SECOND EDITION

CIRCUIT THEORY FUNDAMENTALS AND APPLICATIONS

ARAM BUDAK

Professor of Electrical Engineering
Colorado State University

PRENTICE-HALL, INC., ENGLEWOOD CLIFFS, NJ 07632

Library of Congress Cataloging-in-Publication Data

BUDAK, ARAM.
Circuit theory fundamentals and applications.

Includes index.
1. Electric circuits. 2. Electric networks.
I. Title.
TK454.B77 1987 621.319'2 86-17006
ISBN 0-13-134057-3

Editorial/production supervision and
interior design: Mary Jo Stanley
Cover design: 20/20 Services, Inc.
Manufacturing buyer: Rhett Conklin

Printed in the United States of America

10 9 8 7 6 5 4 3 2 1

ISBN 0-13-134057-3 025

PRENTICE-HALL INTERNATIONAL (UK) LIMITED, *London*
PRENTICE-HALL OF AUSTRALIA PTY. LIMITED, *Sydney*
PRENTICE-HALL OF CANADA INC., *Toronto*
PRENTICE-HALL HISPANOAMERICANA, S.A., *Mexico*
PRENTICE-HALL OF INDIA PRIVATE LIMITED, *New Delhi*
PRENTICE-HALL OF JAPAN, INC., *Tokyo*
PRENTICE-HALL OF SOUTHEAST ASIA PTE. LTD., *Singapore*
EDITORA PRENTICE-HALL DO BRASIL, LTDA., *Rio de Janeiro*

CONTENTS

2 RESISTIVE NETWORKS 47

3 USEFUL NETWORK THEOREMS, POWER, AND ENERGY 115

4 MESH AND NODE EQUATIONS 160

PREFACE

Twenty-five years of experience with circuits—teaching at all levels, experimenting in the laboratory and interacting with circuit-design engineers—has given me definite ideas as to what is relevant and how circuits should be taught at the sophomore level. While it is essential to establish a firm grasp of the fundamentals, it is equally important to develop a sound physical understanding of how circuits work. Without such an understanding students will be unable to apply theory to practice. Indeed, it is not uncommon to see students treat the laboratory portion of a course as if it were unrelated to what is learned in class. They set aside powerful techniques presented in lectures, and make circuits work by trial and error—a practice all too prevalent also in industry. Clearly, theory could and should be the guiding light, but students must acquire the confidence to know when and how theory applies and to realize its limitations. It is my sincere hope that this book will provide the knowledge essential for solving network problems with ease and understanding. For this reason, I have taken a pragmatic approach: a basic and consistent set of circuit analysis techniques is used to solve problems of increasing complexity as the text progresses. The book is written for the undergraduate engineering student who is interested in what he can do with theory and less inclined to follow the details of a derivation however elegant.

At Colorado State University, the book is used at the sophomore level in a two-semester sequence on beginning circuits. The first semester course is taken by all engineers; the second semester course, by electrical engineering majors and other majors who want to learn more about circuits. The entire sequence is also videotaped and played back in various industrial locations in Colorado. The students in these remote locations are mostly mechanical engineers, computer scientists, physicists, and mathematicians who want to acquire the know-how to interact with electrical engineering colleagues.

Chapter 1 gives the fundamental relationships of circuit theory. In Chapters 2 and 3 several useful techniques for solving resistive circuits are presented and applied to a variety of simple but practical problems. In Chapter 4, the foundations for writing mesh and node equations in a systematic manner are laid. The student is now able to solve any resistive network and to write the differential equations for any *RLC* network. In Chapter 5, the Laplace transformation is used as a means of solving these equations. The approach taken is not that of a detailed treatment of Laplace transformation but rather of a development that emphasizes the operational aspects of the transformation. The aim is to give the student as early as possible the necessary skill for solving network problems and interpreting the results. This is done in the next three chapters.

In Chapter 6, the relationship between the frequency and time domain is demonstrated. The step response of first-order systems is derived and applied to *RC* and *RL* networks. The development is such that any current or voltage response can be graphed or expressed mathematically by inspection of the circuit. Chapter 7 deals with the step response of second-order *RLC* networks. A good understanding of second-order systems is essential in modern engineering practice. That is why such a detailed treatment is given. However, if desired, the coverage can be shortened by selecting examples that are representative of responses obtainable from real-axis and complex-conjugate poles. In Chapter 8, the sinusoidal response is covered. Phasors are introduced and used to solve for the sinusoidal steady-state response.

Chapter 9 is devoted to first- and second-order filter functions and their realization with *RLC* networks. Lowpass, highpass, bandpass, bandstop, and other filters are presented. Chapter 10 deals with mutually coupled circuits. Tightly and loosely coupled transformer circuits are discussed. Chapter 11 is on dependent sources. A large number of examples are given to show how dependent sources are handled and how they affect *RLC* networks. Then, from the graphical characterization of three-terminal devices, mathematical and circuit models employing dependent sources are derived. Various methods for biasing, ac and dc gain calculations are demonstrated on a variety of devices. A general approach is taken so that the student is able to take a completely new and unfamiliar device and know what to do with it. Thus, this chapter gives the student the necessary background for the electronics courses that follow. The Fourier series is developed in Chapter 12 in trigonometric, polar, and exponential form. Amplitude and phase spectra are calculated for a variety of waveforms. Examples are given to show how the Fourier series is used to solve circuit problems.

It was a pleasure to write this book and share my ideas with others. I hope that the examples and the explanations presented will give students a physical feel for circuits and encourage them to be creative thinkers. I wish them all the fun and excitement I have had in working with circuits.

Fort Collins, Colorado

ARAM BUDAK

CHAPTER 1

FUNDAMENTAL RELATIONSHIPS IN CIRCUIT THEORY

Variables and equations are used to characterize the various relationships in a system. If the variables are to characterize an actual *physical* system, they must be evaluated by measurement. Consequently, it is necessary to use instruments and give specific instructions on how they are connected. If the instrument readings can be related mathematically, then a theory can be developed to generalize and broaden the scope of applicability of the experimentally observed results. Such is the case with electrical circuits, where theory is developed by using voltage and current measurements. In this chapter we show that a few simple measurements form the basis of fundamental relationships governing circuit elements and their interconnection.

1-1 VOLTAGE AND CURRENT

Two variables $v(t)$ and $i(t)$ characterize the various relationships in an electrical circuit. These variables are functions of time and so may change in value from one instant to the next. The $v(t)$ variable (or simply v) is called the *voltage* variable and the $i(t)$ variable (or simply i) the *current* variable. These variables may also be constant.

The *voltmeter* is the instrument that measures the $v(t)$ variable. The instrument that measures the $i(t)$ variable is called the *ammeter*. Since the readings obtained with these instruments and the knowledge thereby acquired form the basis of circuit theory, knowing how to use the instruments properly is necessary.

Figure 1-1(a) gives the schematic representation of a voltmeter. It has two leads, one of which is marked with a + sign. Although not marked in the diagram, it is understood that the other lead is the negative lead. Instead of the + sign, the former lead may be colored red or connected to a red terminal on the voltmeter proper. It is important that it be distinguished from the other lead, which is the negative, or black, lead or the lead tied to the black terminal of the voltmeter proper. Only one lead need be marked or identified in some manner. The letter V within the circle identifies the voltmeter.

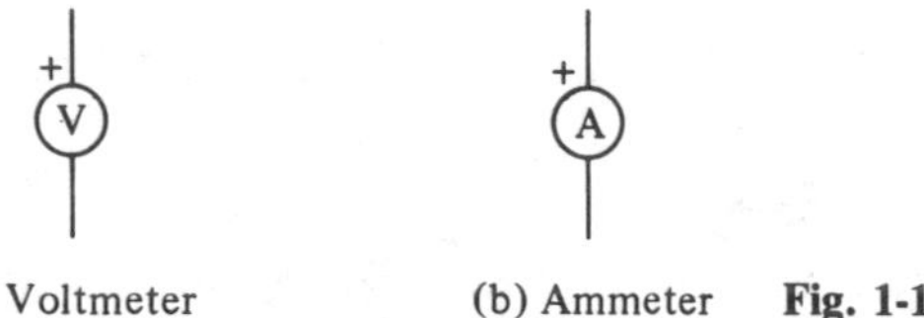

(a) Voltmeter (b) Ammeter **Fig. 1-1**

Figure 1-1(b) shows the schematic representation of an ammeter, the terminal markings of which are similar to the voltmeter. One lead is the +, or red, lead, the other the −, or black, lead. This latter lead is not marked on the diagram. The letter A within the circle identifies the ammeter.

The simplest electrical elements are two-terminal devices that can be characterized by a simple voltage-current relationship. Resistors, capacitors, inductors, and sources, to be characterized shortly, are examples of such electrical elements. These elements are connected together with wires to form circuits or networks. Generally the term *circuit* is used to describe simple interconnections. On the other hand, a network may contain many circuits. In Fig. 1-2(a) an electric circuit consisting of elements 1 and 2 and network N is shown. With each two-terminal element or network we associate a voltage and a current variable. For instance, with element 2 we associate variables v_2 and i_2. With network N we have v_N and i_N and so on.

Voltage is taken as an *across* variable, and so voltage is measured by always connecting the voltmeter *across* an element or *between* two points in a network. In Fig. 1-2(b), for instance, we measure the voltage across element 2 (between e and f) by connecting the voltmeter as shown. The reading of the voltmeter is then associated with the variable v_2, which is shown with its + and − designations next to element 2. Note that the + marking of the v_2 variable matches the + terminal of the voltmeter. If the voltmeter reading is positive, the value of the variable v_2 is positive by definition. If the voltmeter reading is negative, the value of v_2 is negative. For example, if the voltmeter reading is plus five, the voltage *across* element 2 is $v_2 = +5$. On the other hand, if the voltmeter reading is minus ten, $v_2 = -10$. In other words, the variable v_2 may assume positive as well as negative values depending on the sign of the voltmeter reading. It is important to know that this one-to-one correspondence between the voltmeter reading and the value assigned to the variable is based on the particular connection shown; that is, the + end of the voltmeter and the

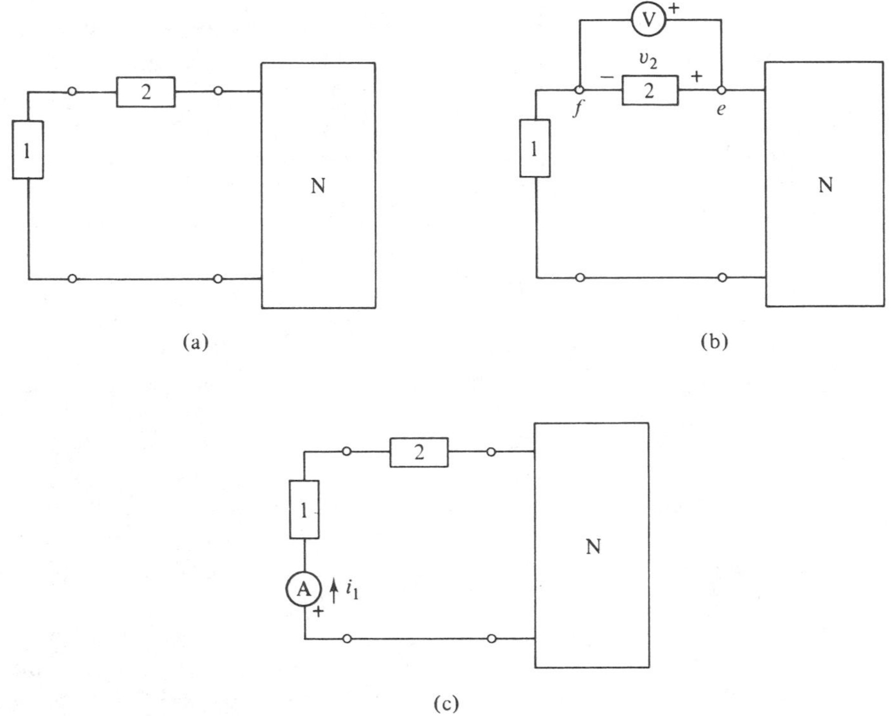

Fig. 1-2

+ marking of the variable refer to the same point on element 2. If these two polarity markings were not in agreement—v_2 marked + on the left and − on the right—the variable value would be taken as the negative of the voltmeter reading. Positive reading would then correspond to a negative voltage. Whether a voltage variable is marked in the + − or − + order in a circuit is not significant. In general, one designation or the other is chosen arbitrarily.

For emphasis, we repeat: voltage measurements are always taken across an element or between two points in a circuit. *To speak of voltage at a point without specifying the location of the other point is meaningless.*

Voltage is measured in units of volts, abbreviated V.

The voltmeter designation given in Fig. 1-1(a) is for an ideal voltmeter. *Ideal voltmeters do not draw any current*. Hence the circuit is not disturbed when the ideal voltmeter is connected to measure voltage.

Current is taken as a *through* variable and thus is measured by *inserting* the ammeter in the circuit. So in order to measure the current through element 1 in Fig. 1-2(a), one of the wires tied to element 1 is cut and the ammeter introduced as shown in Fig. 1-2(c). The ammeter reading is then associated with the current variable i_1 marked on the diagram. Note that i_1 has an arrow associated with it and that this arrow goes from the + terminal of the ammeter to the other terminal. When connected in this way, the variable i_1 is assigned, by definition, a positive value if the meter reading is positive. A negative reading means that the value of i_1 is taken as negative. If the arrow of i_1 is turned around without changing the ammeter connection, however, the variable value is the negative of the ammeter reading. Stated differently, *when the ammeter marking and the current arrow marking match,* as in Fig. 1-2(c), *the ammeter reading and variable value are one and the same*. If the polarities are not lined up as shown, the reading and the variable value differ by a negative sign. Again, whether a current variable is marked with the arrow one way or the other is unimportant, for the choice, in general, is arbitrary.

In talking about current, we mean the current *through* an element or the current in a wire. Current is measured in units of amperes, abbreviated A.

The ammeter designation given in Fig. 1-1(b) is for an ideal ammeter. *The voltage across ideal ammeters is zero*. Hence the circuit is not disturbed when an ideal ammeter is connected to measure current.

Voltage and current variables in a circuit are designated as shown in Fig. 1-3. *Always associate + and − signs with a voltage variable* (clearly indicating where the signs belong) *and an arrow with the current variable*. The voltage v_1 is *between* points a and b, or v_1 is across the terminal leads of N_1. To determine v_1, a voltmeter is connected between a and b with the + lead at a. The voltage v_2 is *between* points c and d or across the top terminals of N_2. To measure v_2, the + lead of the voltmeter is connected to c and the other lead to d. The current i_1 represents the current *through* the wire marked e. To measure it, the wire must be *cut* at e and the ammeter *inserted* with the + terminal on the left side. Similarly, to measure i_2, cut the lead at f and *insert* the ammeter with the + lead on the right.

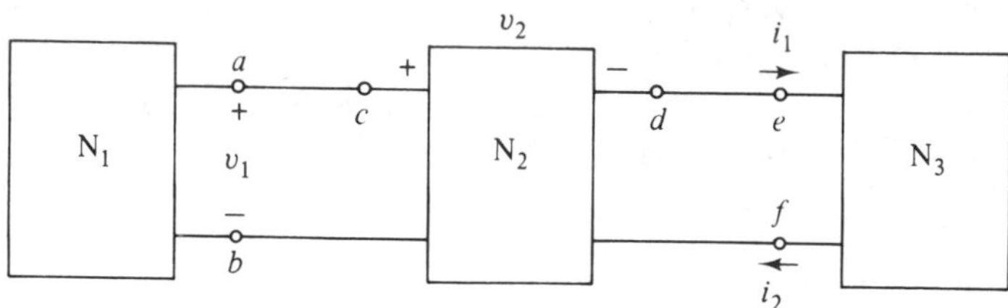

Fig. 1-3

Example 1-1

In the network of Fig. 1-4(a), we wish to determine the values of the v_1 and i_2 variables. To do so, voltmeter and ammeter readings are taken as in Fig. 1-4(b). What is the value of v_1? What is the value of i_2? (Here the standard symbols for the voltmeter and ammeter are not used in order to show the numerical values of meter deflections.)

Solution. The voltmeter shows an upscale deflection of 100. (If the voltmeter had a digital readout, it would have indicated +100.) The polarity marking of the variable v_1 is in opposition to the voltmeter marking. So

$$v_1 = -100 \text{ V} \quad \text{Ans.}$$

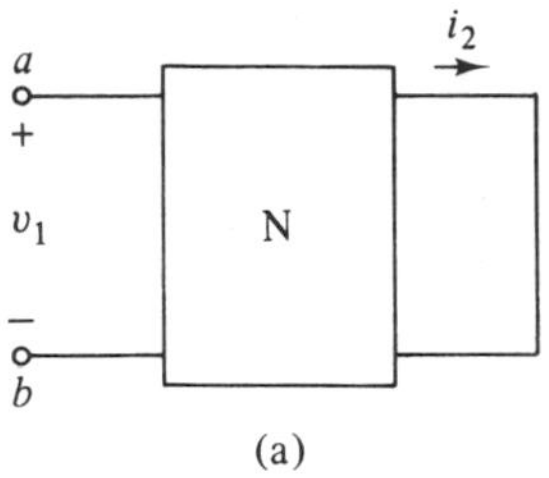

(a)

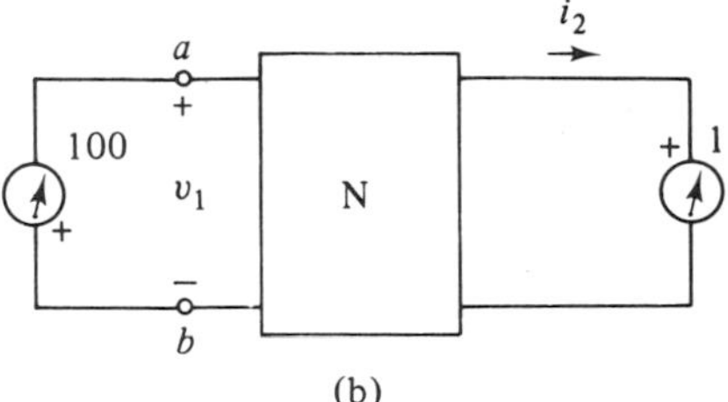

(b)

Fig. 1-4

The current i_2 goes through the + terminal of the ammeter. Thus the ammeter reading represents the value of the i_2 variable—that is,

$$i_2 = 1 \text{ A} \qquad \text{Ans.}$$

Example 1-2

(a) In Fig. 1-5, $v_1 = 20$ V. What is v_2?
(b) If $i = -2$ A, how should the ammeter be connected to obtain a reading of +2 A?

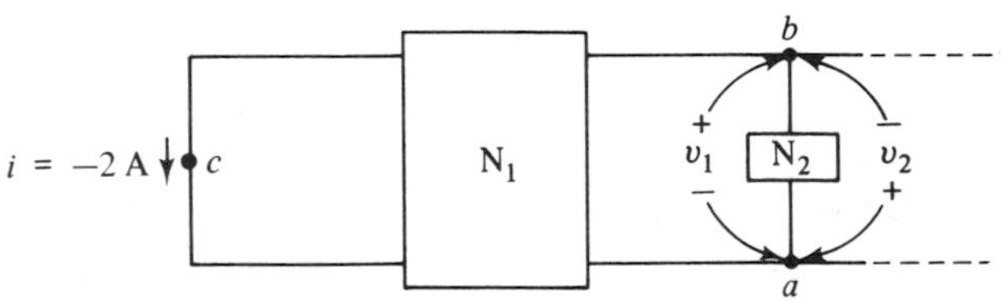

Fig. 1-5

Solution.

(a) Both v_1 and v_2 are measurements taken between the same two points—namely, a and b. The measurement of v_2 calls for the + end of the voltmeter to be connected to the point a, whereas v_1 is measured with the + end of the voltmeter at point b. So

$$v_2 = -v_1 = -20 \text{ V} \quad \text{Ans.}$$

(b) Cut wire at c and insert ammeter with the positive terminal on the bottom.

Example 1-3

In Fig. 1-6 the ammeter reading varies with time as shown. Obtain the value of i for $t = 5$, 10, and 15 s.

Solution. The arrow of the i variable points away from the + terminal of the ammeter. Therefore the value of the i variable is the negative of the ammeter reading.

$$\text{At} \quad \begin{Bmatrix} t = 5, & i = -10 \text{ A} \\ t = 10, & i = 0 \\ t = 15, & i = 10 \text{ A} \end{Bmatrix} \quad \text{Ans.}$$

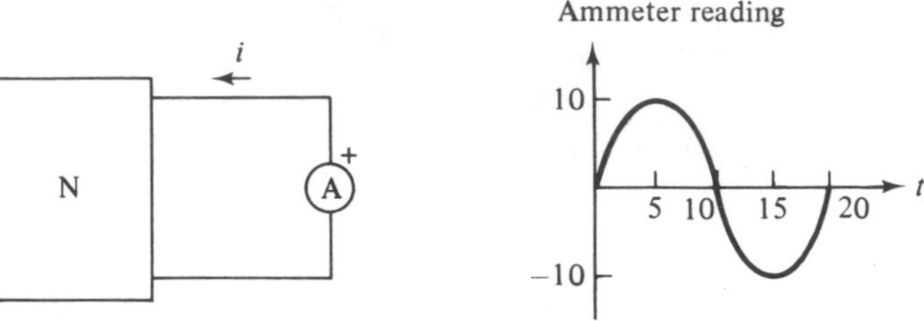

Fig. 1-6

Example 1-4

(a) How is i_2 related to i_1 in Fig. 1-7?
(b) If $i_1 = -6$ A, what is i_2?

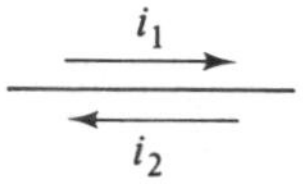

i_1 →
← i_2

Fig. 1-7

Solution.

(a) i_1 and i_2 are measured in opposite senses. So

$$i_2 = -i_1 \quad \text{Ans.}$$

(b)

$$i_2 = -(-6) = 6 \text{ A} \quad \text{Ans.}$$

1-2 KIRCHHOFF'S LAWS

Current Law

In a circuit, a *node* is a junction involving the connection of two or more wires. If we explore with an ammeter the current distributions at the nodes of an actual network, we soon discover that there is a law governing this distribution. Consider, for instance, the node shown by a dot in Fig. 1-8(a). Three wires, and hence three currents, are associated with this node. Suppose that we direct all three current variables into the node and label them i_1, i_2, and i_3. See Fig. 1-8(a). To measure these currents, we connect three ammeters as in Fig. 1-8(b). Note that the negative terminals of all three ammeters face the node; therefore the variable values are the same as the ammeter readings. In obtaining the ammeter readings, we find that

$$i_1 + i_2 + i_3 = 0 \tag{1-1a}$$

In other words, the sum of the three ammeter readings is zero, or the sum of the current variables directed into the node is zero. This means, of course, that all values are not of the same sign. For instance, if i_1 and i_2 are positive, then i_3 must be negative so as to satisfy Eq. (1-1a).

Next, suppose that instead of directing all current variables into the node, we

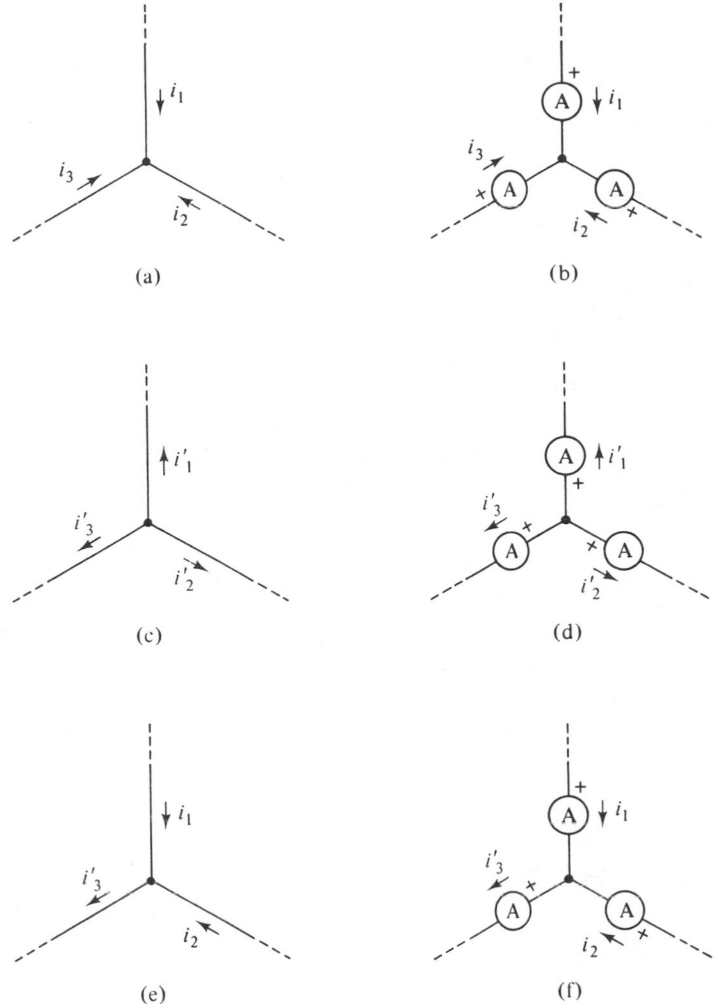

Fig. 1-8

direct them all away from the node as in Fig. 1-8(c). Correspondingly, we connect the ammeters as in Fig. 1-8(d) in order to obtain the values of i'_1, i'_2, and i'_3. Note that the positive terminals of all three ammeters face the node. Again, the ammeter readings show that

$$i'_1 + i'_2 + i'_3 = 0 \tag{1-1b}$$

Thus we can state that the sum of the current variables directed away from the node is zero. Indeed, if we had recognized that

$$i_1 = -i'_1, \qquad i_2 = -i'_2, \qquad i_3 = -i'_3$$

we could have obtained Eq. (1-1b) directly from Eq. (1-1a) as follows.

$$i_1 + i_2 + i_3 = (-i_1') + (-i_2') + (-i_3') = -(i_1' + i_2' + i_3') = 0$$

Finally, suppose that we direct two of the current variables into and one away from the node as in Fig. 1-8(e). When the ammeter readings, taken as shown in Fig. 1-8(f), are ordered, we find that

$$i_1 + i_2 = i_3' \quad \text{or} \quad i_1 + i_2 - i_3' = 0 \tag{1-1c}$$

So we can state that the sum of the two currents coming into the node is equal to the current going out of the node, or the sum of currents taken in one sense minus those taken in the opposite sense is zero. Again, Eq. (1-1c) could have been obtained directly from Eq. (1-1a) by recognizing that $i_3 = -i_3'$. We could have written

$$i_1 + i_2 + i_3 = i_1 + i_2 + (-i_3') = 0$$

$$i_1 + i_2 = i_3'$$

Alternatively, we could have started with Eq. (1-1b) and obtained Eq. (1-1c) as shown below by using $i_1' = -i_1$ and $i_2' = -i_2$.

$$i_1' + i_2' + i_3' = (-i_1) + (-i_2) + i_3' = 0$$

$$i_1 + i_2 = i_3'$$

It was the German physicist Kirchhoff who first observed this fundamental property of currents at a node, and the law governing the currents *at every node* of a circuit is known as *Kirchhoff's Current Law*. It can be stated in three ways, depending on how the current variables are designated at a node. Consider the general case of n wires coming together to form the node p in Fig. 1-9.

1. If all the n currents are directed toward the node p as in Fig. 1-9(a), then Kirchhoff's Current Law can be stated as

   Sum of all currents entering a node = 0

   Stated mathematically,

$$\sum_{j=1}^{n} i_j = 0 \tag{1-2a}$$

2. If all the n currents are directed away from the node p as in Fig. 1-9(b), Kirchhoff's Current Law can be stated as

   Sum of all currents leaving a node = 0

$$\sum_{j=1}^{n} i_j' = 0 \tag{1-2b}$$

3. If some of the currents are directed toward and the rest away from the node p as in Fig. 1-9(c), Kirchhoff's Current Law can be stated as

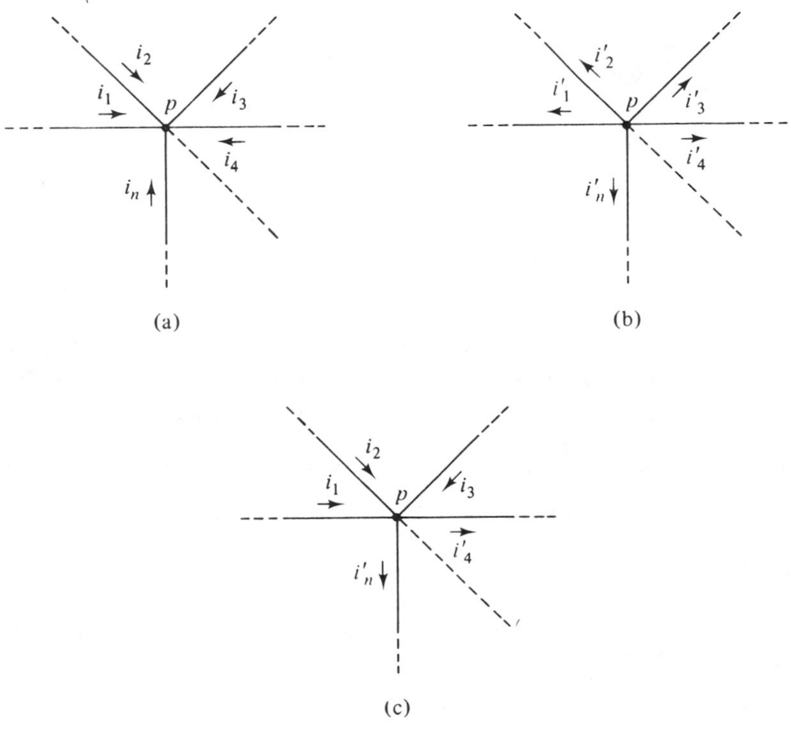

Fig. 1-9

Sum of currents entering the node = Sum of currents leaving the node

$$\sum_{j=1}^{k} i_j = \sum_{j=k+1}^{n} i'_j \tag{1-2c}$$

In Eq. (1-2c) k currents are directed toward and $n - k$ currents are directed away from the node. Alternatively, Eq. (1-2c) can be written

$$\sum_{j=1}^{k} i_j \quad \sum_{j=k+1}^{n} i'_j = 0$$

that is, the sum of currents taken in one sense minus the sum taken in the other sense is zero.

Since $i_j = -i'_j$, the three forms of Kirchhoff's Current Law given by Eq. (1-2) are equivalent statements. It should be emphasized that Kirchhoff's Current Law holds at every node of the circuit and is valid at every instant of time. As time changes, the currents entering and leaving a node may change in value, but the sum of currents coming in is always equal to the sum of currents going out.

Example 1-5

What is i in Fig. 1-10?

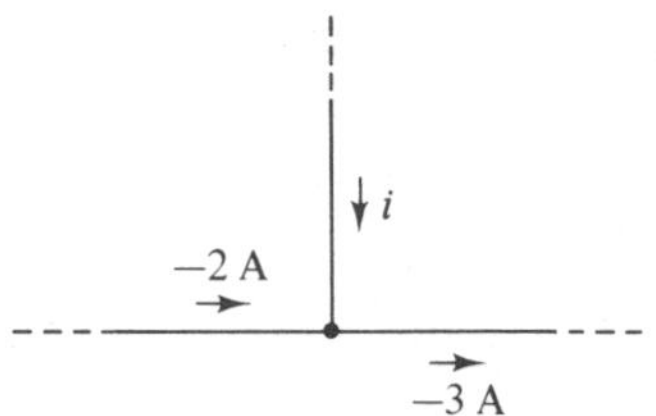

Fig. 1-10

Solution. Three currents are involved with the node. Two are known, and one is unknown. Note that

Currents coming into the node: $-2, i$

Current coming out of the node: -3

We now solve for the current i by three methods.

1. Since the current into a node is the negative of the current out of the node (reversal of the ammeter connection causes a reversal of the sign of the reading), we can express all currents as *incoming* currents: $-2, i, 3$. So, by Kirchhoff's Current Law, we have

$$\sum_{j=1}^{3} i_j = 0$$

$$(-2) + i + 3 = 0$$

$$i = -1 \text{ A} \quad \text{Ans.}$$

2. Since the current out of a node is the negative of the current into a node, we can express all currents as *outgoing* currents: $2, -i, -3$. By Kirchhoff's Current Law, therefore, we have

$$\sum_{j=1}^{3} i'_j = 0$$

$$2 + (-i) + (-3) = 0$$

$$i = -1 \text{ A} \quad \text{Ans.}$$

3. We equate the sum of the currents coming into the node to the current coming out of the node to obtain

$$(-2) + i = -3$$

$$i = -1 \text{ A} \quad \text{Ans.}$$

Example 1-6

In Fig. 1-11, what is i?

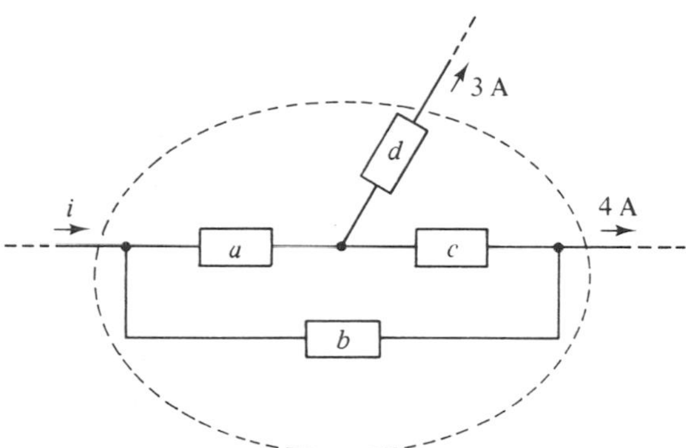

Fig. 1-11

Solution. Create a supernode by enclosing elements a, b, c, and d within a closed surface; that is, put the elements in a sack and let the three leads pierce the sack. Apply Kirchhoff's Current Law, Currents in = Currents out, to the supernode (to the closed surface) and obtain

$$i = 3 + 4 = 7 \text{ A} \quad \text{Ans.}$$

Voltage Law

In a circuit, a *loop* is a closed path containing circuit elements. Exploring the voltages around a loop with a voltmeter soon shows that there is a law governing them. Consider, for instance, the loop shown with a clockwise arrow in Fig. 1-12(a). Three elements, and hence three voltages, are associated with this loop. Suppose that we label these voltages v_1, v_2, v_3 and orient their polarities all in the same sense: + to − in a clockwise direction. See Fig. 1-12(a). To measure these voltages, we connect three voltmeters as in Fig. 1-12(b). Note that the polarity markings of the voltmeters match the + and − designations of the variables, and thus the variable values are the same as the voltmeter readings. When we obtain the voltmeter readings, we find that

$$v_1 + v_2 + v_3 = 0 \tag{1-3a}$$

Thus the sum of the voltages taken in the + to − sense around the loop adds up to zero. In other words, all values are not of the same sign—one is of opposite sign.

In Fig. 1-12(c) all voltages are marked in the − to + sense in going clockwise around the loop. The voltmeters are connected as shown in Fig. 1-12(d) to measure voltages v_1', v_2', and v_3'. Noting that the voltmeter readings are the same as the variable values, we find that

$$v_1' + v_2' + v_3' = 0 \tag{1-3b}$$

Thus the sum of voltages taken in the − to + sense around the loop adds up to zero. Having Eq. (1-3a), we could have obtained Eq. (1-3b) by recognizing that

$$v_1' = -v_1, \qquad v_2' = -v_2, \qquad v_3' = -v_3$$

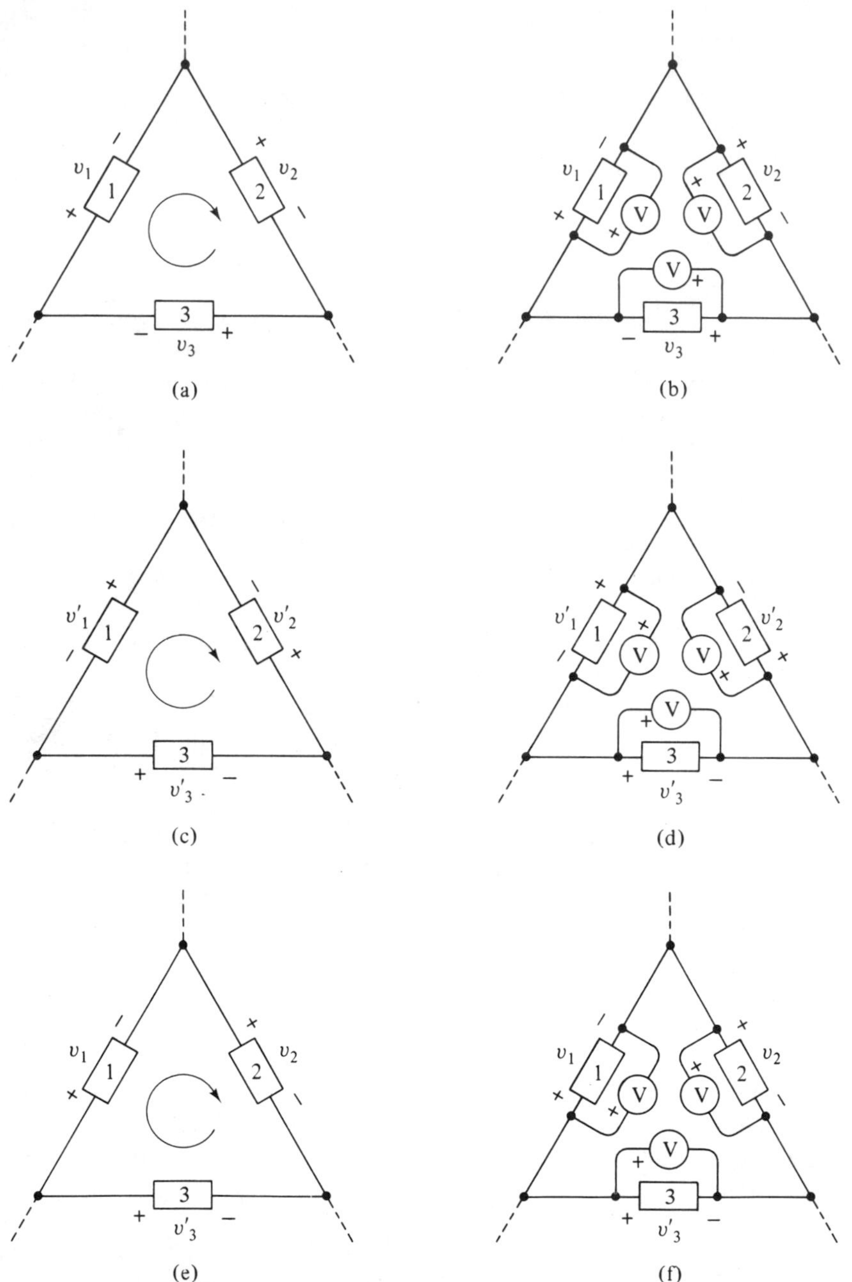

Fig. 1-12

In Fig. 1-12(e) v_1 and v_2 are designated in the + to − sense, whereas v_3' is designated in the − to + sense in going clockwise around the loop. As shown in Fig. 1-12(f), the voltmeters are connected so that they measure the variable values (not their negatives). The result is

$$v_1 + v_2 = v_3' \quad \text{or} \quad (v_1 + v_2) - v_3' = 0 \tag{1-3c}$$

which indicates that, around the loop, the sum of voltages taken in the + to − sense equals the voltages taken in the − to + sense, or the sum of voltages in one sense minus those in the other sense is zero. By recognizing that $v_3' = -v_3$, we see that Eq. (1-3c) reduces to Eq. (1-3a). Alternatively, by using $v_1 = -v_1'$ and $v_2 = -v_2'$, Eq. (1-3c) can be made the same as Eq. (1-3b).

Again, Kirchhoff observed this fundamental property of voltages around a loop. The law governing the voltages *around every loop* in a circuit, known as *Kirchhoff's Voltage Law,* can be stated in three different ways, depending on how the voltage variables are designated around a loop. Consider the general case of n elements that form the loop q shown in Fig. 1-13.

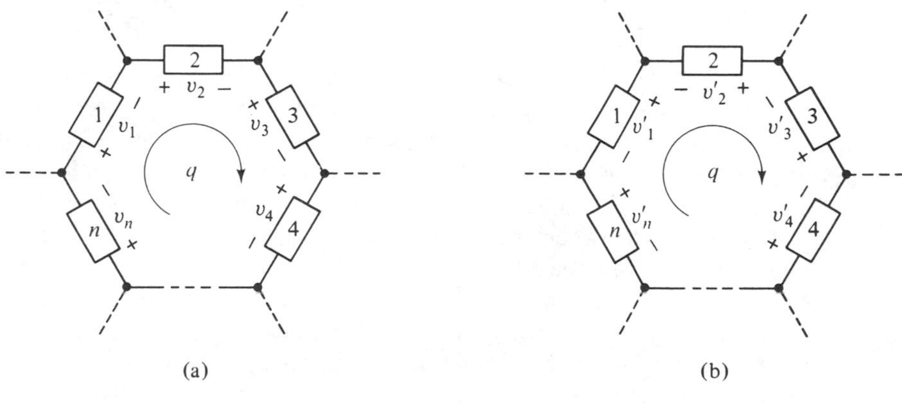

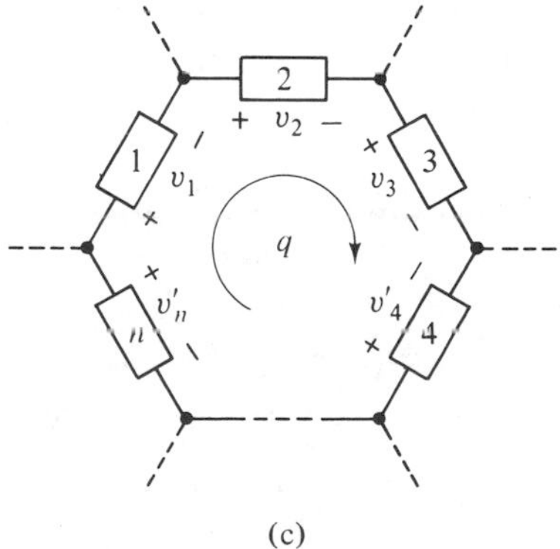

Fig. 1-13

1. If all voltages are designated in the + to − sense around the loop as in Fig. 1-13(a), then Kirchhoff's Voltage Law can be stated as

$$\sum_{j=1}^{n} v_j = 0 \tag{1-4a}$$

2. If all voltages are designated in the − to + sense around the loop as in Fig. 1-13(b), Kirchhoff's Voltage Law can be stated as

$$\sum_{j=1}^{n} v_j' = 0 \tag{1-4b}$$

3. If some of the voltages are designated + to − and the rest − to + around the loop as in Fig. 1-13(c), Kirchhoff's Voltage Law can be stated as

$$\sum_{j=1}^{k} v_j = \sum_{j=k+1}^{n} v_j' \quad \text{or} \quad \sum_{j=1}^{k} v_j - \sum_{j=k+1}^{n} v_j' = 0 \tag{1-4c}$$

In Eq. (1-4c) k voltages are designated in the + to − and $n - k$ voltages in the − to + sense.

Since $v_j = -v_j'$, the three forms of Kirchhoff's Voltage Law given by Eq. (1-4) are equivalent statements. The law is also valid if the loop is taken in the counterclockwise sense. It should be emphasized that Kirchhoff's Voltage Law holds around every loop of the circuit and is valid at every instant of time. The voltages around the loop may change their values with time, but their sum is always governed by Eq. (1-4).

Implicit in the statement of Kirchhoff's Voltage Law is the understanding that voltages appear across the elements that are drawn as boxes in Fig. 1-12 and 1-13 and that zero voltage is associated with the wires connecting the elements. In other words, in a circuit diagram the voltages are concentrated at the elements and not at the connecting wires. When the voltages across the connecting wires cannot be neglected, however, the wires themselves can be regarded as elements across which voltages are present.

Often an alternative form of Kirchhoff's Voltage Law is used: *the sum of voltages between any two nodes in a circuit is the same regardless of the path taken to go from one node to the other*. (If such were not the case, voltages would not sum to zero around the loops that are formed by the paths.) Consider, for instance, part of a circuit shown in Fig. 1-14(a). Loop k has four elements, and hence four voltages, associated with it. Two of these voltages, v_1 and v_2, appear in the − to + sense; the other two, v_3 and v_4, appear in the + to − sense *as we go around loop k in the clockwise sense*. Consequently, by Kirchhoff's Voltage Law, Eq. (1-4c), we have

Sum of voltages in one sense = Sum of voltages in the other sense

$$v_1 + v_2 = v_3 + v_4$$

Had we gone clockwise around loop l instead of loop k, we would have obtained

$$v_3 + v_4 = v_5$$

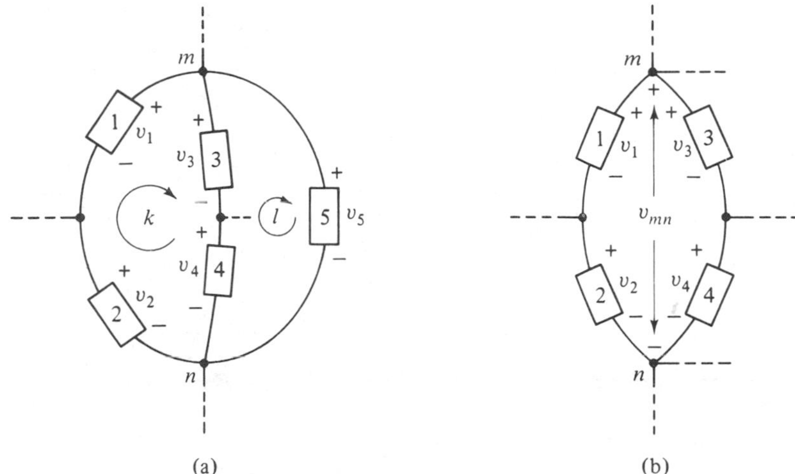

Fig. 1-14

On the other hand, if we had gone clockwise around the loop composed of elements 1, 2, and 5 (which is not designated with an arrow in the diagram), Kirchhoff's Voltage Law would have given us

$$v_1 + v_2 = v_5$$

So we see that

$$v_1 + v_2 = v_3 + v_4 = v_5 = v_{mn}$$

where we have introduced v_{mn} to designate the voltage *between* nodes *m* and *n*. Indeed, if element 5 were considered a voltmeter, it would read v_{mn}. Regardless of the *path* taken in going from *m* to *n*, therefore, we always obtain the same voltage, v_{mn}. This voltage is shown in Fig. 1-14(b). Its polarity markings are such that the positive sign is at *m* and the negative sign at *n*. By convention, the first subscript is considered positive, the second negative. It follows that $v_{nm} = -v_{mn}$.

From Fig. 1-14(b) we see that, along the left path from *m* to *n*, v_{mn} (+ to −) is equal to v_1 (+ to −) plus v_2 (+ to −). Or, along the right path from *m* to *n*, v_{mn} (+ to −) is equal to v_3 (+ to −) plus v_4 (+ to −). In other words, voltages summed in the + to − sense along any path from *m* to *n* give v_{mn} in the same sense. Nevertheless, it should be emphasized that we can designate voltage variables along a path or around a loop in any sense that we wish. For instance, in Fig. 1-15 $v_{13} = v_1 + v_2$, since, along the top path from node 1 to node 3, v_1 and v_2 as well as v_{13} are all in the + to − sense. On the other hand, along the right path from node 3 to node 5, $v_{35} = v_3 + (-v_4)$. Here v_4 must be reversed so as to make its sense the same as that of v_3 and v_{35}—that is, + to − as we go from node 3 to node 5. Similarly, along the left path from node 5 to node 1, $v_{51} = (-v_5) + (-v_6)$, where both v_5 and v_6 are reversed in order to make their polarities conform with the polarity of v_{51}—that is, +

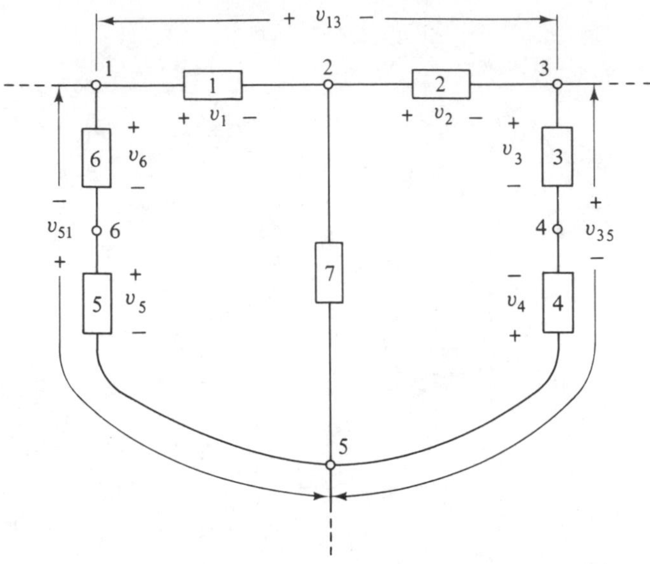

Fig. 1-15

to − as we go from node 5 to node 1. Inspection of the circuit diagram also shows that

$$\underbrace{v_{13} + v_{35}}_{\substack{\text{Right path from} \\ \text{node 1 to node 5}}} = \underbrace{-v_{51}}_{\substack{\text{Left path from} \\ \text{node 1 to node 5}}}$$

Example 1-7

Obtain v_1 and v_2 in Fig. 1-16.

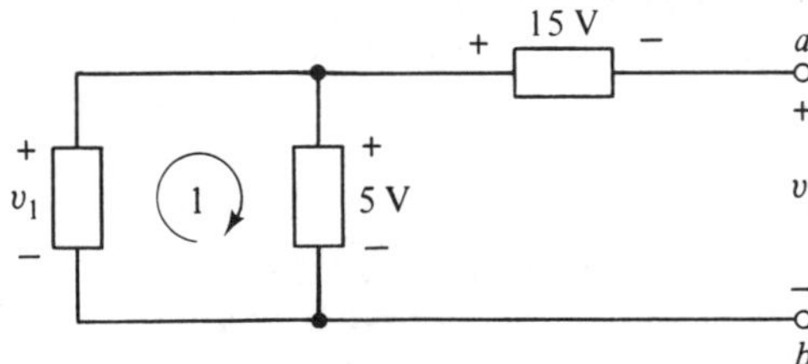

Fig. 1-16

Solution. Apply Kirchhoff's Voltage Law around *loop 1* to obtain v_1.

$v_1 + (-5) = 0$ (Sum of voltages around the loop, taken in the − to + sense, equals zero.)

$v_1 = 5$ V Ans.

Sum the voltages in the + to − sense along any path from a to b to obtain v_2.

$$v_2 = (-15) + 5 = -10 \text{ V} \quad \text{Ans.}$$

Example 1-8

In Fig. 1-17, find v_1 and v_2.

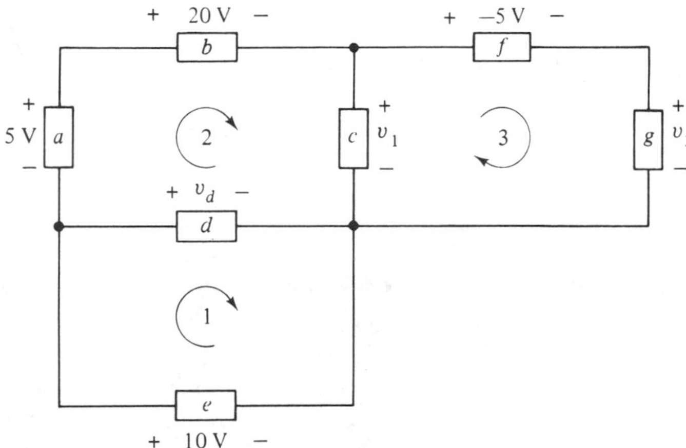

Fig. 1-17

Solution. To obtain v_1, apply Kirchhoff's Voltage Law to the loop consisting of elements a, b, c, and e. This loop is a combination of loops 1 and 2 and may be called a superloop.

$$10 + 5 = 20 + v_1$$ (Sum of voltages taken in the − to + sense = Sum of voltages taken in the + to − sense)

$$v_1 = -5 \text{ V} \quad \text{Ans.}$$

Apply Kirchhoff's Voltage Law to loop 3 and obtain v_2.

$$v_1 - [(-5) + v_2] = 0$$ [(Sum of voltages in the − to + sense) − (Sum of voltages in the + to − sense) = 0]

$$v_2 = -5 + 5 = 0 \quad \text{Ans.}$$

Kirchhoff's Current and Voltage Laws are laws that are based on the connective features of a network. The Current Law governs the sum of the currents at any node of the network. The Voltage Law governs the sum of voltages around any loop in the network. These laws say nothing about the elements themselves.

Kirchhoff's Current and Voltage laws are independent of each other. Together they are used to solve circuit problems.

1-3 TWO-TERMINAL CHARACTERIZATION OF ELEMENTS

Figure 1-18(a) shows a two-terminal electrical element. One terminal is marked with a dot for identification purposes. Three variables are associated with the two leads. One variable is the voltage between the leads. It is labeled v with + on the top and

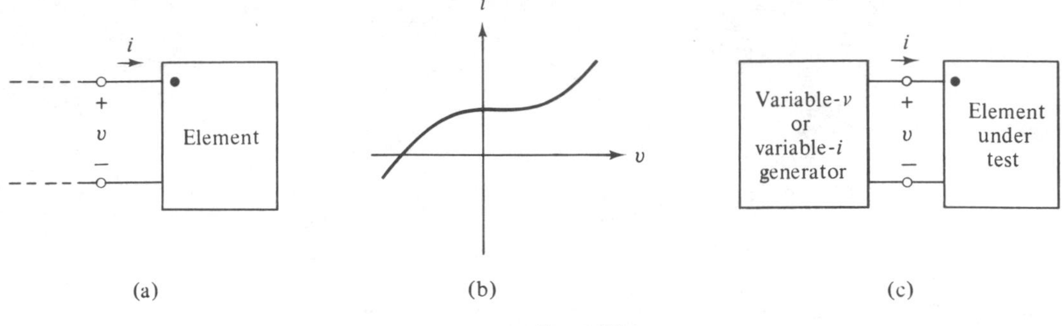

Fig. 1-18

− on the bottom. The other two variables are the currents in each lead. If the current in the top lead is labeled i and is taken into the box as shown, then, by Kirchhoff's Current Law, the current in the bottom lead must be i, and it must be coming out of the box. If this situation is understood, it is not necessary to show the current in the bottom lead. Consequently, only two variables, v and i, are associated with a two-terminal element. In Fig. 1-18(a) the broken lines on the left imply that the element is connected to another circuit.

The element is characterized if we can determine the functional relationship between v and i. If we obtain an expression relating v to i, we have determined a mathematical *model,* or equation, to represent the terminal characteristics of the element. Indeed, this functional relationship is used to *define* the element.

To see how v and i are related, we *measure* v and i for different sets of values and plot a graph as shown in Fig. 1-18(b). We then try to describe this curve mathematically. If it is a simple curve, such as a straight line, it is easy to write the equation for the curve, thereby establishing the functional relationship between v and i. In some cases, we may be able to do so only over a limited range of the variables, and therefore we can establish a mathematical model for the element only if the v and i variables stay within that range. In other cases, we may be able to fit the curve mathematically in two or more separate ranges of the variables, thereby characterizing the element with two or more models, one for each range. In still other cases, we may not be able to obtain an accurate model for the element at all. This does not mean that such an element is useless but rather that it is not going to be an easy task to use it with other elements and predict what the outcome will be. Indeed, the manufacturer and the designer of the elements try to produce a device that obeys simple mathematical relationships so that its performance in a circuit can easily be predicted.

To obtain the element-describing curve shown in Fig. 1-18(b), it is necessary to vary the terminal variables. This variation is achieved by connecting the element under test to a variable v- or variable i-producing network as in Fig. 1-18(c). Typically, this network is a time-varying voltage or current source, to be described shortly, or a manually variable dc (direct current) source. Even though the v and i variables are common to both boxes shown in Fig. 1-18(c), this procedure provides the characteristic curve for the box on the right and not for the box on the left. It is the box on the left that causes changes in the terminal variables, whereas the box on the right is subjected to these changes.

Henceforth, unless otherwise indicated, we will adopt the sign conventions shown in Fig. 1-18(a) and (c), which are + on the top, − on the bottom for the voltage variable, and an arrow directed to the right in the upper lead of the box under test. In this way, a consistent set of polarity markings is used in measuring the terminal variables of any element that is to be characterized. In the remainder of the chapter the characteristics of five circuit elements are discussed.

1-4 VOLTAGE SOURCES

Any two-terminal element having the i vs. v characteristic shown in Fig. 1-19(a) is called a *voltage source*. All voltage sources are characterized by a *vertical line*. The v-axis intercept, v_s, represents the value of the voltage source. The higher the voltage of the voltage source, the larger v_s is. If the voltage source is a function of time—that is, its value changes from one instant to the next—then the intercept changes. However, at any given time the characteristic curve is a vertical line. When v_s is negative, the line is to the left of the i axis.

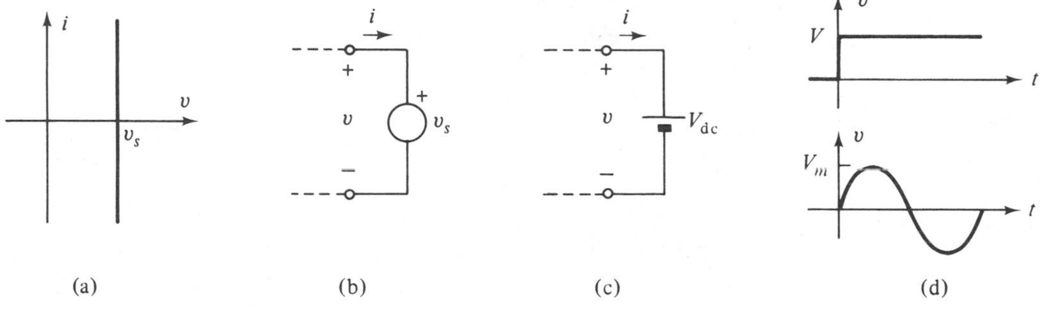

Fig. 1-19

The mathematical model of the voltage source shown in Fig. 1-19(a) is

$$v = v_s \tag{1-5}$$

As Fig. 1-19(a) and Eq. (1-5) show, the voltage is fixed at the value of v_s *regardless of the value of i through the voltage source*. We cannot determine the current through the voltage source by looking at the voltage source alone. We can only determine its voltage, v_s. The current through the voltage source is determined by the external circuit to which the voltage source is connected. The current may be positive, zero, or negative.

A voltage source described by the vertical line in Fig. 1-19(a) is an *ideal voltage source*. The designer and manufacturer of voltage sources try their best to obtain such a curve. Although they might not be able to produce the ideal characteristic, they may come close to it. Actual voltage sources also have limited current capability; that is, the source acts as a voltage source only over a specified range of current values.

A voltage source is schematically presented in Fig. 1-19(b). This diagram serves as the *circuit model* for the voltage source. Note that the schematic diagram gives us the equation $v = v_s$ (by Kirchhoff's Voltage Law). The circuit model gives the same information as the curve of Fig. 1-19(a). It says no more or less. They both say $v = v_s$. This mathematical model is the *defining equation for the voltage source*. Thus Fig. 1-19(a) or Fig. 1-19(b) or Eq. (1-5) can be used to characterize a voltage source completely.

When independent of time, the voltage source is called a *dc* source, battery, or dc power supply and is schematically represented as in Fig. 1-19(c). The longer (upper) line of the battery symbol designates the + terminal of the battery. For the battery shown, $v = V_{dc}$. Two widely used voltage-source waveforms are shown in Fig. 1-19(d). The top waveform represents a voltage step of amplitude V. The bottom waveform represents a sinusoidal voltage of peak amplitude V_m.

When a voltage source is applied (connected) to nodes a and a' in a network, the voltage between a and a' is forced to take on the value of the voltage source. The voltage between a and a' is thus fixed regardless of what is happening in the remainder of the network. This voltage is *independent* of everything else that may be going on in the network.

To illustrate, consider the circuit shown in Fig. 1-20, which represents an idealized version of a car's battery and the associated accessories that it runs.

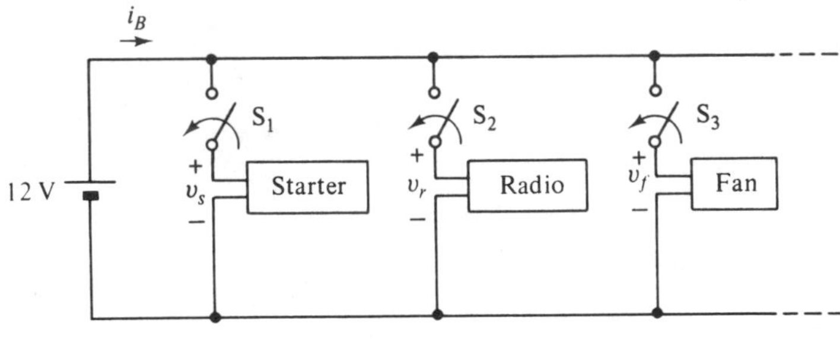

Fig. 1-20

When switch S_1 is closed, v_s becomes 12 V (by Kirchhoff's Voltage Law applied to the loop containing the battery, S_1, and the starter), and the starter becomes activated. When switch S_2 is closed, v_r becomes 12 V (by Kirchhoff's Voltage Law applied to the loop containing the battery, S_2, and the radio), and the radio is turned on. When switch S_3 is closed, v_f becomes 12 V (by Kirchhoff's Voltage Law applied to the loop containing the battery, S_3, and the fan), and the fan is turned on. Thus all accessories receive the full 12 V of the battery when the switches are closed. Other accessories can also be connected across the battery without affecting the voltages supplied to the radio, fan, and similar accessories. However, the current through the battery, i_B, depends on the number of accessories that are switched on. As the number of electrical devices that are activated increases, the current supplied by the battery increases, but the voltage remains constant at 12 V. (Later we will learn how the current changes as additional elements are connected across the voltage source.)

1-5 CURRENT SOURCES

Any two-terminal element having the i vs. v characteristic shown in Fig. 1-21(a) is called a *current source*. All current sources are characterized by a *horizontal line*. The i-axis intercept, i_s, represents the value of the current source. The higher the value of the current source, the larger i_s is. If the current source is a function of time—that is, its value changes from one instant to the next—then the intercept changes. However, at any given time the characteristic curve is a horizontal line. When i_s is negative, the line is below the v axis.

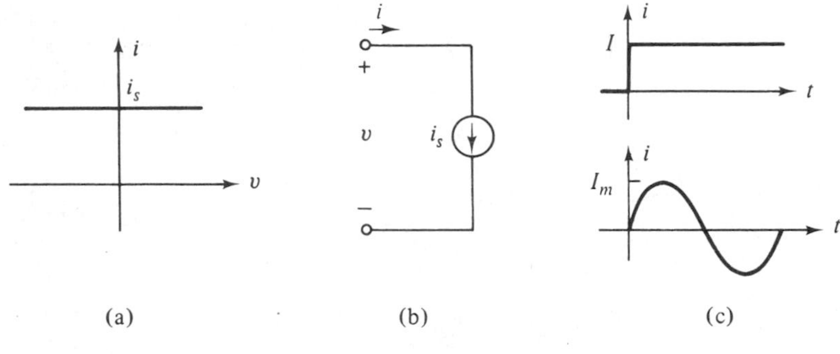

Fig. 1-21

The horizontal line shown in Fig. 1-21(a) is modeled mathematically by

$$i = i_s \tag{1-6}$$

As Fig. 1-21(a) and Eq. (1-6) show, the current is fixed at the value i_s *regardless of the value of v across the current source*. We cannot determine the voltage across the current source by looking at the current source alone. We can only determine its current i_s. The voltage across the current source is determined by the external circuit to which the current source is connected. The voltage may be positive, zero, or negative.

A current source described by the horizontal line in Fig. 1-21(a) is an *ideal current source*. Again, the designer and manufacturer of current sources try their best to produce such a curve. Actual current sources have limited voltage capability; that is, the source acts like a current source only over a specified range of voltage values.

A current source is schematically presented in Fig. 1-21(b). This diagram serves as the circuit model for the current source. Note that the circuit model gives us the equation $i = i_s$ (by Kirchhoff's Current Law). The schematic representation gives the same information as the curve of Fig. 1-21(a). It says no more or less. They both say

$i = i_s$. This mathematical model is the *defining equation for the current source*. Thus Fig. 1-21(a) or Fig. 1-21(b) or Eq. (1-6) can be used to characterize a current source completely. Two widely used current-source waveforms are shown in Fig. 1-21(c). The top waveform represents a step current of amplitude I, the bottom one a sinusoidal current of peak amplitude I_m.

When a current source is connected between two nodes in a network, current i_s is injected to one of the nodes, and current i_s is taken out of the other node. The value of i_s is *independent* of everything else that may be occurring in the network.

As an example of a current source driving a load, consider the circuit shown in Fig. 1-22. The 10 A current source is connected to five lamps. By Kirchhoff's Current Law, it is seen that the current through each lamp is 10 A. If a sixth lamp is added, the current through it will also be 10 A, while the current through the other lamps remains the same. However, the voltage across the current source, v, will increase in order to supply the voltage for the additional lamp.

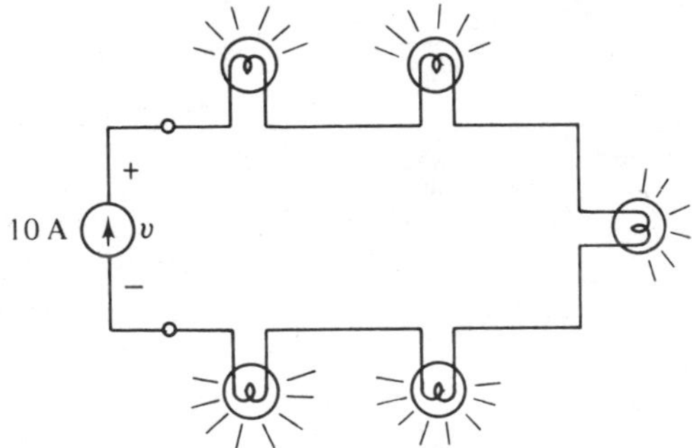

Fig. 1-22

1-6 RESISTORS AND OHM'S LAW

Any two-terminal element having the i vs. v characteristic shown in Fig. 1-23(a) is called a *resistor*. All resistors are characterized by a line with *positive* slope going through the origin. The slope is $1/R$. The reciprocal of the slope, R, represents the value of the resistor. For a given resistor, the value of R is constant. The characteristic curve displayed in Fig. 1-23(a) does not change if the leads of the resistor are reversed.

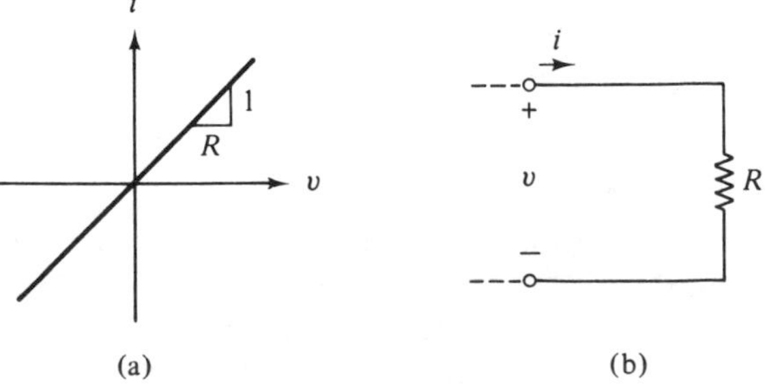

Fig. 1-23

The mathematical model for the resistor is obtained from Fig. 1-23 by writing the equation for the straight line

$$i = \frac{v}{R} \tag{1-7a}$$

This equation can also be written

$$v = iR \tag{1-7b}$$

Equation (1-7b) is a statement of *Ohm's Law*. It is also the resistor-defining equation. The constant R represents the *resistance* of the resistor. Resistance is measured in ohms, abbreviated Ω. Dimensionally, we have $1\ \Omega = 1\ \text{V}/1\ \text{A}$. A kilo-ohm, abbreviated kΩ, is 1000 Ωs.

Ohm's Law allows us to calculate the current through a resistor if the voltage across it is given. We can also calculate the voltage across a resistor if the current through it is given. The voltage across and the current through a resistor may assume different values, depending on the external circuit, but *their ratio is always constant.*

A resistor described by the straight line shown in Fig. 1-23(a) is schematically represented as in Fig. 1-23(b). This diagram serves as the circuit model for the resistor.

It should be clear that Ohm's Law ($v = iR$) is valid only when v and i are measured according to the polarity markings in Fig. 1-23(b). If v or i is measured differently, then Ohm's Law is modified accordingly. For instance, if i is taken (measured) the other way, as in Fig. 1-24(a), then both the direction of i and the sign of i are changed [see Fig. 1-24(b)], so that the terminal variables are put in the standard form on which all element-defining measurements are based. When Ohm's Law is applied to Fig. 1-24(b), we obtain

$$(-i) = \frac{v}{R} \tag{1-8a}$$

or

$$v = -iR \tag{1-8b}$$

The negative sign appearing in Eq. (1-8) does not mean that we have negative resistance but rather that we chose to designate i in an opposite sense—going to the left as in Fig. 1-24(a).

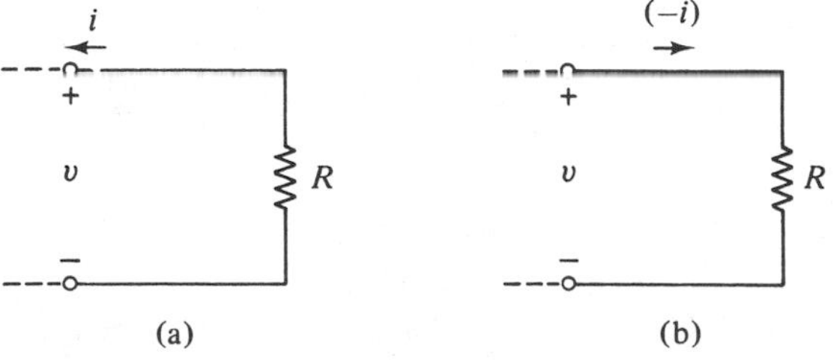

Fig. 1-24

The schematic representation given in Fig. 1-23(b) is a symbolic way of saying what the curve of Fig. 1-23(a) says. Either representation characterizes a resistor completely. Manufacturers try to fabricate resistors that behave as Fig. 1-23(a).

Two equations are necessary for the solution of the v and i variables associated with a two-terminal element. One equation comes from the element itself. So for a voltage source, $v = v_s$; for a current source, $i = i_s$; and for a resistor, $v = iR$. The other equation, which comes from the circuit external to the element, represents constraints imposed on the terminal variables by the external circuit.

Example 1-9

Obtain v and i for the circuit shown in Fig. 1-25.

Solution. By Kirchhoff's Voltage Law applied to the loop as shown, obtain

$$10 - v = 0$$

$$v = 10 \text{ V} \quad \text{Ans.}$$

Since we know v and R *for the resistor,* we can use Ohm's Law to obtain

$$i = \frac{v}{R} = \frac{10}{2} = 5 \text{ A} \quad \text{Ans.}$$

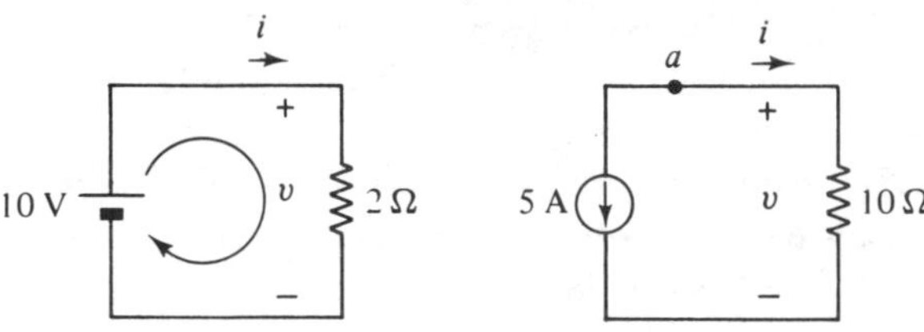

Fig. 1-25 **Fig. 1-26**

Example 1-10

Obtain v for the circuit shown in Fig. 1-26.

Solution. By Kirchhoff's Current Law applied to node a, obtain

$$i + 5 = 0$$

Then

$$i = -5 \text{ A}$$

Since we know i and R *for the resistor,* we can use Ohm's Law to obtain

$$v = iR = -5 \times 10 = -50 \text{ V} \quad \text{Ans.}$$

Example 1-11

The voltage across a resistor is $v = 15 \sin 100t$. The current through it is $i = 7.5 \sin 100t$.

(a) What is R?

(b) Using the given voltage and current, plot the i vs. v curve for this resistor.

Solution

(a) By Ohm's Law,

$$R = \frac{v}{i} = \frac{15 \sin 100t}{7.5 \sin 100t} = 2\ \Omega \quad \text{Ans.}$$

(b) As given, v and i are functions of t, but we are asked to plot the i vs. v curve. We can do so by using the result of (a) to obtain the expression for i in terms of v.

$$i = \frac{v}{R} = \frac{v}{2}.$$

Since $v = 15 \sin 100t$, its maximum value is $+15$ V, and its minimum value is -15 V. Since $i = 7.5 \sin 100t$, its maximum value is 7.5 A, and its minimum value is -7.5 A. Thus the bounds on v and i are established. The slope of the i vs. v curve is $\frac{1}{2}$. The resulting curve is shown in Fig. 1-27.

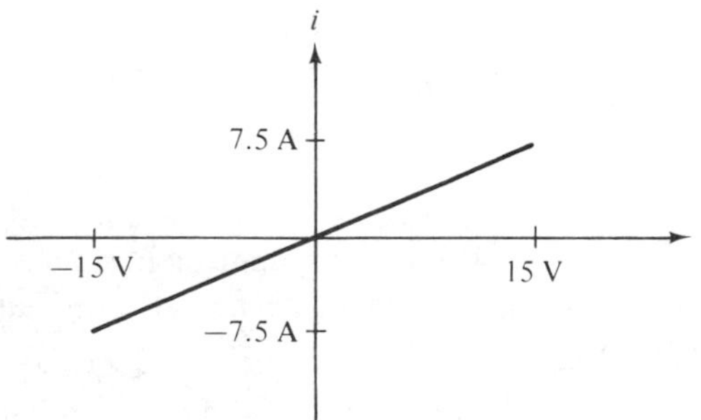

Fig. 1-27

Example 1-12

What is the value of i in Fig. 1-28?

Solution. Redraw the circuit as shown in Fig. 1-29 so that the terminal variables are designated in standard form. By Ohm's Law,

$$i = \frac{-6}{2} = -3\ \text{A} \quad \text{Ans.}$$

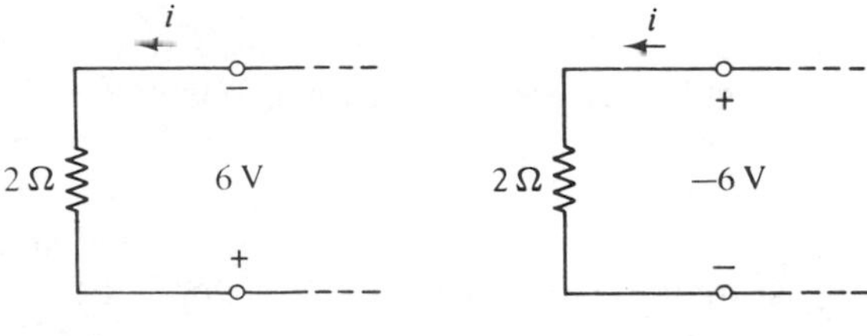

Fig. 1-28 **Fig. 1-29**

Example 1-13

The i vs. v characteristic of a device is shown in Fig. 1-30. Obtain a model for the device.

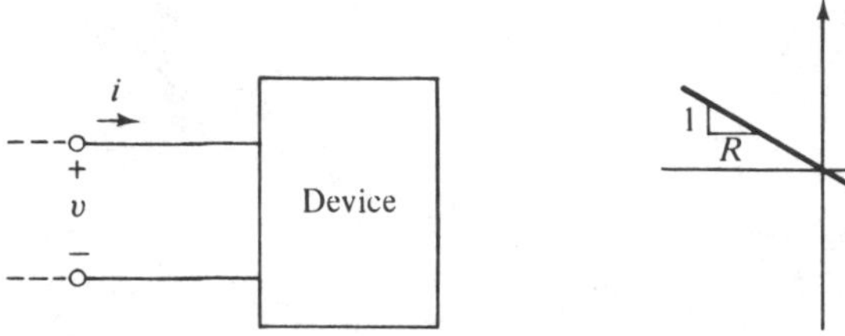

Fig. 1-30

Solution. From the graph of Fig. 1-30

$$i = -\frac{v}{R}$$

which can be written as

$$i = \frac{v}{-R} = \frac{v}{R'} \quad \text{Ans.}$$

where $R' = -R$

Thus the model for this device is a resistor of value R' that is negative. Symbolically, we present such a resistor as in Fig. 1-31. Using dependent sources (discussed in Chapter 11) and resistors, it is possible to construct such negative resistance devices that operate over a limited range of v and i values.

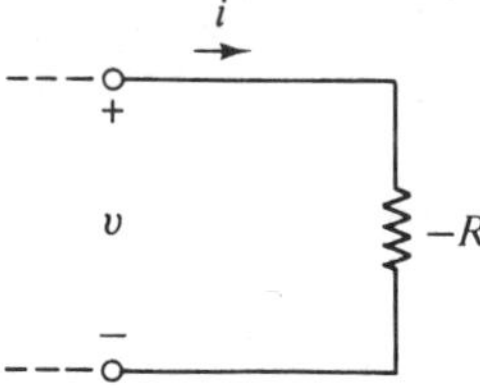

Fig. 1-31

1-7 CAPACITORS

Any two-terminal element with the i vs. dv/dt characteristic shown in Fig. 1-32(a) is called a *capacitor*. Unlike the preceding three elements (v_s, i_s, and R), the capacitor is defined not by an i vs. v curve but by an i vs. dv/dt curve. Had we plotted i vs. v, the shape of the curve would have depended on the i or v waveform, a result that is highly undesirable because it is not unique. On the other hand, the i vs. dv/dt curve is a straight line passing through the origin with a slope of C as shown, and this result is *independent* of the i or v waveform.

The mathematical model for the capacitor is obtained from Fig. 1-32(a) by writing the equation of the straight line*

$$i = C\frac{dv}{dt} \tag{1-9a}$$

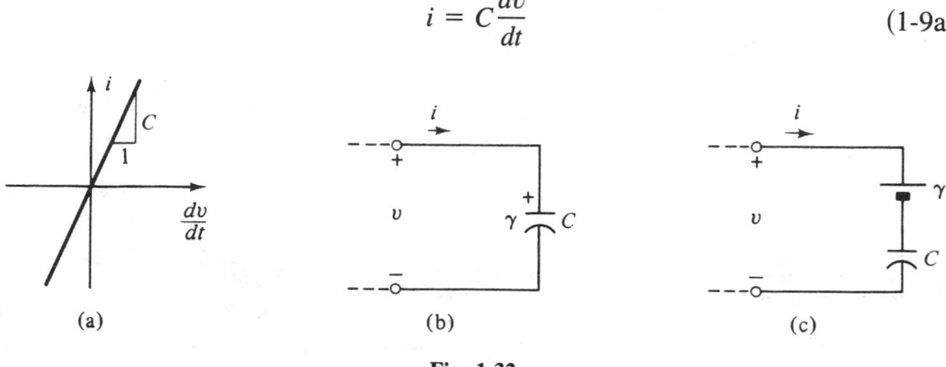

Fig. 1-32

It is also desirable to have the expression for v as a function of i. Separating the variables in Eq. (1-9a) and then integrating between the fixed lower limit t_0 and variable upper limit t, we obtain

$$dv = \frac{1}{C} i\, dt, \qquad \int_{v(t_0)}^{v(t)} dv = \frac{1}{C}\int_{t_0}^{t} i\, dt'$$

$$v(t) - v(t_0) = \frac{1}{C}\int_{t_0}^{t} i\, dt', \qquad v(t) = v(t_0) + \frac{1}{C}\int_{t_0}^{t} i\, dt'$$

Usually, the constant t_0 is taken as zero and is considered to represent the time at which voltages or currents are applied to a circuit. Hence $v(t)$ can be written

$$\begin{aligned} v(t) &= \underbrace{v(0)}_{\gamma} + \frac{1}{C}\int_0^t i\, dt' \\ v &= \gamma + \frac{1}{C}\int_0^t i\, dt' \end{aligned} \tag{1-9b}$$

Either Eq. (1-9a) or Eq. (1-9b) can be taken as the defining equation for a capacitor. The constant C represents the *capacitance* of the capacitor. Capacitance is measured in farads, abbreviated F. Dimensionally, we have 1 F = 1 (ampere × second)/1 volt. A microfarad, abbreviated μF, is 10^{-6} F. The constant γ represents the *initial voltage* $v(0)$ on the capacitor. It is the value of voltage that appears across the

*In cases where the slope C varies with time, Eq. (1-9a) is modified to

$$i = \frac{d}{dt}(Cv) = \frac{dq}{dt}$$

where $q = Cv$ represents the charge on the capacitor.

capacitor at $t = 0$ and represents the accumulated (integrated) result of past events (prior to $t = 0$) to which the capacitor has been subjected. Henceforth, unless stated otherwise, γ will be taken as zero.

The schematic representation of a capacitor appears in Fig. 1-32(b). This diagram serves as the circuit model for the capacitor. Note how the initial voltage γ is put on the diagram. Figure 1-32(b) and Eq. (1-9b) are equivalent statements. Sometimes it is desirable to designate the initial voltage separately. We can do so by interpreting Eq. (1-9b) as a statement of Kirchhoff's Voltage Law representing the sum of two voltages: γ and $(1/C)\int_0^t i\,dt'$. The first voltage is constant and hence can be represented by a battery. The second voltage is the voltage acquired by the capacitor after $t = 0$ and thus can be represented as the voltage across a "fresh" capacitor—one having zero initial voltage. The resulting circuit is shown in Fig. 1-32(c). *Even though there are two elements in this equivalent representation, it should be realized that the actual terminals of the capacitor are still where v and i are designated.* The internal structuring is merely for convenience of presentation. It does not describe a physical situation.

For any capacitor in a network, i and v are governed by Eq. (1-9a) or Eq. (1-9b). Either equation applies a specific constraint between the i and v variables. Since there are two variables, another equation involving i and v is needed in order to solve for the values of i and v. (Two variables require two independent equations for solution.) The second equation is obtained by considering the circuit to which the capacitor is connected. For instance, if the capacitor is connected to a voltage source, v_s, then we have our second equation—$v = v_s$. If v_s is known, Eq. (1-9a) can be used to calculate i.

Example 1-14

The circuit shown in Fig. 1-33 is energized with the constant current I_{dc} at $t = 0$. Obtain the expression for the voltage v across the capacitor.

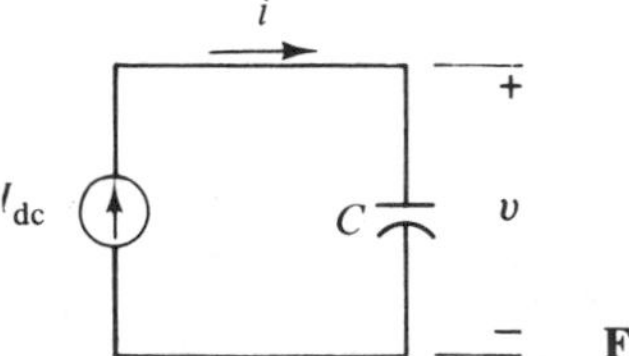

Fig. 1-33

Solution. The voltage across the capacitor is related to the current through it by Eq. (1-9b).

$$v = \gamma + \frac{1}{C}\int_0^t i\,dt'$$

No initial voltage is given. Therefore assume $\gamma = 0$. The current through the capacitor is given as $i = I_{dc}$. Then

$$v = \frac{1}{C}\int_0^t I_{dc}\,dt' = \frac{I_{dc}}{C}\int_0^t dt' = \frac{I_{dc}}{C}t'\bigg|_0^t = \frac{I_{dc}}{C}t \quad \text{Ans.}$$

This result indicates that if the capacitor is driven with a constant current source, the voltage across it increases linearly with time. Thus, *time* can be measured by reading the *voltage* across the capacitor.

Example 1-15

(a) In Fig. 1-34, $v = V_m \sin \omega t$. What is i? Draw the resulting i vs. v curve.
(b) Repeat (a) for $v = E$, where E is a constant.
(c) Discuss the results of (a) and (b).

Solution.

(a) By Eq. (1-9a),

$$i = C\frac{dv}{dt} = C\frac{d}{dt}(V_m \sin \omega t) = V_m\omega C \cos \omega t \quad \text{Ans.}$$

Thus the voltage across and the current through the capacitor are given by

$$v = V_m \sin \omega t$$
$$i = V_m\omega C \cos \omega t$$

It is possible to use this equation set to draw the i vs. v curve, employing t as a parameter. However, the curve can be drawn much more readily if t is eliminated altogether. We can do so as follows.

$$\left(\frac{v}{V_m}\right)^2 + \left(\frac{i}{V_m\omega C}\right)^2 = \sin^2 \omega t + \cos^2 \omega t$$

Since $\sin^2 \omega t + \cos^2 \omega t = 1$, we have

$$\left(\frac{v}{V_m}\right)^2 + \left(\frac{i}{V_m\omega C}\right)^2 = 1$$

which is the equation of an ellipse. It is sketched in Fig. 1-35.

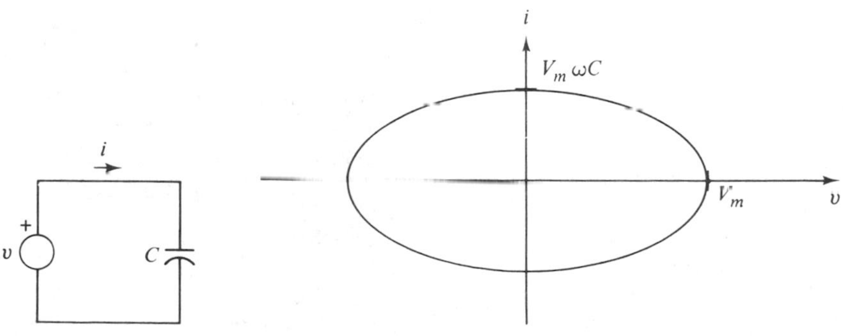

Fig. 1-34 **Fig. 1-35**

(b) If $v = E$, then

$$i = C\frac{dv}{dt} = C\frac{dE}{dt} = 0 \quad \text{Ans.}$$

So equations

$$v = E$$

$$i = 0$$

represent the terminal conditions for this case. The i vs. v curve is merely a point as shown in Fig. 1-36.

(c) This example shows that if we were to describe the capacitor in terms of the i vs. v graph, we would have obtained different graphs, depending on the type of waveforms used to obtain the curve. Thus, as Fig. 1-35 shows, the curve is an ellipse if the voltage is a sine wave. On the other hand, as Fig. 1-36 shows, there is no curve but a point if the voltage is a constant. This kind of presentation is confusing if not useless. It does not uniquely describe the terminal properties of the capacitor. However, had we plotted i vs. dv/dt, we would have obtained a straight line in (a) and a point (at the origin) on this straight line in (b), thereby always giving points on a line with slope C.

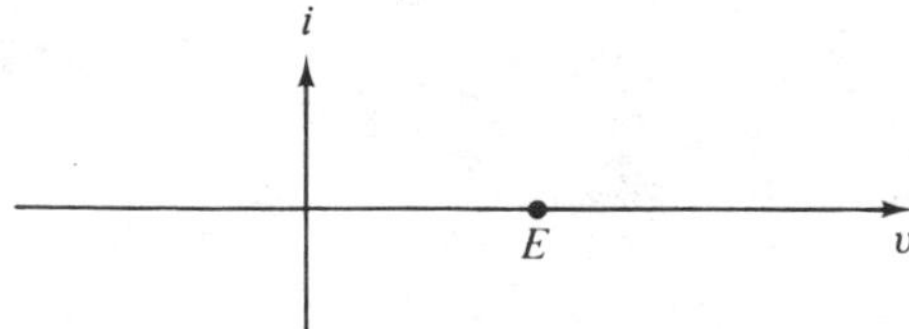

Fig. 1-36

Example 1-16

The triangular voltage waveform shown in Fig. 1-37 is applied to the capacitor. What is the current waveform?

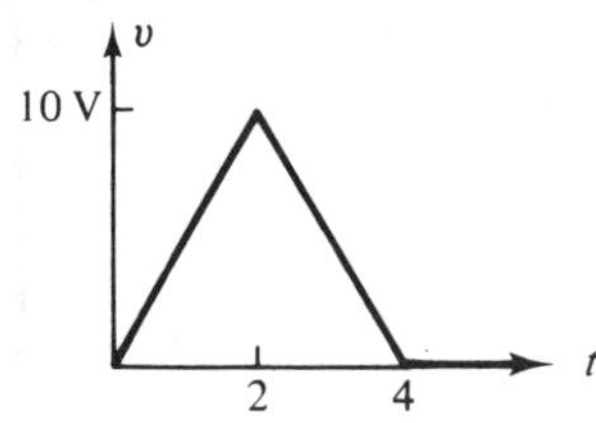

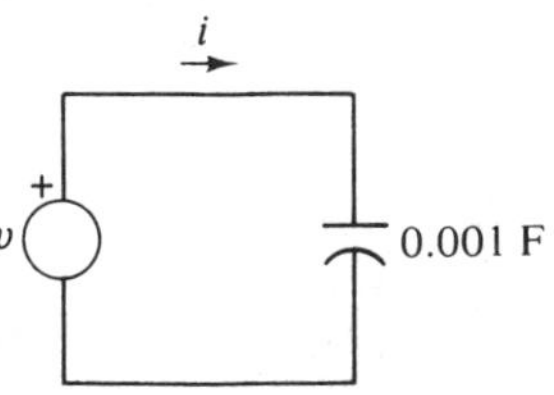

Fig. 1-37

Solution. The current i is given by

$$i = C\frac{dv}{dt} = 0.001\frac{dv}{dt}$$

Inspection of the v vs. t curve shows that

$$\frac{dv}{dt} = \begin{cases} \dfrac{10}{2} = 5, & 0 < t < 2 \\ -\dfrac{10}{2} = -5, & 2 < t < 4 \\ 0, & 4 < t \end{cases}$$

So

$$i = 0.001\,\frac{dv}{dt} = \begin{cases} 0.005\ \text{A}, & 0 < t < 2 \\ -0.005\ \text{A}, & 2 < t < 4 \\ 0, & 4 < t \end{cases}$$

The resulting current is sketched in Fig. 1-38.

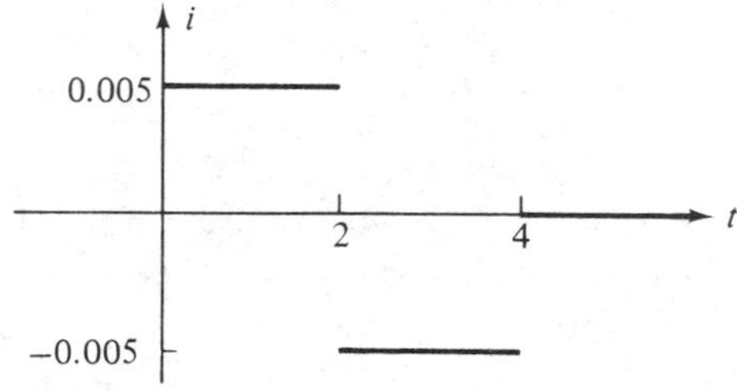

Fig. 1-38

1-8 INDUCTORS

Any two-terminal element having the v vs. di/dt characteristic shown in Fig. 1-39(a) is called an *inductor*. Although the terminal variables are v and i, the plot is v vs. di/dt. Had we plotted i vs. v, the shape of the curve would have depended on the i or v waveform, a result that is not desirable because it is not unique. On the other hand, the v vs. di/dt curve is a straight line passing through the origin with a slope L as shown, and this result is *independent* of the i or v waveform.

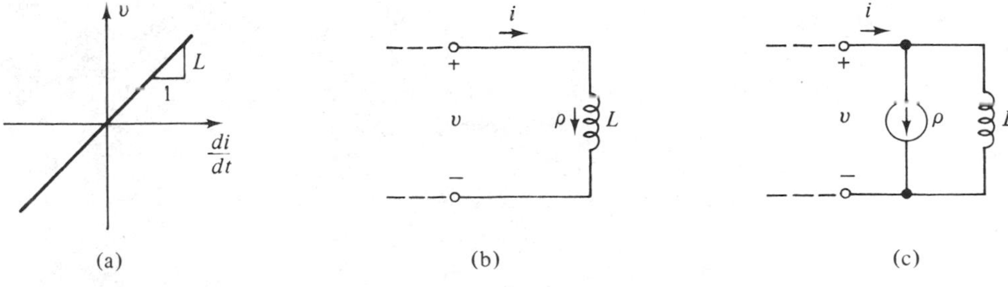

Fig. 1-39

The mathematical model for the inductor is obtained from Fig. 1-39(a) by writing the equation for the straight line*

$$v = L\frac{di}{dt} \tag{1-10a}$$

It is also desirable to have the expression for i as a function of v. Separating the variables in Eq. (1-10a) and then integrating between limits 0 and t, we obtain

$$di = \frac{1}{L}v\,dt, \qquad \int_{i(0)}^{i(t)} di = \frac{1}{L}\int_0^t v\,dt'$$

$$i(t) - i(0) = \frac{1}{L}\int_0^t v\,dt', \qquad i(t) = \underbrace{i(0)}_{\rho} + \frac{1}{L}\int_0^t v\,dt' \tag{1-10b}$$

$$i(t) = \rho + \frac{1}{L}\int_0^t v\,dt'$$

Either Eq. (1-10a) or Eq. (1-10b) can be taken as the defining equation for an inductor. The constant L represents the *inductance* of the inductor. Inductance is measured in henries, abbreviated H. Dimensionally, we have 1 H = 1 (volt × second)/1 ampere. The constant ρ represents the *initial current* $i(0)$ in the inductor. As the value of current that exists in the inductor at $t = 0$, it represents the accumulated result of past events to which the inductor has been subjected. Henceforth, unless specifically mentioned, ρ will be taken as zero.

The schematic presentation of an inductor appears in Fig. 1-39(b). This diagram serves as the circuit model for the inductor. Note how the initial current ρ is put on the diagram. Figure 1-39(b) and Eq. (1-10b) are equivalent statements. Sometimes it is desirable to designate the initial current separately. We can do so by interpreting Eq. (1-10b) as a statement of Kirchhoff's Current Law that represents the sum of two currents: ρ and $(1/L)\int_0^t v\,dt'$. The first current is constant, which means that it can be represented by a constant current source. The second current is the current acquired by the inductor after $t = 0$ and so can be represented as the current through a "fresh" inductor—one having zero initial current. The resulting circuit is shown in Fig. 1-39(c). *Even though there are two elements in this equivalent presentation, it should be noted that the actual terminals of the inductor are still at the v and i designations.* As before, the internal structuring is merely for convenience and does not reflect a physical situation.

For any inductor in the network, i and v are governed by Eq. (1-10a) or Eq. (1-10b). Either equation applies a specific constraint between the i and v variables. If

*In cases where the slope L varies with time, Eq. (1-10a) is modified to

$$v = \frac{d}{dt}(Li) = \frac{d\lambda}{dt}$$

where $\lambda = Li$ represents the flux linkages of the inductor.

v and i are to be determined, another relation between v and i must be found. This second relation is obtained by considering the characteristics of the network to which the inductor is connected. For instance, if the inductor is connected to a current source, i_s, then $i = i_s$. If i_s is known, Eq. (1-10a) can be used to calculate v.

Example 1-17

In Fig. 1-40 the battery is applied to the inductor by closing the switch S at $t = 0$. What is the resulting current through the inductor? The initial current in the inductor is zero.

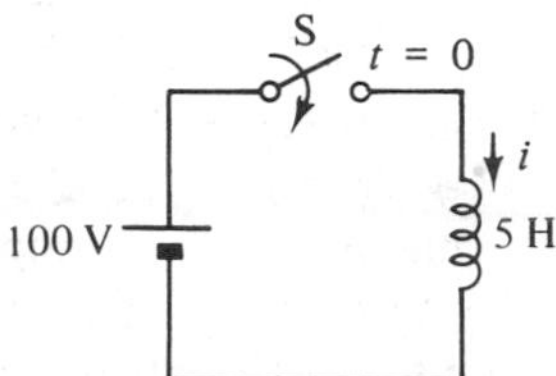

Fig. 1-40

Solution. Using Eq. (1-10b) with $\rho = 0$, we can calculate i.

$$i = \frac{1}{L}\int_0^t v\, dt' = \frac{1}{5}\int_0^t 100\, dt' = 20t'\Big|_0^t = 20t \quad \text{Ans.}$$

Example 1-18

The voltage across an inductor is $v = 5 \sin 0.2t$ volts. The current through it is $i = -0.1 \cos 0.2t$ amperes. What is the value of the inductance?

Solution. By Eq. (1-10a),

$$v = L\frac{di}{dt}$$

Therefore

$$L = \frac{v}{di/dt} = \frac{5 \sin 0.2t}{(d/dt)(-0.1 \cos 0.2t)} = \frac{5 \sin 0.2t}{0.02 \sin 0.2t} = 250 \text{ H} \quad \text{Ans.}$$

1-9 OTHER ELEMENTS

As the variety of basic electrical elements (building blocks) increases, the circuit designer can become more versatile. For instance, we may wish that we had an element described by the terminal characteristic shown in Fig. 1-41.

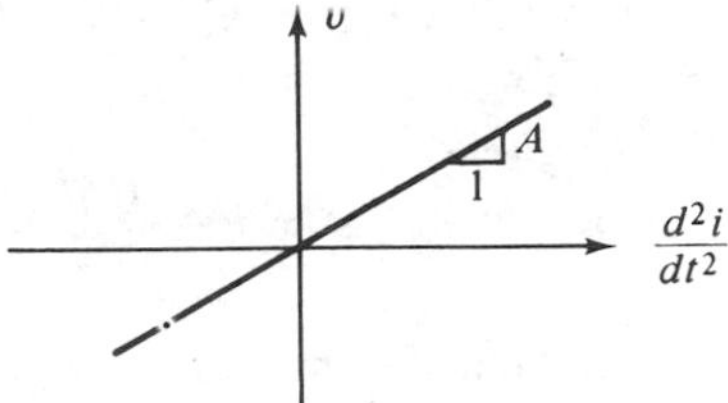

Fig. 1-41

The mathematical model for this element would be

$$v = A\frac{d^2i}{dt^2}$$

We could even name this element ourselves and decide on a symbolic presentation for it as we please! However, it should be noted that having a mathematical description of an element is one thing and having the actual physical realization of it is another. Even if building such a device were technically feasible, manufacturing it could be prohibitive unless a large market is demonstrably available.

Sooner or later the engineer realizes that the voltage source described by Fig. 1-19(a) or the inductor described by Fig. 1-39(a) is nonexistent. Each represents idealized characteristics that the manufacturer attempts to bring close to realization. The chief problem in modeling is to recognize that, in practice, we are dealing with *approximations* that may produce the desired behavior over a limited range of variables if certain other restrictions, such as constant-temperature environment, are met. It may be possible, for a given device, to obtain closer agreement between the observed behavior and the mathematical model over a wide range of variables by using more complicated models. Quite often the engineer has to choose between a simple model that is readily understandable and a complicated model that gives more accurate results but is more difficult to use.

1-10 LINEAR CIRCUITS

Sources are described by *one* variable. Thus $v = v_s$ and $i = i_s$ characterize completely a voltage and a current source, respectively. By considering the voltage source alone, we have no way of knowing the current through it. Similarly, the current source by itself tells us nothing about the voltage across it. In order to determine these variables, we must know about the entire circuit. The external circuit must be given before the current through a voltage source or the voltage across a current source can be found.

On the other hand, resistors, capacitors, and inductors are described by a functional relationship involving the current through and the voltage across them. We do not know about the current or the voltage, but we do know how they are related. Given one, we can find the other by considering the element alone. Again, the entire circuit must be given in order to determine both variables associated with an element.

Consider now the i vs. v relationships of a resistor, capacitor, and inductor. Since initial conditions can be treated as separate sources [(see Figs. 1-32(c) and 1-39(c)], they are omitted in the following discussion.

$$i = \frac{1}{R}v, \qquad i = C\frac{dv}{dt}, \qquad i = \frac{1}{L}\int_0^t v\,dt' \tag{1-11}$$

From Eq. (1-11) we see that the current through each element is linearly related to the voltage across it. So if the voltage across each element is doubled, the current through each element doubles. *If the voltages are multiplied by some constant K, the resulting currents become K times larger.*

Instead of expressing i as a function of v, we can express v as a function of i, obtaining

$$v = Ri, \qquad v = \frac{1}{C}\int_0^t i\,dt', \qquad v = L\frac{di}{dt} \tag{1-12}$$

We then see that multiplying the currents by K results in voltages that are K times larger. As a result of this property, we say that resistors, capacitors, and inductors are linear elements. In general, any element in which the voltage and current variables are related by

$$i = A\frac{d^n v}{dt^n} \quad \text{or} \quad v = B\frac{d^n i}{dt^n} \qquad (n = 0, 1, 2, \ldots) \tag{1-13}$$

is called a *linear* element, provided that A and B do not depend on v or i. A circuit composed of linear elements and sources is called a *linear circuit*. (By sources, we mean independent and linearly dependent sources. This distinction is discussed in Chapter 11.)

In a linear circuit that is driven by a *single* voltage or current source, all resulting voltages and currents are linearly dependent on the source. Thus if the value of the source is doubled or tripled, all resulting currents and voltages are doubled or tripled. If the source is multiplied by K, where K can be positive or negative, all resulting currents and voltages are multiplied by K. In other words, currents and voltages in a linear circuit are directly proportional to the source producing them.

1-11 OPEN AND SHORT CIRCUITS

A pair of terminals is said to be open-circuited when *no current* is drawn from either terminal. See Fig. 1-42(a). The voltage across the terminals can have any value, depending on the circuit N under consideration. This voltage is called the *open-circuit voltage*, v_{oc}. Alternatively, terminals 1–1′ can be considered open-circuited if external to the network N there is infinite resistance between 1–1′.

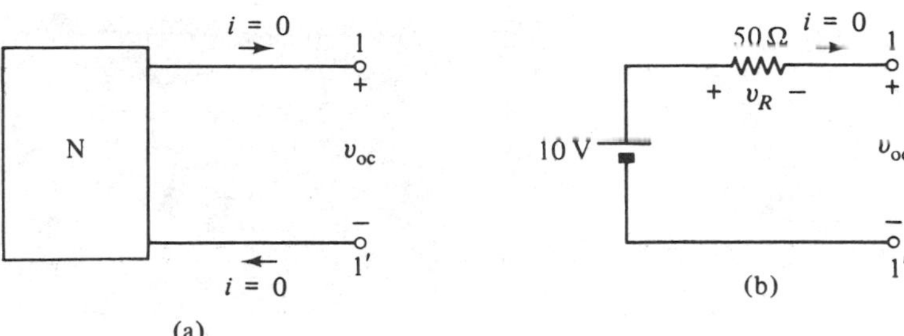

Fig. 1-42

An example of an open circuit is given in Fig. 1-42(b). When Kirchhoff's Current Law is applied to either node, 1 or 1′, it is seen that no current is drawn from the terminals—that is, $i = 0$. Consequently, the current through the 50 Ω resistor is zero. Moreover, by Ohm's Law ($v_R = iR$), the voltage across the resistor is zero. Therefore, by Kirchhoff's Voltage Law (applied to the loop involving 10 V, v_R, and v_{oc}), we obtain $v_{oc} = 10$ V.

A pair of terminals is said to be short-circuited when *the voltage* across these terminals is *zero,* regardless of the value of current flowing from one terminal to the other. See Fig. 1-43(a). The current through the short circuit is called the *short-circuit current,* i_{sc}. Alternatively, terminals 1–1′ can be considered short-circuited if external to the network N there is zero resistance between 1–1′.

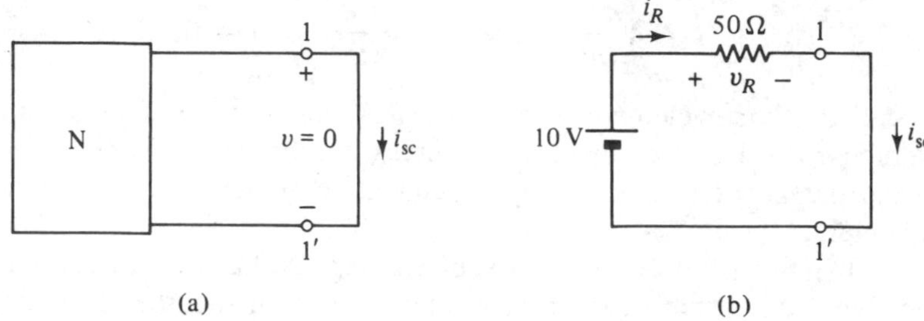

Fig. 1-43

An example of a short circuit is given in Fig. 1-43(b). By Kirchhoff's Voltage Law, $v_R = 10$ V. By Ohm's Law, the current through the resistor is $i_R = v_R/R = 10/50 = 0.2$ A. Then, by Kirchhoff's Current Law applied to node 1, $i_{sc} = i_R = 0.2$ A.

1-12 SUMMARY

Two variables v and i describe the characteristics of electric networks. These variables are measured by a voltmeter and an ammeter.

Two laws, known as Kirchhoff's laws, place constraints on the i and v variables, based on the connective features of the circuit elements. Kirchhoff's Current Law

$$\sum i = 0$$

is obeyed at every node in the network at all times. Kirchhoff's Voltage Law

$$\sum v = 0$$

is obeyed in every loop of the network at all times.

Elements are described in terms of the v and i relationships at their terminals.

The five basic elements discussed in this chapter are

Voltage source	$(v = v_s)$
Current source	$(i = i_s)$
Resistor	$(v = iR)$
Capacitor	$\left(i = C\dfrac{dv}{dt}\right)$
Inductor	$\left(v = L\dfrac{di}{dt}\right)$

The equation defining an element places one constraint on the terminal v and i variables. Another equation is needed to solve for the two terminal variables. This second equation is obtained by considering the characteristics of the circuit to which the element is connected.

When two terminals are open-circuited, the terminal currents are zero, but the open-circuit voltage may have a value other than zero. When two terminals are short-circuited, the terminal voltage is zero, but the short-circuit current may have a value other than zero.

The equation defining a resistor, $v = iR$, is also known as Ohm's Law.

PROBLEMS

1-1. For each circuit shown in Fig. 1-44, find the unknown current.

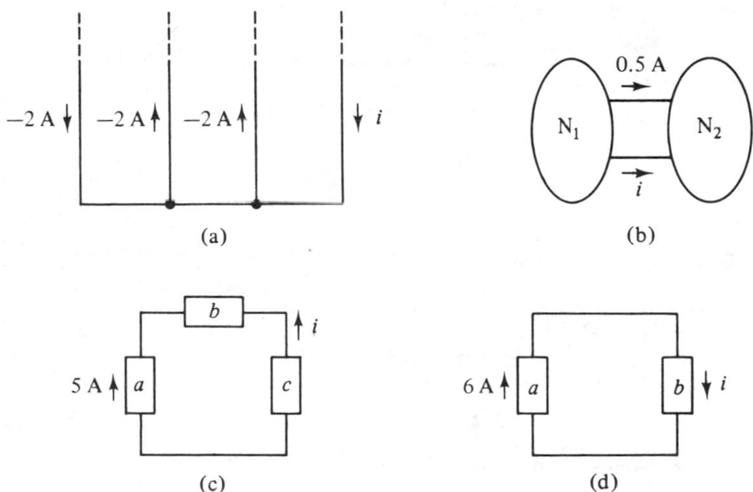

Fig. 1-44

1-2. In Fig. 1-45 what does the ammeter read?

1-3. In Fig. 1-46 ammeters 1 and 2 read −2 A and 3 A, respectively. What does ammeter 3 read?

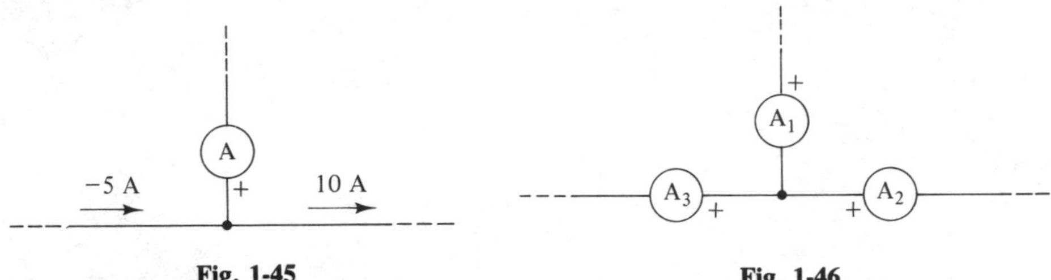

Fig. 1-45 **Fig. 1-46**

1-4. In Fig. 1-47 the ammeter reads −2 A. Find i_1 and i_2.

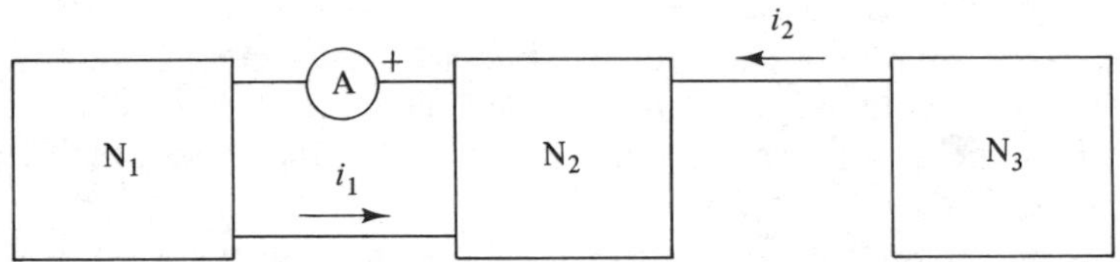

Fig. 1-47

1-5. Refer to Fig. 1-48.

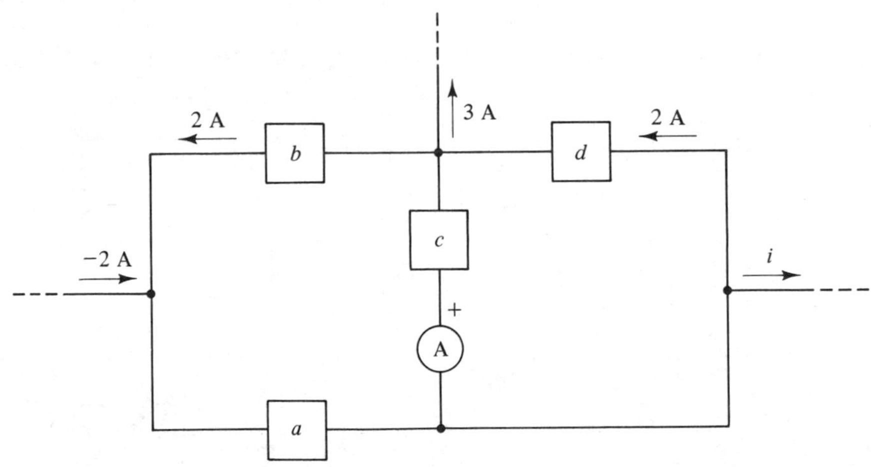

Fig. 1-48

(a) What does the ammeter read?
(b) What is i?

1-6. For each circuit shown in Fig. 1-49, find the unknown voltage.

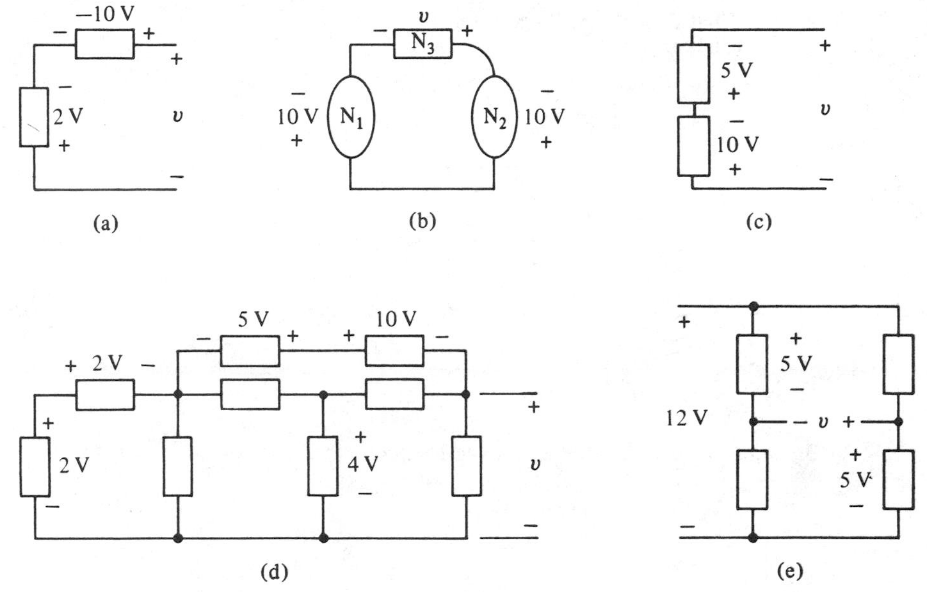

Fig. 1-49

1-7. In Fig. 1-50 voltmeters 1 and 2 read −10 V and 5 V, respectively.

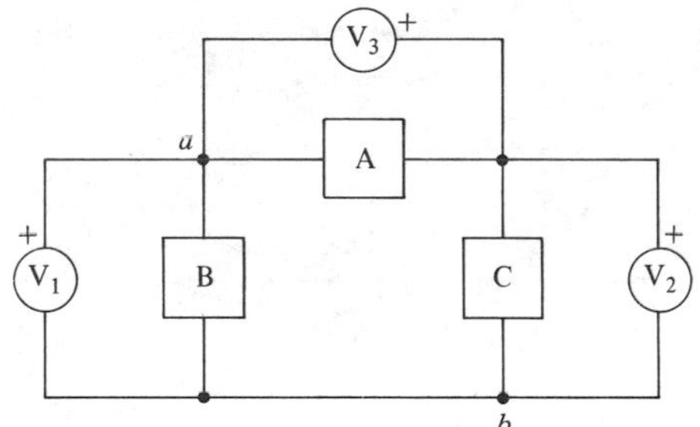

Fig. 1-50

(a) What does the voltmeter 3 read?
(b) What is v_{ab}?

1-8. Refer to Fig. 1-51.

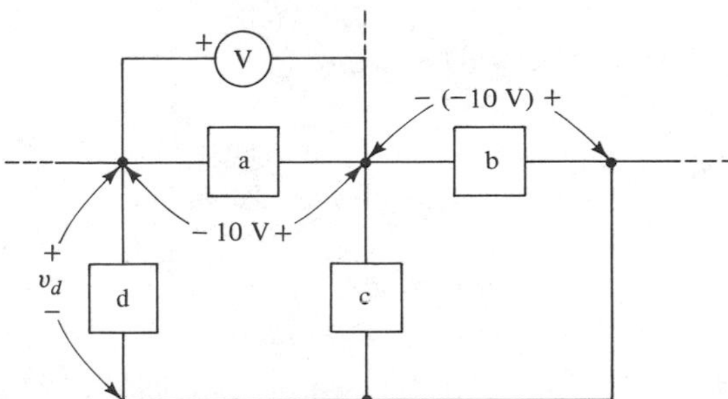

Fig. 1-51

(a) What does the voltmeter read?
(b) What is v_d?

1-9. Determine the unknown current for each circuit shown in Fig. 1-52.

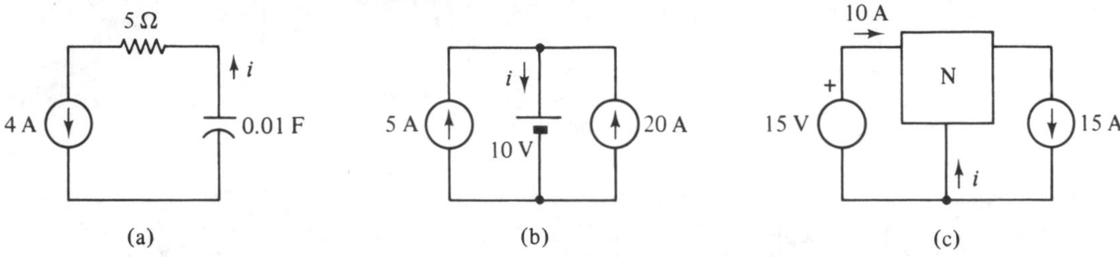

Fig. 1-52

1-10. Determine the unknown voltage for each circuit shown in Fig. 1-53.

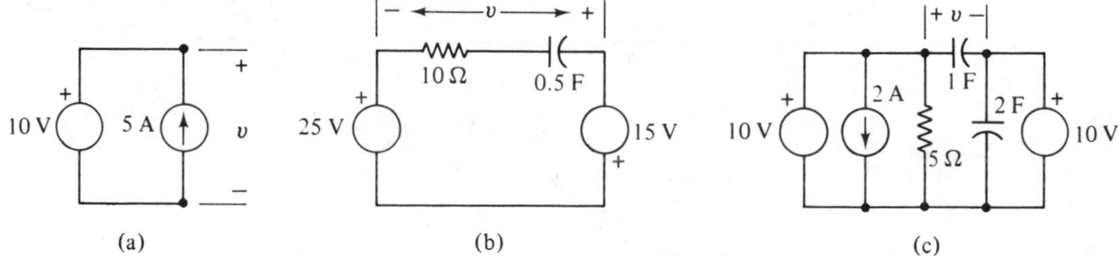

Fig. 1-53

1-11 In Fig. 1-54 voltmeters 1 and 2 read 5 V and −6 V, respectively.

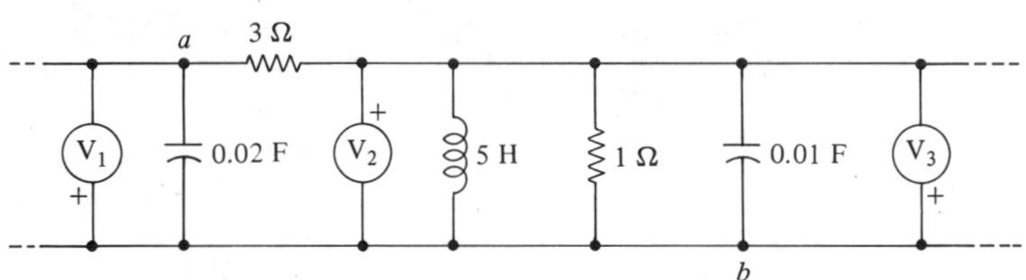

Fig. 1-54

(a) What does voltmeter 3 read?
(b) What is v_{ab}?

1-12. For the four circuits shown in Fig. 1-55, calculate i.

1-13. Calculate v for each circuit shown in Fig. 1-56.

1-14. For the circuit shown in Fig. 1-57, plot the i vs. v characteristic curve.

1-15. The terminal variables of a box are measured and graphed as shown in Fig. 1-58. What is in the box?

1-16. Refer to Fig. 1-59. What do the four instruments read?

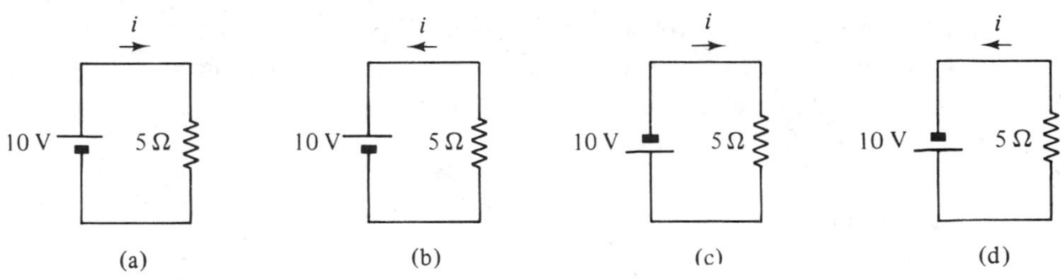

Fig. 1-55

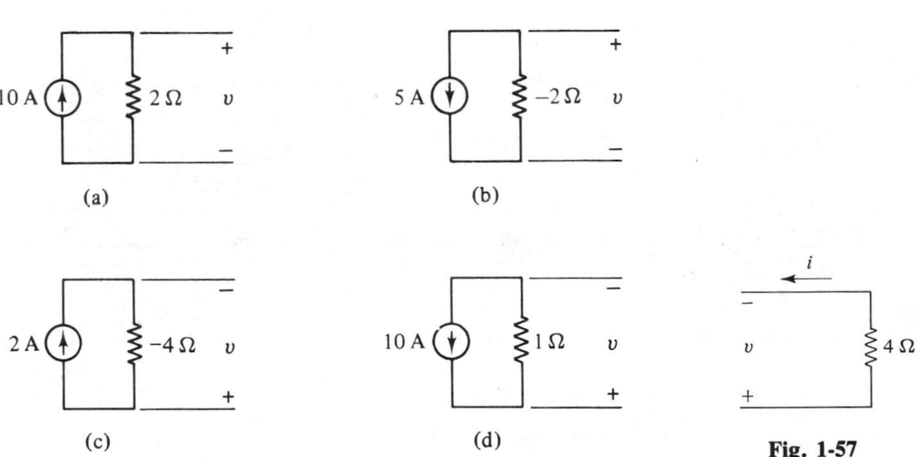

Fig. 1-57

Fig. 1-56

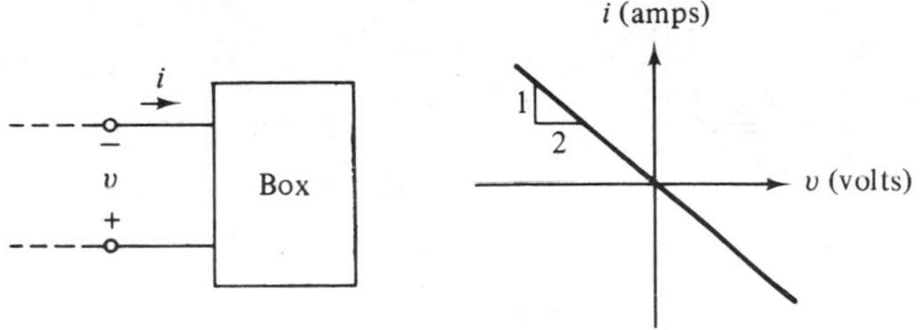

Fig. 1-58

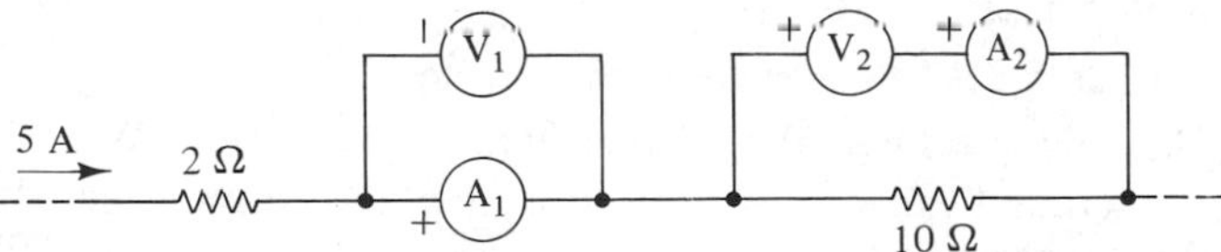

Fig. 1-59

1-17. In Fig. 1-60 the voltmeter reads −10 V. What is i_1?

1-18. In Fig. 1-61 $v_1 = -10$ V. What do the three instruments read?

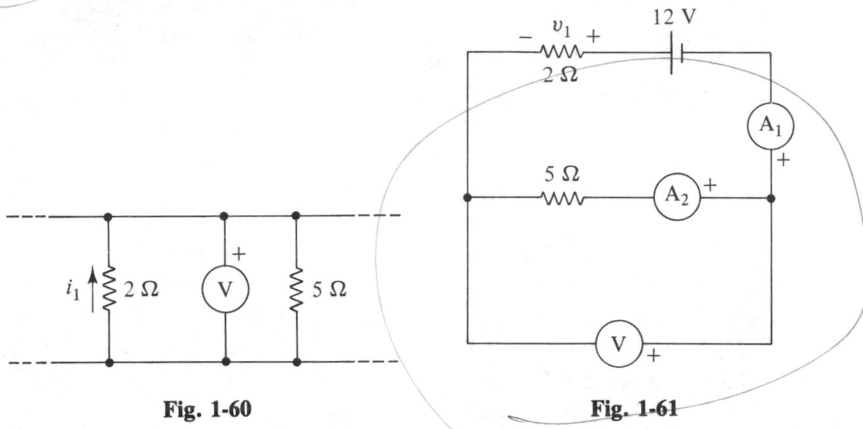

Fig. 1-60 **Fig. 1-61**

1-19. In Fig. 1-62 the ammeter and voltmeter readings are −2 A and 10 V, respectively. What is i_s?

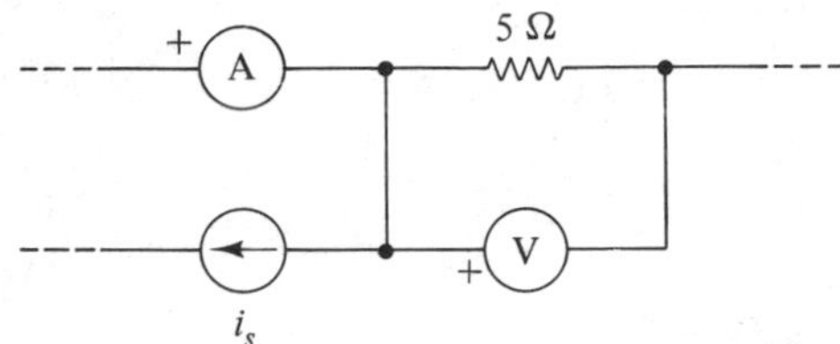

Fig. 1-62

1-20. In Fig. 1-63 the ammeter reads 2 A. Find v_3 and i_b.

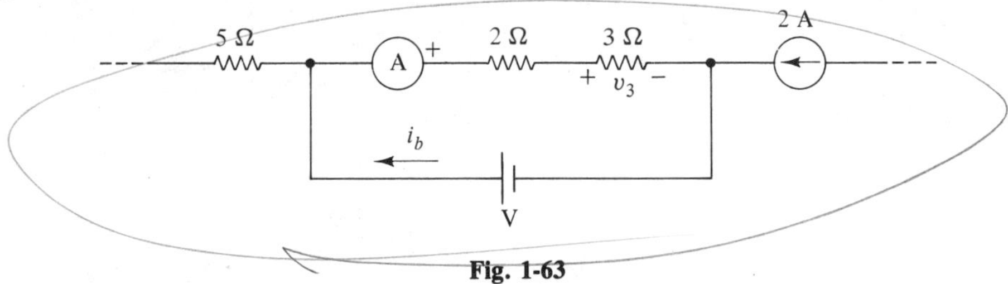

Fig. 1-63

1-21. In Fig. 1-64 the voltmeter reads 0. Find i and v.

1-22. Plot the $\int_0^t i\,dt'$ vs. v curve for a capacitor.

1-23. The voltage across a 0.01 F capacitor is $v = t + \sin t$. What is i through it?

1-24. The terminal variables of an element are measured and graphed as shown in Fig. 1-65. What is the element?

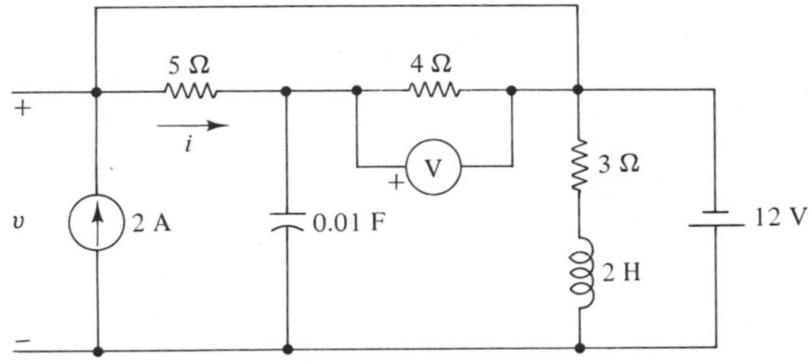

Fig. 1-64

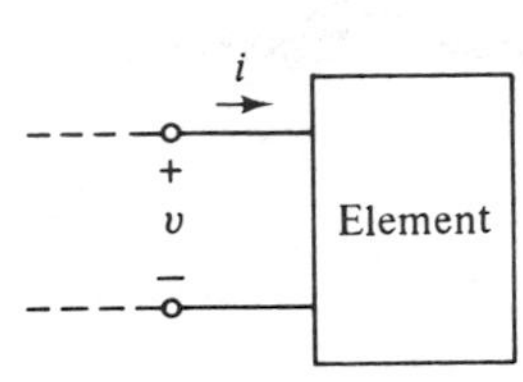

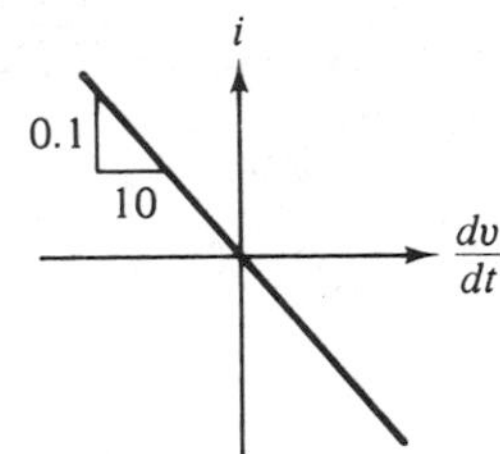

Fig. 1-65

1-25. Graph for $t \geq 0$ the i vs. v curve for a 1 F capacitor if (a) $v = t$; (b) $i = e^{-t}$.

1-26. A 0.01 F capacitor is driven by the current waveform shown in Fig. 1-66. Sketch the resulting voltage waveform. Give values.

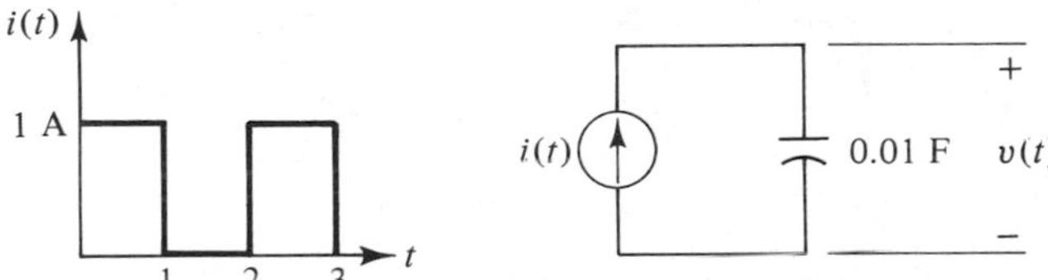

Fig. 1-66

1-27. For the i_s given in Fig. 1-67, obtain the expressions for $v(t)$.

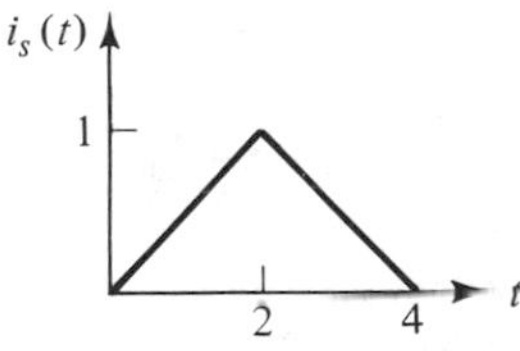

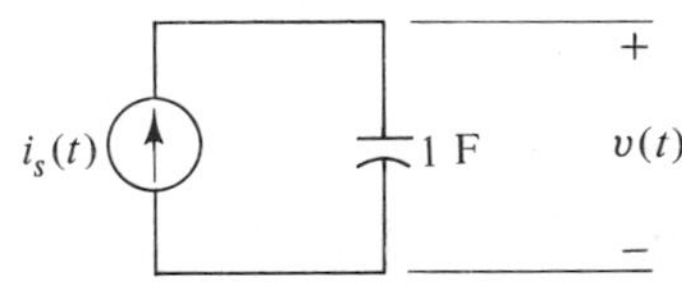

Fig. 1-67

1-28. In Fig. 1-68 what v waveform would result in the i waveform shown?

1-29. In Fig. 1-69 $i = t$ for $t \geq 0$. For $t \geq 0$ plot the following: v vs. t, i vs. v, i vs. dv/dt.

1-30. The voltage source in Fig. 1-70 has the waveform shown. Draw the i vs. t and i vs. v curves. Give values.

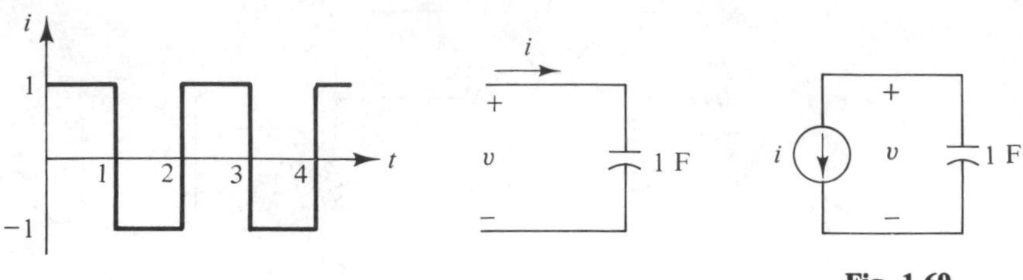

Fig. 1-69

Fig. 1-68

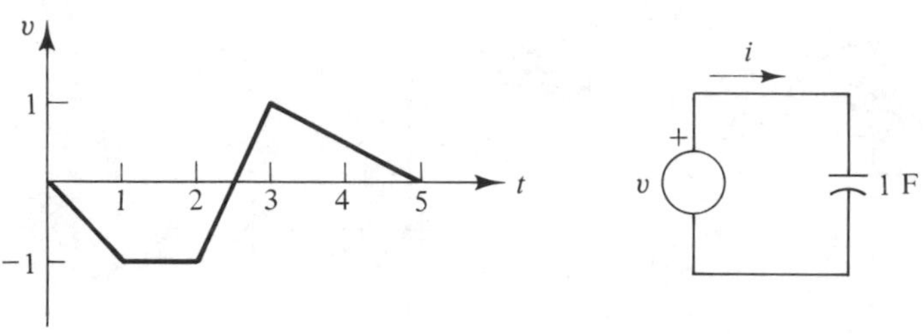

Fig. 1-70

1-31. A 1 A step current is applied to the capacitor with an initial voltage of 3 V as shown in Fig. 1-71. Sketch v vs. t. When is the voltage across the capacitor zero?

1-32. In Fig. 1-72 the initial voltage across the capacitor is 10 V as shown. Obtain the expression for $v(t)$.

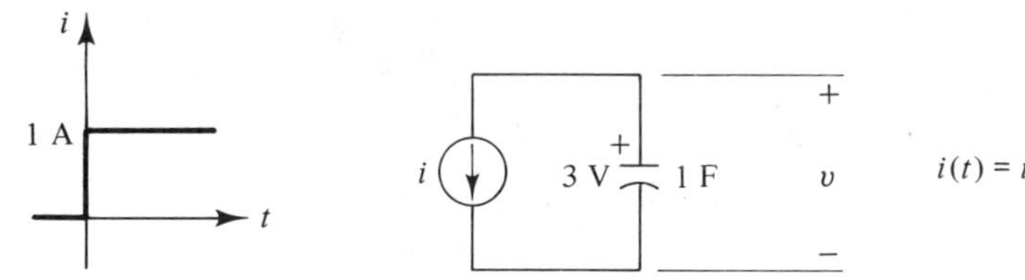

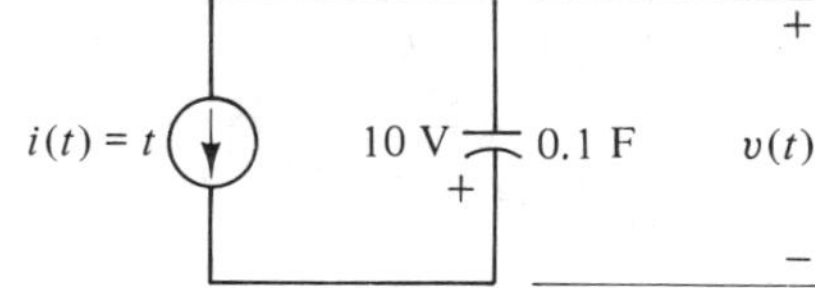

Fig. 1-71

Fig. 1-72

1-33. A current source given by $i = t$ is applied to a 10 H inductor at $t = 0$. What is the resulting voltage?

1-34. (a) The current through an inductor L is $I_m \sin \omega t$. What is the voltage across it?
(b) Using the i and v obtained in (a), sketch the i vs. v curve.
(c) Using the i and v obtained in (a), sketch the v vs. di/dt curve.

1-35. The voltage across a 1 H inductor is $\sin t$.
(a) Sketch the resulting current waveform.
(b) Sketch the i vs. v curve. Give values.

1-36. In Fig. 1-73 sketch the current waveforms. Give values.

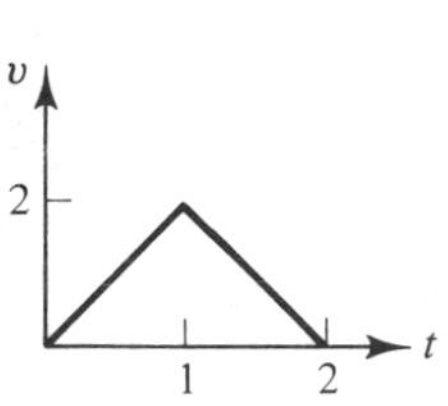

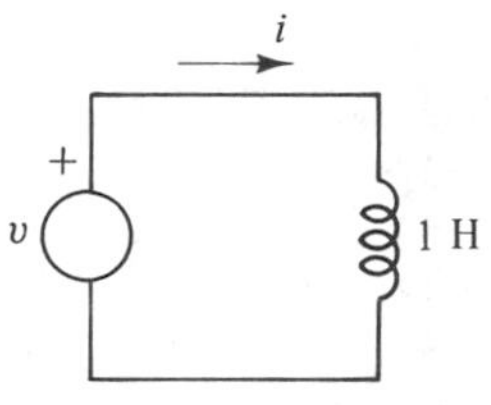

Fig. 1-73

1-37. For the circuit shown in Fig. 1-74 sketch the $v(t)$ vs. t and $i(t)$ vs. $v(t)$ curves.

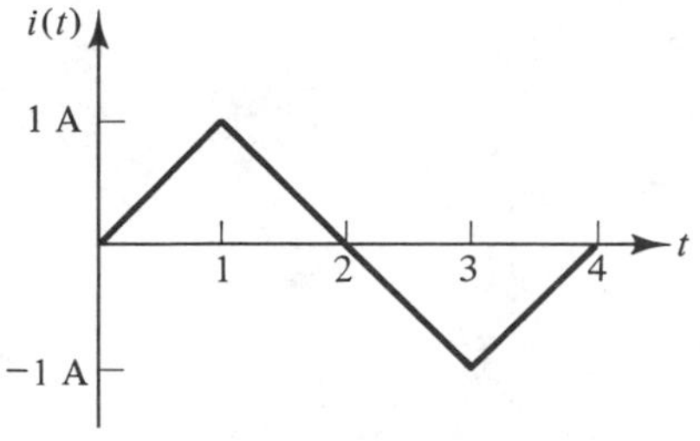

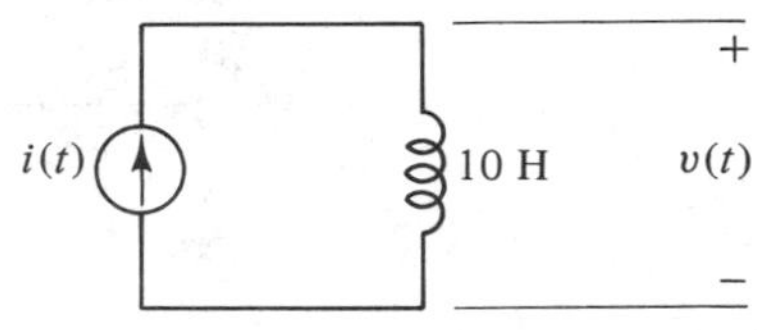

Fig. 1-74

1-38. In Fig. 1-75 obtain the expression for $i(t)$.

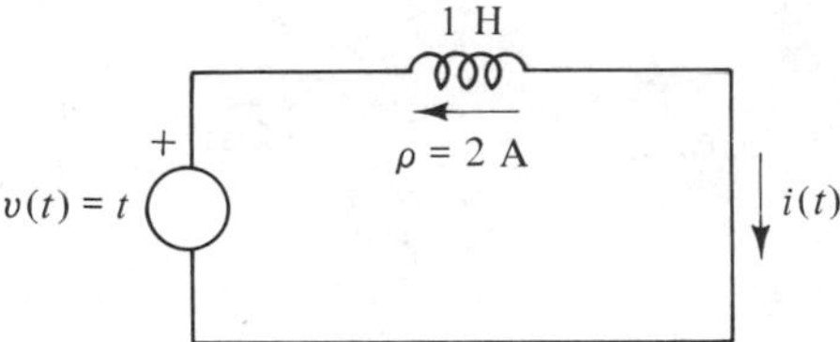

Fig. 1-75

1-39. In Fig. 1-76 sketch the i vs. t, i vs. v, and v vs. di/dt curves.

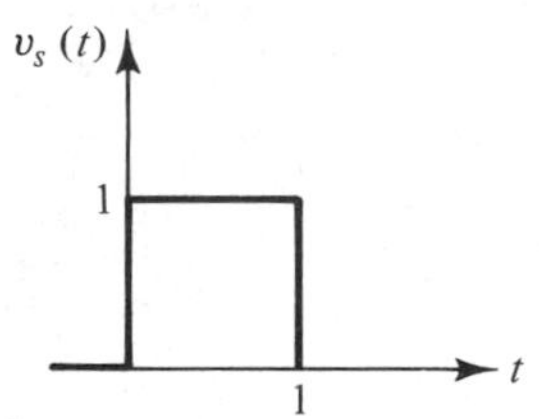

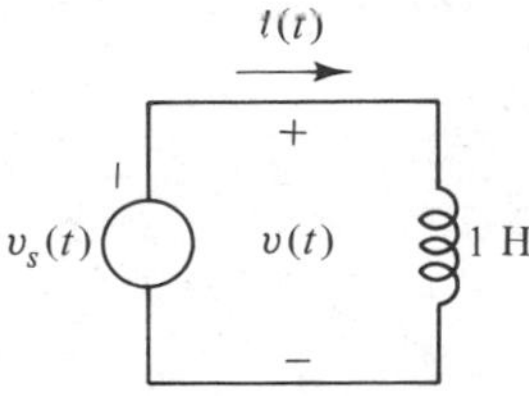

Fig. 1-76

1-40. In Fig. 1-77, the switch S is closed at $t = 0$, thereby short-circuiting terminals 1–1′.

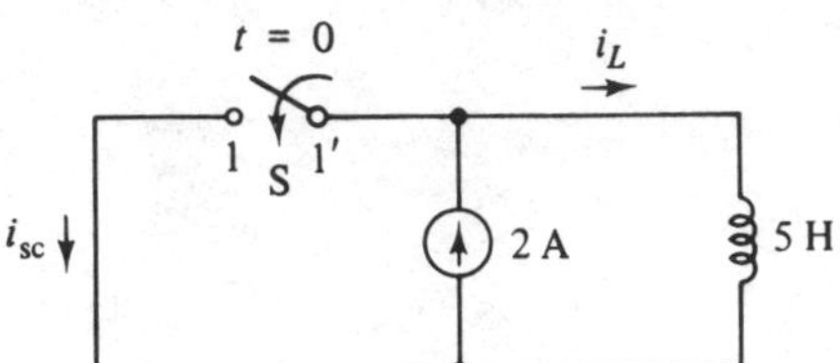

Fig. 1-77

(a) What is the current through the inductor before the switch is closed?
(b) What is the current through the inductor and the current through the short circuit 10 s after the switch is closed?

1-41. Sketch i vs. $\int_0^t v\, dt'$ for an inductor.

1-42 Refer to Fig. 1-78.

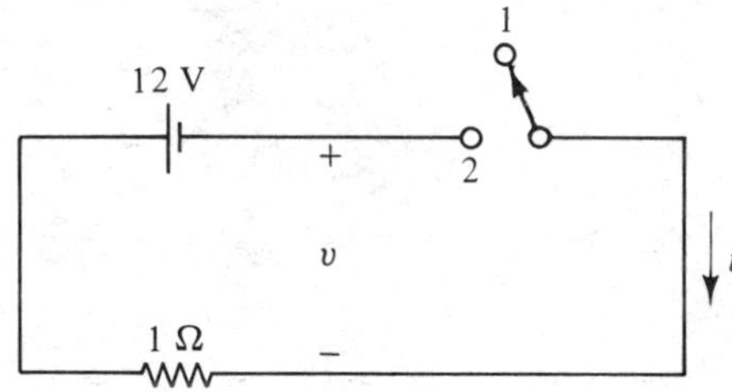

Fig. 1-78

(a) The switch is in position 1. Obtain v and i.
(b) The switch is in position 2. Obtain v and i.

CHAPTER 2

RESISTIVE NETWORKS

Networks consisting of resistors and a voltage or current source are easily analyzed by using Ohm's Law and Kirchhoff's two laws.

2-1 EQUIVALENCE; SERIES AND PARALLEL CONNECTIONS

Two networks are said to be *equivalent* with respect to their terminal behavior if *their terminal characteristics are identical*. The terminal characteristics are described in terms of the functional relationship between the v and i variables.

Two elements (or networks) are said to be connected in *series* if they are chain connected as in Fig. 2-1(a). *Because no other connections are made at the common node A, the same current i flows through both elements*. This statement can be verified by applying Kirchhoff's Current Law to node A between the two elements.

Two elements (or networks) are said to be connected in *parallel* if their terminals are connected together as in Fig. 2-1(b). Because both elements are connected between nodes B and C, the *same voltage v exists across them*. This statement can be verified by applying Kirchhoff's Voltage Law to the loop containing elements 1 and 2.

The network shown in Fig. 2-2 is a series-parallel-connected network. Element 1 is connected in series with element 2. (At node A only elements 1 and 2 are connected.) Element 3 is connected in parallel with element 4. (Elements 3 and 4 are

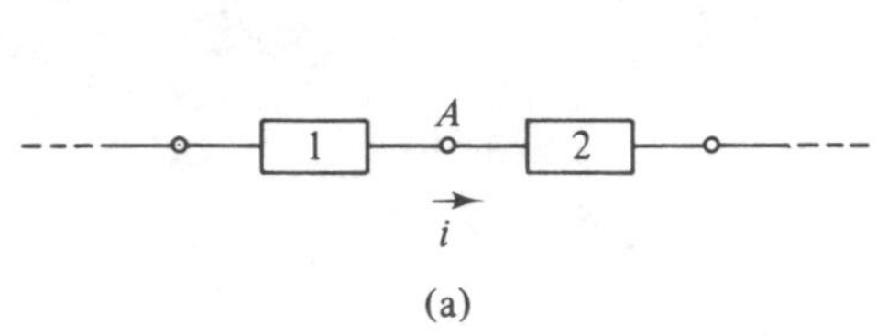

(a)

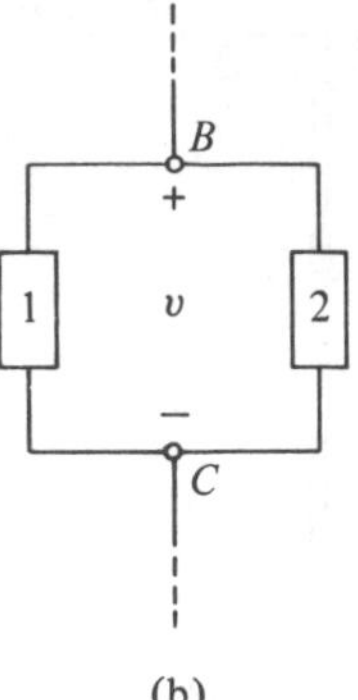

(b)

Fig. 2-1

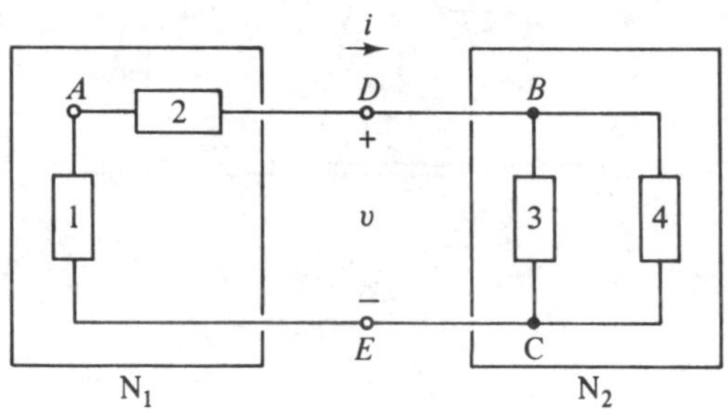

Fig. 2-2

connected between nodes B and C.) The combination of elements 1 and 2 (box labeled N_1) is connected in series with the combination of elements 3 and 4 (box labeled N_2), since the same current i flows through N_1 and N_2. Alternatively, the combination of elements 1 and 2 can be considered connected in parallel with the combination of elements 3 and 4, since the same voltage v exists across N_1 and N_2. If a third network, N_3, were connected between nodes D and E, N_1 would no longer be in series with N_2. However, N_1, N_2, and N_3 will all be in parallel.

2-2 SERIES, PARALLEL, AND SERIES-PARALLEL CONNECTION OF RESISTORS

In Fig. 2-3(a), two resistors are connected in series. The same current i flows through R_1 and R_2. By Ohm's Law, the voltages across R_1 and R_2 are

$$v_1 = iR_1, \qquad v_2 = iR_2$$

By Kirchhoff's Voltage Law, the voltage v appearing across terminals 1–2 is

$$v = v_1 + v_2 = iR_1 + iR_2 = i(R_1 + R_2) = iR_{eq}$$

(a) (b)

Fig. 2-3

where $R_{eq} = R_1 + R_2$. Thus if we take the series combination of R_1 and R_2 out and substitute instead a single resistor of value $(R_1 + R_2)$, the terminal behavior (i vs. v curve) will be the same. So the network in Fig. 2-3(a) can be equivalently represented as in Fig. 2-3(b). This result is independent of the order in which the resistors are connected; that is, in Fig. 2-3(a), R_1 and R_2 can be interchanged.

When n resistors are connected in series, the equivalent resistance becomes

$$R_{eq} = R_1 + R_2 + R_3 + \cdots + R_n \tag{2-1}$$

Stated in words, the equivalent resistance of n resistors connected in series is the sum of the individual resistances.

In Fig. 2-4(a), two resistors are connected in parallel. The same voltage v appears across R_1 and R_2. By Ohm's Law, the currents through R_1 and R_2 are

$$i_1 = \frac{v}{R_1}, \qquad i_2 = \frac{v}{R_2}$$

By Kirchhoff's Current Law, the current i coming in at node 1 is

$$i = i_1 + i_2 = \frac{v}{R_1} + \frac{v}{R_2} = v\left(\frac{1}{R_1} + \frac{1}{R_2}\right) = v\left(\frac{R_1 + R_2}{R_1 R_2}\right) = \frac{v}{R_{eq}}$$

where $$R_{eq} = \frac{R_1 R_2}{R_1 + R_2} \qquad \text{or} \qquad \frac{1}{R_{eq}} = \frac{1}{R_1} + \frac{1}{R_2}$$

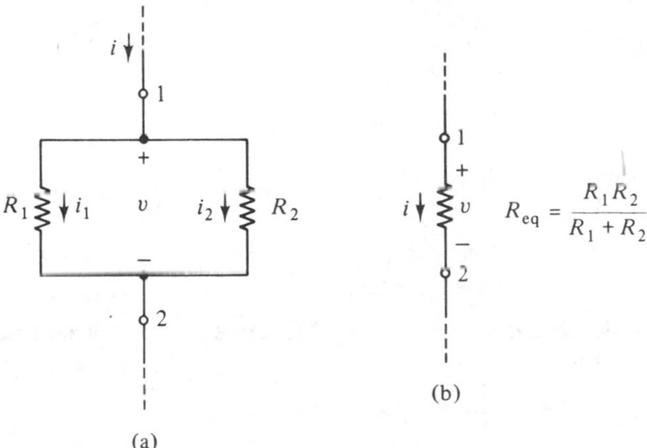

Fig. 2-4

Thus if we take the parallel combination of R_1 and R_2 out and substitute instead a single resistor of value $R_1 R_2/(R_1 + R_2)$, the terminal behavior (i vs. v curve) will be the same. Consequently, the network in Fig. 2-4(a) can be equivalently represented as in Fig. 2-4(b). Stated in words, the equivalent resistance of *two* resistors connected in parallel is equal to the product over the sum of the two individual resistances. This equivalent resistance is *always smaller* than either resistance except when one resistance is zero; then the equivalent resistance is zero. This result is independent of the order in which the resistors are connected; that is, in Fig. 2-4(a), R_1 and R_2 can be interchanged.

When n resistors are connected in parallel, the equivalent resistance is obtained from

$$\frac{1}{R_{eq}} = \frac{1}{R_1} + \frac{1}{R_2} + \frac{1}{R_3} + \cdots + \frac{1}{R_n} \tag{2-2}$$

Stated in words, the reciprocal of the equivalent resistance is the sum of the reciprocals of the individual resistances.

By using the series and parallel connection rules for resistors given by Eqs. (2-1) and (2-2), the equivalent resistance of series-parallel-connected resistors can readily be obtained. However, not all circuits are connected in series, parallel, or series-parallel. In such cases, the equivalent resistance is found by calculating the v/i ratio at the terminals.

Example 2-1

Obtain the equivalent resistance of the two networks shown in Fig. 2-5.

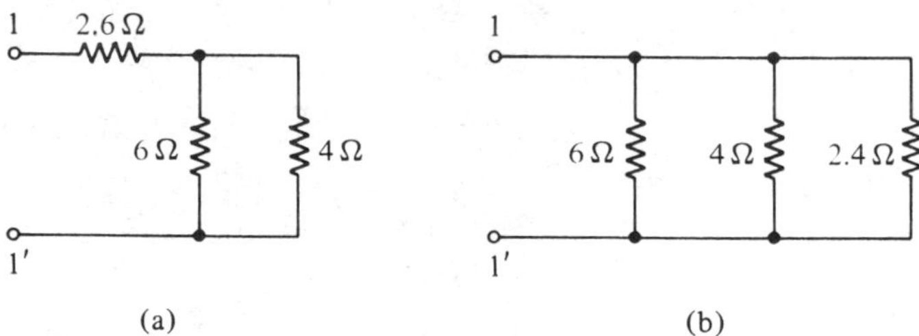

Fig. 2-5

Solution. Consider first the circuit in Fig. 2-5(a). The 6 Ω and 4 Ω resistors are in parallel. The combination can be replaced with an equivalent resistance of

$$\frac{6 \times 4}{6 + 4} = 2.4\ \Omega$$

This 2.4 Ω resistor is in series with the 2.6 Ω resistor. Therefore the equivalent resistor appearing between terminals 1–1′ is

$$2.4 + 2.6 = 5\ \Omega \quad \text{Ans.}$$

Consider next the circuit in Fig. 2-5(b). The equivalent resistance between 1–1′ is obtained by using Eq. (2-2).

$$\frac{1}{R_{eq}} = \frac{1}{6} + \frac{1}{4} + \frac{1}{2.4} = \frac{1}{1.2}$$

$$R_{eq} = 1.2\ \Omega \quad \text{Ans.}$$

Alternatively, the first two (or any other two) resistors can be replaced by a resistor having a resistance of

$$\frac{6 \times 4}{6 + 4} = 2.4$$

This resistor itself is in parallel with the remaining 2.4 Ω resistor. So by using the product over the sum rule again, the equivalent resistance at terminals 1–1′ is obtained.

$$\frac{2.4 \times 2.4}{2.4 + 2.4} = \frac{2.4}{2} = 1.2\ \Omega \quad \text{Ans.}$$

The equivalent resistance of three parallel resistances *cannot* be found by taking the product of all three resistances divided by their sum.

Example 2-2

In Fig. 2-6, what is the equivalent resistance seen to the right of 1–1′, 2–2′, and 3–3′?

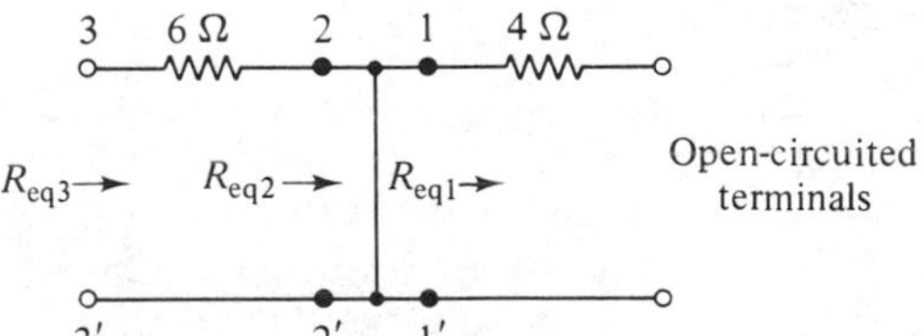

Fig. 2-6

Solution. To the right of 1–1′ we find the 4 Ω in series with an open circuit (infinite resistance). Thus we obtain

$$R_{eq1} = 4 + \infty = \infty \quad \text{Ans.}$$

In other words, to the right of 1–1′ we still have an open circuit.

To the right of 2–2′ we find a short circuit (zero resistance) in parallel with R_{eq1}, which is infinite. Therefore we have

$$R_{eq2} = 0 \quad \text{Ans.}$$

In other words, to the right of 2–2′ we still have a short circuit.

To the right of 3–3′ we have 6 Ω in series with R_{eq2}, which is zero. So we have

$$R_{eq3} = 6 + R_{eq2} = 6\ \Omega \quad \text{Ans.}$$

Example 2-3

In Fig. 2-7, what is the resistance seen looking into terminals 1–1′? All edge resistances are 1 Ω.

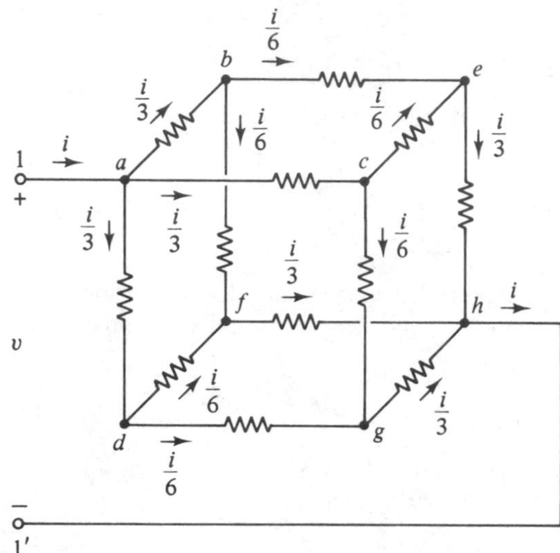

Fig. 2-7

Solution. The simple series and parallel connection rules cannot be used for this problem because the elements of the network do not form such combinations. Therefore the equivalent resistance is obtained by finding from Fig. 2-7 the i vs. v relationship at terminals 1–1′. Because of the symmetry of the network geometry and associated element values, the current i coming into the node a divides into three equal parts as shown. The three $i/3$ currents arriving at nodes b, c, and d each split further equally into two $i/6$ currents as shown. At nodes e, g, and f two $i/6$ currents come together to form an $i/3$ coming out as shown. At node h the three $i/3$'s coming in form the i coming out. Note that this current appearing at node 1′ is the same as the current at node 1 (since Kirchhoff's Current Law must apply for the entire network when it is placed in a bag and only terminals 1–1′ are brought out). Now consider any path between 1 and 1′. For example, sum the voltages along path *abeh*.

$$v_{ab} + v_{be} + v_{eh} = \frac{i}{3} \times 1 + \frac{i}{6} \times 1 + \frac{i}{3} \times 1 = \frac{5}{6}i$$

The voltage along this path must equal the voltage v appearing across the input terminals. So

$$v = \frac{5}{6}i = R_{eq}i$$

This terminal relationship could have been obtained from a $\frac{5}{6}$ Ω resistor connected across 1–1′. Therefore

$$R_{eq} = \frac{5}{6}\ \Omega \quad \text{Ans.}$$

2-3 SERIES AND PARALLEL CONNECTION OF SOURCES

Voltage sources can be connected in *series* as shown in Fig. 2-8(a). Since the terminal voltage is $(v_1 + v_2)$, an equivalent voltage source of value $(v_1 + v_2)$ can be used to represent the terminal characteristic. If actual voltage sources are to act as voltage sources, terminals 1–1′ should not be short-circuited.

Two voltage sources can be connected in *parallel* if the two source voltages are *equal* and the voltage *polarities match*. See Fig. 2-8(b). If these two conditions are not met, Kirchhoff's Voltage Law would be violated around the loop containing the two sources. In practice, such a violation may result in damage to the sources.

Current sources can be connected in *parallel* as shown in Fig. 2-8(c). Since the terminal current is $(i_1 + i_2)$, an equivalent current source of value $(i_1 + i_2)$ can be used to represent the terminal characteristic. If actual current sources are to act as current sources, terminals 1–1′ should not be open-circuited.

Two current sources can be connected in *series* if the two source currents are *equal* and the currents are in the *same sense*. See Fig. 2-8(d). If these two conditions are not met, Kirchhoff's Current Law would be violated at the junction of the two sources. If, in practice, such an unallowable connection is made by mistake, the sources stop acting like current sources, and their i vs. v characteristics change (sometimes drastically) with the result that Kirchhoff's Current Law is not violated.

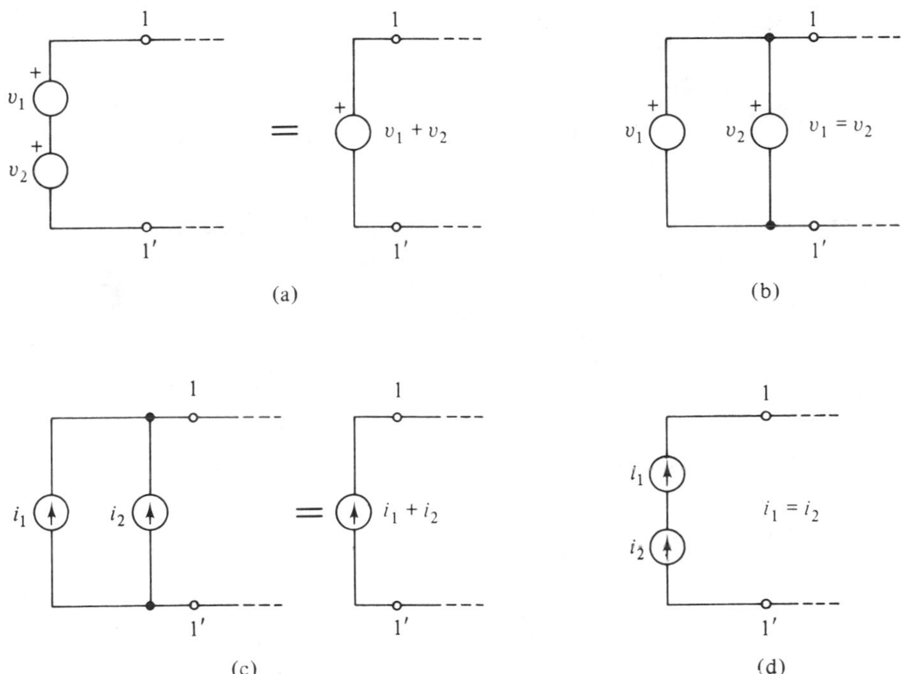

Fig. 2-8

A voltage source can be connected in series with a current source. This situation is shown in Fig. 2-9(a). Since the terminal current is decided by the current source, the combination is equivalent to a current source as far as the *terminal characteristic* is concerned.

A voltage and a current source can also be connected in parallel as in Fig. 2-9(b). Since the voltage at the terminals is v, regardless of the value of the current source, the combined *terminal characteristic* is equivalent to the voltage source of value v.

Similarly, the terminal equivalences shown in Fig. 2-9(c) are valid.

(a)

(b)

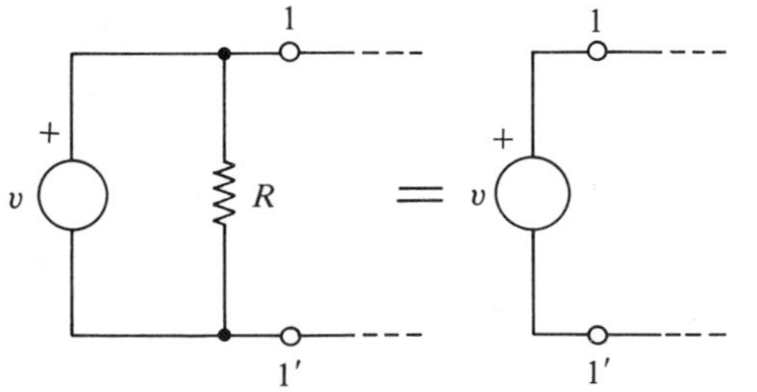

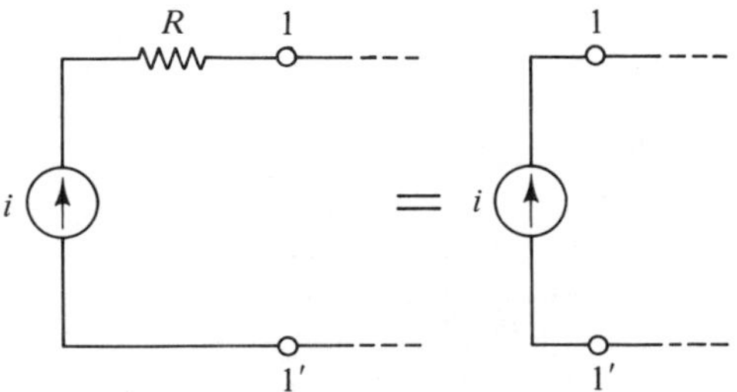

(c)

Fig. 2-9

2-4 NONIDEAL SOURCES

The i vs. v curve for a resistor is a line through the origin. For a voltage source, it is a vertical line. For a current source, it is a horizontal line. By combining sources with resistors, it is possible to obtain a variety of i vs. v characteristics. Conversely, from a measured i vs. v characteristic we may be able to construct an equivalent circuit involving sources and resistors, thereby finding a circuit model for the device under test.

Consider, for instance, the resistor-voltage-source combination shown in Fig. 2-10(a). To represent graphically the terminal characteristic of the combination, we need the equation relating v to i. Inspection of the network shows that

$$v = v_R + V_{dc}$$

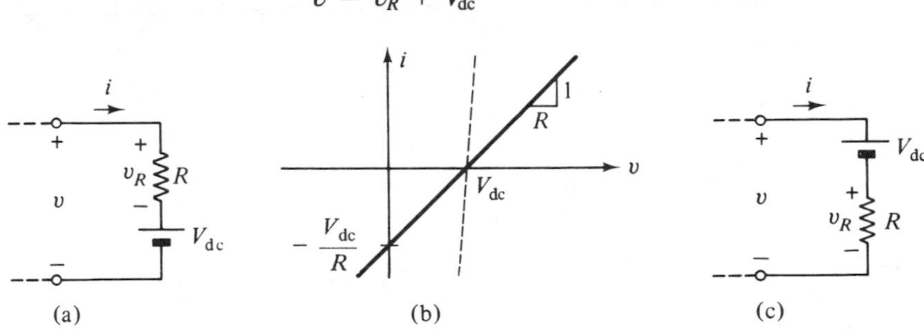

Fig. 2-10

But

$$v_R = iR$$

Therefore

$$v = iR + V_{dc}$$

or

$$i = \frac{v - V_{dc}}{R} = \underbrace{\frac{1}{R}}_{\text{Slope}}v - \underbrace{\frac{V_{dc}}{R}}_{\substack{i\text{-axis} \\ \text{intercept}}}$$

which is the equation of a line with slope $1/R$ and v-axis intercept V_{dc}. It is graphed in Fig. 2-10(b). We can now see the effect of V_{dc}. If V_{dc} is zero, the i vs. v curve is that of a resistor. If V_{dc} is increased from zero, the line is shifted to the right without altering its slope. If V_{dc} is made negative, the line is shifted to the left at constant slope. Thus V_{dc} controls the amount and the direction of the horizontal shift.

If V_{dc} is held constant and R is decreased, the line rotates counterclockwise about the point $(V_{dc}, 0)$. For $R = 0$ the line is vertical at $v = V_{dc}$ and we have an ideal voltage source. Actual voltage sources have terminal characteristics similar to that shown by the dashed line in Fig. 2-10(b) (not quite vertical), thus indicating the presence of a *small* series internal resistance. An equivalent circuit of an actual voltage source is shown in Fig. 2-10(a). As R becomes smaller, the circuit behaves more as an ideal voltage source; that is, the terminal voltage v becomes independent of the current i.

The circuit of Fig. 2-10(c) is obtained from Fig. 2-10(a) by interchanging the position of the resistor and battery. Such an interchange does not alter the terminal characteristics. The terminal variables are still related by $i = (v - V_{dc})/R$.

As another example, consider the circuit given in Fig. 2-11(a). Inspection of the network readily shows the i vs. v relationship:

$$i = I_{dc} + i_R$$

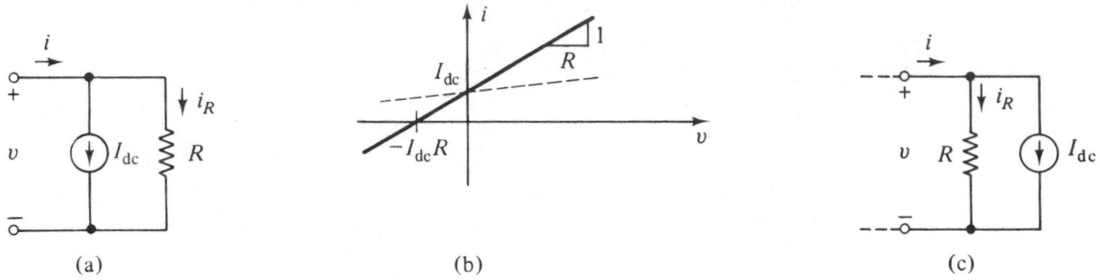

(a) (b) (c)

Fig. 2-11

But

$$i_R = \frac{v}{R}$$

So

$$i = \underbrace{I_{dc}}_{i\text{-axis intercept}} + \underbrace{\frac{1}{R}}_{\text{Slope}} v$$

This equation is graphed in Fig. 2-11(b). We see that the effect of I_{dc} is to move the straight line vertically up ($I_{dc} > 0$) or down ($I_{dc} < 0$) at constant slope.

If I_{dc} is held constant and R is increased, the line rotates clockwise about the point $(0, I_{dc})$. For $R = \infty$ the line is horizontal and we have an ideal current source. Actual current sources have terminal characteristics similar to that shown by the dashed line in Fig. 2-11(b) (not quite horizontal), thereby indicating the presence of a *large* parallel internal resistance. The equivalent circuit of an actual current source is shown in Fig. 2-11(a). As R becomes larger, the circuit behaves more like an ideal current source; that is, the terminal current i becomes independent of the voltage v.

The circuit of Fig. 2-11(c) is obtained from Fig. 2-11(a) by interchanging the position of the resistor and current source. Such an interchange does not affect the terminal characteristics. (The current i is still given by $i = I_{dc} + v/R$.)

Example 2-4

The terminal characteristic of a circuit is determined experimentally and plotted as in Fig. 2-12. Obtain an equivalent circuit presentation for the circuit under test.

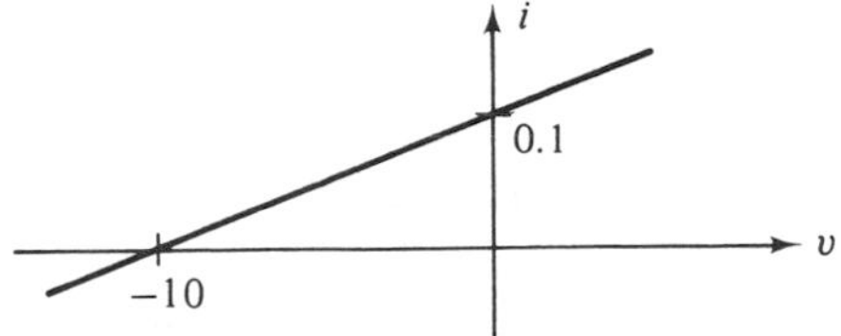

Fig. 2-12

Solution. From the experimental curve we obtain the i vs. v relationship as

$$i = \underbrace{0.1}_{\substack{i\text{-axis}\\ \text{intercept}}} + \underbrace{0.01}_{\text{Slope}}\, v = 0.1 + \frac{v}{100}$$

or

$$v = -10 + 100i$$

We can obtain an equivalent circuit by interpreting the first equation as a statement of Kirchhoff's Current Law: the current i comes into a node and currents $v/100$ and 0.1 come out of the same node. But the current $v/100$ would result from having a 100 Ω resistor connected across the terminals (where v is measured); the other current is a constant current of value 0.1, thus representing a current source. Hence the equivalent circuit of Fig. 2-13(a) can be put together as a circuit that will produce the measured characteristic.

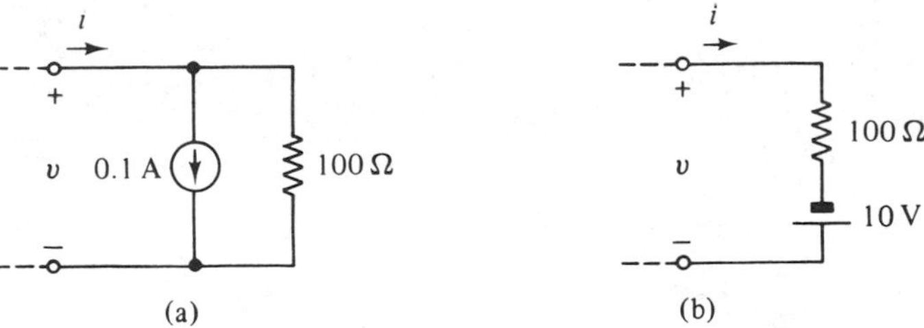

Fig. 2-13

Alternatively, we could start with the second equation and interpret it as a statement of Kirchhoff's Voltage Law: the voltage v is made up of two components, −10 and $100i$. The first is a constant voltage of −10 V and the second is a voltage that would result from i flowing through 100 Ω. Therefore the equivalent circuit of Fig. 2-13(b) can be put together as a second circuit that will produce the measured terminal characteristic. Consequently, the solution to this problem is not unique. Either circuit is a model for the measured characteristic.

Regardless of how sources and resistors are connected, the i vs. v (or v vs. i) characteristic at a pair of terminals is always a straight line.

Example 2-5

Draw the i vs. v curve for the circuit shown in Fig. 2-14.

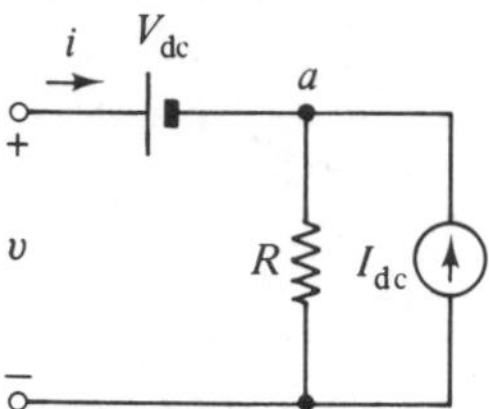

Fig. 2-14

Solution. The circuit, being composed of dc sources and a resistor, would result in a straight line i vs. v characteristic. So we need to find only two points in order to draw the line. Inspection of the circuit shows that v can be calculated easily as the sum of the battery voltage and the voltage across the resistor. If i were zero, the current through the resistor would be I_{dc} (by Kirchhoff's Current Law applied to node a), which causes a voltage of $I_{dc}R$ across the resistor. Therefore

$$v = V_{dc} + I_{dc}R \qquad (i = 0)$$

Similarly, if v were zero, the battery voltage would be applied directly to the resistor, causing a current of V_{dc}/R (directed up) through the resistor. So, by Kirchhoff's Current Law applied to the node a, we have

$$i = -\left(\frac{V_{dc}}{R} + I_{dc}\right) \qquad (v = 0)$$

Having thus found the v- and i-axis intercepts, the i vs. v curve can be drawn as in Fig. 2-15.

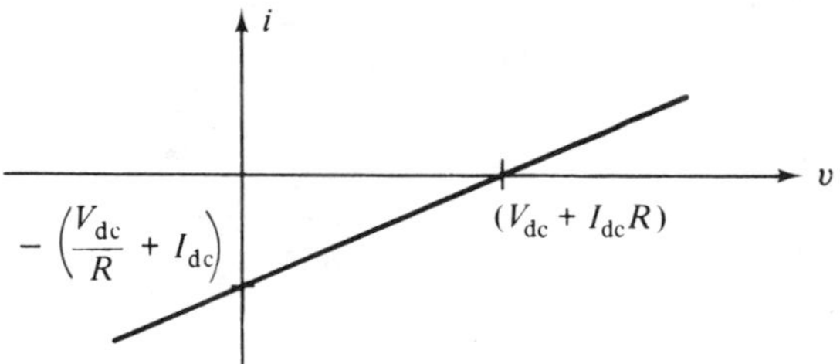

Fig. 2-15

Example 2-6

For the circuit shown in Fig. 2-16, calculate the voltage v across the current source.

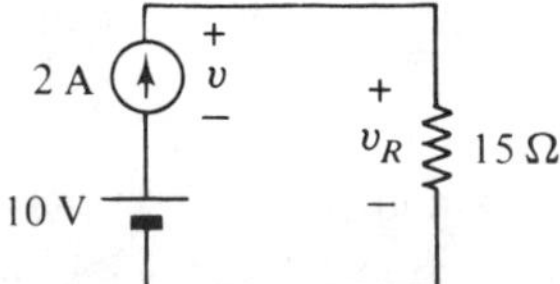

Fig. 2-16

Solution. The current through the 15 Ω resistor is 2 A. Ohm's Law thus gives

$$v_R = 2 \times 15 = 30\,\text{V}$$

By Kirchhoff's Voltage Law,

$$10 + v = v_R$$

It follows that

$$v = v_R - 10 = 30 - 10 = 20\,\text{V} \quad \text{Ans.}$$

2-5 SOURCE CONVERSIONS

A nonideal voltage source can be equivalently represented as a nonideal current source. Similarly, a nonideal current source can be converted to a nonideal voltage source.

The circuit model for a nonideal voltage source appears in Fig. 2-17(a). The corresponding mathematical model is obtained by summing voltages around the loop shown:

$$v = iR + v_s \tag{2-3}$$

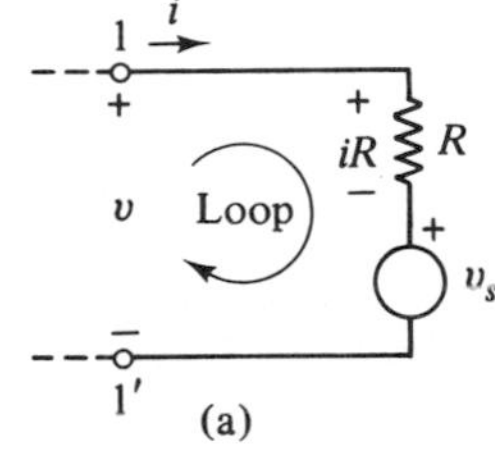

(a)

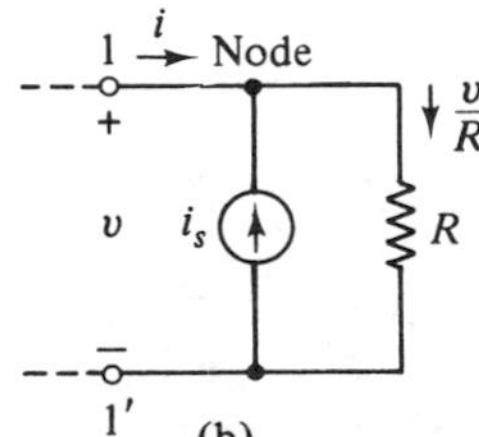

(b)

Fig. 2-17

The circuit model for a nonideal current source is given in Fig. 2-17(b). The corresponding mathematical model is obtained by summing currents at the top node:

$$i + i_s = \frac{v}{R}$$

This equation can be rearranged as

$$v = iR + i_s R \tag{2-4}$$

We now compare Eq. (2-3) with Eq. (2-4), keeping in mind that the terminal variables are the same. We see that the two representations are equivalent if

$$v_s = i_s R \tag{2-5a}$$

or

$$i_s = \frac{v_s}{R} \tag{2-5b}$$

Referring to the voltage source given in Fig. 2-17(a), we see that if we short-circuit terminals 1–1′ (make $v = 0$), the short-circuit current from 1 to 1′ would be $-i = v_s/R$, which must equal i_s according to Eq. (2-5b). So in order to convert a nonideal voltage source to a nonideal current source, merely determine the short-circuit current produced by the voltage source, call it i_s, and withdraw its current-source equivalent as in Fig. 2-17(b).

With reference to the current source given in Fig. 2-17(b), we see that if we open-circuit terminals 1–1′ (make $i = 0$), the open-circuit voltage across terminals 1–1′ would be $v = i_s R$, which must equal v_s by Eq. (2-5a). In converting a nonideal current source to a nonideal voltage source, therefore, simply determine the open-circuit voltage produced by the current source, call it v_s, and redraw its voltage-source equivalent as in Fig. 2-17(a).

As these transformations indicate, any nonideal source can be represented either as a voltage source or as a current source. In solving problems, it does not matter which circuit model is used. From a physical point of view, however, it is more descriptive of the characteristic of the source to label it as a voltage or current source, depending on which terminal variable remains nearly constant as the external demands imposed on the source vary.

Example 2-7

Convert the current source shown in Fig. 2-18 to a voltage source.

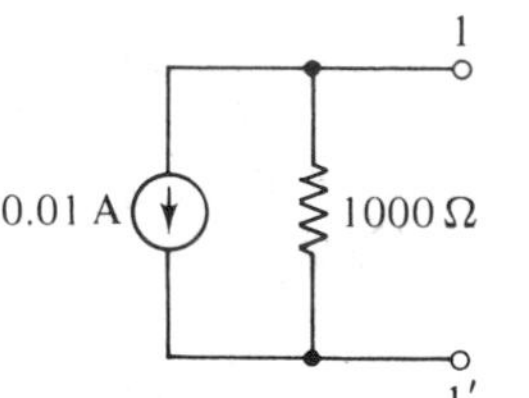

Fig. 2-18

Solution. From Fig. 2-18 the open-circuit voltage is

$$v_{oc} = 0.01 \times 1000 = 10\,\text{V}$$

with the + sign at the bottom. So the voltage-source equivalent can be drawn as in Fig. 2-19.

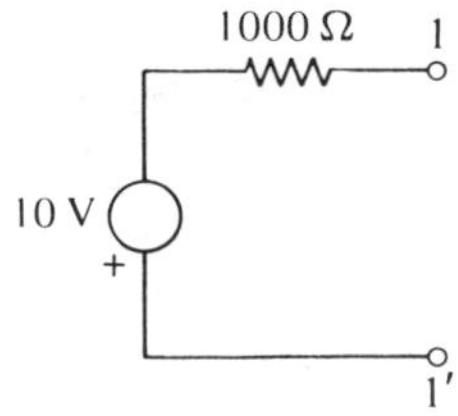

Fig. 2-19

2-6 LABORATORY DISPLAY OF *i* VS. *v* CURVES

By measuring the terminal characteristics of electrical devices we obtain their graphical, mathematical, and circuit models. For a large class of devices, the i vs. v curves are either straight lines over a wide range of terminal variables or straight-line segments with different slopes joined together. Such characteristics can easily be displayed completely on an oscilloscope by making the vertical deflection on the display tube represent current and the horizontal deflection represent voltage. Since oscilloscopes measure voltage and not current, the current to be measured can be passed through a known resistor and the resulting voltage across the resistor can then be applied to the vertical amplifier of the oscilloscope. Thus the vertical deflection is made proportional to current. A sinusoidal voltage source can be used to cause variations in both i and v, thereby generating a continuous set of values that trace the characteristic curve. The connection diagram is shown in Fig. 2-20.

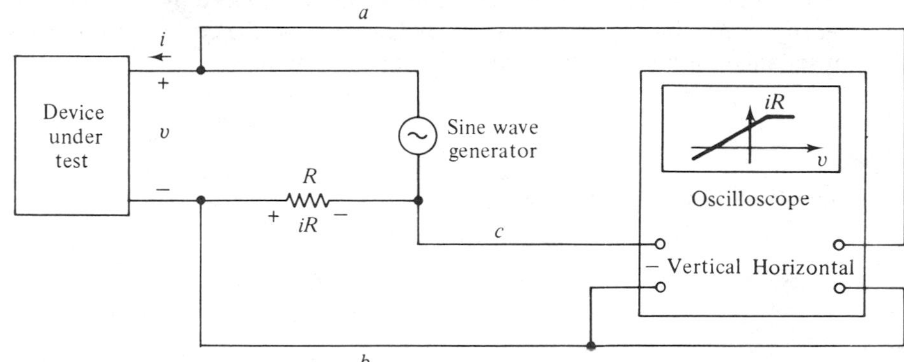

Fig. 2-20

Leads a and b apply the voltage v across the device directly to the horizontal amplifier. Leads c and b apply the voltage $(-iR)$ to the inverting terminals of the vertical amplifier. Thus the vertical deflection represents (iR) and the horizontal v. Since R is a known resistance, i can be calculated from

$$i \text{ in amperes} = \frac{\text{vertical deflection in volts}}{R \text{ in ohms}}$$

In Fig. 2-20 we have assumed that leads a, b, and c do not draw any current. As a result, the oscilloscope does not affect the circuit under test.

2-7 EXCITATION-RESPONSE; INPUT-OUTPUT

A network is *excited* (driven) when one or more voltage and current sources are connected to it. It can also become excited by initial capacitor voltages and initial inductor currents. All currents and voltages in a nonexcited network are zero. Another word for excitation is *input*.

Excitation causes currents through and voltages across the various elements in a network. These currents and voltages are called *responses*. Another word for response is *output*.

The input may be either current or voltage. The output may be either current or voltage. Consequently, input-output relationships may take one of the following forms: voltage-voltage, voltage-current, current-voltage, and current-current.

2-8 VOLTAGE- AND CURRENT-DIVIDER RULES

Suppose that we want to find the input-output relationship for the network shown in Fig. 2-21(a). The input to the resistive network composed of R_1 and R_2 is v_i. The output is v_2. Since R_1 and R_2 are in series, they can be replaced by an equivalent resistance of $(R_1 + R_2)$ that appears across v_i. By Ohm's Law, the current through this equivalent resistance, and hence the current through R_1 and R_2, is

$$i_i = \frac{v_i}{R_1 + R_2}$$

The resulting output voltage is

$$v_2 = i_i R_2$$

$$v_2 = v_i\left(\frac{R_2}{R_1 + R_2}\right) \tag{2-6}$$

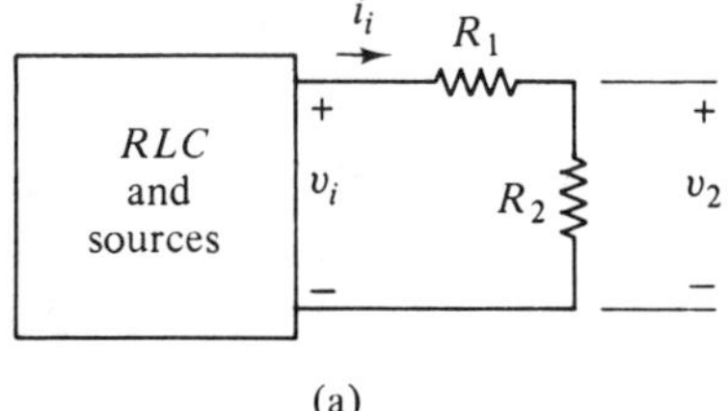

(a)

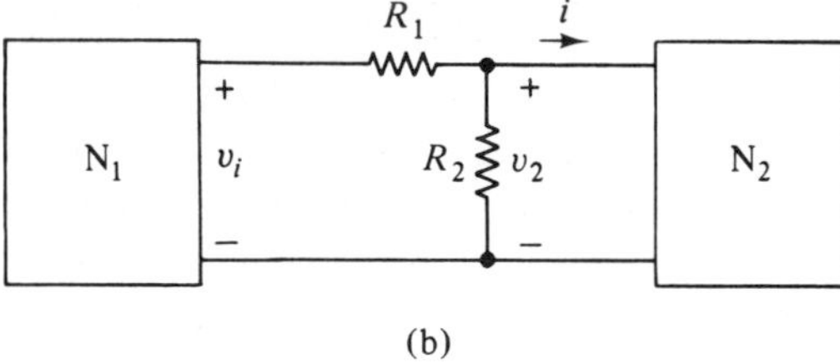

(b)

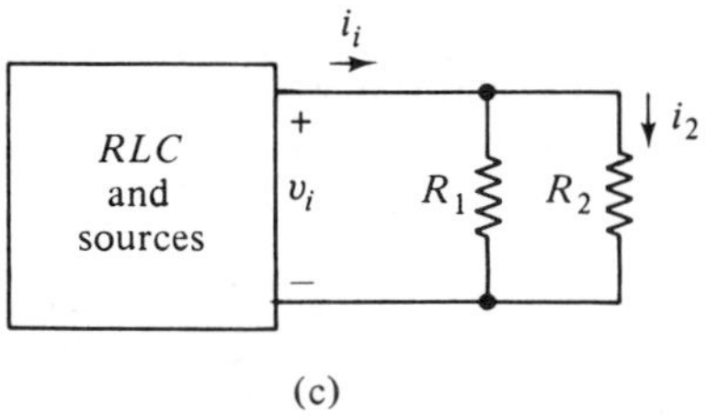

(c)

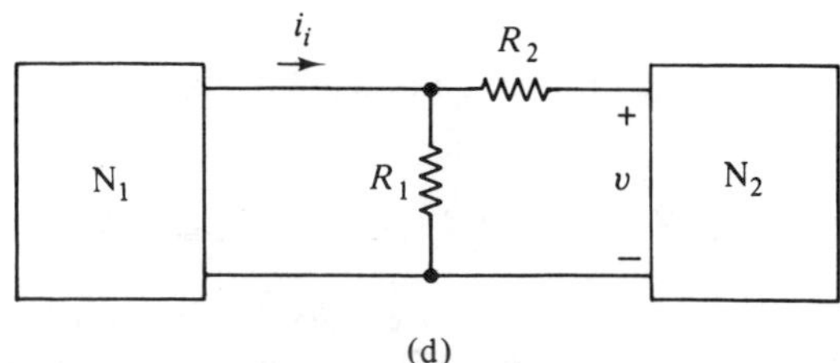

(d)

Fig. 2-21

Except when $R_1 = 0$ or $R_2 = \infty$, the factor $R_2/(R_1 + R_2)$ is less than unity. This factor multiplies the input, v_i, to produce the output voltage across R_2. So except for $R_1 = 0$ or $R_2 = \infty$, the output is less than unity, for the input voltage is divided between R_1 and R_2, and we are interested in the voltage across R_2. Equation (2-6), which is known as the *voltage-divider* rule, allows us to calculate the output voltage if the input voltage to the two series-connected resistors is known.

It should be emphasized that the voltage-divider rule *does not* apply to the circuit of Fig. 2-21(b) unless it can be shown that i to N_2 is zero.

The input to the resistive network shown in Fig. 2-21(c) is the current i_i. The output is the current i_2 through R_2. To obtain the input-output relationship, replace the parallel-R connection with an equivalent resistance of $R_1R_2/(R_1 + R_2)$. The current i_i flows through this resistance and produces a voltage of

$$i_i\frac{R_1R_2}{R_1 + R_2}$$

across it. Since this is also the voltage across R_2, we can obtain the current through R_2 by

$$i_2 = i_i\left(\frac{R_1R_2}{R_1 + R_2}\right)\bigg/R_2$$

$$i_2 = i_i\left(\frac{R_1}{R_1 + R_2}\right) \tag{2-7}$$

Equation (2-7) represents the *current-divider* rule. It tells us how to find the current through R_2 if the input current i_i is known. Since the input current is divided between R_1 and R_2, the current through R_2 is less than the input current. In the special cases when $R_2 = 0$ or $R_1 = \infty$, the output current equals the input current.

It should be emphasized that the current-divider rule *does not* apply to the circuit of Fig. 2-21(d) unless it can be shown that v across N_2 is zero.

Example 2-8

In Fig. 2-22, obtain the output voltage.

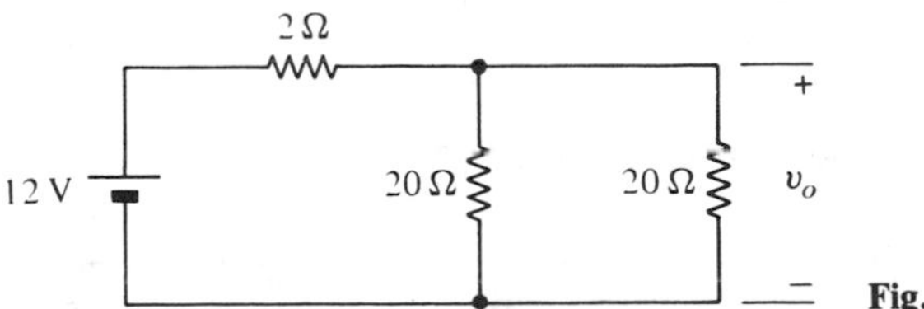

Fig. 2-22

Solution. The input voltage of 12 V divides between the 2 Ω and the 10 Ω, which represents the equivalent resistance of the two parallel-connected 20 Ω resistances. The output is taken across this equivalent resistance. So

$$v_o = 12\left(\frac{10}{10 + 2}\right) = 10 \text{ V} \quad \text{Ans.}$$

Example 2-9

In Fig. 2-23, obtain the output current.

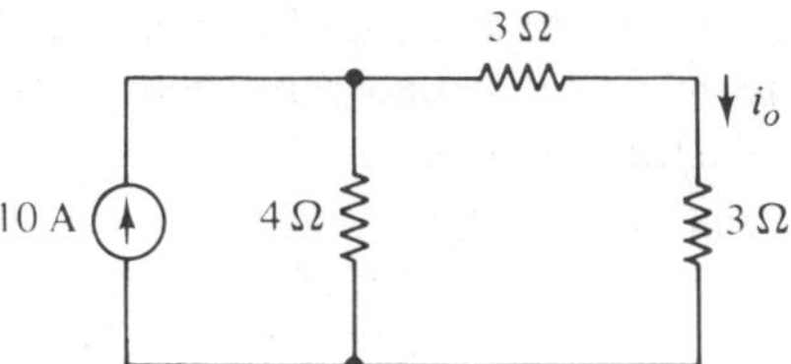

Fig. 2-23

Solution. The input current of 10 A divides between the 4 Ω and the 6 Ω, which represents the equivalent resistance of the two series-connected 3 Ω resistances. The output current is the current through this equivalent resistance. Thus

$$i_o = 10\left(\frac{4}{4 + 6}\right) = 4 \text{ A} \quad \text{Ans.}$$

2-9 ESTABLISHING A REFERENCE: THE GROUND

Frequently it is desirable to make voltage measurements with one lead of the voltmeter connected to a node in the network while the other lead is moved around to other nodes to take readings. In this way, all voltages are measured with respect to a common point (or node) of *reference*. This point is often called *ground* and is designated by one of the symbols shown in Fig. 2-24(a). In practice, ground represents a conducting body, such as a chassis or the earth itself.

To learn how to interpret such measurements, consider first the circuit shown in Fig. 2-24(b). We can easily calculate voltages v_1 and v_2 by using the voltage-divider rule.

$$v_1 = 20\left(\frac{R_1}{R_1 + R_2}\right) = 20\left(\frac{6}{6 + 4}\right) = 12 \text{ V}$$

$$v_2 = 20\left(\frac{R_2}{R_1 + R_2}\right) = 20\left(\frac{4}{6 + 4}\right) = 8 \text{ V}$$

When measuring v_1, the + lead of the voltmeter is connected at a and the − lead at b. When measuring v_2, both leads are removed from their previous connection points and reconnected with the + lead at b and the − lead at c. In transferring leads from one pair of points to another, it is important to ensure that the + and − markings of the variables match the + and − markings of the voltmeter. Quite often this situation is overlooked or the leads are mixed up; later on, while checking calculations, the question of whether a certain reading should have been negative arises. Such uncertainties are avoided if *all* voltages are measured with one lead, say the negative, of the voltmeter connected to point c. This point then becomes the common reference node for all measurements. This fact can be further emphasized by connecting point

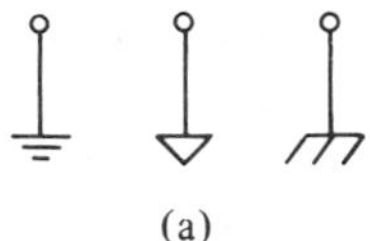

(a)

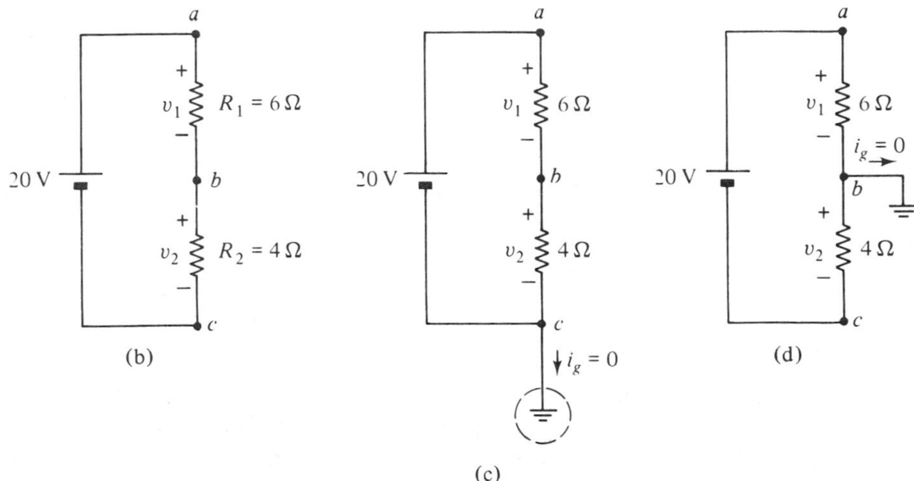

(c)

Fig. 2-24

c to a chassis ground as shown in Fig. 2-24(c). It should be obvious that connecting the point c to a ground point *does not alter the voltages or currents* in the circuit because here the current in the ground lead is zero. (Apply Kirchhoff's Current Law to the closed surface designated by the dashed line to verify that $i_g = 0$.) Consequently, v_1 is still 12 V and v_2 is still 8 V. However, voltages are now measured with respect to ground by connecting the positive lead of the voltmeter to a and then to b. Note that with this measurement technique we are moving only one lead of the voltmeter about, and so there is little chance of making errors in the sign of the readings. Furthermore, the entire measurement procedure is simpler and faster. When the free (+) lead of the voltmeter is connected to b, the voltmeter reads v_2—that is, 8 V. When the free lead is connected to a, the voltmeter reads $(v_1 + v_2)$, which is 20 V. Knowing v_2 and $(v_1 + v_2)$, we can calculate v_1. Consequently, with this procedure we cannot measure v_1 directly, but we can determine it from the other two measured results.

Suppose that, instead of referencing point c to ground, we reference point b to ground as in Fig. 2-24(d) and connect the − lead of the voltmeter to point b. Again, voltages and currents in the circuit are not disturbed because here also the ground-lead current is zero. The voltmeter readings, however, are different. When the + lead is connected to a, the voltmeter measures v_1, which is 12 V. When the + lead is connected to c, the voltmeter measures $-v_2$, which is -8 V.

In an electronic circuit, ground usually means a wire or a chassis to which many components are connected. For instance, in Fig. 2-25(a) the voltage source, resistors R_2 and R_4, each have one end connected to ground. Alternatively, we can draw Fig. 2-25(a) as in 2-25(b). This type of representation is used in schematic diagrams to avoid drawing too many lines. In practice, it may also save wiring costs.

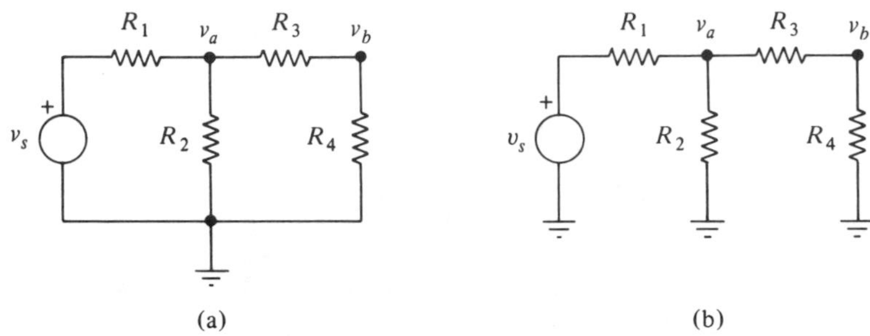

Fig. 2-25

Figures 2-25(a) and (b) present a new designation for voltage variables. Henceforth a voltage such as v_a or v_b appearing next to a node represents the *node-to-ground voltage*. Although no polarities are indicated, it should be understood that the voltage is measured and calculated with the + *at the node and the* − *at ground*.

Refer now to Fig. 2-26(a). Here R_2, R_3, and R_4 are in parallel, since each is connected between node a and ground. If we like, we can say that the series combination of R_1 and v_s is also in parallel with R_2, R_3, and R_4. On the other hand, R_5 is shorted out because it is connected to ground at both ends. (Someone may have made a wrong connection.) Because of the short circuit, the voltage across R_5 is zero. Hence, by Ohm's Law, the current through it is zero. Therefore R_5 can be removed completely from the circuit without affecting any currents or voltages. Quite often the operation of a circuit is clearer if it is redrawn in a form that is more familiar. For

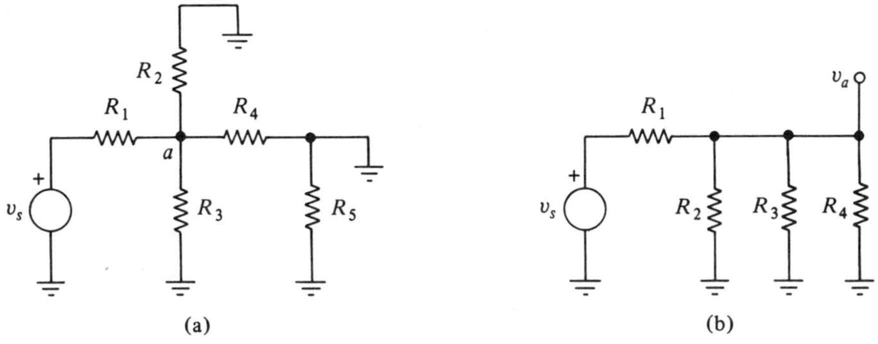

Fig. 2-26

instance, if Fig. 2-26(a) is redrawn as in 2-26(b), we can easily calculate v_a as

$$v_a = v_s \frac{R_p}{R_p + R_1}$$

where R_p is the parallel combination of R_2, R_3, and R_4. It should be clear that v_a does not change if R_4 is repositioned ahead of R_2 instead of behind R_3.

Example 2-10

In Fig. 2-27, $V_{dc} = 120$ V. Calculate v_1, v_2, and the voltage across R_1.

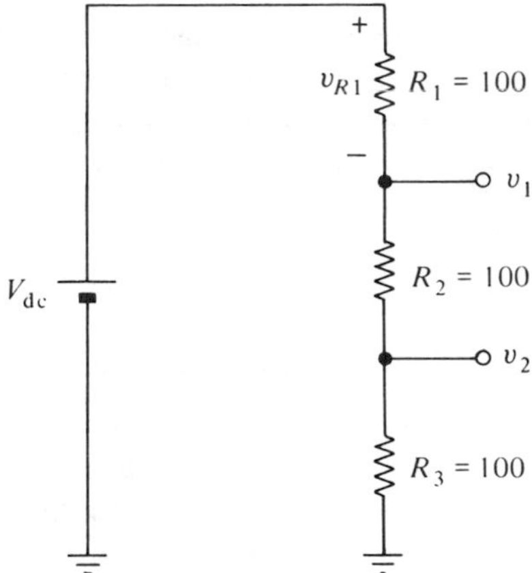

Fig. 2-27

Solution. Use the voltage-divider rule to calculate v_1 and v_2.

$$v_1 = V_{dc}\frac{(R_2 + R_3)}{(R_2 + R_3) + R_1} = 120\left(\frac{200}{200 + 100}\right) - 80 \text{ V} \quad \text{Ans.}$$

$$v_2 = V_{dc}\frac{R_3}{R_3 + (R_1 + R_2)} = 120\left(\frac{100}{100 + 200}\right) = 40 \text{ V} \quad \text{Ans.}$$

$$v_{R1} = V_{dc} - v_1 = 120 - 80 = 40 \text{ V} \quad \text{Ans.}$$

Example 2-11

In Fig. 2-28, calculate v_1, v_2, and the voltage across R_2.

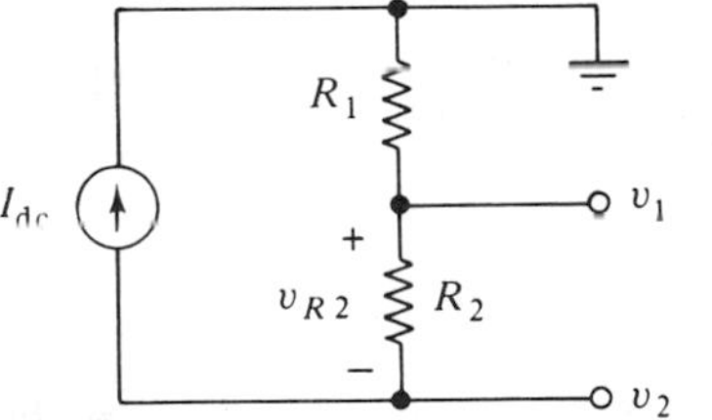

Fig. 2-28

Solution. We could redraw the figure so that the ground is placed at the bottom, its usual location. However, this circuit is simple enough so that we can obtain v_1, v_2, and

v_{R2} by inspection. Since the current through the ground is zero, all of I_{dc} flows through R_1 and R_2. So we have

$$\left.\begin{aligned} v_1 &= -I_{dc}R_1 \\ v_2 &= -I_{dc}(R_1 + R_2) \\ v_{R2} &= v_1 - v_2 = I_{dc}R_2 \end{aligned}\right\} \text{Ans.}$$

2-10 MILLI, MICRO, KILO, AND MEG REPRESENTATIONS

In many applications, very small currents and voltages and very large resistances are frequently encountered. In such cases, currents and voltages are measured in milliamperes (mA), millivolts (mV), microamperes (μA), and microvolts (μV). Resistances are measured in kilo-ohms (kΩ) and megohms (MΩ).

$$1\text{ mA} = 10^{-3}\text{ A} \qquad 1\ \mu\text{A} = 10^{-6}\text{ A}$$

$$1\text{ mV} = 10^{-3}\text{ V} \qquad 1\ \mu\text{V} = 10^{-6}\text{ V}$$

$$1\text{ k}\Omega = 10^{3}\ \Omega \qquad 1\text{ M}\Omega = 10^{6}\ \Omega$$

In Ohm's Law ($v = iR$), v is measured in volts (V), i in amperes (A), and R in ohms (Ω). Since m stands for 10^{-3} and k for 10^3, we have m $\times$ k $= 10^{-3} \times 10^3 = 1$. Consequently, we can use milliamperes for currents and kilo-ohms for resistance and still come up with volts for voltages. For example, with 10 V across 2 kΩ, the current through the resistor is $10/2 = 5$ mA. Similarly, $\mu \times \text{M} = 10^{-6} \times 10^6 = 1$; so microamperes $\times$ megohms $=$ volts.

2-11 CONSTRUCTION OF A SIMPLE CURRENT SOURCE

A simple current source can be constructed by using a voltage source and a resistor as in Fig. 2-29(a). We will now show that the circuit placed within the dashed box can serve as a nonideal current source. Let R_L act as a load on the circuit. The load current is given by

$$i_L = \frac{v_s}{R + R_L} = \frac{v_s}{R}\left[\frac{1}{1 + (R_L/R)}\right] \tag{2-8}$$

If the load resistance is restricted to values much smaller than the source resistance, Eq. (2-8) becomes

$$i_L \cong \frac{v_s}{R} \qquad (R_L \ll R) \tag{2-9}$$

Thus the current through the load, i_L, is rendered *independent of the load resistance* R_L. Stated differently, as long as $R_L \ll R$, the source voltage and source resistance are primarily responsible for the current through R_L. Hence the load resistance sees a current source of value v_s/R.

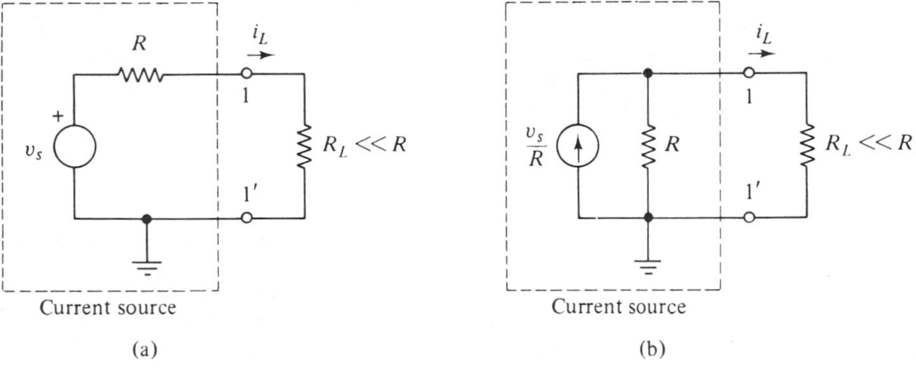

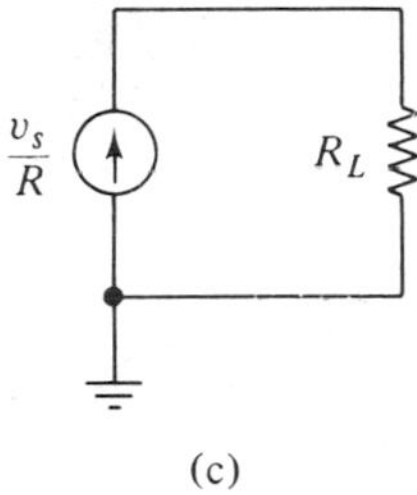

(c)

Fig. 2-29

We can look at this circuit from still another point of view. Since a voltage source in series with a resistor can be equivalently replaced with a current source in parallel with the same resistor, Fig. 2-29(a) can be redrawn as in 2-29(b). Using the current-divider rule, we obtain the load current as

$$i_L = \left(\frac{v_s}{R}\right)\left(\frac{R}{R + R_L}\right) \tag{2-10}$$

As long as $R_L \ll R$, almost all the input current would go through the load. Under this constraint, Eq. (2-10) reduces to (2-9). Indeed, we can go one step further and draw Fig. 2-29(b) as in 2-29(c), to show the circuit's true nature. In making this last simplification, we tacitly assumed that the parallel connection of R with R_L is approximately equal to R_L, which is the case if $R_L \ll R$.

When v_s is constant, as it is for a dc voltage source, the resulting current source, v_s/R, is constant. If v_s is sinusoidal, the current source is sinusoidal.

Example 2-12

Using a voltage source and a resistance, design a 10 mA dc current source for a range of load resistance values from 0 to 100 Ω. How good is the current source?

Solution. The circuit that we must force to act like a current source is given in Fig. 2-30. We must choose V_{dc} and R such that 10 mA results when $R_L = 0$. Then the worst departure from 10 mA would occur when R_L is largest—that is, $R_L = 100\ \Omega$. Even for

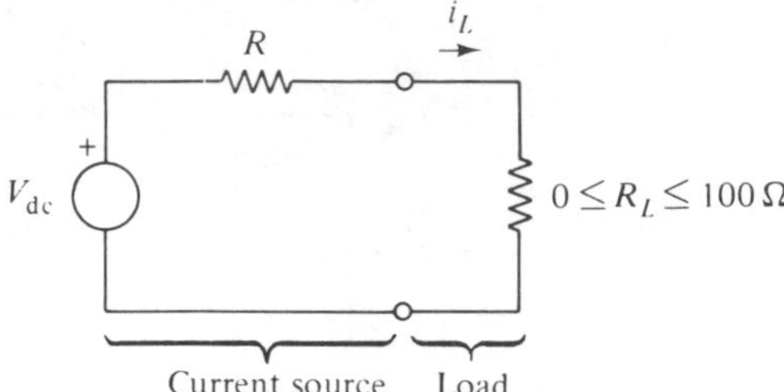

Fig. 2-30

this extreme case R must be chosen so that almost all of V_{dc} appears across R and the current is mainly determined by $V_{dc}/R = 10$ mA. Let us try $V_{dc} = 10$ V and $R = 1$ kΩ and see how good a current source we obtain.

$$i = \frac{V_{dc}}{R + R_L} = \frac{V_{dc}}{R}\left[\frac{1}{1 + (R_L/R)}\right] = 10\left[\frac{1}{1 + (R_L/R)}\right]$$

$$= \begin{cases} 10 \text{ mA} & (R_L = 0) \\ 10\left(\dfrac{1}{1.1}\right) = 9.1 \text{ mA} & (R_L = 100\ \Omega) \end{cases}$$

So within the range of values for R_L, i_1 would vary by about 10%, which may be objectionable. (When $R_L = 100\ \Omega$, the voltage across it is $0.091V_{dc}$, which is about 10% of the input voltage V_{dc}.)

To improve on our design, let us now try $V_{dc} = 100$ V and $R = 10$ kΩ.

$$i_L = \frac{V_{dc}}{R}\left[\frac{1}{1 + (R_L/R)}\right] = 10\left[\frac{1}{1 + (R_L/R)}\right]$$

$$= \begin{cases} 10 \text{ mA} & (R_L = 0) \\ 10\left(\dfrac{1}{1.01}\right) = 9.9 \text{ mA} & (R_L = 100\ \Omega) \end{cases}$$

We see that i_L would be within 1% of 10 mA for the entire range of R_L values. (At worst, the voltage across R_L is $0.0099V_{dc}$, which is about 1% of the input voltage.)
It should be clear that the larger V_{dc} and R, the more the resulting circuit acts like a true current source. Practical considerations generally limit the use of very large voltages. If the conditions on the current source are too stringent, it may be necessary to look for a different circuit to act as a current source.

2-12 ATTENUATORS

Many applications require that signals—voltages or currents—be attenuated (scaled down) by a fixed amount. *Attenuators* are used for this purpose. Almost all electronic instruments use attenuators to allow for the measurement of a wide range of voltage and current values. In turning down the volume on a radio, for instance, we make use of a variable attenuator to reduce the signal.

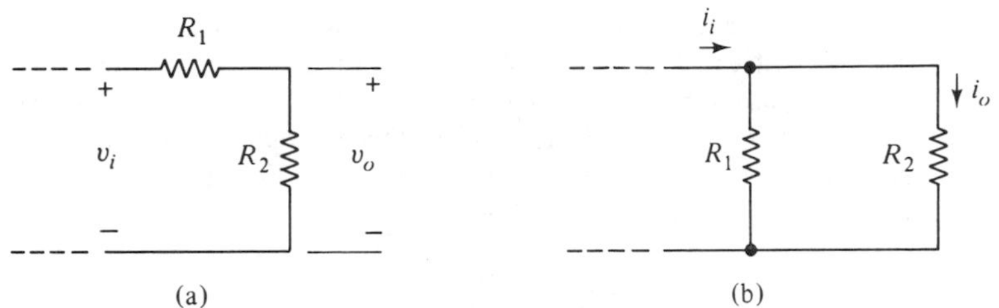

Fig. 2-31

A voltage attenuator composed of two resistors is shown in Fig. 2-31(a). By the voltage-divider rule,

$$v_o = v_i\left(\frac{R_2}{R_1 + R_2}\right) = v_i\left[\frac{1}{1 + (R_1/R_2)}\right] \tag{2-11}$$

Note that the amount of attenuation depends on the ratio of resistances and not on the actual values. The factor $R_2/(R_1 + R_2)$ is known as the *attenuation factor*.

A current attenuator is shown in Fig. 2-31(b). By the current-divider rule,

$$i_o = i_i\left(\frac{R_1}{R_1 + R_2}\right) = i_i\left[\frac{1}{1 + (R_2/R_1)}\right] \tag{2-12}$$

Again, the amount of attenuation is determined by the ratio of resistances.

Example 2-13

Design a 10 : 1 voltage attenuator. Discuss the selection of the element values.

Solution. To design the attenuator, refer to Fig. 2-31(a) and Eq. (2-11). In order for the output to be $\frac{1}{10}$ of the input, the R_1/R_2 ratio must be 9. So

$$R_1 = 9R_2$$

and the solution is not unique. We can arbitrarily pick a value for R_2 and make R_1 nine times R_2 and meet the attenuation requirement. For example, the two circuits shown in Fig. 2-32 provide the desired attenuation. The circuit on the left draws from the source of v_i a current of $v_i/10$ A, which may be objectionable if v_i is more than a few tenths of a volt. (For v_i = 10 V, the source must be able to supply 1 A of current.) On the other

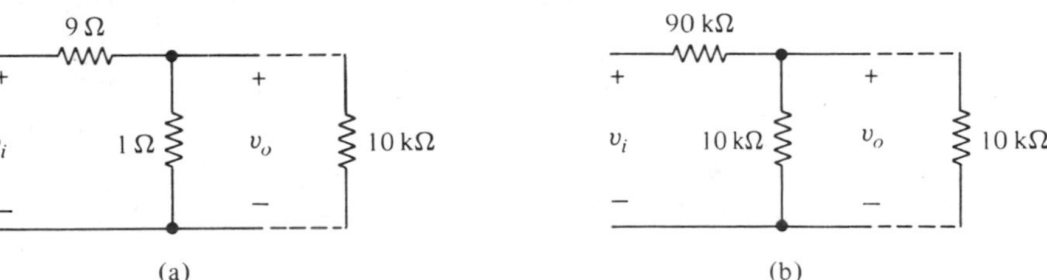

Fig. 2-32

hand, for the circuit on the right, the source need supply only $v_i/100$ mA of current while achieving the desired attenuation. So it would appear that the circuit on the right is the circuit to use in practice. Such would be the case if no other element were connected across the output. However, suppose that the output is *loaded* by a 10 kΩ resistor, as shown by the dashed line, and the attenuator is expected to work with and without loading. Under loaded conditions we have

$$v_o = v_i \frac{(1 \times 10{,}000)/10{,}001}{9 + (1 \times 10{,}000)/10{,}001} = \frac{v_i}{10}\left(\frac{1}{1.00009}\right) \qquad \text{[for Fig. 2-32(a)]}$$

$$= v_i \frac{5}{90 + 5} = \frac{v_i}{10}\left(\frac{1}{1.9}\right) \qquad \text{[for Fig. 2-32(b)].}$$

Thus the attenuation produced by the circuit on the left is very close to the desired value of 10 : 1, whereas the circuit on the right produces almost twice the desired attenuation. These results show that the amount of current drawn from the source and the amount of loading of the output are important factors that should be considered in the design of attenuators.

Example 2-14

Design a two-position attenuator with attenuation factors of 0.1 and 0.2.

Solution. A two-position attenuator requires three resistors as shown in Fig. 2-33(a). There are three unknowns: R_1, R_2, and R_3. There are two design constraints, resulting in two equations: $v_{o1}/v_i = 0.1$ and $v_{o2}/v_i = 0.2$. So one resistance can be chosen arbitrarily. Let this resistance be R_3. Since the same current i flows through all three resistors and $v_{R3} + v_{R2} + v_{R1} = v_i$, we have

$$v_{R3} = iR_3 = v_{o1} = 0.1v_i$$

$$v_{R2} = iR_2 = v_{o2} - v_{o1} = 0.1v_i$$

$$v_{R1} = iR_1 = v_i - v_{o2} = 0.8v_i$$

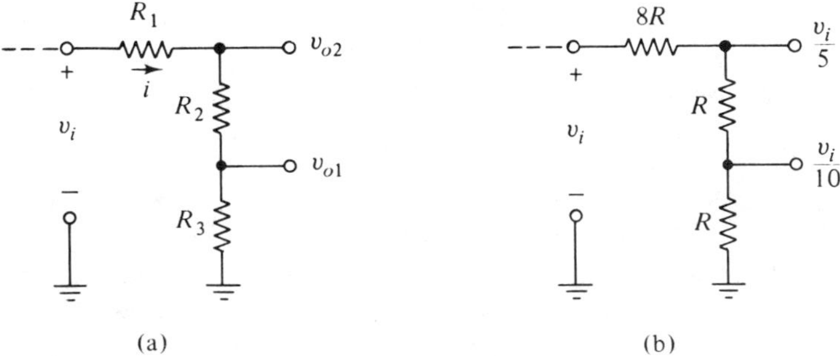

Fig. 2-33

Taking ratios of v_{R2}/v_{R3} and v_{R1}/v_{R3}, we obtain

$$\frac{R_2}{R_3} = 1, \qquad \frac{R_1}{R_3} = 8$$

Thus $R_2 = R_3$ and $R_1 = 8R_3$. We now let $R_3 = R$ and draw the completed design as in Fig. 2-33(b).

2-13 CONTINUOUSLY VARIABLE ATTENUATORS

In order to obtain a continuously variable attenuation, a three-terminal resistor with an adjustable contact is needed. Such resistors are called *potentiometers* and are schematically represented in Fig. 2-34(a). The input is between 1 and 2. The output is between 3 and 1 or between 3 and 2. By positioning the movable arm of the potentiometer, called the *wiper*, anywhere between terminals 1 and 2, various amounts of the total resistance are tapped. To illustrate, consider Fig. 2-34(b), where the output is taken between the wiper and ground. When the wiper is all the way up (at 1), the output is the same as the input V_{dc}. When the wiper is all the way down (at 2), the output is the same as ground and so is zero. Any other setting results in a voltage between V_{dc} and zero. If we let α be a measure of the amount of resistance being tapped, then Fig. 2-34(b) can be drawn as in Fig. 2-34(c), from which we obtain

$$v_o = V\frac{\alpha R}{\alpha R + (1 - \alpha)R} = \alpha V \qquad (0 \le \alpha \le 1)$$

By varying α between zero and one, therefore, the amount of attenuation introduced by the network can be varied continuously.

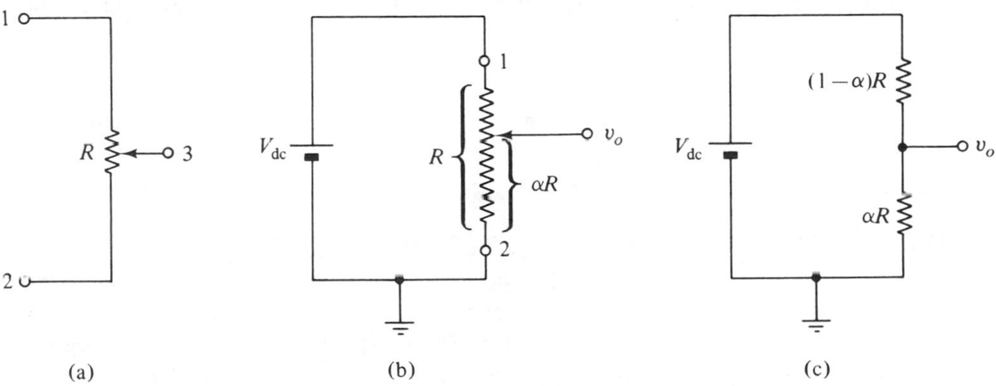

Fig. 2-34

Example 2-15

Show that the circuit in Fig. 2-35 introduces a continuously variable voltage that can be set anywhere between +15 V and −15 V.

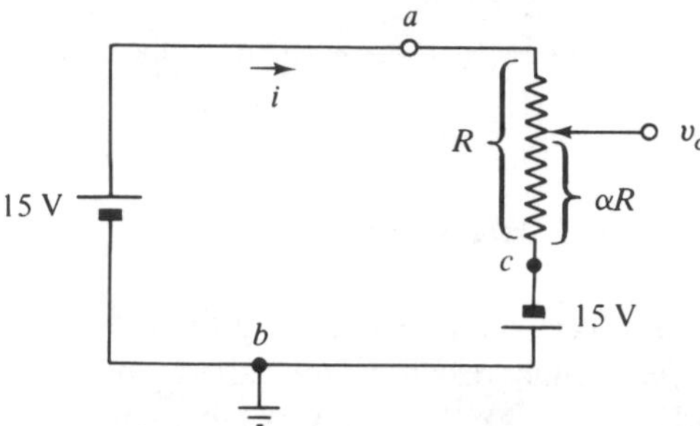

Fig. 2-35

Solution. Inspection of the network shows that

$$v_o = 15\text{ V} \qquad \text{(wiper on top; } \alpha = 1\text{)}$$

$$v_o = -15\text{ V} \qquad \text{(wiper on bottom; } \alpha = 0\text{)}$$

For any other setting, we can obtain v_o by first calculating the current i. The circuit shows the voltage across and the current through R are

$$v_R = v_{ac} = v_{ab} - v_{cb} = v_{ab} + v_{bc} = 15 + 15 = 30\text{ V}$$

$$i = \frac{v_R}{R} = \frac{30}{R}$$

So the voltage across the lower portion of the potentiometer (from wiper to c) is

$$i\alpha R = \left(\frac{30}{R}\right)\alpha R = 30\alpha$$

The output voltage is the sum of this voltage with the −15 V produced by the battery; that is,

$$v_o = 30\alpha + v_{cb} = 30\alpha + (-15)$$

As α varies between zero and one, the output voltage varies between −15 V and +15 V. For $\alpha = 0.5$, $v_o = 0$.

2-14 AMMETER SHUNTS AND VOLTMETER MULTIPLIERS

The basic building block for ammeters and voltmeters is a two-terminal meter that responds when *current* is passed through it. The meter is characterized by its internal resistance R and by the current that produces full-scale reading. This current is designated by I_{fs}. In general, the current through the meter can have any value between zero and I_{fs}. In Fig. 2-36 the meter current is labeled I_M. The maximum value of I_M

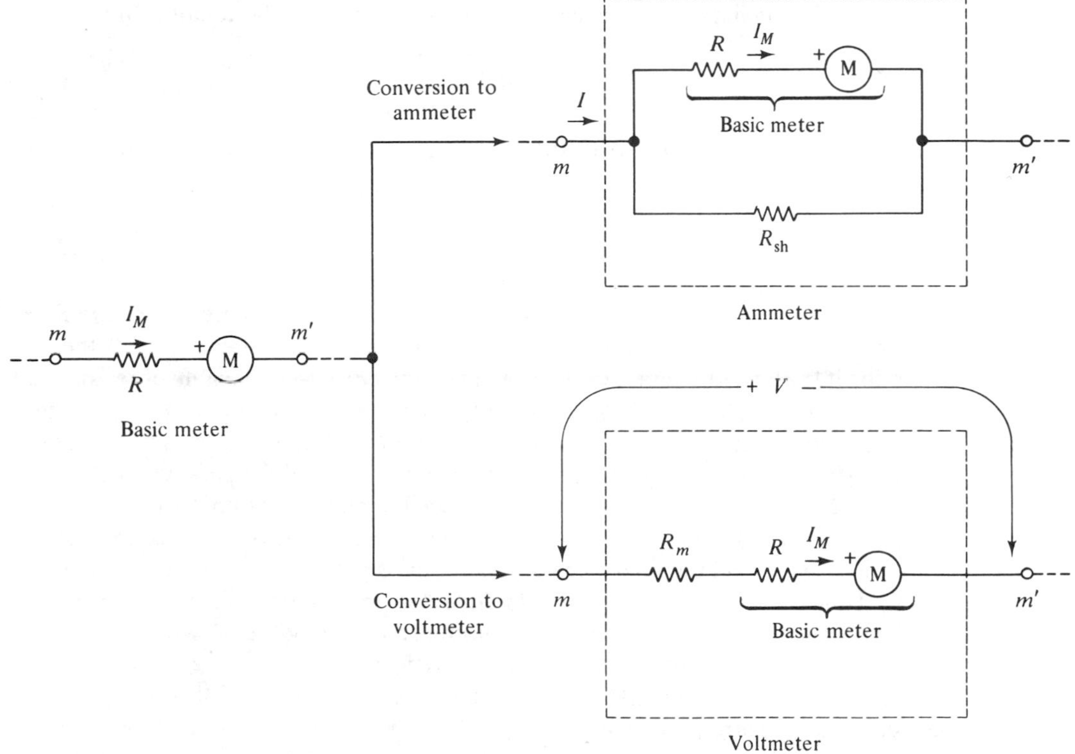

Fig. 2-36

is I_{fs}. When the current through the meter is I_{fs}, the voltage across the terminals marked m–m' is $I_{fs} \times R$. In general, we have $v_{mm'} = I_M R$.

As it stands, the basic meter can be used as an ammeter if the currents to be measured fall within the range of the meter—that is, if they are less than or at most equal to I_{fs}. If the currents to be measured are larger than I_{fs}, an attenuated portion of the currents is sent through the meter while the rest is shunted (by-passed) through a resistance called *shunt resistance*, R_{sh}. The basic meter, together with the shunt resistance, then becomes the ammeter. See Fig. 2-36.

It should be clear by inspection of Fig. 2-36 that

$$I_M = I\left(\frac{R_{sh}}{R_{sh} + R}\right) \qquad \text{(current-divider rule)}$$

where $R_{sh}/(R_{sh} + R)$ represents the attenuation (or proportionality) factor relating the meter current I_M to the line current I being measured. By adjusting the attenuation factor, any line current can be brought within the range of the meter. Different shunt resistances can be used to cover a wide range of line currents. The ammeter scale can be calibrated to indicate the line current I directly by using the relationship

$$I = I_M\left(1 + \frac{R}{R_{\text{sh}}}\right) \tag{2-13}$$

In particular, when the meter reads full scale, the reading corresponds to a line current of

$$I = I_{\text{fs}}\left(1 + \frac{R}{R_{\text{sh}}}\right) \tag{2-14}$$

It should be realized that whenever current measurements are taken, the R–R_{sh} combination shown in Fig. 2-36 is introduced into the circuit, thereby altering the very circuit itself [unless, of course, we have an ideal meter ($R = 0$) capable of reading any current I]. As a result of the changes introduced in the circuit by the ammeter's presence, the current that it would measure would not quite be the current that is present before the meter is connected. The lower the value of the parallel combination of R with R_{sh}, the less the disturbance and hence the more accurate the measurement. The degree of disturbance depends on the relative values of the ammeter resistance $[RR_{\text{sh}}/(R + R_{\text{sh}})]$ and the resistance that is in series with the ammeter in the external circuit. Unless otherwise specified, we shall assume that the changes caused in a circuit as a result of the introduction of an ammeter are negligible or, which is the same thing, that we have an ideal ammeter—that is, $R = 0$.

The basic meter can also be used directly as a voltmeter if the voltages to be measured cause currents that are within the range of the meter—that is, $I_M \leq I_{\text{fs}}$. Expressed in terms of voltage, the meter reading is maximum when the voltage across it is $I_{\text{fs}}R$. If the voltages to be measured cause larger voltages across the basic meter, then an attenuated portion of the voltages is applied to the meter by inserting a resistance, called *multiplier resistance* (R_m), in series with the basic meter. The basic meter, together with the multiplier resistance, becomes the voltmeter. (See Fig. 2-36.) The voltmeter reads the voltage across its terminals, which can easily be calculated from Fig. 2-36 as

$$V = I_M(R_m + R) \tag{2-15}$$

In particular, when the meter reads full scale, the reading corresponds to a terminal voltage of

$$V = I_{\text{fs}}(R_m + R)$$

Alternatively, we can rearrange this equation as

$$\underbrace{V}_{\substack{\text{Voltage being}\\ \text{measured}}} = \underbrace{I_{\text{fs}}R}_{\substack{\text{Voltage across}\\ \text{basic meter}}} \times \underbrace{\left(1 + \frac{R_m}{R}\right)}_{\substack{\text{Multiplying}\\ \text{factor}}} \tag{2-16}$$

By using different multiplier resistances, we can measure a wide range of voltage values. Even though the deflection is caused by current, the scale is calibrated in terms of volts based on Eq. (2-16).

The ideal voltmeter should measure voltages without disturbing the circuit under measurement. This means that its resistance must be infinite. Actual voltmeters do not have infinite resistance. Instead they are designed to have large enough resistances that draw very small current (compared to the other currents in the circuit) while taking the measurement. If such is not the case, the reading on the voltmeter is not a true indication of the voltage that existed in the circuit prior to the connection of the voltmeter. The reading represents the voltage in the altered (due to the introduction of the voltmeter) circuit.

The effect of the voltmeter on the circuit can be assessed by using the kilo-ohm per volt figure that is given with voltmeters. (This figure of merit is the reciprocal of I_{fs} measured in milliamperes.) Thus a 5 kΩ/V voltmeter has 5 kΩ internal resistance on the 1 V full-scale range. It has 50 kΩ resistance on the 10 V full-scale range and so on. If such a voltmeter reads 4 V when used on the 10 V range, it would draw from the circuit 0.08 mA (4 V/50 kΩ). Whether this much voltmeter current is acceptable depends on the current in the element across which the voltage is being measured. For instance, if the current in the element is 10 mA, the 0.08 mA demanded by the voltmeter for measurement may be considered negligible. From now on, unless otherwise specified, we shall assume that the voltmeter has negligible effect on the circuit under test.

Example 2-16

The constants associated with a particular meter are $R = 100\ \Omega$, $I_{fs} = 0.1$ mA.

(a) Using this meter, design an ammeter that reads full scale for 0.1 mA, 1 mA, and 10 mA, depending on the position of the range switch.

(b) Using the meter, design a voltmeter that reads full scale for 0.1 V, 1 V, and 10 V, depending on the position of the range switch.

Solution

(a) In the 0.1 mA range of operation, the meter can be used directly without any shunt resistance because its full-scale reading is 0.1 mA. This situation is shown in Fig. 2-37(a). In the 1 mA range of operation, 0.9 mA must be shunted around the meter when the line current to be measured is 1 mA. See Fig. 2-37(b). Since the voltage across the terminals is the same regardless of the path chosen, we calculate the voltage across the 100 Ω and equate it to the voltage across R_{sh2}.

$$0.1\text{ mA} \times 100\ \Omega = 0.9\text{ mA} \times R_{sh2}$$

Hence

$$R_{sh2} = \frac{100}{9}\ \Omega$$

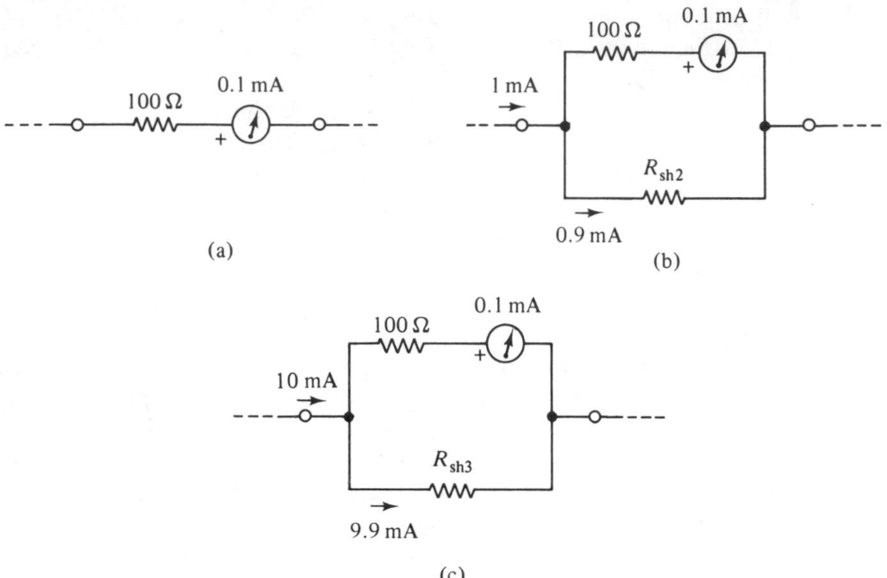

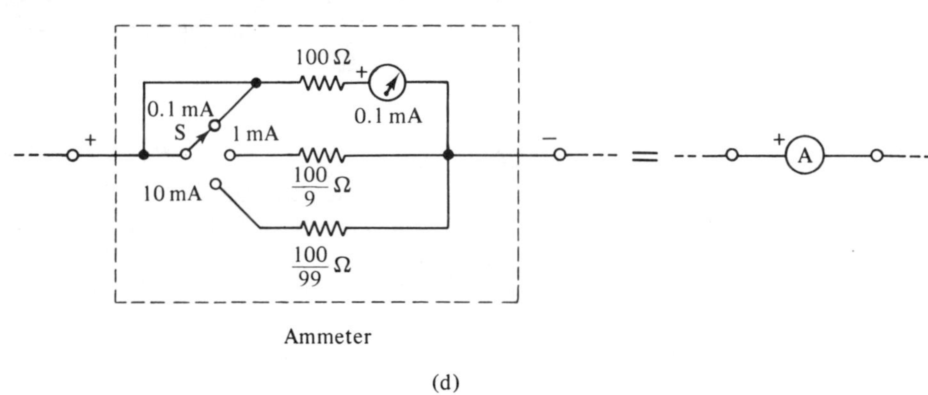

Fig. 2-37

Alternatively, we can use the current-divider rule. We want 0.1 mA through the meter when the line current is 1 mA. So

$$0.1 = 1 \times \frac{R_{sh2}}{100 + R_{sh2}}, \qquad R_{sh2} = \frac{100}{9}\,\Omega$$

In the 10 mA range of operation, 9.9 mA must be shunted around the meter when the line current (which is to be measured) is 10 mA. Again, equating the voltage across the top branch to the voltage across the bottom branch, we obtain

$$0.1 \text{ mA} \times 100\ \Omega = 9.9 \text{ mA} \times R_{sh3}$$

Therefore

$$R_{sh3} = \frac{100}{99}\,\Omega$$

By means of the range switch shown in Fig. 2-37(d), we can put all three circuits together and thus complete the design of the ammeter. When the switch S is in the 0.1 mA position, we have the circuit of Fig. 2-37(a). When it is in the 1 mA position, we have the circuit of Fig. 2-37(b). When it is in the 10 mA position, we have the circuit of Fig. 2-37(c).

(b) In the 0.1 V range of operation, the voltage across the voltmeter should be 0.1 V when the current through the meter is 0.1 mA. This situation is shown in Fig. 2-38(a). Consequently,

$$0.1 = 0.1 \text{ mA} \times (R_{m1} + 0.1) \text{ k}\Omega$$
$$R_{m1} = 0.9 \text{ k}\Omega$$

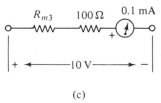

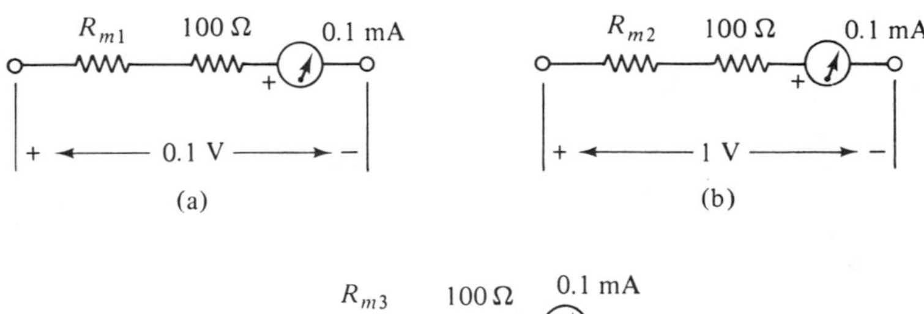

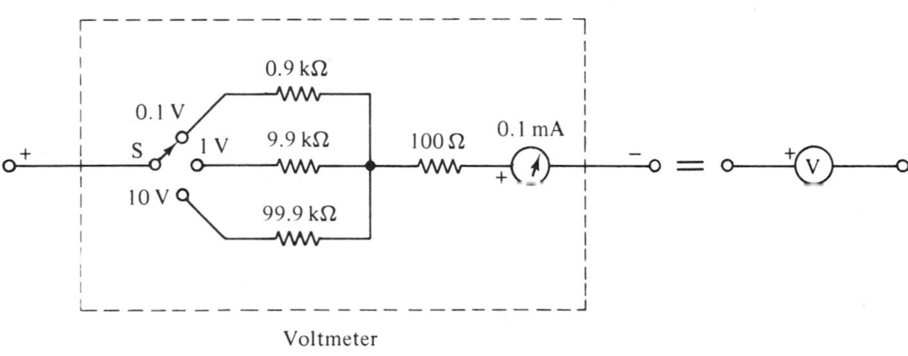

Fig. 2-38

Alternatively, we can use the voltage-divider rule. We want 10 mV(100 Ω × 0.1 mA) across the basic meter when the voltage to be measured is 100 mV. Hence

$$10 = 100\frac{100}{100 + R_{m1}}, \qquad R_{m1} = 900\ \Omega = 0.9\ \text{k}\Omega$$

In the 1 V range, we see from Fig. 2-38(b) that

$$1 = 0.1\ \text{mA} \times (R_{m2} + 0.1)\ \text{k}\Omega, \qquad R_{m2} = 9.9\ \text{k}\Omega$$

Similarly, using Fig. 2-38(c), we obtain the multiplier resistance for the 10 V range of operation.

$$10 = 0.1\ \text{mA} \times (R_{m3} + 0.1)\,\text{k}\Omega, \qquad R_{m3} = 99.9\,\text{k}\Omega$$

As Fig. 2-38(d) shows, we can put all three circuits together by using a range switch and thus complete the design of the voltmeter. When the switch S is in the 0.1 V position, we have the circuit of Fig. 2-38(a). When it is in the 1 V position, we have the circuit of Fig. 2-38(b). When it is in the 10 V position, we have the circuit of Fig. 2-38(c).

Note that this voltmeter would be rated as 10 kΩ/V. (It has 1 kΩ of resistance on the 0.1 V range, 10 kΩ of resistance on the 1 V range, and 100 kΩ of resistance on the 10 V range.)

Example 2-17

(a) A 2 kΩ/V voltmeter is used on the 100 V range to measure the voltage across the 200 kΩ resistor shown in Fig. 2-39. What will it read?

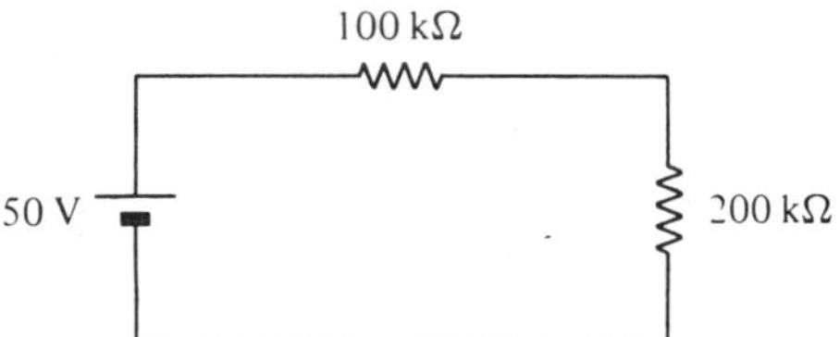

Fig. 2-39

(b) What will the voltmeter read if it is connected across the battery?

Solution.

(a) On the 100 V range, the resistance of the voltmeter is 2 kΩ/V × 100 V = 200 kΩ. When it is connected across the 200 kΩ resistor, the circuit is modified as shown in Fig. 2-40(a). The 50 V source now sees 100 kΩ in series with two 200 kΩs in parallel. By voltage division, the voltage across the parallel combination is

$$50 \times \frac{100}{100 + 100} = 25\ \text{V}$$

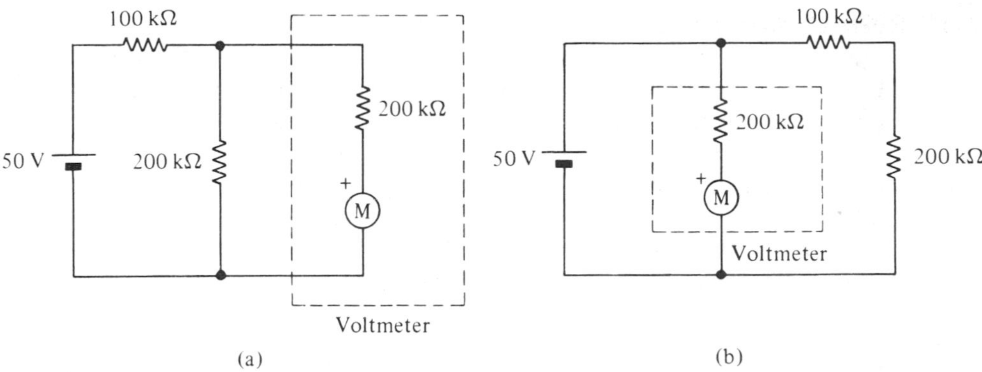

Fig. 2-40

Consequently, the voltmeter will read 25 V. This is considerably different from the $33\frac{1}{3}$ V[50 × 200/(200 + 100)] that exists across the 200 kΩ resistor before the voltmeter is connected.

(b) When the voltmeter is connected across the battery as shown in Fig. 2-40(b), it will read the correct battery voltage—50 V. The battery supplies the 0.25 mA (50 V/200 kΩ) required by the voltmeter without its terminal voltage being affected.

Example 2-18

Given a 1.5 V battery and 100 μA (full-scale) meter with 100 Ω internal resistance, construct an ohmmeter. (See also Problem 2-58.)

Solution. To limit the maximum current through the meter to 100 μA, connect a 14.9 kΩ resistor in series with the meter and the battery as in Fig. 2-41. Thus when the terminals are shorted together, the meter deflection would be maximum (I_M = 1.5 V/15 kΩ = 0.1 mA = 100 μA). Mark this position as 0 Ω on the meter scale to signify that the resistance across the terminals (R_x) is zero. Connect different but known resistors across the terminals and mark the corresponding deflections to agree with the known resistor values. For example, if 15 kΩ is connected across the terminals, the meter will deflect half scale (because the source sees twice as much resistance and the current drops to half its short-circuit value) and this position is marked 15 kΩ and so on. Thus the meter scale is calibrated to read kΩs directly. The maximum deflection corresponds to zero ohms.

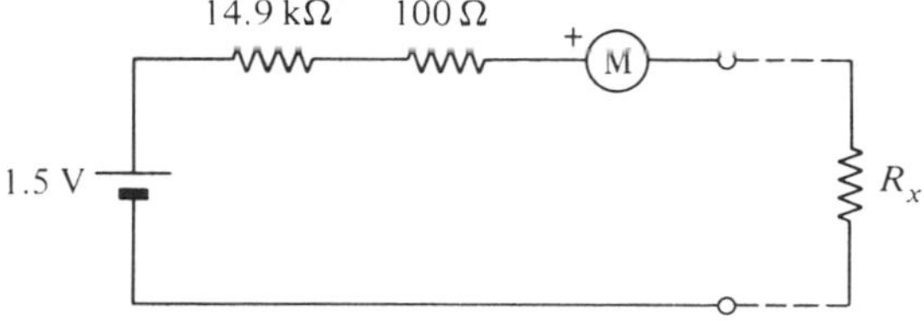

Fig. 2-41

2-15 SIMPLE RESISTANCE MEASUREMENTS

Here we are concerned with two simple methods of resistance measurement that use a voltmeter. A third method appears in Example 2-19 under bridge networks.

The unknown resistance R_x can be determined by connecting it as in Fig. 2-42(a) or (b), where R_k represents a known resistance. Both methods require *two* voltage measurements.

If the circuit connection shown in Fig. 2-42(a) is used, the voltmeter is connected across V_s and then across R_x to measure v_1 and v_2. These voltages are related by

$$v_2 = v_1 \frac{R_x}{R_k + R_x}$$

Solving for R_x, we obtain

$$R_x = \frac{R_k}{(v_1/v_2) - 1} \tag{2-17}$$

Since all the quantities on the right side of the equation are known, R_x can be calculated. The known R_k should be chosen such that v_2 is considerably smaller than v_1, thus improving the accuracy of calculation. [If v_2 were close to v_1, we would, in the denominator of Eq. (2-17), be taking the difference of two numbers that are close

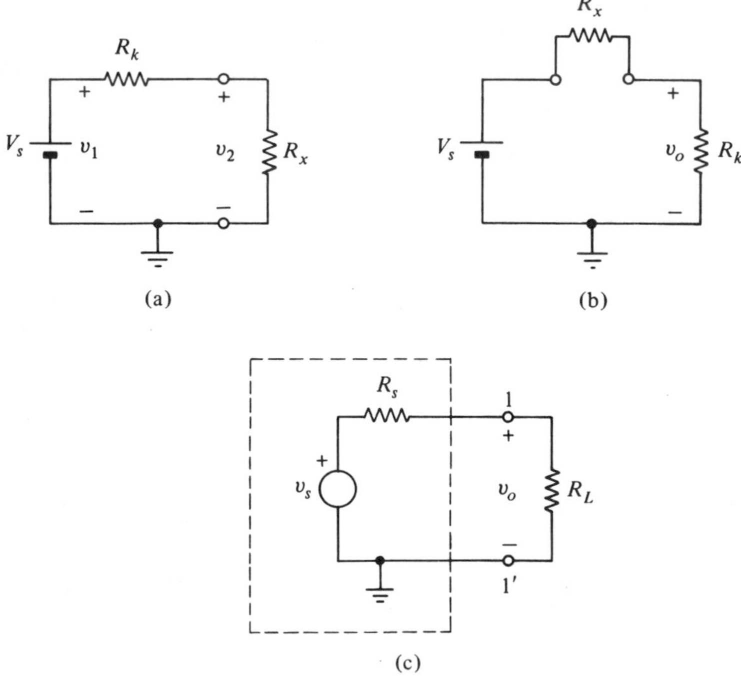

Fig. 2-42

to each other; therefore the result becomes highly sensitive to small errors in the measurement of v_1 and v_2.]

In the circuit connection shown in Fig. 2-42(b), v_o is measured twice, corresponding to two different values of R_k. Generally one value of R_k is chosen as infinity; that is, R_k is simply disconnected from the circuit. The resulting v_o represents the open-circuit voltage v_{oc}, which is equal to V_s. Then a known value of R_k is connected and the new v_o is noted. This v_o will be lower than v_{oc} because of the voltage dropped across R_x, and it is related to V_s by

$$v_o = V_s \frac{R_k}{R_k + R_x}$$

Since $V_s = v_{oc}$, we have

$$v_o = v_{oc} \frac{R_k}{R_k + R_x}$$

Solving for R_x, we obtain

$$R_x = R_k\left(\frac{v_{oc}}{v_o} - 1\right) \tag{2-18}$$

Thus the two measured voltages, v_{oc} (open circuit) and v_o (loaded by R_k), and the known value of R_k allow us to calculate R_x. A sufficiently small R_k should be chosen so that v_{oc}/v_o is far from unity; otherwise R_x, being dependent on the difference of two almost-equal numbers, will not be determined too accurately.

Equation (2-18) shows that for $v_o = \frac{1}{2}v_{oc}$, $R_x = R_k$. So a very simple determination of R_x can be made by loading the output by a known but variable R_k until the output voltage v_o drops down to half its open-circuit value. When this situation occurs, the source voltage divides equally between the unknown and load resistances. The particular value of R_k that does so is equal to the unknown resistance R_x.

The second method of measurement shown in Fig. 2-42(b) is particularly useful in the measurement of internal resistances that are not accessible for direct measurement. For instance, as shown in Fig. 2-42(c), the unknown resistance may be the internal resistance R_s of a battery with only external terminals 1–1′ available for measurement. By taking two measurements of the voltage across these terminals with two different values of R_L, R_s can be determined. (See Problem 2-62.)

2-16 BRIDGE NETWORKS

A bridge network has the configuration shown in Fig. 2-43. The input can be taken either as the voltage v_i or the current i_i. These variables can be dc (direct current) or ac (alternating current). The output is taken as the voltage v_o, which is the difference between the voltage across R_4 and the voltage across R_2. *The bridge is said to be balanced, or nulled, when* $v_o = 0$.

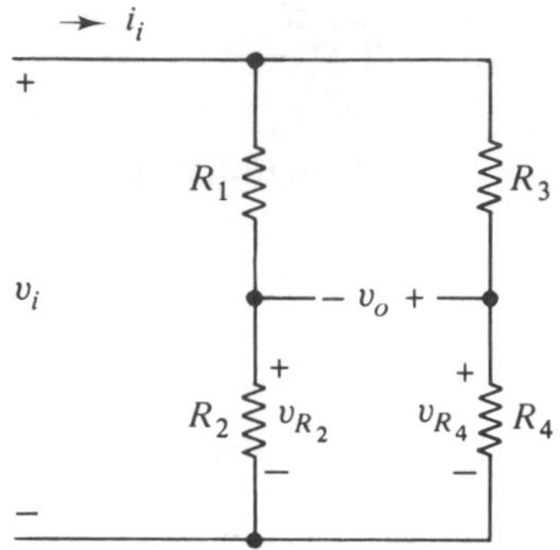

Fig. 2-43

If the input is taken as v_i, the output is

$$v_o = v_{R4} - v_{R2} = v_i \frac{R_4}{R_3 + R_4} - v_i \frac{R_2}{R_1 + R_2} = v_i \frac{(R_1 R_4 - R_2 R_3)}{(R_1 + R_2)(R_3 + R_4)} \tag{2-19}$$

If the input is taken as i_i, the output is

$$\begin{aligned} v_o &= v_{R4} - v_{R2} \\ &= i_i \frac{(R_1 + R_2)}{(R_1 + R_2) + (R_3 + R_4)} \times R_4 - i_i \frac{(R_3 + R_4)}{(R_1 + R_2) + (R_3 + R_4)} \times R_2 \\ &= i_i \frac{(R_1 R_4 - R_2 R_3)}{R_1 + R_2 + R_3 + R_4} \end{aligned} \tag{2-20}$$

Whether the input is v_i or i_i, the bridge is balanced when

$$R_1 R_4 = R_2 R_3 \tag{2-21}$$

As seen from Fig. 2-43, the condition for balance is attained when the *diagonally opposite resistance products are equal to each other.*

Bridge networks are used in a wide variety of applications that rely on the condition of balance one way or another. In some, one of the resistances is varied until v_o is driven to zero, thereby establishing balance. In other applications, we start out with the balanced condition and relate any ensuing changes in v_o to changes in one of the resistances.

Example 2-19

In Fig. 2-44, R_1 and R_3 are 1 kΩ resistances of high precision. The resistance R_2 is a high-precision, calibrated potentiometer. It is adjusted until v_o is zero. If this occurs for $R_2 = 1.94$ kΩ, what is the unknown resistance R_x?

Solution. Since $v_o = 0$, the products of resistances in diagonally opposite arms of the bridge are equal.

$$R_1 R_x = R_2 R_3$$

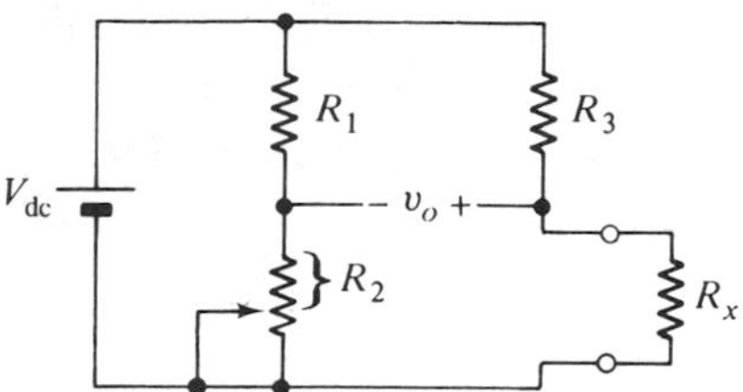

Fig. 2-44

Since $R_1 = R_3$ and $R_2 = 1.94\ \text{k}\Omega$, we have

$$R_x = R_2 = 1.94\ \text{k}\Omega \quad \text{Ans.}$$

Thus we determine the value of the unknown resistance from the values of the other three known resistances.

Example 2-20

In Fig. 2-45 the three Rs are precision 1 kΩ resistances. If $v_o = 10$ mV, what is R_x?

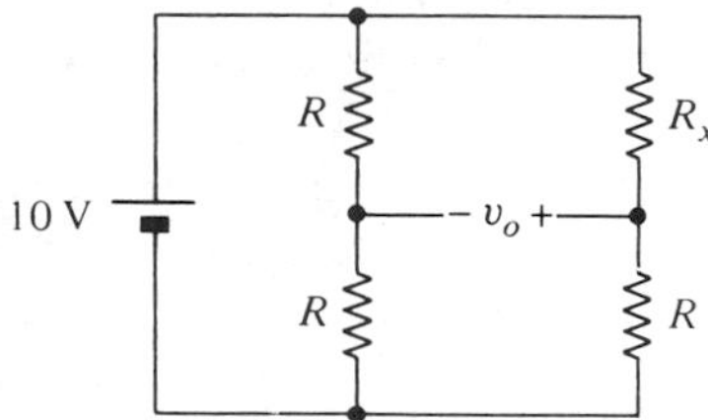

Fig. 2-45

Solution. By inspection of the bridge network, we see that

$$v_o = 10\frac{R}{R + R_x} - 10\frac{R}{R + R}$$

$$10 \times 10^{-3} = 10\frac{1}{1 + R_x} - 5$$

$$1 + R_x = \frac{10}{5 + 0.01}$$

$$R_x = \frac{5 - 0.01}{5 + 0.01} = \frac{1 - 0.002}{1 + 0.002}$$

Since

$$\frac{1}{1 + x} \cong 1 - x \qquad |x| \ll 1$$

we can simplify R_x to

$$R_x \cong (1 - 0.002)(1 - 0.002) \cong (1 - 0.004)\ \text{k}\Omega = 996\ \Omega \quad \text{Ans.}$$

If R_x were equal to 1 kΩ, v_o would have been zero. So we see that a 4 Ω decrease in R_x from 1 kΩ results in +10 mV of unbalance in the output.

2-17 OTHER APPLICATIONS INVOLVING BRIDGE NETWORKS

It is possible to construct resistors that have temperature-dependent resistance values. Such resistors, which are called *thermistors*, are used in temperature measurement and temperature control circuits. It is also possible to construct resistors having resistance values that depend on the elongation or compression applied to them. Called *strain gages*, these resistors are used in measuring the strain in structural elements. In addition, there are resistors with characteristics that are dependent on light, humidity, and other factors. Such resistors can be made part of a bridge circuit that is then nulled when one set of external conditions, such as temperature or humidity, prevails. When external conditions change, the resistance changes. The bridge becomes unbalanced and a voltage develops across the output terminals. This voltage can, in turn, be related to the external conditions causing the unbalance in the bridge circuit.

To illustrate, consider the thermistor-bridge network shown in Fig. 2-46. The two upper resistances are fixed. The two lower resistances, being thermistor resistances, are temperature dependent. The thermistors are matched; that is, they track together in resistance value as a function of temperature. Ideally, when both thermistors are placed in exactly the same environment, their resistance values will be the same and the bridge will be balanced. In practice, v_o will not be exactly zero because it is impossible to have any two resistances that are *exactly* equal. As a result, v_o will be either slightly positive or slightly negative. To balance the bridge under these circumstances, we need a "zero-adjust" capability. This capability is provided by the potentiometer labeled R_a. Its value is much less than the other resistances, for its only function is to compensate for the small differences in the other resistance values.

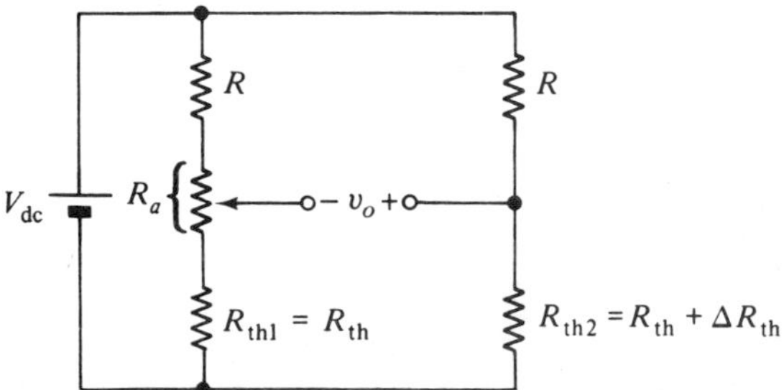

Fig. 2-46

Suppose that both R_{th1} and R_{th2} are placed in an environment at temperature T_1, thus making $R_{th1} = R_{th2} = R_{th}$. We then balance the bridge by adjusting R_a. We may even amplify v_o to obtain a more accurate null. If R_{th2} is taken out of the environment at temperature T_1 and placed in an environment at temperature T_2, R_{th2} becomes

$R_{th} + \Delta R_{th}$, where ΔR_{th} represents the change in resistance of the thermistor due to change of temperature. As a result, v_o is no longer zero but is given by

$$v_o = V_{dc}\frac{R_{th} + \Delta R_{th}}{R + R_{th} + \Delta R_{th}} - V_{dc}\frac{R_{th}}{R + R_{th}} \tag{2-22}$$

In deriving Eq. (2-22), we have assumed that R_a is zero. Rearranging Eq. (2-22), we have

$$v_o = V_{dc}\left[\frac{\dfrac{R}{R_{th}}}{\left(1 + \dfrac{R}{R_{th}}\right)\left(1 + \dfrac{R}{R_{th}} + \dfrac{\Delta R_{th}}{R_{th}}\right)}\right]\left(\frac{\Delta R_{th}}{R_{th}}\right)$$

For $\Delta R_{th} \ll R_{th}$, v_o can be simplified to

$$v_o \cong V_{dc}\left[\frac{\dfrac{R}{R_{th}}}{\left(1 + \dfrac{R}{R_{th}}\right)^2}\right]\left(\frac{\Delta R_{th}}{R_{th}}\right)$$

which shows that as long as resistance changes are small, the output voltage is directly proportional to changes in R_{th2}. For a given thermistor, the change in R_{th2} is related to $(T_2 - T_1)$. So by measuring v_o, $(T_2 - T_1)$ can be determined. If T_1 can be held constant, R_{th1} can be replaced with a resistor, thereby avoiding the necessity of using two thermistors.

In Fig. 2-46 the thermistors can be replaced by strain gages. In this case, v_o represents the difference in strain between the two locations where the strain gages are secured.

Example 2-21

The circuit shown in Fig. 2-47 is balanced at room temperature by adjusting R to 1 kΩ. The temperature coefficient of the thermistor is −2 Ω/°C.

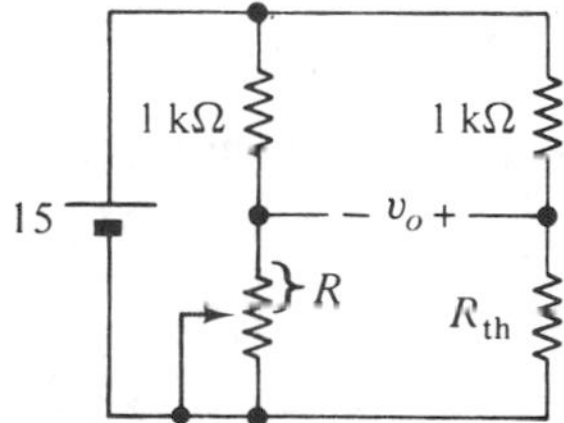

Fig. 2-47

(a) What is the resistance of the thermistor at room temperature?

(b) When the thermistor is placed in a different environment, it is noted that v_o = 150 mV. What is the temperature of the new environment?

Solution.

(a) The bridge is balanced when

$$1\text{ k}\Omega \times R_{th} = 1\text{ k}\Omega \times R$$

Since $R = 1$ kΩ, the thermistor resistance at room temperature is

$$R_{th} = 1\text{ k}\Omega \quad \text{Ans.}$$

(b) When the thermistor is placed in the new environment, its resistance becomes

$$R_{th} = (1 + \Delta R_{th})\text{ k}\Omega$$

where ΔR_{th} accounts for the change in resistance due to the difference in temperature between the new environment and the ambient (room) temperature. The resulting v_o can be obtained by inspection of Fig. 2-47 and by using $R = 1$ kΩ.

$$v_o = 15\left(\frac{R_{th}}{1 + R_{th}} - \frac{R}{1 + R}\right)$$

$$= 15\left(\frac{1 + \Delta R_{th}}{1 + 1 + \Delta R_{th}} - \frac{1}{1 + 1}\right) = \frac{15}{2}\left[\frac{1 + \Delta R_{th}}{1 + (\Delta R_{th}/2)} - 1\right]$$

$$= \frac{15}{4}\frac{\Delta R_{th}}{1 + (\Delta R_{th}/2)}$$

Since $v_o = 0.150$ V, we have

$$0.150 = \frac{15}{4}\frac{\Delta R_{th}}{1 + (\Delta R_{th}/2)}$$

which results in

$$\Delta R_{th} = \frac{2}{49}\text{ k}\Omega \cong 40\ \Omega$$

Since the temperature coefficient of the thermistor is $-2\ \Omega/^\circ$C, the temperature of the new environment is 20°C below the ambient temperature.

Example 2-22

In Fig. 2-48 two identical 100 Ω strain gages are connected in a bridge circuit as shown. The left gage is a dummy gage in that it is not secured to anything. The right gage, the active one, is secured to a bar. (The dummy gage is used to make the bridge balance

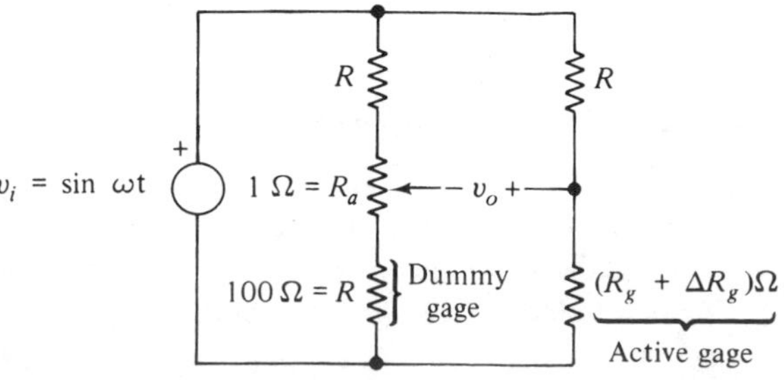

Fig. 2-48

independent of temperature, humidity, and other environmental variations that would affect both sides of the bridge by the same amount and therefore maintain the balance for changes not related to stresses in the bar.) When there is no load on the bar, the bridge is balanced by adjusting the 1 Ω potentiometer. The bar is then put under tension.

(a) Let $R = R_g$ and $R_a = 0$. Show that

$$v_o \cong \frac{1}{4}\left(\frac{\Delta R_g}{R_g}\right)v_i \qquad (\Delta R_g \ll R_g)$$

(b) The gage factor,

$$\text{GF} = \frac{\Delta R_g/R_g}{\Delta l/l}$$

is 6. What is the percent change in length if the measured output is

$$v_o = 0.01 \sin \omega t?$$

Solution

(a) The output voltage is the difference of voltages across the dummy and active gages.

$$v_o = v_i\left(\frac{R_g + \Delta R_g}{R + R_g + \Delta R_g} - \frac{R_g}{R + R_g}\right)\Bigg|_{R=R_g}$$

$$= v_i\left(\frac{R_g + \Delta R_g}{2R_g + \Delta R_g} - \frac{1}{2}\right) = \frac{v_i}{2}\left\{\left[\left(1 + \frac{\Delta R_g}{R_g}\right)\Big/\left(1 + \frac{1}{2}\frac{\Delta R_g}{R_g}\right)\right] - 1\right\}$$

$$= \frac{v_i}{4}\left(\frac{\Delta R_g}{R_g}\right)\Big/\left(1 + \frac{1}{2}\frac{\Delta R_g}{R_g}\right)$$

For $\Delta R_g \ll R_g$, the output simplifies to

$$v_o \cong \frac{1}{4}\left(\frac{\Delta R_g}{R_g}\right)v_i \quad \text{Ans.}$$

(b) Since

$$\text{GF} = \frac{\Delta R_g/R_g}{\Delta l/l}$$

the output can be expressed as

$$v_o \doteq \frac{\text{GF}}{4}\left(\frac{\Delta l}{l}\right)v_i$$

Hence

$$\frac{\Delta l}{l} \cong \frac{4}{\text{GF}}\frac{v_o}{v_i}$$

which for GF = 6, $v_i = \sin \omega t$, and $v_o = 0.01 \sin \omega t$ gives

$$\frac{\Delta l}{l} \cong \frac{4}{6} \times 0.01 = \frac{2}{3} \times 0.01$$

There is a $\frac{2}{3}$% elongation in the bar.

Example 2-23

A *photoresistor* is a two-terminal device that can be equivalently represented by a light-controlled resistor. Its resistance, R_{ph}, depends on the intensity of light. In Fig. 2-49 the photoresistor is used in a bridge structure. The circuit is designed so that the bridge is balanced when a prescribed light intensity causes the photoresistor to assume the value of R_{pho}. Additionally, the output v_o is to be most sensitive to slight variations of light intensity about the prescribed value; that is, a small change in light intensity should result in as large a value for v_o as possible. How should R_1, R_2, and R be selected to achieve this desired result? What is the resulting output for small changes in R_{ph}?

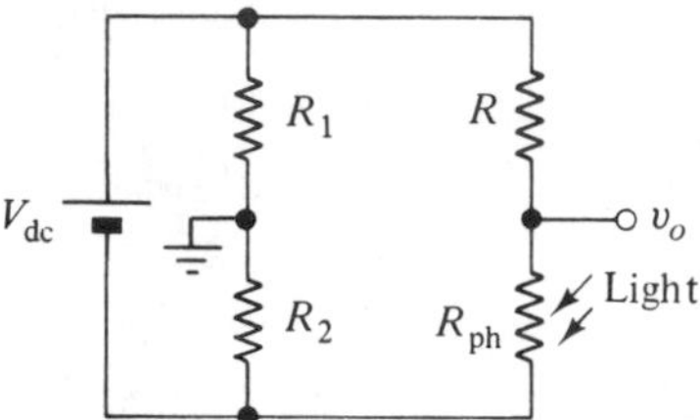

Fig. 2-49

Solution. The output as a function of R_1, R_2, and R is given by

$$v_o = V_{dc}\left(\frac{R_{ph}}{R + R_{ph}} - \frac{R_2}{R_1 + R_2}\right)$$

where R_{ph} represents the resistance of the photoresistor for some value of light intensity. In particular, when the light intensity is at its prescribed value, R_{ph} takes on the value of R_{pho}, and v_o becomes zero. This balance condition requires that

$$R_1 R_{pho} = R_2 R$$

In Fig. 2-50, the output v_o is sketched as a function of R_{ph}. The objective of the design is to make the bridge as sensitive as possible. This requires that the slope of the v_o vs. R_{ph} curve be as steep as possible at the point of balance, thus causing v_o to assume a large positive value ($R_{ph} > R_{pho}$) or a large negative value ($R_{ph} < R_{pho}$) when the light intensity

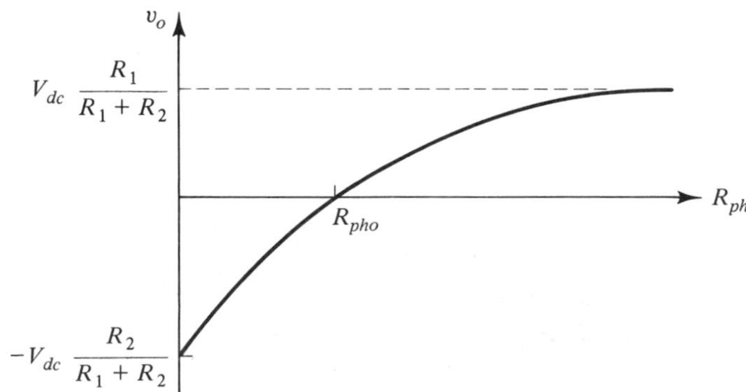

Fig. 2-50

changes about the prescribed value. To determine what it takes to maximize the slope at R_{pho}, we differentiate v_o with respect to R_{ph} and evaluate the result for $R_{ph} = R_{pho}$.

$$\left.\frac{\partial v_o}{\partial R_{ph}}\right|_{R_{ph}=R_{pho}} = V_{dc}\left.\frac{(R + R_{ph}) - (R_{ph})}{(R + R_{ph})^2}\right|_{R_{ph}=R_{pho}} = V_{dc}\frac{R}{(R + R_{pho})^2}$$

The supply voltage V_{dc} and the nominal photoresistor value R_{pho} are fixed; they are not design parameters that can be adjusted. Hence the only design parameter that can be changed to affect the slope is R. Since the slope is always positive and is zero for $R = 0$ and $R = \infty$, it must have a maximum value for some value of R. See Fig. 2-51. To determine the optimum value of R, we differentiate the expression of the slope at balance with respect to R and set the result to zero.

$$\frac{\partial}{\partial R}\left[\left.\frac{\partial v_o}{\partial R_{ph}}\right|_{R_{ph}=R_{pho}}\right] = V_{dc}\frac{(R + R_{pho})^2 - 2R(R + R_{pho})}{(R + R_{pho})^4}$$

$$= V_{dc}\frac{(R_{pho} - R)}{(R + R_{pho})^3} = 0$$

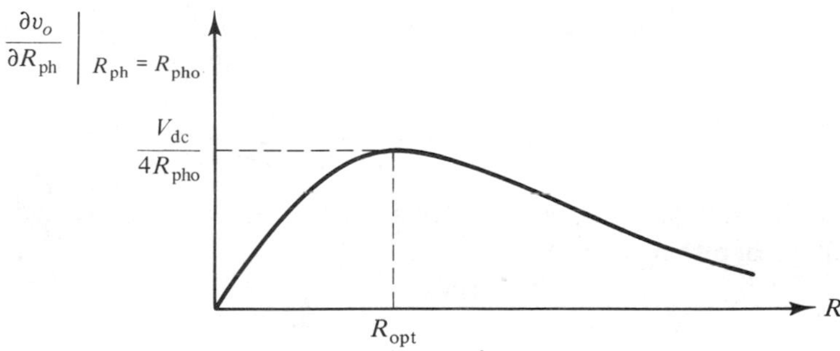

Fig. 2-51

The slope is maximum when $R = R_{pho}$, that is, the free design parameter R must be adjusted to equal to the value of the photoresistance obtained when the prescribed amount of light falls on the photoresistor. Using this result in the condition for balance gives the further condition of $R_1 = R_2$. Thus the bridge design for most sensitivity calls for

$$\left\{\begin{matrix} R_1 = R_2 \\ R = R_{pho} \end{matrix}\right\} \quad \text{Ans.}$$

which results in

$$\left(\left.\frac{\partial v_o}{\partial R_{ph}}\right|_{R_{ph}=R_{pho}}\right)_{max} = \frac{V_{dc}}{4R_{pho}}$$

For small changes, the derivative can be approximated by

$$\frac{\partial v_o}{\partial R_{ph}} \cong \frac{\Delta v_o}{\Delta R_{ph}}$$

Hence, the changes in output about the balance point can be expressed as

$$\Delta v_o \cong \frac{V_{dc}}{4}\left(\frac{\Delta R_{ph}}{R_{pho}}\right)$$

Since the nominal value of v_o is zero, the change in output is the output itself; that is,

$$v_o \cong \frac{V_{dc}}{4}\frac{\Delta R_{ph}}{R_{pho}} \quad \text{Ans.}$$

So for $V_{dc} = 24$ V, a 0.1% change in resistance, caused by a change in light intensity falling on the photoresistor, produces an output of

$$v_o \cong \frac{24}{4} \times 0.001 = 0.006 \text{ V} = 6 \text{ mV}$$

2-18 SUMMARY

When R_1 and R_2 are connected in series, the equivalent resistance is $R_1 + R_2$. When R_1 and R_2 are connected in parallel, the equivalent resistance is

$$\frac{R_1R_2}{R_1 + R_2}$$

When a voltage v is to be divided between two series resistances R_1 and R_2, the voltage across R_2 is given by

$$\pm v\left(\frac{R_2}{R_1 + R_2}\right)$$

When a current i is to be divided between two parallel resistances R_1 and R_2, the current through R_2 is given by

$$\pm i\left(\frac{R_1}{R_1 + R_2}\right)$$

A nonideal voltage source can be characterized as an ideal voltage source in series with a resistor. A nonideal current source can be characterized as an ideal current source in parallel with a resistor. A nonideal voltage source can be equivalently represented by a nonideal current source and vice versa.

Shunts are used to divert part of the current to be measured around the ammeter, thereby increasing the range of the ammeter. Multipliers are used to drop part of the voltage to be measured while the rest is applied to the voltmeter. The range of the voltmeter is thereby increased.

Bridge networks are widely used to obtain balanced conditions and sense departures from balanced conditions. When in balance, the output voltage is zero. Then the resistance products of diagonally opposite arms of the bridge are equal. Departures from balance generate voltages that can be related to changes in one of the resistances in the bridge circuit. The polarity of the voltage tells whether the resistance has gone up or down.

PROBLEMS

2-1. For the networks shown in Fig. 2-52, obtain the equivalent resistance at terminals 1–1′.

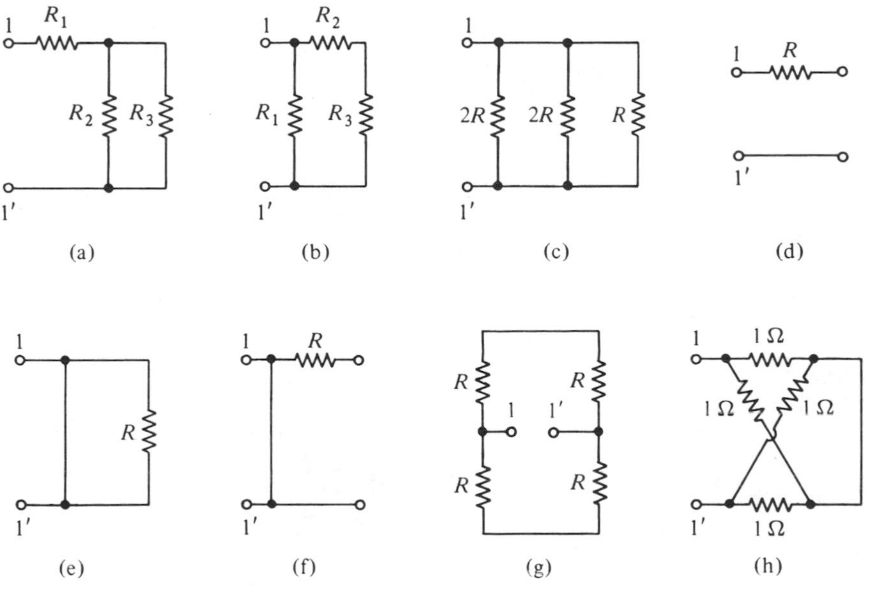

Fig. 2-52

2-2. Find the equivalent resistance of n identical resistors connected in parallel.

2-3. For the two circuits shown in Fig. 2-53, obtain the equivalent resistance seen between terminals 1 and 1′. Assume all resistances are 1 Ω.

2-4. In Fig. 2-7 what is the equivalent resistance seen between corners a and g? a and d?

2-5. For the circuits shown in Fig. 2-54 obtain the equivalent resistance seen between terminals 1 and 1′.

2-6. The network shown in Fig. 2-55 repeats itself indefinitely. What is R_{eq}?

2-7. Obtain equivalent terminal presentations for the source combinations shown in Fig. 2-56.

2-8. For the circuits shown in Fig. 2-57, sketch the i vs. v curves.

2-9. Draw on the same set of axes the i vs. v curves for the two circuits shown in Fig. 2-58.

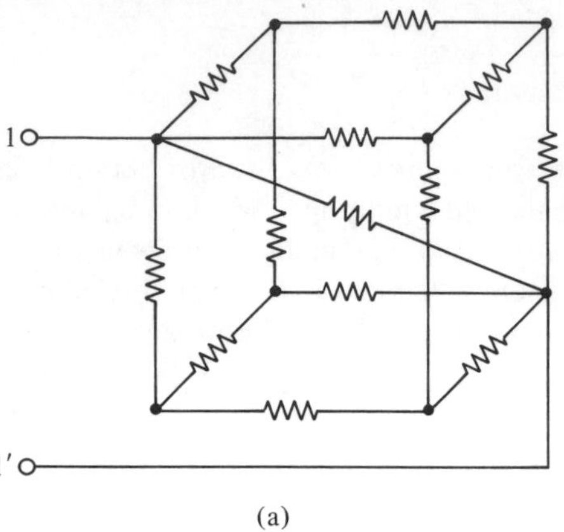

(a)

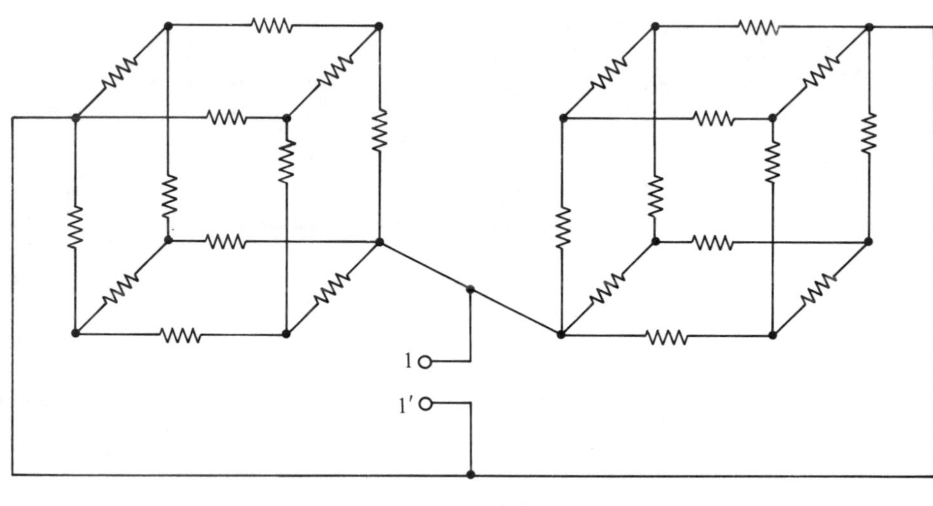

(b)

Fig. 2-53

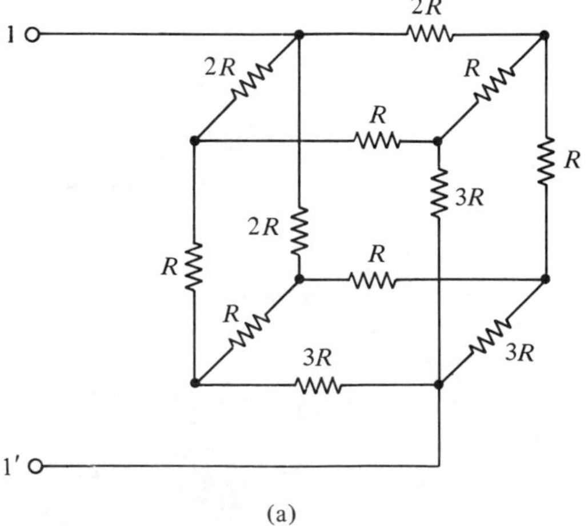

(a)

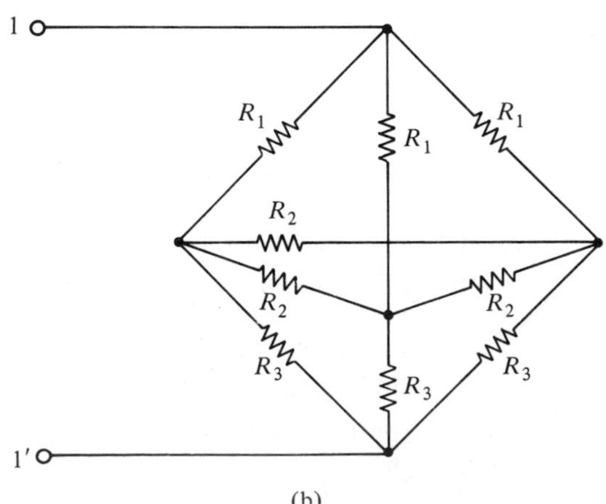

(b)

Fig. 2-54

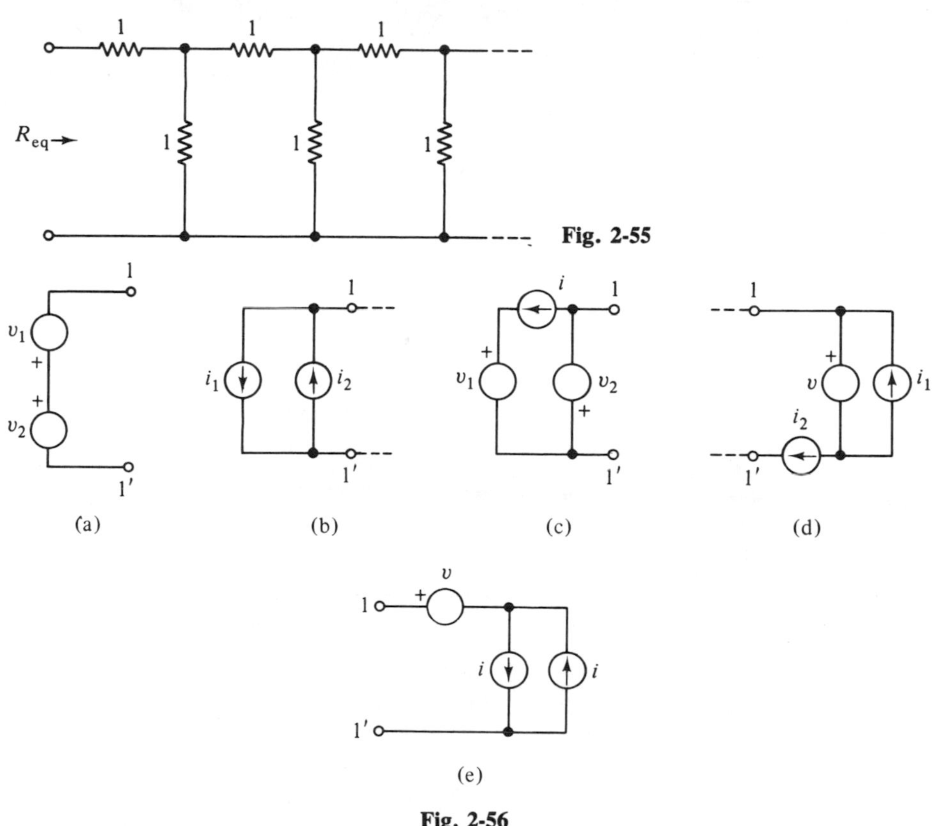

Fig. 2-55

(a) (b) (c) (d)

(e)

Fig. 2-56

(a) (b) (c)

(d) (e) (f) (g)

(h) (i) (j)

Fig. 2-57

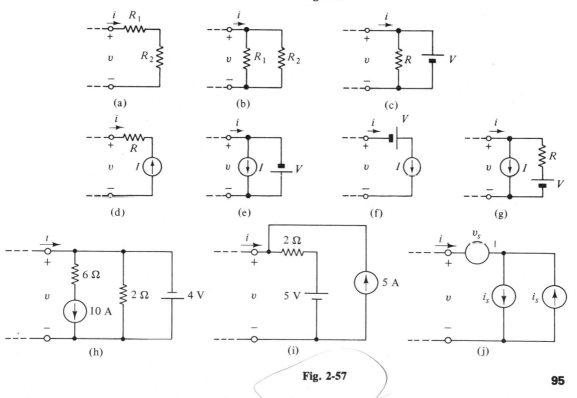

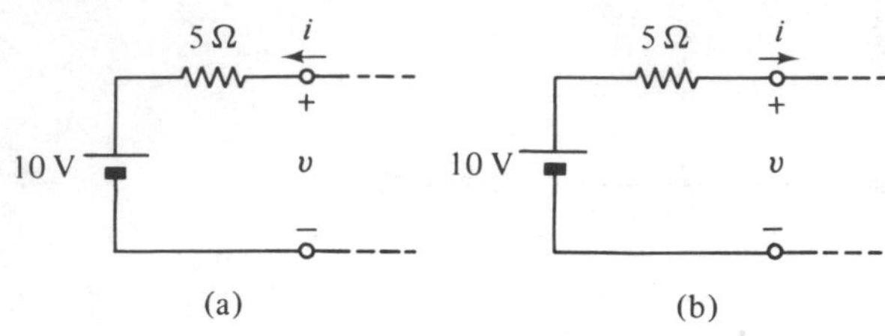

Fig. 2-58

2-10. Draw on the same set of axes the i vs. v curves for the two circuits shown in Fig. 2-59.

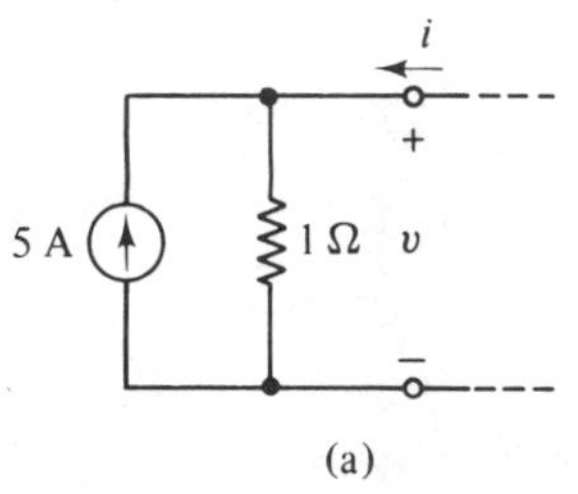

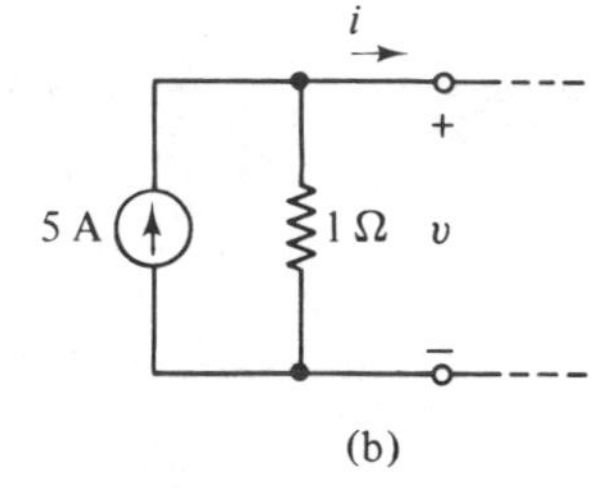

Fig. 2-59

2-11. Measurements are done on a two-terminal box with the polarities as shown in Fig. 2-60, and the results are plotted. What is in the box?

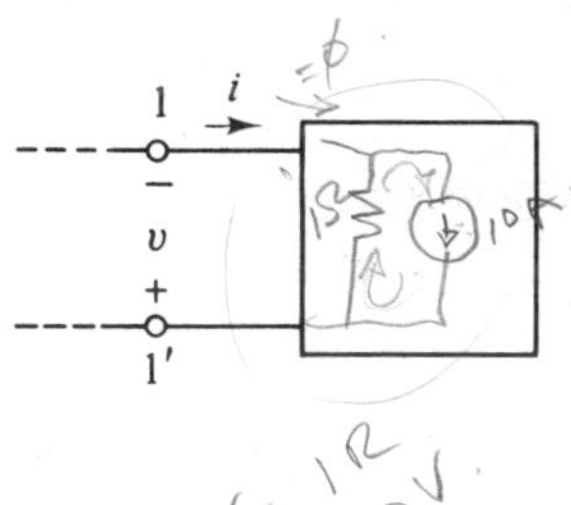

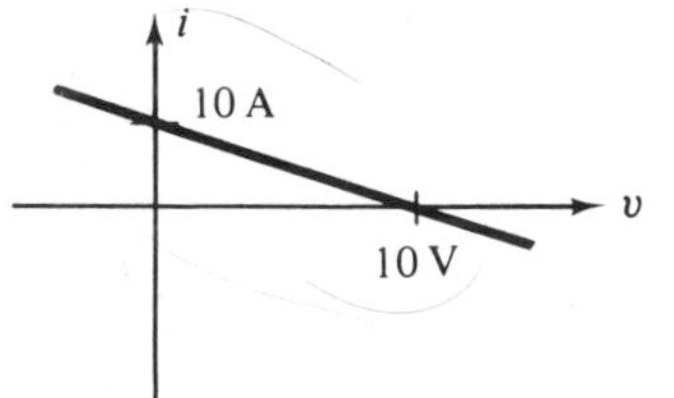

Fig. 2-60

2-12. In Fig. 2-60 suppose the same i vs. v curve is obtained with the polarity of the voltage across terminals 1 and 1′ reversed. What is in the box?

2-13. In Fig. 2-61, the v vs. i curve is as shown. What is in the box?

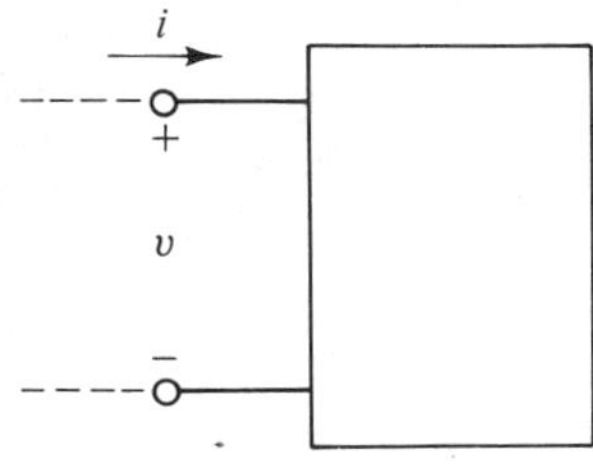

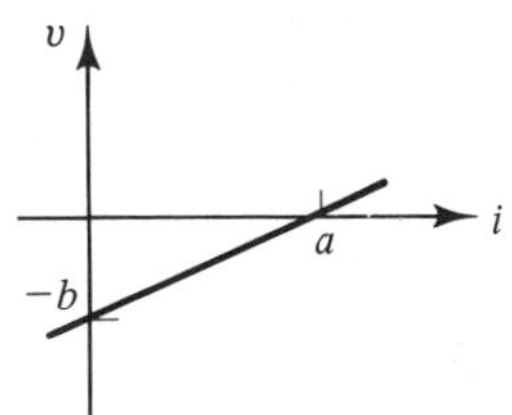

Fig. 2-61

2-14. At the terminals of a current source the voltage is zero. True of false. Explain.

2-15. The equation governing the terminal variables of the two-terminal network shown in Fig. 2-62 is $2v - 10i + 15 = 0$. What is in the box?

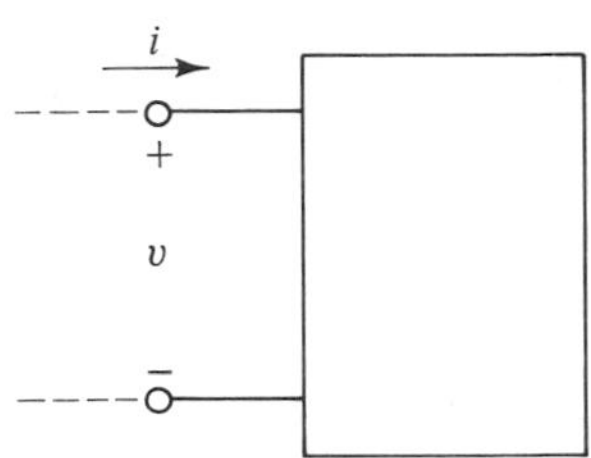

Fig. 2-62

2-16. A two-terminal device and its input characteristic are given in Fig. 2-63. What is the circuit model for the device?

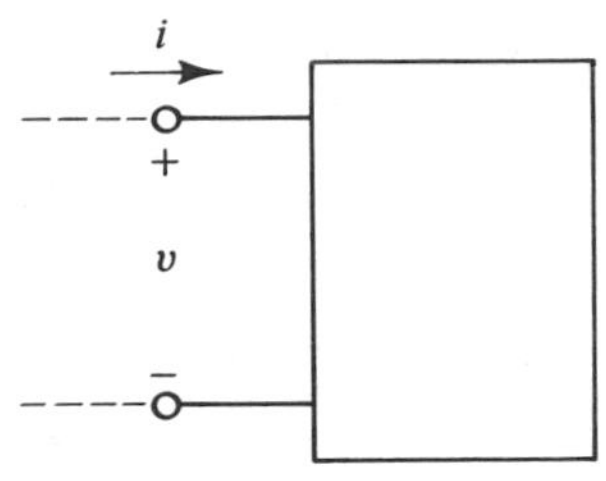

Fig. 2-63

2-17. In Fig. 2-64 obtain the currents and voltages designated by a question mark.

2-18. For each circuit shown in Fig. 2-65 answer the following three questions.
(a) Terminals are open circuited. What is v?
(b) Terminals are short circuited. What is i?
(c) What is the general relationship between v and i? State it as $v = f(i)$.

2-19. Convert the nonideal voltage source shown in Fig. 2-66 to a nonideal current source.

2-20. Figure 2-67 shows an oscilloscope display taken according to the setup shown in Fig. 2-20. Obtain a circuit model for the device. $R = 100\ \Omega$.

2-21. In Fig. 2-68, what would the oscilloscope display? Assume that the oscilloscope does not draw any current.

2-22. In Fig. 2-69, calculate the voltages and currents designated by a question mark.

2-23. In Fig. 2-70, the three trolly cars draw 50 A, 100 A, and 100 A of current as shown. There are no other cars on the track. The trolly wire has a resistance of 0.4 Ω/mi. The track resistance is 0.03 Ω/mi. What are the voltages across the trolly cars?

2-24. In Fig. 2-71, obtain the variables designated by a question mark.

2-25. In Fig. 2-72, $v_a = 100$ mV, $v_b = 250$ mV. What is i?

2-26. In Fig. 2-73, what is i?

2-27. (a) For what range of load resistance values does a 100 V voltage source with 10 Ω internal resistance act like a current source? Assume that 10% variation in current is acceptable.
(b) For what range of load resistance values does the source in (a) act like a voltage source? Assume that 10% variation in voltage is acceptable.

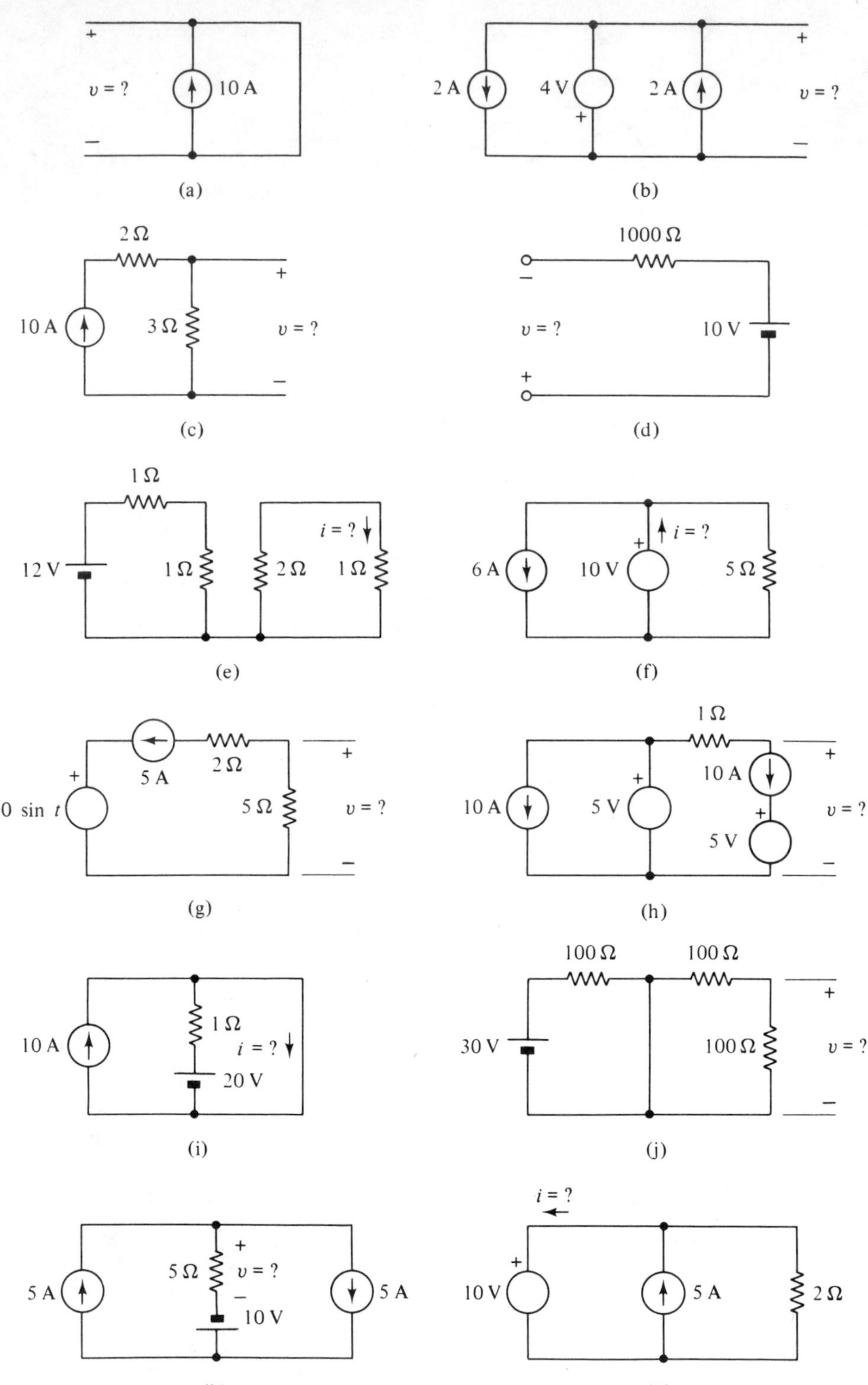

+
v = ?
−
10 A
(a)
2 A
4 V
+
2 A
+
v = ?
−
(b)
2 Ω
10 A
3 Ω
+
v = ?
−
(c)
1000 Ω
−
v = ?
+
10 V
(d)
1 Ω
12 V
1 Ω
2 Ω
i = ?
1 Ω
(e)
6 A
10 V
+
i = ?
5 Ω
(f)
+
10 sin t
5 A
2 Ω
5 Ω
+
v = ?
−
(g)
1 Ω
10 A
+
5 V
10 A
+
5 V
+
v = ?
−
(h)
10 A
1 Ω
i = ?
20 V
(i)
100 Ω
100 Ω
30 V
100 Ω
+
v = ?
−
(j)
5 A
5 Ω
+
v = ?
−
10 V
5 A
(k)
i = ?
+
10 V
5 A
2 Ω
(1)

Fig. 2-64

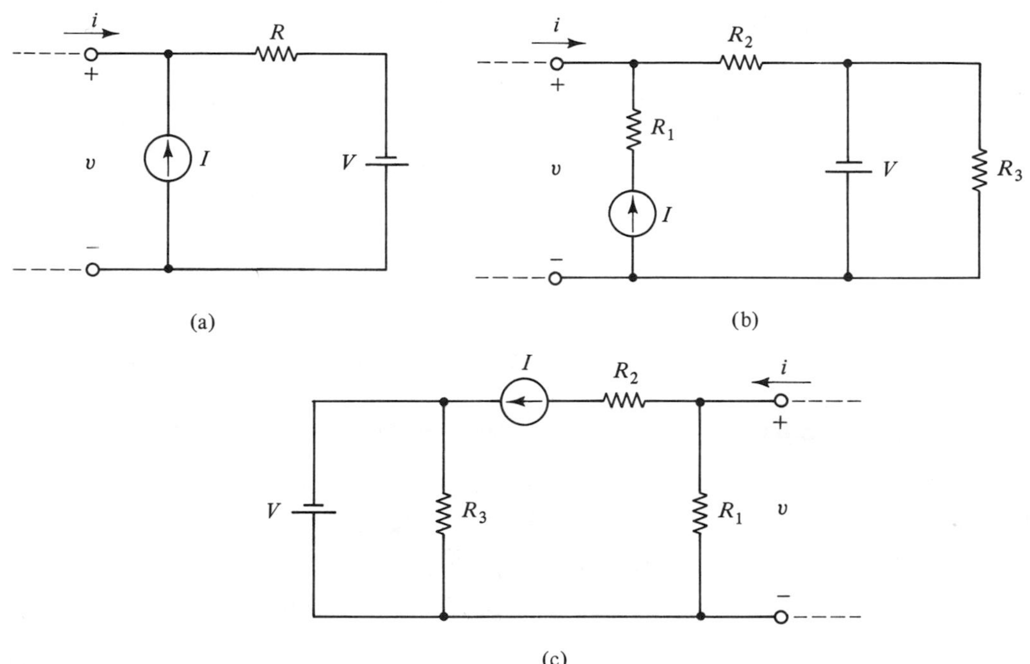

Fig. 2-65

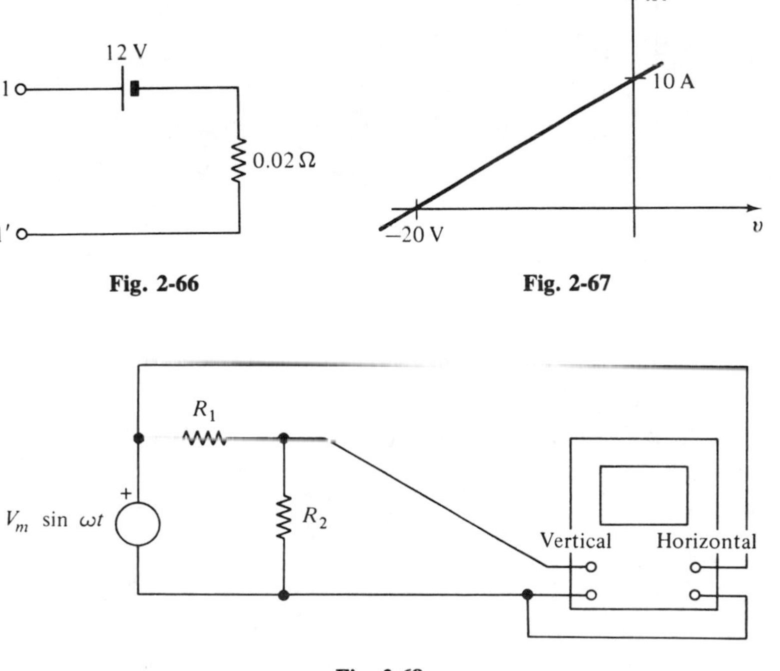

Fig. 2-66

Fig. 2-67

Fig. 2-68

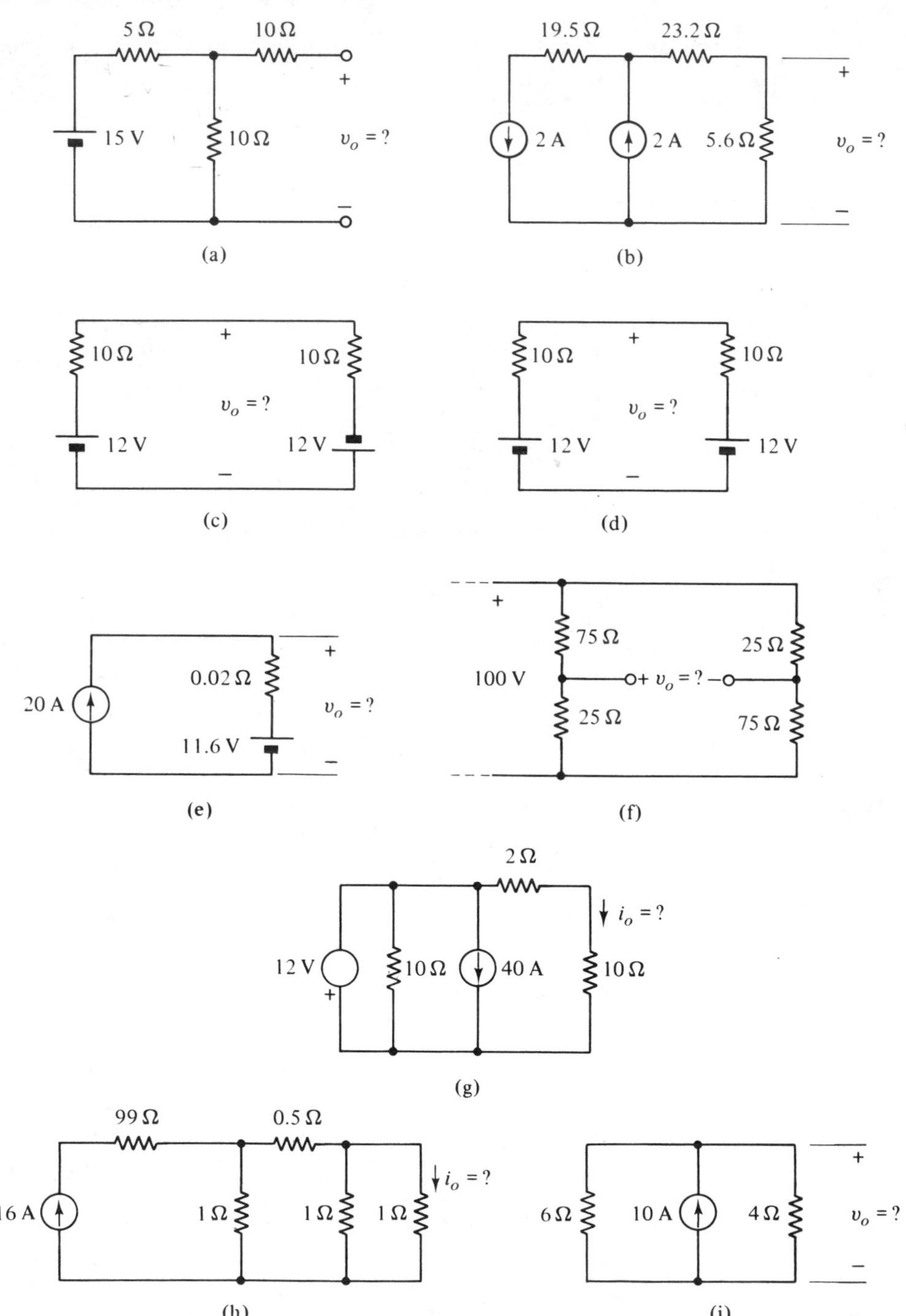

5 Ω
10 Ω
15 V
10 Ω
+
v_o = ?
−
(a)
19.5 Ω
23.2 Ω
2 A
2 A
5.6 Ω
+
v_o = ?
−
(b)
10 Ω
10 Ω
+
v_o = ?
12 V
12 V
−
(c)
10 Ω
10 Ω
+
v_o = ?
12 V
12 V
−
(d)
20 A
0.02 Ω
11.6 V
+
v_o = ?
−
(e)
+
100 V
75 Ω
25 Ω
25 Ω
75 Ω
+ v_o = ? −
(f)
2 Ω
i_o = ?
12 V
+
10 Ω
40 A
10 Ω
(g)
99 Ω
0.5 Ω
16 A
1 Ω
1 Ω
1 Ω
i_o = ?
(h)
6 Ω
10 A
4 Ω
+
v_o = ?
−
(i)

Fig. 2-69

0.4 Ω/mi
50 A
100 A
100 A
550 V
1
2
3
1 mi
1 mi
2 mi
0.03 Ω/mi

Fig. 2-70

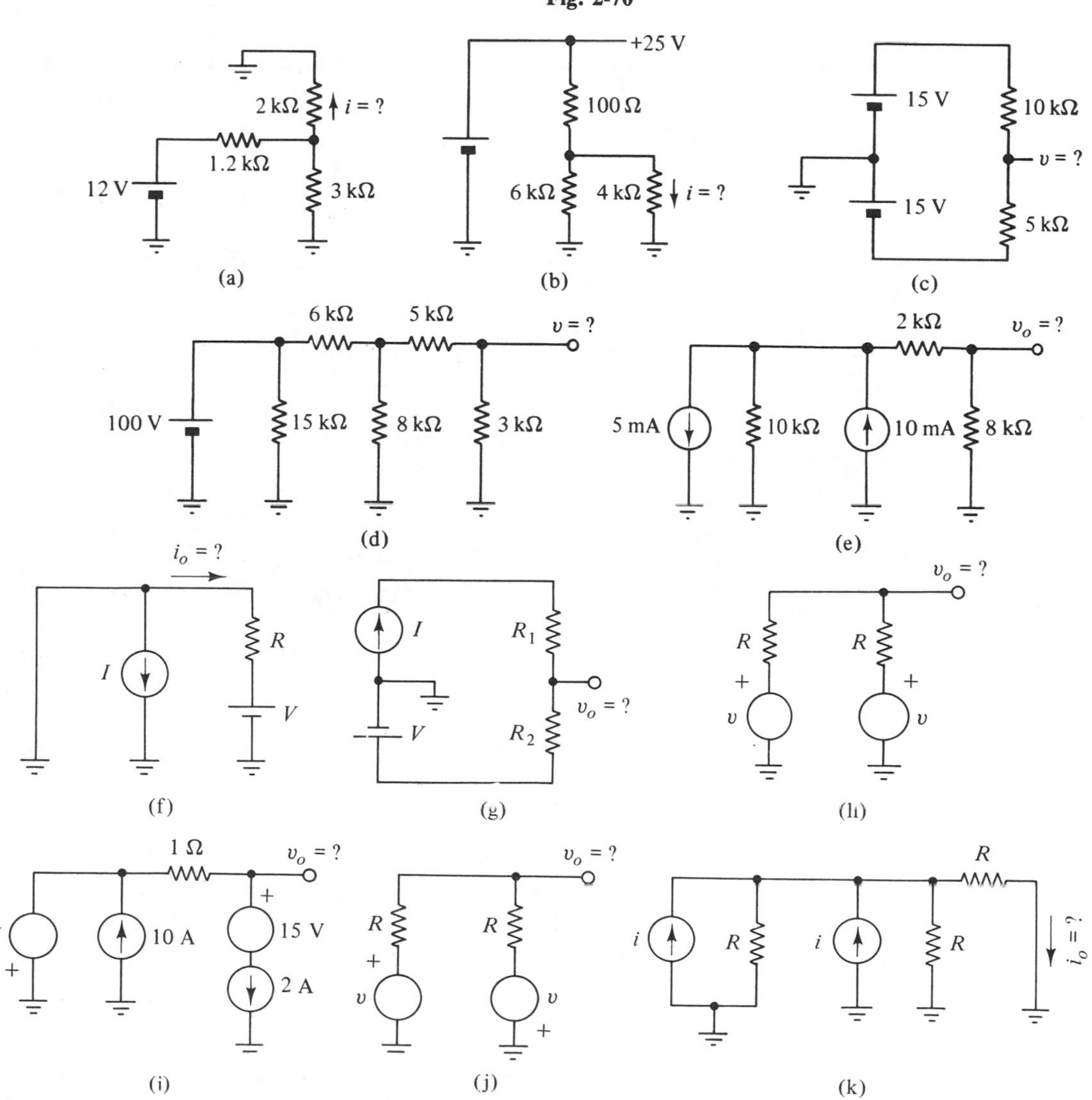

Fig. 2-71

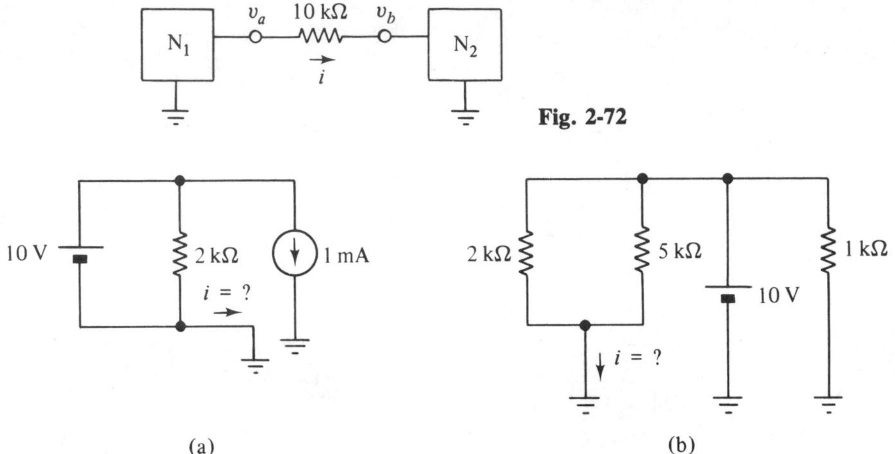

Fig. 2-72

Fig. 2-73

2-28. When does a current source start acting like a voltage source? Assume that the internal resistance of the current source is R.

2-29. Design a 5 : 1 current attenuator.

2-30. In Fig. 2-74, when the source resistance $R_s = 0$, $v_o = 0.5v_s$. What are v_o/v_i and v_o/v_s when $R_s = R_1$?

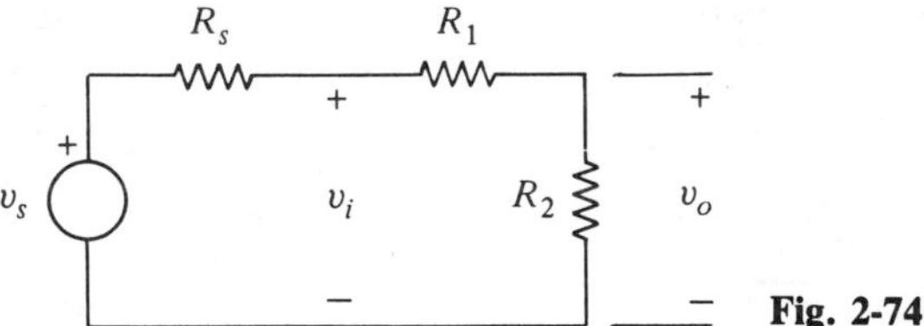

Fig. 2-74

2-31. Design the circuit of Fig. 2-75 such that $v_{o1} = 0.25\ V_{dc}$ and $v_{o2} = 0.75\ V_{dc}$. Give values of R_1 and R_2 in terms of R.

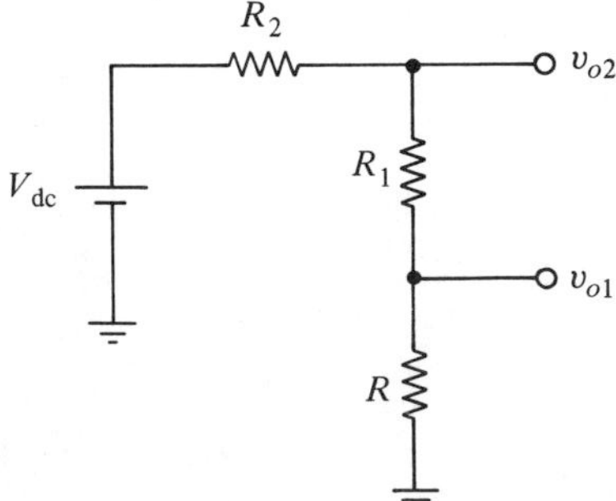

Fig. 2-75

2-32. In Fig. 2-76 select R_1 and R_2 to obtain the desired attenuations shown.

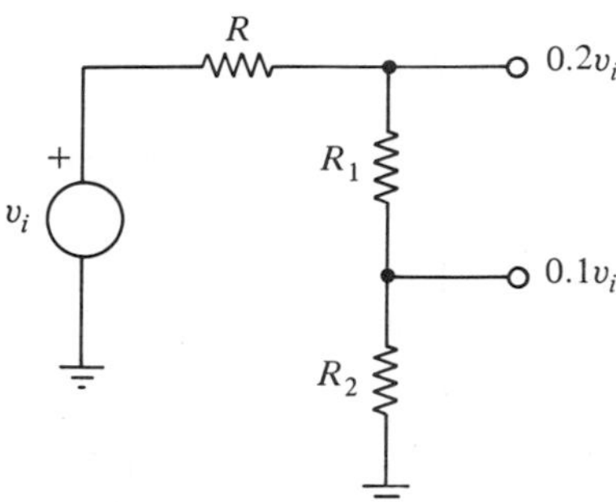

Fig. 2-76

2-33. Design a three-position voltage attenuator that produces the following output voltages:

$$\frac{v_i}{4}, \quad \frac{v_i}{2}, \quad \frac{3}{4} v_i$$

2-34. A signal v_s with 1 kΩ internal source resistance is to be attenuated to 0.1 v_s. The load is 10 kΩ. Design the attenuator, using the load and the source resistances as part of the attenuator.

2-35. (a) In Fig. 2-77, show that the output is given by

$$v_o = v_s\left(\frac{R_2}{R_1 + R_2}\right)\left[\frac{1}{1 + R_s/(R_1 + R_2)}\right]$$

(b) If the source resistance is to have negligible effect on the attenuation factor, what constraints must be placed on resistance values?

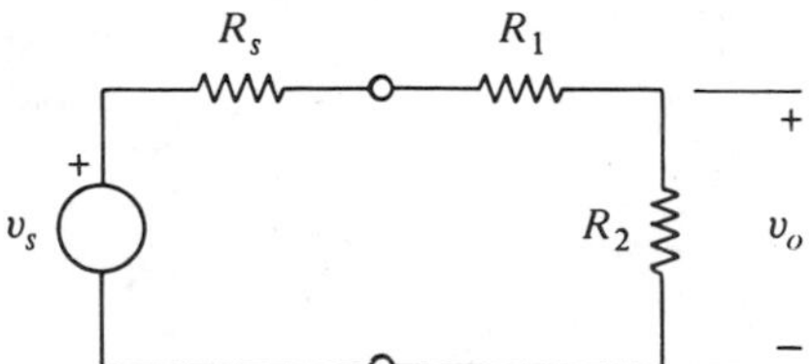

Fig. 2-77

2-36. (a) In Fig. 2-78, show that the output is given by

$$v_o = v_s\left(\frac{R_2}{R_1 + R_2}\right) \Big/ \left[1 + \frac{R_1 R_2/(R_1 + R_2)}{R_L}\right]$$

(b) If the load resistance R_L is to have negligible effect on the attenuation factor, what constraints must be placed on R_1 and R_2?

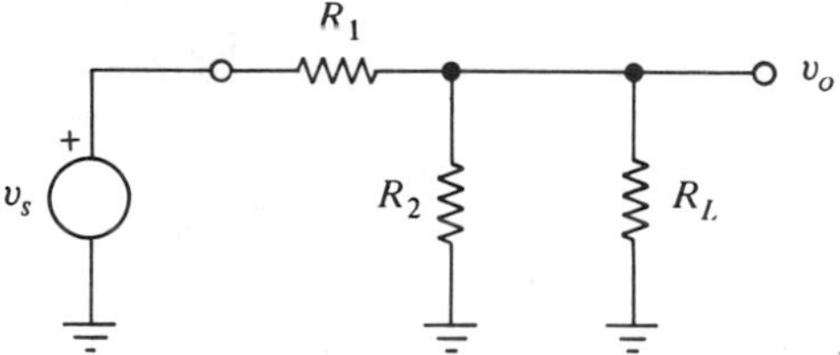

Fig. 2-78

2-37. For the circuit shown in Fig. 2-79, obtain v_o.

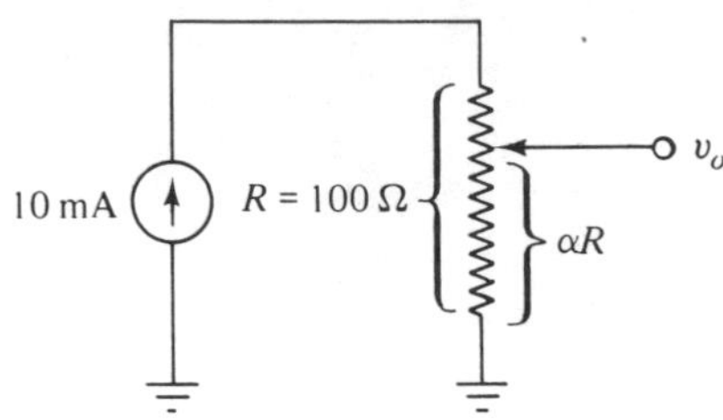

Fig. 2-79

2-38. (a) For the circuit shown in Fig. 2-80, calculate v_o.
(b) On the same set of axes, sketch the v_o vs. α curve for $R_L = \infty$ and $R_L = R$.

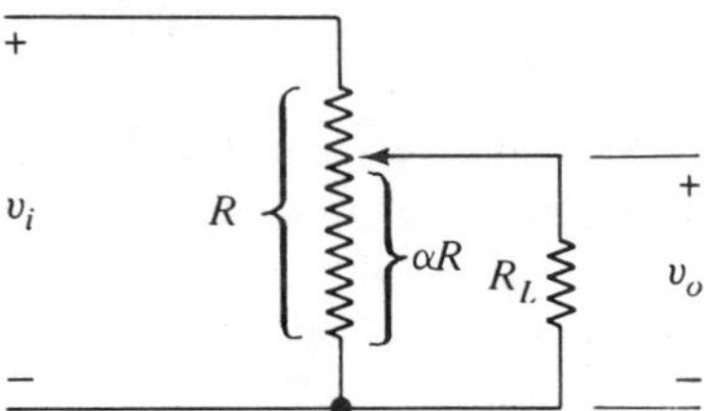

Fig. 2-80

2-39. For the circuits shown in Fig. 2-81, obtain v_o.

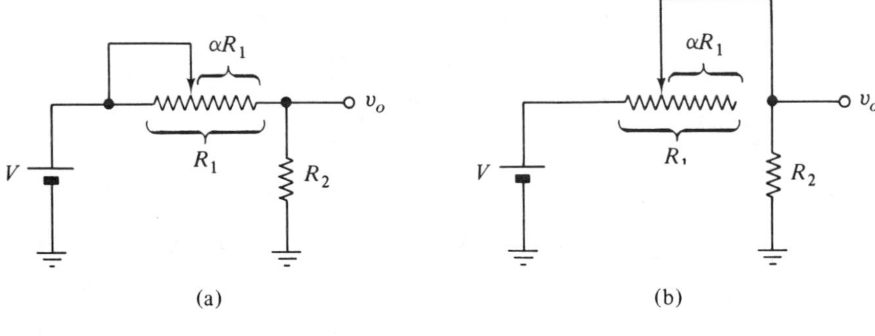

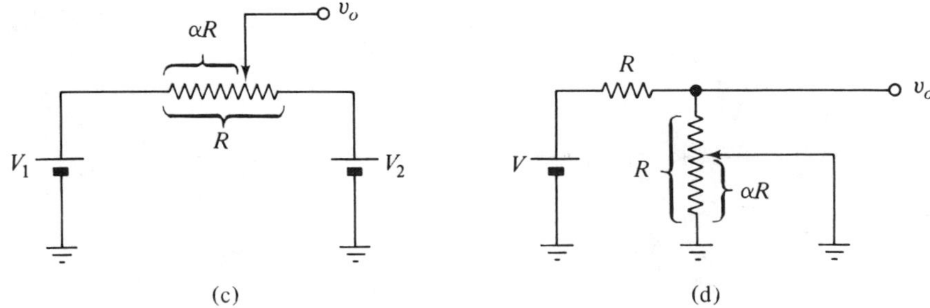

Fig. 2-81

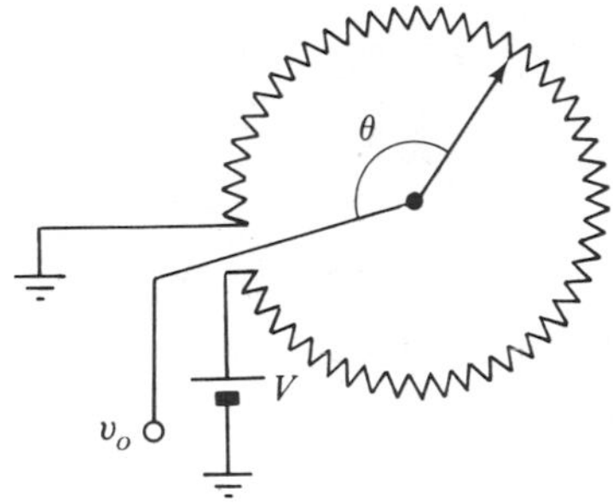

(e) **Fig. 2-81** (*cont.*)

2-40. A four-terminal variable resistor is shown in Fig. 2-82. The center of the resistor (terminal 3) is grounded. What range of voltage values are available at the output? (The wiper covers all positions from terminal 1 to terminal 2).

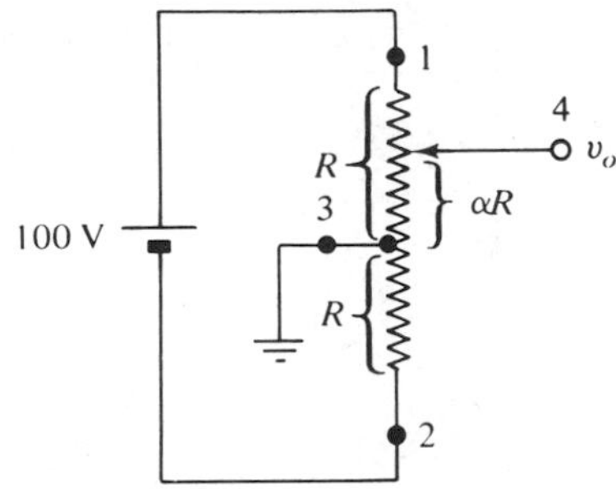

Fig. 2-82

2-41. Given a floating (neither end is grounded) 30 V voltage source. Using this source and resistors, obtain +20 V and −10 V with respect to a common reference.

2-42. Refer to Fig. 2-83.

(a) Obtain v_1 and v_2.
(b) Terminal 1 is loaded with $R_L = R$ (shown dashed). Obtain v_1 and v_2.
(c) Both terminals are loaded with R. Obtain v_1 and v_2.
(d) Terminal 1 is loaded with R and terminal 2 with $2R$. Obtain v_1 and v_2.

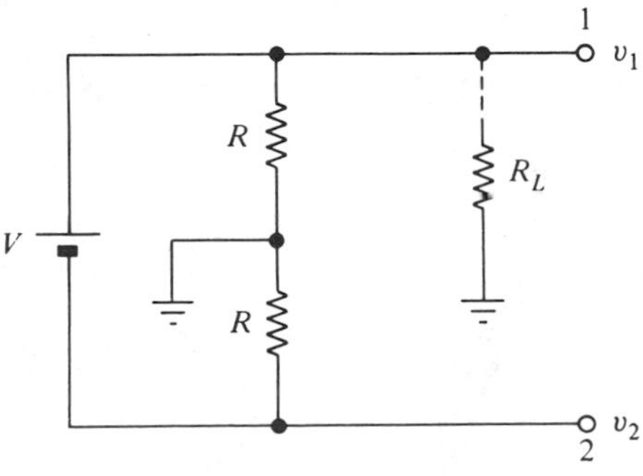

Fig. 2-83

2-43. In Fig. 2-84, obtain v_1, v_2, and v_3.

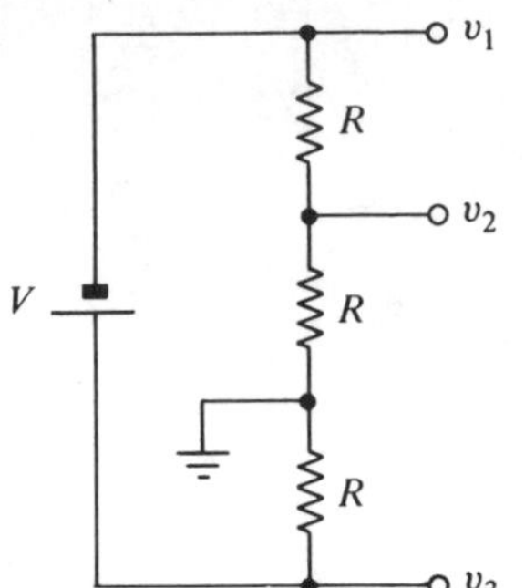

Fig. 2-84

2-44. Obtain v_o for the two circuits shown in Fig. 2-85.

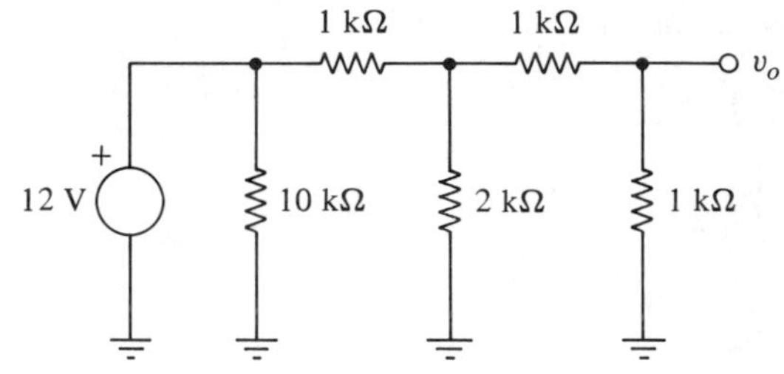

(a)

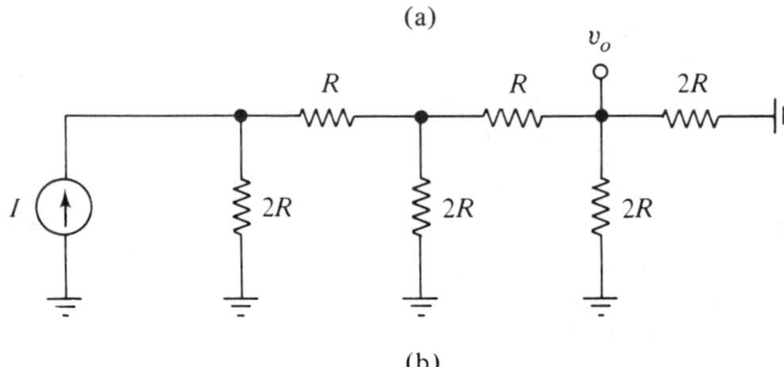

(b)

Fig. 2-85

2-45. In Fig. 2-86 assume the wiper is in the middle.

(a) Find v_o.

(b) Find v_o if R_L is infinite.

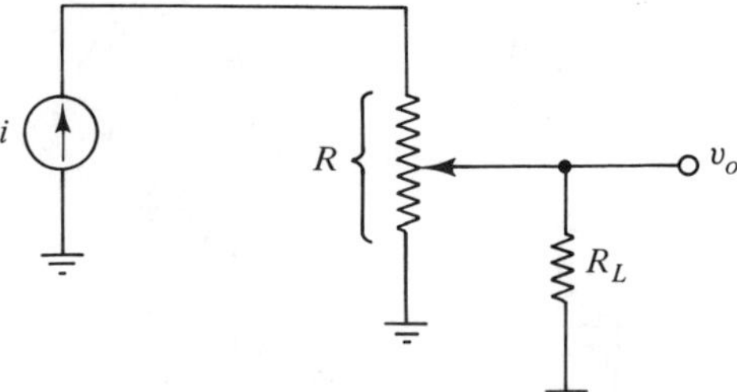

Fig. 2-86

2-46. Refer to Fig. 2-87.

(a) For the general case where N_1 and N_2 are arbitrary, how is v_2 related to v_1? i_2 related to i_1?

(b) For the special case of $i_2 = 0$, how is v_2 related to v_1?

(c) For the special case of $i_1 = 0$, how is v_2 related to v_1?

(d) For the special case of $v_2 = 0$, how is i_2 related to i_1?

(e) For the special case of $v_1 = 0$, how is i_2 related to i_1?

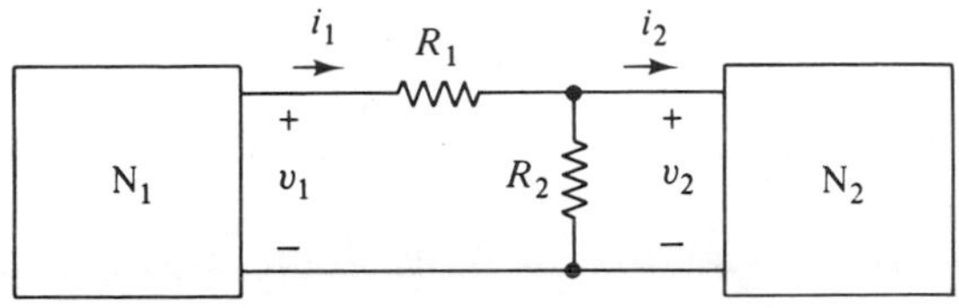

Fig. 2-87

2-47. (a) The resistance of a meter is 200 Ω. The full-scale deflection current is 50 μA. Convert this meter to a 100 V voltmeter.

(b) The voltmeter is used to read the voltage across the 1 MΩ resistor as shown in Fig. 2-88. What will it read? How does the reading compare with the actual voltage?

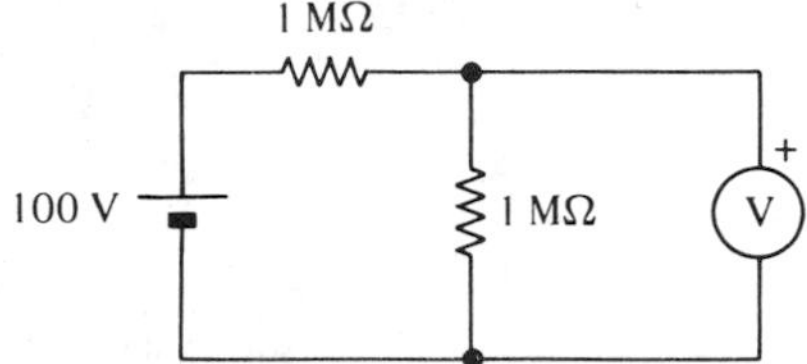

Fig. 2-88

2-48. A 15 V voltage source, a 1 kΩ potentiometer, and a resistor are used to design a 0 to −5 V variable voltage supply. Give the schematic diagram of the circuit and the resistor value.

2-49. (a) A 15 V voltage source, a 1 kΩ potentiometer, and a resistor are used to design a 10 V-to-15 V variable voltage supply. Draw the schematic diagram of the circuit.

(b) The potentiometer is set at the 10 V position. What will this voltage read if the output terminal is loaded with 1 kΩ?

(c) The potentiometer is set at the 15 V position. What will this voltage read if the output terminal is loaded with 1 kΩ?

2-50. A 20 V voltage source, a 1 kΩ potentiometer, and resistors are used to design a +5 V to +10 V variable voltage supply. Draw the schematic diagram of the circuit. Give values.

2-51. (a) In Fig. 2-89, $R_i = \infty$. What is the current attenuation factor?

(b) $R_i = 10R$. What is the attenuation factor?

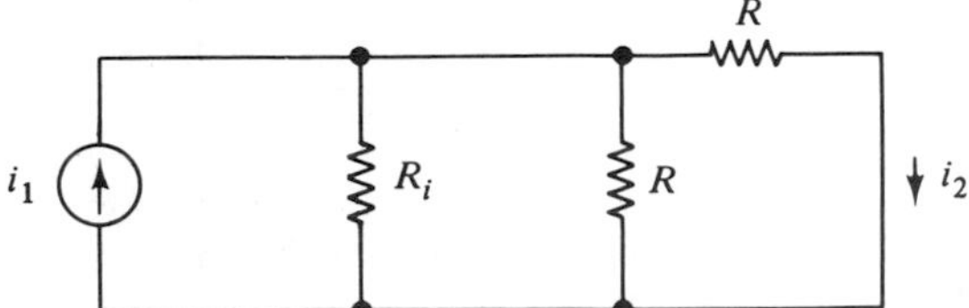

Fig. 2-89

2-52. (a) In Fig. 2-90, $R_L = 0$. What is the current attenuation factor?
(b) $R_L = R/10$. What is the attenuation factor?

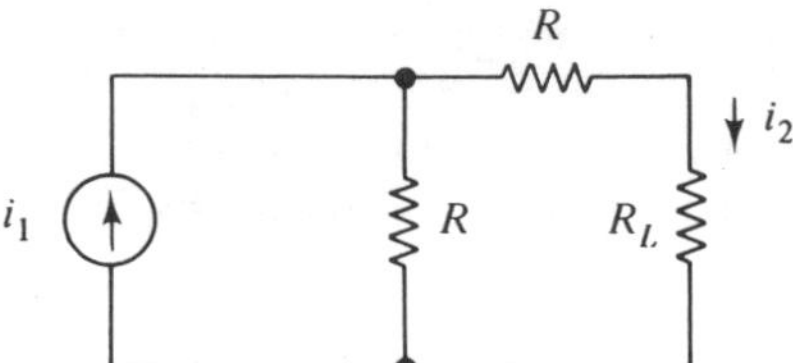

Fig. 2-90

2-53. A 100 Ω meter requires 100 μA for full-scale deflection. How would you convert this meter to a 10 mV full-scale voltmeter?

2-54. How would you modify a meter so that it gives full-scale deflection at twice its nominal full-scale current?

2-55. (a) A 2 kΩ/V voltmeter is used on the 1 V range. What is its resistance?
(b) What is the resistance of the voltmeter when used on the 10 V range?

2-56. A basic 50 Ω, 1 mA meter is converted to a 200 mA full-scale ammeter. What will the ammeter read when it is inserted in the circuit shown in Fig. 2-91? How different is the reading from the actual current in the circuit?

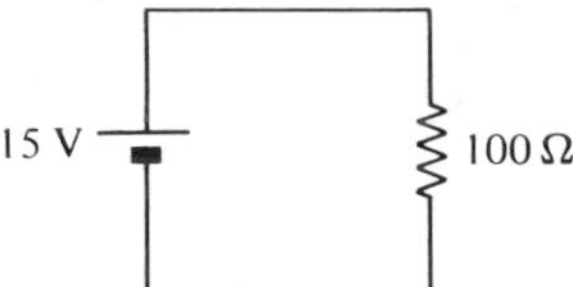

Fig. 2-91

2-57. An ammeter with 50 Ω internal resistance is used to read the current in the circuit shown in Fig. 2-92. What will it read?

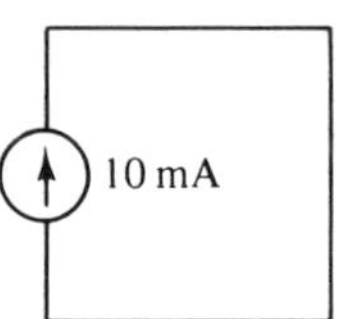

Fig. 2-92

2-58. Explain how the circuit shown in Fig. 2-93 can be used as an ohmmeter. Note that the voltmeter reads the terminal voltage.

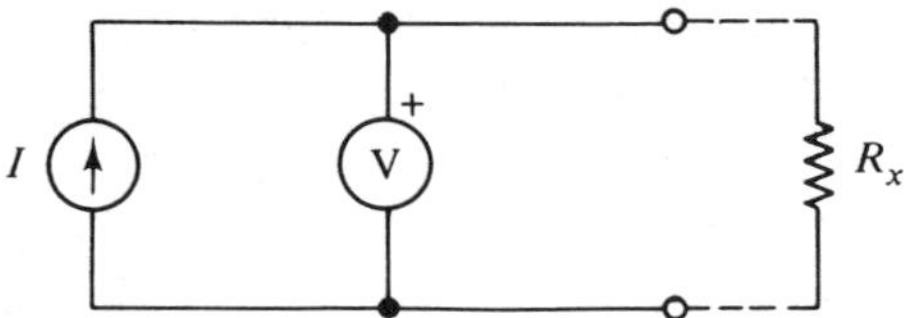

Fig. 2-93

2-59. An unknown resistor is connected in series with an ammeter and a current source as in Fig. 2-94. The reading of the meter is noted. Then R_k is added and adjusted until the

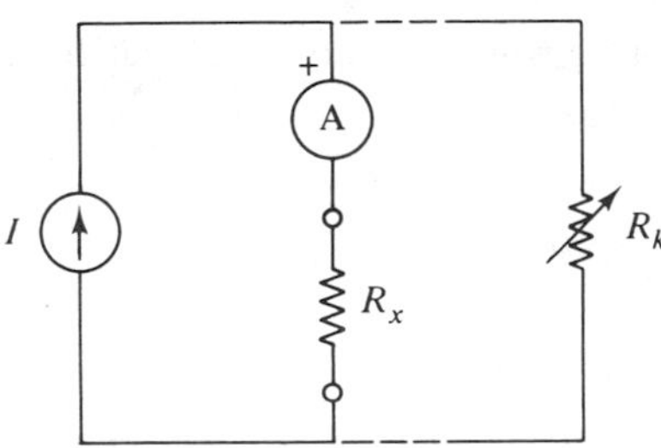

Fig. 2-94

ammeter reading drops to half the previous value. Show that this result occurs when $R_k = R_x$.

2-60. In Fig. 2-95, let $R_L = \infty$ and note the ammeter reading. Call this reading i_1. Let $R_L = R$, which is a known resistor, and note the ammeter reading again. Call this second reading i_2. Show that R_x can be determined from

$$R_x = R\left(\frac{i_1}{i_2} - 1\right)$$

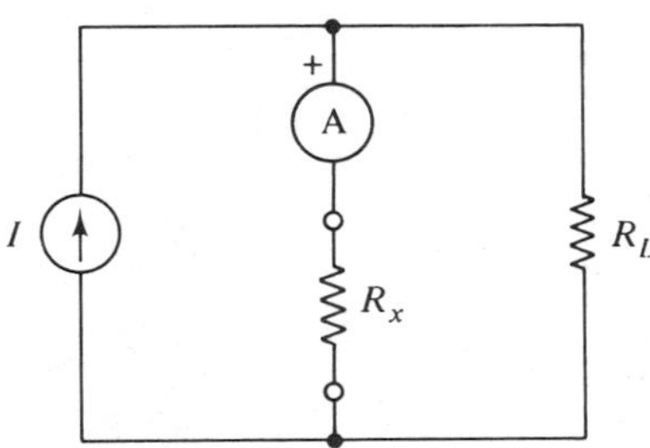

Fig. 2-95

2-61. In Fig. 2-96, let $R_L = 0$ and note the voltmeter reading. Call it v_1. Let $R_L = R$, which is a known resistor, and note the voltmeter reading again. Call it v_2. Show that R_x can be determined from

$$R_x = \frac{R}{(v_1/v_2) - 1}$$

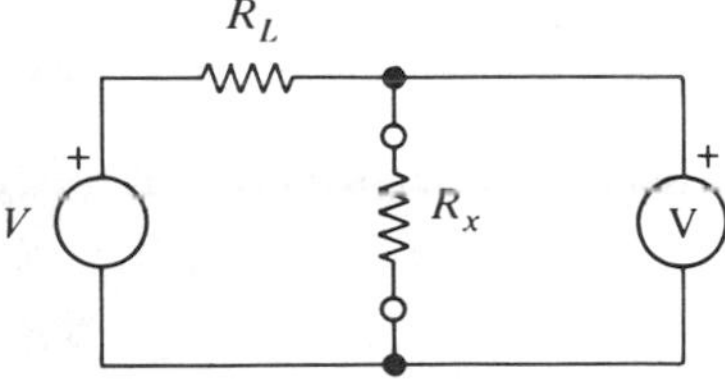

Fig. 2-96

2-62. (a) In Fig. 2-97, let $v_o = v_{o1}$ when $R_L = R_{L1}$ and $v_o = v_{o2}$ when $R_L = R_{L2}$. Show that the internal resistance can be determined from

$$R_s = \frac{R_{L1}[1 - (v_{o1}/v_{o2})]}{(v_{o1}/v_{o2}) - (R_{L1}/R_{L2})}$$

(b) Show that the result of (a) reduces to Eq. (2-18) for $R_{L1} = \infty$.

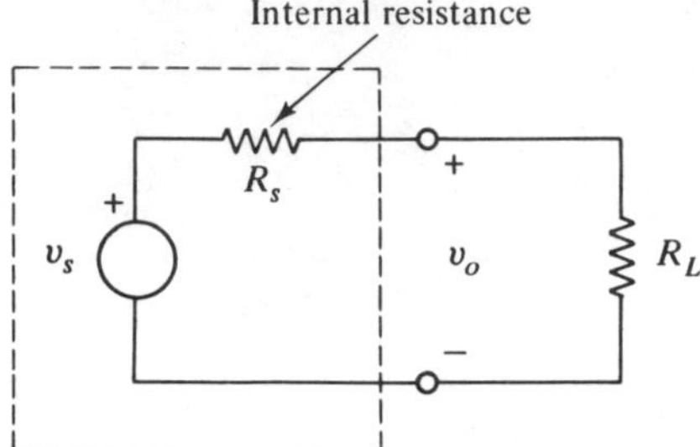

Fig. 2-97

2-63. The open-circuit voltage across the terminals of a network is 12 V. When 20 A is taken out of this network, the terminal voltage drops to 10 V. What is the internal resistance of the network?

2-64. Refer to Fig. 2-98. When $R_L = 0$, $i_o = 10 \sin \omega t$. When $R_L = 10\,\text{k}\Omega$, $i_o = \sin \omega t$. What is R?

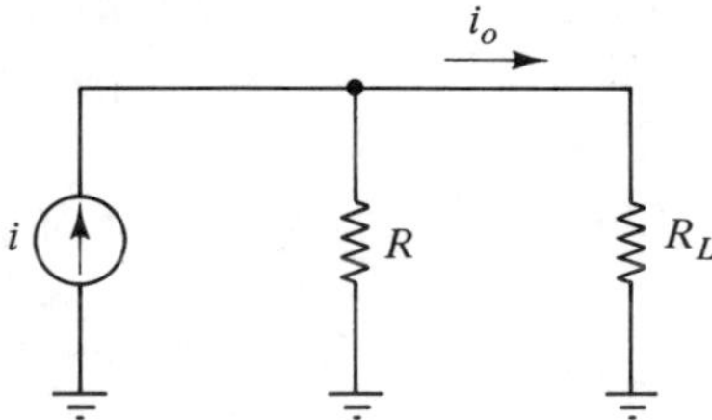

Fig. 2-98

2-65. In Fig. 2-99 for what value of V is $v_o = 0$?

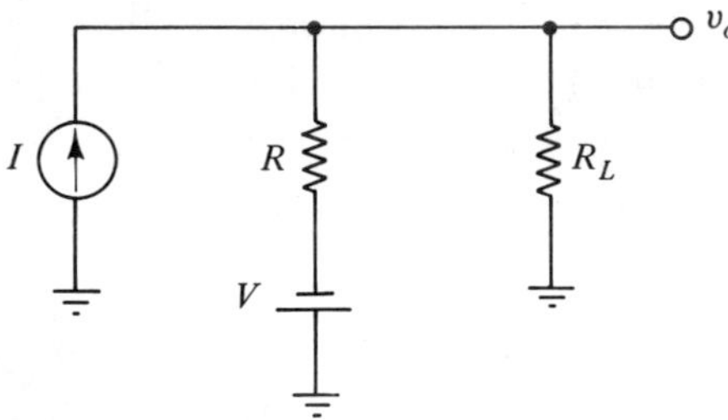

Fig. 2-99

2-66. In Fig. 2-100 what range of voltages are available at the output?

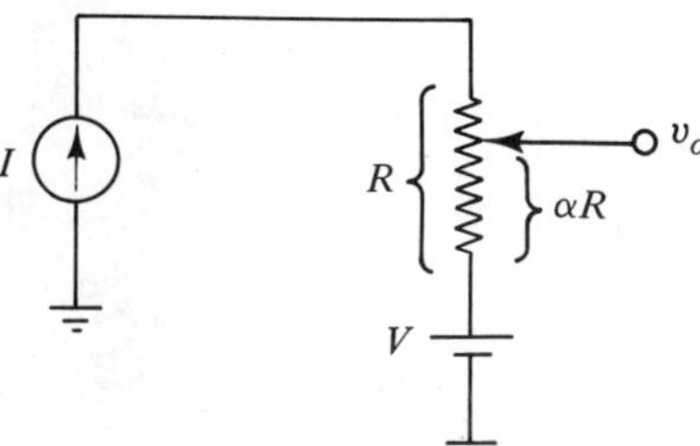

Fig. 2-100

2-67. Find v_o in Fig. 2-101.

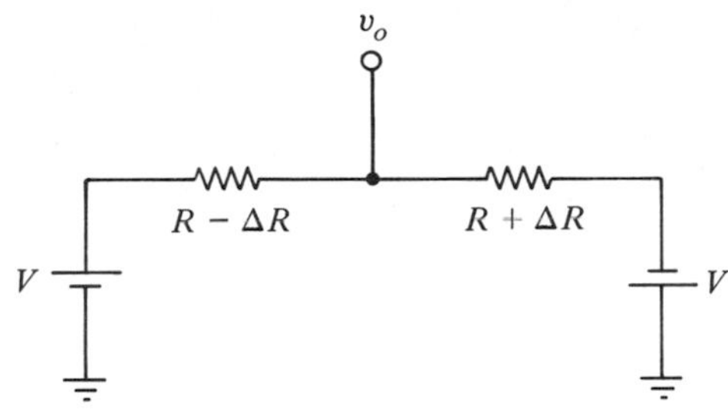

Fig. 2-101

2-68. In Fig. 2-102 what is v_o?

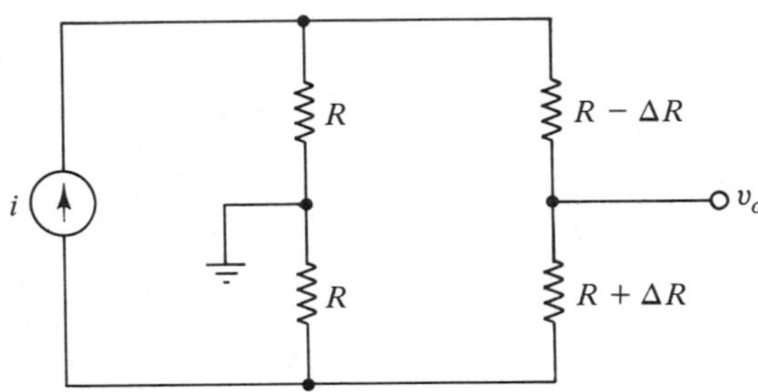

Fig. 2-102

2-69. In Fig. 2-103 obtain v_o.

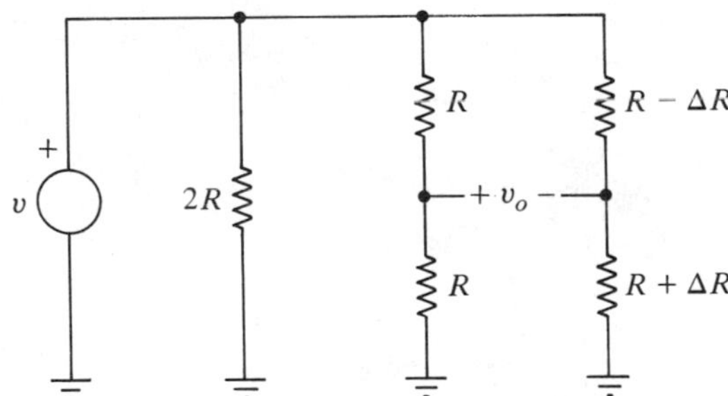

Fig. 2-103

2-70. In Fig. 2-104 what is the voltage across the current source? For what value of α is the bridge in balance?

2-71. In Fig. 2-105 for what range of values of R_x can the bridge be balanced?

2-72. If, in Fig. 2-106, R changes by $\pm 1\ \Omega$, how much does v_o change?

2-73. (a) For the two circuits shown in Fig. 2-107, obtain v_o if $R_2 = R_1$.

(b) If R_2 changes from its value in (a) by $+1\%$, how much does v_o change in the two circuits?

2-74. (a) In Fig. 2-108, $I = 10$ mA and $R = 1$ kΩ. What must be V in order to result in $v = 0$?

(b) V is adjusted to the value given in (a). The resistance R changes by ΔR. What is the output voltage?

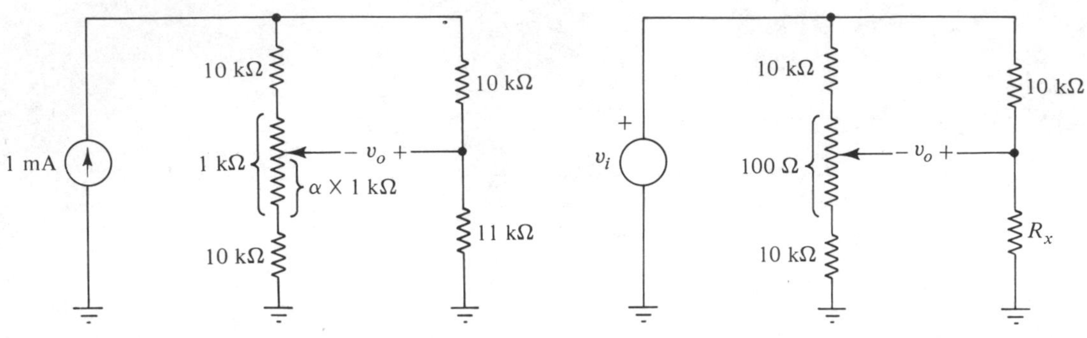

Fig. 2-104

Fig. 2-105

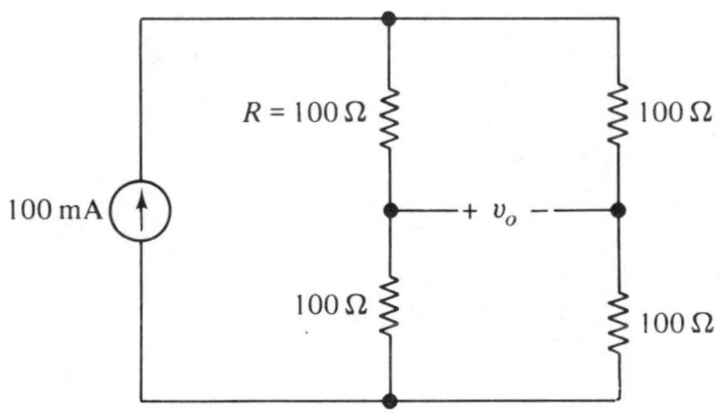

Fig. 2-106

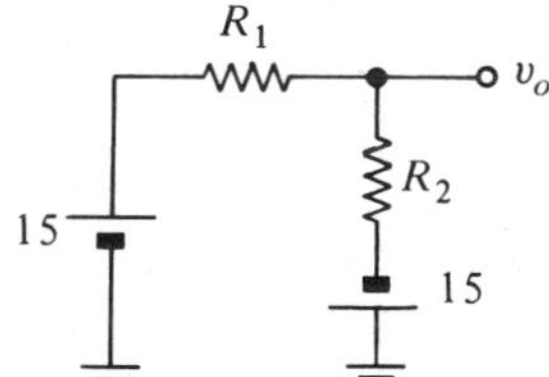

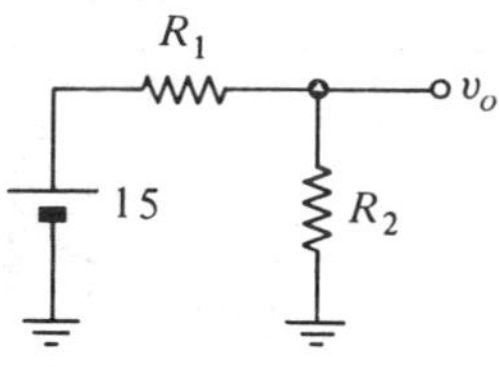

Fig. 2-107

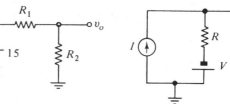

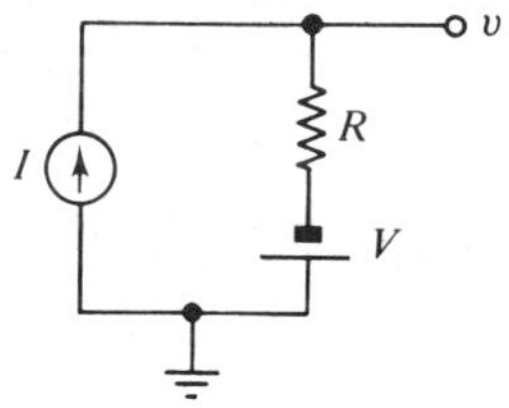

Fig. 2-108

2-75. Obtain i in Fig. 2-109.

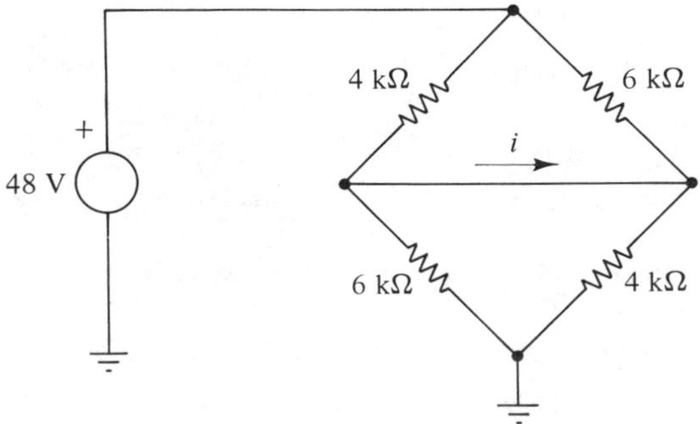

Fig. 2-109

2-76. In Fig. 2-110 obtain i_o.

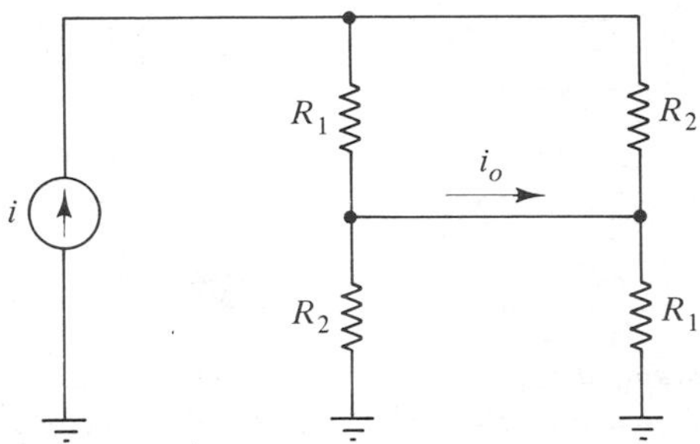

Fig. 2-110

2-77. In Fig. 2-111 obtain i_o.

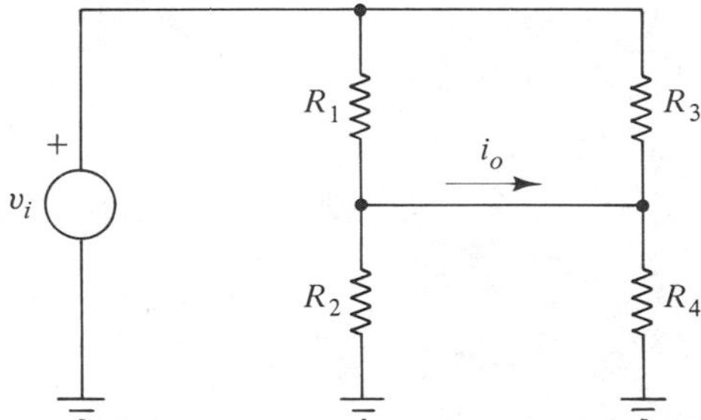

Fig. 2-111

2-78. In Fig. 2-112, V_{st} is a standard cell; that is, its voltage is known accurately. R is a precision potentiometer with an accurately calibrated dial that reads α. V_x is the unknown voltage that is to be calculated. As seen from the diagram, an attenuated portion of V_x is compared against V_{st} by adjusting α until the ammeter *reads* 0. Show that using this value of α and knowing V_{st}, V_x can be found. Assume $V_x > V_{st}$.

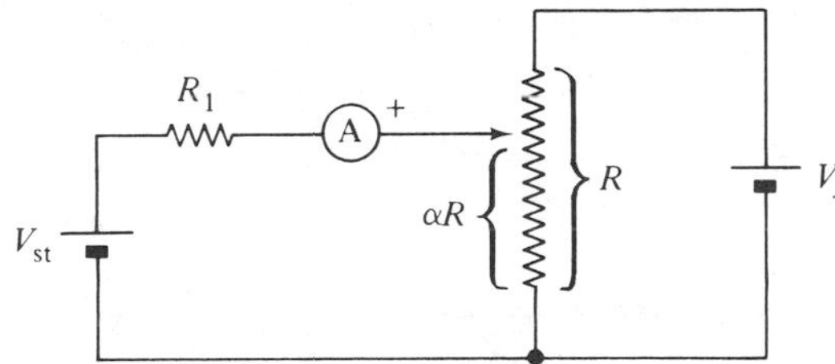

Fig. 2-112

2-79. Junction voltages in semiconductors are temperature sensitive. They can be equivalently represented as voltage sources that vary with the temperature. Two such semiconductor junctions are connected in a bridge circuit as shown in Fig. 2-113. The dummy junction is kept in a constant temperature oven; the voltage across it is measured as 0.6 V. The active junction is used as a temperature probe. When this probe is placed at a certain location, v_o reads 10 mV. If the junction voltage varies -2 mV/°C, what temperature is the probe measuring? (R_a is used for initial nulling of the output when both junctions are placed in the same oven.)

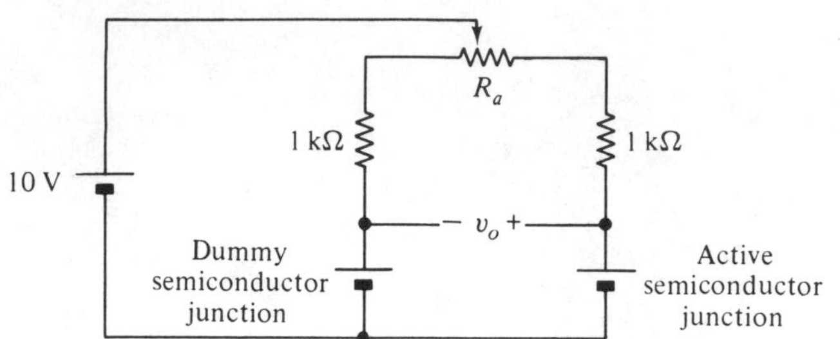

Fig. 2-113

2-80. In Fig. 2-114, design the bridge so that it is balanced for a given value of R_1 and produces the greatest possible output when R_1 changes to $R_1 + \Delta R_1$. Assuming that $\Delta R_1 \ll R_1$, also obtain the expression for the resulting output.

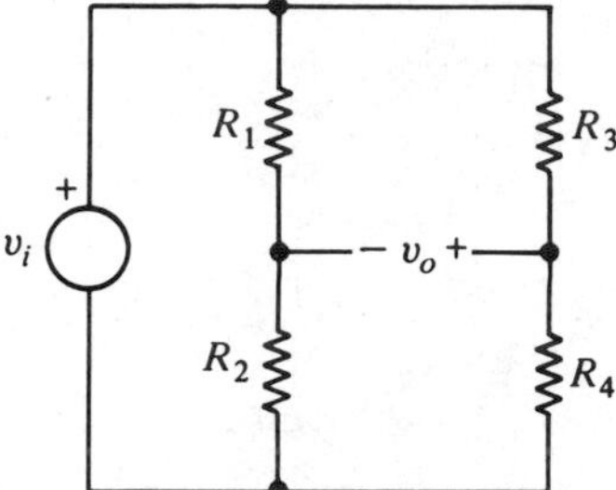

Fig. 2-114

2-81. Refer to Example 2-23. Draw accurately the v_o vs. R_{ph} curves for $R_1/R_2 = 5, 1,$ and 0.2. Which curve is the steepest if all curves are made to go through $R_{ph} = R_{pho}$?

CHAPTER 3

USEFUL NETWORK THEOREMS, POWER, AND ENERGY

Using some simple network theorems, it is possible to simplify response calculations in more complex networks than the ones discussed in the preceding chapter. Furthermore, additional insight is gained in the operation of circuits. Except for relationships involving power, the techniques presented here are for resistive networks. In later chapters they are generalized to include capacitors, inductors, and dependent sources.

3-1 THE SUPERPOSITION PRINCIPLE

We know how to calculate responses in simple circuits when one source (or a combination of sources equivalently represented as a single source) excites a network. When more than one source excites a linear network, the resulting response may be obtained as *the sum of individual responses caused by each source acting alone while all other sources are made zero*. Thus by adding the responses due to sources applied one at a time, we can obtain the response due to all sources acting together. This principle is known as the *superposition principle*.

In using the superposition principle, all sources other than the one under consideration are set to zero. Setting a voltage source to zero means making $v_s = 0$, which is equivalent to *replacing the voltage source* v_s *with a short circuit*. Setting a current source to zero means making $i_s = 0$, which is equivalent to *replacing the current source* i_s *with an open circuit*. The process of setting sources to zero is referred to as *killing the sources*. If three sources are acting on a circuit and the principle of superposition is being used to calculate a response, then we are actually solving three problems, one for each source of excitation.

Example 3-1

In Fig. 3-1, obtain i and v_o by superposition.

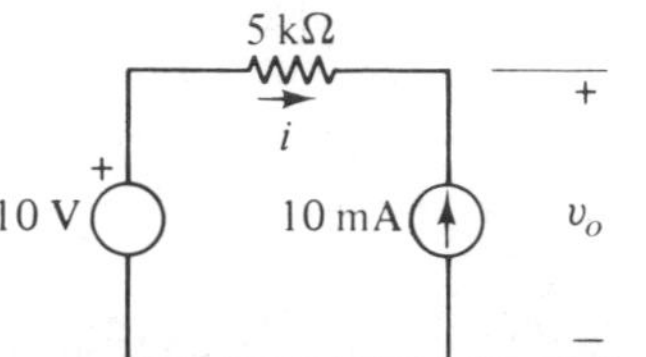

Fig. 3-1

Solution. First we turn on the 10 V voltage source and turn off the 10 mA current source, obtaining the circuit of Fig. 3-2(a). Note that we have replaced the current source with an open circuit and have labeled the resulting responses with the subscript 1, signifying that they are due to the first source acting alone. By inspection of the circuit, we see that

$$i_1 = 0, \qquad v_{o1} = 10\text{ V}$$

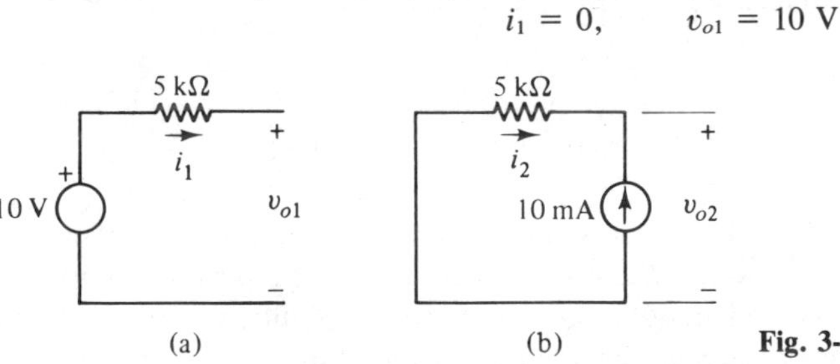

Fig. 3-2

Next, we turn on the 10 mA current source and turn off the 10 V voltage source. The result is Fig. 3-2(b), where we have replaced the voltage source with a short circuit and have designated the resulting responses with the subscript 2, signifying that they are due to the second source acting alone. Again, by inspection of the circuit, we see that

$$i_2 = -10\text{ mA}, \qquad v_{o2} = 10\text{ mA} \times 5\text{ k}\Omega = 50\text{ V}$$

Now we apply the principle of superposition to obtain the desired responses.

$$i = i_1 + i_2 = 0 + (-10) = -10\text{ mA} \quad \text{Ans.}$$

$$v_o = v_{o1} + v_{o2} = 10 + 50 = 60\text{ V} \quad \text{Ans.}$$

At this time it is worthwhile to refer to Figs. 3-1 and 3-2 in order to emphasize the fact that the senses of i_1, i_2, and i, as well as v_{o1}, v_{o2}, and v_o, are all in agreement; that is, the current arrows match, and voltage + and − signs match.

We could also have solved this problem directly without the principle of superposition. Inspection of Fig. 3-1 shows that

$$i = -10\text{ mA}, \qquad v_o = 10 + (10\text{ mA} \times 5\text{ k}\Omega) = 60\text{ V} \quad \text{Ans.}$$

Although it is faster to obtain the answers this way, the purpose of this example is to demonstrate the use of the principle of superposition.

Example 3-2

In Fig. 3-3, obtain v_o by superposition.

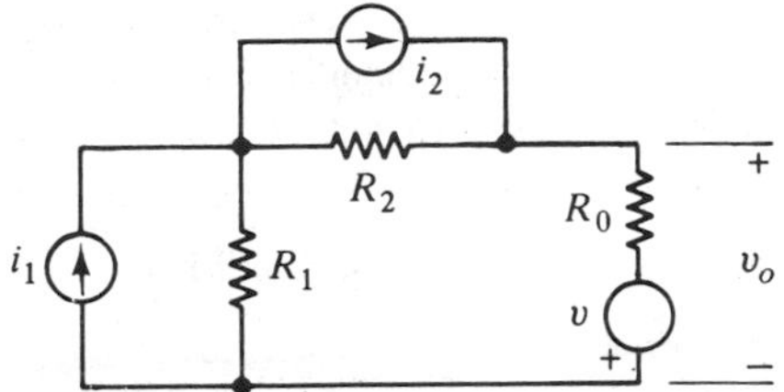

Fig. 3-3

Solution. Break down the problem into three parts, involving one source each, as shown in Fig. 3-4. From Fig. 3-4(a), we obtain

$$v_{o1} = \underbrace{i_1\left(\frac{R_1}{R_1 + R_2 + R_0}\right)}_{\text{By the current-divider rule}} R_0$$

Figure 3-4(b) gives

$$v_{o2} = \underbrace{i_2\left(\frac{R_2}{R_1 + R_2 + R_0}\right)}_{\text{By the current-divider rule}} R_0$$

Figure 3-4(c) gives

$$v_{o3} = \underbrace{-v\left(\frac{R_1 + R_2}{R_1 + R_2 + R_0}\right)}_{\text{By the voltage-divider rule}}$$

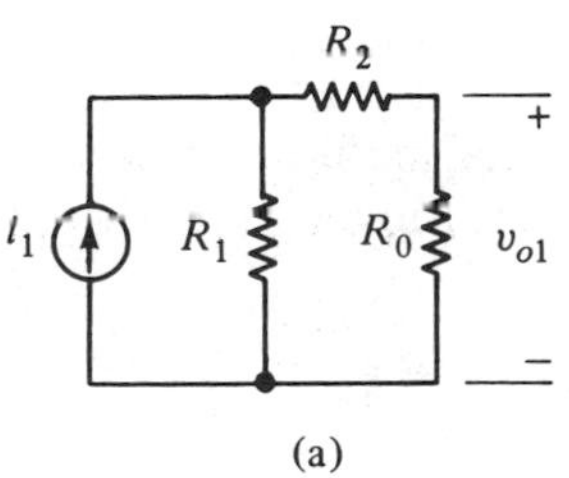

(a)

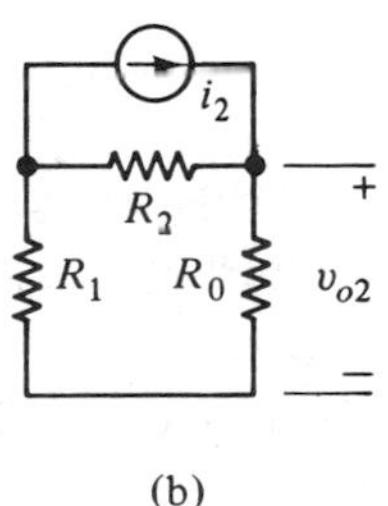

(b)

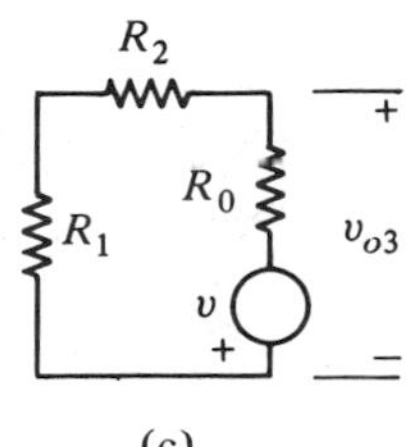

(c)

Fig. 3-4

Using the principle of superposition, we obtain the desired v_o.

$$v_o = v_{o1} + v_{o2} + v_{o3} = \frac{i_1 R_0 R_1 + i_2 R_0 R_2 - v(R_1 + R_2)}{R_0 + R_1 + R_2} \quad \text{Ans.}$$

Example 3-3

Due to distortions the voltage applied to a capacitor is not a pure sine wave but rather the sum of two harmonically related sine waves. It is given by $v_i = V_1 \sin \omega t + V_3 \sin 3\omega t$, where $V_1 \sin \omega t$ is the fundamental and $V_3 \sin 3\omega t$ is the third harmonic component of the voltage. What is the resulting current? Compare the third-harmonic-to-fundamental amplitude ratios in the excitation and response waveforms.

Solution. The current through the capacitor is given by

$$i = C\frac{dv}{dt} = C\frac{d}{dt}(V_1 \sin \omega t + V_3 \sin 3\omega t)$$

$$i = \omega C(V_1 \cos \omega t + 3V_3 \cos 3\omega t) \quad \text{Ans.}$$

The third-harmonic-to-fundamental amplitude ratios in the excitation and response waveforms are

$$\frac{V_3}{V_1}, \qquad \frac{3V_3}{V_1}$$

Thus three times more distortion occurs in the response than in the excitation.

3-2 ADDITION OF SIGNALS

Two or more signals, represented by grounded voltage sources, can be *added* together by means of resistive networks. The number of resistors required for summing is equal to the number of signal sources. The circuit for adding two signals is shown in Fig. 3-5(a). Sources v_1 and v_2 have a common ground. By using superposition, the output is obtained as

$$v_o = v_1\left(\frac{R_2}{R_1 + R_2}\right) + v_2\left(\frac{R_1}{R_1 + R_2}\right) = \frac{v_1 R_2 + v_2 R_1}{R_1 + R_2} \tag{3-1}$$

When R_1 is made equal to R_2, Eq. (3-1) becomes

$$v_o = \frac{1}{2}(v_1 + v_2)$$

So one-half the sum of the two signals is obtained if no load is connected across the output. If there is a load R_L (shown by dashed line) across the output, v_o becomes

$$\begin{aligned} v_o &= v_1\frac{R_2 R_L}{R_2 + R_L}\bigg/\left(R_1 + \frac{R_2 R_L}{R_2 + R_L}\right) + v_2\frac{R_1 R_L}{R_1 + R_L}\bigg/\left(R_2 + \frac{R_1 R_L}{R_1 + R_L}\right) \\ &= \left(\frac{v_1 R_2 + v_2 R_1}{R_1 + R_2}\right)\left[R_L\bigg/\left(\frac{R_1 R_2}{R_1 + R_2} + R_L\right)\right] \end{aligned} \tag{3-2}$$

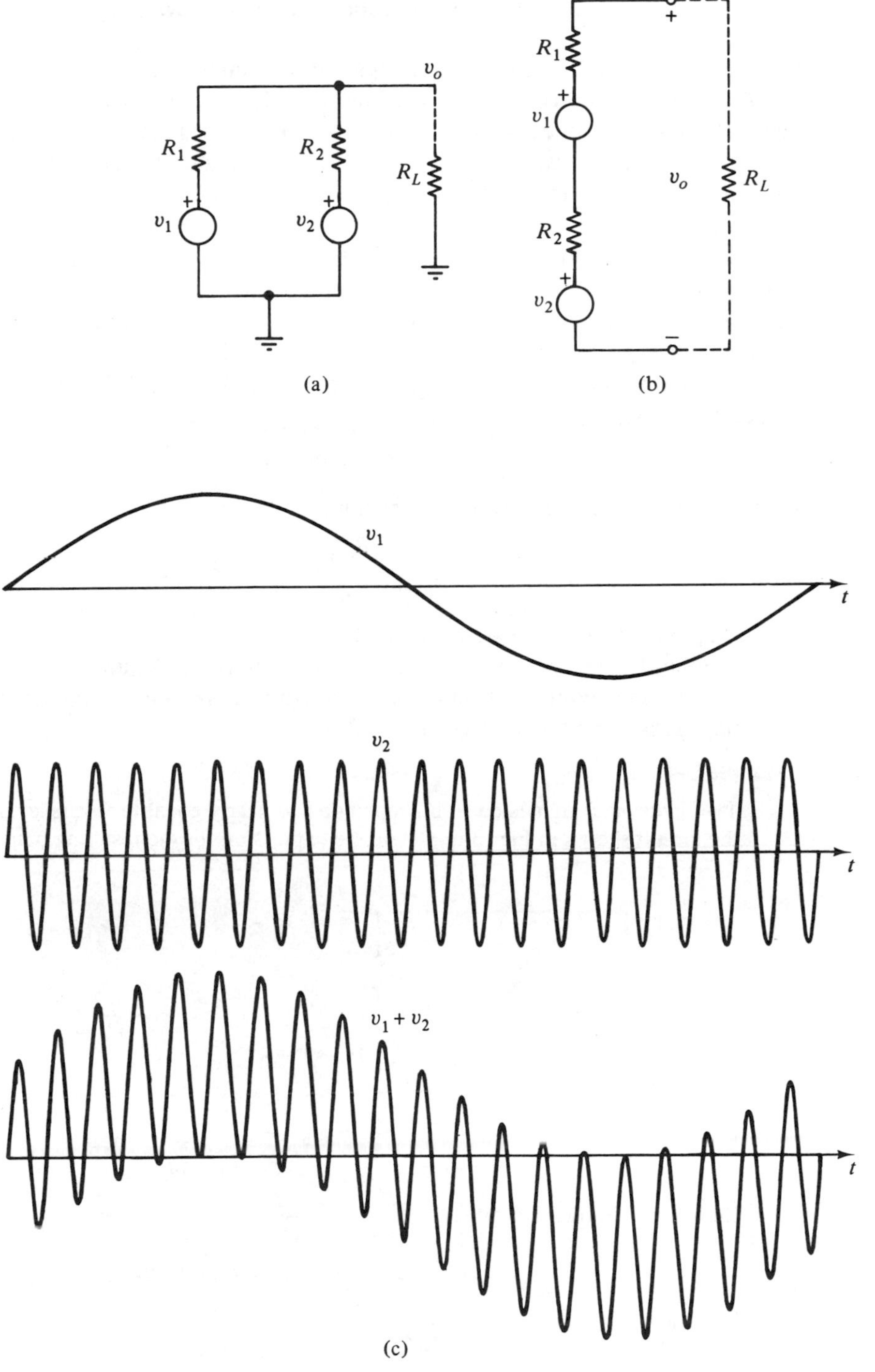

Fig. 3-5

Comparing Eq. (3-1) with Eq. (3-2), we see that an attenuation factor dependent on R_L, R_1, and R_2 is introduced via the bracketed term in Eq. (3-2). For $R_L = \infty$ this attenuation factor reduces to unity and Eq. (3-2) becomes identical with Eq. (3-1). To obtain a *sum signal under loaded conditions* again requires that R_1 be made equal to R_2. Therefore by letting $R_1 = R_2 = R$ in Eq. (3-2), we obtain

$$v_o = \frac{1}{2}(v_1 + v_2)\left[\frac{R_L}{(R/2) + R_L}\right] = \left(\frac{R_L}{R + 2R_L}\right)(v_1 + v_2)$$

If the signal sources are floating—that is, they are not grounded (or at least one of them is not grounded)—they can be added directly by connecting them in series. For two sources, the summing circuit is shown in Fig. 3-5(b). When the output is not loaded ($R_L = \infty$), v_o is

$$v_o = v_1 + v_2$$

Under loaded conditions the output becomes

$$v_o = \frac{R_L}{(R_1 + R_2) + R_L}(v_1 + v_2)$$

which represents an attenuated sum signal.

If v_1 and v_2 are both sinusoidal signals of different frequencies, the sum signal is no longer sinusoidal. This situation is shown in Fig. 3-5(c). Signals can be added by simple resistive networks as in Fig. 3-5.

Example 3-4

Two sinusoidal signals equal in amplitude and nearly equal in frequency are applied to the circuit shown in Fig. 3-6. Obtain the expression for the resulting output and sketch it.

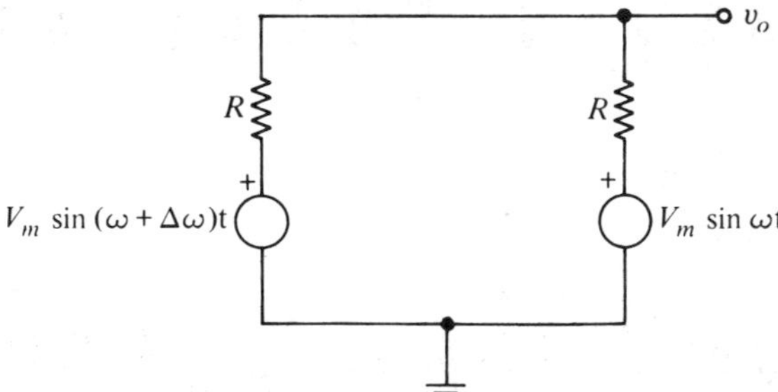

Fig. 3-6

Solution. Figure 3-6 gives

$$v_o = \frac{1}{2}[V_m \sin \omega t + V_m \sin (\omega + \Delta\omega)t]$$

$$= \frac{V_m}{2}[\sin \omega t + \sin (\omega t + \Delta\omega t)]$$

By using the trigonometric identity

$$\sin A + \sin B = 2 \cos \frac{1}{2}(A - B) \sin \frac{1}{2}(A + B)$$

we have

$$v_o = V_m \cos \left[\left(\frac{\Delta\omega}{2} \right) t \right] \sin \left(\omega + \frac{\Delta\omega}{2} \right) t$$

This resulting waveform is not a sine wave. Nevertheless, we may think of it as a sine wave with time-varying amplitude given by

$$V_m \cos \left[\left(\frac{\Delta\omega}{2} \right) t \right]$$

This amplitude varies slowly at the rate of $\Delta\omega/2$ radians per second, whereas the main sine wave varies at the much faster rate of $(\omega + \Delta\omega/2)$ radians per second. The result is the waveform shown in Fig. 3-7. Note that the envelope (shown dashed) varies twice as fast as the cosine wave. The envelope frequency, $\Delta\omega$, represents the difference of the two frequencies and is called the *beat* frequency, which is distinctly audible if v_o is listened to on an audio system.

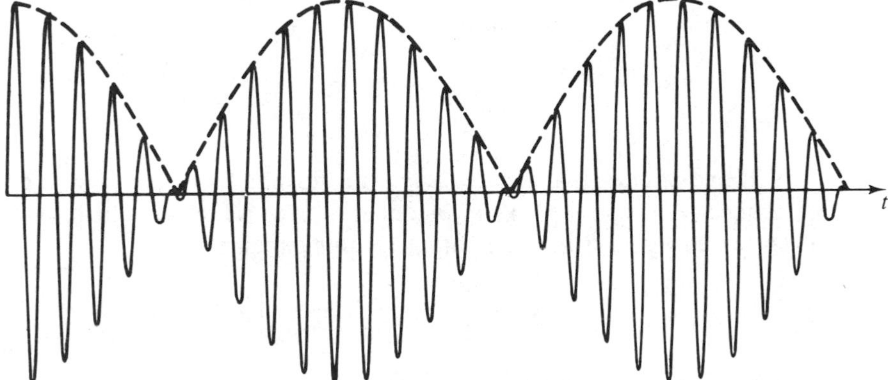

Fig. 3-7

3-3 SUBTRACTION OF SIGNALS

Two signal sources having a common ground *cannot* be subtracted from each other by using a resistive network if the output is also referred to ground. The usual procedure is to use an amplifier with a gain of -1 so that one of the signals is *inverted first* and *then summed* with the other signal. The schematic diagram of the circuit is shown in Fig. 3-8(a). The output, being proportional to the sum of v_1 with $(-v_2)$, is given by

$$v_o = \frac{1}{2}[v_1 + (-v_2)] = \frac{1}{2}(v_1 - v_2)$$

Thus a difference signal is obtained.

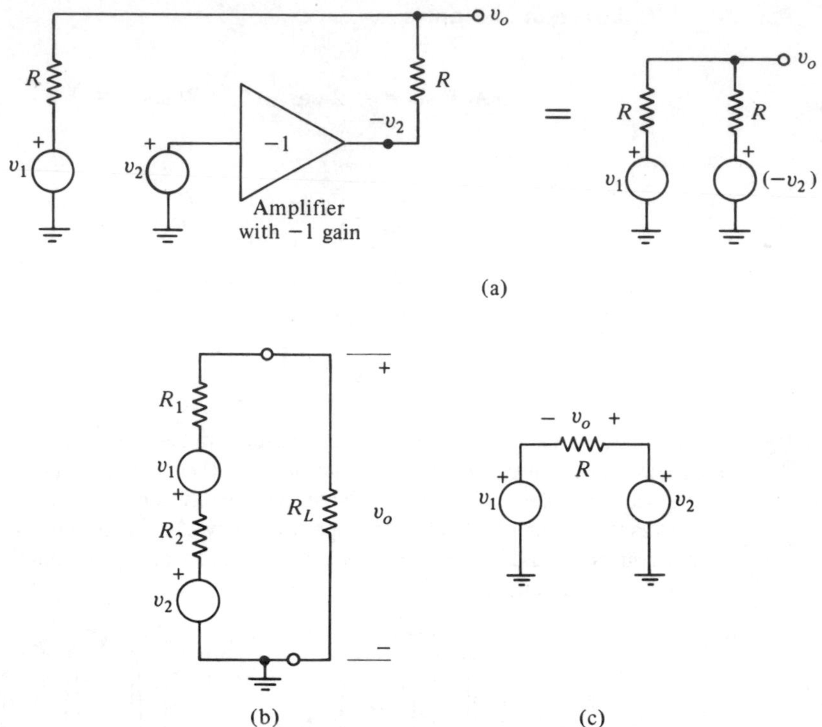

Fig. 3-8

If one of the signal sources, say v_1, is floating (not connected to ground), it can be connected so that it bucks v_2 (is opposite in sense to v_2), which may be grounded as shown in Fig. 3-8(b). The output for this circuit is

$$v_o = \left[\frac{R_L}{(R_1 + R_2) + R_L}\right](v_2 - v_1)$$

which, for $R_L = \infty$ (no load), reduces to

$$v_o = v_2 - v_1$$

If we are allowed to have a floating output, then the circuit shown in Fig. 3-8(c) can be used to obtain the difference signal. The output is independent of R (provided $R \neq 0$) and is given by

$$v_o = v_2 - v_1$$

3-4 LEVEL SHIFTING

A signal is level-shifted if its dc level is changed. A signal can be shifted up or down by adding a dc source with appropriate polarity to it. If one of the sources is floating, say the signal source v, the circuit of Fig. 3-9(a) can be used. With no load connected across the output, v_o is given by $v_o = v + V_{dc}$.

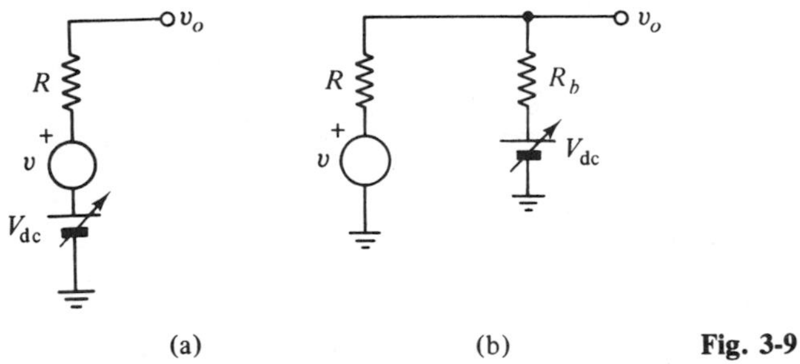

Fig. 3-9

By varying the dc source V_{dc}, v can be shifted up (constant positive value added to it) or shifted down by making V_{dc} negative. The circuit is essentially a summing circuit with one of the signals acting as the level shifter.

If both the signal and the dc source are grounded, the circuit shown in Fig. 3-9(b) can be used to change the level of the signal source. By superposition, the output is

$$v_o = \frac{vR_b + V_{dc}R}{R + R_b} = \frac{R_b}{R + R_b}\left(v + V_{dc}\frac{R}{R_b}\right)$$

So by varying V_{dc}, the signal v can be shifted up (V_{dc} positive) or down (V_{dc} negative).

Example 3-5

A 10 V peak sine wave is to be attenuated 2 : 1, and its average level is to be shifted from 0 to −6 V. Design the circuit.

Solution. Draw the circuit as in Fig. 3-10. Since the attenuation factor for the signal is $\frac{1}{2}$, the resistances must equal. Therefore choose $R_1 = R_2$. The component in the output due to the dc source is

$$-V_{dc}\frac{R_1}{R_1 + R_2} = -\frac{V_{dc}}{2}$$

Since this component is to be −6 V, choose $V_{dc} = 12$ V. The desired output is shown in Fig. 3-10.

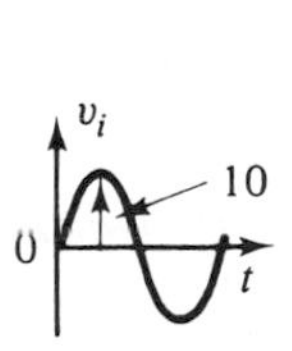

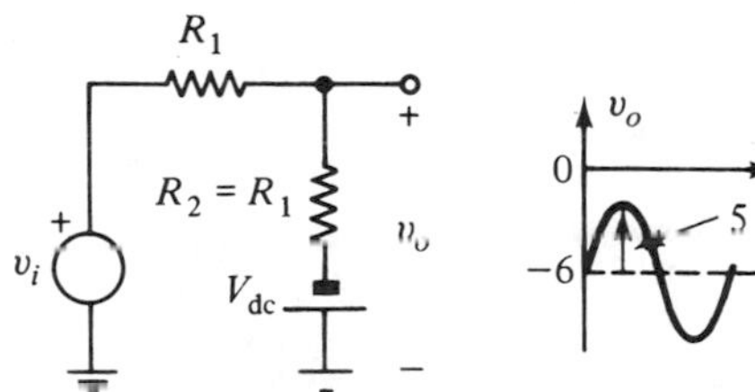

v_o 0 t 5 −6

Fig. 3-10

3-5 THÉVENIN AND NORTON EQUIVALENT CIRCUITS

Any two-terminal linear network composed of resistors and sources can be equivalently represented either as a *voltage source in series with a resistor* or as *a current source in parallel with a resistor*. The former is called the *Thévenin equivalent*

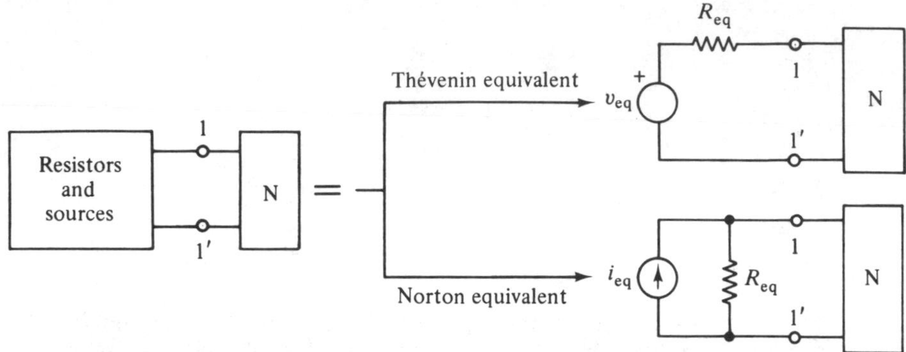

Fig. 3-11

representation and the latter the *Norton equivalent* representation. The equivalence is shown in Fig. 3-11.

Thus no matter how complicated the network to the left of terminals 1–1′ is, it can be simplified to one source and one resistor so that the *terminal* characteristics are indistinguishable from those of the original network.

Whether the Thévenin or the Norton equivalent circuit is used, R_{eq} is the same. To determine R_{eq}, *kill* all independent sources inside the box; that is, replace *voltage sources by short circuits* and *current sources by open circuits*. Then calculate or measure the resistance as seen from the terminals looking into the box. This resistance is R_{eq}. The procedure is illustrated in Fig. 3-12(a).

To obtain the Thévenin equivalent voltage v_{eq}, open-circuit terminals 1–1′ (this step is not necessary if the terminals are not loaded by N) and calculate or measure

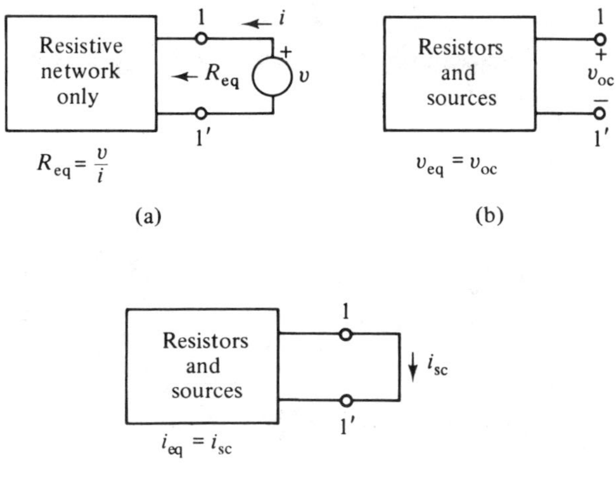

Fig. 3-12

the voltage across terminals 1–1′. This open-circuit voltage is v_{eq}—that is, $v_{oc} = v_{eq}$. The procedure is illustrated in Fig. 3-12(b).

To obtain the Norton equivalent current, short-circuit terminals 1–1′ and calculate or measure the current through the short circuit. This short-circuit current is i_{eq}—that is, $i_{sc} = i_{eq}$. The procedure is shown in Fig. 3-12(c).

From the source transformations presented in Section 2-5 it should be clear that v_{eq} and i_{eq} are related by

$$v_{eq} = i_{eq} R_{eq} \tag{3-3a}$$

or

$$v_{oc} = i_{sc} R_{eq} \tag{3-3b}$$

The Thévenin and Norton equivalent circuits may sufficiently simplify circuit analysis to the point that voltages and currents can be calculated by inspection. To illustrate the usefulness and the general applicability of these equivalent presentations further, consider the combination of the N_1 and N_2 networks shown in Fig. 3-13(a). Suppose that we wish to calculate v and i.

We look to the left into N_1 and represent its terminal behavior with the Thévenin equivalent circuit consisting of v_{eq1} and R_{eq1}. We then look to the right into N_2 and represent its terminal behavior with the equivalent circuit consisting of v_{eq2} and R_{eq2}. The result is Fig. 3-13(b), from which we can easily calculate i and v by using the principle of superposition.

$$i = \frac{v_{eq1} - v_{eq2}}{R_{eq1} + R_{eq2}}, \qquad v = \frac{v_{eq1} R_{eq2} + v_{eq2} R_{eq1}}{R_{eq1} + R_{eq2}}$$

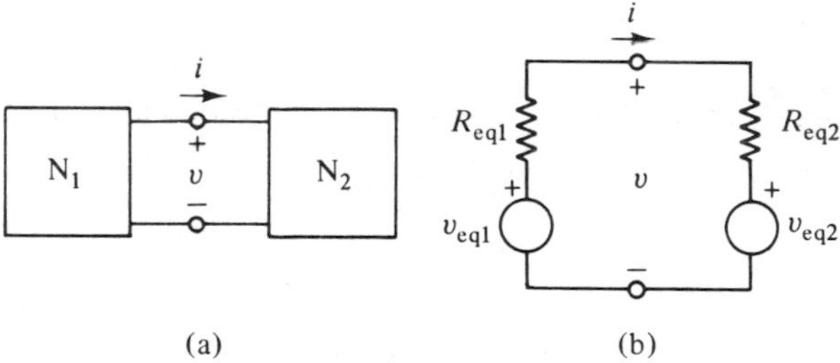

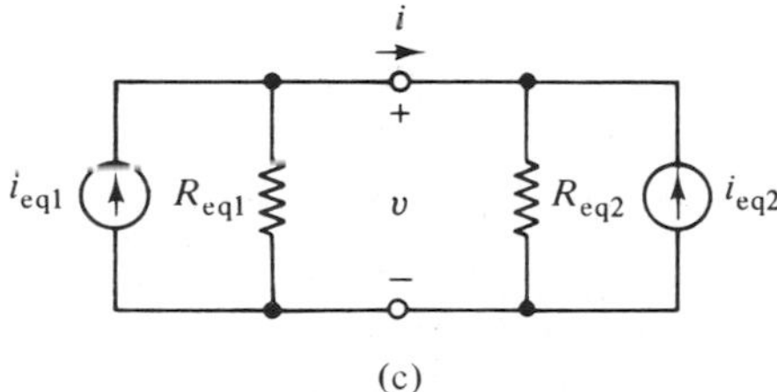

Fig. 3-13

Alternatively, we represent N_1 and N_2 with their Norton equivalent circuits as in Fig. 3-13(c). Again, using the principle of superposition, i and v are readily calculated.

$$i = \frac{i_{eq1} R_{eq1} - i_{eq2} R_{eq2}}{R_{eq1} + R_{eq2}}, \qquad v = (i_{eq1} + i_{eq2})\left(\frac{R_{eq1} R_{eq2}}{R_{eq1} + R_{eq2}}\right)$$

Once v and i are determined, it is a simple matter to calculate the voltages and currents at internal points in N_1 and N_2.

Example 3-6

For the circuit shown in Fig. 3-14, determine the Thévenin and Norton equivalent circuits as seen from terminals 1–1′.

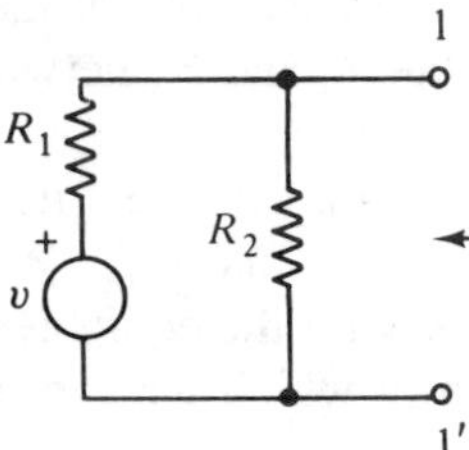

Fig. 3-14

Solution. To calculate R_{eq}, kill the source v and look into the terminals 1–1′ as shown in Fig. 3-15(a). We see that

$$R_{eq} = \frac{R_1 R_2}{R_1 + R_2}$$

To calculate v_{eq}, we use the circuit of Fig. 3-14 as given and find the open-circuit voltage across the 1–1′ terminals.

$$v_{eq} = v_{oc} = v\frac{R_2}{R_1 + R_2}$$

To calculate i_{eq}, we short-circuit the terminals as shown in Fig. 3-15(b) and calculate i_{sc}. Since the voltage across R_2 is zero, there is no current through it and i_{sc} is the same as the current through R_1.

$$i_{eq} = i_{sc} = \frac{v}{R_1}$$

Using R_{eq}, v_{eq}, and i_{eq}, the Thévenin and Norton equivalent circuits can be drawn as in Fig. 3-15(c). Note that

$$i_{sc} = \frac{v}{R_1} = \frac{v_{oc}}{R_{eq}} = \frac{vR_2/(R_1 + R_2)}{R_1 R_2/(R_1 + R_2)} = \frac{v}{R_1}$$

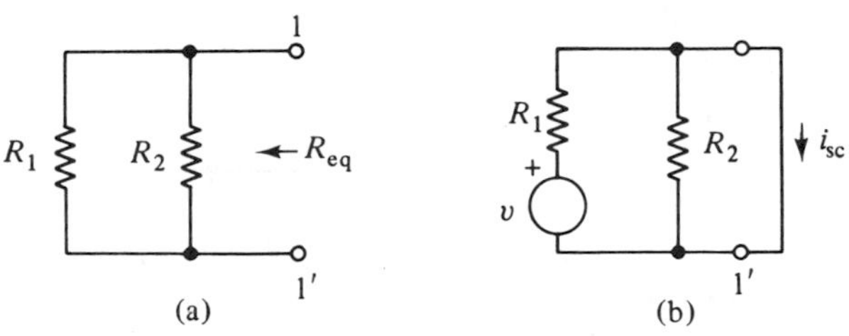

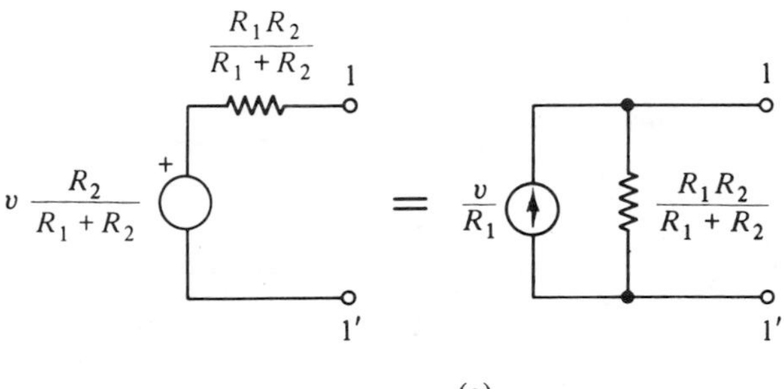

Fig. 3-15

Example 3-7

Obtain v_o for the circuit shown in Fig. 3-16.

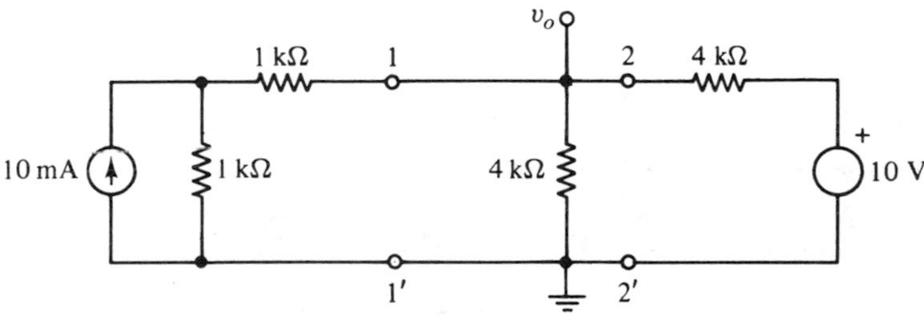

Fig. 3-16

Solution. Redraw the circuit to the left of 1–1′ as in Fig. 3-17(a) and obtain its Norton equivalent.

$$R_{eq1} = 1\ \text{k}\Omega + 1\ \text{k}\Omega - 2\ \text{k}\Omega, \qquad i_{sc1} = 10\ \text{mA} \times \frac{1}{2} = 5\ \text{mA}$$

Redraw the circuit to the right of 2–2′ as in Fig. 3-17(b) and obtain its Norton equivalent.

$$R_{eq2} = 4\ \text{k}\Omega, \qquad i_{sc2} = \frac{10}{4} = 2.5\ \text{mA}$$

Put the equivalent circuits together and draw the circuit of Fig. 3-17(c). The two current sources are in parallel. Therefore they can be combined into one current source as shown.

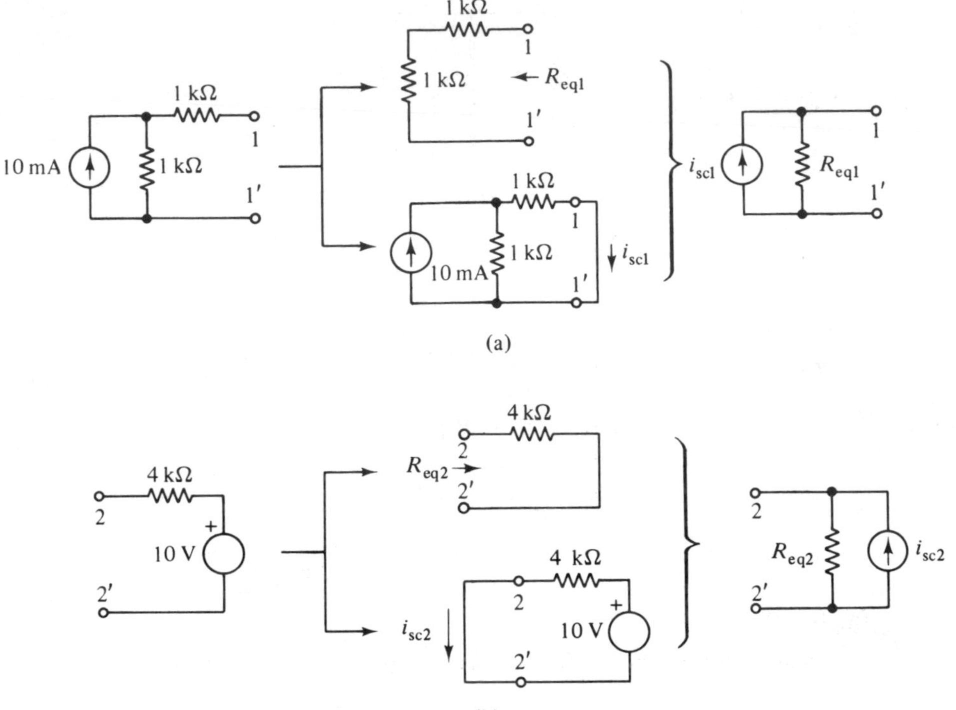

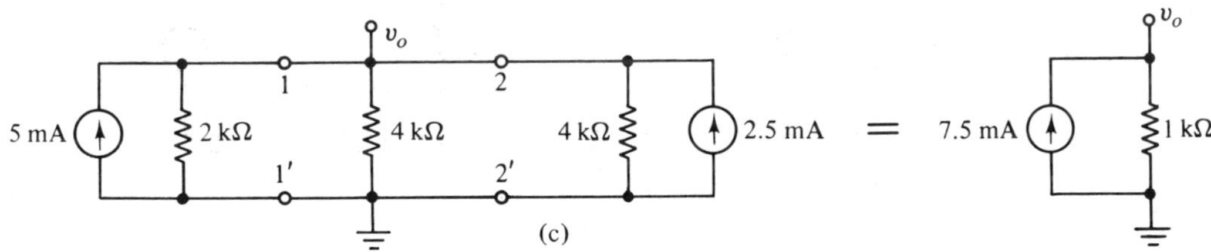

Fig. 3-17

The three resistors are in parallel and so can be equivalently represented by a 1 kΩ resistor. Thus we have

$$v_o = 7.5 \text{ mA} \times 1 \text{ k}\Omega = 7.5 \text{ V} \quad \text{Ans.}$$

Example 3-8

For the circuit shown in Fig. 3-18, obtain v_o.

Solution. Starting on the left, obtain successive Thévenin equivalent circuits looking in from A, B, C, D, and E. The various steps are shown in Fig. 3-19. By inspection of the last equivalent presentation, obtain v_o.

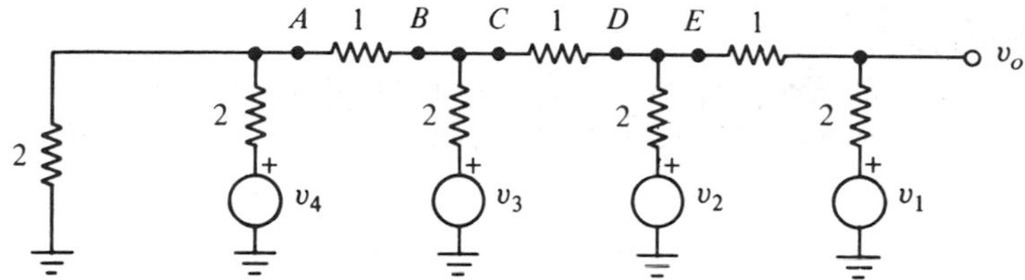

Fig. 3-18

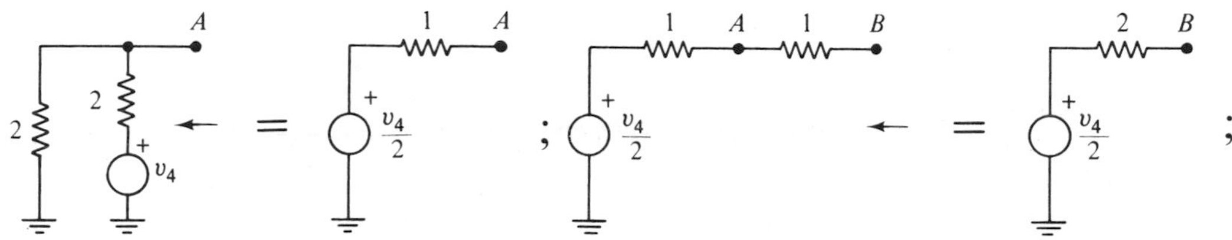

Fig. 3-19

$$v_o = \frac{v_1}{2} + \frac{v_2}{4} + \frac{v_3}{8} + \frac{v_4}{16} \quad \text{Ans.}$$

Note that the output represents a weighted sum of the input signals. The weighting factor is

$$\frac{1}{2^n}$$

where n represents the source number. It should be clear (from the way the circuit equivalents develop) that the result can be extended to any number of sources.

Example 3-9

For the circuit shown in Fig. 3-20, calculate first i_{R_L}. Then rearrange the expression for i_{R_L} and from it identify the Thévenin equivalent circuit facing R_L.

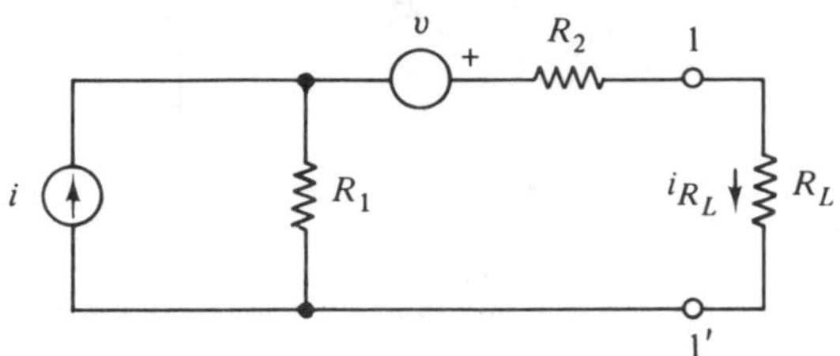

Fig. 3-20

Solution. Use superposition to calculate i_{R_L}.

$$i_{R_L} = i\frac{R_1}{R_1 + R_2 + R_L} + \frac{v}{R_1 + R_2 + R_L} = \frac{(iR_1 + v)}{(R_1 + R_2) + R_L} \tag{3-4}$$

Now refer to Fig. 3-21, which is drawn in terms of the Thévenin equivalent circuit facing R_L. Using it, obtain i_{R_L} as

$$i_{R_L} = \frac{v_{eq}}{R_{eq} + R_L} \tag{3-5}$$

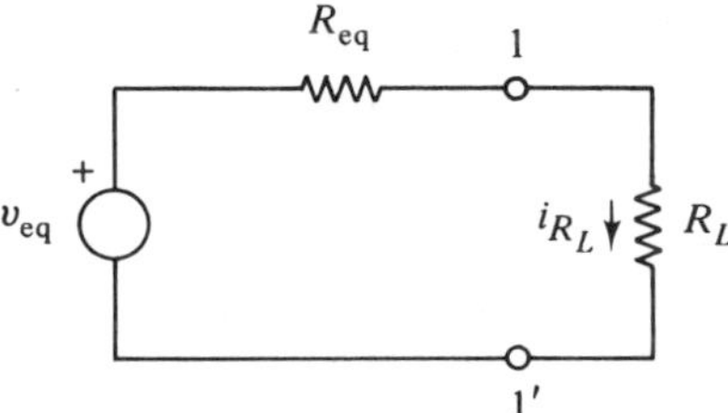

Fig. 3-21

The i_{R_L} given by Eq. (3-5) must agree with i_{R_L} given by Eq. (3-4). Hence, by comparison, we obtain

$$v_{eq} = iR_1 + v, \qquad R_{eq} = R_1 + R_2$$

The comparison method presented here is an alternative way for calculating Thévenin equivalent circuits. In one step it gives both R_{eq} and v_{eq}. However, the calculations are a little more involved because of R_L, which is used as a means by which the various terms in the final expression can be segregated. The general procedure for calculating Thévenin equivalents (see Fig. 3-12) is easier to use because R_L is not involved. Still, it requires two separate calculations: one to determine R_{eq} and another to determine v_{eq}.

Example 3-10

The network N in Fig. 3-22 contains sources and resistors. Let v_{oc} represent the open-circuit voltage appearing across the output terminals. Let i_{sc} represent the short-circuit current that would flow in a short circuit placed across the output terminals. Show that $R_{eq} = v_{oc}/i_{sc}$.

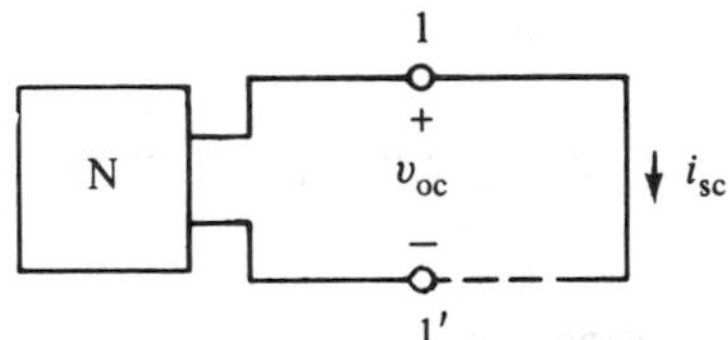

Fig. 3-22

Solution. We know that N can be equivalently presented by the Thévenin equivalent circuit shown in Fig. 3-23. From this figure we see that when terminals 1–1′ are open-circuited,

$$v_{oc} = v_{eq}$$

and when terminals 1–1′ are short-circuited,

$$i_{sc} = \frac{v_{eq}}{R_{eq}}$$

Forming the v_{oc} to i_{sc} ratio, we have

$$\frac{v_{oc}}{i_{sc}} = \frac{v_{eq}}{v_{eq}/R_{eq}} = R_{eq}$$

Thus we can also determine the R_{eq} of a circuit from two calculations or measurements—the open-circuit voltage and the short-circuit current.

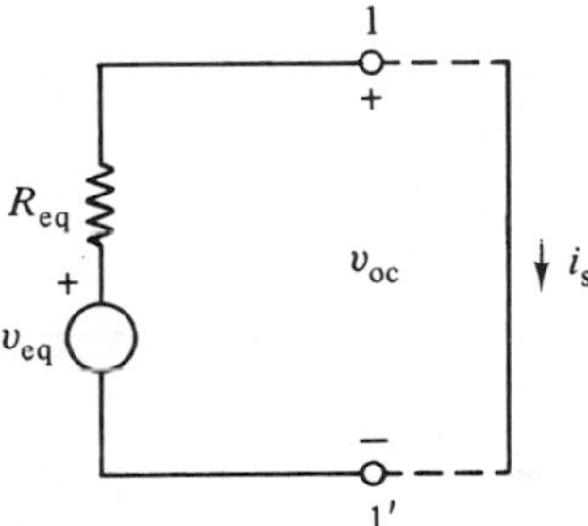

Fig. 3-23

Example 3-11

In Fig. 3-24, what is v_o?

Solution.

Method 1 Starting with the source end, we move to the right, one element at a time, and obtain Thévenin equivalent circuits, thereby simplifying the problem as in Fig.

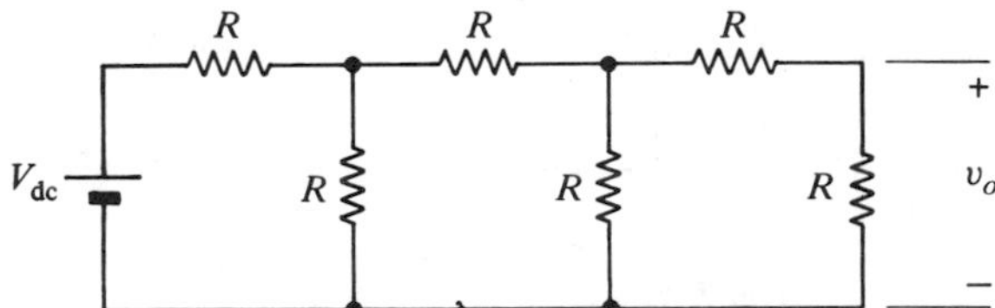

Fig. 3-24

3-25. From the last circuit we have

$$v_o = \frac{1}{5}V_{dc}\left(\frac{R}{R + R + \frac{3}{5}R}\right) = \frac{1}{13}V_{dc} \quad \text{Ans.}$$

Instead of using the Thévenin equivalent circuits successively, we could just as well have proceeded from left to right, using Norton equivalent circuits to simplify, and thus easily obtained the answer.

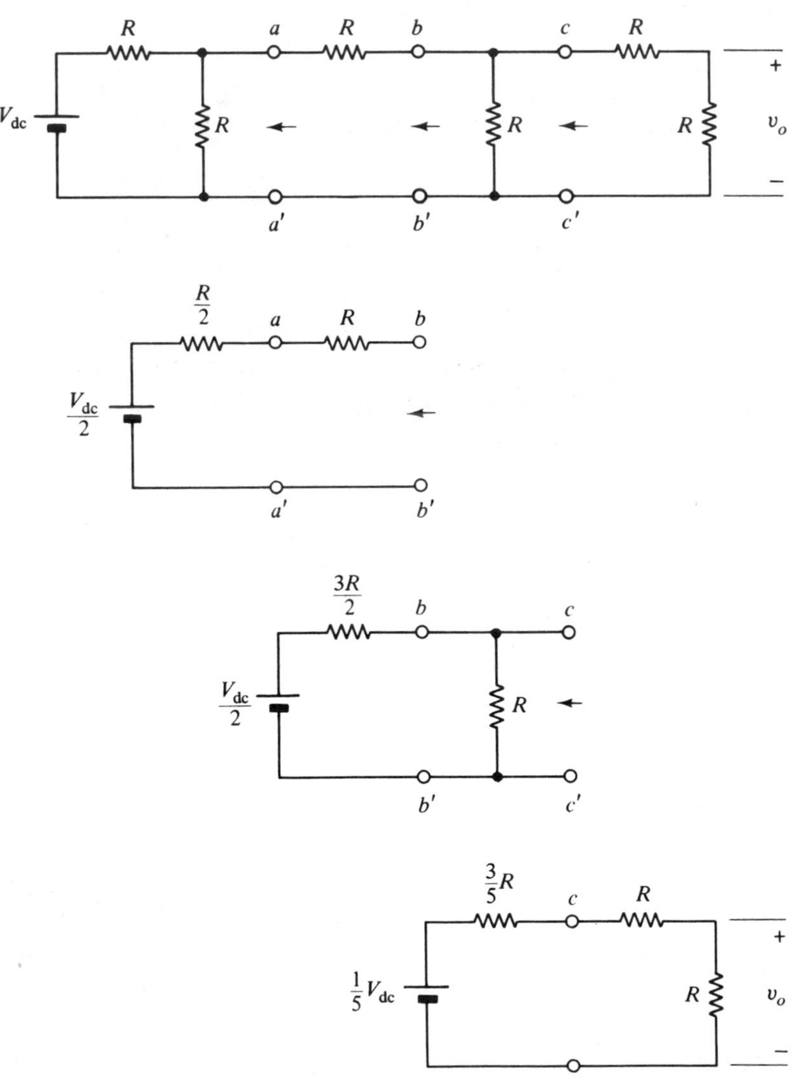

Fig. 3-25

Method 2 Starting from the output side, we move to the left, calculating equivalent resistances as shown in Fig. 3-26.

$$R_{aa'} = R + R = 2R$$

$$R_{bb'} = \frac{RR_{aa'}}{R + R_{aa'}} = \frac{R \times 2R}{R + 2R} = \frac{2}{3}R$$

$$R_{cc'} = R + R_{bb'} = R + \frac{2}{3}R = \frac{5}{3}R$$

$$R_{dd'} = \frac{RR_{cc'}}{R + R_{cc'}} = \frac{R \times \frac{5}{3}R}{R + \frac{5}{3}R} = \frac{5}{8}R$$

$$R_{ee'} = R + R_{dd'} = R + \frac{5}{8}R = \frac{13}{8}R$$

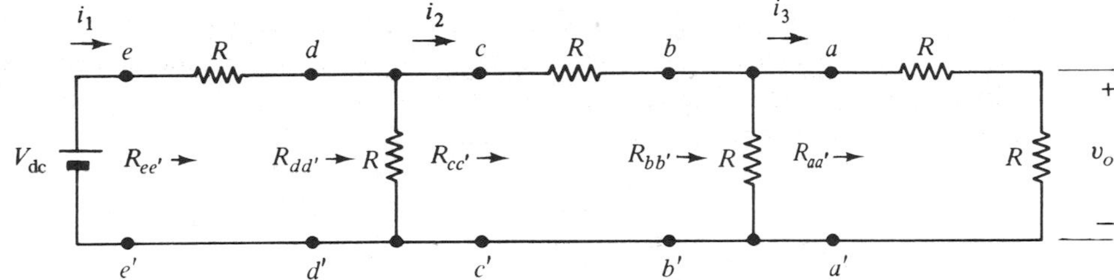

Fig. 3-26

So the battery delivers a current of

$$i_1 = \frac{V_{dc}}{R_{ee'}} = \frac{V_{dc}}{\frac{13}{8}R} = \frac{8}{13}\frac{V_{dc}}{R}$$

We now move back to the output and use the current-divider rule at each junction.

$$i_2 = i_1\frac{R}{R + R_{cc'}} = \frac{8}{13}\frac{V_{dc}}{R}\left(\frac{R}{R + \frac{5}{3}R}\right) = \frac{3}{13}\frac{V_{dc}}{R}$$

$$i_3 = i_2\frac{R}{R + R_{aa'}} = \frac{3}{13}\frac{V_{dc}}{R}\left(\frac{R}{R + 2R}\right) = \frac{1}{13}\frac{V_{dc}}{R}$$

The output voltage is

$$v_o = i_3 R = \frac{1}{13} V_{dc} \quad \text{Ans.}$$

Method 3 We proceed as in method 2 and calculate equivalent resistances. Then instead of using the current-divider rule, we use the voltage-divider rule as we move toward the output.

$$v_{dd'} = V_{dc}\left(\frac{R_{dd'}}{R + R_{dd'}}\right) = V_{dc}\left(\frac{\frac{5}{8}R}{R + \frac{5}{8}R}\right) = \frac{5}{13}V_{dc} = v_{cc'}$$

$$v_{bb'} = v_{cc'}\left(\frac{R_{bb'}}{R + R_{bb'}}\right) = \frac{5}{13}V_{\text{dc}}\left(\frac{\frac{2}{3}R}{R + \frac{2}{3}R}\right) = \frac{2}{13}V_{\text{dc}} = v_{aa'}$$

$$v_o = v_{aa'}\left(\frac{R}{R + R}\right) = \frac{1}{13}V_{\text{dc}} \quad \text{Ans.}$$

3-6 POWER AND ENERGY

Consider the connection of two networks N_1 and N_2 in Fig. 3-27(a). The voltage $v(t)$ and the current $i(t)$ are common to both networks. With $v(t)$ and $i(t)$ variables as designated, the *instantaneous power delivered by* N_1, and thus, *received by* N_2, is given by

$$p(t) = v(t)i(t) \tag{3-6}$$

If the sense of $i(t)$ were reversed, the power received by N_2 would be $v(t)[-i(t)] = -v(t)i(t)$. No loss or gain in power occurs in the connecting wires, which are assumed to have zero resistance. Power is measured in *watts*. Dimensionally, we have 1 watt = 1 volt × 1 ampere.

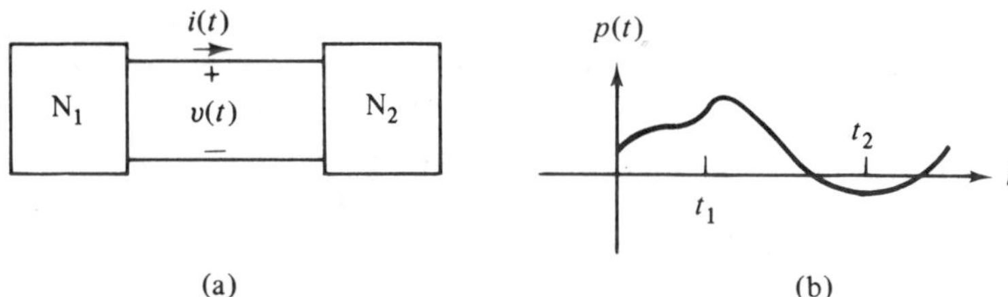

Fig. 3-27

As indicated by Eq. (3-6) and Fig. 3-27(b), power received by N_2 is a function of time. Consequently, it may vary from one instant to the next. In particular, at any given instant, it may be positive or negative. At time t_1, $p(t_1)$ is positive; hence N_1 is delivering and N_2 is *receiving* power. At $t = t_2$, $p(t_2)$ is negative, which means that N_1 is delivering and N_2 is *receiving* negative power. Negative power received by any N is the same as positive power delivered by N. So at $t = t_2$, N_2 is delivering positive power to N_1. In order to avoid confusion, we say that N_2 is receiving power, and hence N_1 delivering power, regardless of the sign of $p(t)$, if the voltage and current senses are as shown in Fig. 3-27.

When two or more sources act on a network, *voltages* and *currents* can be determined by superimposing responses caused by each source while the others are held at zero. The principle of superposition, however, *does not apply to power*. This statement can easily be demonstrated by supposing that $v(t)$ and $i(t)$ in Fig. 3-27(a) are caused by two sources and therefore can be written in superimposed form as

$$v = v_1 + v_2, \qquad i = i_1 + i_2$$

where subscripts 1 and 2 refer to the responses caused by sources 1 and 2, respectively. The power delivered to N_2 is then given by

$$p = vi = (v_1 + v_2)(i_1 + i_2) = (v_1 i_1 + v_2 i_2) + (v_1 i_2 + v_2 i_1)$$

Source 1, if it were to act alone, would deliver a power of $v_1 i_1$. Source 2, if it were to act alone, would deliver a power of $v_2 i_2$. Yet if both sources were to act at the same time, the power delivered would be the sum of the individual powers, $(v_1 i_1 + v_2 i_2)$, *plus* another term involving mixed variables, $(v_1 i_2 + v_2 i_1)$. Because of this added term, power cannot be obtained by superposition.

Since $p(t)$ may be positive for a time and then negative, it is important to know whether, *on the average*, N_2 receives power or delivers power. To determine the outcome, we average $p(t)$ over a specified period. The result is the *average power received by* N_2 (and hence delivered by N_1) over that period. It is given by

$$p_{av} = \frac{1}{t_2 - t_1}\int_{t_1}^{t_2} p(t)\,dt = \frac{1}{t_2 - t_1}\int_{t_1}^{t_2} v(t)i(t)\,dt \tag{3-7}$$

where $(t_2 - t_1)$ is the length of the time interval over which the instantaneous power is averaged. If p_{av} turns out to be a positive number, then N_2 has indeed *received power on the average*. If p_{av} turns out to be a negative number, N_2 has received negative power on the average, which is equivalent to saying that N_2 has actually *delivered positive power on the average*. The average power is measured in watts.

Since power represents the rate of change of energy, it can be written as

$$p = vi = \frac{dw}{dt} \tag{3-8}$$

where w stands for energy in *watt-seconds* (1 watt-second = 1 joule). Separating the variables and integrating between limits of t_1 and t_2, we can solve Eq. (3-8) for w.

$$dw = p\,dt = vi\,dt$$

$$\int_{w(t_1)}^{w(t_2)} dw = \int_{t_1}^{t_2} p\,dt = \int_{t_1}^{t_2} vi\,dt$$

$$w(t_2) - w(t_1) = \int_{t_1}^{t_2} p\,dt = \int_{t_1}^{t_2} vi\,dt$$

$$w(t_2) = w(t_1) + \int_{t_1}^{t_2} p\,dt = w(t_1) + \int_{t_1}^{t_2} vi\,dt \tag{3-9}$$

In Eq. (3-9) $w(t_2)$ and $w(t_1)$ represent the energy associated with N_2 [(see Fig. 3-27(a)] at $t = t_2$ and $t = t_1$, respectively, whereas $\int_{t_1}^{t_2} vi\,dt$ represents the energy *delivered* to N_2 between t_1 and t_2 seconds.

We can rearrange Eq. (3-7) and obtain

$$\int_{t_1}^{t_2} vi\,dt = p_{av}(t_2 - t_1) \tag{3-10}$$

Consequently, Eq. (3-9) can be written

$$w(t_2) = w(t_1) + p_{av}(t_2 - t_1) \tag{3-11}$$

Thus the power delivered by N_1 over a period of $t_2 - t_1$ seconds increases the energy associated with N_2 from $w(t_1)$ to $w(t_2)$.

Quite often t_1 is taken as zero and t_2 as t, and Eq. (3-9) is written

$$w(t) = w(0) + \int_0^t p\, dt' = w(0) + \int_0^t vi\, dt' \tag{3-12}$$

where $w(t)$ and $w(0)$ represent the energy state of N_2 at times t and 0, respectively, and $\int_0^t vi\, dt'$ represents the energy delivered to N_2 during the time interval from 0 to t. Henceforth, unless specifically designated, $w(0)$ is taken as zero.

3-7 POWER AND ENERGY RELATIONSHIPS IN A RESISTOR

For a resistor, the terminal variables are related by

$$v = iR$$

So the power delivered to a resistor is

$$p = vi = i^2R = \frac{v^2}{R} \tag{3-13}$$

Because either i or v is squared, the power delivered to a resistor can never be negative. In other words, a resistor always absorbs power.

The energy absorbed by the resistor is

$$w(t) = \int_0^t p(t')\, dt' = R\int_0^t i^2(t')\, dt' = \frac{1}{R}\int_0^t v^2(t')\, dt' \tag{3-14}$$

All this energy is dissipated (converted to heat) by the resistor.

Example 3-12

A 10 Ω heating unit carries 1.5 A of current.

(a) How many joules of energy are converted to heat in one minute?

(b) If the resistor is to handle this much heat without getting damaged, what must its wattage rating be?

(c) At 6 cents per kilowatt-hour, how much will it cost to run the heater for a month?

Solution.

(a) We obtain the energy dissipated by the resistor by using Eq. (3-14).

$$w = R\int_0^t i^2\, dt' = 10\int_0^{60} 1.5^2\, dt' = 22.5t'\Big|_0^{60}$$

$$= 22.5 \times 60 = 1350 \text{ J} \quad \text{Ans.}$$

(b) The wattage rating of the resistor is given by

$$i^2R = 1.5^2 \times 10 = 22.5 \text{ W} \quad \text{Ans.}$$

Thus the resistor must have a wattage rating of 22.5 W or greater in order to dissipate the required amount of power. If a 10 Ω resistor with a lower wattage rating is used in the circuit, the resistor will still be forced by the 1.5 A current to dissipate 22.5 W. As a result, it may burn itself out before 1350 J are converted to heat.

(c) The resistor converts into heat 22.5 W = 0.0225 kW of power. In a month, it will be on for 24 × 30 = 720 hours. So it will consume 0.0225 kW × 720 hours = 16.2 kWh of energy. At 6 cents per kilowatt-hour, it will cost 6 × 16.2 = 97.2¢ to run the heater for a month.

Example 3-13

A 110 V incandescent light bulb is rated at 100 W.

(a) What is the resistance of the bulb?

(b) How much current does it take from the 110 V source?

(c) How many kilowatt-hours are consumed by the light bulb if it is connected to 110 V and left burning for a month?

(d) How much power will the bulb dissipate if it is connected across 100 V?

Solution.

(a) Equation (3-13) gives the relationship between power, voltage, and wattage.

$$R = \frac{v^2}{p} = \frac{110^2}{100} = 121\ \Omega \quad \text{Ans.}$$

(b) By Ohm's Law,

$$i = \frac{v}{R} = \frac{110}{121} = \frac{10}{11} = 0.909 \text{ A} \quad \text{Ans.}$$

(c) Since the power dissipated is constant at 100 W, Eq. (3-14) gives

$$w = \int_0^t p(t')\, dt' = \int_0^{30\times 24} 100\, dt' = 100t' \Big|_0^{30\times 24}$$

$$= 100 \times 30 \times 24 = 72{,}000 \text{ Wh} = 72 \text{ kWh.} \quad \text{Ans.}$$

(d) Since the resistance of the bulb is 121 Ω and it is connected across 100 V, we have

$$p = \frac{v^2}{R} = \frac{100^2}{121} = 82.6 \text{ W} \quad \text{Ans.}$$

$$i = \frac{v}{R} = \frac{100}{121} = 0.826 \text{ A} \quad \text{Ans.}$$

Strictly speaking, the resistance of the bulb does not stay constant. Due to the lower current the bulb operates at a lower temperature, and its resistance goes down. Here we have neglected this effect.

Example 3-14

A sinusoidal voltage given by $V_m \sin \omega t$ is applied to a resistor at $t = 0$.

(a) Sketch the voltage across, the current through, and the instantaneous power dissipated by the resistor.

(b) What is the average power dissipated by the resistor over a period of $2\pi/\omega$ seconds?

(c) How much energy is delivered to the resistor at the end of $2\pi/\omega$ seconds?

(d) Sketch as a function of time the energy delivered to the resistor.

Solution.

(a) The voltage across, the current through, and the instantaneous power dissipated by the resistor are

$$v = V_m \sin \omega t \quad \text{Ans.}$$

$$i = \frac{v}{R} = \frac{V_m}{R} \sin \omega t \quad \text{Ans.}$$

$$p = vi = \frac{V_m^2}{R} \sin \omega t = \frac{V_m^2}{2R}(1 - \cos 2\omega t) \quad \text{Ans.}$$

These waveforms are sketched in Fig. 3-28.

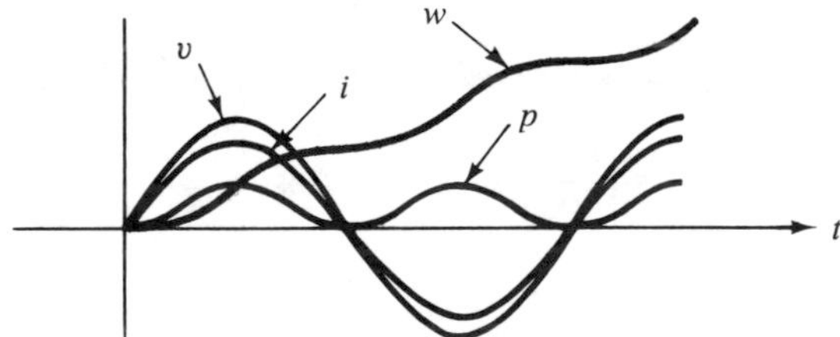

Fig. 3-28

(b) The average power dissipated by the resistor in $2\pi/\omega$ seconds is

$$p_{av} = \frac{1}{2\pi/\omega}\int_0^{2\pi/\omega} p\,dt = \frac{\omega}{2\pi}\int_0^{2\pi/\omega} \frac{V_m^2}{2R}(1 - \cos 2\omega t)\,dt$$

$$= \frac{\omega V_m^2}{4\pi R}\left(t - \frac{1}{2\omega}\sin 2\omega t\right)\Bigg|_0^{2\pi/\omega} = \frac{\omega V_m^2}{4\pi R}\frac{2\pi}{\omega}$$

$$= \frac{V_m^2}{2R}\ \text{W} \quad \text{Ans.}$$

(c) The energy delivered in $2\pi/\omega$ seconds is

$$p_{av}\frac{2\pi}{\omega} = \frac{\pi V_m^2}{\omega R}\ \text{J} \quad \text{Ans.}$$

(d) The energy delivered to the resistor is

$$w(t) = \int_0^t p(t')\,dt' = \int_0^t \frac{V_m^2}{2R}(1 - \cos 2\omega t')\,dt'$$

$$= \frac{V_m^2}{2R}\left(t - \frac{\sin 2\omega t}{2\omega}\right) \quad \text{Ans.}$$

Because of the linear term in t, the energy delivered to the resistor increases with time. See Fig. 3-28.

3-8 MAXIMUM POWER TRANSFER

Consider the voltage source shown in Fig. 3-29(a). Its source resistance R_s is *fixed;* it cannot be altered. Now we ask: What is the maximum power that can be supplied at a given time by this source to a resistive load, assuming that we can *adjust the load resistance* R_L to any (positive) value that we want?

Since all the power supplied by the voltage source ($v_s R_s$ combination shown within the dashed box) goes to the load, let us calculate the power received by R_L.

$$p_L = i^2 R_L = \left(\frac{v_s}{R_s + R_L}\right)^2 R_L \tag{3-15}$$

When $R_L = 0$ or ∞, no power is delivered by the voltage source. Stated differently, a short or open circuit cannot absorb any power. Clearly, for some value of R_L between

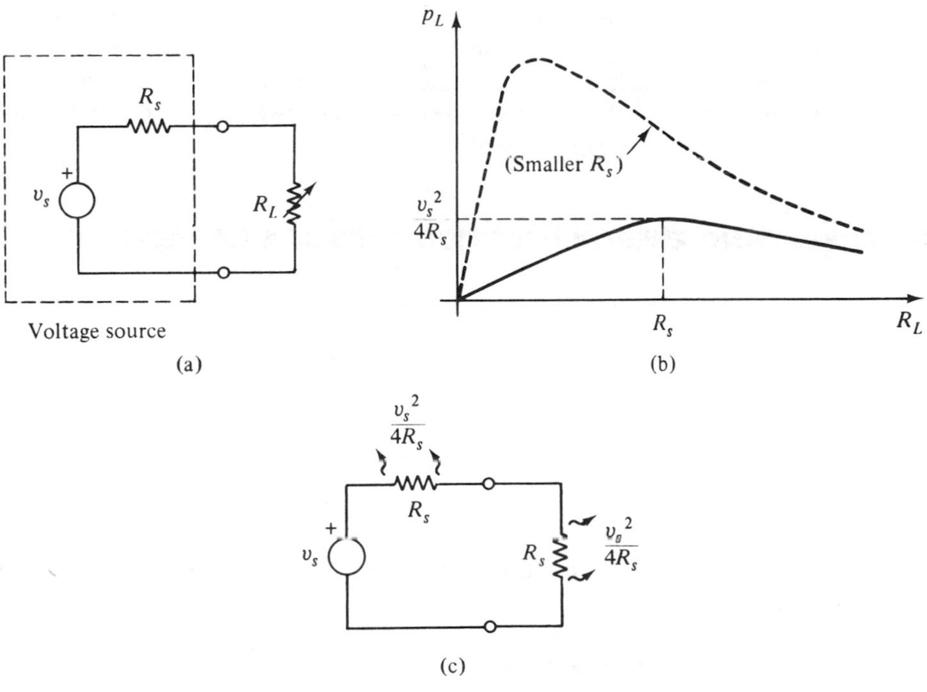

Fig. 3-29

zero and infinity, the power received by R_L must peak as shown in Fig. 3-29(b). To find the value of R_L for which p_L peaks, we differentiate Eq. (3-15) with respect to R_L, set the result equal to zero, and solve for R_L.

$$\frac{dp_L}{dR_L} = \frac{v_s^2[(R_s + R_L)^2 - 2R_L(R_s + R_L)]}{(R_s + R_L)^4} = v_s^2\frac{(R_s - R_L)}{(R_s + R_L)^3} = 0$$

$$R_L = R_s \tag{3-16}$$

Thus when *the load resistance is matched to the source resistance,* the voltage source supplies to the load the maximum power that it can possibly deliver. This power, called the maximum available power, is obtained by substituting Eq. (3-16) into (3-15).

$$(p_L)_{\max} = \left(\frac{v_s}{R_s + R_L}\right)^2 R_L\bigg|_{R_L = R_s} = \frac{v_s^2}{4R_s} \tag{3-17}$$

While $(p_L)_{\max}$ is being dissipated in R_L, an equal amount of power is being dissipated in the internal source resistance as shown in Fig. 3-29(c).

In general, the load resistance, as well as the source resistance, is fixed, in which case the source delivers less power than it is capable of delivering unless, of course, R_s happens to equal R_L.

We can increase the maximum available power from a source by decreasing its internal resistance if it is possible to do so. For instance, by reducing the internal resistance by a factor of 3 and then matching the load resistance to the source resistance, we can obtain three times as much power out of the source, as shown by the dashed curve in Fig. 3-29(b).

3-9 POWER AND ENERGY RELATIONSHIPS IN A CAPACITOR

The terminal variables in a capacitor are related by

$$i = C\frac{dv}{dt}$$

Hence the power delivered to a capacitor is

$$p = vi = vC\frac{dv}{dt} = Cv\frac{dv}{dt} \tag{3-18}$$

If we want to find the energy stored by the capacitor, we use Eq. (3-12) and obtain

$$w(t) = w(0) + \int_0^t p(t')\,dt' = w(0) + \int_0^t \left(Cv\frac{dv}{dt'}\right)dt'$$

$$= w(0) + C\int_{v(0)}^{v(t)} v\,dv = w(0) + \frac{1}{2}Cv^2\Big|_{v(0)}^{v(t)}$$

$$w(t) = w(0) + \frac{1}{2}C[v^2(t) - v^2(0)] \tag{3-19}$$

In Eq. (3-19) the first term on the right, $w(0)$, represents the energy stored in the capacitor at $t = 0$. The second term, $\frac{1}{2}C[v^2(t) - v^2(0)]$, represents the energy delivered to the capacitor from time 0 to t. Now suppose that $v(t) = 0$ for $t \geq t_1$. It follows that $i(t) = 0$ for $t > t_1$ because $i(t) = C\,dv(t)/dt$. With both $v(t)$ and $i(t)$ zero for $t > t_1$, no energy can be associated with the capacitor. So, for $t > t_1$, $w(t)$, given by Eq. (3-19), must be zero. This requirement means that

$$\frac{1}{2}Cv^2(0) = w(0) \tag{3-20}$$

Consequently, Eq. (3-19) simplifies to

$$w(t) = \frac{1}{2}Cv^2(t) \tag{3-21}$$

At any time t *the energy stored in the capacitor is one-half the product of the capacitance and the square of the voltage across it.*

Example 3-15

To a 1 μF capacitor with an initial voltage of 10 V, a 5 mA, 2 ms current pulse is applied as shown in Fig. 3-30.

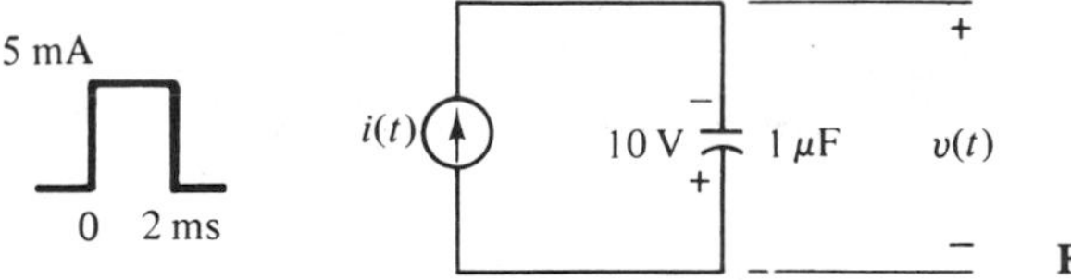

Fig. 3-30

(a) What is the energy stored in the capacitor before and after the current pulse?
(b) Calculate the total energy supplied by the current source.
(c) How much power is being delivered by the current source at $t = 1$ ms?

Solution.

(a) Before the current pulse is applied, the energy stored in the capacitor is due to its initial 10 V. Therefore

$$w(0) = \frac{1}{2}Cv^2(0) = \frac{1}{2} \times 1 \times 10^{-6} \times (-10)^2$$

$$= 50\ \mu\text{J} \quad \text{Ans.}$$

During the pulse, the voltage across the capacitor is given by

$$v = -10 + \frac{1}{C}\int_0^t i(t')\,dt' = -10 + \frac{1}{1 \times 10^{-6}}\int_0^t 5 \times 10^{-3}\,dt'$$

$$= -10 + [5000t']_0^t = -10 + 5000t$$

At the end of the pulse, the voltage across the capacitor is

$$v = -10 + 5000 \times 2 \times 10^{-3} = 0$$

After $t = 2$ ms, the current drops to zero, and the voltage across the capacitor stays at zero volts. Hence the energy stored in the capacitor after the current pulse is

$$w(t) = \frac{1}{2}Cv^2(t) = 0 \quad (t \geq 2 \text{ ms}) \quad \text{Ans.}$$

(b) Since the capacitor initially had 50 μJ of energy in storage and lost all of it, the current source must have received all of the 50 μJ of energy. So the energy supplied by the current source is -50 μJ. Alternatively, we can calculate the energy delivered by the current source by using

$$w(t) = \int_0^t p(t')\,dt' = \int_0^t v(t')i(t')\,dt'$$

where

$$\left.\begin{aligned} v(t) &= -10 + 5000t \\ i(t) &= 5 \times 10^{-3} \end{aligned}\right\} \quad (0 < t < 2 \text{ ms}) \quad \text{and} \quad \left.\begin{aligned} v(t) &= 0 \\ i(t) &= 0 \end{aligned}\right\} \quad (t > 2 \text{ ms})$$

Energy delivery stops after $t = 2$ ms because the vi product is zero thereafter. Thus the energy delivered within the 2 ms period is

$$\begin{aligned} w(t) &= \int_0^{2\times 10^{-3}} v(t)i(t)\,dt \\ &= \int_0^{2\times 10^{-3}} (-10 + 5000t) \times 5 \times 10^{-3}\,dt \\ &= 5 \times 10^{-3}(-10t + 2500t^2)\Big|_0^{2\times 10^{-3}} \\ &= 5 \times 10^{-3}(-10 \times 2 \times 10^{-3} + 2500 \times 4 \times 10^{-6}) \\ &= -50\ \mu\text{J} \quad \text{Ans.} \end{aligned}$$

(c) The power delivered by the current source at $t = 1$ ms is

$$\begin{aligned} p &= v(1 \text{ ms})i(1 \text{ ms}) = (-10 + 5000 \times 1 \times 10^{-3})(5 \times 10^{-3}) \\ &= -25 \text{ mW} \quad \text{Ans.} \end{aligned}$$

Example 3-16

A sinusoidal voltage given by $V_m \sin \omega t$ is applied to a capacitor at $t = 0$.

(a) Sketch the voltage across, the current through, and the instantaneous power delivered to the capacitor.

(b) What is the average power supplied to the capacitor over a period of $2\pi/\omega$ seconds?
(c) How much energy is stored by the capacitor at the end of $2\pi/\omega$ seconds?
(d) Sketch as a function of the time the energy delivered to the capacitor.

Solution.

(a) The voltage across, the current through, and the instantaneous power delivered to the capacitor are

$$v = V_m \sin \omega t \quad \text{Ans.}$$

$$i = C\frac{dv}{dt} = \omega C V_m \cos \omega t \quad \text{Ans.}$$

$$p = vi = \omega C V_m^2 \sin \omega t \cos \omega t = \frac{1}{2}\omega C V_m^2 \sin 2\omega t \quad \text{Ans.}$$

These waveforms are sketched in Fig. 3-31.

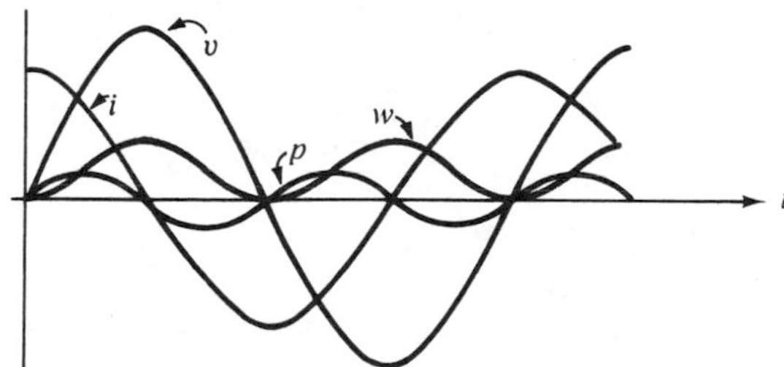

Fig. 3-31

(b) The average power supplied in $2\pi/\omega$ seconds is

$$p_{\text{av}} = \frac{1}{2\pi/\omega}\int_0^{2\pi/\omega} p(t)\, dt = \frac{1}{4}\frac{\omega^2}{\pi} C V_m^2 \int_0^{2\pi/\omega} \sin 2\omega t\, dt$$

$$= \frac{\omega^2 C V_m^2}{4\pi}\left[-\frac{\cos 2\omega t}{2\omega}\right]_0^{2\pi/\omega} = 0 \quad \text{Ans.}$$

(c) The energy stored by the capacitor is

$$w(t) = \frac{1}{2}Cv^2(t) = \frac{1}{2}CV_m^2 \sin^2 \omega t$$

which for $t = 2\pi/\omega$ becomes

$$w\left(\frac{2\pi}{\omega}\right) = \frac{1}{2}CV_m^2 \sin^2 \omega\frac{2\pi}{\omega} = 0 \quad \text{Ans.}$$

This result could have also been obtained directly from $p_{\text{av}} \times 2\pi/\omega = 0$.

(d) The energy delivered to the capacitor is

$$w(t) = \int_0^t p(t')\, dt' = \frac{1}{2}Cv^2(t) = \frac{1}{2}CV_m^2 \sin^2 \omega t \quad \text{Ans.}$$

Unlike the resistor, the energy delivered to the capacitor does not increase with time. See Fig. 3-31.

3-10 POWER AND ENERGY RELATIONSHIPS IN AN INDUCTOR

The terminal variables for an inductor are related by

$$v = L\frac{di}{dt}$$

Therefore the power delivered to an inductor is

$$p = vi = L\frac{di}{dt}i \tag{3-22}$$

If we want to find the energy stored by the inductor, we use Eq. (3-12) and obtain

$$\begin{aligned} w(t) &= w(0) + \int_0^t p(t')\,dt' = w(0) + \int_0^t \left(Li\frac{di}{dt'}\right) dt' \\ &= w(0) + L\int_{i(0)}^{i(t)} i\,di = w(0) + \frac{1}{2}Li^2\Big|_{i(0)}^{i(t)} \end{aligned}$$

$$w(t) = w(0) + \frac{1}{2}L[i^2(t) - i^2(0)] \tag{3-23}$$

In Eq. (3-23) the first term on the right, $w(0)$, represents the energy stored in the inductor at $t = 0$. The second term, $\frac{1}{2}L[i^2(t) - i^2(0)]$, represents the energy delivered to the inductor from time 0 to t. Now suppose that $i(t) = 0$ for $t \geq t_1$. It follows that $v(t) = 0$ for $t > t_1$ because $v(t) = L\,di(t)/dt$. With both $i(t)$ and $v(t)$ zero for $t > t_1$, there can be no energy associated with the inductor. Therefore for $t > t_1$, $w(t)$, given by Eq. (3-23), must be zero. This requires that

$$\frac{1}{2}Li^2(0) = w(0) \tag{3-24}$$

So Eq. (3-23) simplifies to

$$w(t) = \frac{1}{2}Li^2(t) \tag{3-25}$$

At time t *the energy stored in the inductor is one-half the product of the inductance and the square of the current through it.*

Example 3-17

A V-volts step voltage is applied to an inductor by closing the switch at $t = 0$ as shown in Fig. 3-32. Obtain the expressions for power and energy delivered to the inductor as a function of time.

Solution. After $t \geq 0$, the voltage across the inductor is V volts at all times. This constant voltage causes a current of $i(t)$, which is given by

$$i(t) = \frac{1}{L}\int_0^t v\,dt' = \frac{1}{L}\int_0^t V\,dt' = \frac{V}{L}t'\Big|_0^t = \frac{V}{L}t$$

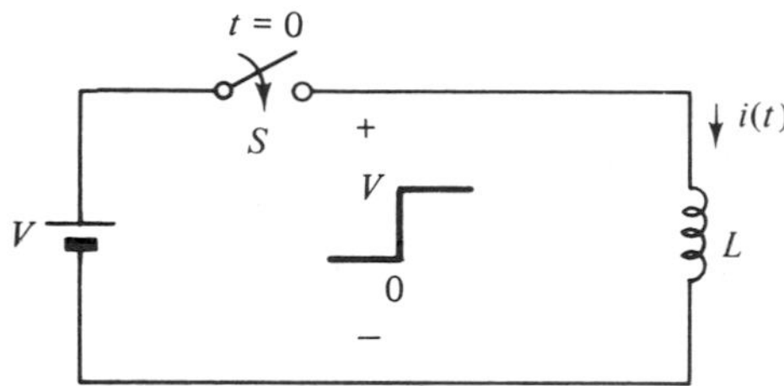

Fig. 3-32

The power delivered to the inductor is

$$p(t) = v(t)i(t) = V\left(\frac{V}{L}t\right) = \frac{V^2}{L}t \quad \text{Ans.}$$

The energy delivered to the inductor is

$$w(t) = \int_0^t p(t')\,dt' = \int_0^t \frac{V^2}{L}t'\,dt' = \frac{V^2}{L}\frac{t'^2}{2}\bigg|_0^t = \frac{1}{2}\frac{V^2}{L}t^2 \quad \text{Ans.}$$

Note that $w(t)$ could also have been obtained directly from

$$w(t) = \frac{1}{2}Li^2(t) = \frac{1}{2}L\left(\frac{V}{L}t\right)^2 = \frac{1}{2}\frac{V^2}{L}t^2$$

Example 3-18

A linearly rising voltage is applied to the *RLC* network shown in Fig. 3-33. How much energy is supplied by the source in one second?

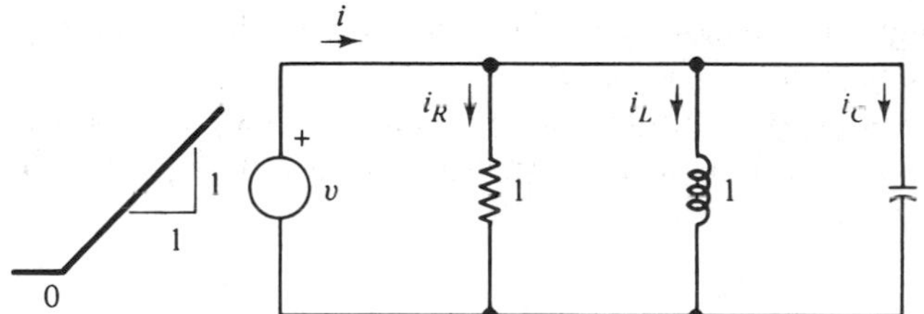

Fig. 3-33

Solution. Since the energy supplied by the voltage source in one second is

$$w(1) = \int_0^1 p(t)\,dt = \int_0^1 v(t)i(t)\,dt$$

we must first find the vi product. The voltage v is given: $v = t$. The current i is the sum of three currents.

$$i = i_R + i_L + i_C$$

where

$$i_R = \frac{v}{R} = t$$

$$i_L = \frac{1}{L}\int_0^t v\,dt' = \int_0^t t'\,dt' = \frac{1}{2}t^2$$

$$i_C = C\frac{dv}{dt} = 1$$

Therefore

$$i = t + \frac{1}{2}t^2 + 1$$

and

$$w(1) = \int_0^1 t\left(t + \frac{1}{2}t^2 + 1\right) dt = \int_0^1 \left(t^2 + \frac{1}{2}t^3 + t\right) dt$$

$$= \frac{t^3}{3} + \frac{1}{8}t^4 + \frac{t^2}{2}\bigg|_0^1 = \frac{1}{3} + \frac{1}{8} + \frac{1}{2} = \frac{23}{24} \text{ J} \quad \text{Ans.}$$

3-11 SUMMARY

A response may be the result of a single excitation or several excitations applied to different parts of the network. When more than one excitation is present, the response can be obtained as a sum of individual responses, each of which can be attributed to one excitation while the others are held zero. This is the principle of superposition.

The characteristics of any two-terminal network composed of resistors and sources can be equivalently presented by the Thévenin or Norton equivalent circuits. The Thévenin equivalent representation uses a resistance in series with a voltage source. The Norton equivalent representation uses a resistance in parallel with a current source. In either case, the resistance is the equivalent resistance obtained looking in from the two terminals. The Thévenin equivalent voltage source is the open-circuit voltage at the two terminals. The Norton equivalent current source is the short-circuit current through the two terminals. The open-circuit voltage equals the short-circuit current times the equivalent resistance.

Power is the product of voltage and current. Energy is the time integral of power. Power dissipated in a resistor is i^2R. The energy stored in a capacitor is $\frac{1}{2}Cv^2$. The energy stored in an inductor is $\frac{1}{2}Li^2$.

PROBLEMS

3-1. In Fig. 3-34, obtain the values of the voltages and currents indicated by a question mark.

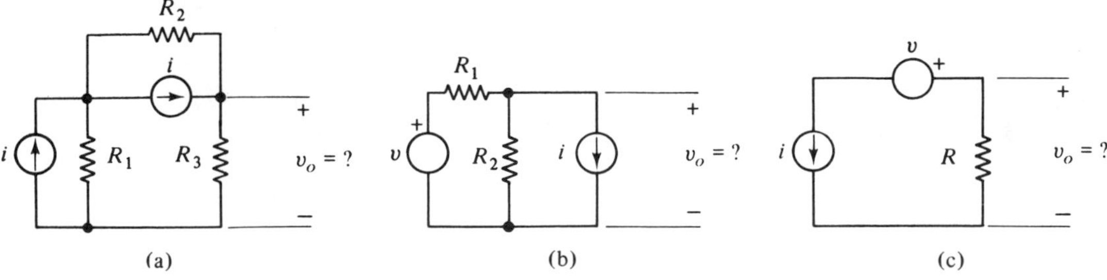

Fig. 3-34

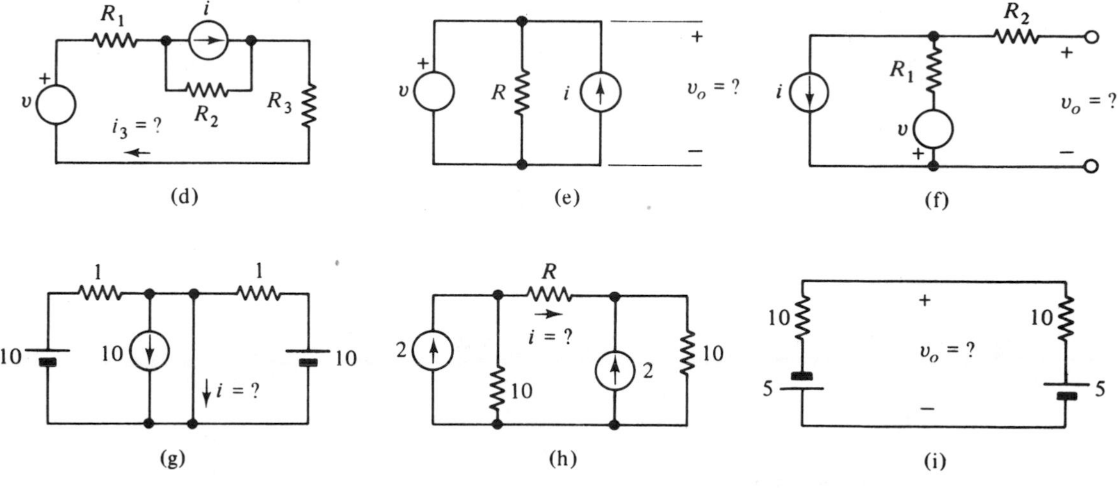

Fig. 3-34 *(cont.)*

3-2. For the circuit shown in Fig. 3-35, obtain v_o.

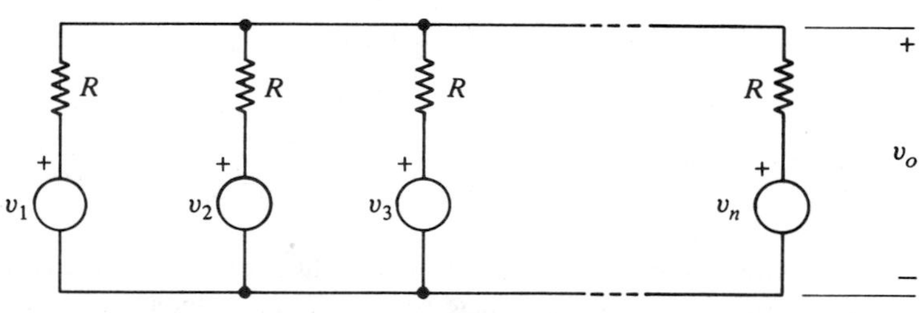

Fig. 3-35

3-3. What would happen to the output voltages of Fig. 3-35 if a load resistance R_L were connected across the output?

3-4. In Fig. 3-36 find i_o and v_o.

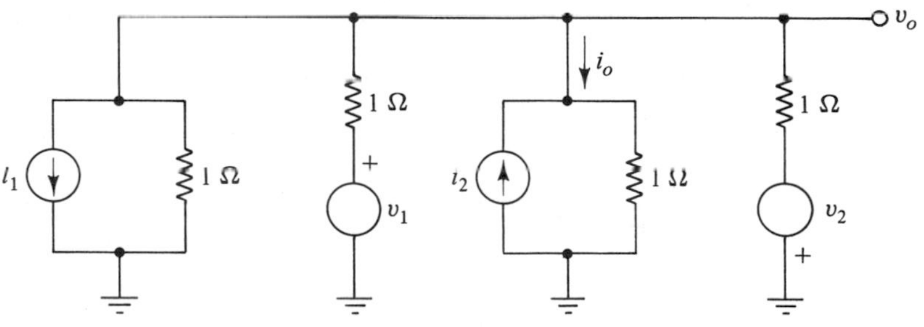

Fig. 3-36

3-5. In Fig. 3-37 v_1, v_2, and v_3 waveforms are as shown. Obtain the v_o waveform.

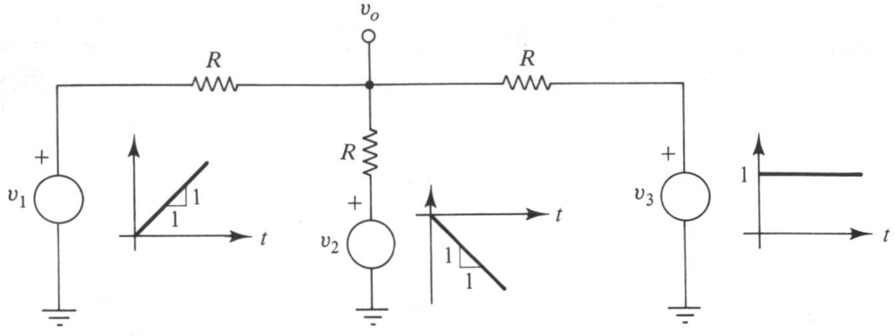

Fig. 3-37

3-6. In Fig. 3-38 obtain v_o and i_o.

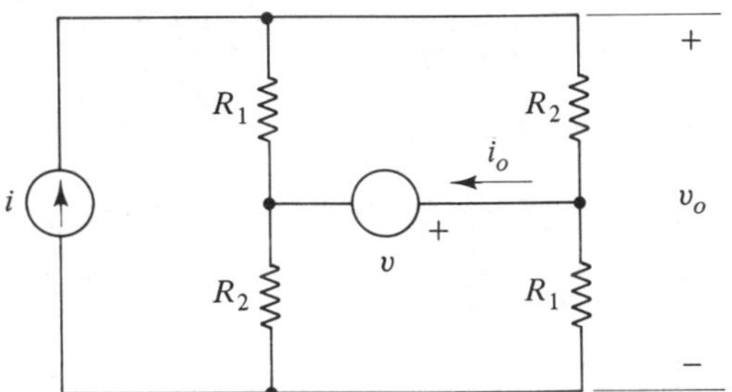

Fig. 3-38

3-7. Voltage source v_1 has an internal resistance of 600 Ω; voltage source v_2 has an internal resistance of 500 Ω; voltage source v_3 has an internal resistance of 600 Ω. Design a simple circuit that produces a voltage of $k(v_1 + v_2 + v_3)$. The constant k should have as large a value as possible. The voltage sources have a common ground.

3-8. Two ideal voltage sources are to be mixed in the ratio of 4 : 1—that is, $v_o = k(4v_1 + v_2)$, where k is arbitrary. Design the circuit.

3-9. Let i_1 and i_2 be two ideal current sources. Design a circuit that sums these currents.

3-10. In Fig. 3-39, n nonideal current sources are connected as shown. What is the current through R_L?

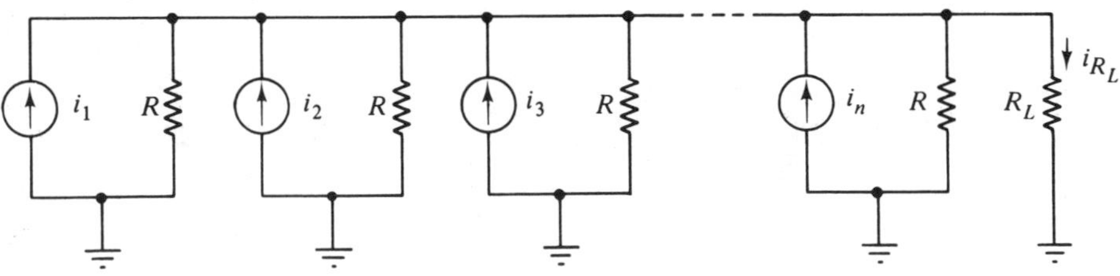

Fig. 3-39

3-11. Two grounded, nonideal current sources, described by (i_1, R_1) and (i_2, R_2) and a resistance are connected to produce an output voltage that is proportional to $(i_1 + 2i_2)$. Design the circuit.

3-12. Given two grounded, ideal current sources i_1 and i_2. Design a circuit that will produce an output current of

$$i_o = \frac{1}{2}i_1 + \frac{1}{3}i_2$$

3-13. Given two grounded, ideal voltage sources. Design a circuit that will give an output current of $i_o = k_1v_1 + k_2v_2$ where k_1 and k_2 are positive.

3-14. Given two grounded, ideal current sources. Design a circuit that will give an output voltage of

$$v_o = \frac{1}{2}i_1 + \frac{1}{3}i_2$$

3-15. What do the circuits shown in Fig. 3-40 accomplish? Explain.

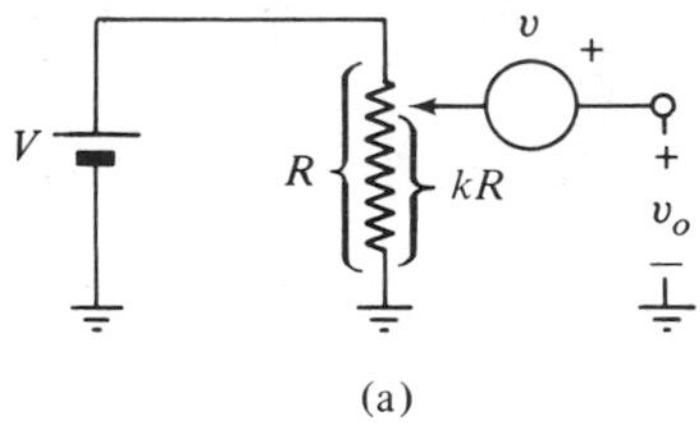

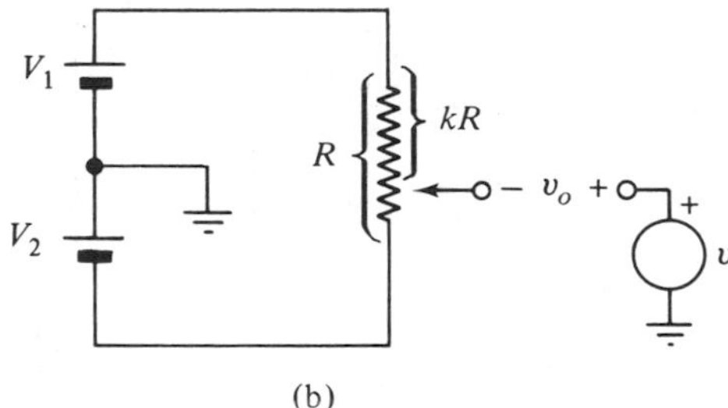

Fig. 3-40

3-16. For the circuit shown in Fig. 3-41 sketch the output voltage. Give maximum, minimum, and average values.

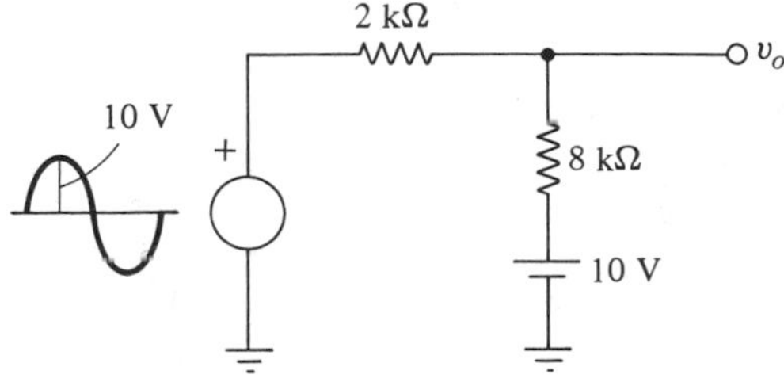

Fig. 3-41

3-17. For the circuit shown in Fig. 3-42 sketch the output v_o.

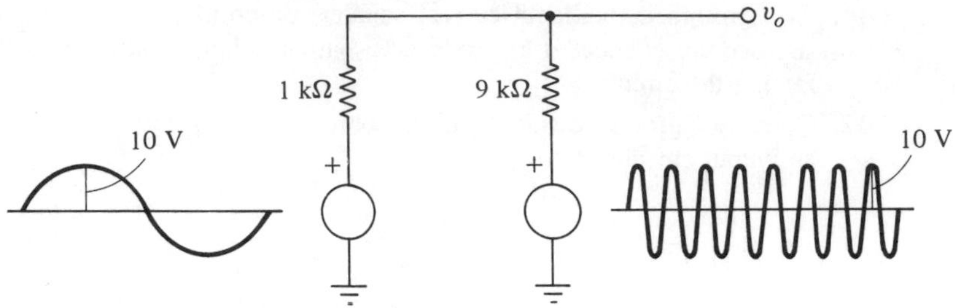

Fig. 3-42

3-18. A 10 V peak sine wave is to be attenuated 2 : 1 and its average level shifted from 0 to −5 V. Give the schematic diagram of the circuit and the element values.

3-19. For the circuits in Fig. 3-43, obtain the Thévenin equivalent circuits.

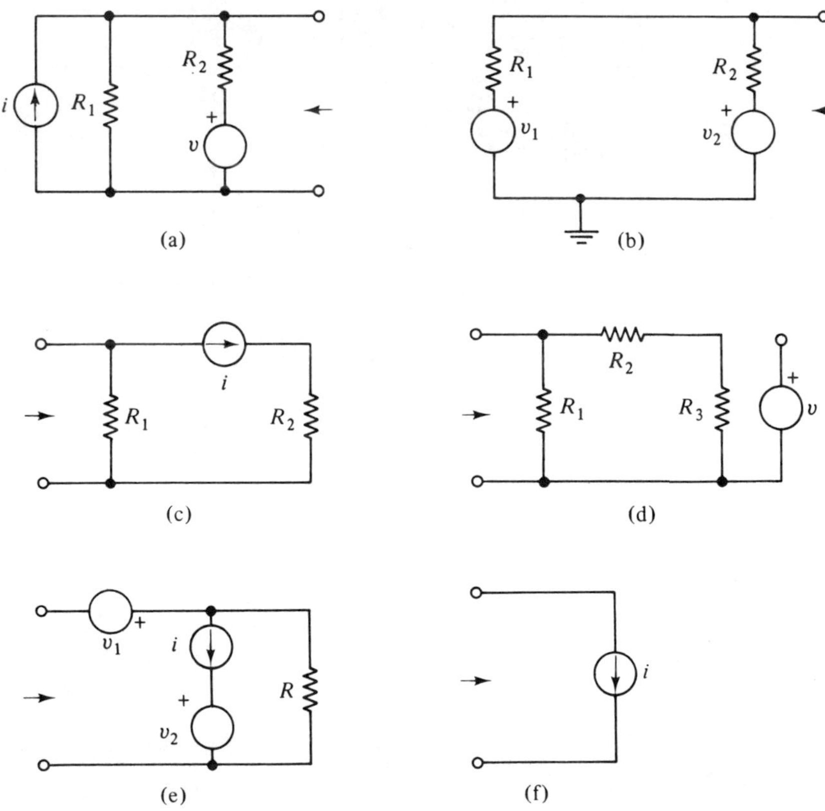

Fig. 3-43

3-20. For the circuits in Fig. 3-44, obtain the Norton equivalent circuits.

(a) (b)

(c) (d)

(e) (f)

Fig. 3-44

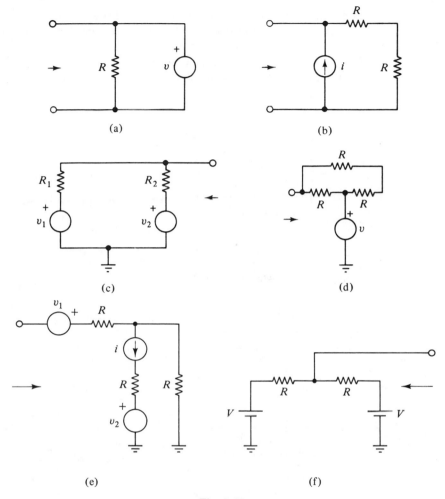

3-21. Refer to Fig. 3-45.

(a) Find the Norton equivalent circuit as seen between a and b.

(b) Find the Thévenin equivalent circuit as seen between b and c.

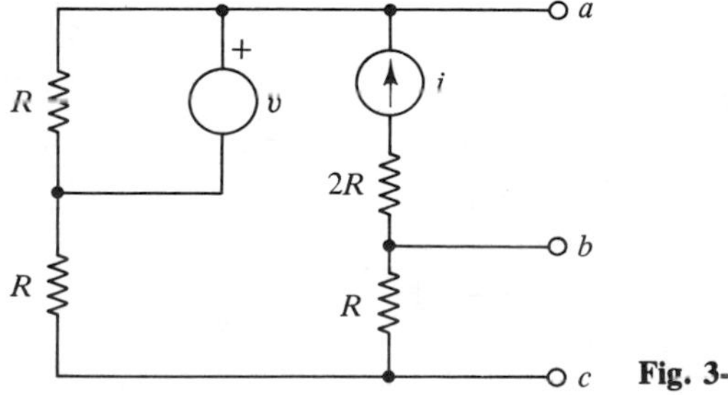

Fig. 3-45

3-22. In Example 3-8 each source is either 0 or 16 V. Show that the output voltage can be set to any integer value from 0 to 15 by the appropriate selection of the four input voltages.

3-23. Refer to Fig. 3-46.

(a) Obtain the expression for the output voltage.

(b) Each source voltage is either 0 or 15 V. What combination of input voltages would result in $v_o = 8$ V?

(c) Repeat (b) for $v_o = 13$ V.

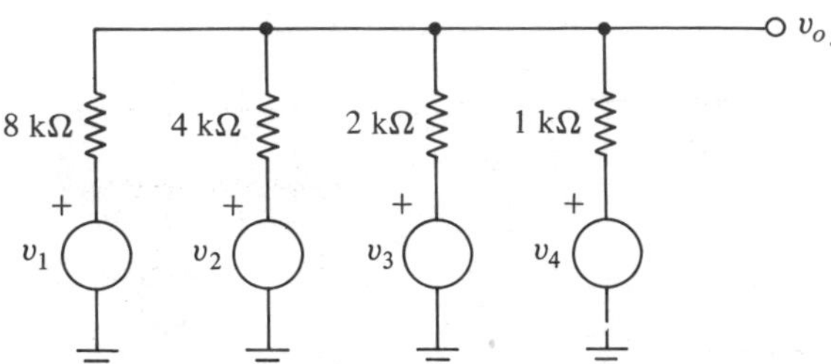

Fig. 3-46

3-24. In Fig. 3-47 for what value of R_L is $R_{\text{in}} = R_L$?

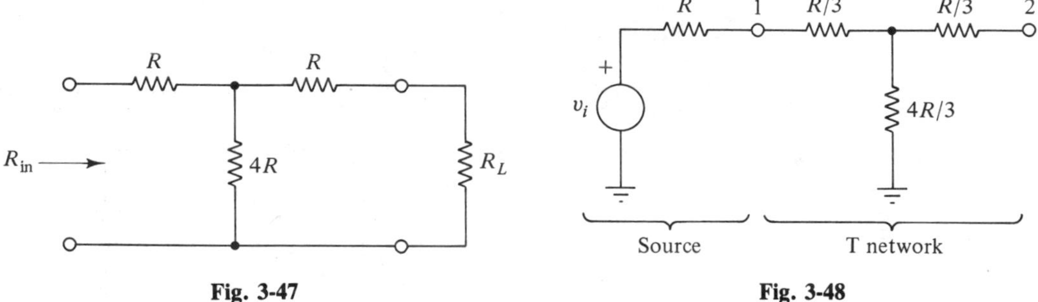

Fig. 3-47 **Fig. 3-48**

3-25. Refer to Fig. 3-48.

(a) Obtain the Thévenin equivalent circuit as seen from the output terminals.

(b) What is the effect of the T network on the source?

3-26. In Fig. 3-49 design the Π network such that the output equivalent circuit is 50 Ω in series with $0.2v_i$.

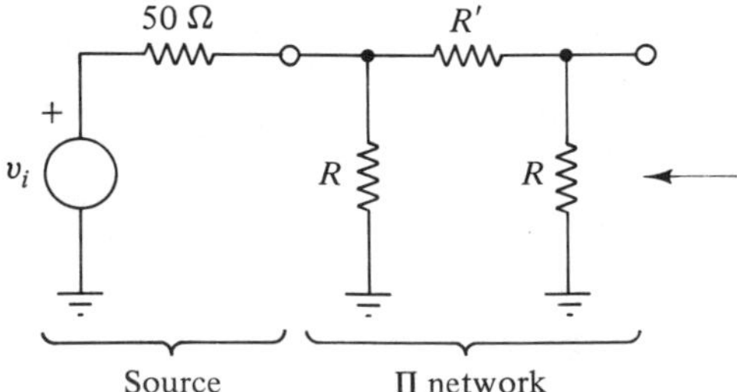

Fig. 3-49

3-27. Making use of the results of Problem 3-26, design the circuit of Fig. 3-50 such that the output equivalent circuit is 50 Ω in series with $0.04v_i$.

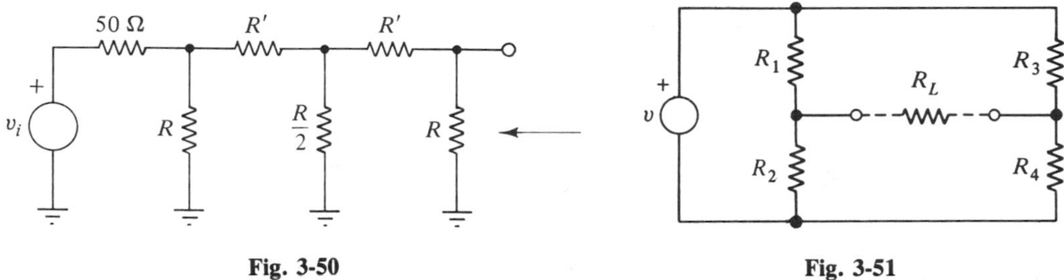

Fig. 3-50 **Fig. 3-51**

3-28. (a) What is the Thévenin equivalent circuit as seen from the output terminals of the bridge in Fig. 3-51?
(b) If R_L is connected across the output, what is the voltage across it?

3-29. (a) What is the Thévenin equivalent circuit as seen from the output terminals of the bridge circuit of Fig. 3-52?
(b) If R_L is connected across the output, what is the current through it?

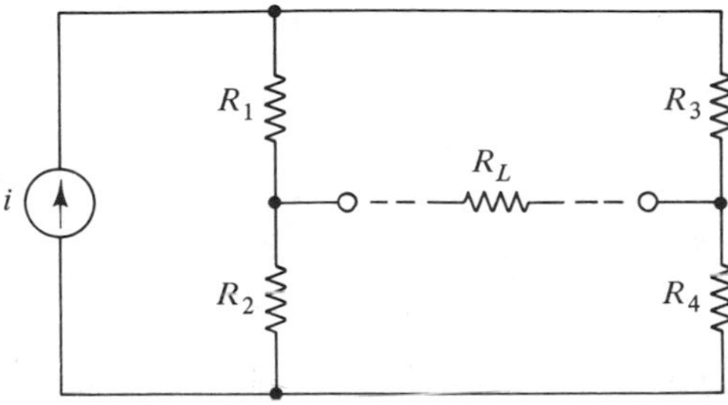

Fig. 3-52

3-30. In Fig. 3-53, obtain i_o.

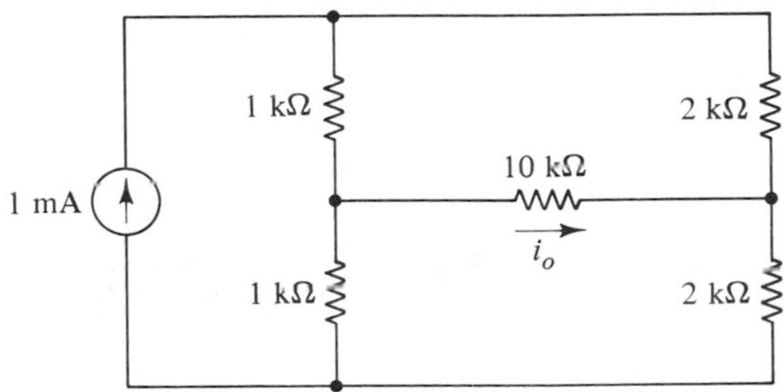

Fig. 3-53

3-31. In Fig. 3-54, calculate the responses designated by a question mark. Boxes labeled N represent resistive networks.

Fig. 3-54

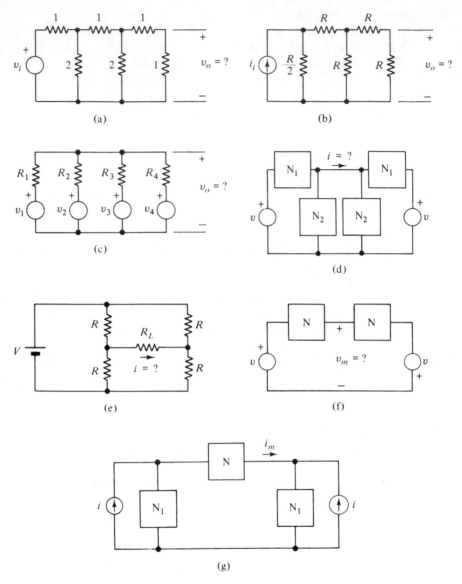

3-32. Find v_{ab} and v_a in Fig. 3-55.

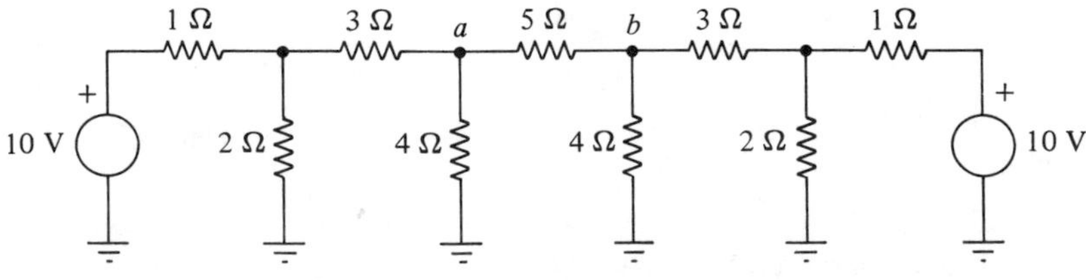

Fig. 3-55

3-33. In Fig. 3-56 obtain i_o and i_2.

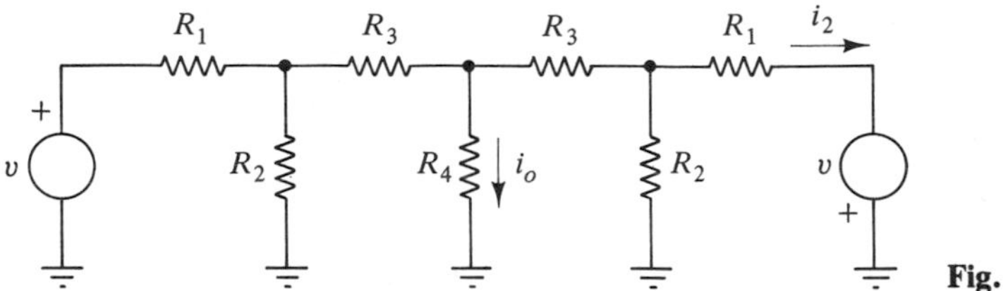

Fig. 3-56

3-34. The voltage across and the current through a device are sketched in Fig. 3-57. Sketch the instantaneous power vs. t.

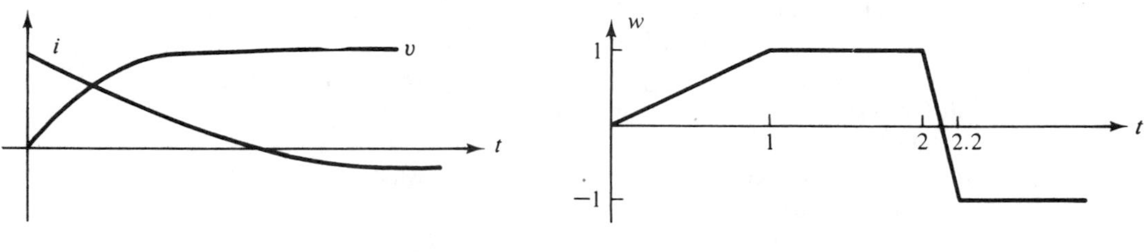

Fig. 3-57

Fig. 3-58

3-35. The energy delivered to a device is sketched in Fig. 3-58. Sketch the instantaneous power delivered to the device. Give values.

3-36. How many joules of heat are generated by a 1 kW toaster in 1 minute?

3-37. A 10 W, 12 Ω resistor is connected across 6 V. How much current would it draw?

3-38. What should be the power rating of a 1 kΩ resistor in a 100 V dc circuit?

3-39. (a) Two $\frac{1}{2}$ W, 25 Ω resistors are connected in series. How much current can be passed through each resistor without damaging it?

(b) Repeat (a) if the resistors are connected in parallel.

3-40. The two circuits shown in Fig. 3-59 have identical voltages ($I_{dc}R$) across them. Is there an advantage in using one circuit over the other?

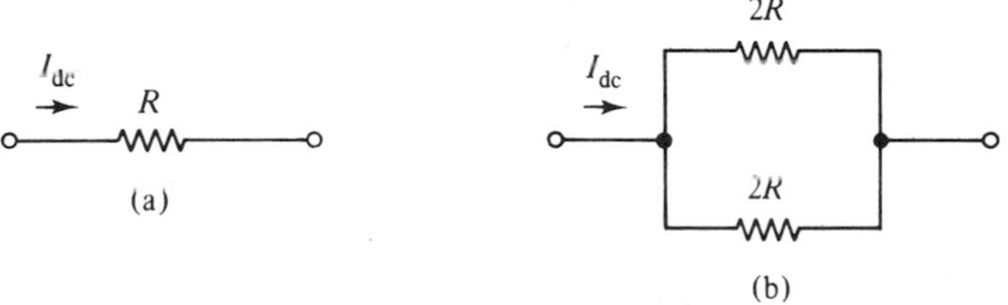

Fig. 3-59

3-41. The two circuits shown in Fig. 3-60 have the same terminal voltage. When will it be advantageous to use the circuit in (b) over (a)?

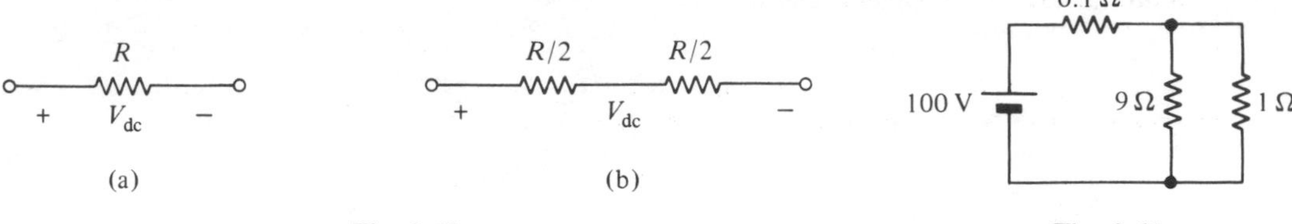

Fig. 3-60

Fig. 3-61

3-42. Calculate the wattage rating of all the resistors shown in Fig. 3-61.

3-43. What is the most power that can be taken out of a 12 V, 0.05 Ω source?

3-44. (a) An 8 Ω speaker is connected to a 16 Ω, 10 V peak sinusoidal source. What is the average power delivered to the speaker over one cycle of the sine wave?
(b) Repeat (a) if a 16 Ω speaker is used.

3-45. The load resistance is fixed at R_L. The source resistance R_s is variable. For what value of R_s is maximum power delivered to R_L by the voltage source?

3-46. A current source described by (i_s, R_s) supplies power to a load resistance R_L. Assuming that R_L can be varied, what is the maximum power that can be taken out of the current source?

3-47. In Fig. 3-62, assume that R can be adjusted. For what value of R is the power received by R maximum?

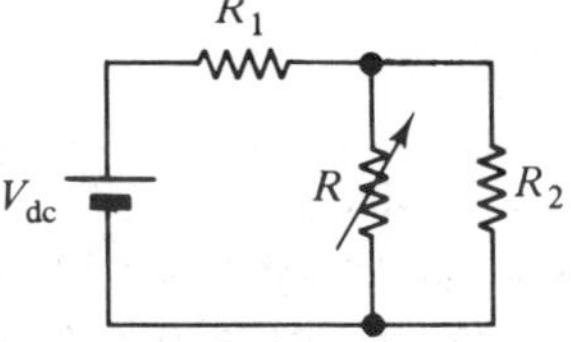

Fig. 3-62

3-48. Refer to Fig. 3-63.
(a) For what value of R_L is the power dissipated in R_L maximum?
(b) For what value of R_L is the power dissipated in R maximum?
(c) For what value of R_L is the power delivered by the current source maximum?

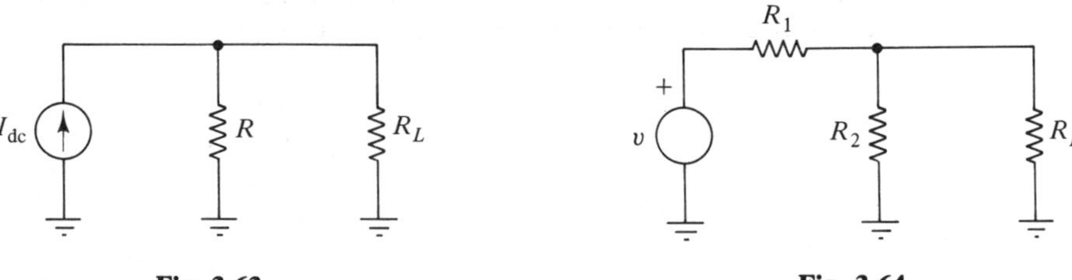

Fig. 3-63

Fig. 3-64

3-49. Refer to Fig. 3-64.
(a) Maximum power is to be delivered to R_L by adjusting R_1 alone. Find the appropriate value of R_1 and the power delivered to R_L.
(b) Repeat (a) if R_2 alone is the adjustable resistor.
(c) Repeat (a) if R_L alone is the adjustable resistor.

3-50. In Fig. 3-65 I_{dc}, R_1, and R_2 are fixed. Resistor R_3 is variable as shown.
(a) For what value of R_3 is the power dissipated in R_1 maximum?
(b) For what value of R_3 is the power dissipated in R_2 maximum?
(c) For what value of R_3 is the power dissipated in R_3 maximum?

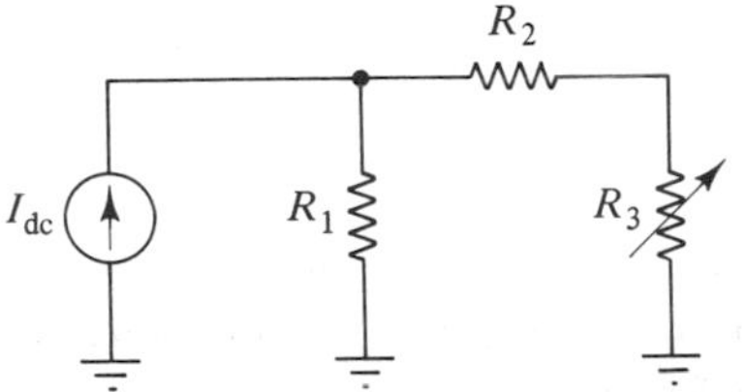

Fig. 3-65

3-51. What size C must be used to store 1 J of energy at 100 V?

3-52. In Fig. 3-66, the current source is turned on for 4 ms at 5 mA and then turned off. The initial voltage across the capacitor is 10 V as shown.
(a) Obtain the initial and final energies stored by the capacitor.
(b) Obtain the expression for power supplied by the current source as a function of time.
(c) How much energy does the current source supply altogether?

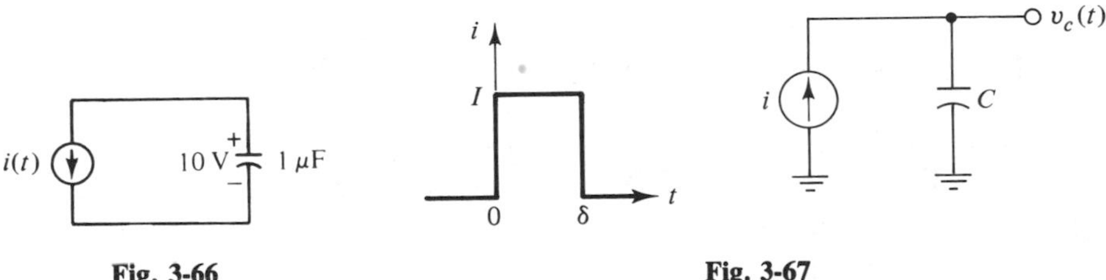

Fig. 3-66 **Fig. 3-67**

3-53. Refer to Fig. 3-67. Obtain the expression for $v_c(t)$, $p_c(t)$, and $\omega_c(t)$ and sketch them vs. t.

3-54. Repeat Prob. 3-53 if the capacitor has an initial voltage of $-\gamma$, that is, $v_c(0) = -\gamma$.

3-55. For the circuit shown in Fig. 3-68, sketch the power delivered by the current source as a function of time. Give values.

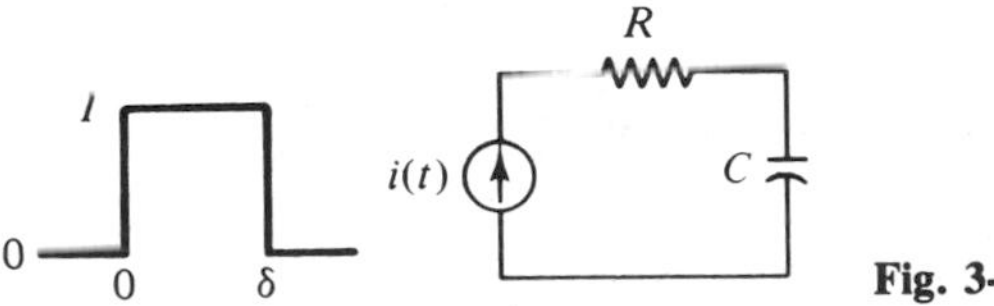

Fig. 3-68

3-56. If all the energy stored in a capacitor is transferred without loss to an inductor, what will the current in the inductor be? Express this current in terms of the voltage across the capacitor.

3-57. In the circuit of Fig. 3-69, how much energy is stored in the inductor at $t = 2$ seconds?

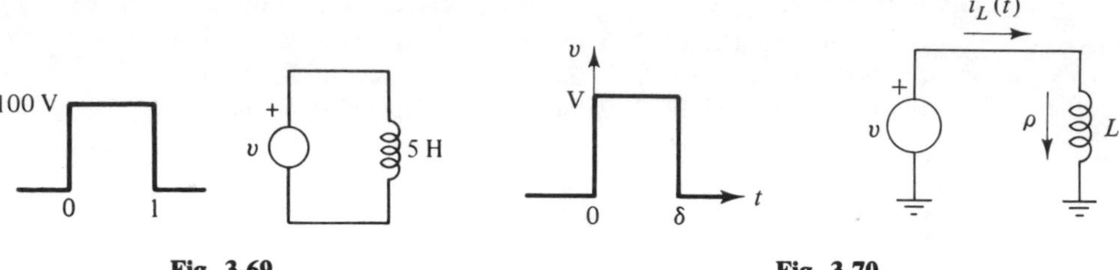

Fig. 3-69 **Fig. 3-70**

3-58. Refer to Fig. 3-70. Sketch $i_L(t)$, $p_L(t)$, and $\omega_L(t)$ vs. t.

3-59. For the circuit shown in Fig. 3-71, calculate the power and energy supplied by the voltage source as a function of time.

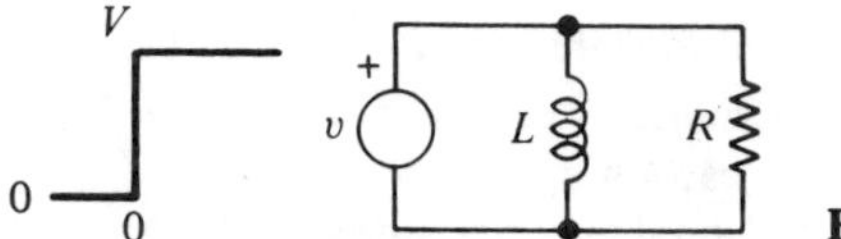

Fig. 3-71

3-60. For the circuits shown in Fig. 3-72, obtain the power delivered by each source.

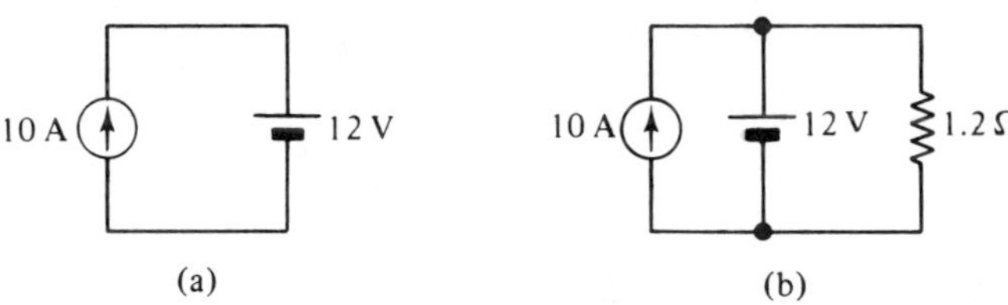

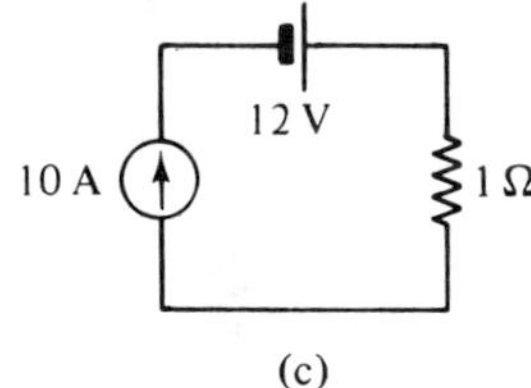

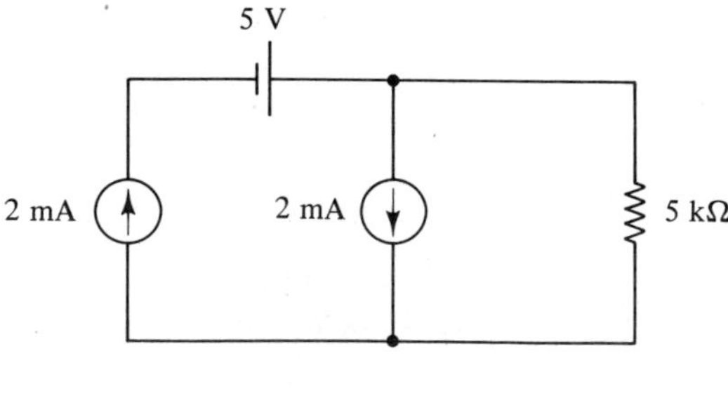

Fig. 3-72

3-61. A sinusoidal current given by $I_m \sin \omega t$ is applied to an inductor.

(a) Sketch the voltage across, the current through, and the instantaneous power received by the inductor.

(b) What is the average power supplied to the inductor over a period of $2\pi/\omega$ seconds?

(c) How much energy is stored by the inductor at the end of $2\pi/\omega$ seconds?

3-62. Refer to Fig. 3-73.

(a) Obtain the power delivered by each source.

(b) What does the sum of the powers obtained in (a) represent?

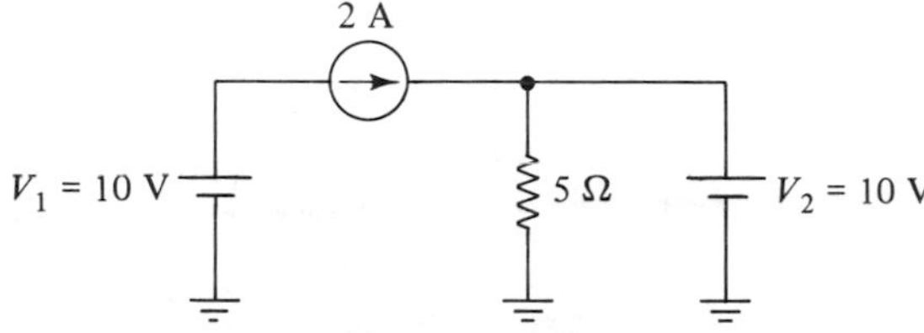

Fig. 3-73

3-63. Two identical black boxes are shown in Fig. 3-74. One contains a 1 V voltage source in series with a 1 Ω resistor. The other contains a 1 A current source in parallel with a 1 Ω resistor. By looking at a box you cannot tell which circuit it contains. You are not allowed to open the boxes, but the two output terminals are available for testing. Can you determine what is in each box by external experimentation?

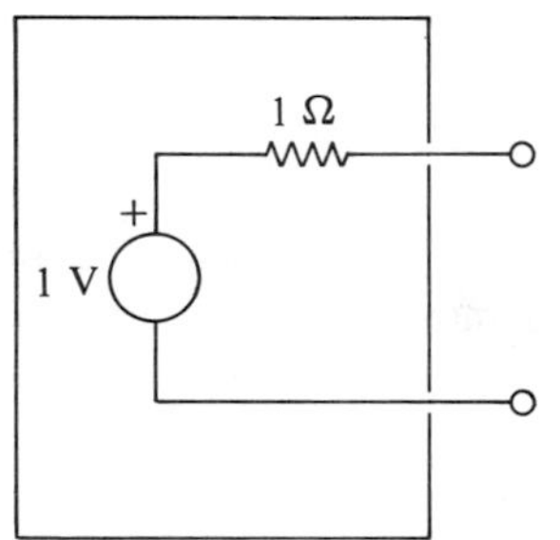

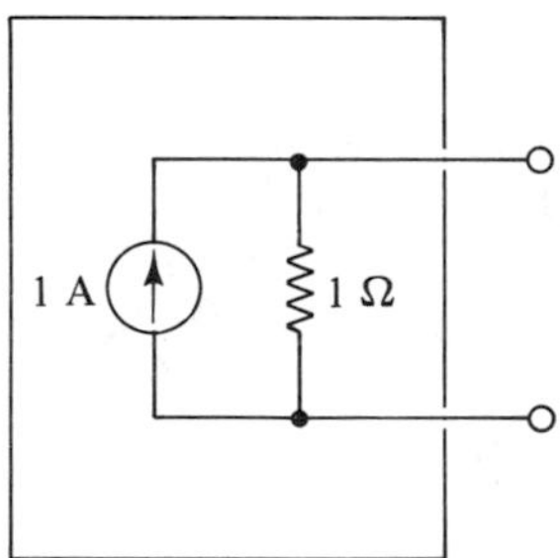

Fig. 3-74

CHAPTER 4

MESH AND NODE EQUATIONS

The techniques presented in preceding chapters allow currents and voltages in simple circuits to be determined easily. As circuit complexity increases, however, a systematic approach for solving for the i and v variables becomes necessary. Two such approaches are discussed here. One deals with the writing of mesh equations that are then solved for the mesh currents. The other deals with the writing of node equations that are then solved for the node voltages.

4-1 MESH EQUATIONS

Most networks can be drawn so that the elements are arranged to form meshes. This situation is shown in Fig. 4-1(a). The meshes are designated by drawing a clockwise arrow within each mesh. These arrows also define the mesh currents i_1, i_2, and i_3 as shown.

The relationship between mesh currents and currents through the branches of a network is governed by the convention set forth in Fig. 4-1(b). Thus when mesh currents i_c and i_d are acting on N (which could be a resistor or a more complicated network with two terminals), the current downward through N is $(i_c - i_d)$. Or if preferred, the current can be directed up and be designated $(i_d - i_c)$. Note that mesh current i_c goes down through N and that mesh current i_d goes up through N.

Returning to Fig. 4-1(a), we see that the currents through the various networks or network elements are as shown in Table 4-1. There is only *one* current through

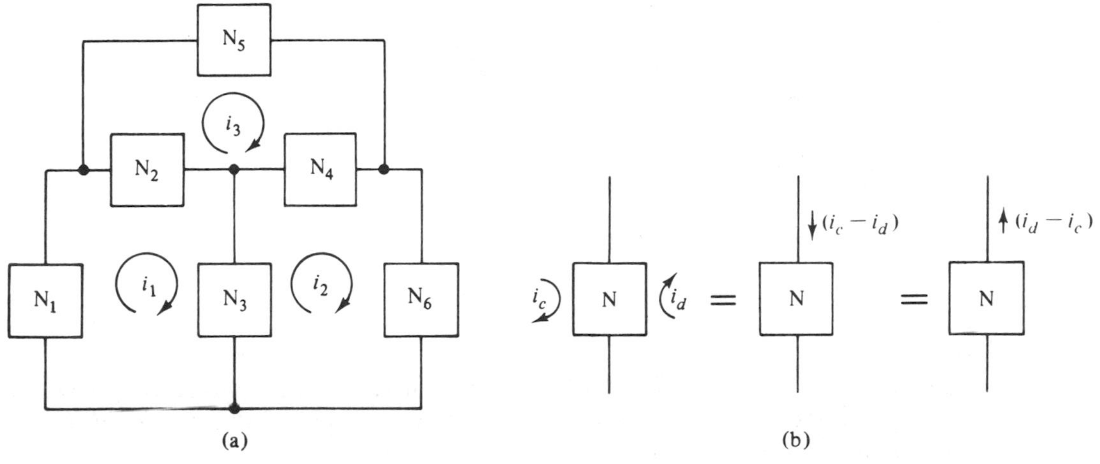

Fig. 4-1

TABLE 4-1

Network	Current	Direction
N_1	i_1	Up
N_2	$i_1 - i_3$	To the right
N_3	$i_1 - i_2$	Down
N_4	$i_2 - i_3$	To the right
N_5	i_3	To the right
N_6	i_2	Down

each element, *not two*. It is only when we choose to designate this current as being the difference of two mesh currents that we use the decomposition into two component parts.

Alternatively, the meshes are called *loops,* and currents i_1, i_2, and i_3 are called *loop currents*. It should also be recognized that the network of Fig. 4-1(a) has other loops than those designated 1, 2, and 3. For instance, $N_1N_5N_6$ also forms a loop. So does $N_2N_5N_6N_3$ or $N_1N_5N_4N_3$. However, when a network is drawn in laid-out fashion as in Fig. 4-1(a), loops 1, 2, and 3 stand out and are identical with meshes 1, 2, and 3.

According to *Kirchhoff's Voltage Law, the sum of voltages around any loop is zero*. To see how these voltages are summed in a systematic way, a typical mesh (loop) consisting of resistors *a*, *b*, *c*, and *d* is shown in Fig. 4-2. The current in this mesh is designated i_2. The currents in the four adjacent meshes are designated i_1, i_3, i_4, and i_5. All mesh currents are arbitrarily taken in a clockwise sense. As a result, the current in each resistor is the difference of the two mesh currents appearing on either side of the resistor. So the current in resistor R_b is $(i_2 - i_3)$, directed to the right; the current through resistor R_d is $(i_2 - i_4)$, directed to left; and so on. Next, we

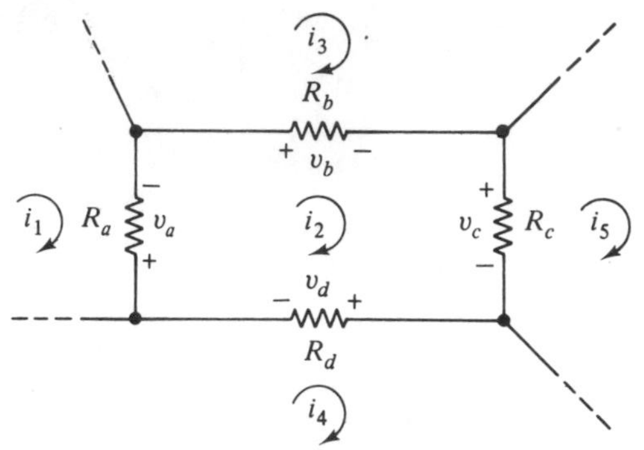

Fig. 4-2

go clockwise around mesh 2 (in the same sense as i_2) and systematically label all voltages in the $+-$ sense as shown. Then when we apply Kirchhoff's Voltage Law around this mesh, we have

$$v_a + v_b + v_c + v_d = 0 \tag{4-1}$$

These voltages can be expressed in terms of mesh currents by using Ohm's Law.

$$v_a = (i_2 - i_1)R_a \tag{4-2a}$$

$$v_b = (i_2 - i_3)R_b \tag{4-2b}$$

$$v_c = (i_2 - i_5)R_c \tag{4-2c}$$

$$v_d = (i_2 - i_4)R_d \tag{4-2d}$$

Note that in each of these voltage expressions the current i_2 appears first. This result follows directly from the way voltages are labeled around the mesh (to conform with the direction of i_2). Substituting Eq. (4-2) into Eq. (4-1), we find

$$(i_2 - i_1)R_a + (i_2 - i_3)R_b + (i_2 - i_5)R_c + (i_2 - i_4)R_d = 0 \tag{4-3}$$

We can reorder Eq. (4-3) so that all terms involving i_1 appear first; next come terms involving i_2, then i_3, and so forth.

$$-i_1R_a + i_2(R_a + R_b + R_c + R_d) - i_3R_b - i_4R_d - i_5R_c = 0 \tag{4-4}$$

This equation has a definite and predictable order to it. Indeed, it could have been written directly from inspection of Fig. 4-2. Certainly i_2 flows through all four resistors; and if it were acting alone, it would have produced a voltage represented by $i_2(R_a + R_b + R_c + R_d)$ in Eq. (4-4). The current i_1 flows only through R_a, and its sense is opposite to that of i_2; thus it would produce a voltage $-i_1R_a$, which represents the first term in Eq. (4-4). Similarly, i_3, which is in opposition to i_2 and flows only through R_b as far as mesh 2 is concerned, produces a voltage of $-i_3R_b$—hence the third term in Eq. (4-4). The remaining two terms are due to i_4 flowing in opposition to i_2 in R_d and i_5 flowing in opposition to i_2 in R_c. As a result of these explanations, we may reinterpret Eq. (4-4) as being a summation (superposition) of terms produced by the current i_2 (the self terms) and the currents in adjacent meshes (the mutual terms). The self terms are taken as positive, whereas all mutual terms are negative.

As another example, consider mesh 3 in Fig. 4-3. The currents in adjacent meshes are labeled i_1, i_2, and i_4. The voltages around mesh 3 are labeled v_L, v_R, and v_C. Their senses are taken to conform with the sense of i_3; that is, the polarities are uniformly marked +− as we go around the mesh in the clockwise sense. By Kirchhoff's Voltage Law applied to mesh 3, we have

$$v_L + v_R + v_C = 0 \tag{4-5}$$

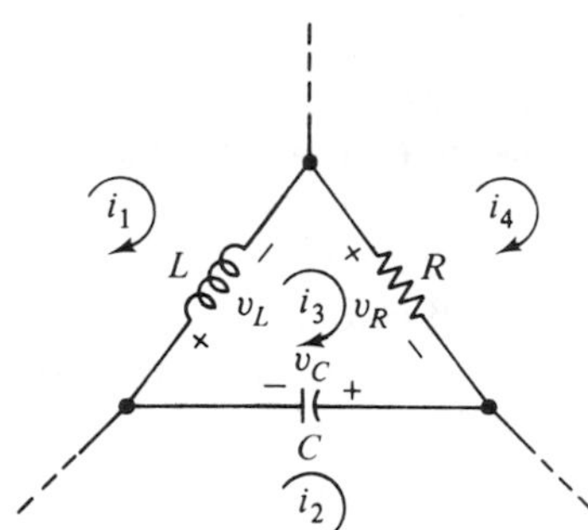

Fig. 4-3

The element-defining equations relate the voltage across an element to the current through the element. Thus

$$v_L = L\frac{d}{dt}(i_3 - i_1) \tag{4-6a}$$

$$v_R = R(i_3 - i_4) \tag{4-6b}$$

$$v_C = \frac{1}{C}\int (i_3 - i_2)\, dt \tag{4-6c}$$

Again, note that in these expressions i_3 occurs first because we are summing the voltages around *mesh 3*.

When the expressions given by Eq. (4-6) are substituted in Eq. (4-5), we obtain

$$L\frac{d}{dt}(i_3 - i_1) + R(i_3 - i_4) + \frac{1}{C}\int (i_3 - i_2)\, dt = 0 \tag{4-7}$$

which can be rearranged so that terms involving i_1 appear first, then terms involving i_2, and so on.

$$-L\frac{di_1}{dt} - \frac{1}{C}\int i_2\, dt + L\frac{di_3}{dt} + i_3R + \frac{1}{C}\int i_3\, dt - i_4R = 0 \tag{4-8}$$

This equation could have been written directly from inspection of Fig. 4-3 as follows. Keeping in mind that we are writing the sum of voltages around *mesh 3*, we write

$$-L\frac{di_1}{dt} \quad \text{as the contribution of } i_1 \text{ to mesh 3}$$

$$-\frac{1}{C}\int i_2\,dt \quad \text{as the contribution of } i_2 \text{ to mesh 3}$$

$$\left(L\frac{di_3}{dt} + i_3R + \frac{1}{C}\int i_3\,dt\right) \quad \text{as the contribution of } i_3 \text{ to mesh 3}$$

$$-Ri_4 \quad \text{as the contribution of } i_4 \text{ to mesh 3}$$

Terms containing i_1, i_2, and i_4 are due to the mutual interaction between mesh 3 and the other meshes. The term containing i_3 is the self term or the voltage caused in mesh 3 by current i_3. To make the writing of these terms as mechanical a procedure as possible, they are taken in the order of the subscripts; that is, terms with i_1 are taken first, terms with i_2 are considered next, and so on. The mutual terms are given a negative sign, the self terms a positive one.

Consider elements L and R appearing between meshes 1 and 2 in Fig. 4-4. If we were to sum the voltages around mesh 1, the contribution from the two elements is

$$v_{1L} + v_{1R} = L\frac{d}{dt}(i_1 - i_2) + (i_1 - i_2)R \tag{4-9}$$

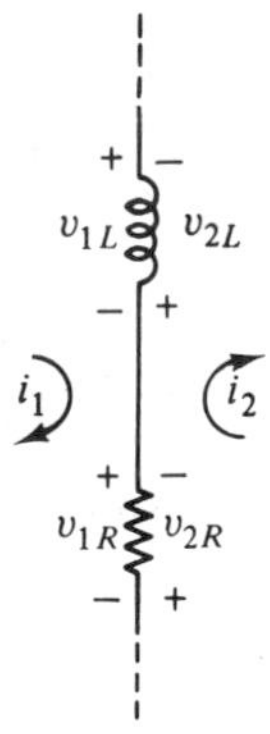

Fig. 4-4

On the other hand, summing the voltages around mesh 2 would result in

$$v_{2R} + v_{2L} = (i_2 - i_1)R + L\frac{d}{dt}(i_2 - i_1) \tag{4-10}$$

In Eq. (4-9) i_1 appears first because we directed our attention to the writing of the equation for mesh 1. In Eq. (4-10) i_2 appears first because we directed our attention to the writing of the equation for mesh 2. Equation (4-9) is the negative of Eq. (4-10). This result occurs because, in considering mesh 1, we sum the voltages from top to bottom, whereas in mesh 2 we sum them from bottom to top with their polarities taken in the opposite sense.

We are now ready to formulate a general procedure for writing a system of equations based on the mesh equations.

1. Draw the network so that the meshes are exposed; that is, the circuit diagram contains no intersecting wires. In most networks it is possible to lay out the network diagram with all its meshes bared.
2. In each mesh, draw clockwise arrows to designate the mesh currents. Sum the voltages around each mesh and set the result equal to zero. This step is equivalent to applying Kirchhoff's Voltage Law around each mesh. If there are n meshes altogether, there are n unknown mesh currents; therefore n equations (one for each mesh) are written. These equations are *independent*.
3. Solve simultaneously the resulting n equations for the *n unknown mesh currents*. The currents through the individual elements can be found by taking the difference between the two adjacent mesh currents. The voltages across the elements can be obtained by using the appropriate element-defining equations.

So in solving for the unknown voltages and currents in a network by the mesh-equations method, *we first solve for the mesh currents*. Then we can easily obtain the element currents and voltages.

Example 4-1

(a) Write the mesh equations for the circuit shown in Fig. 4-5.
(b) Solve for the mesh currents.
(c) Obtain the voltage across R_2 and the output voltage.

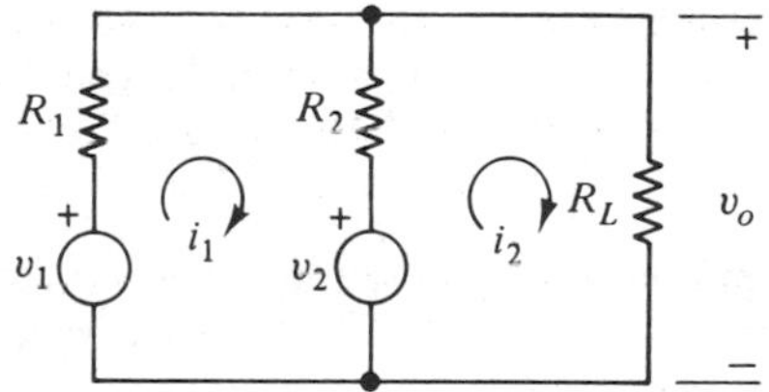

Fig. 4-5

Solution

(a) There are two meshes in the network, and so there are only two mesh currents. They are designated by i_1 and i_2 as shown. Summing the voltages around the first mesh (applying Kirchhoff's Voltage Law), we obtain

$$i_1R_1 + (i_1 - i_2)R_2 = v_1 - v_2 \tag{4-11}$$

Note that we have placed the sources on the right-hand side of the equation. Source v_1, if it were to act alone, would produce current i_1 in the sense shown; hence v_1 is positive on the right-hand side. Source v_2, if it were to act alone, would produce current i_1 in the opposite sense; hence v_2 is negative on the right-hand side. Such arguments, which have their basis in Kirchhoff's laws, help to form a physical picture of what is occurring in the network.

Summing the voltages around the second mesh, we obtain

$$(i_2 - i_1)R_2 + i_2R_L = v_2 \tag{4-12}$$

On the right-hand side, v_2 appears as positive, for if it were to act alone, it would have caused i_2 to flow in the sense shown.

Next, we reorder Eqs. (4-11) and (4-12) so that i_1 terms appear first and i_2 terms next.

$$\begin{aligned} i_1(R_1 + R_2) - i_2R_2 &= v_1 - v_2 \\ -i_1R_2 + i_2(R_2 + R_L) &= v_2 \end{aligned} \tag{4-13}$$

Of course, we could have written this set of equations directly by inspection of Fig. 4-5 by noting the self and mutual terms (with negative signs) and by checking the effect of the individual sources on the mesh currents.

(b) The set of equations given by Eq. (4-13) can be solved for i_1 and i_2 by using *Cramer's rule*.* The determinant is

$$\Delta = \begin{vmatrix} R_1 + R_2 & -R_2 \\ -R_2 & R_2 + R_L \end{vmatrix}$$

Note that the terms along the principal diagonal (shown by dashed line from top left to bottom right) are positive and represent, respectively, the sum of resistances in meshes 1 and 2—that is, $(R_1 + R_2)$ and $(R_2 + R_L)$. On the other hand, the terms along the other diagonal are negative and equal; they represent the mutual effects between meshes 1 and 2 caused by the presence of R_2. The value of the determinant is

$$\Delta = (R_1 + R_2)(R_2 + R_L) - (-R_2)(-R_2) = R_1R_2 + R_1R_L + R_2R_L$$

Each term in the determinant is positive. Indeed, such is always the case when the sources exciting the network are independent. This fact can be used as a check against mistakes in the evaluation of determinants. When all the cancelations are done, no negative term should be left in the expression for the determinant.

To obtain i_1, we form a new determinant by replacing the first column of Δ with the sources in the network as arranged on the right-hand side of Eq. (4-13) and evaluate the resulting determinant.

Sources

$$\Delta_1 = \begin{vmatrix} v_1 - v_2 & -R_2 \\ v_2 & R_2 + R_L \end{vmatrix} = (v_1 - v_2)(R_2 + R_L) - v_2(-R_2)$$

$$= v_1(R_2 + R_L) - v_2R_L$$

Similarly, to obtain i_2, we replace the second column of Δ with the sources obtained from Eq. (4-13) and evaluate the resulting determinant.

Sources

$$\Delta_2 = \begin{vmatrix} R_1 + R_2 & v_1 - v_2 \\ -R_2 & v_2 \end{vmatrix} = v_2(R_1 + R_2) - (v_1 - v_2)(-R_2)$$

$$= v_1R_2 + v_2R_1$$

*A brief review of determinants is presented in Appendix 1.

Then i_1 and i_2 are given by

$$i_1 = \frac{\Delta_1}{\Delta} = \frac{v_1(R_2 + R_L) - v_2 R_L}{R_1 R_2 + R_1 R_L + R_2 R_L} \quad \text{Ans.}$$

$$i_2 = \frac{\Delta_2}{\Delta} = \frac{v_1 R_2 + v_2 R_1}{R_1 R_2 + R_1 R_L + R_2 R_L} \quad \text{Ans.}$$

(c) By inspection of Fig. 4-5, we see that the voltage across R_2 is given by

$$v_{R2} = (i_1 - i_2)R_2 = \left[\frac{v_1 R_L - v_2(R_1 + R_L)}{R_1 R_2 + R_1 R_L + R_2 R_L}\right] R_2 \quad \text{Ans.}$$

The output voltage is given by

$$v_o = i_2 R_L = \frac{(v_1 R_2 + v_2 R_1)R_L}{R_1 R_2 + R_1 R_L + R_2 R_L} \quad \text{Ans.}$$

To obtain a different interpretation of this result, we can rearrange the expression for v_o so that R_L appears by itself in the denominator [divide numerator and denominator by $(R_1 + R_2)$].

$$v_o = \left(\frac{v_1 R_2 + v_2 R_1}{R_1 + R_2}\right) R_L \Big/ \left(\frac{R_1 R_2}{R_1 + R_2} + R_L\right) = \frac{v_{eq} R_L}{R_{eq} + R_L} \tag{4-14}$$

where $$v_{eq} = \frac{v_1 R_2 + v_2 R_1}{R_1 + R_2}, \quad R_{eq} = \frac{R_1 R_2}{R_1 + R_2}$$

Referring to Fig. 4-5, we see that v_{eq} represents the output voltage if R_L were infinite and that R_{eq} represents the equivalent resistance facing R_L with $v_1 = v_2 = 0$. In other words, the expressions for v_{eq} and R_{eq} represent the Thévenin equivalent of the circuit appearing to the left of R_L. This equivalent circuit, when combined with R_L, allows us to calculate v_o as given by Eq. (4-14). In effect, we are saying that in this problem we could have obtained v_o much more easily by making use of the Thévenin equivalent circuit instead of solving the mesh equations. Nonetheless, the aim of this example is to demonstrate the use of the mesh-equations method in solving network problems.

Example 4.2

Refer to Fig. 4-6.

(a) What is the resistance seen by the 10 V source?

(b) What is the output voltage?

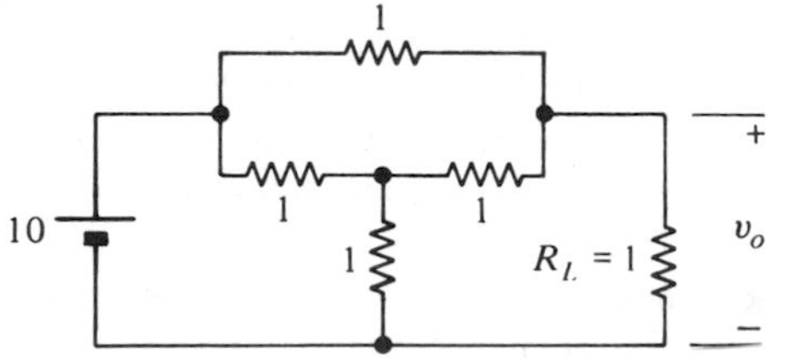

Fig. 4-6

Solution.

(a) In this circuit the resistance seen by the voltage source cannot be obtained easily by using the rules for series and parallel connection of resistances because no single resistor is in series or parallel with any other resistor. Therefore we must calculate the current delivered by the battery in order to determine the equivalent resistance seen by the battery. To obtain this current, we redraw Fig. 4-6 as in Fig. 4-7, indicating the three mesh currents and the equivalent resistance R_{in} that we wish to determine. This resistance is also called the *input resistance* of the network. We then write three equations, one for each mesh, indicating the summation of voltages around that mesh.

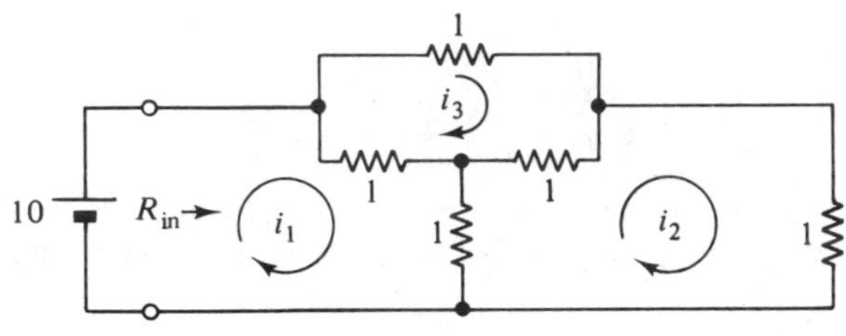

Fig. 4-7

$$(i_1 - i_3) \times 1 + (i_1 - i_2) \times 1 = 10 \qquad \text{(mesh 1)}$$

$$(i_2 - i_1) \times 1 + (i_2 - i_3) \times 1 + i_2 \times 1 = 0 \qquad \text{(mesh 2)}$$

$$(i_3 - i_1) \times 1 + (i_3 - i_2) \times 1 + i_3 \times 1 = 0 \qquad \text{(mesh 3)}$$

These equations are then ordered as

$$\begin{aligned} 2i_1 - i_2 - i_3 &= 10 \\ -i_1 + 3i_2 - i_3 &= 0 \\ -i_1 - i_2 + 3i_3 &= 0 \end{aligned} \qquad (4\text{-}15)$$

The determinant is

$$\Delta = \begin{vmatrix} 2 & -1 & -1 \\ -1 & 3 & -1 \\ -1 & -1 & 3 \end{vmatrix} = \begin{vmatrix} a_{11} & a_{12} & a_{13} \\ a_{21} & a_{22} & a_{23} \\ a_{31} & a_{32} & a_{33} \end{vmatrix}$$

Here we recognize that it is not actually necessary to write the mesh equations and reorder them in order to obtain the determinant. We could write the determinant directly by inspection of the circuit and by remembering two simple rules.

1. The terms along the principal diagonal (shown dashed) are positive and represent the sum of resistances around each mesh. Thus a_{11} is the sum of resistances in mesh 1, which is $1 + 1 = 2$; a_{22} is the sum of resistances in mesh 2, which is $1 + 1 + 1 = 3$; and a_{33} is the sum of resistances in mesh 3, which is $1 + 1 + 1 = 3$.
2. The terms off the principal diagonal are negative and represent the sum of resistances that are mutual to adjacement meshes. Thus

$$a_{12} = -(\text{sum of resistances between meshes 1 and 2}) = -1$$

$$a_{13} = -(\text{sum of resistances between meshes 1 and 3}) = -1$$

$$a_{23} = -(\text{sum of resistances between meshes 2 and 3}) = -1$$

Only half the off-diagonal terms need be evaluated because what is common to meshes i and j is also common to meshes j and i. Stated in equation form,

$$a_{ij} = a_{ji}$$

Therefore in order to describe the determinant, it is sufficient to obtain the terms along the principal diagonal and the terms above this diagonal. (The terms below the diagonal are mirror images of the terms above the diagonal). *Note that the determinant does not contain information about sources. It represents the network with all sources dead.*

We now evaluate the determinant

$$\Delta = 2\begin{vmatrix} 3 & -1 \\ -1 & 3 \end{vmatrix} - (-1)\begin{vmatrix} -1 & -1 \\ -1 & 3 \end{vmatrix} + (-1)\begin{vmatrix} -1 & 3 \\ -1 & -1 \end{vmatrix}$$

$$= 2(9 - 1) + (-3 - 1) - (1 + 3) = 16 - 4 - 4 = 8$$

To obtain i_1, we form a new determinant by crossing out the first column of the determinant and substituting instead the sources appearing in each mesh. We start with sources acting in the clockwise sense in mesh 1 (a_{11} position) and then move to meshes 2 and 3 (a_{21} and a_{31} positions). In this case, only the first mesh contains a source; the others have no sources.

$$\Delta_1 = \begin{vmatrix} 10 & -1 & -1 \\ 0 & 3 & -1 \\ 0 & -1 & 3 \end{vmatrix} = 10\begin{vmatrix} 3 & -1 \\ -1 & 3 \end{vmatrix} = 10(9 - 1) = 80$$

Hence

$$i_1 = \frac{\Delta_1}{\Delta} = \frac{80}{8} = 10$$

The 10 V source delivers 10 A of current. So the source sees a resistance of

$$R_{in} = \frac{10\ \text{V}}{10\ \text{A}} = 1\ \Omega \quad \text{Ans.}$$

To increase our dexterity in solving circuit problems, let us determine i_1 by another method. We start out by splitting the 10 V battery into two 10 V batteries in parallel as shown in Fig. 4-8(a). Thus the burden of supplying the current i_1 is now shared by the two batteries. Note that

$$i_1 = i_{11} + i_{12}$$

We then redraw Fig. 4-7 as in Fig. 4-8(b). Since the voltage between a and b is $10 - 10 = 0$, there is no current flow in the interconnecting wire. Thus this connection can be broken and the circuit redrawn as in Fig. 4-8(c). In the next step we

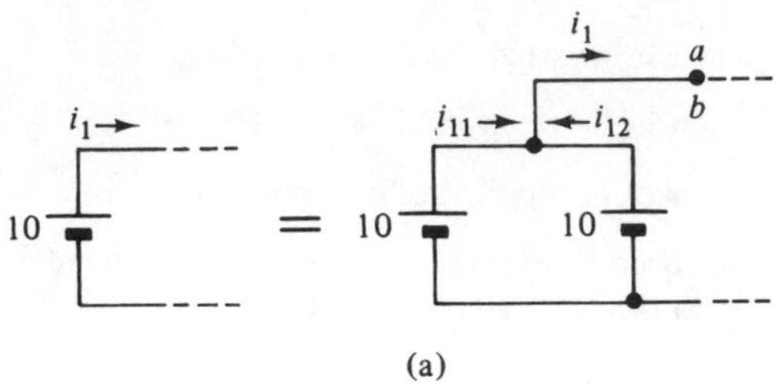
i_1
a
b
i_1
i_{11}
i_{12}
10
=
10
10

(a)

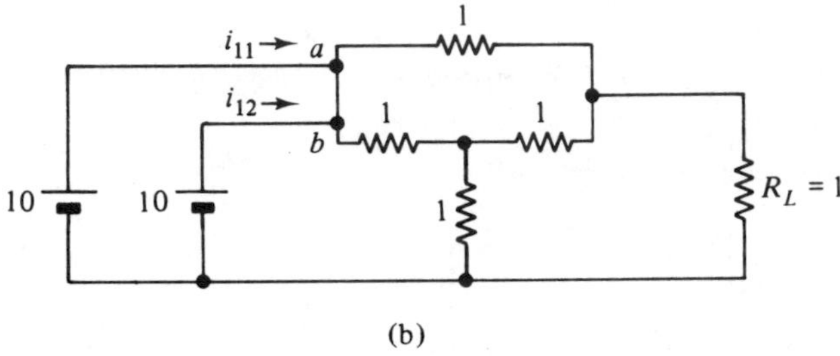
1
i_{11}
a
i_{12}
1
1
b
10
10
1
$R_L = 1$

(b)

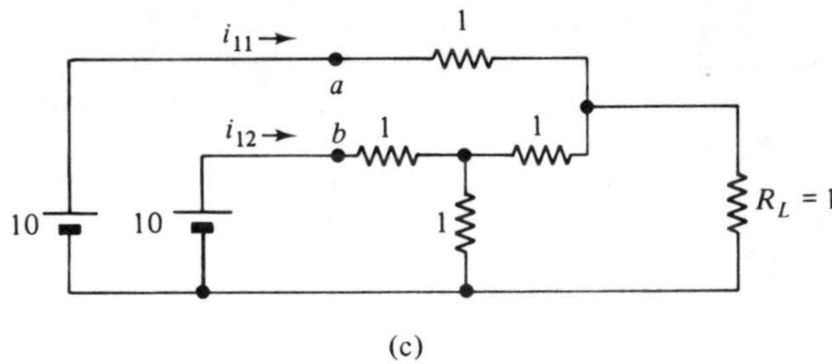
1
i_{11}
a
i_{12}
b
1
1
10
10
1
$R_L = 1$

(c)

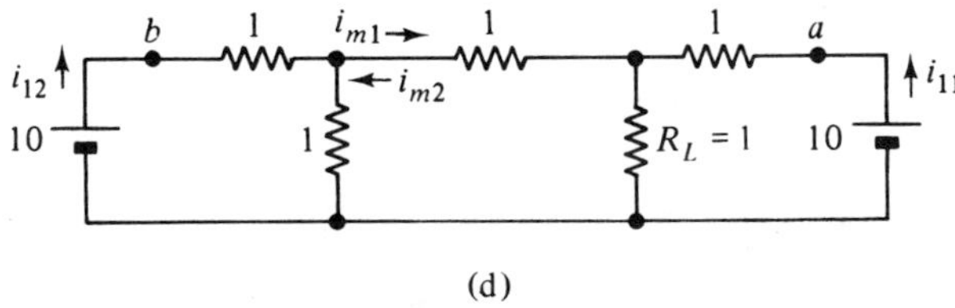
b
1
i_{m1}
1
1
a
i_{12}
i_{m2}
i_{11}
10
1
$R_L = 1$
10

(d)

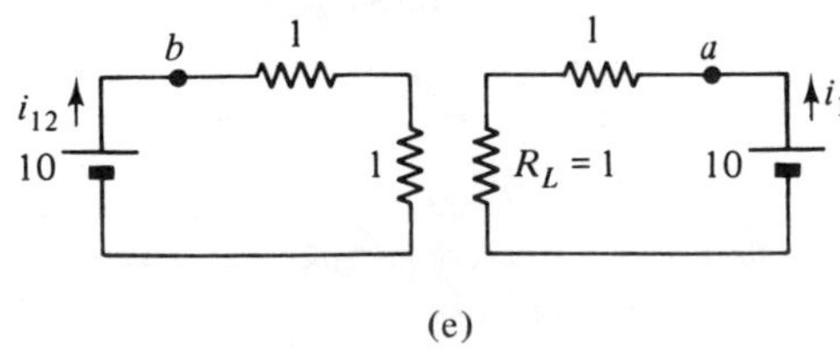
b
1
1
a
i_{12}
i_{11}
10
1
$R_L = 1$
10

(e)

Fig. 4-8

redraw the circuit by rearranging the layout as shown in Fig. 4-8(d). In this form the symmetry of the circuit stands out. As a result, we immediately recognize that the current in the middle resistor, and hence the current in the middle wire, is zero. [To remove any doubt about this situation, think in terms of superposition. Turn the left-hand source on and the right-hand source off. The current in the middle resistor is i_{m1}. Then turn the right-hand source on and the left-hand source off. The current in the middle resistor is i_{m2}. By superposition, the current in the middle resistor is $(i_{m1} - i_{m2})$. Because of symmetry, $i_{m1} = i_{m2}$. So the current in the middle is zero.] Consequently, the two middle wires can be cut without affecting any of the currents and voltages in the circuit. The result is Fig. 4-8(e), from which we can readily determine i_{11} and i_{12}.

$$i_{11} = i_{12} = \frac{10}{2} = 5$$

It follows that

$$i_1 = i_{11} + i_{12} = 10$$

Although we did redraw the circuit many times before obtaining the final answer, with a little practice we could have omitted many of the steps and obtained the result almost by inspection. In general, when circuits possess symmetry, it is possible to simplify analysis considerably.

There is even a faster way of solving this problem if we recognize that the circuit of Fig. 4-6 is a balanced bridge circuit. Redrawing it as in Fig. 4-9 will make the bridge structure stand out. Since the bridge is balanced, the voltage across the middle 1 Ω resistor is zero. So is the current through it. We can either open or short the middle resistor without affecting any current or voltage in the entire circuit. In Fig. 4-9(b), the middle resistor is taken out (there is no current through it), and in Fig. 4-9(c), it is shorted (there is no voltage across it). By inspection of either circuit, we see that $R_{in} = 1\ \Omega$.

(b) To determine the output voltage, we need to determine i_2. Since we have already obtained the determinant, we can easily solve for i_2. We merely replace the second column of the determinant with the right-hand side of Eq. (4-15) to obtain Δ_2.

$$\Delta_2 = \begin{vmatrix} 2 & 10 & -1 \\ -1 & 0 & -1 \\ -1 & 0 & 3 \end{vmatrix} = -10\begin{vmatrix} -1 & -1 \\ -1 & 3 \end{vmatrix} = -10(-3 - 1) = 40$$

Therefore

$$i_2 = \frac{\Delta_2}{\Delta} = \frac{40}{8} = 5$$

$$v_o = i_2 \times 1 = 5\ \text{V} \quad \text{Ans.}$$

Once again it is instructive to obtain this answer by some other method. The decomposition of the network into simpler forms as developed in Fig. 4-8 provides a ready solution. The voltage that we are trying to find is the voltage across R_L. From Fig. 4-8(e) we see that

$$v_o = 10\left(\frac{R_L}{1 + R_L}\right) = 5\ \text{V} \quad \text{Ans.}$$

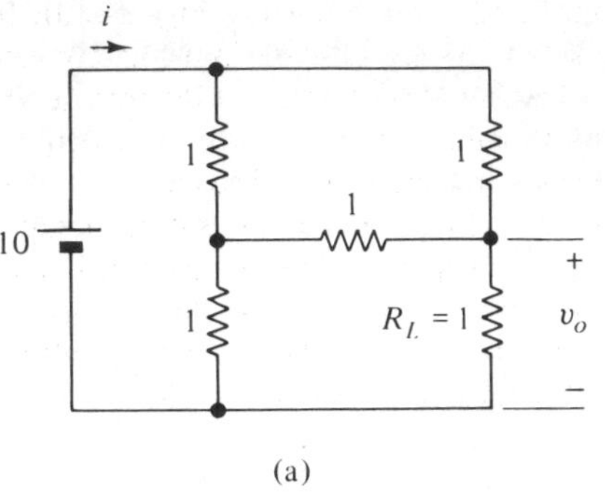

(a)

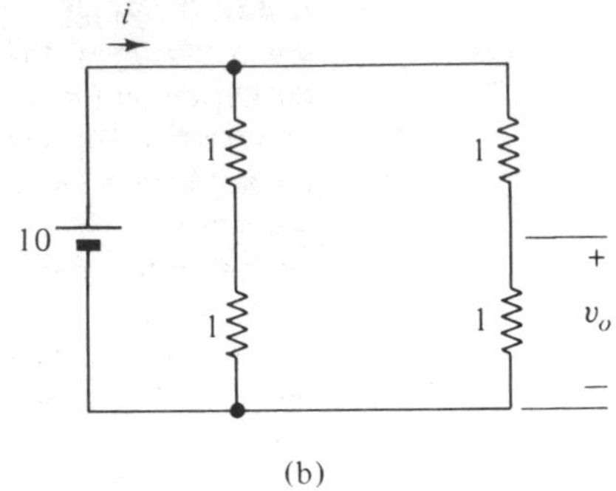

(b)

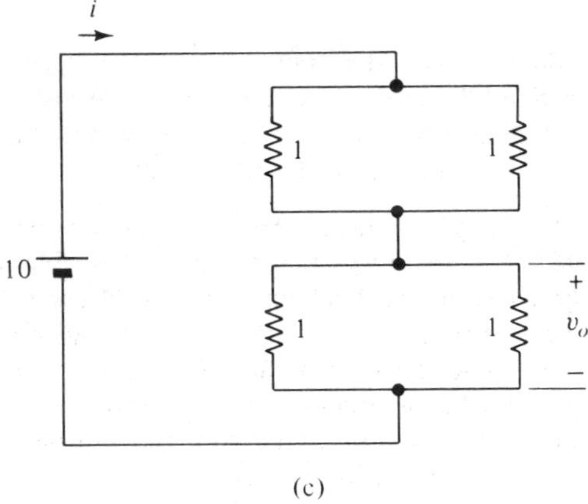

(c)

Fig. 4-9

This voltage can also be easily obtained from the simplified bridge structures shown in Fig. 4-9(b) or (c).

Example 4-3

Using the mesh-analysis method, obtain v_o for the circuit of Fig. 4-10.

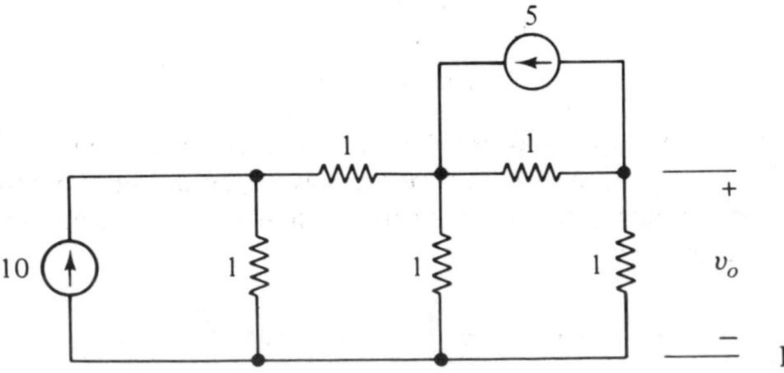

Fig. 4-10

Solution

Method 1 Draw the four mesh currents as in Fig. 4-11. Normally these four currents are the unknowns, and four equations are needed to solve for their values. However, by inspection of Fig. 4-11, we immediately see the values of two of the unknowns.

$$i_1 = 10, \qquad i_4 = -5$$

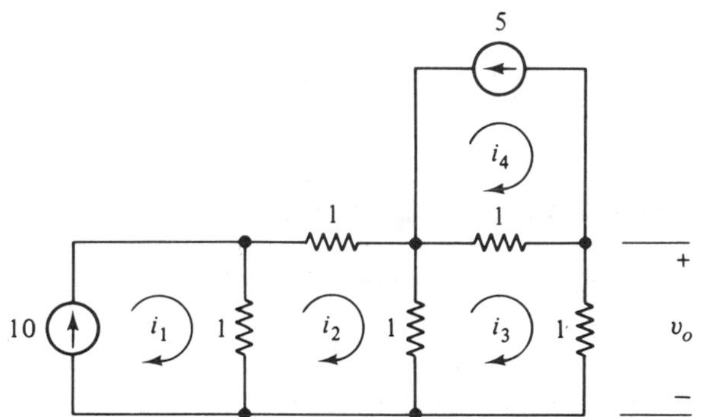

Fig. 4-11

Thus only two unknowns are left—i_2 and i_3. To obtain their values, we must write two independent equations: one for mesh 2 and another for mesh 3.

$$(i_2 - 10) \times 1 + i_2 \times 1 + (i_2 - i_3) \times 1 = 0$$

$$(i_3 - i_2) \times 1 + (i_3 + 5) \times 1 + i_3 \times 1 = 0$$

When rearranged, this set becomes

$$3i_2 - i_3 = 10, \qquad -i_2 + 3i_3 = -5$$

Since we are asked to find v_o, we are interested only in the solution for i_3.

$$i_3 = \frac{\begin{vmatrix} 3 & 10 \\ -1 & -5 \end{vmatrix}}{\begin{vmatrix} 3 & -1 \\ -1 & 3 \end{vmatrix}} = \frac{-15 + 10}{9 - 1} = -\frac{5}{8}$$

Thus

$$v_o = i_3 \times 1 = -\frac{5}{8} \quad \text{Ans.}$$

Method 2 From Fig. 4-10 we note that the two current sources each have a 1 Ω resistor across their terminals. Using source transformations, the current source-1 Ω combinations can be converted into equivalent voltage source-1 Ω combinations as shown in Fig. 4-12. Referring to Fig. 4-12, we write the network determinant and calculate i_b.

$$\Delta = \begin{vmatrix} 3 & -1 \\ -1 & 3 \end{vmatrix} = 9 - 1 = 8$$

$$i_b = \frac{\begin{vmatrix} 3 & 10 \\ -1 & -5 \end{vmatrix}}{\Delta} = \frac{-15 + 10}{8} = -\frac{5}{8}$$

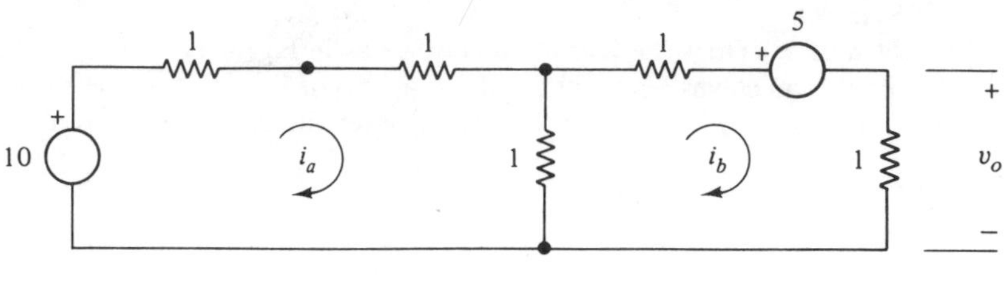

Fig. 4-12

The output is

$$v_o = i_b \times 1 = -\frac{5}{8} \quad \text{Ans.}$$

(When we compare Figs. 4-11 and 4-12, we see that $i_a = i_2$ a nd $i_b = i_3$.)

Example 4-4

Write the mesh equations for the circuit shown in Fig. 4-13.

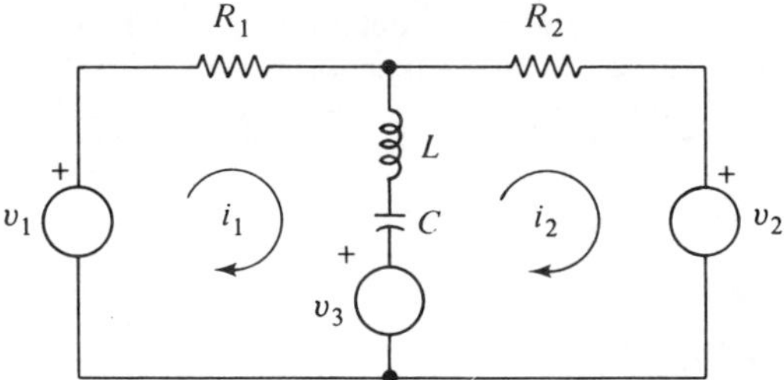

Fig. 4-13

Solution. Let us write them in ordered form directly from Fig. 4-12.

$$\underbrace{\left(L\frac{di_1}{dt} + R_1 i_1 + \frac{1}{C}\int i_1\,dt\right)}_{\text{Self terms}} - \underbrace{\left(L\frac{di_2}{dt} + \frac{1}{C}\int i_2\,dt\right)}_{\text{Mutual terms}} = \underbrace{v_1 - v_3}_{\text{Sources}}$$

$$-\underbrace{\left(L\frac{di_1}{dt} + \frac{1}{C}\int i_1\,dt\right)}_{\text{Mutual terms}} + \underbrace{\left(L\frac{di_2}{dt} + R_2 i_2 + \frac{1}{C}\int i_2\,dt\right)}_{\text{Self terms}} = \underbrace{v_3 - v_2}_{\text{Sources}}$$

Unlike the preceding three examples, we do not yet know how to solve this set of equations for the unknown currents. We must wait until Chapter 5 to learn how to solve integrodifferential equations simultaneously.

4-2 NODE EQUATIONS

Networks can also be analyzed by writing a set of node equations. They can be obtained systematically if one node is established as a reference node and all other node voltages are designated with respect to the reference node. Usually the reference node is drawn as a line at the bottom of the schematic presentation. It can be further identified by calling it ground or attaching the ground symbol to it. In Fig. 4-14(a), the bottom line is taken as the reference. The other node voltages are marked v_1, v_2,and so on, it being understood that v_1 is the voltage between node 1 and the reference, v_2 is the voltage between node 2 and the reference, and so on. This type of designation is also meaningful from a practical standpoint. When measurements are taken, the minus lead of the voltmeter is attached to ground, whereas the plus lead is moved about to read the voltages at the nodes. Implicit in the node-voltage designation is the understanding that the + signs are associated (although not shown) with the nodes and the − sign is at the reference node. See Fig. 4-14(b).

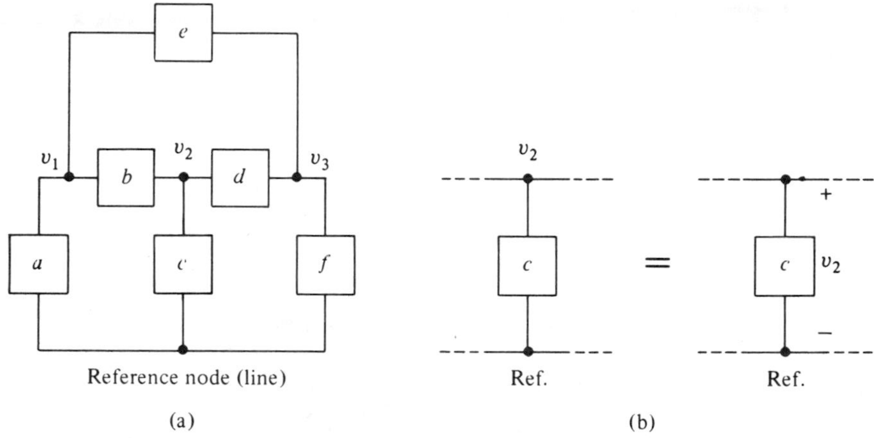

Fig. 4-14

In Fig. 4-14(a) the voltage across element a is v_1(with $+-$, top to bottom). The voltage across element c is v_2. The voltage across element f is v_3. However, the voltage across element b is $(v_1 - v_2)$(with $+-$, left to right) or $(v_2 - v_1)$(with $+-$, right to left). The voltage across element d is $(v_2 - v_3)$with + on the left, and the voltage across element e is $(v_1 - v_3)$ with + on the left. Thus we see that if an element is connected between a node and the reference node, the voltage across it is the node voltage. On the other hand, if an element is connected between two nodes, neither of which is the reference node, the voltage across the element is the difference of the node voltages. This situation is further demonstrated in Fig. 4-15.

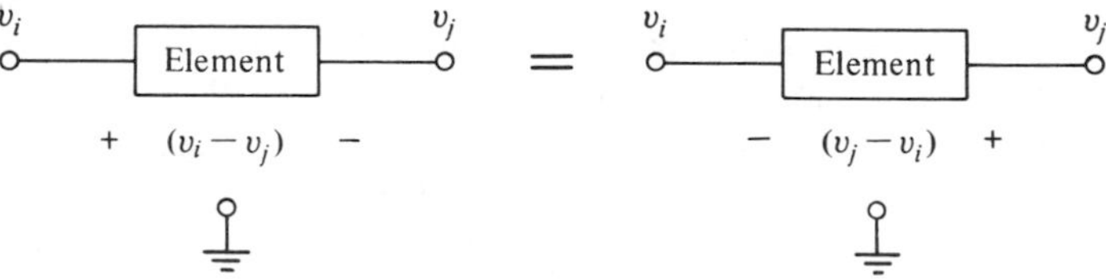

Fig. 4-15

According to *Kirchhoff's Current Law, the sum of currents leaving (or entering) any node is zero*. To see how these currents are summed in a systematic way, refer to Fig. 4-16 and node 2, to which three resistors, R_1, R_2, and R_3, are connected. No other element is connected to node 2. The voltage at this node is v_2. The voltages at the adjacent nodes are v_1 and v_3. Let us adopt the convention that we will consider all currents as leaving node 2 and sum the currents accordingly.

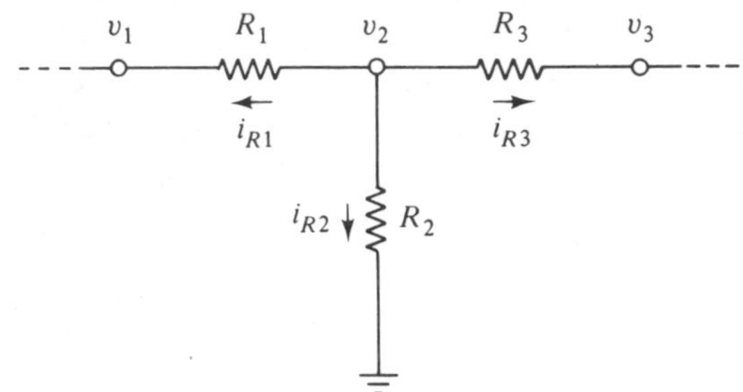

Fig. 4-16

$$i_{R1} + i_{R2} + i_{R3} = 0$$

$$\frac{v_2 - v_1}{R_1} + \frac{v_2}{R_2} + \frac{v_2 - v_3}{R_3} = 0 \qquad (4\text{-}16)$$

Now we define *conductance* as being the *reciprocal of resistance*—that is,

$$G = \frac{1}{R}$$

The symbol G is used for conductance. Conductance is measured in mho, which is ohm spelled backward. Using conductances, Eq. (4-16) becomes

$$(v_2 - v_1)G_1 + v_2G_2 + (v_2 - v_3)G_3 = 0 \qquad (4\text{-}17)$$

Note that in all terms of this equation v_2 appears first. This result occurs because we chose to take the currents as flowing out of node 2. When Eq. (4-17) is reordered so that terms involving v_1 appear first, followed by terms involving v_2, and so on, we have

$$-v_1G_1 + v_2(G_1 + G_2 + G_3) - v_3G_3 = 0 \qquad (4\text{-}18)$$

After studying Eq. (4-18), it is clear that we could have written it directly from inspection of Fig. 4-16. Since we are writing the equation for node 2, node 2 is at the center of our attention. The voltage v_2 is common to all conductances. If v_2 were acting alone (while all other voltages were held at zero), it would have produced a current given by the middle term of Eq. (4-18). Note that this term is positive. The voltage v_1 is associated with G_1 only. If v_1 were acting alone, it would have produced a current of v_1G_1 *toward* node 2 through G_1. Since this current is in opposition to the current flowing *away* from node 2, it appears as $-v_1G_1$ in Eq. (4-18). Similarly, v_3 alone would produce a current of v_3G_3 *toward* node 2 through G_3 and would therefore result in the $-v_3G_3$ (away from node 2) term in Eq. (4-18). Keeping this discussion in mind, we can interpret Eq. (4-18) as being a summation of terms produced by the voltage v_2 (the self terms) and the voltages in adjacent nodes (the mutual terms). The self terms are positive; all mutual terms are negative.

As another example, consider node 3 in Fig. 4-17. The voltages at adjacent nodes are labeled v_1, v_2, and v_4. The currents flowing *away* from node 3 are labeled i_{R1}, i_{R2}, i_L, and i_C. (We note here that if node 4 were the reference node, v_4 would have been zero by definition.)

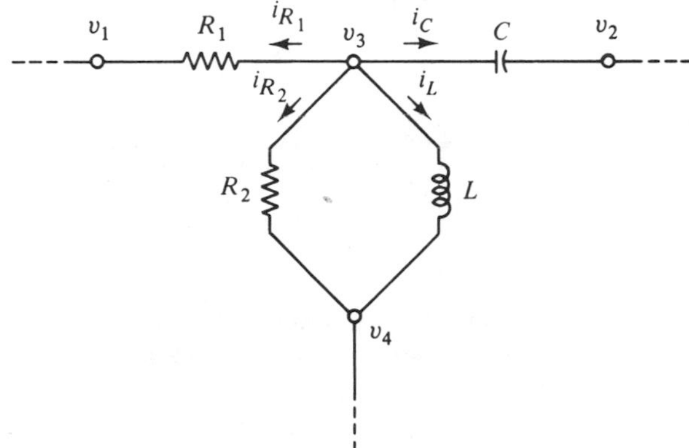

Fig. 4-17

Applying Kirchhoff's Current Law to node 3, we obtain

$$i_{R1} + i_{R2} + i_L + i_C = 0 \tag{4-19}$$

The element-defining equations relate the current through the element to the voltage across the element. Thus

$$i_{R1} = (v_3 - v_1)G_1 \tag{4-20a}$$

$$i_{R2} = (v_3 - v_4)G_2 \tag{4-20b}$$

$$i_L = \frac{1}{L}\int (v_3 - v_4)\, dt \tag{4-20c}$$

$$i_C = C\frac{d}{dt}(v_3 - v_2) \tag{4-20d}$$

Once again we note that v_3 occurs first in these expressions because we are summing currents at *node* 3.

When the expressions given by Eq. (4-20) are substituted in Eq. (4-19), we have

$$(v_3 - v_1)G_1 + (v_3 - v_4)G_2 + \frac{1}{L}\int (v_3 - v_4)\, dt + C\frac{d}{dt}(v_3 - v_2) = 0$$

which can be rearranged so that terms involving v_1 appear first, followed by terms involving v_2, and so on.

$$-v_1G_1 - C\frac{dv_2}{dt} + C\frac{dv_3}{dt} + (G_1 + G_2)v_3 + \frac{1}{L}\int v_3\,dt - G_2v_4 - \frac{1}{L}\int v_4\,dt = 0 \tag{4-21}$$

This equation could have been written directly from inspection of Fig. 4-17 and by turning on *one node voltage at a time*. Thus

v_3 causes $C\dfrac{dv_3}{dt} + v_3(G_1 + G_2) + \dfrac{1}{L}\displaystyle\int v_3\,dt$ (self term)

v_1 causes $-G_1v_1$

v_2 causes $-C\dfrac{dv_2}{dt}$ (mutual terms)

v_4 causes $-v_4G_2 - \dfrac{1}{L}\displaystyle\int v_4\,dt$

Consider next elements C and R connected between nodes 1 and 2 in Fig. 4-18. If we form the sum of element currents shown at node 1, we find

$$i_{1R} + i_{1C} = (v_1 - v_2)G + C\frac{d}{dt}(v_1 - v_2) \tag{4-22}$$

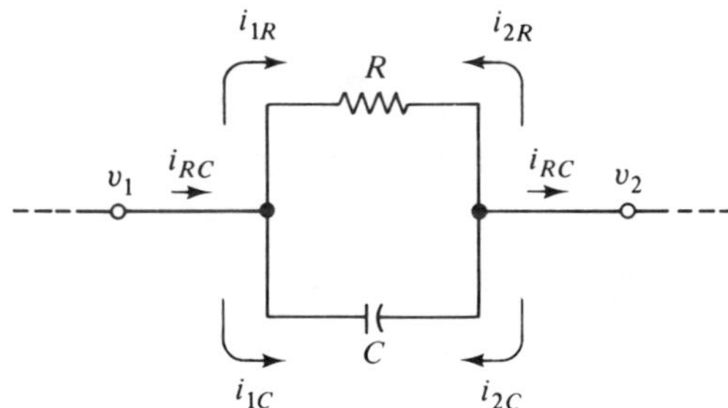

Fig. 4-18

On the other hand, if we form the sum of element currents shown at node 2, we have

$$i_{2R} + i_{2C} = (v_2 - v_1)G + C\frac{d}{dt}(v_2 - v_1) \tag{4-23}$$

Comparison of Eqs. (4-22) and (4-23) shows that $i_{1R} + i_{1C} = -(i_{2R} + i_{2C})$. This result is to be expected since $i_{RC} = i_{1R} + i_{1C}$ enters the RC network on the left and $i_{RC} = -(i_{2R} + i_{2C})$ leaves it on the right, thus obeying Kirchhoff's Current Law.

We are now ready to formulate a general procedure for writing a system of equations based on the node equations.

1. Take one node as the reference node and assign to all other nodes voltages with respect to the reference node.
2. Sum the currents *leaving* each node and set the result to zero. This step is

equivalent to applying Kirchhoff's Current Law to each node. If there are altogether n nodes besides the reference node, there are n unknown node voltages, and so n equations (one for each node) are written. These equations are *independent*.

3. Solve simultaneously the resulting n equations for the *n unknown node voltages*. Once these node voltages are known, the voltages across the elements are easily calculated. Then by using the element-defining equations, the currents through the elements are obtained.

To sum up, in solving for the unknown voltages and currents in a network by the node-equations method, *we solve first for the node voltages*. Then we obtain the element currents and voltages.

Example 4-5

(a) For the circuit shown in Fig. 4-19, write the node equations.

(b) Obtain the output current i_o.

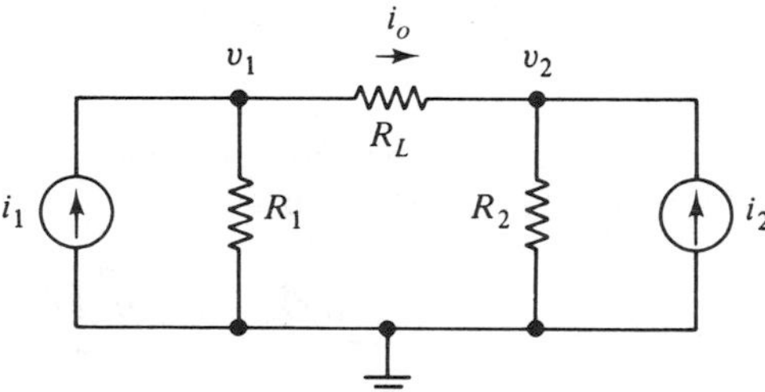

Fig. 4-19

Solution

(a) As Fig. 4-19 shows, voltages are referenced with respect to the bottom line. There are two unknown node voltages—v_1 and v_2. So we need to write two independent equations involving v_1 and v_2. These equations are obtained by applying Kirchhoff's Current Law to nodes 1 and 2.

$$v_1G_1 + (v_1 - v_2)G_L = i_1 \qquad \text{(node 1)}$$

$$v_2G_2 + (v_2 - v_1)G_L = i_2 \qquad \text{(node 2)}$$

These equations can be ordered as

$$\left\{\begin{array}{r} v_1(G_1 + G_L) - v_2G_L = i_1 \\ -v_1G_L + v_2(G_2 + G_L) = i_2 \end{array}\right\} \quad \text{Ans.} \qquad (4\text{-}24)$$

Note that the terms involving the unknown voltages are kept on the left side of the equation and that the terms depicting the known current sources are transferred to the right-hand side. The current i_1 is positive, for if it were to act alone, it would have caused a positive voltage at node 1. Similarly, the current i_2 is positive because it would have caused node 2 voltage to be positive.

(b) The determinant of the set of equations given by Eq. (4-24) is

$$\Delta = \begin{vmatrix} (G_1 + G_L) & -G_L \\ -G_L & (G_2 + G_L) \end{vmatrix} = \begin{vmatrix} a_{11} & a_{12} \\ a_{21} & a_{22} \end{vmatrix}$$

In the a_{11} position of the determinant we have $(G_1 + G_L)$, which represents the sum of conductances tied to node 1. In the a_{22} position of the determinant we have $(G_2 + G_L)$, which represents the sum of conductances tied to node 2. In the a_{12} position we have $-G_L$, which is the negative of the conductance tied between nodes 1 and 2. In the a_{21} position we have $-G_L$, which is the negative of the conductance tied between nodes 2 and 1. Obviously, $a_{12} = a_{21}$.

The value of the determinant is

$$\Delta = (G_1 + G_L)(G_2 + G_L) - G_L^2 = G_1G_2 + G_L(G_1 + G_2)$$

Again note that, after cancellations, all terms in the determinant are positive. This is always the case when the sources exciting the network are independent.

To obtain i_o, we must first solve for v_1 and v_2. Both v_1 and v_2 are obtainable from ratios of determinants.

$$v_1 = \frac{\Delta_1}{\Delta}, \qquad v_2 = \frac{\Delta_2}{\Delta}$$

The determinant Δ_1 is formed by crossing out the *first* column of Δ and replacing it with the current sources coming *into* nodes 1 and 2.

$$\Delta_1 = \begin{vmatrix} i_i & -G_L \\ i_2 & (G_2 + G_L) \end{vmatrix} = i_1(G_2 + G_L) + i_2G_L$$

The determinant Δ_2 is formed by crossing out the *second* column of Δ and replacing it with the current sources coming *into* nodes 1 and 2.

$$\Delta_2 = \begin{vmatrix} (G_1 + G_L) & i_1 \\ -G_L & i_2 \end{vmatrix} = i_2(G_1 + G_L) + i_1G_L$$

Thus

$$v_1 = \frac{i_1(G_2 + G_L) + i_2G_L}{G_1G_2 + G_L(G_1 + G_2)}$$

$$v_2 = \frac{i_1G_L + i_2(G_1 + G_L)}{G_1G_2 + G_L(G_1 + G_2)}$$

If follows that

$$i_o = (v_1 - v_2)G_L = \frac{(i_1G_2 - i_2G_1)G_L}{G_1G_2 + G_L(G_1 + G_2)}$$

We can simplify this expression by dividing the numerator and denominator by $G_1G_2G_L$.

$$i_o = \frac{i_1/G_1 - i_2/G_2}{1/G_L + 1/G_2 + 1/G_1} = \frac{i_1R_1 - i_2R_2}{R_L + R_2 + R_1} \quad \text{Ans.}$$

This last form could have been easily obtained by redrawing Fig. 4-19 as in Fig. 4-20. Note that the current-source-parallel-resistance combinations of Fig. 4-19 have been replaced with voltage-source-series-resistance combinations. From the transformed network, i_o can be calculated by inspection. Therefore an easier way of solving this problem is to use this simpler method. Again, however, the purpose of this example is to obtain practice with node equations and their solutions.

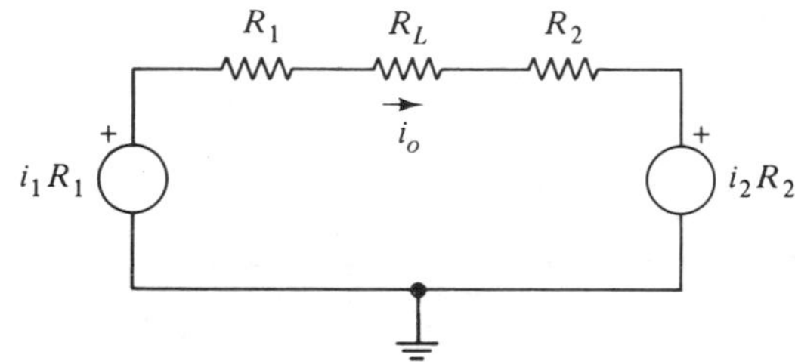

Fig. 4-20

Example 4-6

Refer to Fig. 4-21.

(a) What is the resistance seen by the 1 A source?

(b) What is the output voltage?

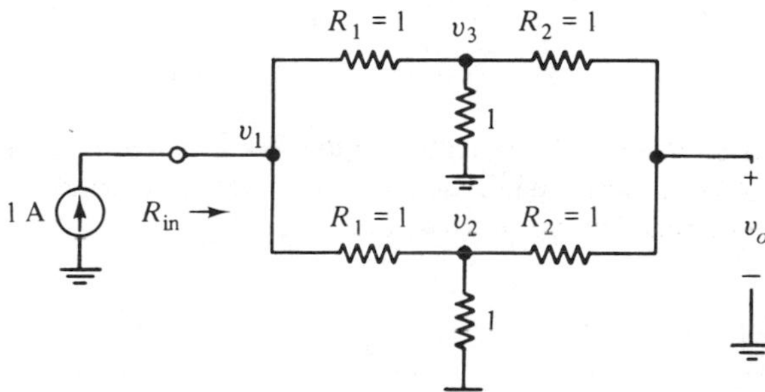

Fig. 4-21

Solution.

(a) Besides the ground node, there are four nodes. Label them v_1, v_2, v_3, and v_o as shown. The input resistance is that single resistance that produces the same voltage v_1 across the input terminals as in the original circuit. So.

$$R_{in} = \frac{v_1}{1\text{A}} = v_1$$

(In this case, R_{in} cannot be found by combining resistances in series and parallel because the network does not possess such combinations.) To calculate R_{in}, we must find v_1. The network determinant is obtained by inspection of Fig. 4-21.

$$\Delta = \begin{vmatrix} 2 & -1 & -1 & 0 \\ -1 & 3 & 0 & -1 \\ -1 & 0 & 3 & -1 \\ 0 & -1 & -1 & 2 \end{vmatrix} = \begin{vmatrix} a_{11} & a_{12} & a_{13} & a_{14} \\ a_{21} & a_{22} & a_{23} & a_{24} \\ a_{31} & a_{32} & a_{33} & a_{34} \\ a_{41} & a_{42} & a_{43} & a_{44} \end{vmatrix}$$

where a_{11} = sum of conductances tied to node 1 = 1 + 1 = 2

a_{22} = sum of conductances tied to node 2 = 1 + 1 + 1 = 3

.
.
.

a_{12} = −conductance tied between nodes 1 and 2 = −1

a_{13} = −conductance tied between nodes 1 and 3 = −1

.
.
.

The value of the determinant is

$$\Delta = 2\begin{vmatrix} 3 & 0 & -1 \\ 0 & 3 & -1 \\ -1 & -1 & 2 \end{vmatrix} - (-1)\begin{vmatrix} -1 & -1 & 0 \\ 0 & 3 & -1 \\ -1 & -1 & 2 \end{vmatrix} + (-1)\begin{vmatrix} -1 & -1 & 0 \\ 3 & 0 & -1 \\ -1 & -1 & 2 \end{vmatrix}$$

$$= 2\left[3\begin{vmatrix} 3 & -1 \\ -1 & 2 \end{vmatrix} + (-1)\begin{vmatrix} 0 & -1 \\ 3 & -1 \end{vmatrix}\right] + \left[(-1)\begin{vmatrix} 3 & -1 \\ -1 & 2 \end{vmatrix} + (-1)\begin{vmatrix} -1 & 0 \\ 3 & -1 \end{vmatrix}\right]$$

$$- \left[(-1)\begin{vmatrix} 0 & -1 \\ -1 & 2 \end{vmatrix} - (-1)\begin{vmatrix} 3 & -1 \\ -1 & 2 \end{vmatrix}\right]$$

$$= 2[3(6-1) - (3)] + [-(6-1) - (1)] - [(1) + (6-1)] = 12$$

To calculate v_1, we need to form Δ_1 by replacing the first column of Δ with the current sources that feed the four nodes. In this case, node 1 receives 1 A; the other nodes have zero current coming in from sources.

$$\Delta_1 = \begin{vmatrix} 1 & -1 & -1 & 0 \\ 0 & 3 & 0 & -1 \\ 0 & 0 & 3 & -1 \\ 0 & -1 & -1 & 2 \end{vmatrix} = \begin{vmatrix} 3 & 0 & -1 \\ 0 & 3 & -1 \\ -1 & -1 & 2 \end{vmatrix} = 12$$

Then

$$v_1 = \frac{\Delta_1}{\Delta} = \frac{12}{12} = 1$$

Consequently,

$$R_{\text{in}} = 1\ \Omega \quad \text{Ans.}$$

Had we studied the circuit a little, we would have seen this result immediately. Because the circuit is symmetrical, the 1 A source coming into node 1 is split evenly, $\frac{1}{2}$ A going each way and producing identical voltages across the two R_1's, shown in Fig. 4-21. As a result, $v_2 = v_3$, and the voltage applied to the two R_2's, connected in series on the right, is zero. Consequently, the current through them is also zero. Alternatively stated, the circuit is a balanced bridge. Therefore the two R_2's can be taken out of the circuit or short-circuited without disturbing voltages v_1, v_2, and v_3. The result is the simplified circuit shown in Fig. 4-22(a) (the two R_2's open-circuited) or Fig. 4-22(b) (the two R_2's short-circuited). Inspection of either circuit shows that $R_{in} = 1$.

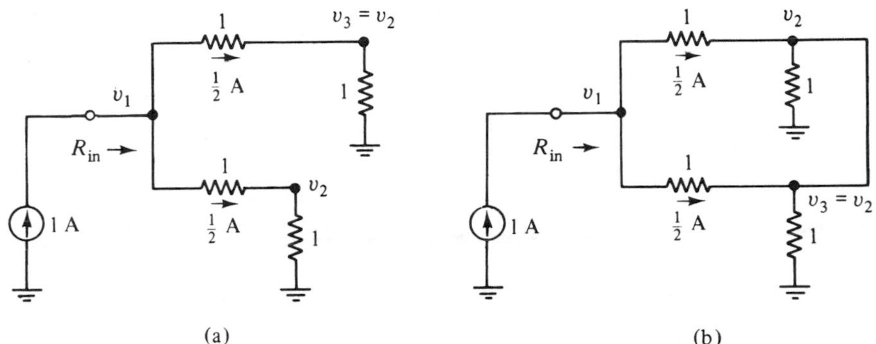

Fig. 4-22

(b) To obtain the output voltage, we calculate Δ_4 by replacing the fourth column of the network determinant with the sources exciting the nodes.

$$\Delta_4 = \begin{vmatrix} 2 & -1 & -1 & 1 \\ -1 & 3 & 0 & 0 \\ -1 & 0 & 3 & 0 \\ 0 & -1 & -1 & 0 \end{vmatrix} = -\begin{vmatrix} -1 & 3 & 0 \\ -1 & 0 & 3 \\ 0 & -1 & -1 \end{vmatrix} = \begin{vmatrix} 0 & 3 \\ -1 & -1 \end{vmatrix} - \begin{vmatrix} 3 & 0 \\ -1 & -1 \end{vmatrix}$$

$$= 3 + 3 = 6$$

Thus

$$v_o = \frac{\Delta_4}{\Delta} = \frac{6}{12} = \frac{1}{2}\text{ V} \quad \text{Ans.}$$

Again, this result could have been obtained directly from either circuit of Fig. 4-22. Because the input resistance is 1 Ω,

$$v_1 = 1\text{ A} \times 1\ \Omega = 1\text{ V}$$

Because the current splits evenly at node 1,

$$v_2 = v_3 = v_1 - \left(\frac{1}{2}\text{ A}\right) \times (1\ \Omega) = 1 - \frac{1}{2} = \frac{1}{2}\text{ V}$$

Because the currents to the right of v_2 and v_3 are zero,

$$v_o = v_2 = v_3 = \frac{1}{2}\text{ V}$$

Example 4-7

Determine the value of i_o in the circuit of Fig. 4-23.

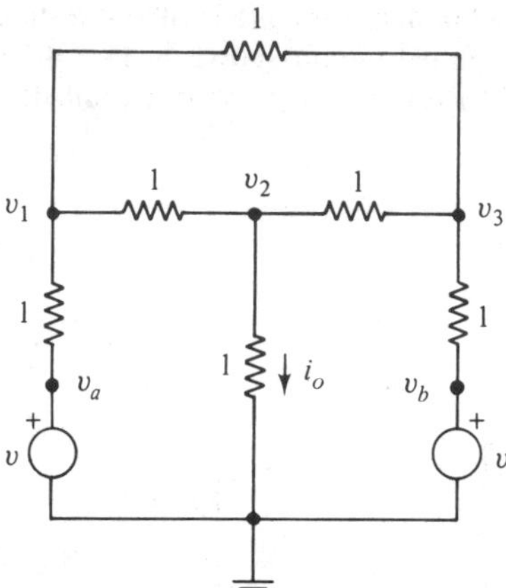

Fig. 4-23

Solution

Method 1 Because the sources are voltage sources, this circuit is ideally set up for analysis by the mesh-equations method. However, to see how voltage sources are handled in the writing of node equations (which are ideally set up for current-source excitations), let us apply the node method of analysis to this problem.

The bottom line is taken as the reference. There are five other nodes in the network, labeled v_a, v_b, v_1, v_2, and v_3. Immediately we see that the voltages at nodes a and b are *constrained* by the two voltage sources to be v volts. So they are known. There are, therefore, three unknown node variables: v_1, v_2, and v_3. Even though we are interested only in v_2 (so that we can determine i_o), we must write three independent equations involving v_1, v_2, v_3 and then solve for v_2. These three independent equations are obtained by applying Kirchhoff's Current Law to nodes 1, 2, and 3.

$$(v_1 - v) \times 1 + (v_1 - v_2) \times 1 + (v_1 - v_3) \times 1 = 0 \quad \text{(node 1)}$$

$$(v_2 - v_1) \times 1 + v_2 \times 1 + (v_2 - v_3) \times 1 = 0 \quad \text{(node 2)}$$

$$(v_3 - v) \times 1 + (v_3 - v_2) \times 1 + (v_3 - v_1) \times 1 = 0 \quad \text{(node 3)}$$

Rearranging, we obtain

$$\begin{aligned} 3v_1 - v_2 - v_3 &= v \\ -v_1 + 3v_2 - v_3 &= 0 \\ -v_1 - v_2 + 3v_3 &= v \end{aligned} \tag{4-25}$$

At this point we observe that if, in Fig. 4-23, we had converted the two voltage sources in series with their 1 Ω resistors into two current sources in parallel with the 1 Ω resistors (feeding nodes 1 and 2, respectively), we would have obtained Fig. 4-24, which is a circuit ideally set up for the node method of analysis (since it is driven by current sources). Had we then written the node equations for this circuit, we would have obtained Eq. (4-25).

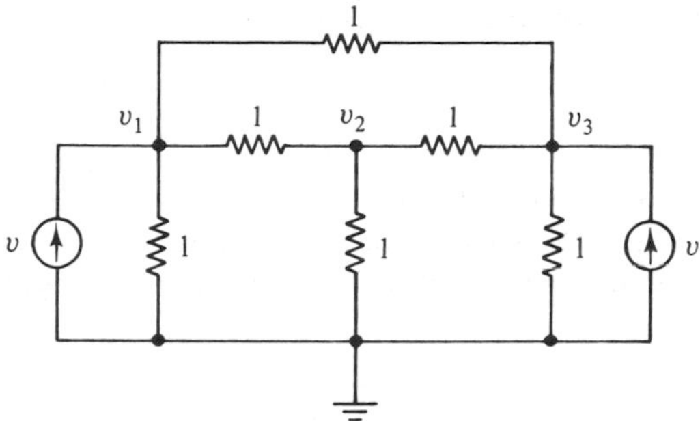

Fig. 4-24

The determinant of the set given by Eq. (4-25) is

$$\Delta = \begin{vmatrix} 3 & -1 & -1 \\ -1 & 3 & -1 \\ -1 & -1 & 3 \end{vmatrix} = 3\begin{vmatrix} 3 & -1 \\ -1 & 3 \end{vmatrix} + \begin{vmatrix} -1 & -1 \\ -1 & 3 \end{vmatrix} - \begin{vmatrix} -1 & -1 \\ 3 & -1 \end{vmatrix}$$

$$= 3(9 - 1) + (-3 - 1) - (1 + 3) = 16$$

This determinant could have been written by inspection of Fig. 4-24 or Fig. 4-23 by leaving out (killing) all the sources. Stated differently, the determinant describes the dead network only; it has no information about the independent sources. The voltage v_2—and hence i_o—is obtained from

$$v_2 = i_o = \frac{\Delta_2}{\Delta}$$

where

$$\Delta_2 = \begin{vmatrix} 3 & v & -1 \\ -1 & 0 & -1 \\ -1 & v & 3 \end{vmatrix} = -v\begin{vmatrix} -1 & -1 \\ -1 & 3 \end{vmatrix} - v\begin{vmatrix} 3 & -1 \\ -1 & -1 \end{vmatrix} = -v(-3 - 1)2 = 8v$$

Thus

$$i_o = \frac{8v}{16} = \frac{v}{2} \quad \text{Ans.}$$

Method 2 Because the circuit is symmetrical, we can easily find i_o without becoming involved with determinants. The current in the top resistor of Fig. 4-23 is zero, as we can see if we think in terms of superposition. The left-hand source by itself would send a current through the top resistor to the right, whereas the right-hand source by itself would send an equal amount of current to the left. The resulting current, the sum of right-hand and left-hand currents, is zero. Therefore this resistor can be removed altogether from the circuit without affecting any current or voltage in the circuit. Next, we redraw the circuit of Fig. 4-23 as in Fig. 4-25(a). Note that we have slightly complicated (for the moment at least) the circuit by using 2 Ω resistors in parallel in the middle branch to take the place of the single 1 Ω resistor in the original circuit. Each 2 Ω resistor carries a current of

$$\frac{i_o}{2}$$

where i_o is the current in the original 1 Ω resistor. Because of the symmetry (think also in terms of superposition), $i_m = 0$. So the middle wires can be cut. The resulting circuit is shown in Fig. 4-25(b). From either the left-half or right-half portion of this circuit we obtain

$$\frac{i_o}{2} = \frac{v}{1 + 1 + 2}$$

$$i_o = \frac{v}{2} \quad \text{Ans.}$$

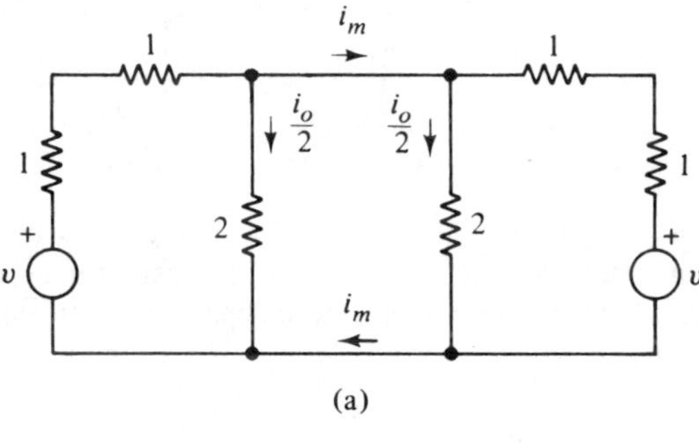

(a)

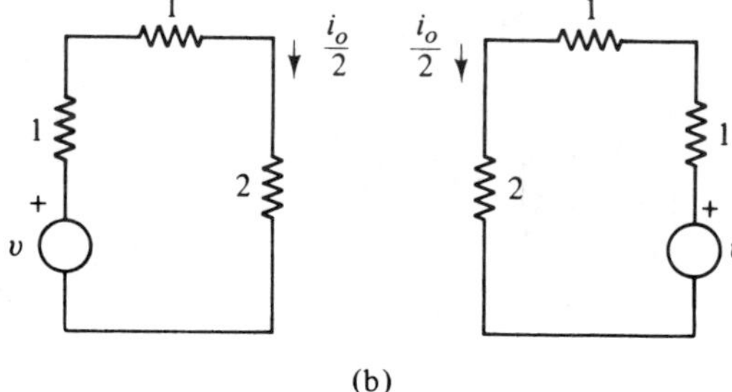

(b)

Fig. 4-25

Example 4-8

For the circuit shown in Fig. 4-26, write the node equations.

Solution. Let us write them in ordered form directly from Fig. 4-26.

$$\underbrace{\left(C\frac{dv_1}{dt} + v_1G_1 + \frac{1}{L}\int v_1\,dt\right)}_{\text{Self terms}} - \underbrace{\left(C\frac{dv_2}{dt} + \frac{1}{L}\int v_2\,dt\right)}_{\text{Mutual terms}} = \underbrace{i_1 + i_2}_{\text{Sources}}$$

$$\underbrace{-\left(C\frac{dv_1}{dt} + \frac{1}{L}\int v_1\,dt\right)}_{\text{Mutual terms}} + \underbrace{\left(C\frac{dv_2}{dt} + v_2G_2 + \frac{1}{L}\int v_2\,dt\right)}_{\text{Self terms}} = \underbrace{-i_2}_{\text{Source}}$$

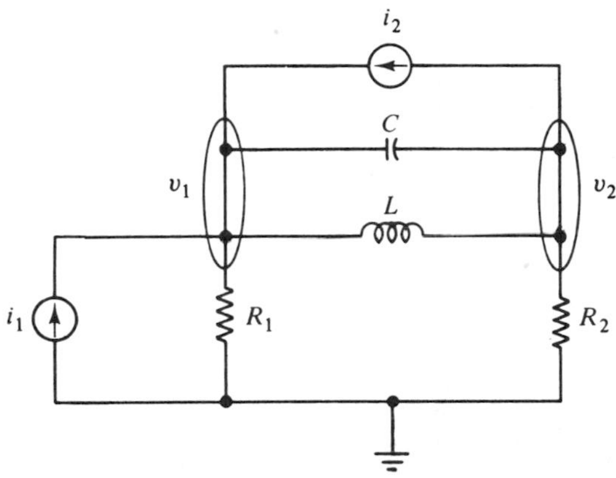

Fig. 4-26

4-3 MIXED SOURCES

In the *mesh-equations method* of analysis, we sum *voltages* around loops. As a result, *voltage sources* are easily incorporated in the summation. On the other hand, a current source requires special handling unless it is in parallel with a resistance; then we can convert the combination to a voltage source in series with the resistance, thereby completely avoiding the handling of current sources.

In the *node-equations method* of analysis, we sum *currents* at nodes, which means that *current sources* are easily incorporated in the summation. On the other hand, a voltage source requires special handling unless it is in series with a resistance. In this case, we can convert the combination to obtain a current source in parallel with thc resistance, thus avoiding altogether the handling of voltage sources.

There are instances, however, in which we cannot use source transformations to convert all sources to voltage sources (for mesh method of analysis) or current sources (for node method of analysis). For instance, if a resistance is not in series with a voltage source, conversion to current source cannot be done; or if a resistance is not in parallel with a current source, conversion to voltage source is not possible. Nonetheless, we can still write a set of equations based on loop- or node-analysis methods as the following example shows. (See also method 1 solutions in Examples 4-3 and 4-7.)

Example 4-9

Solve for the unknown currents and voltages shown in Fig. 4-27 by writing the appropriate set of equations and solving them.

Solution. There are three unknown mesh currents, i_1, i_2, and i_3, requiring three independent equations for solution. There are three unknown node voltages, v_1, v_2, and v_3, also requiring three independent equations for solution. There are two sources of excitation—one voltage, the other current. Because of the number of equations and the type of sources, the mesh method of analysis requires as much work as the node method of analysis. No advantage is gained by using one method rather than the other.

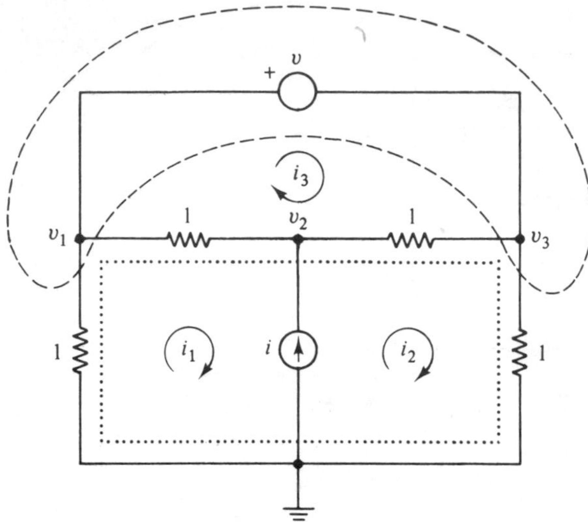

Fig. 4-27

Analysis by Mesh Equations We need to write three equations in order to solve for the three unknown mesh currents. The current source cannot be converted to a voltage source because there is no resistance in parallel with it. However, we see that the current source applies a constraint to mesh currents i_1 and i_2—namely, $i_2 - i_1 = i$. *This is one equation* (constraint equation). The other two equations are obtained by applying Kirchhoff's Voltage Law to *mesh* 3 and to *meshes 1 and 2* combined. The result is a superloop (shown by dots in Fig. 4-27) that avoids (bypasses) the current source, which already has been accounted for by the constraint equation. Four voltages are associated with this superloop: two in mesh 1 and two in mesh 2. The constraint equation, in conjunction with the superloop equation, takes care of meshes 1 and 2.

The three equations needed to solve this problem are

$$-i_1 + i_2 = i \qquad \text{(constraint equation)}$$

$$2i_1 + 2i_2 - 2i_3 = 0 \qquad \text{(superloop equation)}$$

$$-i_1 - i_2 + 2i_3 = -v \qquad \text{(equation for mesh 3)}$$

After dividing the second equation by 2, the network determinant is formed as

$$\Delta = \begin{vmatrix} -1 & 1 & 0 \\ 1 & 1 & -1 \\ -1 & -1 & 2 \end{vmatrix} = -1(2 - 1) - (2 - 1) = -2$$

i_1, i_2, and i_3 are obtained from

$$i_1 = \frac{\begin{vmatrix} i & 1 & 0 \\ 0 & 1 & -1 \\ -v & -1 & 2 \end{vmatrix}}{\Delta} = \frac{i + v}{-2} = -\frac{1}{2}(i + v)$$

$$i_2 = \frac{\begin{vmatrix} -1 & i & 0 \\ 1 & 0 & -1 \\ -1 & -v & 2 \end{vmatrix}}{\Delta} = \frac{-i + v}{-2} = \frac{1}{2}(i - v)$$

$$i_3 = \frac{\begin{vmatrix} -1 & 1 & i \\ 1 & 1 & 0 \\ -1 & -1 & -v \end{vmatrix}}{\Delta} = \frac{2v}{-2} = -v$$

Having found the mesh currents, we can easily calculate the node voltages by inspection of Fig. 4-27.

$$\left.\begin{aligned} v_1 &= -i_1 \times 1 = \frac{1}{2}(i + v) \\ v_2 &= v_1 + (i_3 - i_1) \times 1 = i \\ v_3 &= i_2 \times 1 = \frac{1}{2}(i - v) \end{aligned}\right\} \text{Ans.}$$

Analysis by Node Equations We need to write three equations to solve for the three unknown node voltages. The voltage source cannot be converted to a current source because there is no resistance in series with it. However, we see that *the voltage source applies a constraint to node voltages* v_1 and v_3—namely, $v_1 - v_3 = v$. This is one equation (constraint equation). The other two equations are obtained by applying Kirchhoff's Current Law to *node* 2 and to *nodes 1 and 3 combined*. The result is a supernode (shown by the dashed lines in Fig. 4-27) that avoids the voltage source, which already has been accounted for by the constraint equation. There are four currents leaving this supernode: two at node 1 and two at node 3. The constraint equation, together with the supernode equation, takes care of nodes 1 and 3. The three equations needed to solve this problem are

$$\begin{aligned} -v_1 + v_3 &= -v && \text{(constraint equation)} \\ 2v_1 - 2v_2 + 2v_3 &= 0 && \text{(supernode equation)} \\ -v_1 + 2v_2 - v_3 &= i && \text{(node 2 equation)} \end{aligned}$$

If we replace v_1 by i_1, v_2 by i_3, v_3 by i_2, v by $-i$, and i by $-v$, these equations become identical with the mesh equations given previously. So we take the solutions for the mesh currents given there and make the appropriate substitutions, obtaining

$$\left.\begin{aligned} v_1 &= \frac{1}{2}(i + v) \\ v_2 &= i \\ v_3 &= \frac{1}{2}(i - v) \end{aligned}\right\} \text{Ans.}$$

Having thus found the node voltages, we can readily calcualte the mesh currents by inspection of Fig. 4-27.

$$\left.\begin{aligned} i_1 &= -\frac{v_1}{1} = -\frac{1}{2}(i + v) \\ i_2 &= \frac{v_3}{1} = \frac{1}{2}(i - v) \\ i_3 &= \frac{v_3 - v_2}{1} + i_2 = -v \end{aligned}\right\} \text{Ans.}$$

4-4 MESH OR NODE EQUATIONS?

Certain network problems are suitable for analysis by the mesh-equations methods. Generally such networks contain many series-connected elements. Then there are networks that are suitable for analysis by the node-equations method. These networks usually contain many parallel-connected elements. For instance, the network shown in Fig. 4-28(a) requires *two* equations by the mesh-analysis method. On the other hand, after *the* v_s-R_s combination is converted to a nonideal current source, it requires *five* equations by the node-analysis method (there being five unknown node voltages). This network favors the mesh-analysis method because many elements are connected in series. By contrast, the network of Fig. 4-28(b) contains many elements in parallel and hence requires fewer node equations (2) than mesh equations (6).

4-5 RECAPITULATION

We have learned a number of techniques for solving network problems. Moreover, we have found that some problems can be solved merely by inspection of the network. Several examples of these types of problems and their solutions appear in Fig. 4-29.

Such problems are easy to solve because the networks are simple and composed only of *resistors* and sources. What about networks that contain capacitors and inductors as well? How do we solve problems like those given in Fig. 4-30?

Let us see how far we can get with these circuits by using the methods learned so far. For the circuit in Fig. 4-30(a), we can write the mesh equation

$$v_i = L\frac{di}{dt} + Ri$$

Since $v_o = iR$, we can convert this equation for the current i to an equation for the desired voltage v_o.

$$v_i = \frac{L}{R}\frac{dv_o}{dt} + v_o$$

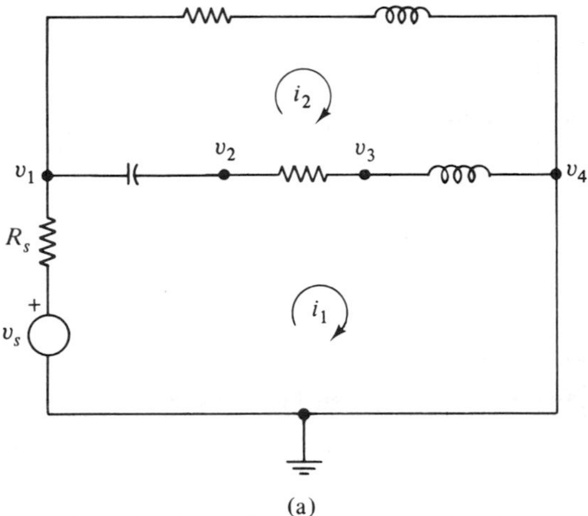

(a)

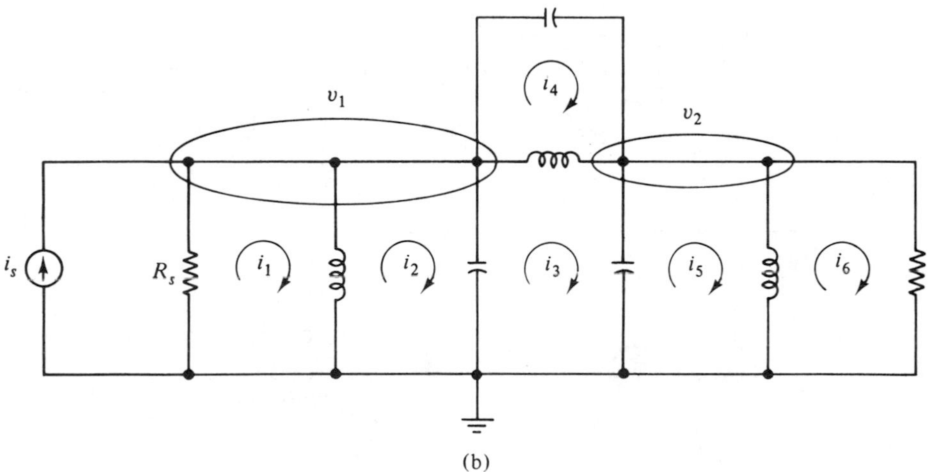

(b)

Fig. 4-28

We can then rearrange this equation so that dv_o/dt (the highest derivative) occurs first, then the term involving v_o, and, finally, on the right-side of the equation we place the term associated with the excitation.

$$\frac{dv_o}{dt} + \frac{R}{L}v_o = \frac{R}{L}v_i \tag{4-26}$$

This is a linear, constant coefficient, differential equation of the first order. To obtain the desired result, we must solve it for v_o.

For the circuit of Fig. 4-30(b), we can write the node equation

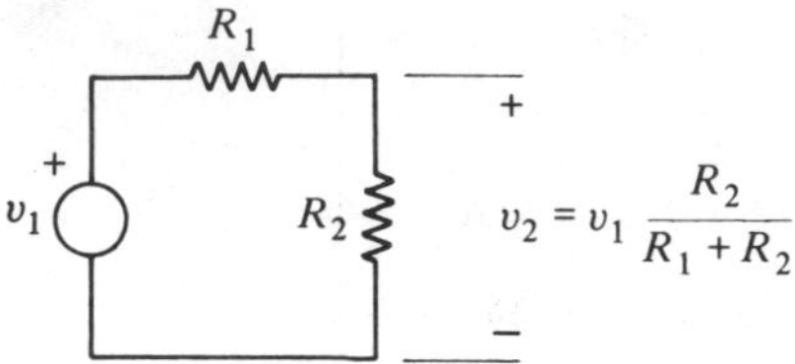

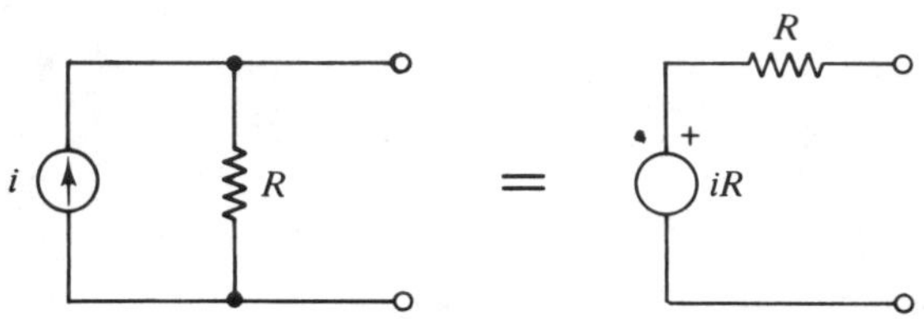

R_3 R_1 R_2 = $\frac{R_3(R_1 + R_2)}{R_1 + R_2 + R_3}$

i R_1 R_2 v v_o = R_1 iR_1 R_2 v $v_o = \frac{iR_1R_2 + vR_1}{R_1 + R_2}$

Fig. 4-29

$$i = C\frac{dv}{dt} + Gv$$

and rearrange it as

$$\frac{dv}{dt} + \frac{G}{C}v = \frac{1}{C}i \tag{4-27}$$

Again, we obtain a linear, constant coefficient, differential equation of the first order, which must be solved for the desired voltage v.

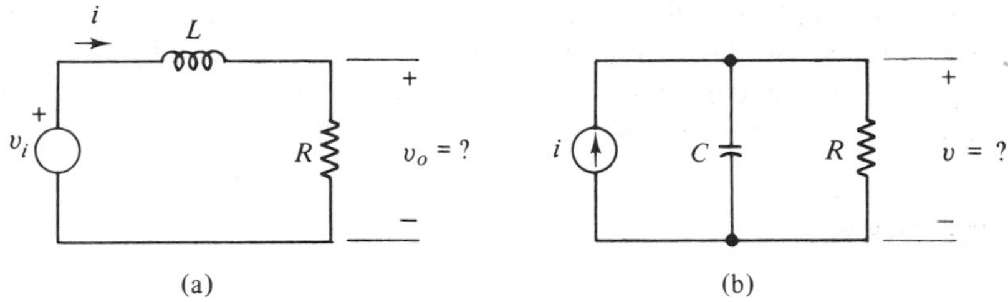

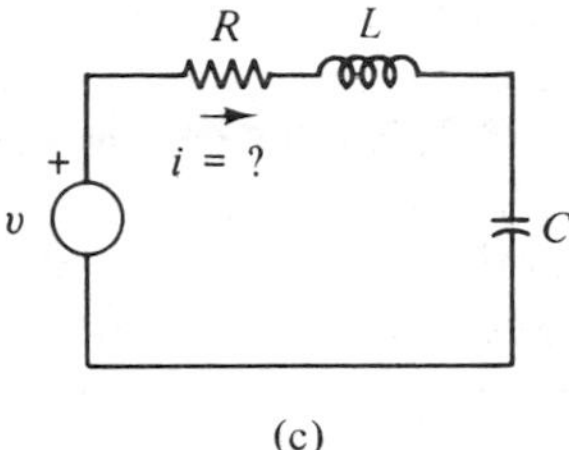

Fig. 4-30

For the circuit of Fig. 4-30(c), we can write the mesh equation to obtain

$$v = iR + L\frac{di}{dt} + \frac{1}{C}\int i\,dt$$

which can then be differentiated with respect to t in order to eliminate the integral:

$$\frac{dv}{dt} = R\frac{di}{dt} + L\frac{d^2 i}{dt^2} + \frac{1}{C}i$$

After dividing by L and reordering, we have

$$\frac{d^2 i}{dt^2} + \frac{R}{L}\frac{di}{dt} + \frac{1}{LC}i = \frac{1}{L}\frac{dv}{dt} \tag{4-28}$$

which is a linear, constant coefficient, differential equation of the second order. Its solution yields the desired current i.

From these three examples, plus others given previously, we see that networks containing *RLC* elements and sources result in differential equations that must be solved for the desired response. At this stage we simply cannot write down the answer by inspection, even for one-mesh or one-node-type problems like those in Fig. 4-30. All we can do is write the differential equation that governs the solution of the problem. Comparing Eqs. (4-26), (4-27), and (4-28), we see that the general form of the differential equation is

$$a_2\frac{d^2 f(t)}{dt^2} + a_1\frac{df(t)}{dt} + a_o f(t) = g(t) \tag{4-29}$$

The a constants are related to the network elements, $f(t)$ is the desired response, and $g(t)$ is related to the excitation. Equation (4-29) is a second-order equation. By making $a_2 = 0$, it becomes a first-order one. In the next chapter we will consider the solution of equations like (4-29).

4-6 SUMMARY

We can use either the mesh or node method of analysis to solve most network problems.

In the mesh method of analysis, we apply Kirchhoff's Voltage Law around each mesh of the circuit and solve the resulting set of equations for the unknown mesh currents. This set of equations can be written systematically if the sources exciting the network are all voltage sources.

In the node method of analysis, we apply Kirchhoff's Current Law to each node except the reference node and solve the resulting set of equations for the unknown node voltages. This set of equations can be written systematically if the sources exciting the network are all current sources.

When a network is excited by both voltage and current sources, it can easily be solved by the mesh or node method of analysis if all sources can be converted to one type. Thus when a resistance appears in series with each voltage source, each source can be converted to a current source. The resulting network contains only current sources and so can be solved by the node method of analysis. Or if a resistance appears in parallel with each current source, then each source can be converted to a voltage source. The resulting network contains only voltage sources and thus can be solved by the mesh method of analysis.

Alternatively, a network excited by both types of sources can be solved by writing constraint equations and mesh or node equations.

PROBLEMS

4-1. (**a**) Apply Kirchhoff's Voltage Law to the two loops shown in Fig. 4-31.
(**b**) Eliminate v_c by combining the two equations obtained in (a). By referring to the network, interpret the resulting equation.

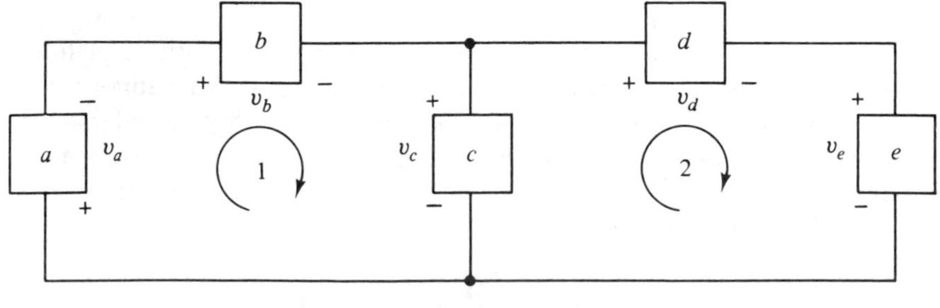

Fig. 4-31

4-2. For loop 3 shown in Fig. 4-32, apply Kirchhoff's Voltage Law.

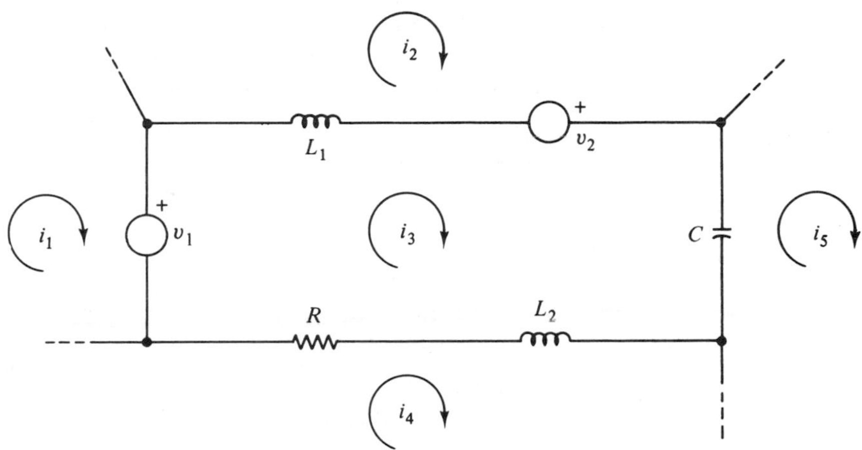

Fig. 4-32

4-3. For the circuits shown in Fig. 4-33, write the mesh equations in ordered form—that is, terms involving i_1 come first, terms involving i_2 next, and so on.

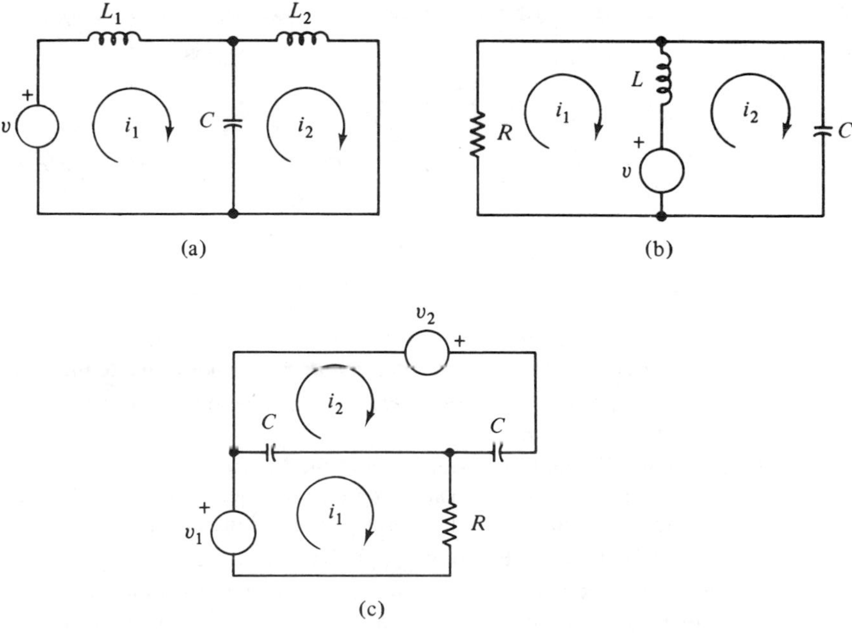

Fig. 4-33

4-4. For the circuits shown in Fig. 4-34, write the equations for the three mesh currents and then order them.

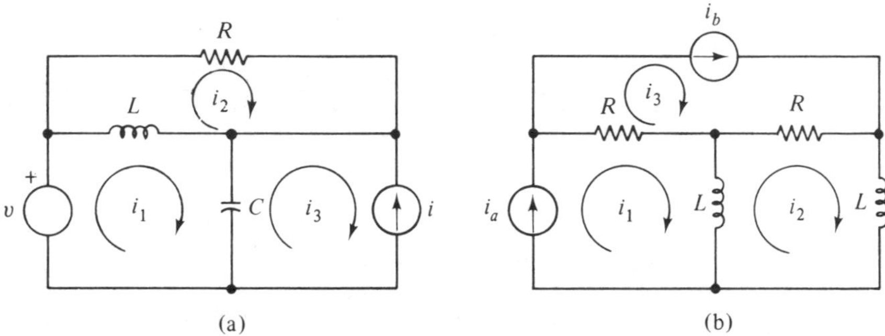

Fig. 4-34

4-5. For the circuits shown in Fig. 4-35, write the mesh determinants by inspection. Do not be concerned with the fact that no sources are involved.

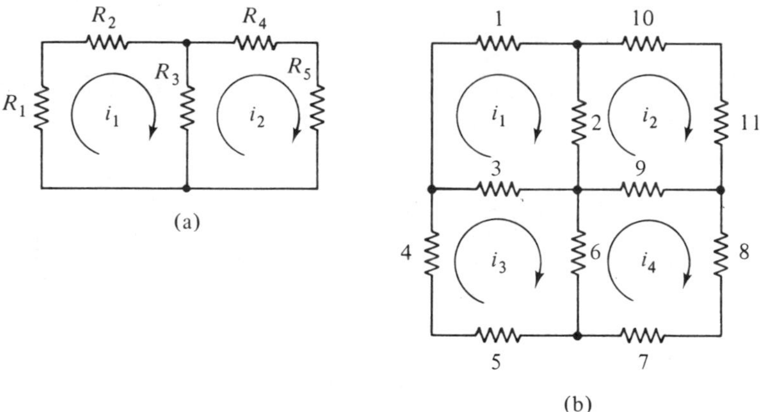

Fig. 4-35

4-6. For the circuits shown in Fig. 4-36, obtain, by inspection, the expressions for the three mesh currents as a ratio of two determinants. Do not evaluate the determinants.

4-7. For the circuits shown in Fig. 4-37, determine the output voltage by using the solutions to the *mesh equations*.

4-8. (**a**) Apply Kirchhoff's Current Law to the two nodes shown in Fig. 4-38.
(**b**) Eliminate i_b and i_c by combining the two equations obtained in part (a) above. By referring to the network, interpret the resulting equation.

4-9. For node 2 shown in Fig. 4-39, apply Kirchhoff's Current Law.

4-10. For the circuits shown in Fig. 4-40, write the node equations in ordered form—that is, terms involving v_1 come first, then come terms involving v_2, and so on.

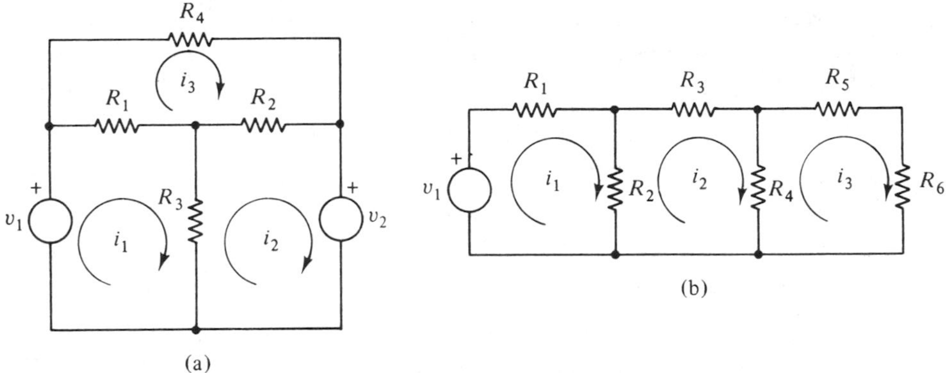

Fig. 4-36

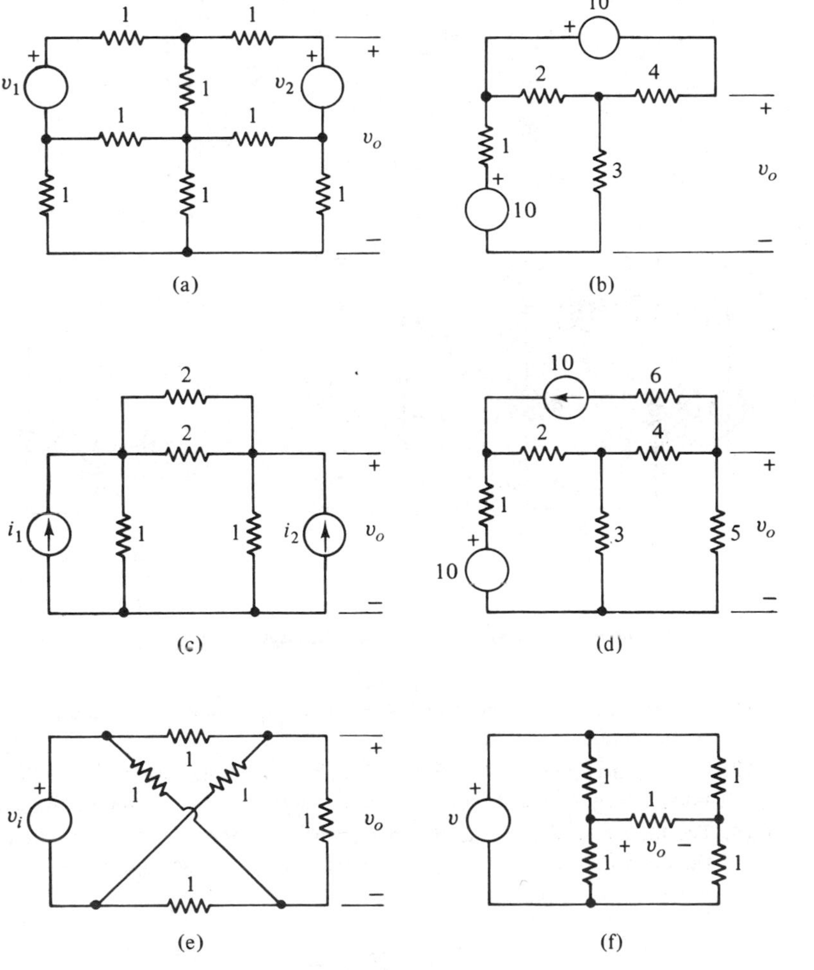

Fig. 4-37

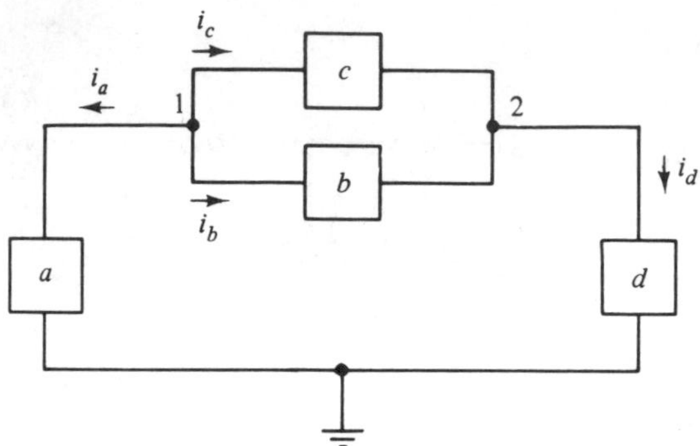

Fig. 4-38

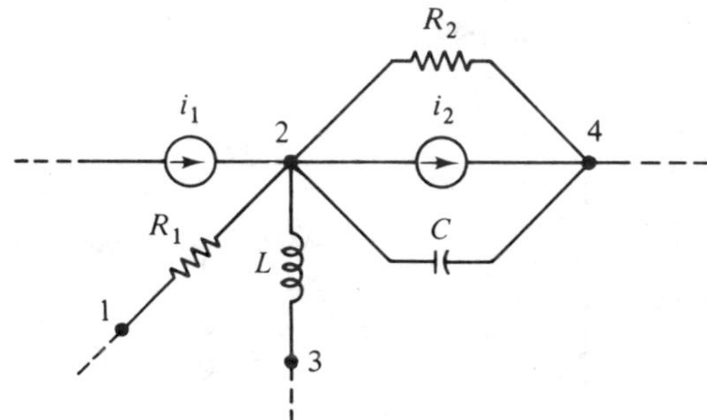

Fig. 4-39

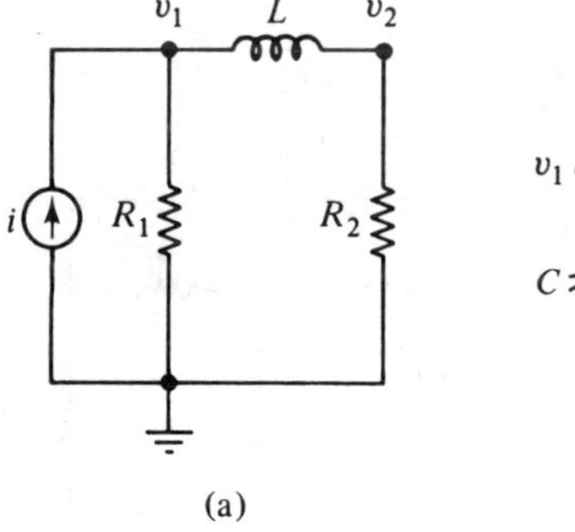

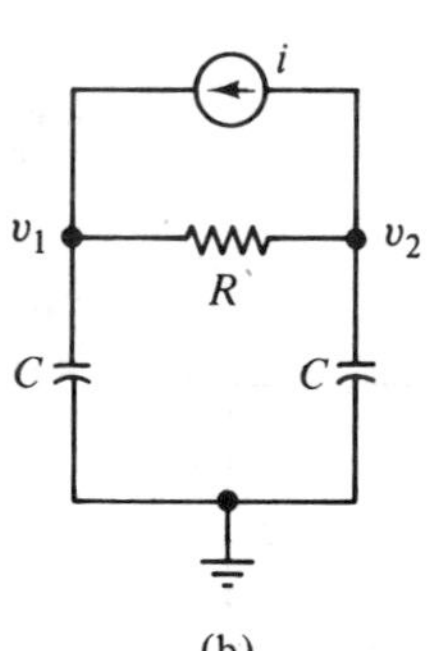

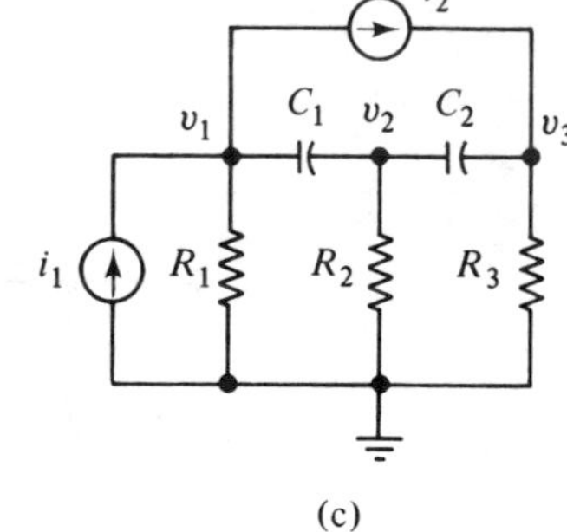

Fig. 4-40

4-11. For the circuits shown in Fig. 4-41, write the equations for the three node voltages and order them.

4-12. For the circuits shown in Fig. 4-42, obtain, by inspection, the expressions for the three node voltages as a ratio of two determinants. Do not evaluate the determinants.

4-13. For the circuits shown in Fig. 4-43, write the appropriate set of equations and solve for the output indicated by a question mark. (Do not use superposition to solve these problems.)

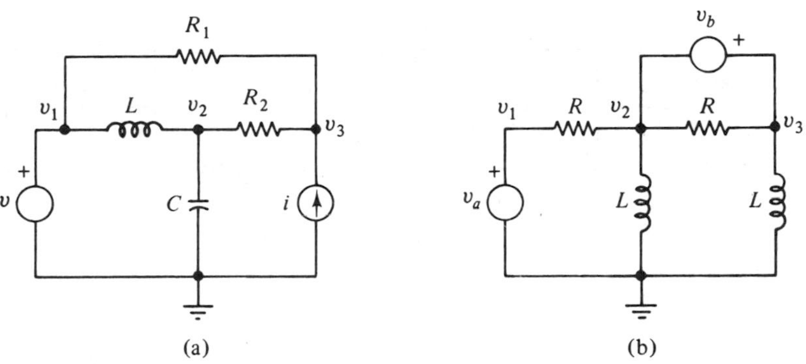

Fig. 4-41

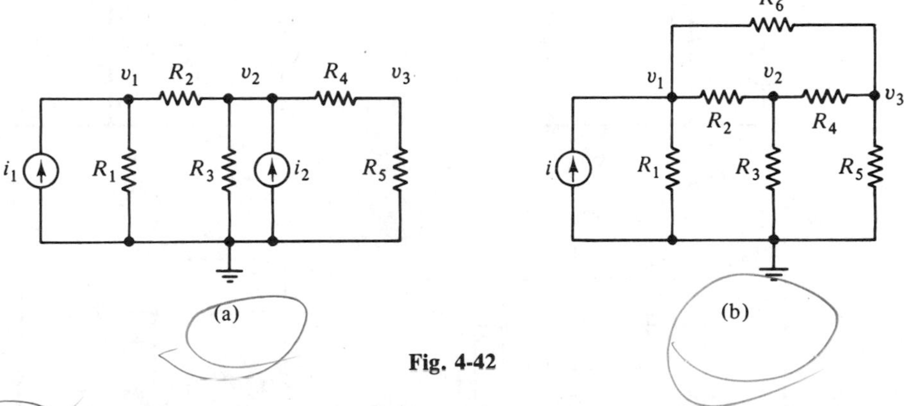

Fig. 4-42

4-14. For the problem given in Example 4-9, check the expression for i_3 by using superposition.

4-15. What is i_0 in Fig. 4-44?

4-16. Write the mesh and node determinants for the network shown in Fig. 4-45.

4-17. In Fig. 4-46, i_3 can be obtained from Δ_3/Δ. What is Δ_3?

4-18. In Fig. 4-47, v_1 can be obtained from Δ_1/Δ. What is Δ_1?

4-19. In a three-mesh network, i_1 is given by

$$i_1 = \frac{\begin{vmatrix} -1 & 0 & -1 \\ 1 & 1 & -1 \\ 0 & -1 & 3 \end{vmatrix}}{\begin{vmatrix} 2 & 0 & -1 \\ 0 & 1 & -1 \\ -1 & -1 & 3 \end{vmatrix}}$$

Draw the schematic diagram of the network.

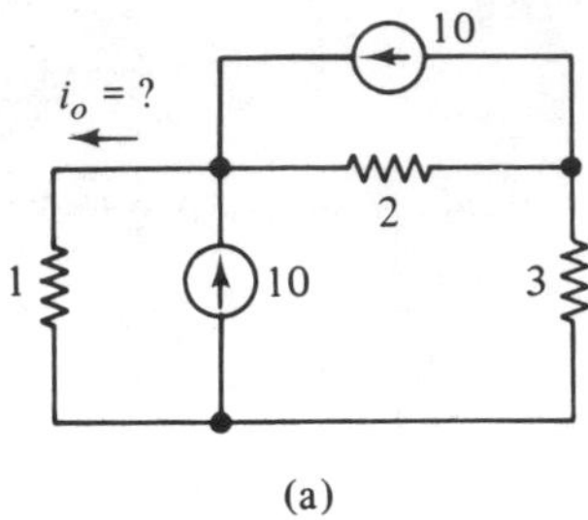

(a)

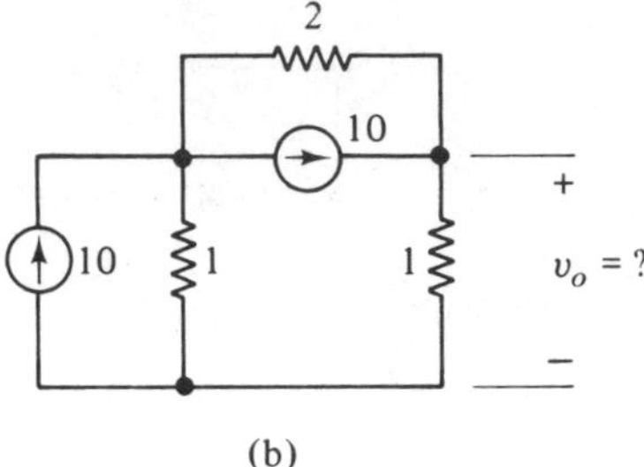

(b)

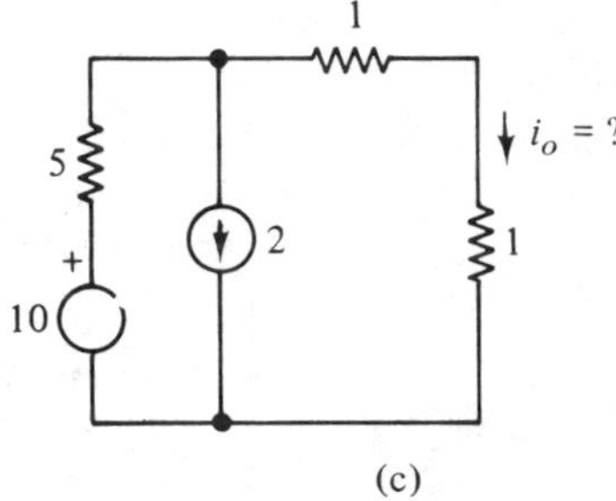

(c)

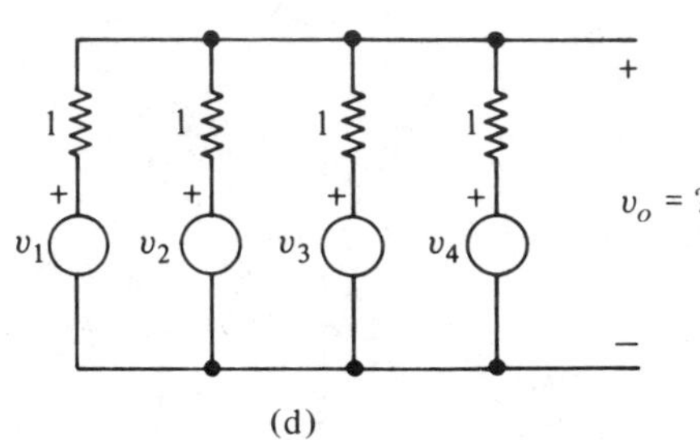

(d)

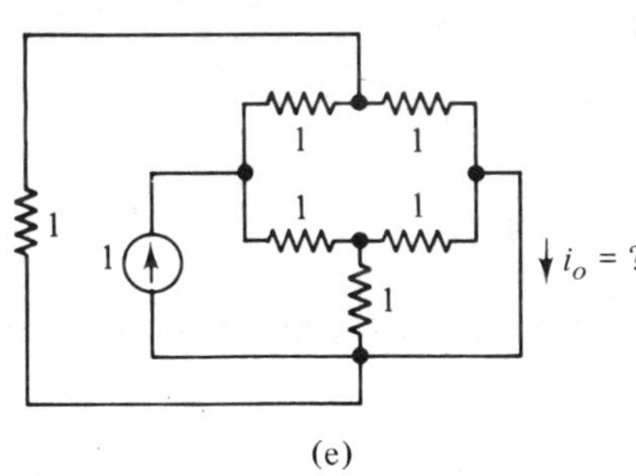

(e)

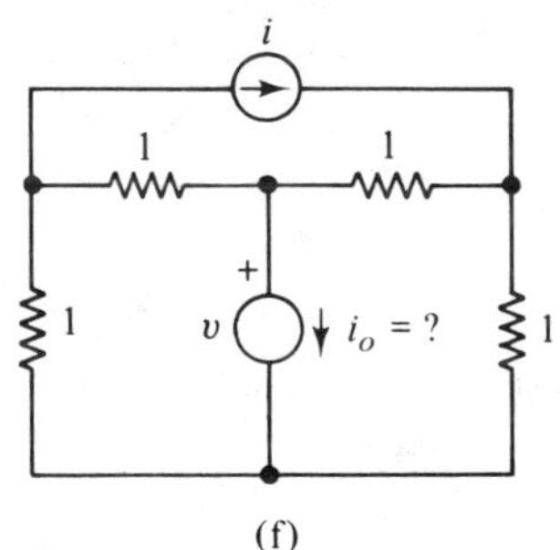

(f)

Fig. 4-43

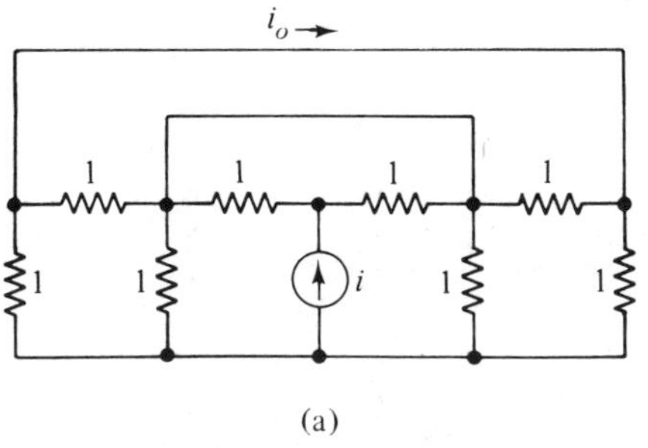

(a)

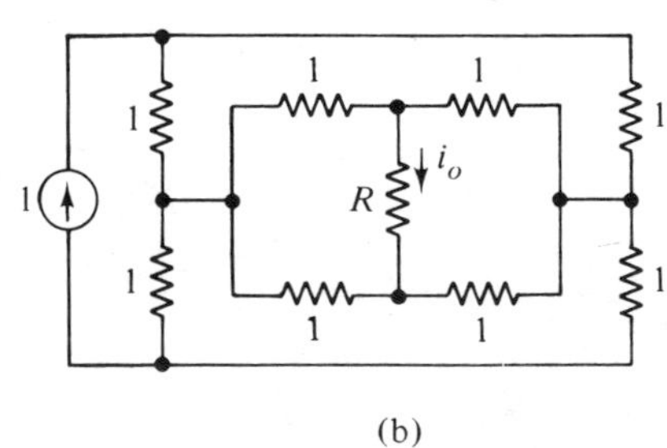

(b)

Fig. 4-44

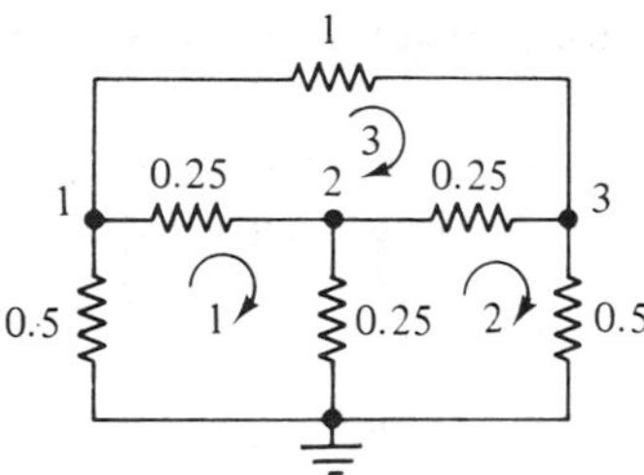

Fig. 4-45

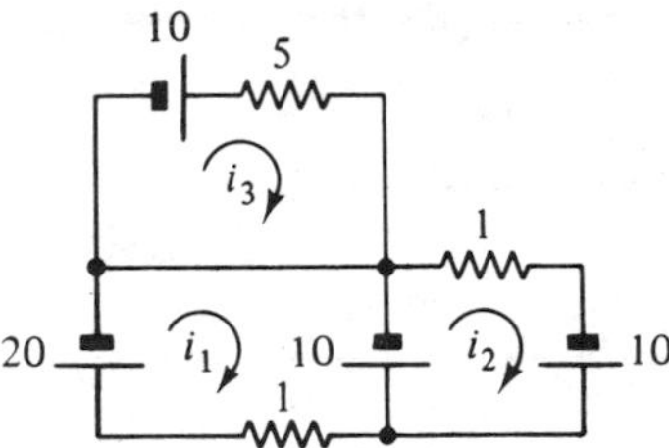

Fig. 4-46

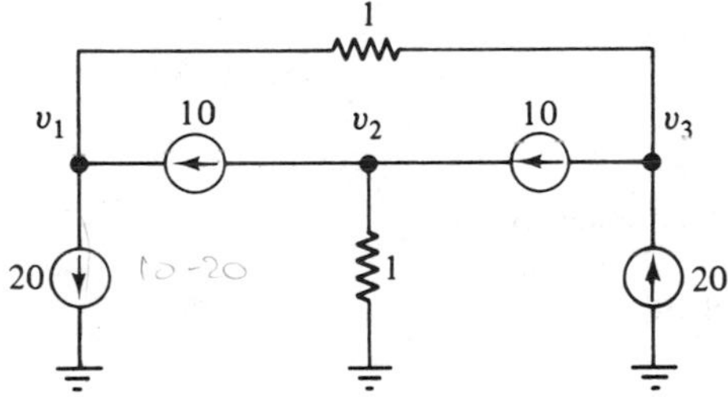

Fig. 4-47

4-20. In a three-node network (excluding the reference mode), v_2 is given by

$$v_2 = \frac{\begin{vmatrix} 2 & 1 & -1 \\ -1 & 0 & -1 \\ 1 & 1 & 2 \end{vmatrix}}{\begin{vmatrix} 2 & -1 & -1 \\ -1 & 3 & -1 \\ -1 & -1 & 2 \end{vmatrix}}$$

Draw the schematic diagram of the network.

4-21. In a three-mesh network, the current i_1 is given by

$$i_1 = \frac{\begin{vmatrix} -8 & -2 & 0 \\ 0 & 6 & -2 \\ 8 & -2 & 4 \end{vmatrix}}{\begin{vmatrix} 4 & -2 & 0 \\ -2 & 6 & -2 \\ 0 & -2 & 4 \end{vmatrix}}$$

The network contains one voltage source. Draw the network and give element values.

4-22. Refer to Fig. 4-48. Show that all currents and hence all voltages in the circuit can be calculated by inspection of the circuit.

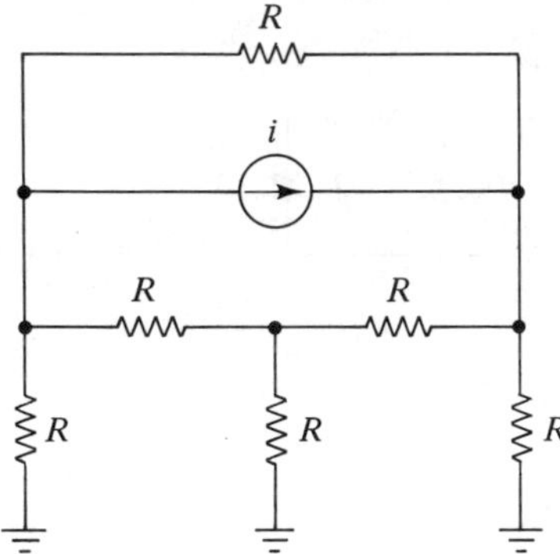

Fig. 4-48

4-23. Refer to Fig. 4-49.

(**a**) Evaluate the mesh determinant Δ.

(**b**) Obtain i_1, i_2, and i_3.

(**c**) Explain the results of (b).

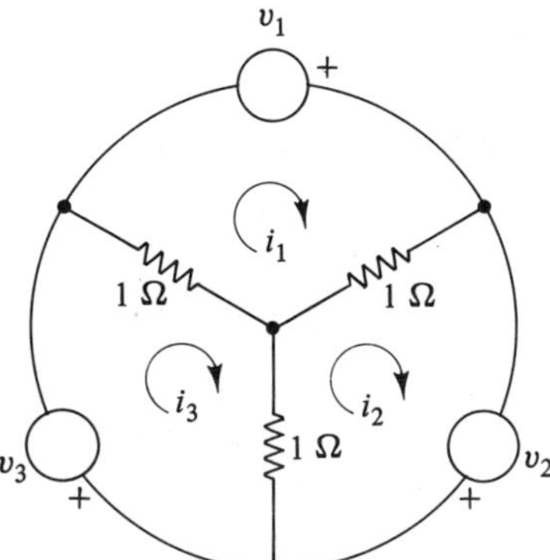

Fig. 4-49

CHAPTER 5

SOLVING NETWORK PROBLEMS BY LAPLACE TRANSFORMATION

Calculating voltages and currents in a resistive network to which excitation is applied is a straightforward process. It is not such a simple matter to calculate voltages and currents in networks that also contain energy storage elements, like capacitors and inductors, which have characteristics defined by derivative relationships $[v = L(di/dt),\ i = C(dv/dt)]$. The resulting equations are differential equations, and their solutions require greater effort. Such equations can be solved by classical methods. Engineers working with circuits, however, prefer the Laplace-transform method, which is simpler to use and gives insight into the operation of circuits. This chapter provides a working knowledge of Laplace transformation and applies it to the solution of networks employing *RLC* elements.

Laplace transformation requires familiarity with complex numbers. The reader unfamiliar with these numbers should consult Appendix 2 in order to acquire the necessary skill.

5-1 LAPLACE TRANSFORMATION

The variables $v(t)$ and $i(t)$ are *time-domain variables*. They are measured in the time domain (at a particular instant of time) by using voltmeters and ammeters. In addition, they can be displayed on an oscilloscope as a function of time. Experimental work gives us information about $v(t)$ and $i(t)$. Therefore no matter which approach we use in solving network problems, we like to see or interpret the end result in terms of what is happening in the familiar time domain. In order to obtain a solution, however, we may get away from the time domain for awhile, but our eventual purpose is to return to the time domain so as to interpret results. Because it gives us a means of solving network equations with little effort, we turn now to the Laplace transformation.

The *Laplace transform* of the function $f(t)$ is given by

$$\mathscr{L}\{f(t)\} = \int_0^\infty f(t)e^{-st}\, dt = F(s) \tag{5-1}$$

Because the limits of integration are $t = 0$ and $t = \infty$, the Laplace transform of $f(t)$ is not a function of time but rather a function of s, which is introduced via the factor e^{-st}. The variable s is called the *complex-frequency variable*. The transformed function, $F(s)$, is a function in the complex-frequency domain or, briefly, in the frequency domain. Note that we denote functions in *the time domain by the lower-case f and functions in the frequency domain by the uppercase F*.

Two functions which are the same for $t > 0$ but different for $t < 0$ will have the same Laplace transform because the integration in Eq. (5-1) is over the positive time interval only.

In order to be Laplace transformable, a function must be piecewise continuous and of exponential order. If $f(t)$ contains only a finite number of finite-isolated discontinuities, it is piecewise continuous. If, for M a positive constant and γ a real number, $|f(t)| < Me^{\gamma t}$ as t approaches infinity, $f(t)$ is of exponential order. Most functions associated with actual circuits are Laplace transformable. We can, however, construct a function that is not Laplace transformable. For instance, $f(t) = e^{t^2}$ cannot be Laplace transformed because it is not of exponential order. (There are no M and γ that will make $|e^{t^2}|$ less than $Me^{\gamma t}$ as $t \to \infty$.)

Upon transformation the two electrical variables, $v(t)$ and $i(t)$, become $V(s)$ and $I(s)$. They are given by

$$V(s) = \int_0^\infty v(t)e^{-st}\, dt, \qquad I(s) = \int_0^\infty i(t)e^{-st}\, dt \tag{5-2}$$

Thus voltages and currents become functions of s. Time is no longer there. We cannot display $V(s)$ and $I(s)$ on an oscilloscope. Nonetheless, we can work with these variables in the frequency domain and learn to use them and even relate their frequency-domain properties to their time-domain properties.

We must excite an *RLC* network in order to obtain a response. (Without excitation all responses are zero.) A very general *excitation function is* e^{kt}. Depending on the value of k, it can represent an exponential decay ($k < 0$), a constant ($k = 0$), or an exponential growth ($k > 0$). Assuming that the excitation is zero prior to $t = 0$ and is e^{kt} after $t = 0$, the excitation can be represented by one of the waveforms shown in Fig. 5-1.

By allowing k to be a complex number and combining two complex exponential functions with proper scale factors, it is possible to generate exponentially

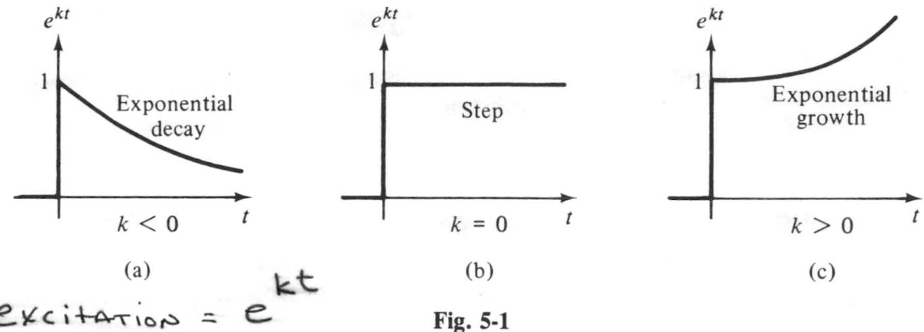

Fig. 5-1

damped sine waves, sine waves, and exponentially growing sine waves as shown below.

$$\left(\frac{1}{2j}\right)e^{(-\alpha+j\beta)t} - \left(\frac{1}{2j}\right)e^{(-\alpha-j\beta)t} = \frac{e^{-\alpha t}(e^{j\beta t} - e^{-j\beta t})}{2j} = e^{-\alpha t}\sin\beta t \tag{5-3a}$$

$$\left(\frac{1}{2j}\right)e^{j\beta t} - \left(\frac{1}{2j}\right)e^{-j\beta t} = \frac{e^{j\beta t} - e^{-j\beta t}}{2j} = \sin\beta t \tag{5-3b}$$

$$\left(\frac{1}{2j}\right)e^{(\alpha+j\beta)t} - \left(\frac{1}{2j}\right)e^{(\alpha-j\beta)t} = \frac{e^{\alpha t}(e^{j\beta t} - e^{-j\beta t})}{2j} = e^{\alpha t}\sin\beta t \tag{5-3c}$$

These waveforms are sketched in Fig. 5-2.

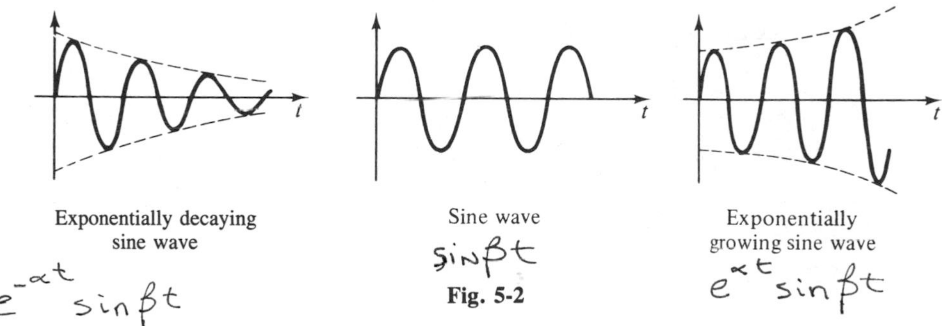

Exponentially decaying sine wave

Sine wave

Exponentially growing sine wave

Fig. 5-2

The Laplace transform of the function e^{kt} is obtained by using Eq. (5-1)

$$\mathscr{L}\{e^{kt}\} = \int_0^\infty e^{kt}e^{-st}\,dt \tag{5-4}$$

$$\mathscr{L}\{e^{kt}\} = \int_0^\infty e^{(k-s)t}\,dt = \left.\frac{e^{(k-s)t}}{(k-s)}\right|_0^\infty \tag{5-5}$$

The exponent $k - s$ is complex. However, we can require that Re $\{k - s\}$ be negative. As a result,

$$e^{(k-s)t} \longrightarrow 0 \quad \text{as} \quad t \longrightarrow \infty$$

Consequently, the evaluation at the upper limit results in zero. At the lower limit we have

$$\left.\frac{e^{(k-s)t}}{k-s}\right|_{t=0} = \frac{1}{k-s}$$

So Eq. (5-5) simplifies to

$$\mathcal{L}\{e^{kt}\} = \frac{1}{s-k} \tag{5-6}$$

For $k = 0$, Eq. (5-6) reduces to

$$\mathcal{L}\{1\} = \frac{1}{s} \tag{5-7}$$

This is an important and much-used result. It represents the Laplace transform of the unit-step function shown in Fig. 5-1(b). Such a function results when a 1 V dc voltage or a 1 A dc current is applied to a circuit at $t = 0$.

Other widely used excitation functions are the sine and cosine waves. Since these waves can be expressed in terms of exponentials,

$$\sin \omega t = \frac{e^{j\omega t} - e^{-j\omega t}}{2j}, \qquad \cos \omega t = \frac{e^{j\omega t} + e^{-j\omega t}}{2}$$

we can easily obtain their Laplace transforms. For instance,

$$\begin{aligned}\mathcal{L}\{\sin \omega t\} &= \int_0^\infty (\sin \omega t)e^{-st}\,dt = \int_0^\infty \left(\frac{e^{j\omega t} - e^{-j\omega t}}{2j}\right)e^{-st}\,dt \\ &= \frac{1}{2j}\left[\int_0^\infty e^{j\omega t}e^{-st}\,dt - \int_0^\infty e^{-j\omega t}e^{-st}\,dt\right]\end{aligned} \tag{5-8}$$

The first integral within the brackets is the Laplace transform of e^{kt} with $k = j\omega$. The second integral is the Laplace transform of e^{kt} with $k = -j\omega$. Thus Eq. (5-8) can be evaluated by using (5-6) with $k = \pm j\omega$.

$$\mathcal{L}\{\sin \omega t\} = \frac{1}{2j}\left(\frac{1}{s-j\omega} - \frac{1}{s+j\omega}\right) = \frac{1}{2j}\left[\frac{(s+j\omega)-(s-j\omega)}{(s-j\omega)(s+j\omega)}\right] = \frac{\omega}{s^2+\omega^2} \tag{5-9}$$

Similarly, we obtain

$$\mathcal{L}\{\cos \omega t\} = \int_0^\infty \left(\frac{e^{j\omega t} + e^{-j\omega t}}{2}\right)e^{-st}\,dt = \frac{s}{s^2+\omega^2} \tag{5-10}$$

The Laplace transform of commonly used functions is given in Table 5-1. The transforms are obtained by applying Eq. (5-1).

TABLE 5-1

$f(t)(t \geq 0)$	$F(s)$
1	$\frac{1}{s}$
$e^{-\alpha t}$	$\frac{1}{s + \alpha}$
$\sin \omega t$	$\frac{\omega}{s^2 + \omega^2}$
$\cos \omega t$	$\frac{s}{s^2 + \omega^2}$
$e^{-\alpha t} \sin \omega t$	$\frac{\omega}{(s + \alpha)^2 + \omega^2}$
$e^{-\alpha t} \cos \omega t$	$\frac{s + \alpha}{(s + \alpha)^2 + \omega^2}$
t	$\frac{1}{s^2}$
$te^{-\alpha t}$	$\frac{1}{(s + \alpha)^2}$

5-2 OPERATIONAL RULES

Using the transformation defined by Eq. (5-1), we can develop five operational rules that are necessary for obtaining the frequency-domain solution of linear, constant coefficient, differential equations. It is assumed that the functions under consideration are Laplace transformable.

1. If $f_1(t)$ and $f_2(t)$ are two functions of time, then

$$\mathscr{L}\{f_1(t) + f_2(t)\} = F_1(s) + F_2(s)$$

Thus the Laplace transform of the sum of two functions is the sum of the Laplace transforms of each individual function.

2. If a is not a function of t, then

$$\mathscr{L}\{af(t)\} = a\mathscr{L}\{f(t)\} = aF(s)$$

So the Laplace transform of a constant times $f(t)$ is the Laplace transform of $f(t)$ multiplied by the constant.

3.

$$\mathscr{L}\left\{\frac{df((t)}{dt}\right\} = sF(s) - f(0) \tag{5-11}$$

provided that $df(t)/dt$ is Laplace transformable. Equation (5-11) states that the Laplace transform of the time derivative of a function is equal to s times the Laplace transform of the function minus the initial value of the function. Implicit in Eq. (5-11) is the understanding that $f(t)$ is differentiable. In particular, if $f(t)$ takes a jump at $t = 0$, it does not possess a derivative at $t = 0$. However, we can still use Eq. (5-11) if derivative is understood to mean the right-hand derivative—that is

$$\left.\frac{df(t)}{dt}\right|_{t \to 0 \text{ from the right}}$$

in which case $f(0)$ is taken as $f(0^+)$—that is,

$$f(0^+) = f(t)|_{t \to 0 \text{ from the right}}$$

If $f(0) = 0$, then Eq. (5-11) reduces to

$$\mathcal{L}\left\{\frac{df(t)}{dt}\right\} = sF(s) \tag{5-12}$$

In this case, differentiation with respect to t in the time domain goes over in the frequency domain as multiplication with s

4.
$$\mathcal{L}\left\{\frac{d^2f(t)}{dt^2}\right\} = s^2F(s) - sf(0) - f'(0) \tag{5-13}$$

where $f'(0)$ denotes the derivative of $f(t)$ with respect to t evaluated at $t = 0$. This result assumes that $d^2f(t)/dt^2$ is Laplace transformable.

5.
$$\mathcal{L}\left\{\int_0^t f(t')\,dt'\right\} = \frac{1}{s}F(s) \tag{5-14}$$

The Laplace transform of the integral of $f(t')$ between the limits of 0 and t is $1/s$ times the Laplace transform of $f(t')$. Thus integration with respect to t' in the time domain goes over as division by s in the frequency domain.

Example 5-1

Show that

$$\mathcal{L}\left\{\frac{df(t)}{dt}\right\} = sF(s) - f(0)$$

Solution.

$$\mathcal{L}\left\{\frac{df(t)}{dt}\right\} = \int_0^\infty \left[\frac{df(t)}{dt}\right]e^{-st}\,dt$$

Integrating by parts, we obtain

$$\mathcal{L}\left\{\frac{df(t)}{dt}\right\} = e^{-st}f(t)\Big|_0^\infty - \int_0^\infty f(t)(-se^{-st})dt$$

With Re $\{s\} > 0$, the evaluation of the first term results in zero at the upper limit and $f(0)$ at the lower limit. Hence we obtain

$$\mathcal{L}\left\{\frac{df(t)}{dt}\right\} = -f(0) + s\int_0^\infty f(t)e^{-st}\,dt$$

By definition, the integral on the right represents the Laplace transform of $f(t)$. Consequently, we have

$$\mathcal{L}\left\{\frac{df(t)}{dt}\right\} = sF(s) - f(0) \quad \text{Ans.}$$

Example 5-2

Show that

$$\mathcal{L}\left\{\int_0^t f(t')dt'\right\} = \frac{1}{s}F(s)$$

Solution.

$$\mathcal{L}\left\{\int_0^t f(t')\,dt'\right\} = \int_0^\infty \left[\int_0^t f(t')\,dt'\right]e^{-st}\,dt$$

Integrating by parts, we have

$$\mathcal{L}\left\{\int_0^t f(t')\,dt'\right\} = \frac{e^{-st}}{-s}\int_0^t f(t')\,dt'\,\bigg|_0^\infty - \int_0^\infty \left(\frac{e^{-st}}{-s}\right)f(t)\,dt$$

The evaluation of the first term at the upper limit results in zero. The evaluation of the first term at the lower limit results in zero, too, because the interval of integration is zero. So we obtain

$$\mathcal{L}\left\{\int_0^t f(t')\,dt'\right\} = \frac{1}{s}\int_0^\infty f(t)e^{-st}\,dt$$

The integral on the right is, by definition, the Laplace transform of $f(t)$. Therefore we can write the result as

$$\mathcal{L}\left\{\int_0^t f(t')\,dt'\right\} = \frac{1}{s}F(s) \quad \text{Ans.}$$

5-3 LAPLACE TRANSFORMATION OF DIFFERENTIAL EQUATIONS

Consider the linear, constant coefficient, second-order differential equation

$$a_2\frac{d^2f(t)}{dt^2} + a_1\frac{df(t)}{dt} + a_0f(t) = g(t) \tag{5-15}$$

The a coefficients and $g(t)$ are known. The problem is to find the solution—that is, obtain $f(t)$ for a given set of initial conditions. We now assume that the known $g(t)$ and the unknown $f(t)$ are Laplace transformable. Let the Laplace transforms of $f(t)$

and $g(t)$ be $F(s)$ and $G(s)$, respectively, and transform both sides of Eq. (5-15) by using the operational rules given in Section 5-2.

$$\mathcal{L}\left\{a_2\frac{d^2f(t)}{dt^2} + a_1\frac{df(t)}{dt} + a_0f(t)\right\} = \mathcal{L}\{g(t)\}$$

$$\mathcal{L}\left\{a_2\frac{d^2f(t)}{dt^2}\right\} + \mathcal{L}\left\{a_1\frac{df(t)}{dt}\right\} + \mathcal{L}\{a_0f(t)\} = \mathcal{L}\{g(t)\} \quad \text{(rule 1)}$$

$$a_2\mathcal{L}\left\{\frac{d^2f(t)}{dt^2}\right\} + a_1\mathcal{L}\left\{\frac{df(t)}{dt}\right\} + a_0\mathcal{L}\{f(t)\} = \mathcal{L}\{g(t)\} \quad \text{(rule 2)}$$

$$a_2[s^2F(s) - sf(0) - f'(0)] + a_1[sF(s) - f(0)] + a_0F(s) = G(s) \quad \text{(rules 3 and 4)} \tag{5-16}$$

Thus *the differential equation,* given by Eq. (5-15), *is transformed to the algebraic equation* of (5-16), which can now be easily solved for the transform of the desired solution.

$$F(s) = \frac{G(s) + a_2[sf(0) + f'(0)] + a_1f(0)}{a_2s^2 + a_1s + a_0} \tag{5-17}$$

If all initial conditions are zero—that is, $f(0) = f'(0) = 0$—this equation simplifies to

$$F(s) = \frac{G(s)}{a_2s^2 + a_1s + a_0} \tag{5-18}$$

which is the frequency-domain solution to the differential equation (with zero initial conditions). To return to the time domain, we need to find the inverse transform of $F(s)$—that is,

$$f(t) = \mathcal{L}^{-1}\{F(s)\} = \mathcal{L}^{-1}\left\{\frac{G(s)}{a_2s^2 + a_1s + a_0}\right\}$$

For the moment, however, we are satisfied in obtaining the Laplace transform of the desired solution. In a later section we will learn how to obtain the inverse transformation.

5-4 LAPLACE TRANSFORMATION OF KIRCHHOFF'S LAWS AND ELEMENT-DEFINING EQUATIONS

In the time domain, Kirchhoff's current and voltage laws are

$$\sum i(t) = 0 \quad \text{at every node}$$

$$\sum v(t) = 0 \quad \text{for every loop}$$

Let $I(s)$ be the Laplace transform of $i(t)$ and $V(s)$ be the Laplace transform of $v(t)$. Then, on transformation, Kirchhoff's laws become

$$\sum I(s) = 0 \tag{5-19a}$$

$$\sum V(s) = 0 \tag{5-19b}$$

In the time domain, the terminal variables for a resistor are related by

$$v(t) = Ri(t)$$

Upon transformation, this equation becomes

$$V(s) = RI(s) \tag{5-20}$$

In the frequency domain, then, the voltage across a resistor is related to the current through it by Eq. (5-20). R is called the *impedance,* or resistance, of the resistor. $1/R = G$ is called the *admittance,* or conductance, of the resistor.

In the time domain, the terminal variables for a capacitor are related by

$$i(t) = C\frac{dv(t)}{dt} \tag{5-21a}$$

or

$$v(t) = \gamma + \frac{1}{C}\int_0^t i(t')\, dt' \tag{5-21b}$$

where γ represents the initial value (the $t = 0$ value) of the voltage across the capacitor—that is, $\gamma = v(0)$.

Upon transformation, Eq. (5-21a) becomes

$$I(s) = C[sV(s) - v(0)] \tag{5-22}$$

Since $v(0) = \gamma$, Eq. (5-22) can be written

$$I(s) = C[sV(s) - \gamma] \tag{5-23}$$

Since $\mathcal{L}\{\gamma\} = (1/s)\gamma$, Eq. (5-21b) transforms into

$$V(s) = \frac{\gamma}{s} + \frac{1}{sC}I(s) \tag{5-24}$$

Equations (5-23) and (5-24) are equivalent statements, as can be seen by solving (5-23) for $V(s)$. In particular, if the initial value of the voltage across the capacitor is zero, (5-24) reduces to

$$V(s) = \frac{1}{sC}I(s) \tag{5-25}$$

Thus, in the frequency domain, the voltage across a capacitor *with zero initial voltage* is found by multiplying the current through it by $1/sC$. See Eq. (5-25). $1/sC$ is called the *impedance* of the capacitor, sC is called the *admittance* of the capacitor.

The terminal variables for an inductor in the time domain are related by

$$v(t) = L\frac{di(t)}{dt} \tag{5-26a}$$

or

$$i(t) = \rho + \frac{1}{L}\int_0^t v(t')\,dt' \tag{5-26b}$$

where ρ represents the initial value of the current through the inductor—that is, $\rho = i(0)$. If we transform Eq. (5-26), we obtain

$$V(s) = L[sI(s) - i(0)] = sLI(s) - \rho L \tag{5-27a}$$

or

$$I(s) = \frac{\rho}{s} + \frac{1}{L}\frac{V(s)}{s} \tag{5-27b}$$

In particular, if the initial value of the current through the inductor is zero, Eq. (5-27) becomes

$$V(s) = sLI(s) \tag{5-28}$$

In the frequency domain, therefore, the voltage across an inductor *with zero initial current* is found by multiplying the current through it by sL. See Eq. (5-28). sL is called the *impedance* of the inductor; $1/sL$ is called the *admittance* of the inductor.

The element-defining relations in the time and frequency domains are summarized in Table 5-2. *Initial conditions are assumed to be zero*. Impedances are designated by the symbol Z and admittances by the symbol Y. It should be clear that

TABLE 5-2

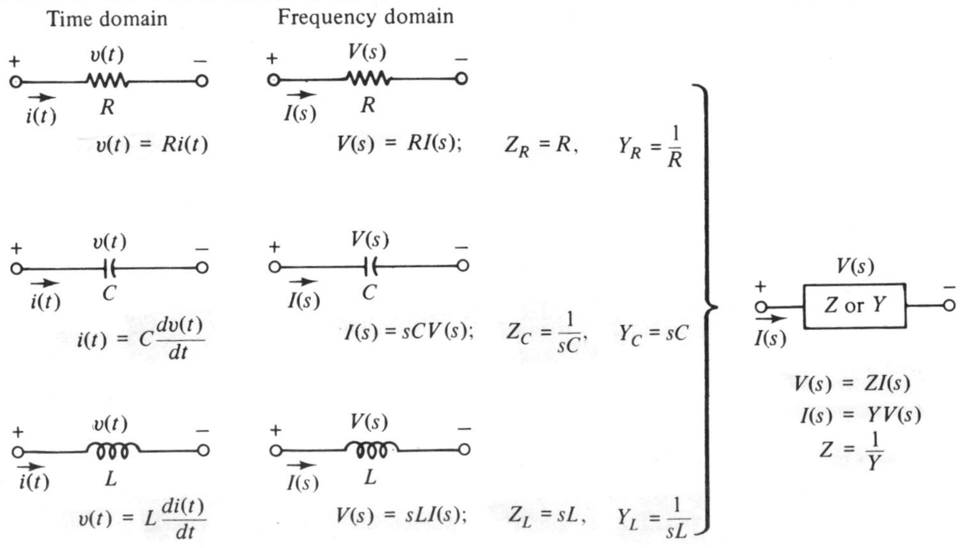

Time domain	Frequency domain		
+ $v(t)$ −, $i(t)$ → R	+ $V(s)$ −, $I(s)$ → R		
$v(t) = Ri(t)$	$V(s) = RI(s)$;	$Z_R = R$,	$Y_R = \frac{1}{R}$
+ $v(t)$ −, $i(t)$ → C	+ $V(s)$ −, $I(s)$ → C		
$i(t) = C\frac{dv(t)}{dt}$	$I(s) = sCV(s)$;	$Z_C = \frac{1}{sC}$,	$Y_C = sC$
+ $v(t)$ −, $i(t)$ → L	+ $V(s)$ −, $I(s)$ → L		
$v(t) = L\frac{di(t)}{dt}$	$V(s) = sLI(s)$;	$Z_L = sL$,	$Y_L = \frac{1}{sL}$

+ $V(s)$ −, $I(s)$ → Z or Y

$V(s) = ZI(s)$

$I(s) = YV(s)$

$Z = \frac{1}{Y}$

$$Y = \frac{1}{Z}, \qquad V = IZ, \qquad I = VY$$

It takes only one equation, $V = IZ$ or $I = VY$, to describe the terminal properties of a resistor, capacitor, or inductor. It is this generality that makes the concept of impedance (or admittance) so useful. Note that in the frequency domain all relationships are algebraic. No derivative or integral relationships appear in the frequency-domain expressions.

When a capacitor has an initial voltage γ and an inductor has an initial current ρ, we have the situation shown in Fig. 5-3(a), in which the initial condition is represented either next to the element itself or as a separate source in conjunction with the element. This latter designation makes it conceptually easier to write the relationship between the terminal voltage and current. Recalling that the transform of a constant is the constant divided by s, we can redraw Fig. 5-3(a) as in Fig. 5-3(b) to emphasize the fact that initial-condition sources must be divided by s in the frequency-domain representation. Thus initial conditions are treated as step-function sources applied to the network at $t = 0$.

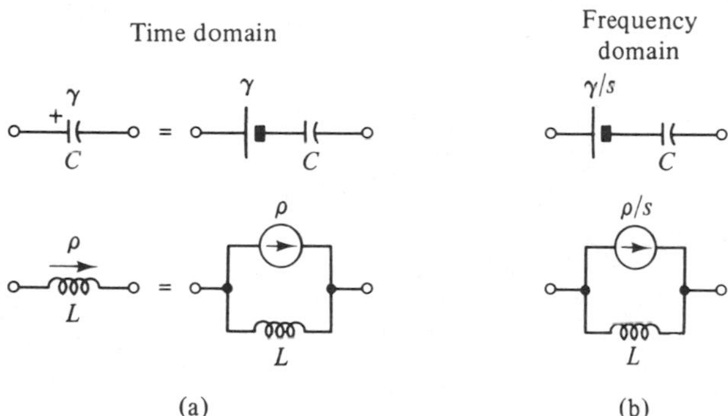

Fig. 5-3

Henceforth initial conditions are assumed to be zero unless their nonzero values are specifically indicated next to capacitors and inductors.

5-5 LAPLACE TRANSFORMATION OF NETWORK EQUATIONS

In order to see how the Laplace transformation is applied to the solution of network problems, consider the network of Fig. 5-4(a). The initial conditions are zero. We wish to find $V_o(s)$. The solution will be obtained by using mesh equations first. By inspection of Fig. 5-4(a), the two time-domain equations are written

$$\begin{aligned}\left(L\frac{di_1}{dt} + \frac{1}{C}\int_0^t i_1\,dt'\right) - \left(\frac{1}{C}\int_0^t i_2\,dt'\right) &= v_i \\ -\left(\frac{1}{C}\int_0^t i_1\,dt'\right) + \left(Ri_2 + \frac{1}{C}\int_0^t i_2\,dt'\right) &= 0\end{aligned} \tag{5-29}$$

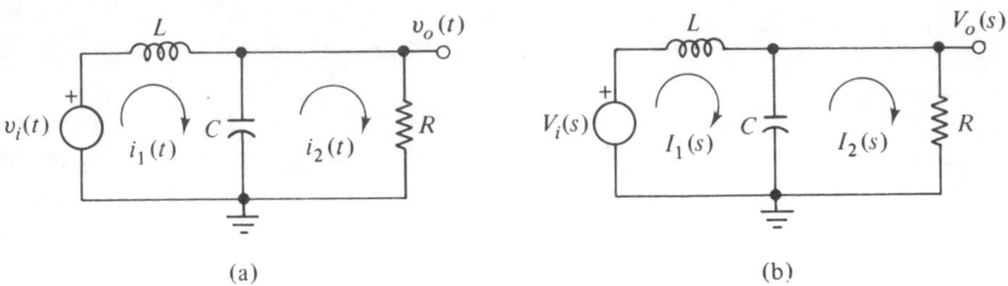

Fig. 5-4

In these equations the functional dependence on time, being understood, is omitted and currents and voltages are written i_1, i_2, v_i. The two unknowns are i_1 and i_2. Let their transforms be I_1 and I_2, where the functional dependence on s, being understood, is also left out. Let $\mathcal{L}\{v_i\} = V_i$. When the set given by Eq. (5-29) is transformed, we have

$$\left[L(sI_1) + \frac{1}{C}\left(\frac{I_1}{s}\right)\right] - \left[\frac{1}{C}\left(\frac{I_2}{s}\right)\right] = V_i$$

$$-\left[\frac{1}{C}\left(\frac{I_1}{s}\right)\right] + \left[R(I_2) + \frac{1}{C}\left(\frac{I_2}{s}\right)\right] = 0$$

When ordered, the transformed set becomes

$$\begin{aligned}\left(sL + \frac{1}{sC}\right)I_1 - \left(\frac{1}{sC}\right)I_2 &= V_i \\ -\left(\frac{1}{sC}\right)I_1 + \left(R + \frac{1}{sC}\right)I_2 &= 0\end{aligned} \tag{5-30}$$

Thus the time-domain integrodifferential equations become the frequency domain algebraic equations. Compare Eq. (5-29) with Eq. (5-30). The transformed equations suggest that we could have written them directly by inspection of Fig. 5-4(b), in which all variables are designated with their transforms. So making use of the fact that the voltage across an inductor is $I(sL)$ and across a capacitor $I(1/sC)$, the mesh equation can be easily written as in Eq. (5-30). The determinant of this set of equations is

$$\Delta = \begin{vmatrix} \left(sL + \dfrac{1}{sC}\right) & -\dfrac{1}{sC} \\ -\dfrac{1}{sC} & \left(R + \dfrac{1}{sC}\right) \end{vmatrix} = \begin{vmatrix} a_{11} & a_{12} \\ a_{21} & a_{22} \end{vmatrix}$$

Examination of the elements of the determinant shows that we could have eliminated all the previous work and written the determinant directly from the network diagram of Fig. 5-4(a). In the a_{11} position we have the sum of impedances in mesh 1—that is, sL for the inductor and $1/sC$ for the capacitor. In the a_{12} position we have the negative of the sum of impedances between meshes 1 and 2, which, in this case, is $-1/sC$. Since $a_{21} = a_{12}$, we have $-1/sC$ in the a_{21} position. In the a_{22} position we have the sum of impedances in mesh 2—that is, R for the resistor and $1/sC$ for the capacitor. Note that the determinant provides a description of the elements of the network and the way in which they are connected with *all sources made zero*.

The value of the determinant is

$$\Delta = a_{11}a_{22} - a_{12}a_{21} = \left(sL + \frac{1}{sC}\right)\left(R + \frac{1}{sC}\right) - \left(-\frac{1}{sC}\right)\left(-\frac{1}{sC}\right)$$

$$= sRL + \frac{L}{C} + \frac{R}{sC} = \frac{LR}{s}\left(s^2 + \frac{1}{RC}s + \frac{1}{LC}\right) \tag{5-31}$$

As Eq. (5-31) shows, once the negative terms are canceled, all the terms in the determinant are positive. Such is always the case when the network is excited only by independent sources. (If the sense of either mesh current is reversed, all the terms of the determinant become negative.)

In order to solve for V_o, we need to find I_2 first. In order to find I_2, we need to form Δ_2 and evaluate it. Δ_2 is obtained by replacing the second column of Δ with the sources acting on the two meshes. In this case, we have one source, V_i, acting in mesh 1. Mesh 2 contains no sources.

$$\Delta_2 = \begin{vmatrix} sL + \dfrac{1}{sC} & V_i \\ -\dfrac{1}{sC} & 0 \end{vmatrix} = V_i\frac{1}{sC}$$

So I_2 is

$$I_2 = \frac{\Delta_2}{\Delta} = V_i\frac{1}{sC}\bigg/\frac{LR}{s}\left(s^2 + \frac{1}{RC}s + \frac{1}{LC}\right) = \left[\frac{1}{RLC}\bigg/\left(s^2 + \frac{1}{RC}s + \frac{1}{LC}\right)\right]V_i$$

Since

$$V_o = I_2R$$

we have

$$V_o = \left[\frac{1}{LC}\bigg/\left(s^2 + \frac{1}{RC}s + \frac{1}{LC}\right)\right]V_i \tag{5-32}$$

Thus we have obtained V_o by the method of mesh analysis. Had we solved this problem by the node-analysis method, we would have arrived at the answer with much less work because in Fig. 5-4(b) there is only one unknown node voltage—namely, V_o. Therefore we need write only one equation. By inspection of Fig. 5-4(b), the node equation for the output node (top node) can be written

$$\underbrace{\frac{V_o - V_i}{sL}}_{\substack{\text{Current}\\\text{through}\\\text{inductor}}} + \underbrace{V_o sC}_{\substack{\text{Current}\\\text{through}\\\text{capacitor}}} + \underbrace{\frac{V_o}{R}}_{\substack{\text{Current}\\\text{through}\\\text{resistor}}} = 0 \tag{5-33}$$

When Eq. (5-33) is solved for V_o, we obtain Eq. (5-32).

As another illustration, consider the network shown in Fig. 5-5. The variables are designated with capital letters, thereby indicating that we are in the frequency domain. A current source excites the network, and there are two unknown node voltages: V_i and V_o. So we will use the node-analysis method of solution to obtain V_o. Working in the frequency domain, we have

$$\underbrace{(V_i - V_o)\frac{1}{sL}}_{\substack{\text{Current}\\\text{through } L}} + \underbrace{(V_i - V_o)sC}_{\substack{\text{Current}\\\text{through } C}} + \underbrace{V_i G_s}_{\substack{\text{Current}\\\text{through } R_s}} = \underbrace{I_i}_{\substack{\text{Current}\\\text{source}}} \qquad \text{(node } i\text{)}$$

$$\underbrace{(V_o - V_i)\frac{1}{sL}}_{\substack{\text{Current}\\\text{through } L}} + \underbrace{(V_o - V_i)sC}_{\substack{\text{Current}\\\text{through } C}} + \underbrace{V_o G_L}_{\substack{\text{Current}\\\text{through } R_L}} = 0 \qquad \text{(node } o\text{)}$$

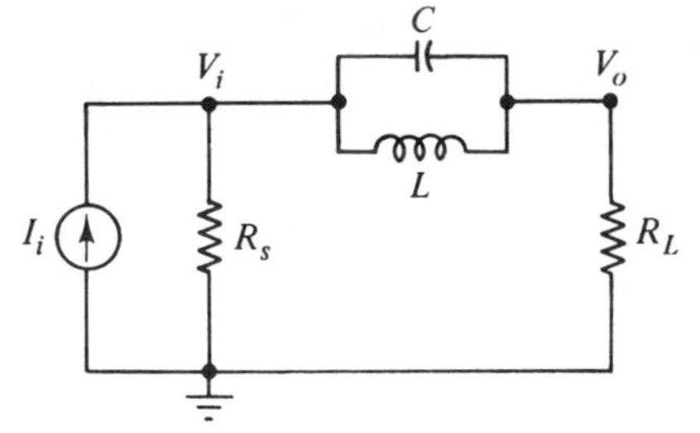

Fig. 5-5

Rearranging, we have

$$V_i\left(sC + G_s + \frac{1}{sL}\right) - V_o\left(sC + \frac{1}{sL}\right) = I_i$$

$$-V_i\left(sC + \frac{1}{sL}\right) + V_o\left(sC + G_L + \frac{1}{sL}\right) = 0$$

The determinant is

$$\Delta = \begin{vmatrix} \left(sC + G_s + \dfrac{1}{sL}\right) & -\left(sC + \dfrac{1}{sL}\right) \\ -\left(sC + \dfrac{1}{sL}\right) & \left(sC + G_L + \dfrac{1}{sL}\right) \end{vmatrix} = \begin{vmatrix} a_{11} & a_{12} \\ a_{21} & a_{22} \end{vmatrix}$$

where

$$a_{11} = \text{sum of admittances connected to node } i\text{: } \left(sC + G_s + \frac{1}{sL}\right)$$

$$a_{12} = a_{21} = -(\text{sum of admittances connected between nodes } i \text{ and } o)\text{:} -\left(sC + \frac{1}{sL}\right)$$

$$a_{22} = \text{sum of admittances connected to node } o\text{: } \left(sC + G_L + \frac{1}{sL}\right)$$

Clearly, the determinant can be written directly from the network diagram. Since we need to solve for V_o, we must form Δ_2, which is easily obtained by replacing the second column of Δ with I_i and 0 (representing current sources coming into nodes i and o).

$$\Delta_2 = \begin{vmatrix} \left(sC + G_s + \dfrac{1}{sL}\right) & I_i \\ -\left(sC + \dfrac{1}{sL}\right) & 0 \end{vmatrix}$$

Consequently,

$$\begin{aligned} V_o = \frac{\Delta_2}{\Delta} &= I_i\left(sC + \frac{1}{sL}\right)\Big/\left[\left(sC + G_s + \frac{1}{sL}\right)\left(sC + G_L + \frac{1}{sL}\right) - \left(sC + \frac{1}{sL}\right)^2\right] \\ &= \left\{\left(sC + \frac{1}{sL}\right)\Big/\left[\left(sC + \frac{1}{sL}\right)(G_s + G_L) + G_sG_L\right]\right\}I_i \\ &= \frac{R_sR_L}{R_s + R_L}\left\{\left(sC + \frac{1}{sL}\right)\Big/\left[\left(sC + \frac{1}{sL}\right) + \frac{1}{R_s + R_L}\right]\right\}I_i \\ &= \frac{R_sR_L}{R_s + R_L}\left[\left(s^2 + \frac{1}{LC}\right)\Big/\left(s^2 + s\frac{1}{(R_s + R_L)C} + \frac{1}{LC}\right)\right]I_i \end{aligned}$$

Example 5-3

For the network with mixed-source excitations shown in Fig. 5-6, set up the equations based on the mesh- as well as node-analysis methods.

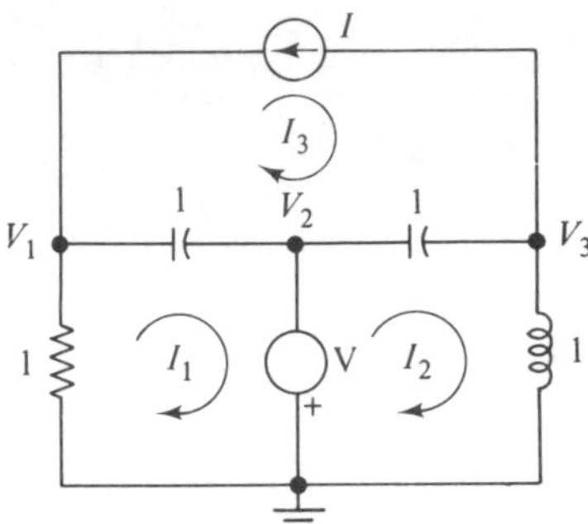

Fig. 5-6

Solution.

Equations Based on Mesh Analysis There are three mesh currents: I_1, I_2, and I_3. Since there is one current source, we must write one constraint equation. The other two equations are written for meshes 1 and 2.

$$\left.\begin{aligned} I_3 &= -I && \text{(constraint equation)} \\ I_1\left(1 + \frac{1}{s}\right) - I_3\frac{1}{s} &= V && \text{(mesh 1)} \\ I_2\left(s + \frac{1}{s}\right) - I_3\frac{1}{s} &= -V && \text{(mesh 2)} \end{aligned}\right\} \text{Ans.}$$

Equations Based on Node Analysis There are three node voltages: V_1, V_2, and V_3. Since there is one voltage source, we need to write one constraint equation. The other two equations are written for nodes 1 and 3.

$$\left.\begin{aligned} V_2 &= -V && \text{(constraint equation)} \\ V_1(s + 1) - V_2 s &= I && \text{(node 1)} \\ -V_2 s + V_3\left(s + \frac{1}{s}\right) &= -I && \text{(node 3)} \end{aligned}\right\} \text{Ans.}$$

5-6 IMPEDANCE AND ADMITTANCE

We have already seen that the impedance of a resistor is R, whereas its admittance is $1/R = G$. The impedance of an inductor is sL; the admittance is $1/sL$. The impedance of a capacitor is $1/sC$; the admittance is sC. We will now generalize these results and define impedance.

Consider a two-terminal network that contains resistors, capacitors, and inductors. (See Fig. 5-7.) These elements may be connected in any manner imaginable. The network *does not contain any independent sources. Neither does it contain any initial conditions* in the form of initial voltages on capacitors and initial currents through inductors. In other words, the network is dead; it contains no excitation. Let the terminal variables be designated by $V(s)$ and $I(s)$. Then *impedance is defined* as

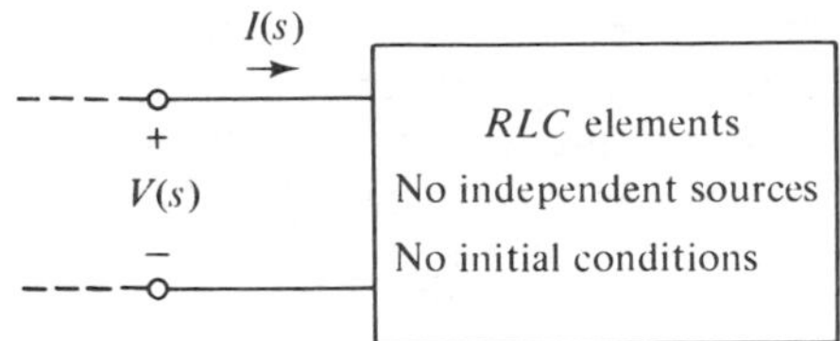

Fig. 5-7

$$Z(s) = \frac{V(s)}{I(s)} \tag{5-34}$$

Note that all variables are functions of s. The impedance function relates voltage to current in the *frequency domain*.

Again, by reference to Fig. 5-7, *admittance is defined* as

$$Y(s) = \frac{I(s)}{V(s)} \tag{5-35}$$

Clearly,

$$Z(s) = \frac{1}{Y(s)} \tag{5-36}$$

The definition of Z (or Y) shows us how to find the impedance looking into a network. Merely apply a voltage source and calculate the resulting current. Then form the V/I ratio. Or apply a current source and calculate the resulting voltage. Again, form the V/I ratio. We must be sure, however, that the network meets the criteria set forth in Fig. 5-7; that is, it does not contain any independent sources or initial conditions and is composed of *RLC* elements only. If any independent sources or initial conditions exist within the network, we must kill them before we calculate Z. This means that we make all independent voltage and current sources zero.

Example 5-4

Calculate the input impedance (or simply impedance) of the network shown in Fig. 5-8.

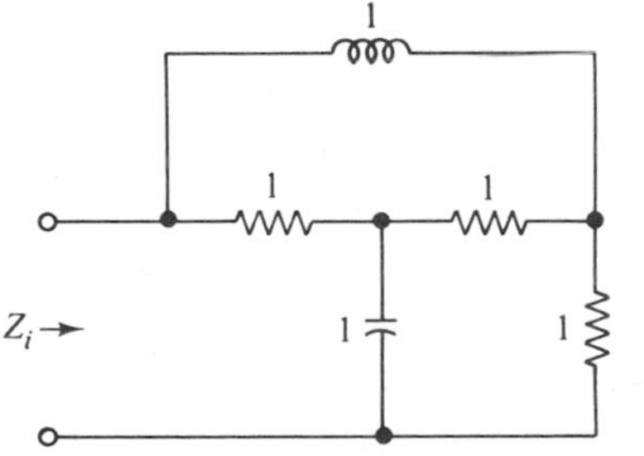

Fig. 5-8

Solution. To find Z_i, we must apply either a voltage source or a current source at the input terminals and calculate the other input variable. If we apply a voltage source, there will be three mesh currents, resulting in a 3 × 3 determinant. If we apply a current source, there will be three node voltages, again resulting in a 3 × 3 determinant. So no advantage is gained by choosing current excitation over voltage excitation. The amount of work involved is the same in both cases. Therefore let us solve for Z_i by applying a voltage source, V_1, as shown in Fig. 5-9 and then solve for the resulting current I_1 by using mesh analysis.

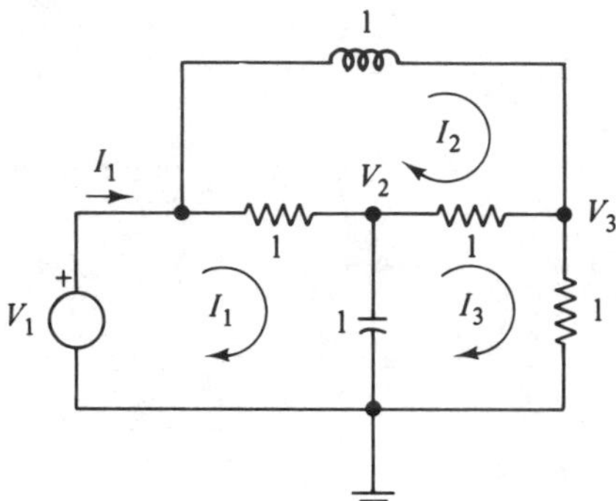

Fig. 5-9

We obtain Δ and Δ_1 by inspection of the network.

$$\Delta = \begin{vmatrix} \left(1 + \frac{1}{s}\right) & -1 & -\frac{1}{s} \\ -1 & (2 + s) & -1 \\ -\frac{1}{s} & -1 & \left(2 + \frac{1}{s}\right) \end{vmatrix} = \left(1 + \frac{1}{s}\right)\left[(2 + s)\left(2 + \frac{1}{s}\right) - 1\right]$$

$$+ \left[-\left(2 + \frac{1}{s}\right) - \frac{1}{s}\right]$$

$$- \frac{1}{s}\left[1 + \frac{1}{s}(2 + s)\right]$$

$$= 2\left(s + 2 + \frac{1}{s}\right)$$

$$\Delta_1 = \begin{vmatrix} V_1 & -1 & -\frac{1}{s} \\ 0 & (2 + s) & -1 \\ 0 & -1 & \left(2 + \frac{1}{s}\right) \end{vmatrix} = V_1\left[(2 + s)\left(2 + \frac{1}{s}\right) - 1\right] = V_1 2\left(s + 2 + \frac{1}{s}\right)$$

$$I_1 = \frac{\Delta_1}{\Delta} = \frac{V_1 2[s + 2 + (1/s)]}{2[s + 2 + (1/s)]} = V_1$$

The input impedance is

$$Z_i = \frac{V_1}{I_1} = 1 \quad \text{Ans.}$$

5-7 SERIES AND PARALLEL CONNECTION OF IMPEDANCES

In Fig 5-10(a) the impedance Z_1 is connected in series with impedance Z_2. (Symbolically, impedances can be drawn like resistors.) The same current I flows through Z_1 and Z_2. The voltage across Z_1 is IZ_1; the voltage across Z_2 is IZ_2. The voltage across the Z_1Z_2 combination is

$$V = V_1 + V_2 = IZ_1 + IZ_2 = I(Z_1 + Z_2) = IZ_{eq}$$

where

$$Z_{eq} = Z_1 + Z_2 \tag{5-37}$$

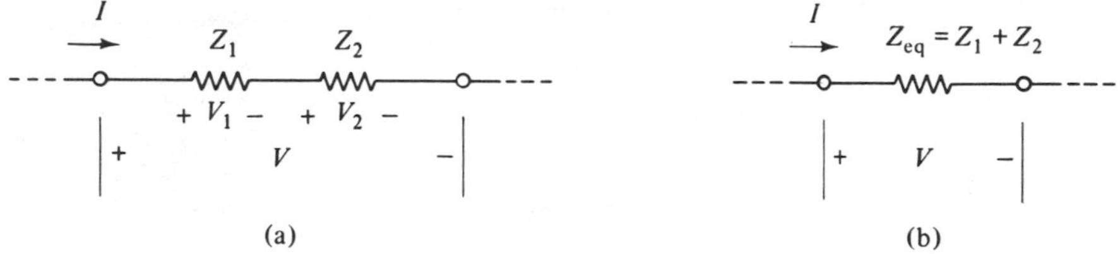

(c) (d)

Fig. 5-10

Thus the terminal behavior of two impedances in series is identical to the terminal behavior of a single impedance whose value is the sum of the two impedances. See Fig. 5-10(b).

In Fig. 5-10(c) two inductors are connected in series. The impedance between terminals 1 and 2 is

$$Z_{eq} = Z_1 + Z_2 = sL_1 + sL_2 = s\underbrace{(L_1 + L_2)}_{L_{eq}}$$

So at the terminals we see an equivalent inductance of $L_1 + L_2$.

In Fig. 5-10(d) two capacitors are connected in series. The impedance between terminals 1 and 2 is

$$Z_{eq} = \frac{1}{sC_1} + \frac{1}{sC_2} = \frac{1}{s}\left(\frac{1}{C_1} + \frac{1}{C_2}\right) = \frac{1}{s\underbrace{[C_1C_2/(C_1 + C_2)]}_{C_{eq}}}$$

which means that at the terminals we see an equivalent capacitance of $C_1C_2/(C_1 + C_2)$.

If n impedances are connected in series, then

$$Z_{eq} = Z_1 + Z_2 + \cdots + Z_n \tag{5-38}$$

that is, *the equivalent impedance is the sum of the individual impedances.*

In Fig. 5-11(a) the impedance Z_1 is connected in parallel with impedance Z_2. The same voltage V exists across Z_1 and across Z_2. The current through Z_1 is VY_1; the current through Z_2 is VY_2. The current through the Z_1Z_2 combination is

$$I = I_1 + I_2 = VY_1 + VY_2 = V(Y_1 + Y_2) = VY_{eq}$$

where

$$Y_{eq} = Y_1 + Y_2 \tag{5-39}$$

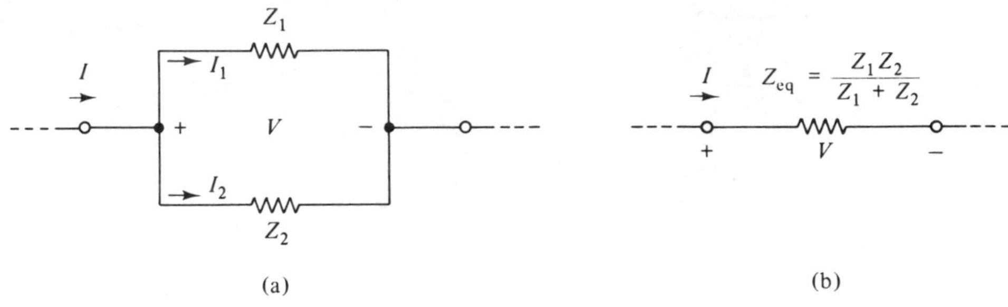

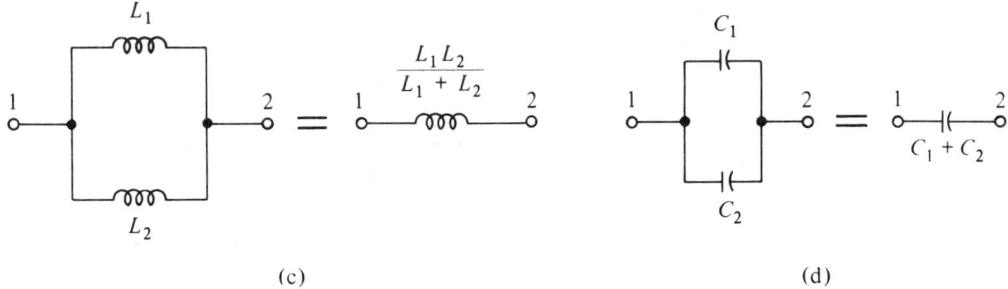

Fig. 5-11

Thus the terminal behavior of two admittances in parallel is identical to the terminal behavior of a single admittance whose value is the sum of the two admittances. Since admittance is the inverse of impedance, Eq. (5-39) can be written

$$\frac{1}{Z_{eq}} = \frac{1}{Z_1} + \frac{1}{Z_2} = \frac{Z_1 + Z_2}{Z_1Z_2}, \qquad Z_{eq} = \frac{Z_1Z_2}{Z_1 + Z_2} \tag{5-40}$$

Therefore the equivalent impedance is the product of the two impedances divided by their sum. See Fig. 5-11(b).

In Fig. 5-11(c) two inductors are connected in parallel. The admittance between terminals 1 and 2 is

$$Y_{eq} = Y_1 + Y_2 = \frac{1}{sL_1} + \frac{1}{sL_2} = \frac{1}{s}\left(\frac{1}{L_1} + \frac{1}{L_2}\right) = \frac{1}{s\underbrace{[L_1L_2/(L_1 + L_2)]}_{L_{eq}}}$$

Consequently, at the terminals we see an equivalent inductance of $L_1L_2/(L_1 + L_2)$.

In Fig. 5-11(d) two capacitors are connected in parallel. The admittance between terminals 1 and 2 is

$$Y_{eq} = sC_1 + sC_2 = s\underbrace{(C_1 + C_2)}_{C_{eq}}$$

At the terminals, then, we see an equivalent capacitance of $C_1 + C_2$.

If n admittances are connected in parallel,

$$Y_{eq} = Y_1 + Y_2 + \cdots = Y_n \tag{5-41}$$

that is, *the equivalent admittance is the sum of individual admittances*. The product over sum rule given by Eq. (5-40) can also be used, provided that impedances are combined two at a time.

Whether we speak in terms of the impedance or the admittance of an element is unimportant. Each describes the terminal properties. However, when elements are connected in series, it is easier to deal with impedances because the equivalent impedance is found by addition of individual impedances. On the other hand, when elements are connected in parallel, it is easier to deal with admittances because the equivalent admittance is the sum of individual admittances.

Example 5-5

Calculate the input impedance of the network shown in Fig. 5-12.

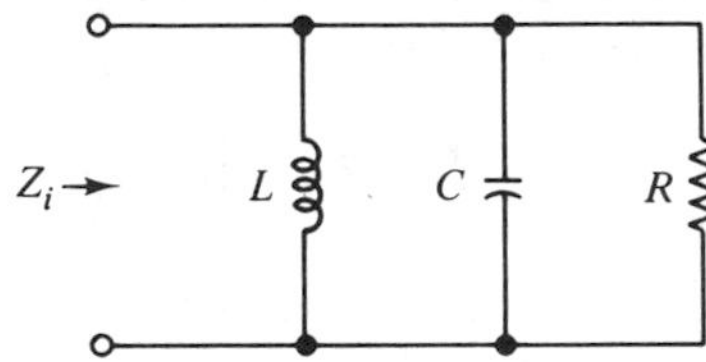

Fig. 5-12

Solution. Since all three elements are in parallel, it is easier to calculate the input admittance Y_i first.

$$Y_i = Y_L + Y_C + Y_R = \frac{1}{sL} + sC + G = \frac{s^2LC + sLG + 1}{sL}$$

The input impedance is

$$Z_i = \frac{1}{Y_i} = \frac{sL}{s^2LC + sLG + 1} \quad \text{Ans.}$$

Example 5-6

What is the input impedance of the network shown in Fig. 5-13?

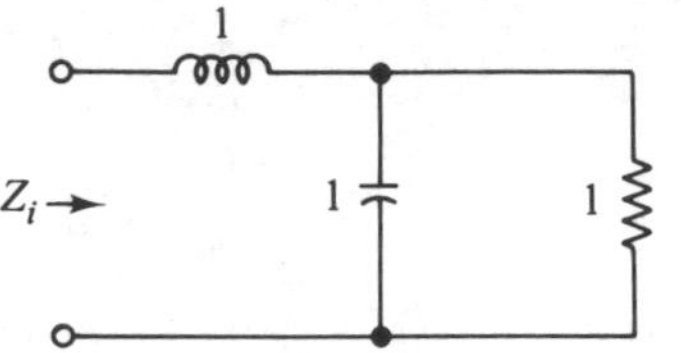

Fig. 5-13

Solution. The inductor is in series with the parallel combination of the resistor and the capacitor. So

$$Z_i = Z_L + Z_{RC} = s + \frac{(1/s) \times 1}{(1/s) + 1} = s + \frac{1}{s+1} = \frac{s^2 + s + 1}{s+1} \quad \text{Ans.}$$

Example 5-7

Obtain the input impedance of the network shown in Fig. 5-14.

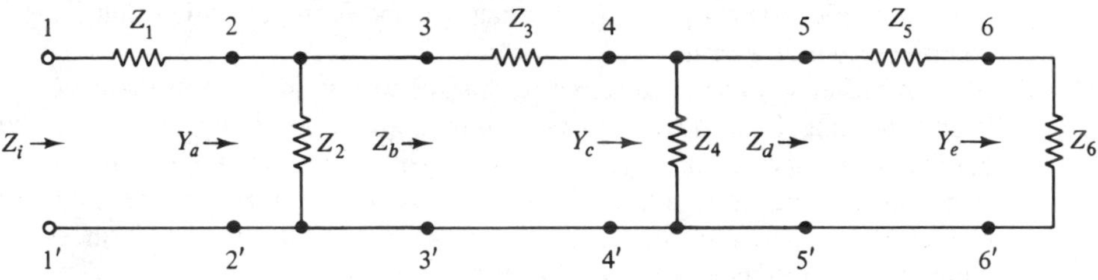

Fig. 5-14

Solution. We can work this problem by starting at the right and moving to the left while applying the rules for series and parallel connection of impedances. Or we can start at the left end and proceed as follows.

$$Z_i = Z_1 + Z_a = Z_1 + \frac{1}{Y_a}$$

where Y_a is the admittance of the circuit to the right of 2–2′. But

$$Y_a = Y_2 + Y_b = Y_2 + \frac{1}{Z_b}$$

where Z_b is the impedance of the circuit to the right of 3–3′.

Continuing in a similar manner, we obtain

$$Z_b = Z_3 + Z_c = Z_3 + \frac{1}{Y_c} \qquad (Y_c = \text{admittance to the right of 4–4}')$$

$$Y_c = Y_4 + Y_d = Y_4 + \frac{1}{Z_d} \qquad (Z_d = \text{impedance to the right of 5–5}')$$

$$Z_d = Z_5 + Z_e = Z_5 + \frac{1}{Y_e} \qquad (Y_e = \text{admittance to the right of } 6\text{–}6')$$

$$= Z_5 + \frac{1}{Y_6}$$

Combining all terms in one equation gives

$$Z_i = Z_1 + \cfrac{1}{Y_2 + \cfrac{1}{Z_3 + \cfrac{1}{Y_4 + \cfrac{1}{Z_5 + \cfrac{1}{Y_6}}}}} \qquad \text{Ans.}$$

From the pattern exhibited by the expression for Z_i, it is clear how to calculate the input impedance of networks that contain repeating sections like those of Fig. 5-14.

5-8 SOURCE CONVERSIONS

A voltage source in series with an impedance can be converted into a current source in parallel with the same impedance. This two-terminal equivalence is illustrated in Fig. 5-15(a). The equivalence is established by showing that, for the same current I taken out of terminal 1, the voltage V across terminals 1–1′ is the same for both circuits. Thus from Fig. 5-15(a) we have

$$\underbrace{V = V_s - IZ_s}_{\substack{\text{From}\\\text{voltage}\\\text{source}}} = \underbrace{\left(\frac{V_s}{Z_s} - I\right)Z_s}_{\substack{\text{From}\\\text{current}\\\text{source}}}$$

The value of the current source is obtained by calculating the short-circuit current produced by the voltage source—namely, V_s/Z_s.

Similarly, a current source in parallel with an impedance can be converted into a voltage source in series with the same impedance. The value of the voltage source is obtained by calculating the open-circuit voltage produced by the current source—namely, I_sZ_s. See Fig. 5-15(b).

Note that all variables are frequency-domain variables.

Example 5-8

Convert the source shown in Fig. 5-16 into a current source.

Solution. The short-circuit current produced by the voltage source is

$$I_{sc} = VY = VsC$$

So the current-source equivalent can be drawn as in Fig. 5-17.

(a)

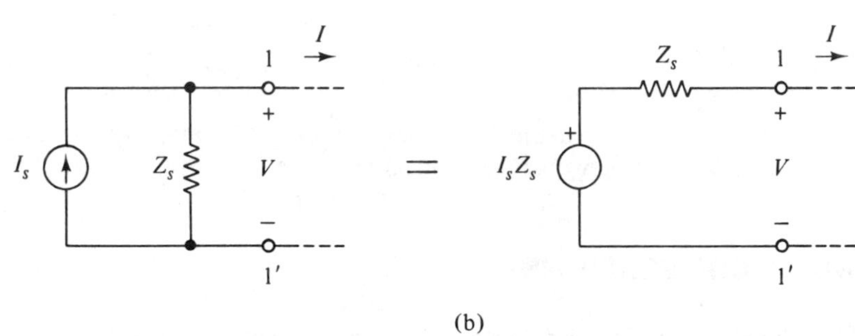

(b)

Fig. 5-15

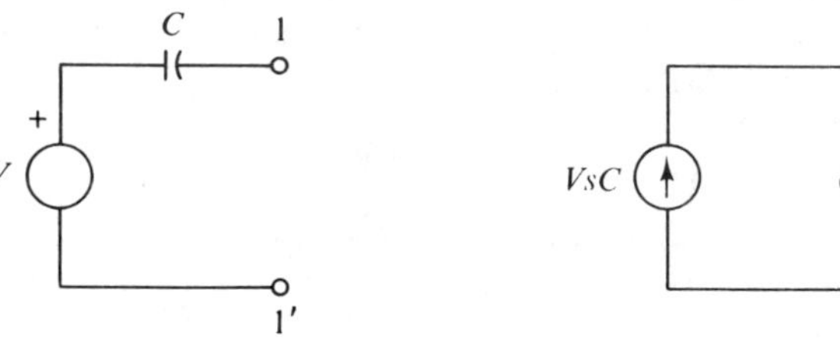

Fig. 5-16 **Fig. 5-17**

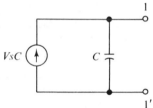

5-9 VOLTAGE- AND CURRENT-DIVIDER RULES

Referring to Fig. 5-18(a), we see that

$$I_i = \frac{V_i}{Z_{\text{eq}}} = \frac{V_i}{Z_1 + Z_2} = V_i\left(\frac{Y_1Y_2}{Y_1 + Y_2}\right)$$

$$V_2 = I_iZ_2 = \frac{I_i}{Y_2}$$

$$V_2 = V_i\left(\frac{Z_2}{Z_1 + Z_2}\right) = V_i\left(\frac{Y_1}{Y_1 + Y_2}\right) \tag{5-42}$$

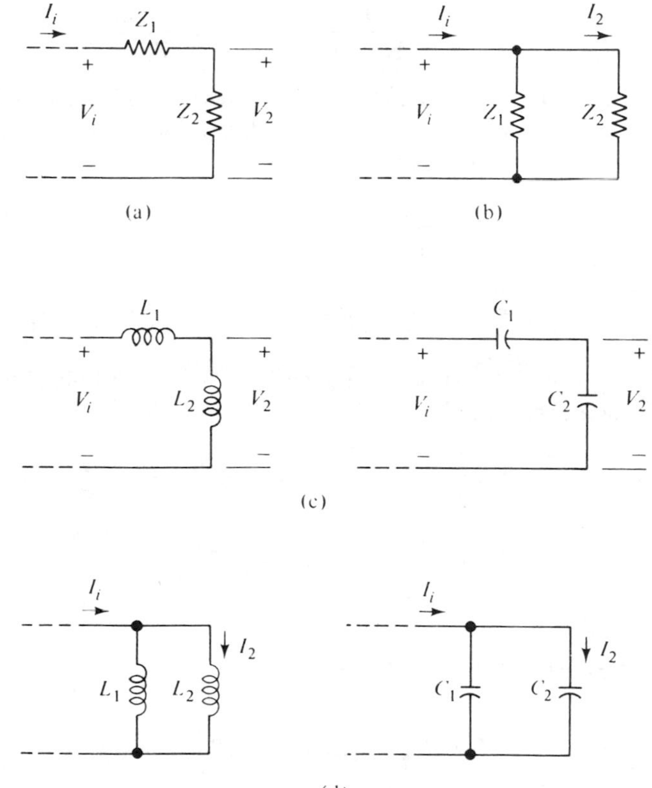

Fig. 5-18

Thus the voltage across Z_2 is equal to the input voltage times the factor

$$\frac{Z_2}{Z_1 + Z_2} \quad \text{or} \quad \frac{Y_1}{Y_1 + Y_2}$$

Equation (5-42) represents a statement of the voltage-divider rule.

By reference to Fig. 5-18(b), we see that

$$V_i = I_i Z_{eq} = I_i\left(\frac{Z_1 Z_2}{Z_1 + Z_2}\right) = I_i\left(\frac{1}{Y_1 + Y_2}\right)$$

$$I_2 = \frac{V_i}{Z_2} = V_i Y_2$$

$$I_2 = I_i\left(\frac{Z_1}{Z_1 + Z_2}\right) = I_i\left(\frac{Y_2}{Y_1 + Y_2}\right) \tag{5.43}$$

So the current through Z_2 is the input current times the factor

$$\frac{Y_2}{Y_1 + Y_2} \quad \text{or} \quad \frac{Z_1}{Z_1 + Z_2}$$

Equation (5-43) represents a statement of the current-divider rule.

Referring to Fig. 5-18(c), we can determine the voltage division between two inductors and two capacitors.

$$V_2 = V_i\left(\frac{Z_2}{Z_1 + Z_2}\right) = V_i\left(\frac{sL_2}{sL_1 + sL_2}\right) = V_i\left(\frac{L_2}{L_1 + L_2}\right)$$

$$V_2 = V_i\left(\frac{Y_1}{Y_1 + Y_2}\right) = V_i\left(\frac{sC_1}{sC_1 + sC_2}\right) = V_i\left(\frac{C_1}{C_1 + C_2}\right)$$

Using Fig. 5-18(d), we can determine the current division between two inductors and two capacitors.

$$I_2 = I_i\left(\frac{Z_1}{Z_1 + Z_2}\right) = I_i\left(\frac{sL_1}{sL_1 + sL_2}\right) = I_i\left(\frac{L_1}{L_1 + L_2}\right)$$

$$I_2 = I_i\left(\frac{Y_2}{Y_1 + Y_2}\right) = I_i\left(\frac{sC_2}{sC_1 + sC_2}\right) = I_i\left(\frac{C_2}{C_1 + C_2}\right)$$

Example 5-9

In Fig. 5-19, obtain I_o in terms of I_i.

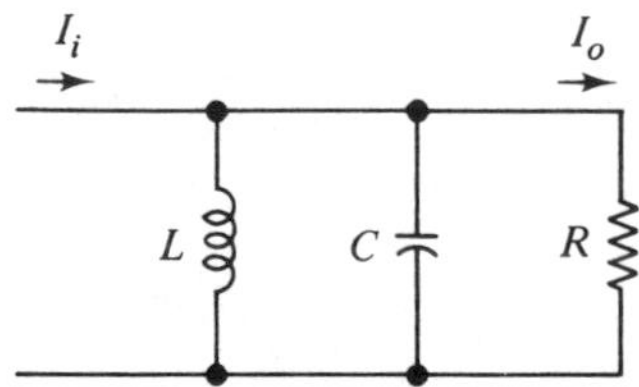

Fig. 5-19

Solution. Treat the LC combination as one impedance; that is,

$$Z_{LC} = \frac{sL \times (1/sC)}{sL + (1/sC)} = \frac{(1/C)s}{s^2 + (1/LC)}$$

Then, using the current-divider rule, divide I_i between Z_{LC} and R. Thus

$$I_o = I_i\left(\frac{Z_{LC}}{Z_{LC} + R}\right) = I_i\left\{\left[\frac{(1/C)s}{s^2 + (1/LC)}\right] \Big/ \left[\frac{(1/C)s}{s^2 + (1/LC)} + R\right]\right\}$$

$$= I_i\left[\frac{(1/RC)s}{s^2 + (1/RC)s + (1/LC)}\right] \quad \text{Ans.}$$

5-10 THE PRINCIPLE OF SUPERPOSITION

In Chapter 3 we learned that in a resistive network with more than one source of excitation the response can be calculated as the sum of individual responses obtained by turning on one source at a time while the other sources are held at zero. Thus we arrived at the response by superimposing responses due to each source acting alone. Here we generalize the principle of superposition to obtain responses in *RLC* networks.

Consider, for example, the *RLC* network shown in Fig. 5-20(a). A voltage source V_1 and a current source I_1 are used for excitation, and we wish to determine by superposition the two responses: V_2 and I_2. In Fig. 5-20(b) the voltage source is turned on and the current source turned off (terminals 2–2′ are open-circuited). The resulting responses are V_{21} and I_{21}, the second subscript "1" denoting that these responses are caused by the first source. In Fig. 5-20(c) the current source is turned on and the voltage source turned off (terminals 1–1′ are short-circuited). The resulting responses are V_{22} and I_{22}, the second subscript "2" denoting that these responses are caused by the second source. The desired responses are obtained by superposition.

$$V_2 = V_{21} + V_{22}, \qquad I_2 = I_{21} + I_{22}$$

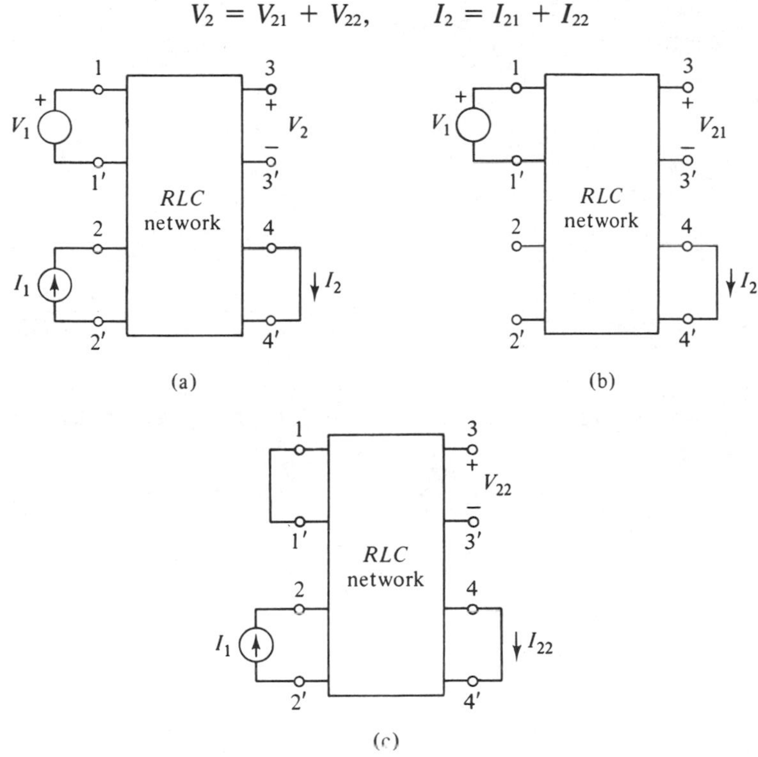

Fig. 5-20

Example 5-10

In Fig. 5-21, obtain I_o and V_o by superposition.

Solution. First, turn the current source on and the voltage source off as in Fig. 5-22(a). Obtain I_{o1} by the current-divider rule and V_{o1} by combining parallel impedances.

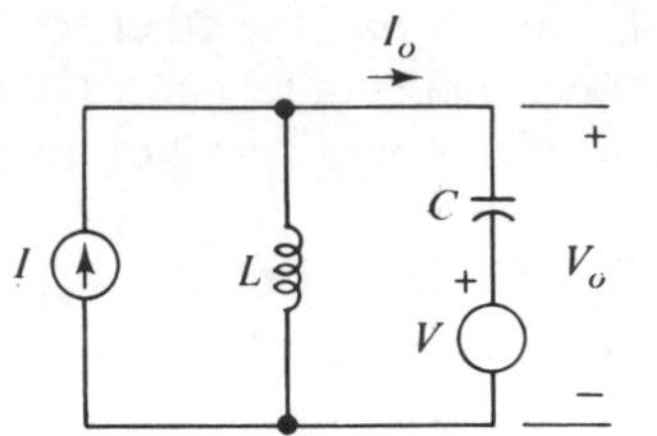

Fig. 5-21

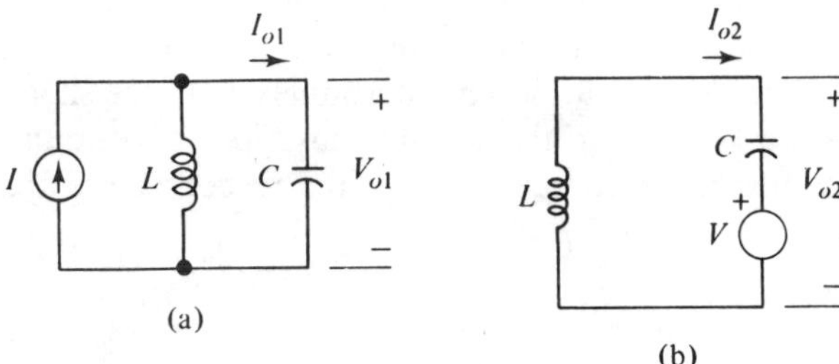

Fig. 5-22

$$I_{o1} = I\left[\frac{sL}{sL + (1/sC)}\right] = I\left[\frac{s^2}{s^2 + (1/LC)}\right]$$

$$V_{o1} = IZ_{LC1} = I\left[\frac{sL \times (1/sC)}{sL + (1/sC)}\right] = I\left[\frac{(1/C)s}{s^2 + (1/LC)}\right]$$

Then turn the voltage source on and the current source off as in Fig. 5-22(b). Obtain I_{o2} by combining series impedances and V_{o2} by the voltage-divider rule.

$$I_{o2} = -\frac{V}{Z_{LC2}} = -\frac{V}{sL + (1/sC)} = -\frac{1}{L}\left[\frac{s}{s^2 + (1/LC)}\right]V$$

$$V_{o2} = V\left[\frac{sL}{sL + (1/sC)}\right] = V\left[\frac{s^2}{s^2 + (1/LC)}\right]$$

The desired responses are

$$I_o = I_{o1} + I_{o2} = I\left[\frac{s^2}{s^2 + (1/LC)}\right] + \frac{-(s/L)V}{s^2 + (1/LC)} = \frac{[Is - (V/L)]s}{s^2 + (1/LC)} \quad \text{Ans.}$$

$$V_o = V_{o1} + V_{o2} = I\left[\frac{(1/C)s}{s^2 + (1/LC)}\right] + V\left[\frac{s^2}{s^2 + (1/LC)}\right] = \frac{[(I/C) + Vs]s}{s^2 + (1/LC)} \quad \text{Ans.}$$

Alternatively, this problem can be solved by converting the current-source-inductance combination into an equivalent voltage-source-inductance combination as shown in Fig. 5-23. We see directly from this figure that

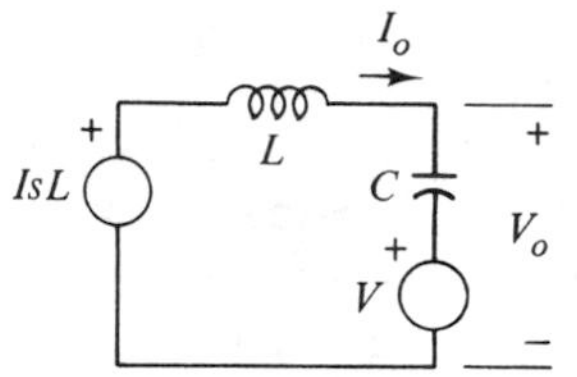

Fig. 5-23

$$I_o = \frac{IsL - V}{sL + (1/sC)} = \frac{[Is - (V/L)]s}{s^2 + (1/LC)}$$

$$V_o = \frac{IsL \times (1/sC) + V \times sL}{sL + (1/sC)} \qquad \text{(by superposition)}$$

$$= \frac{[(I/C) + Vs]s}{s^2 + (1/LC)}$$

5-11 THÉVENIN AND NORTON EQUIVALENT CIRCUITS

The terminal behavior of a network composed of *RLC* elements and sources can be represented by an equivalent voltage source in series with an equivalent impedance or by an equivalent current source in parallel with the same equivalent impedance. Figure 5-24 illustrates the equivalence. The voltage-source-series-impedance combination is the *Thévenin equivalent* representation. The current-source-parallel-impedance combination is the *Norton equivalent* representation.

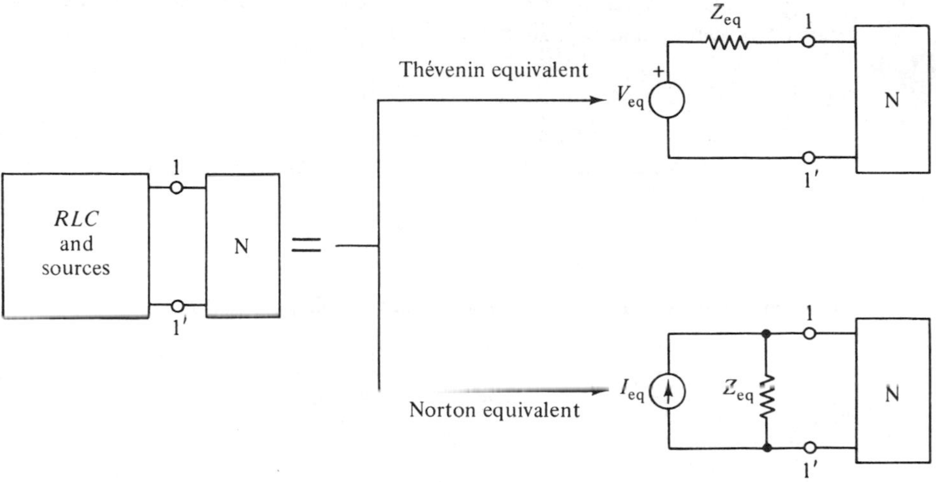

Fig. 5-24

From the discussion on source conversions given in Section 5-8 it should be clear that V_{eq} and I_{eq} are related by

$$V_{eq} = I_{eq}Z_{eq} \tag{5-44}$$

To determine Z_{eq}, make all independent sources inside the *RLC* network zero and then calculate the impedance looking in. When possible, Z_{eq} can be calculated by applying the rules for series and parallel combinations. If the combination rules cannot be used, a voltage or a current source is applied at terminals 1–1′ and the ratio of V/I is formed to find Z_{eq}. This step is illustrated in Fig. 5-25(a).

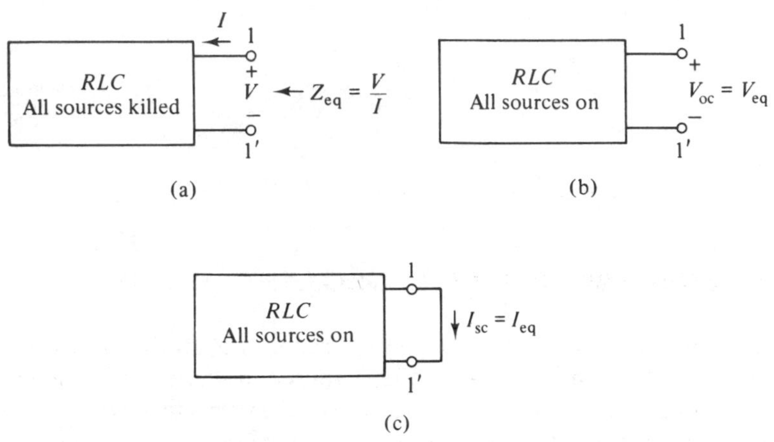

Fig. 5-25

To obtain the Thévenin equivalent voltage V_{eq}, open-circuit terminals 1–1′ as shown in Fig. 5-25(b) (this step is not necessary if terminals 1–1′ are not loaded by another network) and calculate V_{oc}. This open-circuit voltage is V_{eq}; that is

$$V_{eq} = V_{oc} \tag{5-45}$$

To obtain the Norton equivalent current I_{eq}, short-circuit terminals 1–1′ as shown in Fig. 5-25(c) and calculate I_{sc}. This short-circuit current is I_{eq}; that is,

$$I_{eq} = I_{sc} \tag{5-46}$$

Example 5-11

(a) In the circuit of Fig. 5-26, obtain the voltage across R_L.

(b) When is the bridge balanced?

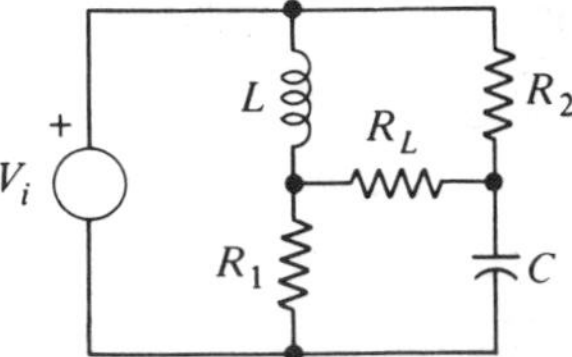

Fig. 5-26

Solution.

(a) Redraw the circuit as in Fig. 5-27(a). This circuit is identical in all respects (except for the current delivered by source V_i) with the original circuit, since the top of L and the top of R_2 are still driven by V_i. Next, obtain two Thévenin equivalent circuits: one for the circuit to the left of 1–1′ and another for the circuit to the right of 2–2′. The result is Fig. 5-27(b), where

$$V_{eq1} = V_i\left(\frac{R_1}{sL + R_1}\right) = V_i\left[\frac{R_1/L}{s + (R_1/L)}\right]$$

$$V_{eq2} = V_i\left[\frac{1/sC}{R_2 + (1/sC)}\right] = V_i\left[\frac{1/R_2C}{s + (1/R_2C)}\right]$$

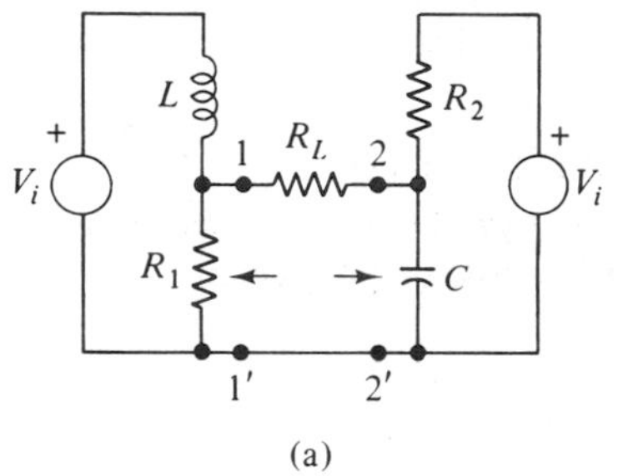

(a)

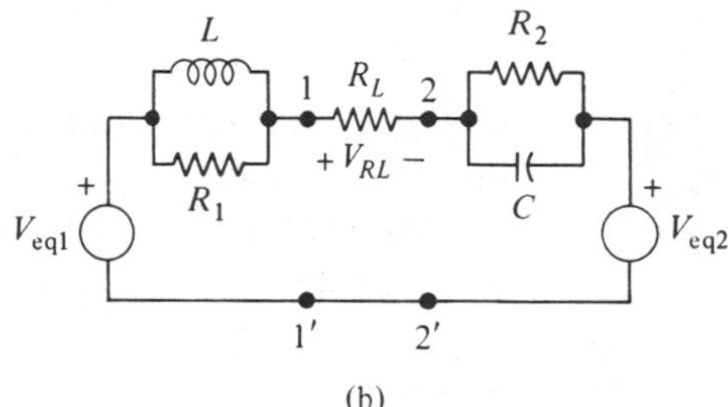

(b)

Fig. 5-27

From the figure note that Z_{eq1} is the parallel combination of R_1 with sL and Z_{eq2} is the parallel combination of R_2 with $1/sC$. From Fig. 5-27(b), V_{R_L} is

$$V_{R_L} = \underbrace{\left\{(V_{eq1} - V_{eq2})\Big/\left[\frac{R_1 sL}{R_1 + sL} + R_L + \frac{R_2(1/sC)}{R_2 + (1/sC)}\right]\right\}}_{\text{Current through } R_L} R_L$$

$$= V_i\left[\frac{R_1}{sL + R_1} - \frac{1/R_2C}{s + (1/R_2C)}\right]R_L\Big/\left[\frac{sLR_1}{sL + R_1} + R_L + \frac{1/C}{s + (1/R_2C)}\right]$$

$$V_{R_L} = V_i\frac{s}{R_2}\left(R_1R_2 - \frac{L}{C}\right)R_L\Big/\left[sLR_1\left(s + \frac{1}{R_2C}\right) + R_L(sL + R_1)\left(s + \frac{1}{R_2C}\right) + \frac{1}{C}(sL + R_1)\right] \quad \text{Ans.}$$

(b) A balanced bridge requires that V_{R_L} be zero. Consequently, we must have

$$R_1R_2 = \frac{L}{C}$$

which can be written

$$R_1R_2 = Z_LZ_C \tag{5-47}$$

where

$$Z_L = sL \qquad \text{and} \qquad Z_C = \frac{1}{sC}$$

Referring to Fig. 5-26 and Eq. (5-47), we see the condition for balance: the products of impedances in diagonally opposite arms of the bridge must equal.

Example 5-12

Refer to Fig. 5-28.

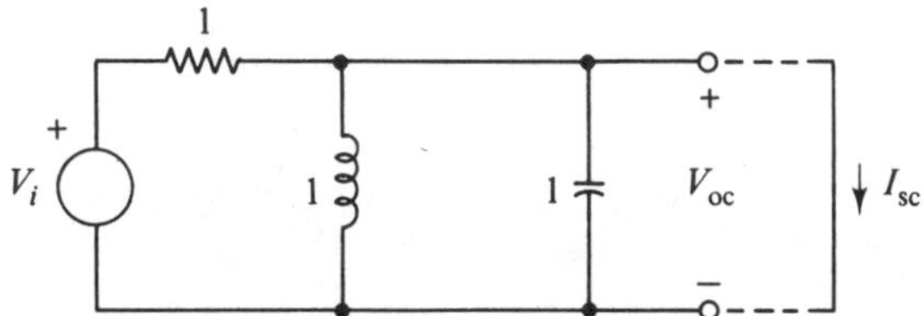

Fig. 5-28

(a) Obtain the open-circuit voltage and the short-circuit current.
(b) Form the ratio of open-circuit voltage to short-circuit current. Show that this ratio represents the impedance looking in from the output terminals.
(c) Show that V_{oc}/I_{sc} always gives Z_{eq}.

Solution.

(a) By inspection of the circuit,

$$V_{oc} = V_i\left\{\left[\frac{s \times (1/s)}{s + (1/s)}\right]\Big/\left[1 + \frac{s \times (1/s)}{s + (1/s)}\right]\right\} = V_i\left(\frac{s}{s^2 + s + 1}\right) \quad \text{Ans.}$$

$$I_{sc} = \frac{V_i}{1} = V_i \quad \text{Ans.}$$

(b)
$$\frac{V_{oc}}{I_{sc}} = \frac{V_i[s/(s^2 + s + 1)]}{V_i} = \frac{s}{s^2 + s + 1}$$

Dimensionally, the ratio of V_{oc}/I_{sc} represents impedance. Hence

$$\frac{V_{oc}}{I_{sc}} = Z = \frac{s}{s^2 + s + 1}$$

$$Y = \frac{1}{Z} = \frac{s^2 + s + 1}{s} = s + 1 + \frac{1}{s}$$

From this expression of Y we recognize that we have three admittances connected in parallel. The first is s, which represents the admittance of a 1 F capacitor. The second is 1, which represents the admittance of a 1 Ω resistor. The third is $1/s$, which represents the admittance of a 1 H inductor. Thus Z represents the parallel connection of a 1 F capacitor, a 1 Ω resistor, and a 1 H inductor. Now if we refer to Fig. 5-28, we see that Z is the same as the impedance looking back from the output terminals (with V_i set to zero).

(c) The two-terminal behavior of a network can be represented by the Thévenin equivalent as shown in Fig. 5-29. From this figure we see that

$$V_{oc} = V_{eq}, \qquad I_{sc} = \frac{V_{eq}}{Z_{eq}}$$

So

$$\frac{V_{oc}}{I_{sc}} = \frac{V_{eq}}{V_{eq}/Z_{eq}} = Z_{eq} \quad \text{Ans.}$$

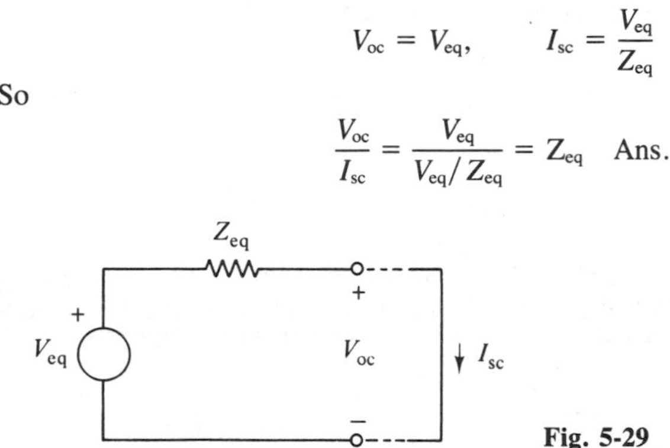

Fig. 5-29

5-12 TRANSFER FUNCTION

When dealing with one pair of terminals, we use the concept of impedance to relate voltage and current at the terminals. When dealing with two or more pairs of terminals, we use the concept of transfer function to relate the voltage and current at one pair of terminals to the voltage and current at another pair of terminals. The case of three pairs of terminals is illustrated in Fig. 5-30. One pair of terminals is considered as input and is labeled 1–1′; the other two pairs of terminals are considered as outputs and are labeled 2–2′ and 3–3′. There are *no independent sources inside the network N*. The network is excited either by a voltage source, as in Fig. 5-30(a), or by a current source, as in Fig. 5-30(b). In either case, there is only *one source* exciting the network. We now define transfer function as

$$T(s) = \frac{\text{output } (s)}{\text{input } (s)} = \frac{\text{response } (s)}{\text{excitation } (s)} \tag{5-48}$$

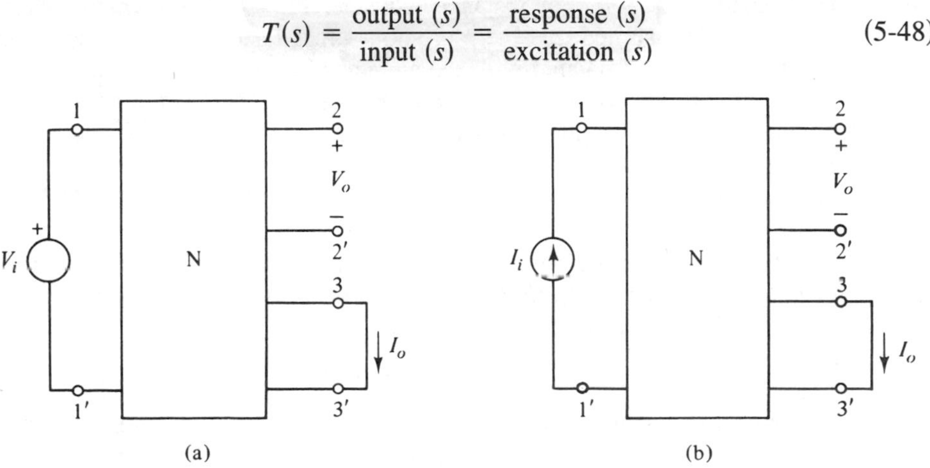

Fig. 5-30

In Fig. 5-30(a) the input is a voltage source. Two outputs are considered: one for voltage, the other for current. Therefore there are two transfer functions, one for each output. These transfer functions are

$$T_1(s) = \frac{V_o(s)}{V_i(s)} \qquad \text{(transfer voltage ratio)} \tag{5-49}$$

$$T_2(s) = \frac{I_o(s)}{V_i(s)} \qquad \text{(transadmittance)} \tag{5-50}$$

In Fig. 5-30(b), the input is a current source. Again, two different kinds of outputs are considered: one for voltage, the other for current. The corresponding transfer functions are

$$T_1(s) = \frac{V_o(s)}{I_i(s)} \qquad \text{(transimpedance)} \tag{5-51}$$

$$T_2(s) = \frac{I_o(s)}{I_i(s)} \qquad \text{(transfer current ratio)} \tag{5-52}$$

So altogether there are four possible combinations of variables:

$$\frac{\text{Voltage}}{\text{Voltage}}, \qquad \frac{\text{Current}}{\text{Voltage}}, \qquad \frac{\text{Voltage}}{\text{Current}}, \qquad \frac{\text{Current}}{\text{Current}}$$

The Voltage/Voltage and Current/Current ratios are dimensionless. The Voltage/Current ratio has dimensions of impedance; the Current/Voltage ratio has dimensions of admittance. Consequently, they are called *transimpedance* and *transadmittance*, respectively.

If more than one source is exciting a network, we use the principle of superposition to find the output. In this case, each input contributes to the output through its own transfer function. For instance, consider Fig. 5-31(a), where sources V and I excite N. It is assumed that there are no sources inside N. This also means that the initial conditions associated with the elements inside the box are all zero.

If we turn on the voltage source and turn off the current source, we have the situation illustrated in Fig. 5-31(b). The output voltage V_{o1} is related to the input voltage V through the transfer function T_V; that is,

$$V_{o1} = VT_V$$

By turning on the current source and turning off the voltage source, we have the situation shown in Fig. 5-31(c). The output voltage V_{o2} is related to the input current through the transfer function T_I; that is,

$$V_{o2} = IT_I$$

By superposition, the output is

$$V_o = V_{o1} + V_{o2} = VT_V + IT_I$$

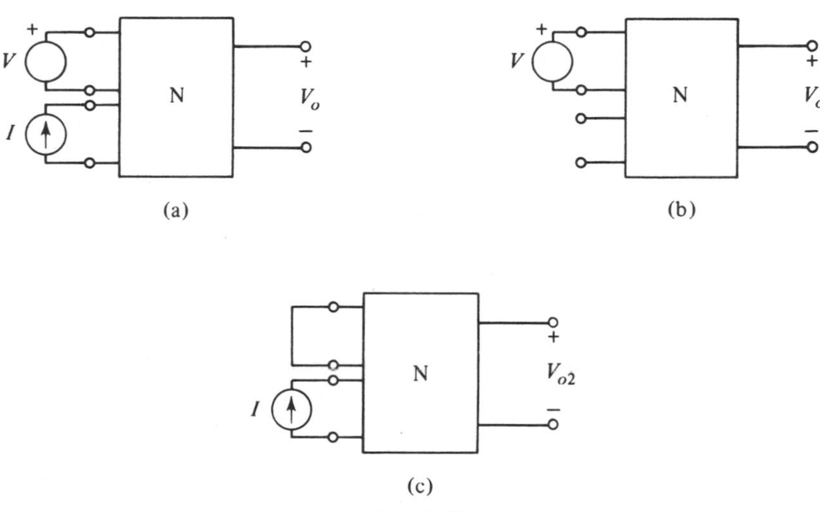

Fig. 5-31

Thus two transfer functions are used to calculate the output. (Of course, the output can always be calculated without specifically calculating transfer functions—which is what we did prior to the introduction of the concept of transfer functions.)

Example 5-13

What is the transfer function for the network shown in Fig. 5-32?

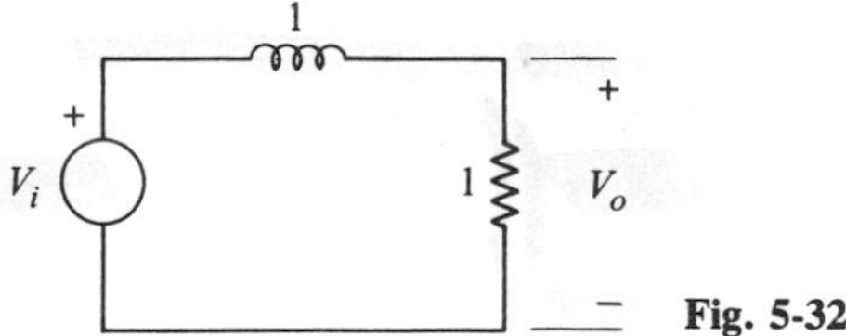

Fig. 5-32

Solution. Obtain V_o by the voltage-divider rule.

$$V_o = V_i\left(\frac{1}{s+1}\right)$$

The transfer function is

$$\frac{\text{Output}}{\text{Input}} = \frac{V_o}{V_i} = \frac{1}{s+1} \qquad \text{(voltage ratio)} \quad \text{Ans.}$$

Example 5-14

Find all the transfer functions associated with the network in Fig. 5-33.

Solution. As shown, there are three responses: I_1, I_2, and V_1. Therefore there are three transfer functions.

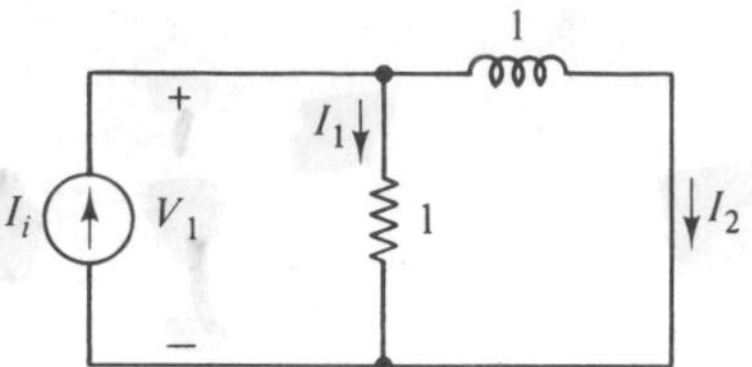

Fig. 5-33

Response: I_1

$$I_1 = I_i\left(\frac{s}{s+1}\right)$$

$$\frac{\text{Response}}{\text{Excitation}} = \frac{I_1}{I_i} = \frac{s}{s+1} \qquad \text{(current ratio)} \quad \text{Ans.}$$

Response: I_2

$$I_2 = I_i\left(\frac{1}{s+1}\right)$$

$$\frac{\text{Response}}{\text{Excitation}} = \frac{I_2}{I_i} = \frac{1}{s+1} \qquad \text{(current ratio)} \quad \text{Ans.}$$

Response: V_1

$$V_1 = I_i\left(\frac{s}{s+1}\right)$$

$$\frac{\text{Response}}{\text{Excitation}} = \frac{V_1}{I_i} = \frac{s}{s+1} \qquad \text{(input impedance)} \quad \text{Ans.}$$

Strictly speaking, this last function is not a transfer function but the input impedance.

Example 5-15

Obtain the transfer function associated with each excitation shown in Fig. 5-34.

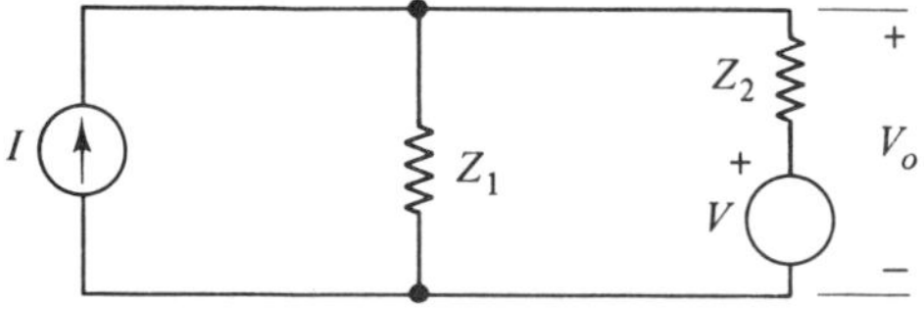

Fig. 5-34

Solution. The output V_o can be written

$$V_o = IT_1 + VT_2$$

where T_1 relates the input current to the output when $V = 0$ and T_2 relates the input voltage to the output when $I = 0$. By inspection of the network,

$$T_1 = \left.\frac{V_o}{I}\right|_{V=0} = \frac{Z_1Z_2}{Z_1 + Z_2}$$

$$T_2 = \frac{V_o}{V}\bigg|_{I=0} = \frac{Z_1}{Z_1 + Z_2}$$

Note that T_1 also represents the impedance seen by the source I while V is held at zero.

5-13 FREQUENCY-DOMAIN SOLUTIONS BY VARIOUS METHODS

The currents or voltages in a finite, lumped, linear network that is drawn without any intersecting wires can be solved in a systematic way by writing mesh or node equations. The *mesh equations* are particularly easy to set up if *all the sources are voltage sources*. On the other hand, the *node equations* can be readily written when *all sources are current sources*.

When mixed sources are present, either mesh or node equations can be used. Prior to writing the equations, it may be desirable to convert all sources to one kind by using source conversions. Doing so may not always be possible, however, because an impedance may not occur in series with every voltage source or an impedance may not be in parallel with every current source unless additional impedances are deliberately introduced for the purpose of solving the problem. Then once the solution is obtained, the impedances are removed from the calculated response by making them zero or infinity, depending on how they are introduced (series or parallel) in the circuit. These and other types of techniques are discussed in the solution of the problem presented in Fig. 5-35.

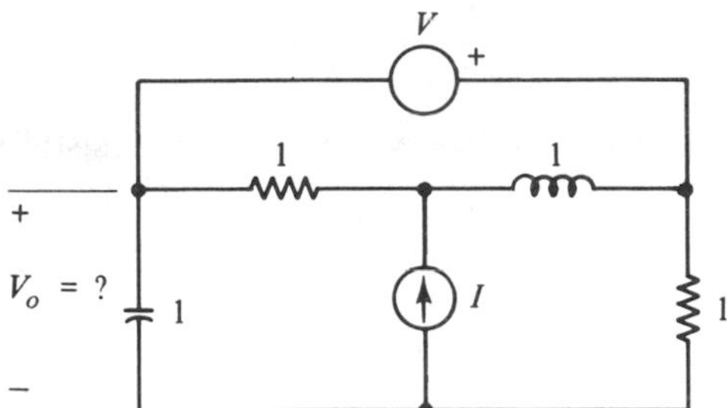

Fig. 5-35

Method 1

Let us first use the superposition principle to determine V_o. The effect of each source is shown in Fig. 5-36. From Fig. 5-36(a) we see that the inductor is in parallel with the top resistor and that the combination is in series with the parallel combination of the capacitor with the other resistor. (Here it may be helpful to redraw the circuit as in Fig. 5-36(b) in order to see that there are two parallel circuits in series with each other.) Since all of I goes through the parallel combination of the capacitor and resistor, we have

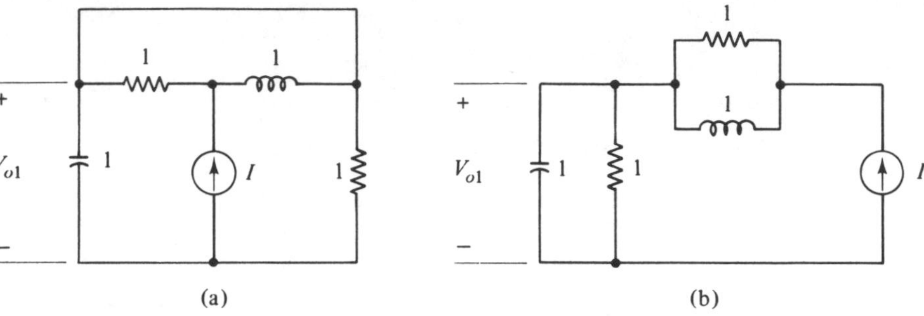

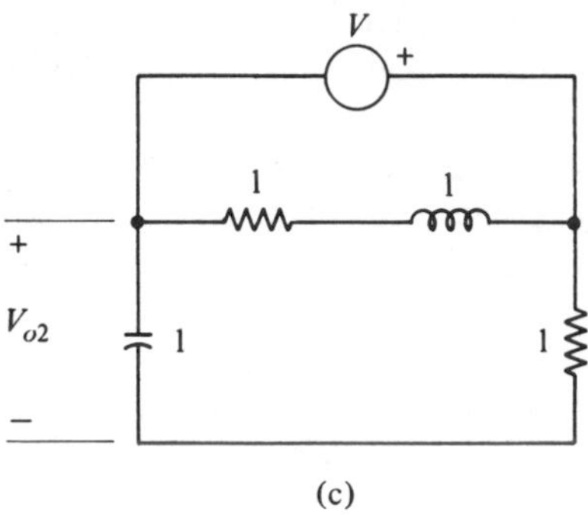

Fig. 5-36

$$V_{o1} = I\left[\frac{1 \times (1/s)}{1 + (1/s)}\right] = I\left(\frac{1}{s+1}\right)$$

From Fig. 5-36(c) we see that V is divided between the resistor and capacitor. So

$$V_{o2} = -V\left[\frac{(1/s)}{1 + (1/s)}\right] = -V\left(\frac{1}{s+1}\right)$$

The desired output is

$$V_o = V_{o1} + V_{o2} = I\left(\frac{1}{s+1}\right) - V\left(\frac{1}{s+1}\right) = \frac{I - V}{s+1} \quad \text{Ans.}$$

Very little effort is involved in finding the answer. In general, solutions can be readily obtained for simple circuits by the superposition principle.

Method 2

Next, let us solve the problem of Fig. 5-35 by the mesh-analysis method. The circuit is redrawn in Fig. 5-37 to show the three mesh currents. The corresponding equations are

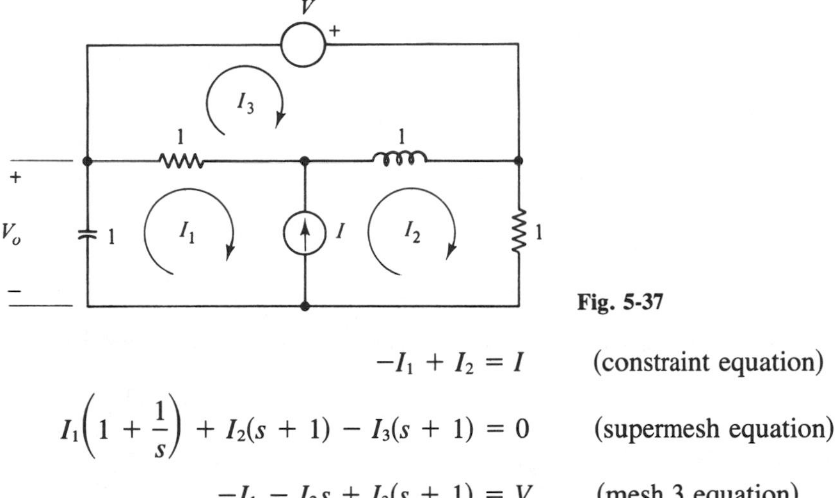

Fig. 5-37

$$-I_1 + I_2 = I \qquad \text{(constraint equation)}$$

$$I_1\left(1 + \frac{1}{s}\right) + I_2(s + 1) - I_3(s + 1) = 0 \qquad \text{(supermesh equation)}$$

$$-I_1 - I_2 s + I_3(s + 1) = V \qquad \text{(mesh 3 equation)}$$

The desired solution is

$$V_o = -I_1\frac{1}{s} = -\frac{1}{s}\frac{\Delta_1}{\Delta}$$

where

$$\Delta = \begin{vmatrix} -1 & 1 & 0 \\ \left(1 + \frac{1}{s}\right) & (s + 1) & -(s + 1) \\ -1 & -s & (s + 1) \end{vmatrix} = -\frac{(s + 1)^2}{s}$$

$$\Delta_1 = \begin{vmatrix} I & 1 & 0 \\ 0 & (s + 1) & -(s + 1) \\ V & -s & (s + 1) \end{vmatrix} = (s + 1)(I - V)$$

$$V_o = -\frac{1}{s}\frac{(s + 1)(I - V)}{-[(s + 1)^2/s]} = \frac{I - V}{s + 1} \qquad \text{Ans.}$$

By comparison with the superposition method, the solution by the mesh-analysis method is much more laborious. Nonetheless, when the rules are applied correctly, the solution is eventually obtained. Because of mixed sources, the determinant does not have all positive terms along the principal diagonal, and the terms off the principal diagonal are not symmetric. As a result, we cannot write the determinant by inspection.

Method 3

Here we solve the problem of Fig. 5-35 by rerouting the current source as shown in Fig. 5-38(a). The current I is directed away from node 0 and into node 1 as before.

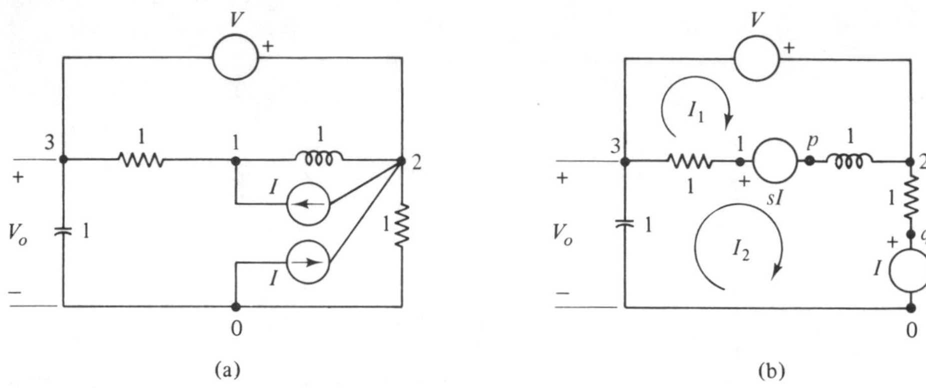

Fig. 5-38

Since the current I is brought in and taken out of node 2, the net effect on node 2 is zero. Thus no voltage or current in any of the elements of the *original* circuit is changed. Using source conversions, we are able to *convert* both current sources into voltage sources because now there is an impedance in parallel with each current source. (The current source was reoriented to produce this situation.) The result is Fig. 5-38(b), which is a two-mesh problem involving voltage sources only. Note that two new nodes, p and q, are generated by the conversions. These nodes are "fictitious" nodes and do not enter in the calculation of element voltages and currents. For instance, the voltage across the inductor is not $(V_2 - V_p)$ of Fig. 5-38(b) but rather $(V_2 - V_1)$ of Fig. 5-38(a) or (b). Similarly, the voltage across the right-hand resistor is not $(V_2 - V_q)$ but rather V_2 (node 0 being taken as reference). When in doubt, we can always *refer back to the original circuit* to see where the element terminals are connected and thus be able to calculate the actual element voltages and currents.

By mesh analysis, we have

$$I_2 = \frac{\Delta_2}{\Delta}$$

where

$$\Delta = \begin{vmatrix} (s + 1) & -(s + 1) \\ -(s + 1) & \left(s + 2 + \dfrac{1}{s}\right) \end{vmatrix} = \frac{(s + 1)^2}{s}$$

$$\Delta_2 = \begin{vmatrix} (s + 1) & (V + sI) \\ -(s + 1) & -(sI + I) \end{vmatrix} = (s + 1)(V - I)$$

So

$$V_o = -I_2\frac{1}{s} = -\frac{1}{s}\,\frac{(s + 1)(V - I)}{(s + 1)^2/s} = \frac{I - V}{s + 1} \quad \text{Ans.}$$

The work involved in this method is less than for method 2 because the determinants are one order smaller. [It should also be clear that in Fig. 5-38(a) we can just as easily tie the midpoint of the two current sources to node 3 rather than node 2 and then convert the resulting current-source-parallel-impedance combinations to voltage-source-series-impedance combinations.]

Method 4

If we introduce a resistance in parallel with the current source as in Fig. 5-39(a), we can convert the current-source-resistance combination into a voltage-source-resistance combination as shown in Fig. 5-39(b). The resulting network is a three-mesh network containing voltage sources only. Therefore the mesh determinant can be readily set up.

$$\Delta = \begin{vmatrix} \left(R + 1 + \dfrac{1}{s}\right) & -R & -1 \\ -R & (s + R + 1) & -s \\ -1 & -s & (s + 1) \end{vmatrix} = \left(s + 2 + \frac{1}{s}\right)(R + 1)$$

$$\Delta_1 = \begin{vmatrix} -IR & -R & -1 \\ IR & (s + R + 1) & -s \\ V & -s & (s + 1) \end{vmatrix} = (s + 1)[V(R + 1) - IR]$$

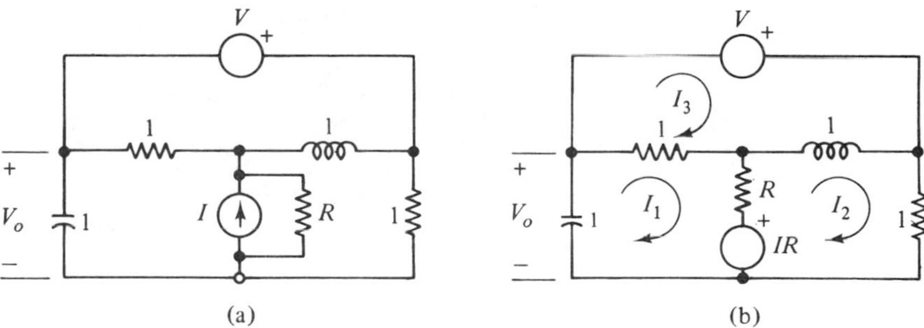

Fig. 5-39

Then

$$V_o = -I_1\frac{1}{s} = -\frac{1}{s}\frac{\Delta_1}{\Delta} = -\frac{1}{s}\frac{(s + 1)[V(R + 1) - IR]}{[s + 2 + (1/s)](R + 1)}$$

$$= -\frac{1}{s}\frac{(s + 1)\{V[1 + (1/R)] - I\}}{[s + 2 + (1/s)][1 + (1/R)]}$$

Next, we undo the original introduction of R by letting $R \to \infty$ in the expression for V_o. The result is

$$V_o = -\frac{1}{s}\frac{(s+1)(V-I)}{s+2+(1/s)} = \frac{I-V}{s+1} \quad \text{Ans.}$$

This method is laborious, but it allows us to avoid confronting ideal current sources in mesh analysis.

Method 5

We now turn to analysis by node equations. The circuit of Fig. 5-35 is redrawn as in Fig. 5-40 to show the three node voltages. The corresponding equations are

$$V_1 - V_o = V \qquad \text{(constraint equation)}$$

$$V_1\left(1+\frac{1}{s}\right) - V_2\left(1+\frac{1}{s}\right) + V_o(s+1) = 0 \qquad \text{(supernode equation, shown dashed)}$$

$$-V_1\frac{1}{s} + V_2\left(1+\frac{1}{s}\right) - V_o = I \qquad \text{(node 2 equation)}$$

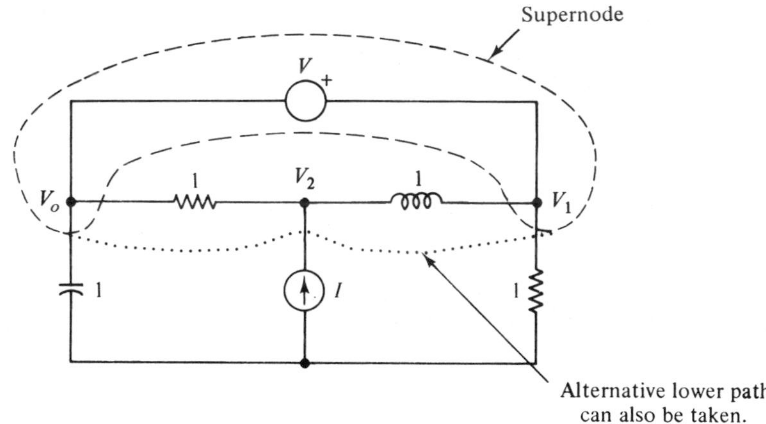

Fig. 5-40

The desired solution is

$$V_o = \frac{\Delta_3}{\Delta}$$

where

$$\Delta = \begin{vmatrix} 1 & 0 & -1 \\ \left(1+\frac{1}{s}\right) & -\left(1+\frac{1}{s}\right) & (s+1) \\ -\frac{1}{s} & \left(1+\frac{1}{s}\right) & -1 \end{vmatrix} = -\left(1+\frac{1}{s}\right)(s+1)$$

$$\Delta_3 = \begin{vmatrix} 1 & 0 & V \\ \left(1 + \frac{1}{s}\right) & -\left(1 + \frac{1}{s}\right) & 0 \\ -\frac{1}{s} & \left(1 + \frac{1}{s}\right) & I \end{vmatrix} = \left(1 + \frac{1}{s}\right)(V - I)$$

$$V_o = \frac{(1 + 1/s)(V - I)}{-(1 + 1/s)(s + 1)} = \frac{I - V}{s + 1} \quad \text{Ans.}$$

Because of mixed sources, it is not possible to write down the determinant by inspection. We must first write the equations. As in the mesh-analysis (method 2), quite a bit of work is involved here also.

Method 6

Here we rearrange the position of the voltage source in order to associate an impedance in series with it (so that we can convert it to a current source). From Fig. 5-35 we see that the voltage V acts only in the top mesh in a clockwise sense. Suppose that this voltage is pushed through node 2 as in Fig. 5-41(a). (If another branch is connected to 2, a third voltage source will have appeared in that branch as a result of pushing the original voltage source through node 2.) Note that there is still a voltage V acting in the clockwise sense in the top mesh. Even though we now have two new voltage sources acting in the lower right mesh, their net effect is zero because they oppose each other. So we have not altered any of the element currents or voltages in the circuit if we recognize that nodes p and q represent the right-hand node of the original circuit of Fig. 5-35. Note that $V_p = V_2 + V = V_q$. We can convert the voltage-source-series-impedance combinations of Fig. 5-41(a) to the current-source-parallel-impedance combinations. The resulting circuit is shown in Fig. 5-41(b), where nodes p and q are no longer available. They have been absorbed by the source conversions. Since the voltage across the inductor is $(V_p - V_1)$ and the voltage across the right-hand resistor is V_q, Fig. 5-41(b) alone *cannot* be used to calculate these voltages. However, we can calculate V_1 and V_2 from Fig. 5-41(b). Then, $(V_p - V_1)$ and V_q can be evaluated from $V_p - V_1 = (V_2 + V) - V_1$, $V_q = V_2 + V$.

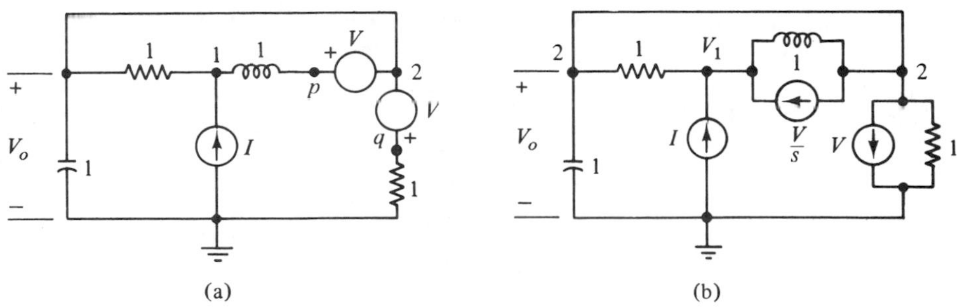

Fig. 5-41

As a result of the source conversions, the original circuit is converted to a two-node problem. Using Fig. 5-41(b), we can write the determinants Δ and Δ_2 and then obtain the output. Since the output voltage is the same as the node 2 voltage, we have

$$V_o = \frac{\Delta_2}{\Delta}$$

$$V_o = \frac{\begin{vmatrix} \left(1 + \frac{1}{s}\right) & \left(I + \frac{V}{s}\right) \\ -\left(1 + \frac{1}{s}\right) & \left(-V - \frac{V}{s}\right) \end{vmatrix}}{\begin{vmatrix} \left(1 + \frac{1}{s}\right) & -\left(1 + \frac{1}{s}\right) \\ -\left(1 + \frac{1}{s}\right) & \left(s + 2 + \frac{1}{s}\right) \end{vmatrix}} = \frac{\left(1 + \frac{1}{s}\right)\left[-V\left(1 + \frac{1}{s}\right) + \left(I + \frac{V}{s}\right)\right]}{\left(1 + \frac{1}{s}\right)\left[\left(s + 2 + \frac{1}{s}\right) - \left(1 + \frac{1}{s}\right)\right]}$$

$$= \frac{I - V}{s + 1} \quad \text{Ans.}$$

This problem could just as well have been solved by moving the original voltage source counterclockwise, thereby pushing it through the left node; then voltage sources would appear in series with the capacitor and in series with the left resistor.

Method 7

Suppose that we introduce a resistance R (or any other impedance that can be tagged) in series with the voltage source as shown in Fig. 5-42(a). We can then convert the voltage-source-R combination to the current-source-R combination shown in Fig. 5-42(b). The resulting network is a three-node network containing current sources only. Therefore the node determinant can be readily set up. Noting that node 3 is the output node, we have

$$\Delta = \begin{vmatrix} \left(G + 1 + \frac{1}{s}\right) & -\frac{1}{s} & -G \\ -\frac{1}{s} & \left(1 + \frac{1}{s}\right) & -1 \\ -G & -1 & (s + G + 1) \end{vmatrix} = \frac{(s + 1)^2}{s}(G + 1)$$

$$\Delta_3 = \begin{vmatrix} \left(G + 1 + \frac{1}{s}\right) & -\frac{1}{s} & VG \\ -\frac{1}{s} & \left(1 + \frac{1}{s}\right) & I \\ -G & -1 & -VG \end{vmatrix} = \frac{(s + 1)}{s}[-VG + I(s + G)]$$

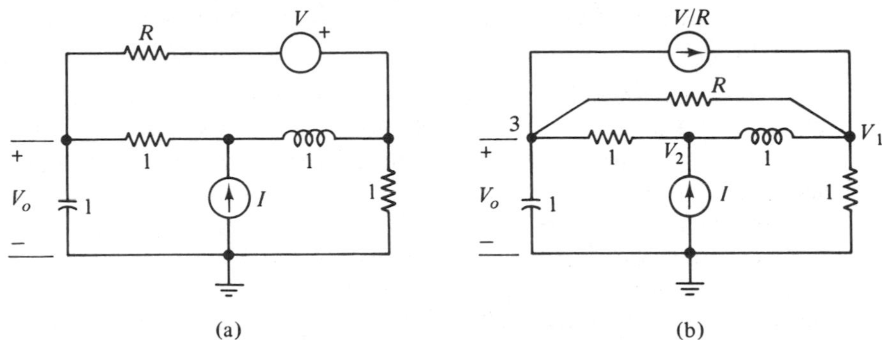

Fig. 5-42

Thus

$$V_o = \frac{\Delta_3}{\Delta} = \frac{(1 + 1/s)[I(s + G) - VG]}{[(s + 1)^2/s](G + 1)}$$

Now we undo the presence of R in the expression for V_o by letting $G \to \infty$ $(R \to 0)$. The result is

$$V_o = \frac{I - V}{s + 1} \quad \text{Ans.}$$

As in method 4, a great deal of work is involved here.

It is time to recapitulate. We solved the problem by seven different methods. It is obvious that the easiest solution to *this problem* by far is superposition (method 1). However, we discussed the other methods of solution so as to review the available options and compare the amounts of work involved. With a little practice it is possible to determine which method of approach is best for a given problem. For this reason, we developed the versatility of solving problems by different methods. To be sure, all methods have their genesis in the two Kirchhoff laws.

5-14 THE NATURE OF THE RESPONSE

If we go back and examine the frequency-domain solutions of all the examples and problems presented so far, we see that the response $R(s)$ is the ratio of two polynomials; that is,

$$R(s) = \frac{N(s)}{D(s)} = \frac{a_m s^m + a_{m-1} s^{m-1} + \cdots + a_1 s + a_0}{b_n s^n + b_{n-1} s^{n-1} + \cdots + b_1 s + b_0} \tag{5-53}$$

where $N(s)$ = numerator polynomial
m = degree of numerator polynomial
$a_m, a_{m-1}, \ldots, a_1, a_0$ = coefficients of numerator polynomial
$D(s)$ = denominator polynomial

n = degree of denominator polynomial = order of $R(s)$
$b_n, b_{n-1}, \ldots, b_1, b_0$ = coefficients of denominator polynomial

Equation (5-53) is true for any *RLC* network that is excited by independent sources with Laplace transforms of the form $(c_0 + c_1s + c_2s^2 + \cdots)/(d_0 + d_1s + d_2s^2 + \cdots)$. The network can also contain linear, dependent sources (which are discussed in Chapter 11).

In general, the degree of the numerator polynomial, m, is less than the degree of the denominator, n. [If $m \geq n$, then $R(s)$ is divided out by long division until the remaining function is in proper form—that is, its numerator degree is less than n.] The a and b coefficients are all real numbers, since they are dependent on R's, L's, and C's.

5-15 POLES

Frequently it is necessary to factor the denominator polynomial, a process that can be achieved by setting the denominator polynomial equal to zero

$$D(s) = b_ns^n + b_{n-1}s^{n-1} + \cdots + b_1s + b_0 = 0 \tag{5-54}$$

and then solving for the n roots of the resulting equation. The roots of $D(s) = 0$ are called *the poles of* $R(s)$ and are designated by the symbol p_i $(i = 1, 2, \ldots)$. Thus Eq. (5-54), and hence (5-53), can be written

$$D(s) = b_n(s - p_1)(s - p_2) \cdots (s - p_n) \tag{5-55}$$

$$R(s) = \frac{a_ms^m + a_{m-1}s^{m-1} + \cdots + a_1s + a_0}{b_n(s - p_1)(s - p_2) \cdots (s - p_n)} \tag{5-56}$$

If the denominator polynomial is of first or second degree, the poles can easily be determined. If the denominator polynomial is of third or higher degree, except for simple cases factorable by inspection, we resort to numerical methods, using the digital computer, to find the poles. A pole can be either real or complex. When complex, the poles occur in conjugate pairs; that is, if $c + jd$ is a pole, then $c - jd$ is also a pole. If this were not the case, the b coefficients would not all be real numbers. We designate the location of the poles by drawing an × in the complex plane, whose abscissa represents real values and the ordinate imaginary values. The complex plane (or s plane) is shown in Fig. 5-43. The abscissa is labeled Re s and the ordinate j Im s. The abscissa is also known as the *real axis* and the ordinate as the *imaginary axis*. All points above the real axis constitute the *upper half-plane,* all those below the *lower half-plane*. All points to the right of the imaginary axis constitute the *right half-plane,* and all points to the left of it constitute the *left half-plane*.

Referring to Fig. 5-43, we see that the pole designated by a is at the origin. The pole designated by b is in the right half-plane and on the real axis. It is on the positive real axis. The poles designated by cc' are a pair of complex-conjugate, right half-plane poles. The poles designated by dd' are a pair of conjugate, imaginary axis

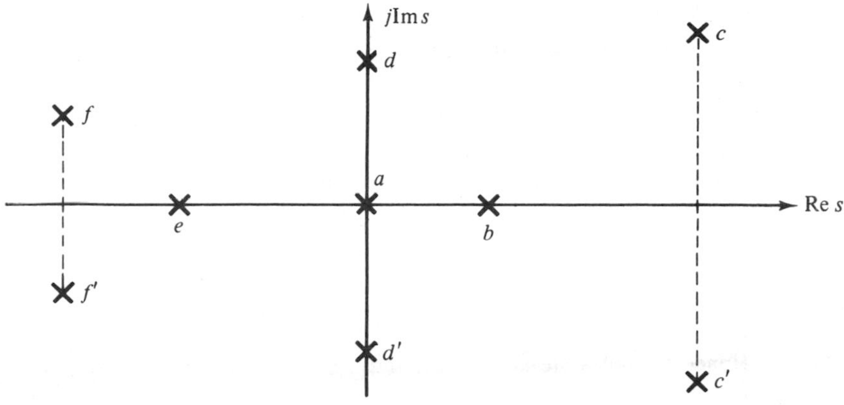

Fig. 5-43

poles. The pole at e is a left half-plane, real axis pole. It is on the negative real axis. The poles designated by ff' are a pair of complex-conjugate, left half-plane poles.

If the poles of a function are given, we can construct the denominator polynomial of that function to within a scale factor. Thus the pole diagram in Fig. 5-44 corresponds to a denominator polynomial of

$$D(s) = b_5(s + 1)(s - j2)(s + j2)(s + 2 - j)(s + 2 + j) \tag{5-57}$$

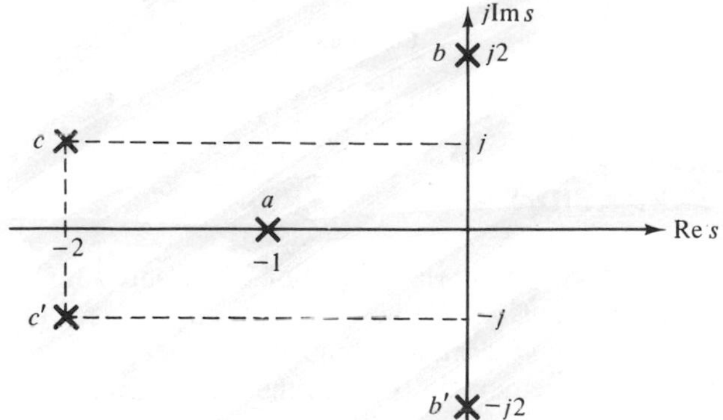

Fig. 5-44

The first factor $(s + 1)$ results from the pole at a, which is at $s = -1$. The second and third factors result from the poles at bb', which are at $s = \pm j2$. The third and fourth factors result from the poles at cc', which are at $-2 \pm j$. Equation (5-57) can be simplified to

$$\begin{aligned} D(s) &= b_5(s + 1)(s^2 + 4)[(s + 2)^2 + 1] \\ &= b_5(s^5 + 5s^4 + 13s^3 + 25s^2 + 36s + 20) \end{aligned}$$

The scale factor b_5 cannot be determined from Fig. 5-44. It must be specified separately.

Example 5-16

Indicate in the s plane the location of the poles of

$$F(s) = \frac{N(s)}{s^3 + s^2 + s + 1}$$

Solution. The denominator polynomial is

$$D(s) = s^3 + s^2 + s + 1$$

It can be factored, by inspection, as

$$D(s) = (s + 1)(s^2 + 1) = (s + 1)(s - j)(s + j)$$

Hence the poles are at -1, $+j$, and $-j$. The locations of these poles are sketched in Fig. 5-45.

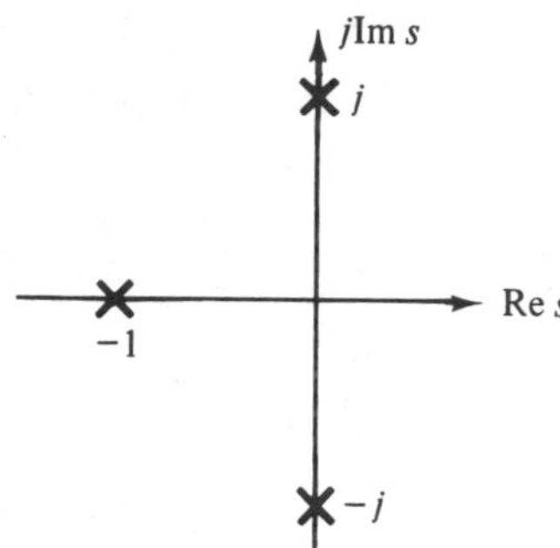

Fig. 5-45

5-16 INVERSE TRANSFORMATION VIA PARTIAL-FRACTION EXPANSION

So far we have learned how to set up appropriate equations and solve for the voltages and currents in the *frequency domain*. We now present a method for converting *frequency-domain* solutions into *time-domain* solutions.

The transformation back into the time domain is called the *inverse transformation* and is designated by the symbol $\mathcal{L}^{-1}$. Thus

$$\mathcal{L}^{-1}\{F(s)\} = f(t) \tag{5-58}$$

The first step in the inverse transformation process is to write the denominator of $F(s)$ in factored form—that is,

$$F(s) = \frac{N(s)}{b_n(s - p_1)(s - p_2) \cdots (s - p_n)} \tag{5-59}$$

where the p's represent the *poles of* $F(s)$. *Note that the poles are those values of* s *that make* $F(s)$ *infinite*. The next step is to break down $F(s)$ into the sum of simpler terms. Such a decomposition is obtained when $F(s)$ is expanded in *partial fractions*.

Simple Poles

Assume that the degree of the denominator of $F(s)$ is greater than the degree of the numerator and that the poles are simple; that is, no two poles are alike. Then the partial fraction expansion of $F(s)$ is given by

$$F(s) = \frac{K_1}{s - p_1} + \frac{K_2}{s - p_2} + \cdots + \frac{K_n}{s - p_n} \tag{5-60}$$

where

$$\begin{aligned} K_1 &= (s - p_1)F(s)\,|_{s=p_1} \\ K_2 &= (s - p_2)F(s)\,|_{s=p_2} \\ &\vdots \\ K_n &= (s - p_n)F(s)\,|_{s=p_n} \end{aligned}$$

Thus a two-step procedure is used to evaluate the K's. For instance, to evaluate K_1, we first multiply both sides of $F(s)$ by $(s - p_1)$ and obtain

$$\begin{aligned} (s - p_1)F(s) &= \frac{N(s)\cancel{(s - p_1)}}{b_n\cancel{(s - p_1)}(s - p_2)\cdots(s - p_n)} \\ &= K_1 + \frac{K_2(s - p_1)}{(s - p_2)} + \cdots + \frac{K_n(s - p_1)}{(s - p_n)} \end{aligned}$$

Then we let $s = p_1$ so that all terms on the right-hand side except K_1 become nullified.

$$\frac{N(p_1)}{b_n(p_1 - p_2)\cdots(p_1 - p_n)} = K_1$$

Thus the value of K_1 is determined. Similarly, $K_2, \ldots, K_n$ are obtained.

Next, consider a typical term in the expansion:

$$\frac{K_i}{s - p_i} \tag{5-61}$$

Referring to Table 5-1 and realizing that K_i is simply a constant, we see that Eq. (5-61) is the Laplace transform of $K_i e^{p_i t}$. So

$$\mathcal{L}^{-1}\left\{\frac{K_i}{s - p_i}\right\} = K_i e^{p_i t} \tag{5-62}$$

Since $F(s)$ is the sum of terms like Eq. (5-61), then $f(t)$ must be the sum of terms like Eq. (5-62). Consequently, we have

$$\begin{aligned} F(s) &= \frac{K_1}{s - p_1} + \frac{K_2}{s - p_2} + \cdots + \frac{K_n}{s - p_n} \\ f(t) &= K_1 e^{p_1 t} + K_2 e^{p_2 t} + \cdots + K_n e^{p_n t} \end{aligned} \tag{5-63}$$

This is a remarkable result. It states that if the degree of the numerator of $F(s)$ is lower than the degree of the denominator and if all poles of $F(s)$ are simple, then $f(t)$ is the sum of n exponentials, *one for each pole of* $F(s)$. The poles appear as exponents in each term. Thus the waveform of $f(t)$ is determined by the location of the poles, which may be real, or may appear in complex-conjugate pairs.

Example 5-17

(a) Expand

$$F(s) = \frac{1}{(s+1)(s+2)}$$

into partial fractions.

(b) Obtain $f(t)$.

Solution.

(a)
$$\frac{1}{(s+1)(s+2)} = \frac{K_1}{s+1} + \frac{K_2}{s+2}$$

$$K_1 = \left.\frac{\cancel{(s+1)}}{\cancel{(s+1)}(s+2)}\right|_{s=-1} = 1$$

$$K_2 = \left.\frac{\cancel{(s+2)}}{(s+1)\cancel{(s+2)}}\right|_{s=-2} = -1$$

So the partial fraction expansion of $F(s)$ is

$$F(s) = \frac{1}{s+1} - \frac{1}{s+2} \quad \text{Ans.}$$

(b) Since $\mathcal{L}^{-1}\{1/(s+\alpha)\} = e^{-\alpha t}$, we have

$$\mathcal{L}^{-1}\left\{\frac{1}{s+1} - \frac{1}{s+2}\right\} = \mathcal{L}^{-1}\left\{\frac{1}{s+1}\right\} - \mathcal{L}^{-1}\left\{\frac{1}{s+2}\right\} = e^{-t} - e^{-2t} \quad \text{Ans.}$$

Example 5-18

$$\text{Obtain } \mathcal{L}^{-1}\left\{\frac{a_1 s + a_o}{s^2 + \omega^2}\right\}.$$

Solution.

Method 1 From Table 5-1 we know that

$$\mathcal{L}^{-1}\left\{\frac{s}{s^2 + \omega^2}\right\} = \cos \omega t$$

and

$$\mathcal{L}^{-1}\left\{\frac{\omega}{s^2 + \omega^2}\right\} = \sin \omega t$$

We therefore rearrange the given function as

$$\mathcal{L}^{-1}\left\{\frac{a_1 s + a_0}{s^2 + \omega^2}\right\} = \mathcal{L}^{-1}\left\{\frac{a_1 s}{s^2 + \omega^2} + \frac{a_0}{s^2 + \omega^2}\right\}$$

$$= a_1 \mathcal{L}^{-1}\left\{\frac{s}{s^2 + \omega^2}\right\} + \frac{a_0}{\omega}\mathcal{L}^{-1}\left\{\frac{\omega}{s^2 + \omega^2}\right\}$$

$$= a_1 \cos \omega t + \frac{a_0}{\omega} \sin \omega t \quad \text{Ans.}$$

Since

$$A \sin \theta + B \cos \theta = \sqrt{A^2 + B^2} \sin\left(\theta + \tan^{-1}\frac{B}{A}\right)$$

$$= \sqrt{A^2 + B^2} \cos\left(\theta - \tan^{-1}\frac{A}{B}\right)$$

we can alternatively rewrite the answer as

$$\sqrt{a_1^2 + \left(\frac{a_0}{\omega}\right)^2} \sin\left[\omega t + \tan^{-1}\left(\frac{a_1 \omega}{a_0}\right)\right] \quad \text{Ans.}$$

Method 2 From Table 5-1 we know that

$$\mathcal{L}^{-1}\left\{\frac{1}{s + \alpha}\right\} = e^{-\alpha t}$$

We therefore expand the given function into partial fractions to obtain the standard terms as follows.

$$\frac{a_1 s + a_0}{s^2 + \omega^2} = \frac{a_1 s + a_0}{(s - j\omega)(s + j\omega)} = \frac{K_1}{s - j\omega} + \frac{K_2}{s + j\omega}$$

$$K_1 = \frac{a_1 s + a_0}{\cancel{(s - j\omega)}(s + j\omega)} \times \cancel{(s - j\omega)}\Bigg|_{s=j\omega} = \frac{a_1 j\omega + a_0}{2j\omega} = \frac{a_1}{2} - j\frac{a_0}{2\omega}$$

$$K_2 = \frac{a_1 s + a_0}{(s - j\omega)\cancel{(s + j\omega)}} \times \cancel{(s + j\omega)}\Bigg|_{s=-j\omega} = \frac{a_1(-j\omega) + a_0}{-j2\omega} = \frac{a_1}{2} + j\frac{a_0}{2\omega}$$

Note that K_2 is the complex conjugate of K_1. This result is to be expected, for the poles corresponding to the K's are complex conjugates of each other. Since

$$\mathcal{L}^{-1}\left\{\frac{K_1}{s - j\omega} + \frac{K_2}{s + j\omega}\right\} = K_1 e^{j\omega t} + K_2 e^{-j\omega t}$$

we have

$$\mathcal{L}^{-1}\left\{\frac{a_1 s + a_0}{s^2 + \omega^2}\right\} = \left(\frac{a_1}{2} - j\frac{a_0}{2\omega}\right)e^{j\omega t} + \left(\frac{a_1}{2} + j\frac{a_0}{2\omega}\right)e^{-j\omega t}$$

$$= a_1\underbrace{\left(\frac{e^{j\omega t} + e^{-j\omega t}}{2}\right)}_{\cos \omega t} + \frac{a_0}{\omega}\underbrace{\left(\frac{e^{j\omega t} - e^{-j\omega t}}{2j}\right)}_{\sin \omega t} = a_1 \cos \omega t + \frac{a_0}{\omega} \sin \omega t \quad \text{Ans.}$$

Example 15-19

$$R(s) = \frac{1}{(s^3 + 3s^2 + 4s + 2)}.\ \text{Obtain } r(t).$$

Solution. We must first factor the denominator in order to obtain the poles of $R(s)$. After some trial and error, we recognize that the denominator is factorable as

$$R(s) = \frac{1}{(s + 1)(s^2 + 2s + 2)}$$

Furthermore, we can factor $(s^2 + 2s + 2)$ by finding the roots of

$$s^2 + 2s + 2 = 0 = (s - r_1)(s - r_2)$$

By the quadratic formula, the roots are

$$r_{1,2} = -1 \pm \sqrt{1 - 2} = -1 \pm j$$

Thus we have

$$R(s) = \frac{1}{(s + 1)(s + 1 - j)(s + 1 + j)}$$

which we expand into partial fractions.

$$R(s) = \frac{K_1}{s + 1} + \frac{K_2}{s + 1 - j} + \frac{K_3}{s + 1 + j}$$

$$K_1 = \left.\frac{1}{(s + 1 - j)(s + 1 + j)}\right|_{s=-1} = \left.\frac{1}{s^2 + 2s + 2}\right|_{s=-1} = 1$$

$$K_2 = \left.\frac{1}{(s + 1)(s + 1 + j)}\right|_{s=-1+j} = \frac{1}{(-1 + j + 1)(-1 + j + 1 + j)}$$

$$= \frac{1}{j2j} = -\frac{1}{2}$$

$$K_3 = \text{conjugate of } K_2 = -\frac{1}{2}$$

$$R(s) = \frac{1}{s + 1} - \frac{1}{2}\frac{1}{s + 1 - j} - \frac{1}{2}\frac{1}{s + 1 + j}$$

$$r(t) = e^{-t} - \frac{1}{2}e^{(-1+j)t} - \frac{1}{2}e^{(-1-j)t}$$

$$= e^{-t} - e^{-t}\underbrace{\left(\frac{e^{jt} + e^{-jt}}{2}\right)}_{\cos t} = e^{-t}(1 - \cos t) \quad \text{Ans.}$$

Example 5-20

Obtain the inverse transform of

$$F(s) = \frac{s + a}{(s + b)(s^2 + c^2)}$$

Solution. First expand $F(s)$ into partial fractions.

$$F(s) = \frac{K_1}{s + b} + \frac{K_2}{s - jc} + \frac{K_3}{s + jc}$$

$$K_1 = \frac{s + a}{s^2 + c^2}\bigg|_{s=-b} = \frac{a - b}{b^2 + c^2}$$

$$K_2 = \frac{s + a}{(s + b)(s + jc)}\bigg|_{s=jc} = \frac{a + jc}{(b + jc)2jc}$$

$$K_3 = \text{complex conjugate of } K_2$$

Then

$$F(s) = \left(\frac{a - b}{b^2 + c^2}\right)\Big/(s + b) + \left[\frac{a + jc}{(b + jc)2jc}\right]\Big/(s - jc) + \left[\frac{a - jc}{(b - jc)2(-j)c}\right]\Big/(s + jc)$$

$$f(t) = \left(\frac{a - b}{b^2 + c^2}\right)e^{-bt} + \left[\frac{a + jc}{(b + jc)2jc}e^{jct}\right] + \text{(its complex conjugate)}$$

When a function and its complex conjugate are added, we obtain twice the real part of the function.

$$(A + jB) + (A - jB) = 2A = 2 \text{ Re } \{(A + jB)\}$$

Thus

$$\begin{aligned} f(t) &= \left(\frac{a - b}{b^2 + c^2}\right)e^{-bt} + 2 \text{ Re } \left\{\frac{a + jc}{2jc(b + jc)}e^{jct}\right\} \\ &= \left(\frac{a - b}{b^2 + c^2}\right)e^{-bt} + \text{Re } \left\{\frac{\sqrt{a^2 + c^2}e^{j\tan^{-1}(c/a)}}{ce^{j\pi/2}\sqrt{b^2 + c^2}e^{j\tan^{-1}(c/b)}}e^{jct}\right\} \\ &= \frac{a - b}{b^2 + c^2}e^{-bt} + \frac{\sqrt{a^2 + c^2}}{c\sqrt{b^2 + c^2}} \text{ Re } \{e^{j[ct + \tan^{-1}(c/a) - (\pi/2) - \tan^{-1}(c/b)]}\} \end{aligned}$$

Since

$$\text{Re } \{e^{j\theta}\} = \cos\theta \tag{5 64}$$

$f(t)$ becomes

$$\begin{aligned} f(t) &= \frac{a - b}{b^2 + c^2}e^{-bt} + \frac{\sqrt{a^2 + c^2}}{c\sqrt{b^2 + c^2}} \cos\left(ct + \tan^{-1}\frac{c}{a} - \frac{\pi}{2} - \tan^{-1}\frac{c}{b}\right) \\ &= \frac{a - b}{b^2 + c^2}e^{-bt} + \frac{\sqrt{a^2 + c^2}}{c\sqrt{b^2 + c^2}} \sin\left(ct + \tan^{-1}\frac{c}{a} - \tan^{-1}\frac{c}{b}\right) \quad \text{Ans.} \end{aligned}$$

Multiple Poles

Assume that the degree of the denominator of $F(s)$ is greater than the degree of the numerator and that $F(s)$ contains poles of multiplicity 2—that is, the denominator of $F(s)$ has factors like $(s - p_i)^2$, where p_i represents the pole. Then in the partial fraction expansion of $F(s)$, the terms corresponding to the double pole are given by

$$F(s) = \frac{N(s)}{\cdots(s - p_i)^2\cdots} = \cdots + \left[\frac{K_{i1}}{(s - p_i)^2} + \frac{K_{i2}}{s - p_i}\right] + \cdots \qquad (5\text{-}65)$$

where $K_{i1} = (s - p_i)^2 F(s)\,\big|_{s=p_i}$

$$K_{i2} = \left\{\frac{d}{ds}[(s - p_i)^2 F(s)]\right\}_{s=p_i}$$

A little study of Eq. (5-65) will show why the indicated operations give the respective K_i values. (See Problem 5-29.) Note that a double-order pole contributes two terms to the partial-fraction expansion.

In general, if $F(s)$ has a pole of multiplicity n at $s = p_i$, then

$$F(s) = \frac{N(s)}{\cdots(s - p_i)^n\cdots}$$

$$= \cdots + \left[\frac{K_{i1}}{(s - p_i)^n} + \frac{K_{i2}}{(s - p_i)^{n-1}} + \frac{K_{i3}}{(s - p_i)^{n-2}} + \cdots + \frac{K_{in}}{s - p_i}\right] + \cdots \qquad (5\text{-}66)$$

where $K_{i1} = (s - p_i)^n F(s)\,\big|_{s=p_i}$

$$K_{i2} = \left\{\frac{d}{ds}[(s - p_i)^n F(s)]\right\}_{s=p_i}$$

$$K_{i3} = \frac{1}{2!}\left\{\frac{d^2}{ds^2}[(s - p_i)^n F(s)]\right\}_{s=p_i}$$

$$\vdots$$

$$K_{in} = \frac{1}{(n-1)!}\left\{\frac{d^{n-1}}{ds^{n-1}}[(s - p_i)^n F(s)]\right\}_{s=p_i}$$

An nth-order pole contributes n terms to the partial-fraction expansion.

Example 5-21

Obtain the inverse transform of $\dfrac{1}{s^2(s^2 + 1)^2}$.

Solution. The given function has six poles. Two of them are at $s = 0$, two at $s = +j$, and two at $s = -j$. Thus it has three sets of poles of multiplicity 2. The expansion contains six terms, two for each double pole.

$$\frac{1}{s^2(s-j)^2(s+j)^2} = \left(\frac{K_{11}}{s^2} + \frac{K_{12}}{s}\right) + \left[\frac{K_{21}}{(s-j)^2} + \frac{K_{22}}{s-j}\right] + \left[\frac{K_{31}}{(s+j)^2} + \frac{K_{32}}{s+j}\right]$$

$$K_{11} = \frac{1}{(s-j)^2(s+j)^2}\bigg|_{s=0} = \frac{1}{(s^2+1)^2}\bigg|_{s=0} = 1$$

$$K_{12} = \left\{\frac{d}{ds}\left[\frac{1}{(s^2+1)^2}\right]\right\}_{s=0} = \frac{-4s}{(s^2+1)^3}\bigg|_{s=0} = 0$$

$$K_{21} = \frac{1}{s^2(s+j)^2}\bigg|_{s=j} = \frac{1}{j^2(2j)^2} = \frac{1}{4}$$

$$K_{22} = \left\{\frac{d}{ds}\left[\frac{1}{s^2(s+j)^2}\right]\right\}_{s=j} + \left[\frac{-2}{s^2(s+j)^3} + \frac{-2}{s^3(s+j)^2}\right]_{s=j} = j\frac{3}{4}$$

$$K_{31} = \text{conjugate of } K_{21} = \frac{1}{4}$$

$$K_{32} = \text{conjugate of } K_{22} = -j\frac{3}{4}$$

So we have

$$\frac{1}{s_2} + \frac{1/4}{(s-j)^2} + \frac{j(3/4)}{s-j} + \frac{1/4}{(s+j)^2} - \frac{j(3/4)}{s+j} \tag{5-67}$$

From Table 5-1, we know that

$$\mathcal{L}^{-1}\left\{\frac{1}{s^2}\right\} = t, \qquad \mathcal{L}^{-1}\left\{\frac{1}{(s+\alpha)^2}\right\} = te^{-\alpha t}, \qquad \mathcal{L}^{-1}\left\{\frac{1}{s+\alpha}\right\} = e^{-\alpha t}$$

Thus the inverse transform of Eq. (5-67) is

$$t + \frac{1}{4}te^{jt} + j\frac{3}{4}e^{jt} + \frac{1}{4}te^{-jt} - j\frac{3}{4}e^{-jt} = t + \frac{t}{2}\underbrace{\left(\frac{e^{jt}+e^{-jt}}{2}\right)}_{\cos t} - \frac{3}{2}\underbrace{\left(\frac{e^{jt}-e^{-jt}}{2j}\right)}_{\sin t}$$

$$= t + \frac{t}{2}\cos t - \frac{3}{2}\sin t \quad \text{Ans.}$$

Example 5-22

In Fig. 5-46, $i_i = t$. What is v_o?

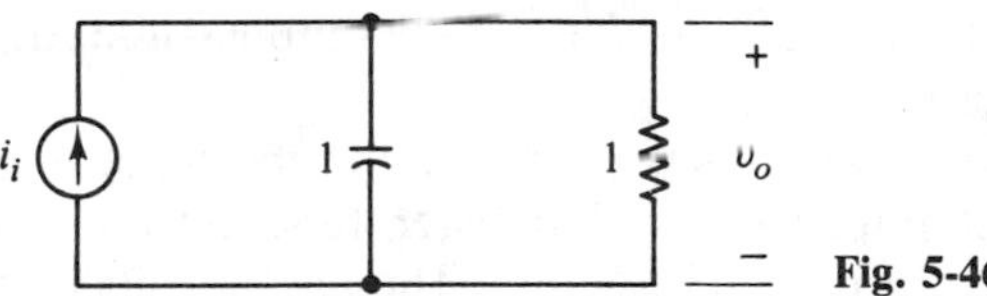

Fig. 5-46

Solution. First, obtain $V_o(s)$.

$$V_o(s) = I_i(s)Z = I_i(s)\left(\frac{1 \times 1/s}{1 + 1/s}\right) = I_i\left(\frac{1}{s+1}\right)$$

Since $i_i(t) = t$, $I_i(s) = 1/s^2$. Then

$$V_o = \frac{1}{s^2(s+1)}$$

Next, expand V_o into partial fractions.

$$V_o = \frac{K_{11}}{s^2} + \frac{K_{12}}{s} + \frac{K_2}{s+1}$$

$$K_{11} = \left.\frac{1}{s+1}\right|_{s=0} = 1$$

$$K_{12} = \left\{\frac{d}{ds}\left(\frac{1}{s+1}\right)\right\}_{s=0} = -\left.\frac{1}{(s+1)^2}\right|_{s=0} = -1$$

$$K_2 = \left.\frac{1}{s^2}\right|_{s=-1} = 1$$

It follows that

$$V_o = \frac{1}{s^2} - \frac{1}{s} + \frac{1}{s+1}$$

This is the frequency-domain solution. To obtain the time-domain solution, take the inverse transform of V_o.

$$v_o(t) = t - 1 + e^{-t} \quad \text{Ans.}$$

5-17 SUMMARY

Using Laplace transformation, we can transform ordinary, linear, constant coefficient, differential equations into algebraic equations that can be solved easily for the transform of the desired variable. By means of partial-fraction expansion, we can decompose the transform of the variable into the sum of simple terms, the inverse transforms of which are readily recognizable.

All the techniques associated with the solution of resistive networks can be applied to the solution of *RLC* networks if we operate in the frequency domain and replace R with Z. The impedance of a resistor is R, of an inductor sL, of a capacitor $1/sC$. The impedance of complicated networks can always be found by forming the $V(s)/I(s)$ ratio at the terminals under consideration while all internal independent sources are set to zero.

The transfer function allows us to describe the input-output relationships in a network. Both input impedance and transfer function are frequency-domain concepts. They are ratios of polynomials in s. The coefficients of these polynomials are determined by the R's, L's, and C's.

If $F(s) = N(s)/D(s)$, then the poles of $F(s)$ are those values of s that make $D(s)$ zero. Alternatively, the poles of $F(s)$ are those values of s that make $F(s)$ infinite. If $D(s)$ is of degree n, then $F(s)$ has n poles. The poles play a central role in the partial-fraction expansion and inverse transformation of $F(s)$. The individual terms in $f(t)$ are determined by the poles of $F(s)$.

PROBLEMS

5-1. Obtain the Laplace transform of the following functions.

(a) $\cos \omega t$ (b) $e^{-\alpha t} \sin \omega t$ (c) t

(d) $1 - e^{-\alpha t}$ (e) $\sin (\omega t + \theta)$ (f) $e^{-\alpha_1 t} - e^{-\alpha_2 t}$

5-2. The functions $f_1(t)$ and $f_2(t)$ are Laplace transformable; a_1 and a_2 are constants. Show that $\mathcal{L}[a_1 f_1(t) + a_2 f_2(t)] = a_1 F_1(s) + a_2 F_2(s)$.

5-3. Given the differential equations and initial conditions, obtain $Y(s)$.

$$Y(s) = \int_0^\infty y e^{-sx}\, dx$$

(a) $\dfrac{d^2y}{dx^2} + y = \sin x, \qquad y(0) = 0, \qquad y'(0) = 1$

(b) $\dfrac{d^2y}{dx^2} + \dfrac{dy}{dx} + y - 1 = 0, \qquad y(0) = y'(0) = 0$

5-4. For the networks shown in Fig. 5-47, obtain the voltages and currents designated by a question mark. Write the necessary equations (mesh, node, and constraint) and solve them.

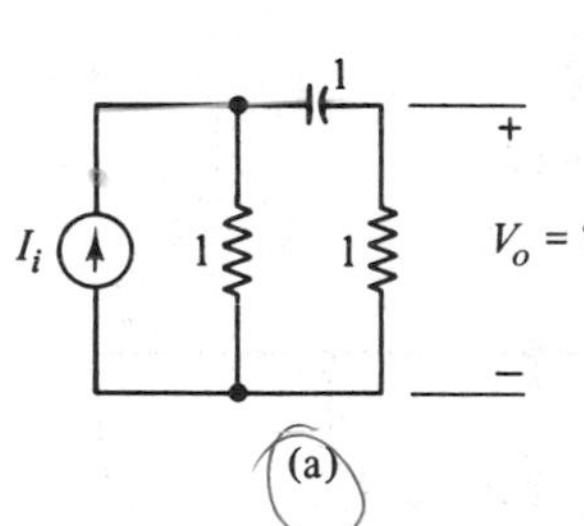

(a)

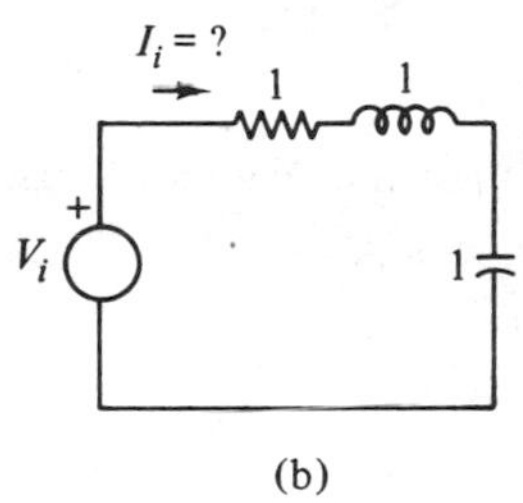

(b)

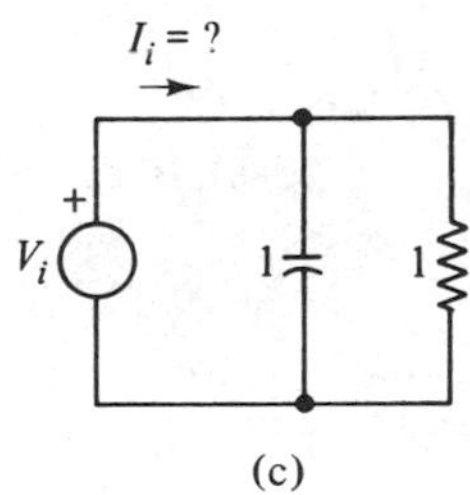

(c)

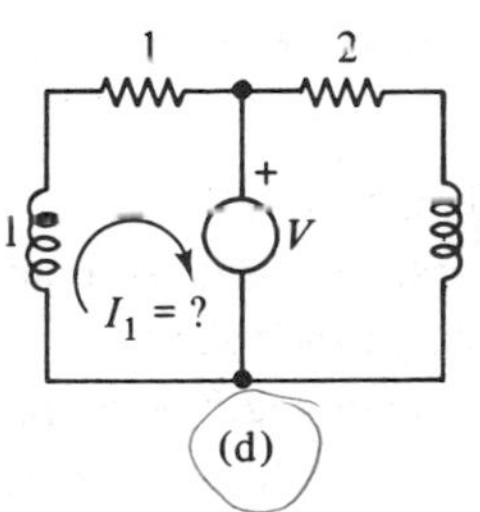

(d)

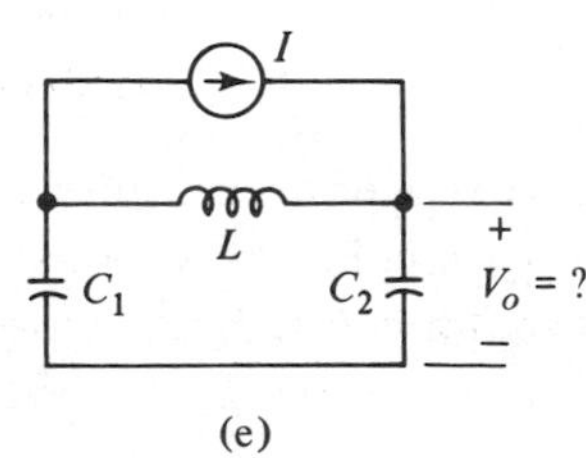

(e)

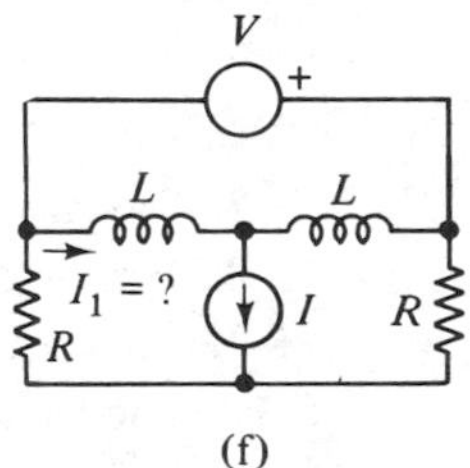

(f)

Fig. 5-47

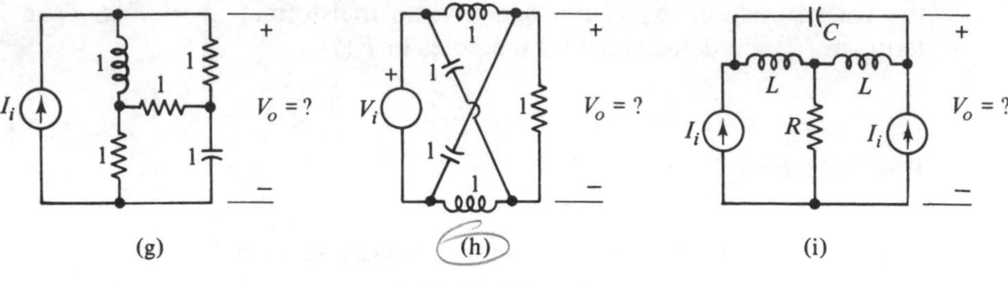

Fig. 5-47 (*cont.*)

5-5. For the networks shown in Fig. 5-48, obtain the mesh and node determinants. Do not be concerned that the networks are not excited.

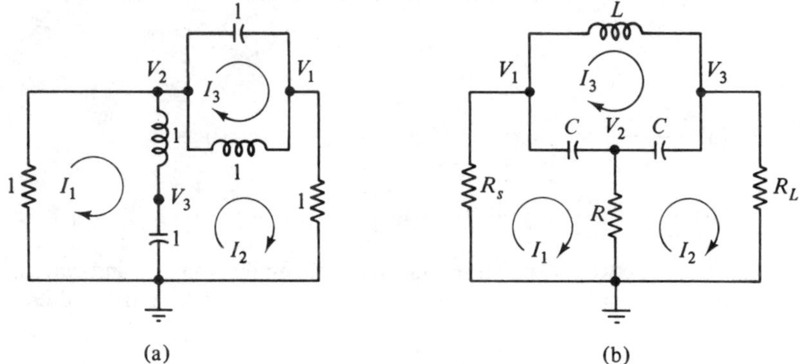

Fig. 5-48

5-6. In the circuits shown in Fig. 5-49, calculate V_o and I_o.

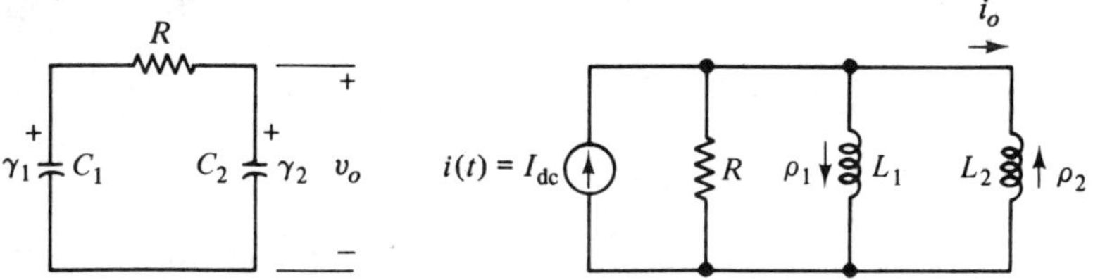

Fig. 5-49

5-7. Calculate the impedance of the networks shown in Fig. 5-50.

5-8. For the circuits shown in Fig. 5-51, obtain the response indicated by a question mark.

5-9. For each circuit shown in Fig. 5-52, derive the condition for balance.

5-10. For the circuits shown in Fig. 5-53, obtain the Thévenin and Norton equivalent circuits.

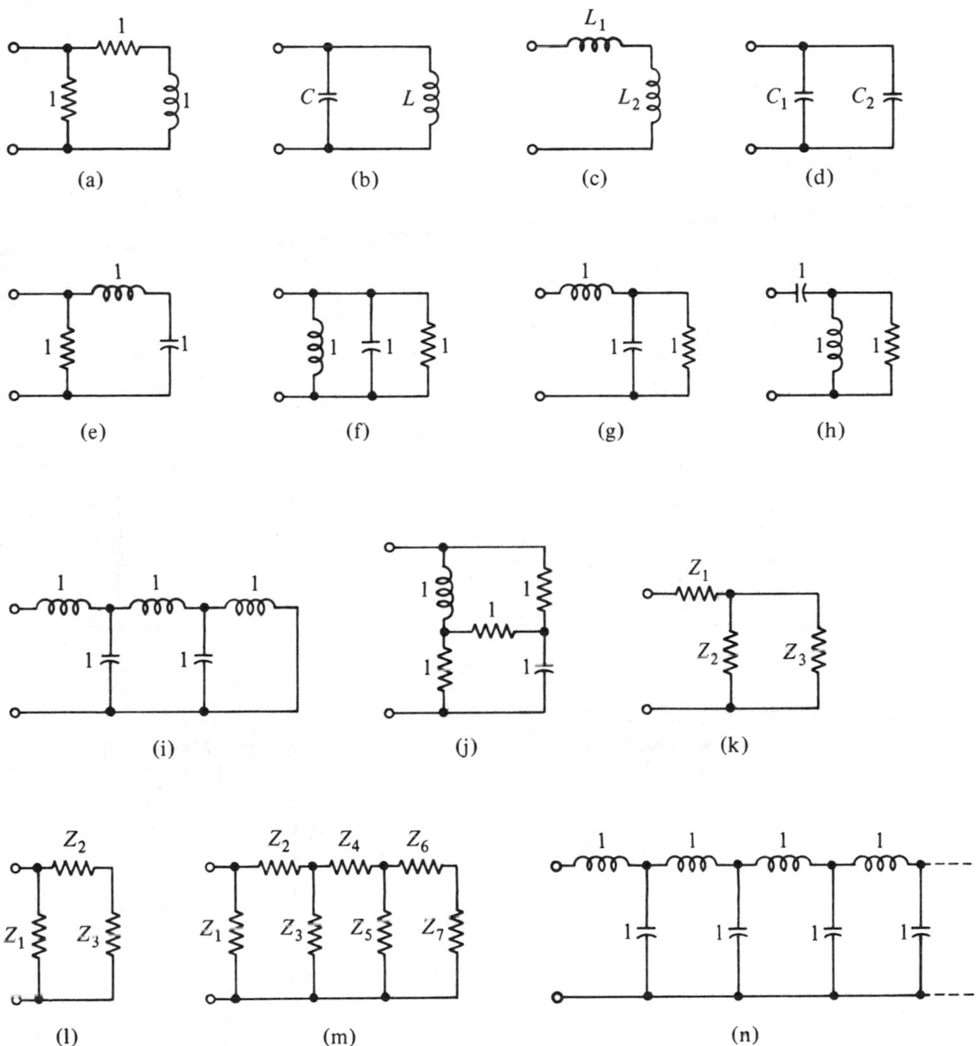
1
1
1
(a)
C
L
(b)
L_1
L_2
(c)
C_1
C_2
(d)
1
1
1
(e)
1
1
1
(f)
1
1
1
(g)
1
1
1
(h)
1
1
1
1
1
(i)
1
1
1
1
1
(j)
Z_1
Z_2
Z_3
(k)
Z_2
Z_1
Z_3
(l)
Z_2
Z_4
Z_6
Z_1
Z_3
Z_5
Z_7
(m)
1
1
1
1
1
1
1
1
(n)

Fig. 5-50

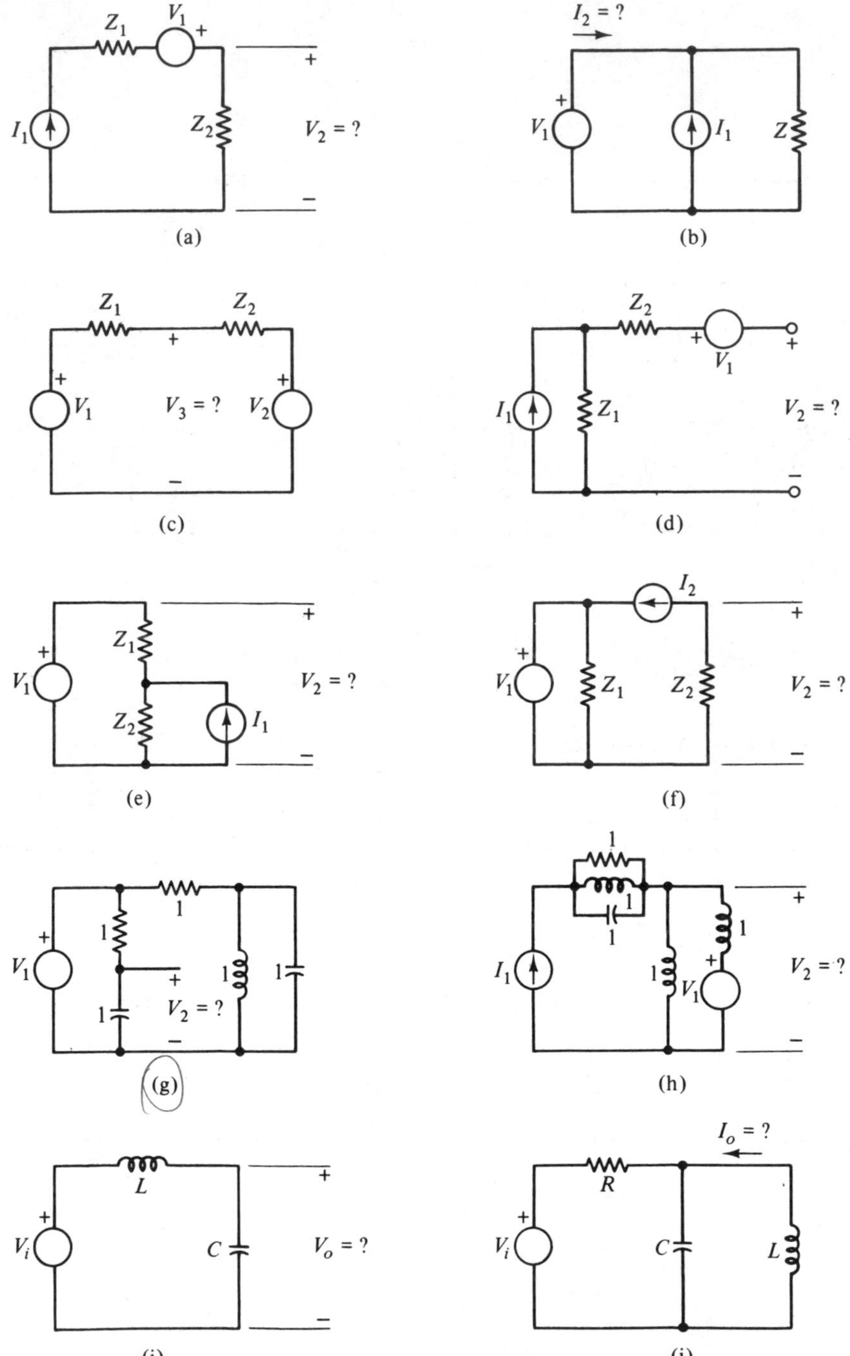

Z_1
V_1
+
+
I_1
Z_2
$V_2 = ?$
−
(a)
$I_2 = ?$
+
V_1
I_1
Z
(b)
Z_1
Z_2
+
+
+
V_1
$V_3 = ?$
V_2
−
(c)
Z_2
+
V_1
+
I_1
Z_1
$V_2 = ?$
−
(d)
+
Z_1
+
V_1
$V_2 = ?$
Z_2
I_1
−
(e)
I_2
+
+
V_1
Z_1
Z_2
$V_2 = ?$
−
(f)
1
+
1
V_1
+
1
1
$V_2 = ?$
1
−
(g)
1
1
1
+
1
I_1
1
+
V_1
$V_2 = ?$
−
(h)
+
L
+
V_i
C
$V_o = ?$
−
(i)
$I_o = ?$
R
+
V_i
C
L
(j)

Fig. 5-51

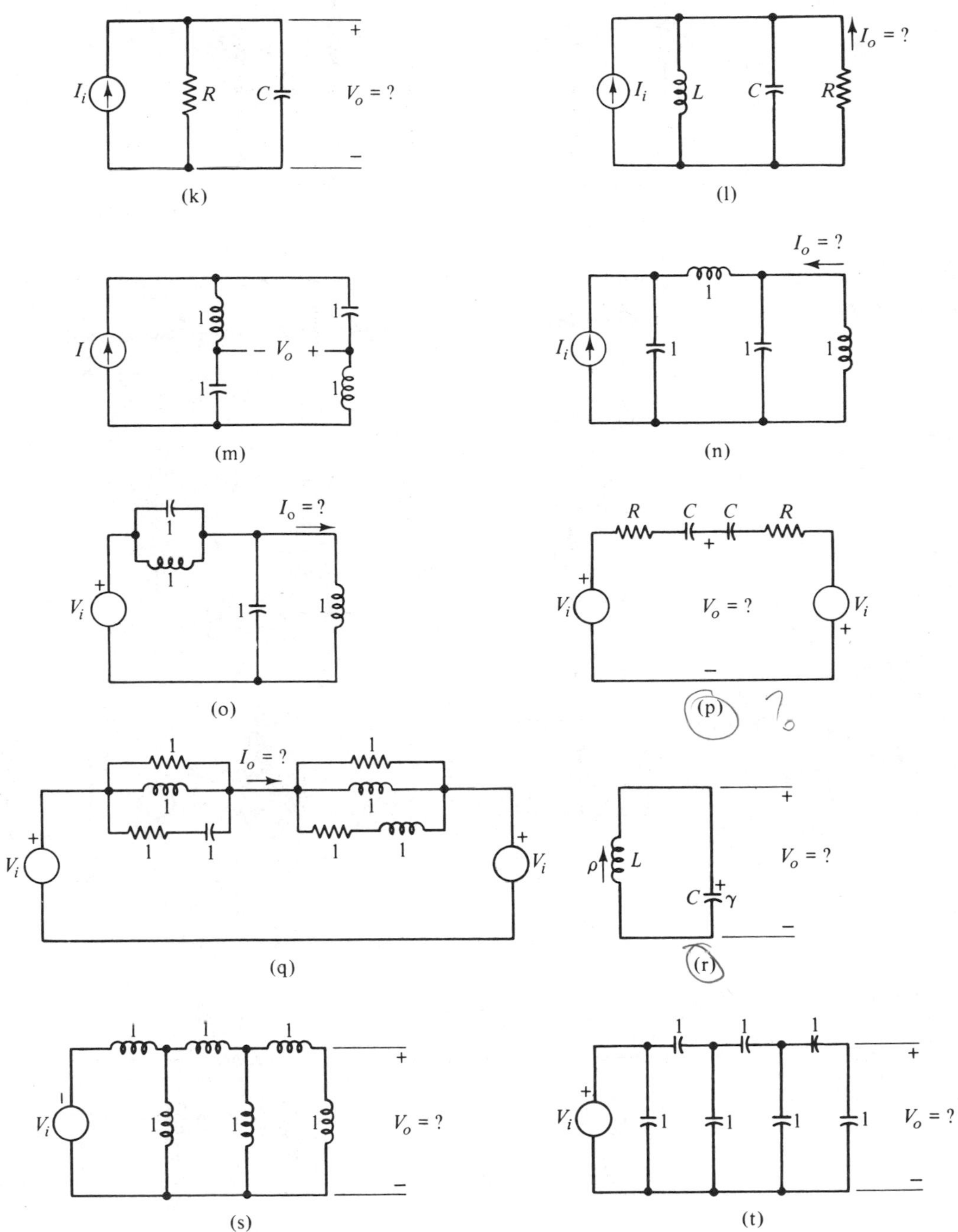

I_i
R
C
$V_o = ?$
(k)
$I_o = ?$
I_i
L
C
R
(l)
I
V_o
(m)
$I_o = ?$
I_i
(n)
$I_o = ?$
V_i
(o)
R C C R
V_i
$V_o = ?$
V_i
(p)
$I_o = ?$
V_i
V_i
(q)
ρ
L
C
γ
$V_o = ?$
(r)
V_i
$V_o = ?$
(s)
V_i
$V_o = ?$
(t)

Fig. 5-51 (*cont.*)

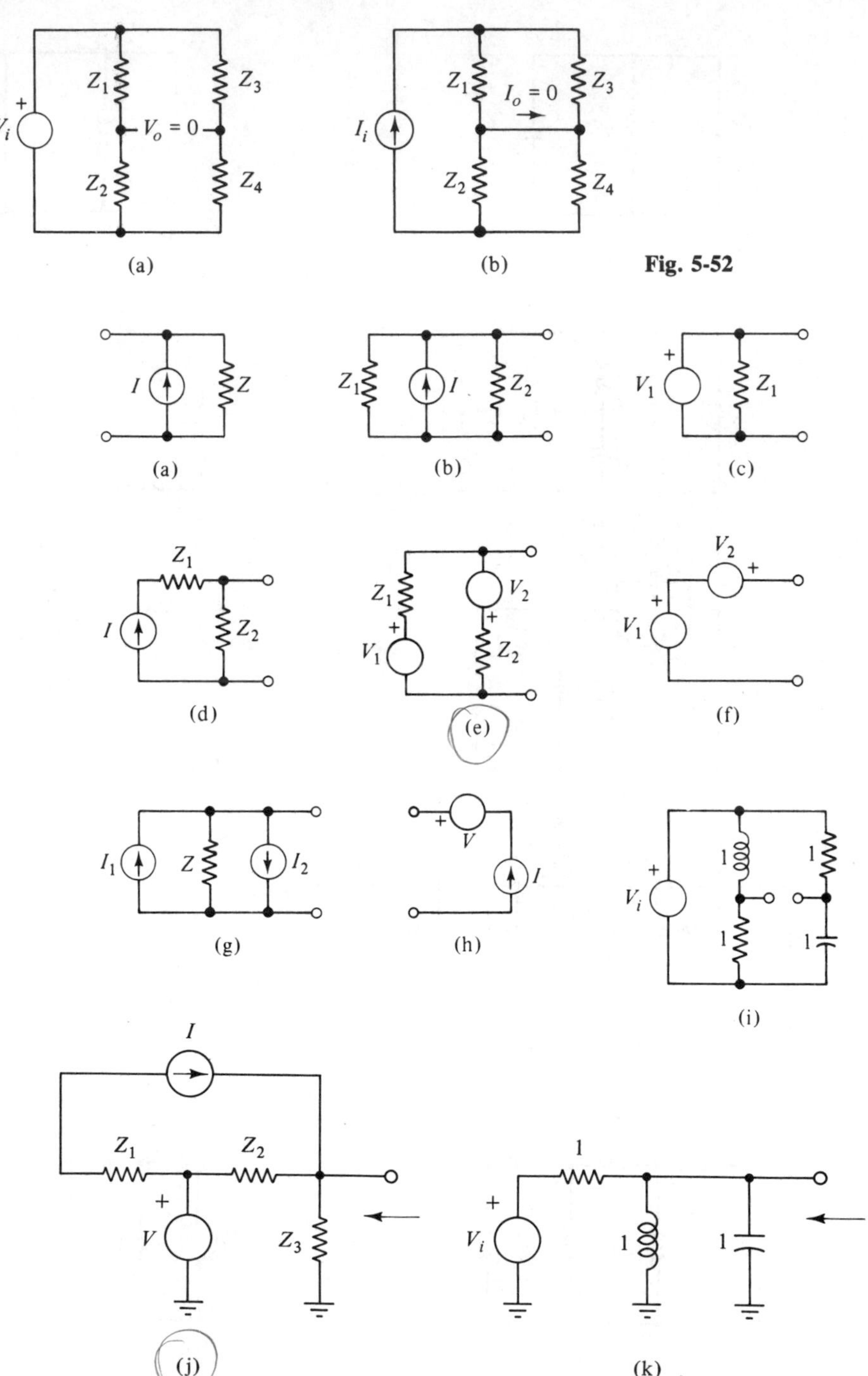

Fig. 5-52

Fig. 5-53

5-11. Calculate the transfer functions of the circuits shown in Fig. 5-54. The inputs and outputs are as designated.

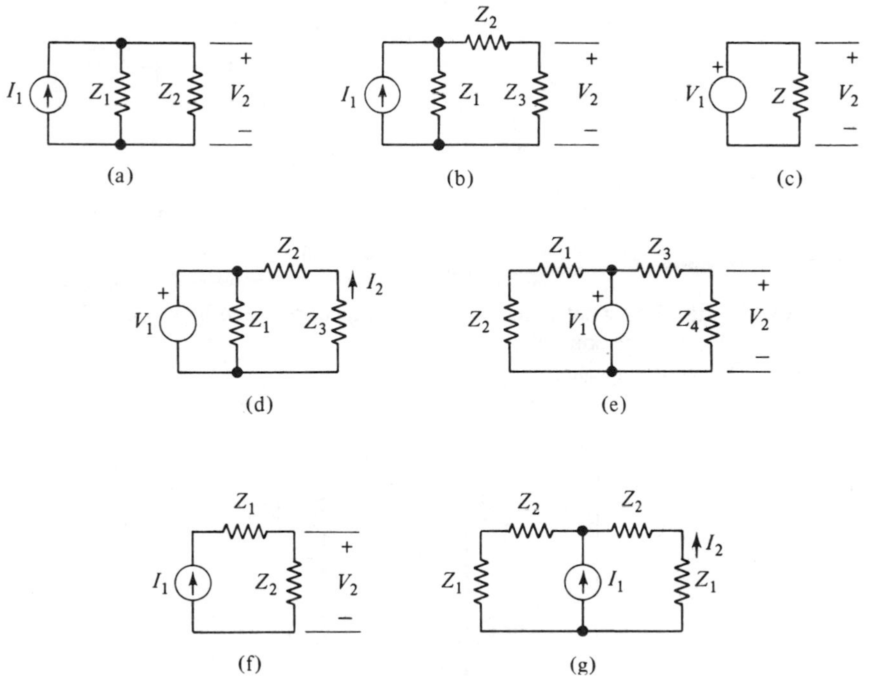

Fig. 5-54

5-12. Refer to Fig. 5-55.

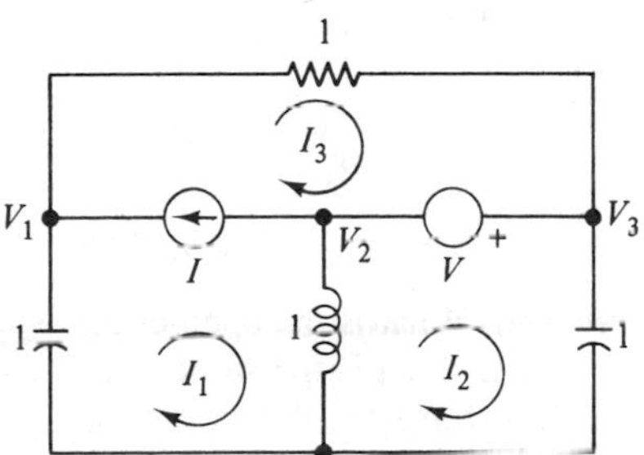

Fig. 5-55

(a) Write the necessary equations in ordered form for the solution of the three currents.
(b) Write the necessary equations in ordered form for the solution of the three voltages.
(c) Show how you would reroute and eliminate the current source.
(d) Show how you would rearrange and eliminate the voltage source.

5-13. In Fig. 5-56, what is I_1 if
(**a**) $V_2 = V_1$? (**b**) $V_2 = -V_1$?

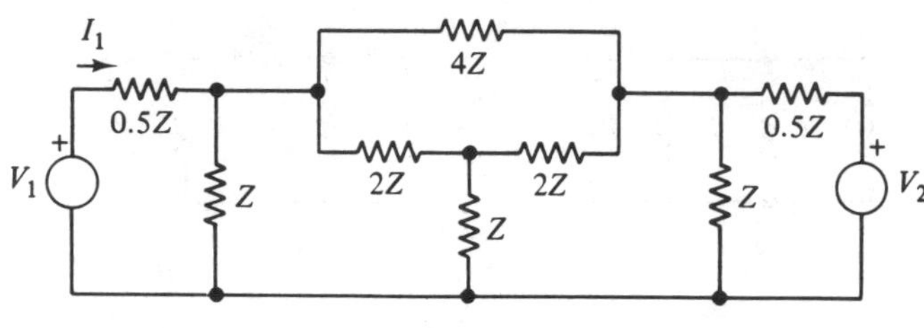

Fig. 5-56

5-14. In Fig. 5-57 what is the equivalent impedance seen between a and b if the source is
(**a**) a voltage source?
(**b**) a current source?

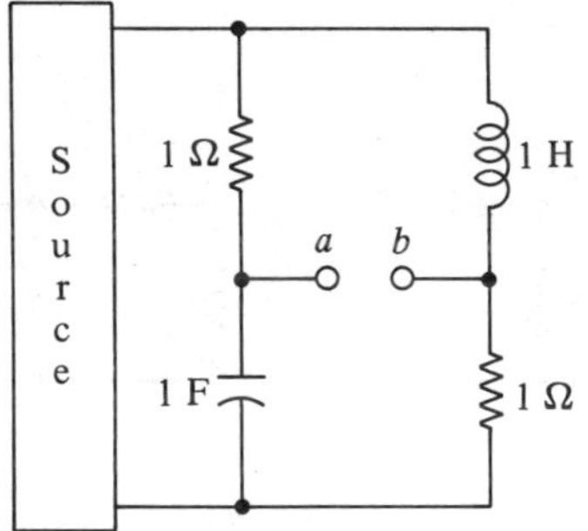

Fig. 5-57

5-15. Refer to Fig. 5-58.

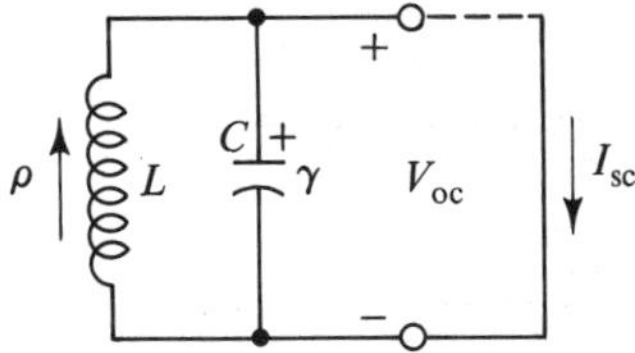

Fig. 5-58

(**a**) Terminals are open circuited. What is the open-circuit voltage $V_{oc}(s)$?
(**b**) Terminals are short circuited. What is the short-circuit current $I_{sc}(s)$?
(**c**) What is the impedance $Z(s)$ seen from the terminals?
(**d**) What are the Thévenin and Norton equivalent circuits as seen from the output terminals?

5-16. When the input is a unit-step function, the response is sin t. What is the transfer function $T(s)$?

5-17. A system described by the transfer function $T(s) = 1/(s + 1)$ has an output of $1 - e^{-t}$. What must have been the input?

5-18. Perform the indicated operations.

(a) $\dfrac{(-1-j)^2}{1+j}$ (b) $\dfrac{(1+j)(-1+j)+(1+j2)j}{(1+j)(2+j)}$

(c) $\dfrac{(1+j)(1-j)}{(-1+j2)(-1-j2)}$

5-19. Obtain the magnitude and angle.

(a) $\dfrac{j(1+j)}{1-j}$ (b) $\dfrac{(1-j)(1+j)-(j+2)}{(-2+j3)(-2+j4)}$

5-20. Assume a, b, c, d, M, and ϕ are real numbers. Perform the indicated operations.

(a) $\text{Re}\left\{\dfrac{a+jb}{c+jd}\right\}$ (b) $\text{Mag}\left\{\dfrac{a+jb}{c+jd}\right\}$

(c) $\text{Im}\,\{(a+jb)e^{(c+jd)}\}$ (d) $\text{Ang}\left\{\dfrac{jc}{a+jb}+jd\right\}$

(e) $\text{Im}\left\{\dfrac{a-jb}{Me^{j\phi}}\right\}$ (f) $\text{Ang}\left\{\dfrac{a-jb}{Me^{-j\phi}}\right\}$

(g) $e^{j\phi}+(e^{j\phi})^*$ (h) $\text{Mag}\left\{\dfrac{1+j}{e^{j(\pi/2)}}\right\}$

5-21. Assume a, b, c, d, M, and ϕ are real numbers. Perform the indicated operations.

(a) $\text{Im}\,\{e^{(-\alpha+j\beta)t}\}$ (b) $\text{Re}\,\{(a+jb)e^{j\phi}\}$

(c) $\text{Re}\,\{(ae^{j\phi})+(ae^{j\phi})^*\}$ (d) $\text{Ang}\left\{\dfrac{1+e^{j\phi}}{e^{j\phi}}\right\}$

(e) $\text{Re}\left\{\left(\dfrac{1+e^{ja}}{e^{jb}}\right)\left(\dfrac{1+e^{ja}}{e^{jb}}\right)^*\right\}$ (f) $\text{Im}\left\{\dfrac{e^{-j(\pi/2)}(1+j)}{1+e^{j(\pi/2)}}\right\}$

(g) $\text{Re}\,\{je^{jt}\}$ (h) $\text{Re}\,\{\cos\,(a+jb)\}$

5-22. Obtain the poles of the following functions.

(a) $\dfrac{(s^2+1)(s+2)}{s^3+s^2-2}$ (b) $\dfrac{s(s^2-1)}{s^3+s^2+s+1}$ (c) $\dfrac{1}{(s^2+1)[(s+1)^2+1]}$

5-23. The poles of a function are at $-\alpha \pm j\beta$. What is the denominator polynomial of the function? Give the polynomial in descending powers of s.

5-24. Expand $\dfrac{1}{s(s+1)(s^2+1)[(s+1)^2+1]}$ into partial fractions.

5-25. The poles of the response function $R(s)$ are at 0, -1, $\pm j$, $-1 \pm j$. What waveforms are expected in $r(t)$?

5-26. Obtain the inverse transform of the following functions.

(a) $\dfrac{1}{(s+a)(s+b)}$ (b) $\dfrac{s+c}{(s+a)(s+b)}$

(c) $\dfrac{1}{s(s+a)(s+b)}$ (d) $\dfrac{1}{s^2-a^2}$

(e) $\dfrac{s}{s^2 - a^2}$ (f) $\dfrac{s + a}{s(s^2 + b^2)}$

(g) $\dfrac{s + c}{(s + \alpha)^2 + \beta^2}$ (h) $\dfrac{s}{(s^2 + a^2)(s^2 + b^2)}$

(i) $\dfrac{s}{(s + \alpha)^2 + \beta^2}$ (j) $\dfrac{1}{s[(s + \alpha)^2 + \beta^2]}$

(k) $\dfrac{2s - 4}{(s + 2)^2 + 4}$ (l) $\dfrac{2}{s^3 + s^2 + s + 1}$

5-27. Obtain the inverse Laplace transform of the following functions. The answer should not contain any j's.

(a) $\left[\dfrac{1}{2}\left(\dfrac{1 + j}{s + j}\right) + \dfrac{1}{2}\left(\dfrac{1 + j}{s + j}\right)^*\right]$ (b) $\dfrac{a_1 s + a_0}{(s + \alpha)^2 + \beta^2}$

(c) $\left(\dfrac{a + jb}{s - jc}\right) + \left(\dfrac{a + jb}{s - jc}\right)^*$ (d) $\left(\dfrac{1 + j}{2}\right)\left(\dfrac{1}{s + 1 - j}\right)$ + conjugate

5-28. Solve the following differential equations, subject to the initial conditions indicated.

(a) $\dfrac{dy}{dx} + y = e^{-2x}, \quad y(0) = 1$

(b) $\dfrac{d^2y}{dx^2} + y = 0, \quad y(0) = 0, \quad y'(0) = 1$

(c) $\dfrac{d^3y}{dx^3} + \dfrac{d^2y}{dx^2} + \dfrac{dy}{dx} + y = 1$ All initial conditions are zero.

(d) $\dfrac{d^2z}{dx^2} - 2\dfrac{dz}{dx} + 1 = 0, \; z(0) = 0, \; z'(0) = 1$

(e) $\dfrac{d^2z}{dy^2} + z = 1, \; z(0) = z'(0) = 0$

(f) $\dfrac{d^2z}{dx^2} + 3\dfrac{dz}{dx} + 2z = 0, \; z(0) = 1, \; z'(0) = 0$

5-29. Show that in Eq. (5-65) the K_i's are obtained by the indicated operations.

5-30. Obtain the inverse transform of the following.

(a) $\dfrac{1}{s^2(s + 1)}$ (b) $\dfrac{1}{s(s + 1)^2}$ (c) $\dfrac{1}{(s^2 + 1)^2}$ (d) $\dfrac{1}{s^2(s + 1)(s + 2)}$

5.31. In Fig. 5-59 obtain for $t > 0$ the responses indicated by a question mark.

5.32. In Fig. 5-60 obtain for $t > 0$ the responses indicated by a question mark.

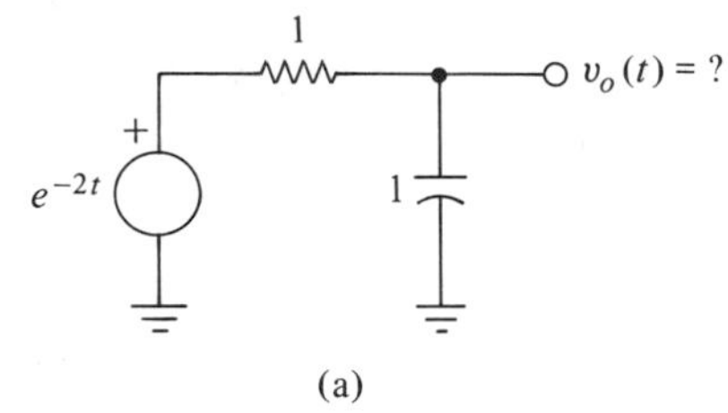

(a)

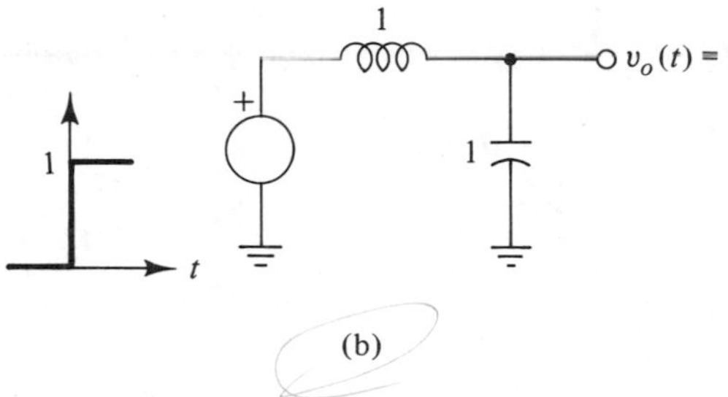

(b)

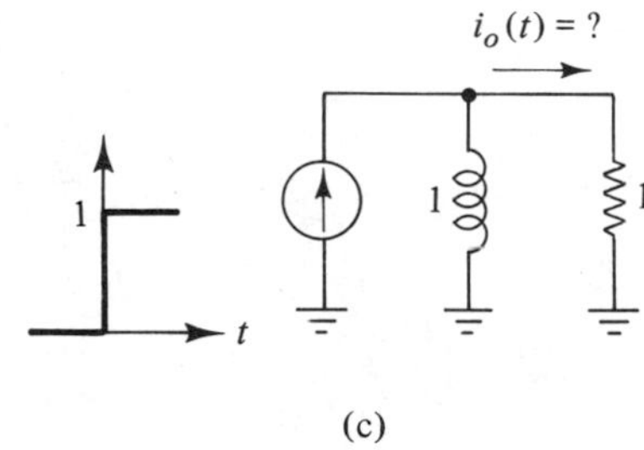

(c)

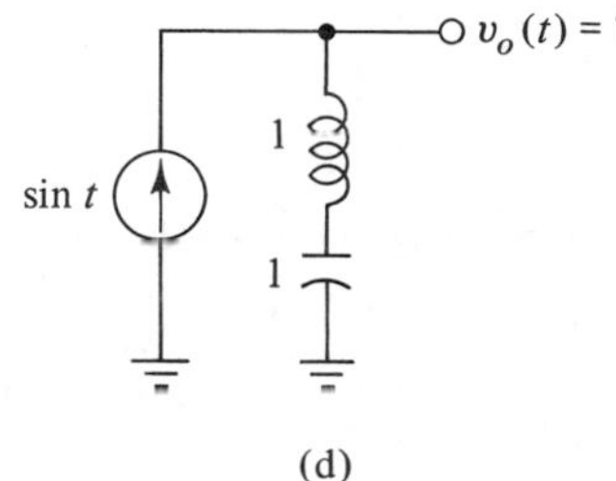

(d)

Fig. 5-59

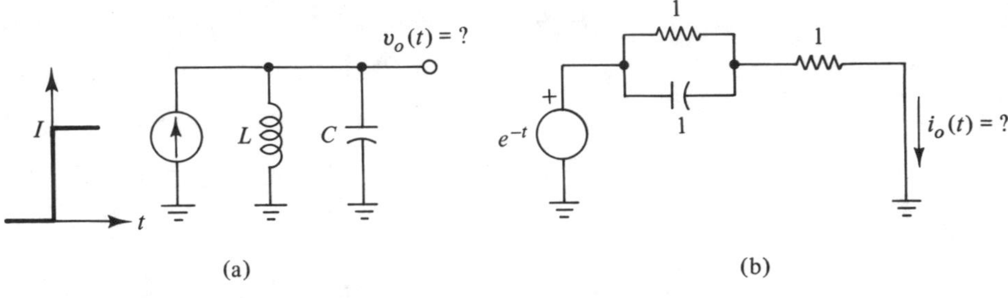

(a) (b)

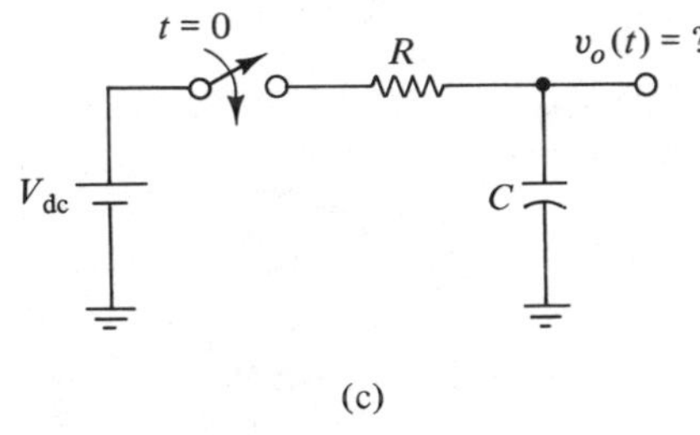

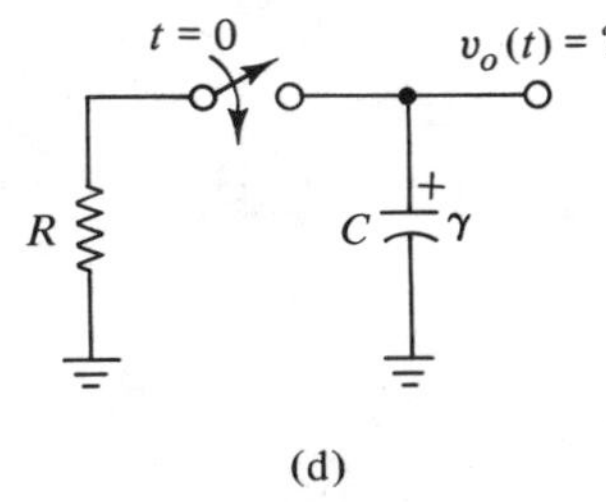

(c) (d)

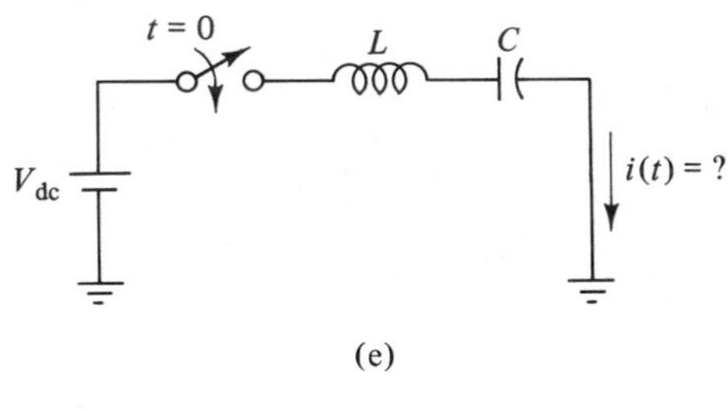

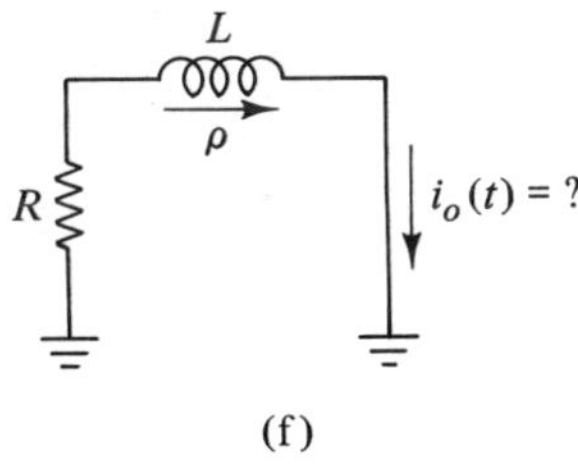

(e) (f)

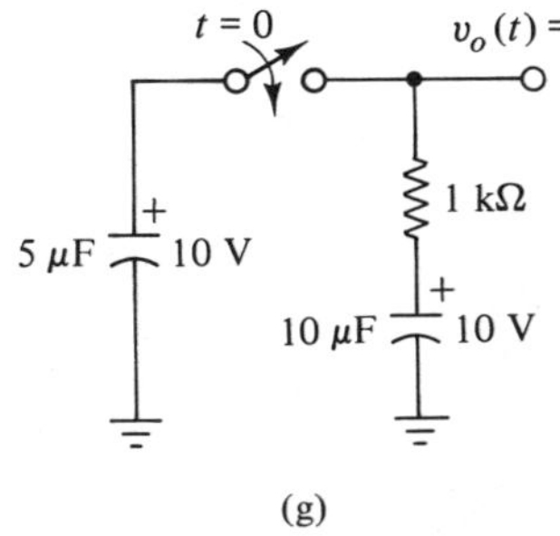

(g)

Fig. 5-60

CHAPTER 6

THE NATURAL AND FORCED RESPONSE AND THE STEP RESPONSE

When one or more sources of excitation are applied to a network, responses are produced throughout the network. Although the direct result of the excitations, these responses contain, in general, terms that are not related in any way to the waveforms imposed on the network by the excitations. Such terms are characteristic of the network and constitute the *natural* part of the response. The other part of the response, which is due to the forcing action produced by the excitations, is called the *forced* part of the response. In actual *RLC* networks the natural part eventually becomes zero; then the response becomes the same as the forced part of the response. When the excitations are constant or sine waves, the forced part of the response is particularly simple to calculate. Here and in the following chapters we study the response of networks that are excited by dc and ac sources.

6-1 NATURAL AND FORCED PARTS OF RESPONSE

The input impedance relates the input current to the input voltage. The transfer function relates the output voltage or current to the input voltage or current. Both the input impedance and the transfer function describe the characteristics of the network. Consequently, once they are calculated for a particular network, the response in that network can be determined for any kind of input. For instance, if the transfer function $T(s)$ is known, then the response $R(s)$ is calculated from

$$\begin{aligned} \text{Response} &= \text{Transfer function} \times \text{Excitation} \\ R(s) &= T(s)E(s) \end{aligned} \tag{6-1}$$

We know that in an *RLC* network $T(s)$ *is a ratio of two polynomials*. Referring to Table 5-1, we see that commonly used *excitation waveforms* have Laplace transforms that are also *ratios of polynomials*. As a result, the *response* itself is the *ratio of two polynomials* and can be written

$$R(s) = \frac{N(s)}{D(s)} \tag{6-2}$$

where $N(s)$ is the numerator polynomial and $D(s)$ the denominator polynomial. Furthermore, for the types of inputs and networks considered in this book, the degree of $D(s)$ is always greater than the degree of $N(s)$. Therefore we can easily expand the response in partial fractions. Referring to Eq. (6-1), we see that some of the poles of $R(s)$ will come from $T(s)$ and that the rest will come from $E(s)$. To identify the origin of the poles, let us designate the transfer function poles by the subscript n (for natural) and the excitation poles by the subscript f (for forced). We can then write Eq. (6-2) as

$$R(s) = \frac{N(s)}{\underbrace{[(s - p_{n1})(s - p_{n2}) \cdots]}_{\substack{\text{Factors involving} \\ \text{transfer function poles}}}\underbrace{[(s - p_{f1})(s - p_{f2}) \cdots]}_{\substack{\text{Factors involving} \\ \text{excitation poles}}}} \tag{6-3}$$

We now assume that all poles are simple; that is, no two poles have the same value. In the partial-fraction expansion there is a term pertaining to each pole. If we keep the terms arising from the transfer function poles in one group and the terms arising from the excitation poles in another group, Eq.(6-3) can be written

$$\begin{aligned} R(s) &= \underbrace{\left(\frac{K_{n1}}{s - p_{n1}} + \frac{K_{n2}}{s - p_{n2}} + \cdots\right)}_{\substack{\text{Terms belonging to} \\ \text{transfer function poles} \\ R_n(s)}} + \underbrace{\left(\frac{K_{f1}}{s - p_{f1}} + \frac{K_{f2}}{s - p_{f2}} + \cdots\right)}_{\substack{\text{Terms belonging to} \\ \text{excitation poles} \\ R_f(s)}} \\ &= R_n(s) + R_f(s) \end{aligned} \tag{6-4}$$

where $R_n(s)$ represents the *natural part* and $R_f(s)$ the *forced part* of the response. The natural part of the response depends on the poles of the transfer function and hence is characteristic of the network. To emphasize this point, we may speak of the transfer function poles as network poles. The forced part of the response depends on the poles of excitation and thus is characteristic of the input functions. It should be noted that there is but *one response* that, for convenience, is decomposed into its *natural* and *forced parts*. When we view a response on an oscilloscope, we see only *one waveform*. This waveform is given by the inverse transform of Eq. (6-4) as

$$r(t) = \underbrace{(K_{n1}e^{p_{n1}t} + K_{n2}e^{p_{n2}t} + \cdots)}_{r_n(t)} + \underbrace{(K_{f1}e^{p_{f1}t} + K_{f2}e^{p_{f2}t} + \cdots)}_{r_f(t)} \tag{6-5}$$

If we know the excitation waveform, we can, by examining the response waveform carefully, delineate its natural and forced components.

Example 6-1

The input to a network is 5 sin t. The output is $2.5e^{-t} + 3.54 \sin(t - 0.785)$. What is the natural response? What is the forced response?

Solution. The input is sinusoidal. The output contains an exponential and a sine wave. Therefore the exponential part of the output waveform must have come from the natural behavior of the network. So

$$\left.\begin{aligned} r_n(t) &= 2.5e^{-t} \\ r_f(t) &= 3.54 \sin(t - 0.785) \end{aligned}\right\} \quad \text{Ans.}$$

By examining the forced response, we see how the network has reshaped the input waveform. The amplitude of the sine wave has changed from 5 to 3.54, and an angle of −0.785 radian has been added. Nonetheless, the forced response is still sinusoidal and has the same frequency as the input.

Example 6-2

In Fig. 6-1 the sine wave is applied to the inductor at $t = 0$. What are the natural and forced parts of the response $i(t)$?

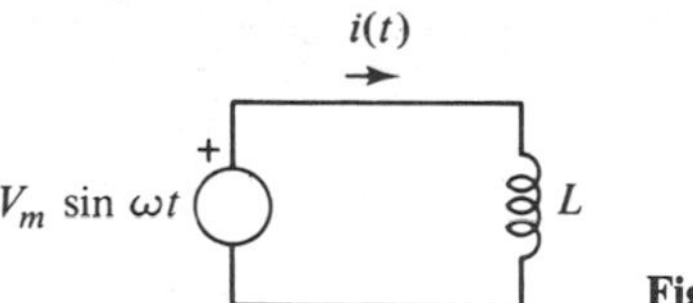

Fig. 6-1

Solution.
Method 1 Since this is a simple problem, we need not use the Laplace transformation to solve for $i(t)$.

$$i(t) = \frac{1}{L}\int_0^t V_m \sin \omega t' \, dt' = \frac{-V_m}{\omega L} \cos \omega t' \Big|_0^t = \frac{V_m}{\omega L} - \frac{V_m}{\omega L} \cos \omega t$$

The input is a sine wave. The output is a constant plus a cosine wave. Therefore

$$\left.\begin{aligned} i_n(t) &= \frac{V_m}{\omega L} \\ i_f(t) &= \frac{-V_m}{\omega L} \cos \omega t = \frac{V_m}{\omega L} \sin\left(\omega t + \frac{3\pi}{2}\right) \end{aligned}\right\} \quad \text{Ans.}$$

If we compare the input with the forced part of the output

$$V_m \sin \omega t \qquad \text{(input)}$$

$$\frac{V_m}{\omega L} \sin\left(\omega t + \frac{3\pi}{2}\right) \qquad \text{(forced part of output)}$$

we see again that the amplitude and angle of the sine wave are modified by the network.

Method 2 To interpret the result from the standpoint of poles, let us solve the problem by Laplace transformation. By reference to Fig. 6-1, we obtain

$$I(s) = \frac{V(s)}{sL}$$

where

$$V(s) = \mathcal{L}\{V_m \sin \omega t\} = V_m \frac{\omega}{s^2 + \omega^2}$$

It follows that

$$I(s) = \frac{V_m}{L} \frac{\omega}{s(s^2 + \omega^2)} = \frac{V_m}{L} \frac{\omega}{s(s - j\omega)(s + j\omega)}$$

The response, $I(s)$, has three poles, which are located at $s = 0$, $s = +j\omega$, and $s = -j\omega$. The pole at $s = 0$ comes from the network (division by sL), and the poles at $s = \pm j\omega$ come from the input sine wave. If we segregate the partial fraction expansion according to the poles, we have

$$I(s) = \left(\frac{K_1}{s}\right) + \left(\frac{K_2}{s - j\omega} + \frac{K_3}{s + j\omega}\right)$$

where $K_1 = V_m/\omega L$, $K_2 = -V_m/2\omega L$, and $K_3 = K_2$. Therefore

$$I(s) = \left(\frac{V_m}{\omega L s}\right) + \left[\frac{-V_m}{2\omega L}\left(\frac{1}{s - j\omega} + \frac{1}{s + j\omega}\right)\right]$$

$$= \underbrace{\left(\frac{V_m}{\omega L s}\right)}_{\text{Natural}} + \underbrace{\left(\frac{-V_m}{\omega L} \frac{s}{s^2 + \omega^2}\right)}_{\text{Forced}}$$

$$i(t) = \underbrace{\frac{V_m}{\omega L}}_{\text{Natural}} + \underbrace{\frac{-V_m}{\omega L} \cos \omega t}_{\text{Forced}}$$

So we see that the pole at $s = 0$ causes the natural part of the solution and that the poles at $s = \pm j\omega$ cause the forced part of the solution.

Example 6-3

In Fig. 6-2 the input is applied at $t = 0$. What is the output?

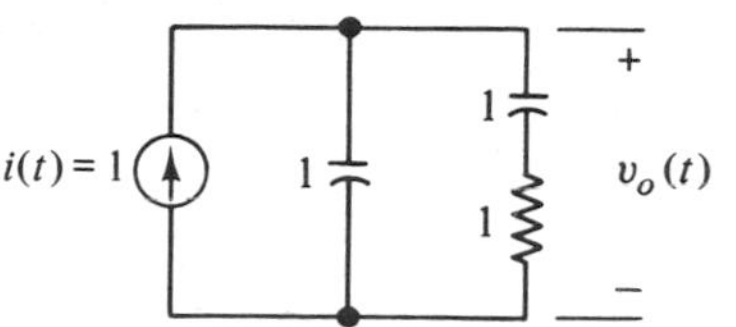

Fig. 6-2

Solution. From the network we see that

$$V_o(s) = I(s)Z(s) = \left(\frac{1}{s}\right)\left[\frac{1/s(1 + 1/s)}{1/s + (1 + 1/s)}\right]$$
$$= \left(\frac{1}{s}\right)\left[\frac{s + 1}{s(s + 2)}\right] = \frac{s + 1}{s^2(s + 2)} \tag{6-6}$$

The excitation has a pole at $s = 0$. The input impedance of the network has poles at $s = 0$ and $s = -2$. Consequently, at $s = 0$ the response $V_o(s)$ has two poles, and we are not able to tell which pole came from the excitation and which from the network. As a result, we are not able to separate completely the forced and natural parts of the response. (This situation always occurs when one or more poles of the excitation are coincident with the poles of the network.) Nonetheless, we can still expand Eq. (6-6) into partial fractions and obtain the inverse transform.

$$V_o(s) = \frac{K_{11}}{s^2} + \frac{K_{12}}{s} + \frac{K_2}{s + 2}$$

where $K_{11} = \left.\frac{s + 1}{s + 2}\right|_{s=0} = \frac{1}{2}$

$$K_{12} = \left.\left[\frac{d}{ds}\left(\frac{s + 1}{s + 2}\right)\right]\right|_{s=0} = \left.\frac{1}{(s + 2)^2}\right|_{s=0} = \frac{1}{4}$$

$$K_2 = \left.\frac{s + 1}{s^2}\right|_{s=-2} = -\frac{1}{4}$$

Thus

$$V_o(s) = \frac{1}{2}\frac{1}{s^2} + \frac{1}{4}\frac{1}{s} - \frac{1}{4}\frac{1}{s + 2}$$

$$v_o(t) = \frac{1}{2}t + \frac{1}{4} - \frac{1}{4}e^{-2t} \quad \text{Ans.}$$

Note that the first two terms in the output, $\frac{1}{2}t$ and $\frac{1}{4}$, have come from the two poles at $s = 0$ and that the third term has come from the remaining pole of the network. In this problem we cannot clearly decompose the output into distinct natural and forced parts.

6-2 RELATIONSHIPS BETWEEN POLE LOCATIONS AND RESPONSE

The response may, in general, have poles at the origin, $s = 0$, on the negative real axis, $s = -\alpha_1(\alpha_1 > 0)$, on the positive real axis, $s = \alpha_2(\alpha_2 > 0)$, on the imaginary axis, $s = \pm j\beta$, in the left half-plane, $s = -\alpha_3 \pm j\beta_3(\alpha_3 > 0)$ and in the right half-plane, $s = \alpha_4 \pm j\beta_4(\alpha_4 > 0)$. Such a response is represented by

$$R(s) = \frac{N(s)}{s(s+\alpha_1)(s-\alpha_2)\underbrace{(s-j\beta)(s+j\beta)}_{(s^2+\beta^2)}\underbrace{(s+\alpha_3-j\beta_3)(s+\alpha_3+j\beta_3)}_{[(s+\alpha_3)^2+\beta_3^2]}\underbrace{(s-\alpha_4-j\beta_4)(s-\alpha_4+j\beta_4)}_{[(s-\alpha_4)^2+\beta_4^2]}\cdots} \tag{6-7}$$

where the dots in the denominator signify the presence of other poles. If we assume that the degree of the denominator polynomial is greater than the degree of the numerator polynomial and that the poles are simple, then the partial-fraction expansion of $R(s)$ is given by

$$\begin{aligned} R(s) = {} & \frac{K_1}{s} + \frac{K_2}{s+\alpha_1} + \frac{K_3}{s-\alpha_2} + \frac{K_4}{s-j\beta} + \frac{K_4^*}{s+j\beta} \\ & + \frac{K_5}{s+\alpha_3-j\beta_3} + \frac{K_5^*}{s+\alpha_3+j\beta_3} + \frac{K_6}{s-\alpha_4-j\beta_4} + \frac{K_6^*}{s-\alpha_4+j\beta_4} + \cdots \end{aligned} \tag{6-8}$$

where the designation $*$ implies the conjugate of the K under consideration. (That the K's corresponding to complex-conjugate poles are conjugates of each other can be seen by direct evaluation.) The resulting $r(t)$ is

$$\begin{aligned} r(t) = {} & K_1 + K_2e^{-\alpha_1 t} + K_3e^{\alpha_2 t} + K_4e^{j\beta t} + K_4^*e^{-j\beta t} \\ & + K_5e^{-\alpha_3 t}e^{j\beta_3 t} + K_5^*e^{-\alpha_3 t}e^{-j\beta_3 t} + K_6e^{\alpha_4 t}e^{j\beta_4 t} + K_6^*e^{\alpha_4 t}e^{-j\beta_4 t} + \cdots \end{aligned} \tag{6-9}$$

Since the *sum of a function and its conjugate is twice the real part of the function,* we can write Eq. (6-9) as

$$\begin{aligned} r(t) = {} & K_1 + K_2e^{-\alpha_1 t} + K_3e^{\alpha_2 t} + 2\,\text{Re}\,\{K_4e^{j\beta t}\} + 2\,\text{Re}\,\{K_5e^{-\alpha_3 t}e^{j\beta_3 t}\} \\ & + 2\,\text{Re}\,\{K_6e^{\alpha_4 t}e^{j\beta_4 t}\} + \cdots \end{aligned} \tag{6-10}$$

The constants K_4, K_5, and K_6 are, in general, complex and thus can be expressed in magnitude and angle form—that is,

$$\begin{aligned} K_4 &= |K_4|\,e^{j\theta_4} \\ K_5 &= |K_5|\,e^{j\theta_5} \\ K_6 &= |K_6|\,e^{j\theta_6} \end{aligned} \tag{6-11}$$

So Eq. (6-10) can be rewritten

$$r(t) = K_1 + K_2e^{-\alpha_1 t} + K_3e^{\alpha_2 t} + 2\,\text{Re}\,\{|K_4|e^{j\theta_4}e^{j\beta t}\} + 2\text{Re}\,\{|K_5|e^{j\theta_5}e^{-\alpha_3 t}e^{j\beta_3 t}\}$$
$$+ 2\,\text{Re}\,\{|K_6|e^{j\theta_6}e^{\alpha_4 t}e^{j\beta_4 t}\} + \cdots \tag{6-12}$$
$$= K_1 + K_2e^{-\alpha_1 t} + K_3e^{\alpha_2 t} + 2|K_4|\,\text{Re}\,\{e^{j(\beta t+\theta_4)}\} + 2|K_5|e^{-\alpha_3 t}\,\text{Re}\,\{e^{j(\beta_3 t+\theta_5)}\}$$
$$+ 2|K_6|e^{\alpha_4 t}\,\text{Re}\,\{e^{j(\beta_4 t+\theta_6)}\} + \cdots \tag{6-13}$$

Since

$$\text{Re}\,\{e^{j\theta}\} = \cos\theta$$

Equation (6-13) can be simplified to

$$r(t) = K_1 + K_2e^{-\alpha_1 t} + K_3e^{\alpha_2 t} + 2|K_4|\cos(\beta t + \theta_4) + 2|K_5|e^{-\alpha_3 t}\cos(\beta_3 t + \theta_5)$$
$$+ 2|K_6|e^{\alpha_4 t}\cos(\beta_4 t + \theta_6) + \cdots \tag{6-14}$$

This is a very important result. It relates the time-domain waveforms in the response to the frequency-domain pole locations as follows.

A pole at the origin produces a constant: K_1.

A pole on the negative real axis at $s = -\alpha_1$ produces a decaying exponential: $K_2e^{-\alpha_1 t}$.

A pole on the positive real axis at $s = \alpha_2$ produces a growing exponential: $K_3e^{\alpha_2 t}$

A pair of conjugate poles on the imaginary axis at $s = \pm j\beta$ produces a sinusoid: $2|K_4|\cos(\beta t + \theta_4)$.

A pair of complex-conjugate poles in the left half-plane at $s = -\alpha_3 \pm j\beta_3$ produces an exponentially decaying sinusoid: $2|K_5|e^{-\alpha_3 t}\cos(\beta_3 t + \theta_5)$.

A pair of complex-conjugate poles in the right half-plane at $s = \alpha_4 \pm j\beta_4$ produces an exponentially growing sinusoid: $2|K_6|e^{\alpha_4 t}\cos(\beta_4 t + \theta_6)$.

No other waveforms are present in the response if the poles are simple. If the response also has poles of multiplicity k, then the response contains, additionally, waveforms given by $K_i' t^{(i-1)}e^{\alpha t}\cos(\beta t + \theta_i)$, $i = 1, 2, \ldots, k$, where α or β or both may be zero. The resulting waveforms can be obtained by multiplying the waveforms given in Eq. (6-14) by $t^{(i-1)}$.

At this point we should pause and reflect on the significance of the result presented by Eq. (6-14). It states that the response in a network is the sum of simple waveforms: dc, growing and decaying exponentials, sine waves, and exponentially growing or decaying sine waves. The constants designated with K's may be positive, zero, or negative. As a result, the response may produce a variety of different waveforms. Whereas the shape of the individual waveforms is determined by the pole locations, the K's fix the sign, the size, and the phase angle (θ's) of the various components of the response. The values of the K's depend on both the numerator and the denominator polynomials of the transfer function and on the input.

To summarize the possible waveforms that can be generated by simple poles, as well as to demonstrate the relationship between the frequency and time domains, refer to Fig. 6-3. As a pole on the real axis is moved from left to right, we obtain a damped exponential, a constant, and a growing exponential. As a pair of complex-conjugate poles is moved from left to right, we obtain an exponentially damped sine wave, a sine wave, and an exponentially growing sine wave. Poles in the left half-plane (to the left of the imaginary axis) produce decaying waveforms. Poles in the right half-plane (to the right of the imaginary axis) produce growing waveforms. Simple complex-conjugate pole pairs on the imaginary axis (which separates the left and right half-planes) produce waveforms that neither decay nor grow but remain the same.

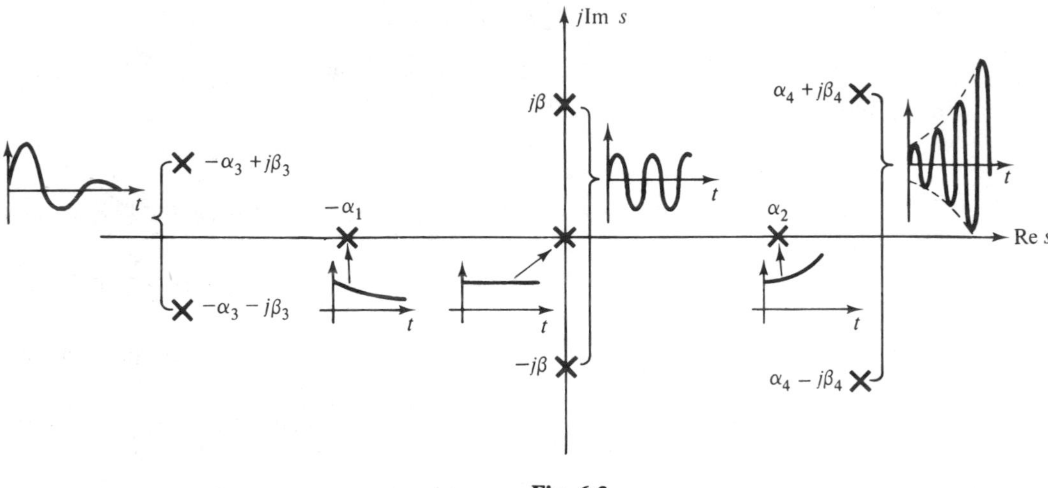

Fig. 6-3

6-3 THE STEP RESPONSE OF NETWORKS

Networks are often excited by a step function. In addition, the step function is widely used to test networks. The step function is very easy to generate. As shown in Fig. 6-4(a), when a switch is closed at $t = 0$ on a dc source, such as a battery or dc power supply, a step voltage is produced at terminals 1–1′. The battery-switch combination can be equivalently represented by a voltage-source symbol with a step voltage beside it. [See Fig. 6-4(a).] Similarly, a step-current source is produced by opening a switch on a current source as shown in Fig. 6-4(b). Circuits using transistors or other active elements can be designed to act as step-current generators.

In Fig. 6-4(c) a *unit-step function* is applied to a network described by the transfer function $T(s)$. We wish to determine the resulting response $r(t)$. [Instead of $T(s)$ we could also use $Z(s)$ or $Y(s)$, in which case the response would be the input voltage or the input current.] In the frequency domain the response is given by

$$R(s) = T(s)E(s)$$

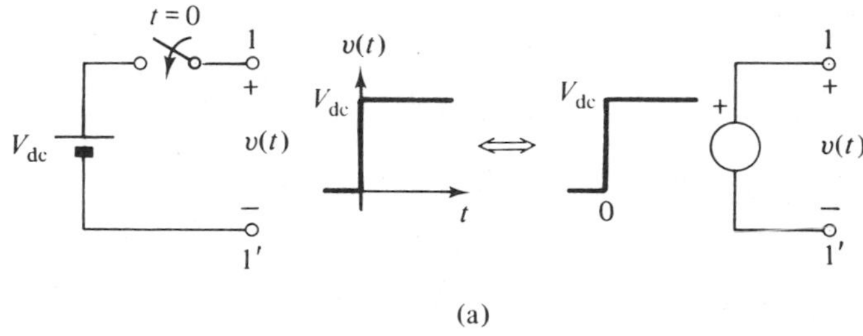

(a)

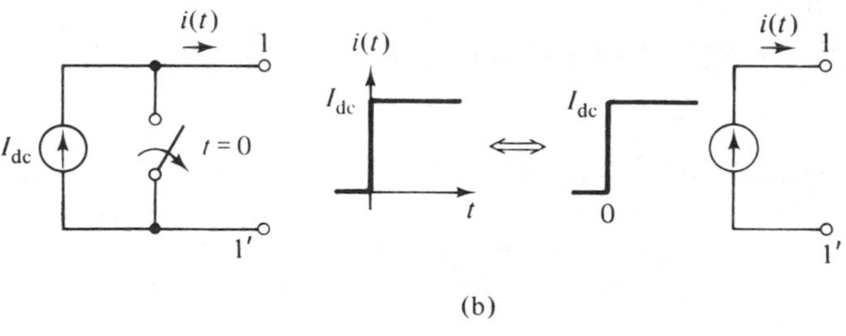

(b)

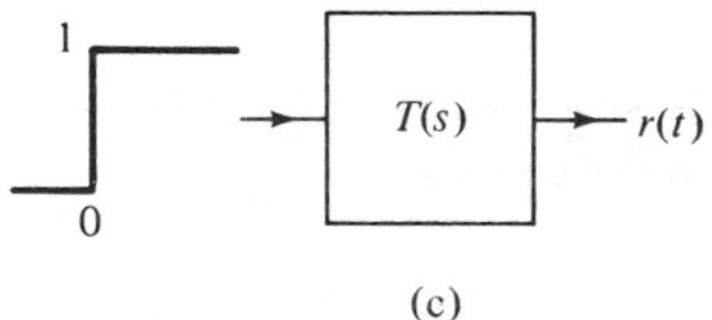

(c)

Fig. 6-4

Since $E(s) = 1/s$, we have

$$R(s) = \frac{T(s)}{s} \tag{6-15}$$

The pole of excitation is at $s = 0$. The poles of the network are not explicitly shown; they can be obtained from the denominator polynomial of $T(s)$. The partial-fraction expansion of Eq. (6-15) for simple poles is given by

$$R(s) = \frac{K_1}{s} + R_n(s) \tag{6-16}$$

where K_1/s represents the forced part of the solution arising from the unit-step input and $R_n(s)$ represents the natural part of the response arising from the poles of $T(s)$. The constant K_1 is easily evaluated as

$$K_1 = sR(s)\,\big|_{s=0} = T(0)$$

So we have

$$R(s) = \frac{T(0)}{s} + R_n(s)$$

The corresponding time-domain response is

$$r(t) = T(0) + r_n(t) \qquad (t > 0) \tag{6-17}$$

This $r(t)$ is known as the *unit-step response* of the network. At the input the step is one unit high; at the output it is $T(0)$ units high. Additionally, the output contains $r_n(t)$, which represents the natural reaction of the network to being jolted by the unit step. If the input is a step A units high instead of one unit high, the resulting response is A times larger than the unit-step response—that is,

$$r(t) = A[T(0) + r_n(t)]$$

Because the excitation is discontinuous at $t = 0$, the response may also be discontinuous at $t = 0$; then the response has different values immediately to the left and to the right of $t = 0$. The former is called the $t = 0^-$ value and the latter the $t = 0^+$ value. The $t = 0^-$ value is obtained from initial conditions (to be discussed later) and the $t = 0^+$ value from Eq. (6-17). If the two values are the same, the response is continuous at $t = 0$, and Eq. (6-17) is valid for $t = 0$ also.

6-4 CALCULATION OF THE STEP RESPONSE OF FIRST-ORDER SYSTEMS

A *first-order* system is characterized by a transfer function (or an input impedance or admittance function) having *one pole*.

$$T(s) = \frac{N(s)}{s + \alpha} \tag{6-18}$$

The most general form of $N(s)$ that is associated with a first-order system is

$$N(s) = a_1 s + a_0$$

So $T(s)$ can be written

$$T(s) = \frac{a_1 s + a_0}{s + \alpha} \tag{6-19}$$

When such a system is excited by a unit-step function, the response is given by

$$R(s) = \frac{1}{s}\left(\frac{a_1 s + a_0}{s + \alpha}\right) = \frac{a_0/\alpha}{s} + \frac{(-a_1\alpha + a_0)/-\alpha}{s + \alpha}$$

$$r(t) = \frac{a_0}{\alpha} + \left(a_1 - \frac{a_0}{\alpha}\right)e^{-\alpha t} \qquad (t > 0) \tag{6-20}$$

Since $a_0/\alpha = T(0)$, the response can also be written

$$r(t) = T(0) + \left(a_1 - \frac{a_0}{\alpha}\right)e^{-\alpha t} \qquad \alpha \neq 0 \qquad (t > 0)$$

Thus the step response of first-order system is *a constant plus a damped exponential*. (We have assumed that $\alpha > 0$.) The constant represents the forced response and the exponential the natural response. It is important to emphasize that although the system is being driven by a step, the output is not just a step but a combination of a step and an exponential. Since the exponential part becomes less and less significant in time, it is called the *transient* part of the solution. Transient part and natural part are terms used synonymously to designate the exponentially decaying portion of the output.

As long as the transient part is nonzero, there is no resemblance between the input and output waveforms. The response becomes a scaled replica [with scale factor $T(0) = a_0/\alpha$] of the excitation only after the transient part has vanished. Thereupon, the response is at steady state (at its final constant value).

If a_1 were zero in $T(s)$, the transfer function and its unit-step reponse would have been

$$T_0(s) = \frac{a_0}{s + \alpha}, \qquad r_0(t) = \frac{a_0}{\alpha}(1 - e^{-\alpha t}) \qquad (t > 0)$$

To see the effect of a_1 on the response, we rearrange Eq. (6-20) as

$$r(t) = \underbrace{\frac{a_0}{\alpha}(1 - e^{-\alpha t})}_{r_0(t)} + a_1 e^{-\alpha t}$$

Since

$$\frac{dr_0}{dt} = a_0 e^{-\alpha t}$$

the unit-step response of $T(s)$ can be expressed in terms of the unit-step response of $T_0(s)$ as follows.

$$r(t) = r_0(t) + \frac{a_1}{a_0}\frac{dr_0(t)}{dt}$$

With $a_1 = 0$, we get $r_0(t)$. As a_1 is increased or decreased from zero, the character of the response changes because

$$\frac{a_1}{a_0}\frac{dr_0(t)}{dt}$$

is added to $r_0(t)$. Since dr_0/dt is largest in magnitude at $t = 0^+$ and diminishes to zero as time approaches infinity, the effect of a_1 is to modify the initial development of the response and leave the final value intact.

Example 6-4

Obtain the unit-step response of the network shown in Fig. 6-5.

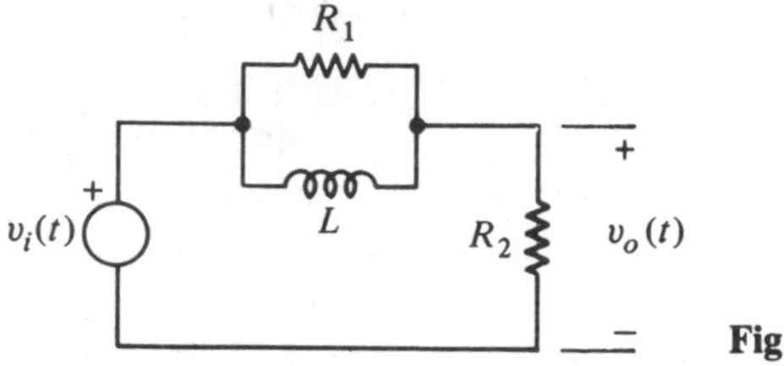

Fig. 6-5

Solution. The input-output relationship of the network is described by the transfer function

$$\frac{V_o(s)}{V_i(s)} = T(s) = R_2 \Big/ \left(R_2 + \frac{sLR_1}{sL + R_1}\right)$$

$$= \left[\left(\frac{R_2}{R_1 + R_2}\right)s + \frac{1}{L}\left(\frac{R_1R_2}{R_1 + R_2}\right)\right] \Big/ \left[s + \frac{1}{L}\left(\frac{R_1R_2}{R_1 + R_2}\right)\right] = \frac{a_1 s + a_0}{s + \alpha}$$

where $a_1 = \dfrac{R_2}{R_1 + R_2}$, $\quad a_0 = \dfrac{1}{L}\left(\dfrac{R_1R_2}{R_1 + R_2}\right)$, $\quad \alpha = \dfrac{1}{L}\left(\dfrac{R_1R_2}{R_1 + R_2}\right)$

Making use of Eq. (6-20), we obtain the output voltage.

$$v_o(t) = \frac{a_0}{\alpha} + \left(a_1 - \frac{a_0}{\alpha}\right)e^{-\alpha t}$$

$$= 1 + \left(\frac{R_2}{R_1 + R_2} - 1\right)e^{-t/[L(R_1+R_2)/R_1R_2]}$$

$$= 1 - \frac{R_1}{R_1 + R_2}\, e^{-t/[L(R_1+R_2)/R_1R_2]} \qquad \text{Ans.}$$

6-5 SKETCH OF THE STEP RESPONSE OF FIRST-ORDER SYSTEMS

The unit-step response of a first-order system with pole at $-\alpha(\alpha > 0)$ is given by Eq. (6-20), which is reproduced here for convenience.

$$r(t) = \frac{a_0}{\alpha} + \left(a_1 - \frac{a_0}{\alpha}\right)e^{-\alpha t} \qquad (t > 0) \tag{6-21}$$

Since

$$e^{-\alpha t} \longrightarrow 1 \text{ as } t \longrightarrow 0$$

$$e^{-\alpha t} \longrightarrow 0 \text{ as } t \longrightarrow \infty$$

we have

$$r(0^+) = a_1 = \text{initial value of response} = I$$

$$r(\infty) = \frac{a_0}{\alpha} = \text{final value of response} = F$$

Thus the response can be expressed in terms of the initial and final values.

$$r(t) = F + (I - F)e^{-\alpha t} \qquad (t > 0) \tag{6-22}$$

In order to facilitate the sketching of the response, we evaluate $r(t)$ at $t = 1/\alpha$.

$$r\left(\frac{1}{\alpha}\right) = F + (I - F)e^{-1} = F + (I - F)0.37 = I + (F - I)0.63 \tag{6-23}$$

As Eq. (6-23) shows, at $t = 1/\alpha$ the response has spanned 63% of the change between the initial and final values. Since $-\alpha$ is the pole of the system $[T(s) = (a_1 s + a_0)/(s + \alpha)]$, $1/\alpha$ represents the reciprocal of the magnitude of the pole and has the dimensional unit of a second. We designate $1/\alpha$ by the symbol τ and call it *time constant*. Thus we have

$$\begin{gathered} \tau = \frac{1}{\alpha} \\ \text{Time constant} = \frac{1}{|\text{pole}|} \end{gathered} \tag{6-24}$$

In the time span of a time constant (which is determined by the system), *63% of the change between the initial and final values takes place*. Using this concept of time constant, Eq. (6-22) can be expressed as

$$r(t) = F + (I - F)e^{-t/\tau} \qquad (t > 0) \tag{6-25}$$

Finally, we make two other observations:

$$r(5\tau) = F + (I - F)e^{-5} = F + (I - F)0.00674 \cong F \tag{6-26}$$

$$\left.\frac{dr(t)}{dt}\right|_{t=0^+} = -\frac{1}{\tau}(I - F)e^{-t/\tau}\Big|_{t=0} = \frac{F - I}{\tau} \tag{6-27}$$

From Eq. (6-26) we see that in five time constants the response is, for all practical purposes, at its final value. In other words, *the transition from the initial to the final value is completed in five time constants*. The smaller the system time constant, the faster the response reaches its final (steady-state) value.

Equation (6-27) indicates that the initial slope of the response is equal to the total *change* in the response divided by the time constant. In other words, *if the response were to maintain its initial rate of change (slope), it would arrive at the final value in one time constant.*

As shown by Eq. (6-25), we need to know only *three* values in order to draw the response: the initial value I, the final value F, and the time constant τ. Equations (6-23), (6-26), and (6-27) merely facilitate the drawing of the response. Depending on the relative values of I and F, the response is represented by one of the waveforms shown in Fig. 6-6.

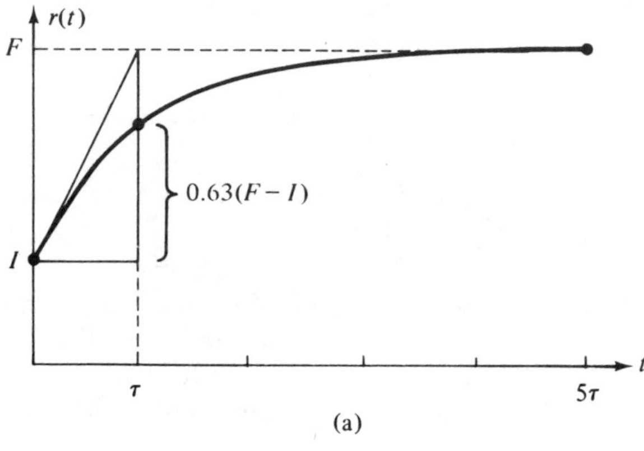

(a)

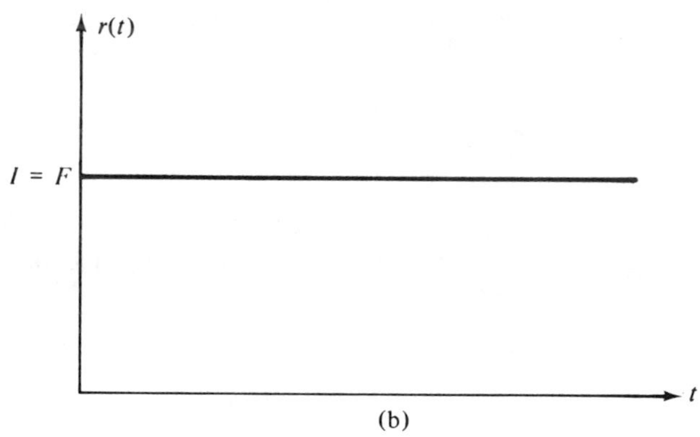

(b)

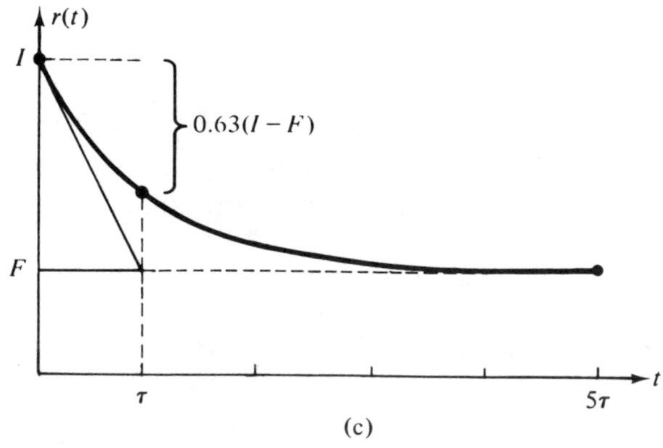

(c)

Fig. 6-6

In Fig. 6-6(a), $F > I$ and the response rises exponentially to the final value. Note that the response starts out along the hypotenuse of the triangle [that establishes the initial slope of $(F - I)/\tau$] and in one time constant covers 63% of the change $(F - I)$. In 5τ, it is, for all practical purposes, at the final value.

In Fig. 6-6(b), $I = F$ and the response is constant. No exponential is involved because the transfer function reduces to a constant as shown below.

$$T(s) = \frac{a_1 s + a_0}{s + \alpha} = \frac{Is + \alpha F}{s + \alpha}, \qquad T(s)\Big|_{I=F} = I\frac{(s + \alpha)}{(s + \alpha)} = I = F$$

In Fig. 6-6(c), $I > F$ and the response decays exponentially to the final value. Again note that the response starts out along the hypotenuse of the triangle [that establishes the initial slope of $-(I - F)/\tau$] and in one time constant covers 63% of the change. In 5τ, it is at the final value.

The responses in Fig. 6-6 are drawn with positive values for I and F. Of course, either or both can be negative. In any event, the transition between the initial and final values is exponential in nature (unless $I = F$), covering 63% of the change in one time constant. Steady state is reached in five time constants.

Example 6-5

Sketch $r(t) = 10 - 15e^{-t/2}$.

Solution. The initial value, the final value, and the time constant are given by

$$r(0^+) = 10 - 15 = -5, \qquad r(\infty) = 10, \qquad \tau = 2$$

Using these values, $r(t)$ can be sketched as shown in Fig. 6-7.

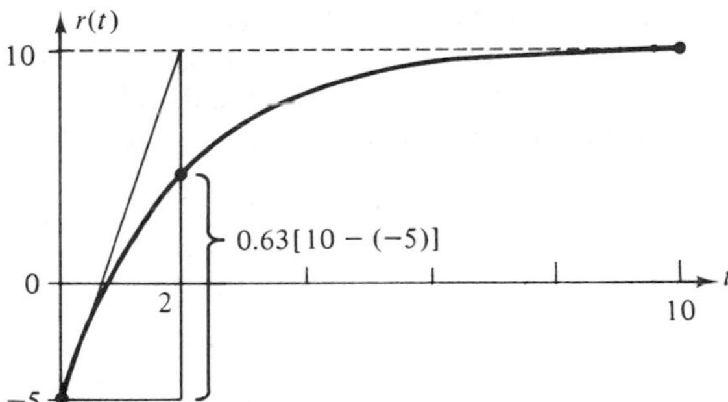

Fig. 6-7

Example 6-6

Obtain the expression of the response shown in Fig. 6-8. The initial and final values are connected by an exponential curve.

Solution. By inspection of Fig. 6-8, we obtain

$$r(0^+) = -5, \qquad r(\infty) = -15$$

The total change in the response is $F - I = -15 - (-5) = -10$. In one time constant, the response should be at $I + (F - I)0.63 = -5 - 10 \times 0.63 = -11.3$. From

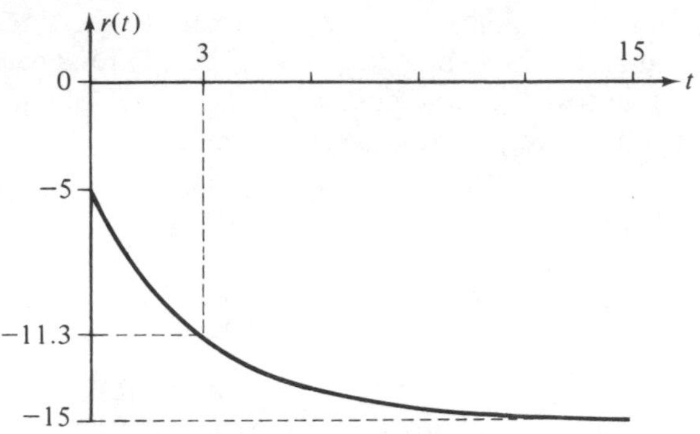

Fig. 6-8

Fig. 6-8 we see that it takes 3 seconds for the response to reach −11.3. Hence $\tau = 3$. Consequently, the response is given by

$$r(t) = F + (I - F)e^{-t/\tau} = -15 + [-5 - (-15)]e^{-t/3}$$
$$= -15 + 10e^{-t/3} \quad \text{Ans.}$$

6-6 DETERMINATION OF τ, I, AND F BY INSPECTION OF THE NETWORK

All networks characterized by a single pole can be reduced (after making all excitations zero) to the *RC* or the *RL* network in Fig. 6-9. To determine the pole of either network, we excite it by a current source in parallel or a voltage source in series with the resistor. Then we pick a response, such as the voltage across the resistor, and form the response/excitation ratio. The pole is the value of s that makes the denominator polynomial of the ratio zero. So for the networks shown in Fig. 6-9 we obtain

$$s + \frac{1}{RC} = 0, \qquad s = -\frac{1}{RC} \tag{6-28}$$

$$s + \frac{R}{L} = 0, \qquad s = -\frac{R}{L} \tag{6-29}$$

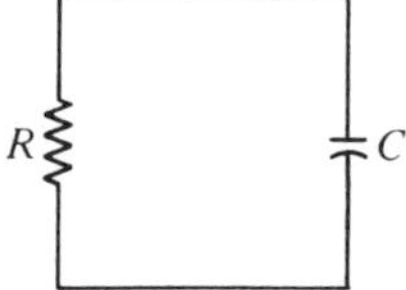

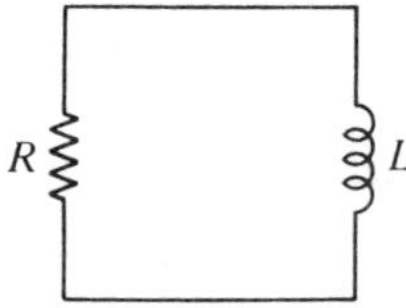

Fig. 6-9

The pole of the *RC* network is at $-1/RC$. The pole of the *RL* network is at $-R/L$. Consequently, the time constants associated with these networks are

$$\tau_{RC} = RC \tag{6-30}$$

$$\tau_{RL} = \frac{L}{R} \tag{6-31}$$

For one-pole networks these time constants can be determined by inspection of the network. For instance, consider the network of Fig. 6-10(a). Since the pole—and hence the time constant—is a characteristic of the network and not of its excitation, we remove the excitations by replacing the voltage source with a short circuit and the current source with an open circuit. The result is Fig. 6-10(b). Then by using the series and parallel combination rules or other techniques, we reduce this network to the single-resistor, single-inductor circuit shown in Fig. 6-10(c). Thus we obtain

$$R_{eq} = R_3 + \frac{R_1R_2}{R_1 + R_2}, \qquad L_{eq} = L_1 + L_2, \qquad \tau = \frac{L_{eq}}{R_{eq}}$$

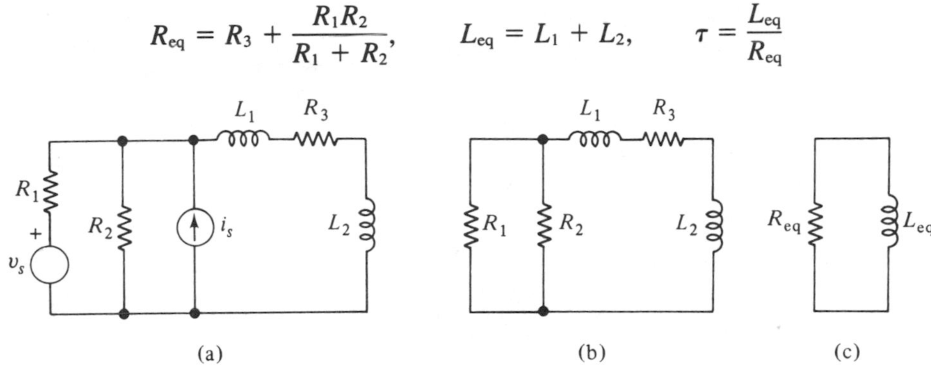

Fig. 6-10

When such a reduction to a single resistor-inductor or resistor-capacitor combination is not possible, the network is *not* a one-pole network. Consequently, the system is not of first order, and its step response cannot be described by a *single* exponential connecting the initial and final value points.

Let us turn to the determination of the initial and final values of voltages and currents in a *step-excited* first-order system. These values are obtained by replacing the inductors and capacitors with simple equivalent circuits that are *valid only for* $t = 0$ *and* $t > 5\tau$. These equivalent circuits are developed from the equations that describe the inductor and the capacitor.

For the inductor shown in Fig. 6-11(a) we have

$$v_L(t) = L\frac{di_L(t)}{dt} \tag{6-32a}$$

$$i_L(t) = \underbrace{i_L(0)}_{\rho} + \frac{1}{L}\int_0^t v_L(t')\,dt' \tag{6-32b}$$

In order to change the current through the inductor, time must elapse so that the integral of the voltage across it develops a nonzero value. [See Eq. (6-32b).] [We certainly cannot sum (integrate) infinitesimal amounts over zero time and expect to ac-

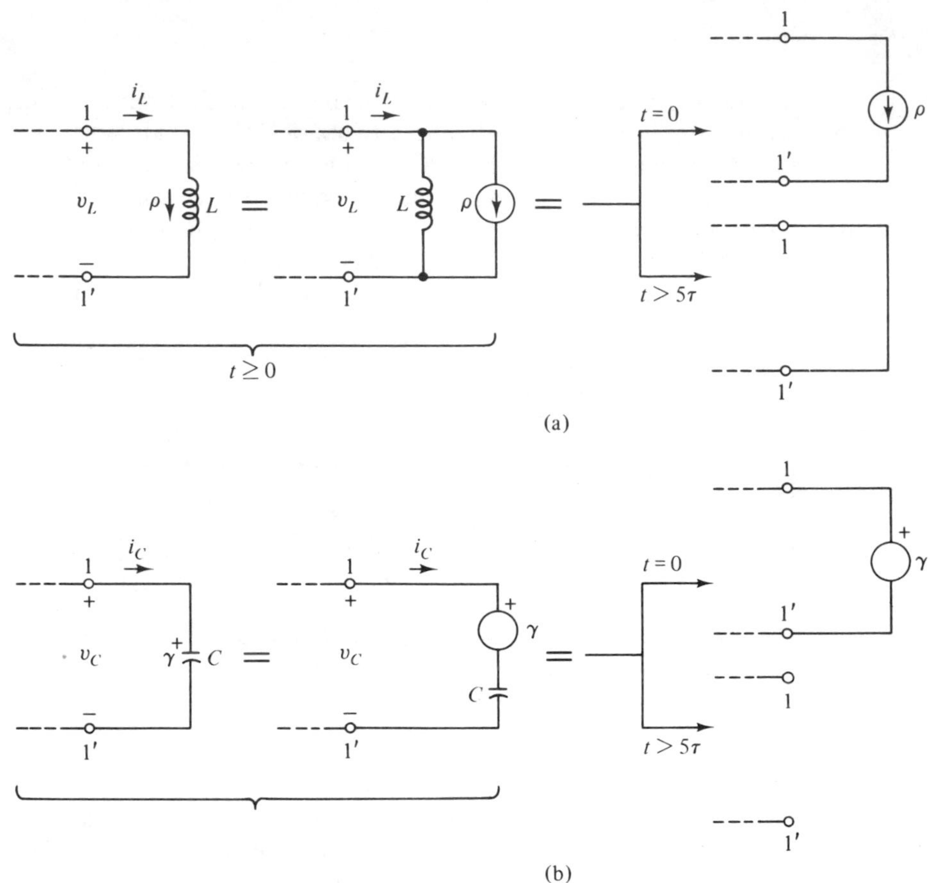

Fig. 6-11

quire a value other than zero.] Consequently, *the current in the inductor is a continuous function of time*. The $i_L(t)$ vs. t curve can have a sudden change in slope, but it *cannot jump* from one value to another at any time.* So the current through the inductor has the same value immediately before, at the time of, and immediately after the application of the step excitation—that is,

$$i_L(0^-) = i_L(0) = i_L(0^+) = \rho$$

Therefore *for the instant of $t = 0$ only, the inductor can be replaced with a dc current source of value ρ*. This initial value of current either is given or is determined from conditions existing in the network prior to the step excitation.

Although the current in the inductor cannot jump at $t = 0$, the voltage across it, being the derivative of the current, can take a jump.

*This development excludes impulse functions. The inductor current can jump if the inductor is subjected to a voltage impulse. In actual circuits, voltage impulses do not occur.

The step response of a first-order system

$$r(t) = F + (I - F)e^{-t/\tau}$$

shows that $r(t)$ becomes constant (attains the value of F) after five time constants. Consequently, dr/dt is zero for $t > 5\tau$. Since $r(t)$ represents either a current or a voltage, all voltage and current derivatives in a first-order network eventually become zero. Thus for the inductor we have

$$\left.\frac{di_L(t)}{dt}\right|_{t>5\tau} = 0$$

Since the voltage across the inductor is $v_L(t) = L\, di_L(t)/dt$, it becomes zero after five time constants; that is

$$v_L(t)\,\big|_{t>5\tau} = 0 \tag{6-33}$$

As a result, *for $t > 5\tau$ the inductor can be replaced with a short circuit*. The equivalent circuits for the inductor and the conditions for which they hold are represented in Fig. 6-11(a).

For the capacitor shown in Fig. 6-11(b) we have

$$i_C(t) = C\frac{dv_C(t)}{dt} \tag{6-34a}$$

$$v_C(t) = \underbrace{v_C(0)}_{\gamma} + \frac{1}{C}\int_0^t i_C(t')\, dt' \tag{6-34b}$$

Comparing Eqs. (6-34) and (6-32), we see that what is true for the voltage across the inductor is also true for the current through the capacitor and vice versa. Thus we can make the following statements concerning the capacitor in a first-order network that is step-excited.

1. *The voltage across the capacitor is a continuous function of time,* and so it *cannot jump* from one value to another at any time.*

   $$v_C(0^-) = v_C(0) = v_C(0^+) = \gamma$$

   For the instant of $t = 0$ only, therefore, the capacitor can be replaced with a dc voltage source of value γ. The current through the capacitor, being the derivative of the voltage across it, can take a jump.
2. After five time constants the current through the capacitor is, for all practical purposes, zero. So $t > 5\tau$ *the capacitor can be replaced with an open circuit.*

*The capacitor voltage can jump if the capacitor is subjected to a current impulse. In actual circuits, current impulses do not occur.

The equivalent circuits for the capacitor and the conditions for which they hold are shown in Fig. 6-11(b).

Although the results presented here are developed for first-order systems, the equivalent circuits given in Fig. 6-11 are also valid for higher-order systems that have left half-plane poles and that are step-excited. The only difference is that more than one time constant will be involved, and therefore the responses in the network will become constant only after the exponential with the largest time constant [corresponding to the pole(s) closest to the imaginary axis] has decayed to zero.

It should be emphasized that the voltage across a capacitor and the current through an inductor are continuous functions of time in all circumstances that exclude impulse functions. This property depends on the integral relationships involved and not on the excitations used.

6-7 EXAMPLES OF STEP RESPONSES IN FIRST-ORDER NETWORKS

The expression for any current or voltage in a network that is characterized by one pole and excited by step function sources is given by

$$r(t) = F + (I - F)e^{-t/\tau}$$

where F = final value of the response
I = initial value of the response
τ = time constant associated with the network

Since F, I, and τ can all be determined by inspection of the network, the response is easily obtained.

Example 6-7

In Fig. 6-12 the switch is closed at $t = 0$, thereby exciting the RL circuit with a step voltage V_{dc} units high. Obtain the expression for the current and sketch it for $R = R_1$, $R_1/2$, and 0.

Solution. First, we determine the time constant. We replace the voltage source with

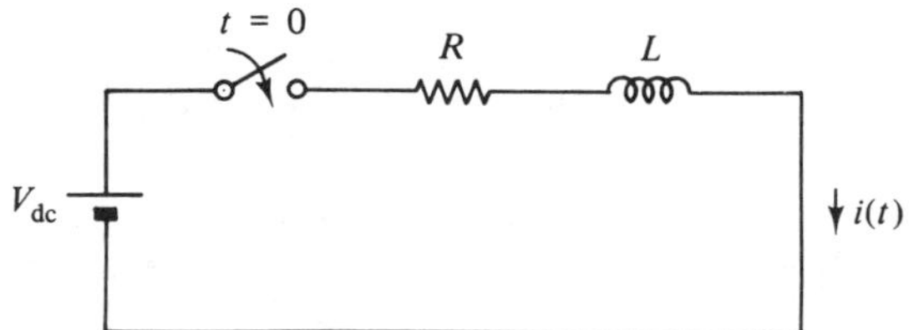

Fig. 6-12

a short circuit and redraw the network with the switch closed as in Fig. 6-13(a). From this figure we obtain

$$\tau = \frac{L}{R}$$

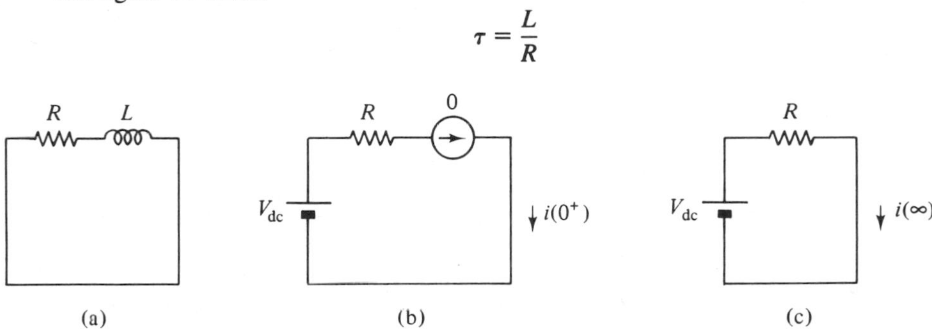

Fig. 6-13

Next, we determine the initial value of the current. Before the switch is closed, the current through the inductor is zero. Since the current through the inductor is a continuous function of time, the current is still zero immediately after the switch is closed. Hence at $t = 0$ the inductor can be replaced with a current source of zero value (open circuit) as in Fig. 6-13(b). From the figure we see that

$$i(0^+) = 0$$

Finally, we determine the final value of the current. We replace the inductor with a short circuit and redraw the network as in Fig. 6-13(c). From the figure we see that

$$i(\infty) = \frac{V_{dc}}{R}$$

The expression for the current is

$$\begin{aligned} i(t) &= i(\infty) + [i(0^+) - i(\infty)]e^{-t/\tau} \\ &= \frac{V_{dc}}{R} + \left(0 - \frac{V_{dc}}{R}\right)e^{-t/(L/R)} \\ &= \frac{V_{dc}}{R}[1 - e^{-(R/L)t}] \qquad (t \geq 0) \quad \text{Ans.} \end{aligned} \tag{6-35}$$

This current is sketched in Fig. 6-14 for $R = R_1$, $R_1/2$, and 0. When $R = R_1$, the current reaches the 63% of V_{dc}/R_1 at $t = \tau_1 = L/R_1$. When R is replaced by $R_1/2$, both the final value of the current and the time constant of the circuit are doubled. It now takes twice as long to reach the 63% of $2V_{dc}/R_1$. When $R \to 0$, the final value of the current and the time constant of the circuit become infinite. As a result, the current never reaches the final value. Since, for $R = 0$, the expression for the current [Eq. (6-35)] becomes indeterminate (0/0), we use l'Hospital's rule to evaluate $i(t)$.

$$i(t) = \lim_{R \to 0} \left\{ \frac{(d/dR)[V_{dc}(1 - e^{-(R/L)t}]}{dR/dR} \right\} = \frac{V_{dc}}{L} t$$

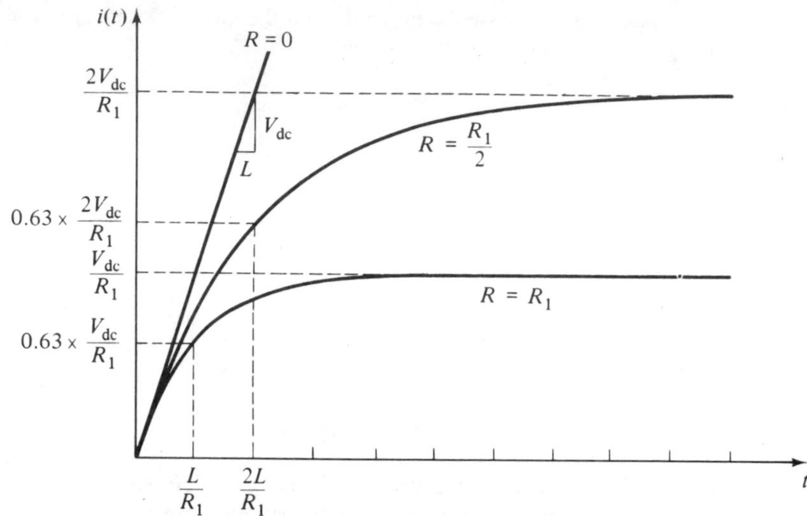

Fig. 6-14

Alternatively, we obtain $i(t)$ directly from Fig. 6-12 (with $R = 0$) as follows.

$$i(t) = \frac{1}{L}\int_0^t v_L(t')\,dt' = \frac{1}{L}\int_0^t V_{dc}\,dt' = \frac{V_{dc}}{L}t$$

So, for $R = 0$, the current rises linearly with t as shown in Fig. 6-14.

Example 6-8

In Fig.6-15 the switch is opened at $t = 0$, thereby exciting the RC network with a step current I_{dc} units high. Obtain $v_o(t)$ and sketch it.

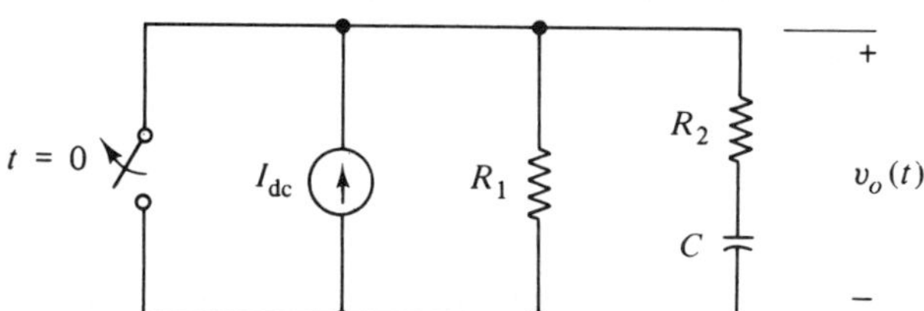

Fig. 6-15

Solution.

Determination of τ With the switch open and the source I_{dc} replaced with an open circuit, Fig. 6-15 is redrawn as in Fig. 6-16(a), and τ is obtained as

$$\tau = R_{eq}C = (R_1 + R_2)C$$

Determination of $v_o(0^+)$ Before the switch is opened, the voltage across the capacitor is zero (there being no excitation across the R_2C circuit). Since the voltage across the capacitor is a continuous function of time, the voltage is still zero immediately after the opening of the switch. Hence at $t = 0$ the capacitor can be replaced with a voltage

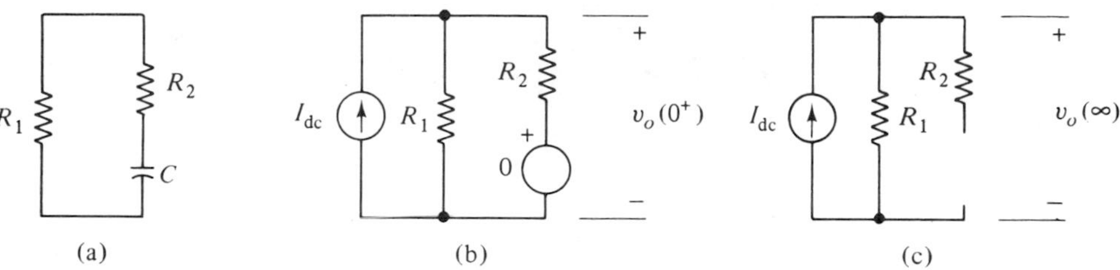

Fig. 6-16

source of zero value (short circuit) as in Fig. 6-16(b). From this figure we obtain the initial value of the output voltage.

$$v_o(0^+) = I_{dc}\left(\frac{R_1R_2}{R_1 + R_2}\right)$$

Determination of $v_o(\infty)$ At $t = \infty$ (indeed for $t > 5\tau$) the capacitor current is zero. Therefore it can be replaced with an open circuit and the network redrawn as in Fig. 6-16(c). From this figure we obtain the final value of the output voltage.

$$v_o(\infty) = I_{dc}R_1$$

Determination of $v_o(t)$

$$\begin{aligned} v_o(t) &= v_o(\infty) + [v_o(0^+) - v_o(\infty)]e^{-t/\tau} \\ &= I_{dc}R_1 + \left[I_{dc}\left(\frac{R_1R_2}{R_1 + R_2}\right) - I_{dc}R_1\right]e^{-t/(R_1+R_2)C} \\ &= I_{dc}R_1\left[1 - \left(\frac{R_1}{R_1 + R_2}\right)e^{-t/(R_1+R_2)C}\right] \quad \text{Ans.} \end{aligned}$$

The output waveform is sketched in Fig. 6-17.

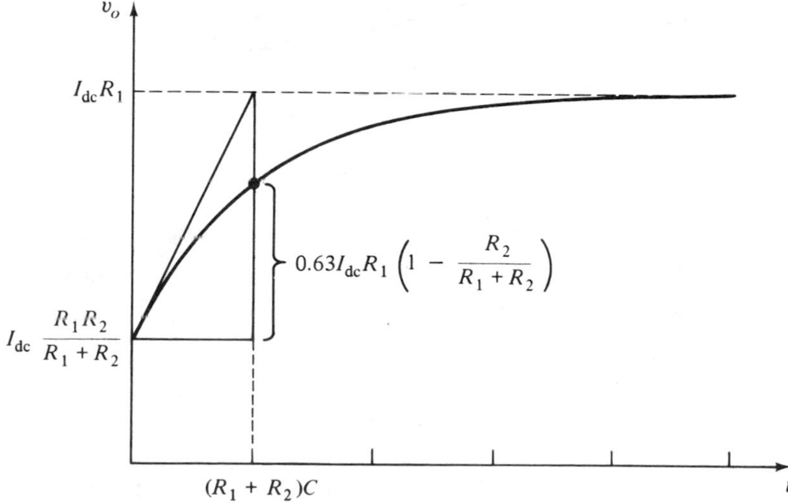

Fig. 6-17

Example 6-9

In Fig. 6-18, sketch $v_o(t)$ for $RC = 10$ and $RC = 1$.

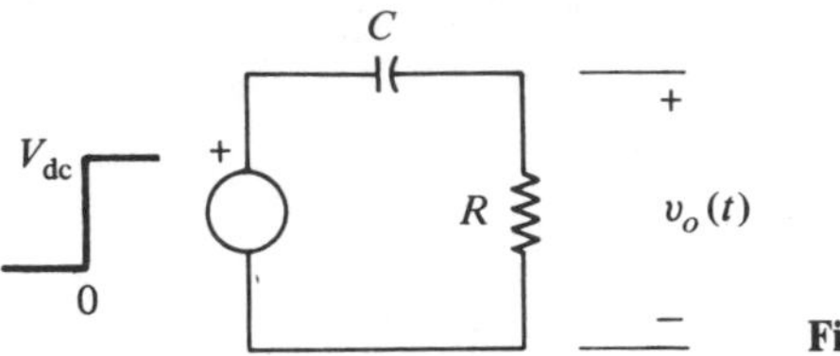

Fig. 6-18

Solution. By inspection of the network, we obtain

$$\tau = RC$$

$$v_o(0^+) = V_{dc} \qquad [\text{since } v_C(0) = 0]$$

$$v_o(\infty) = 0 \qquad [\text{since } i_C(\infty) = 0]$$

The output is sketched in Fig. 6-19(a) for $RC = 10$ and in Fig. 6-19(b) for $RC = 1$. In the latter case, the time constant is ten times smaller. Hence the transition between the initial and final values is ten times faster.

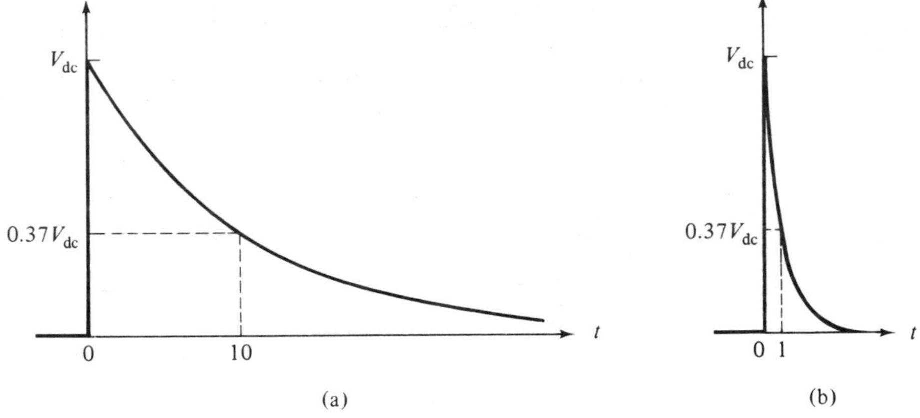

Fig. 6-19

Example 6-10

In Fig. 6-20 the switch is closed at $t = 0$. Obtain the expression for $v_o(t)$ and sketch it for $C_2 = C_1$ and $\gamma_2 = -3\gamma_1$.

Solution. *At* $t = 0^-$

$$v_o(0^-) = \gamma_2 \qquad (\text{there being no voltage across } R)$$

At $t = 0^+$

$$v_o(0^+) = \gamma_1 \qquad (\text{since the voltage across } C_1 \text{ cannot jump})$$

At $t = \infty$

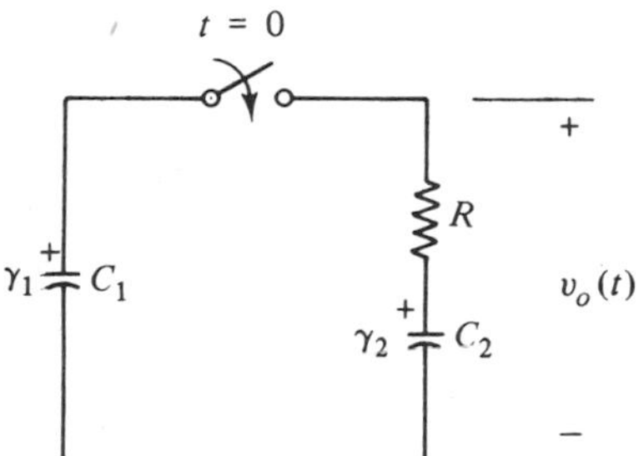

Fig. 6-20

The current through the resistor is zero [since $i_C(\infty) = 0$]. Consequently, the voltage across the resistor is zero, and we can replace the resistor with a short circuit without affecting the $t = \infty$ conditions. We then redraw the circuit as in Fig. 6-21, where the initial conditions are represented as dc voltage sources in series with the capacitors. Although the capacitors act like open circuits, we do not replace them with open circuits in this case in order to see how the voltages divide (between the two open circuits arising from capacitors). By superposition, we obtain

$$v_o(\infty) = \gamma_1\left(\frac{C_1}{C_1 + C_2}\right) + \gamma_2\left(\frac{C_2}{C_1 + C_2}\right) = \frac{\gamma_1 C_1 + \gamma_2 C_2}{C_1 + C_2}$$

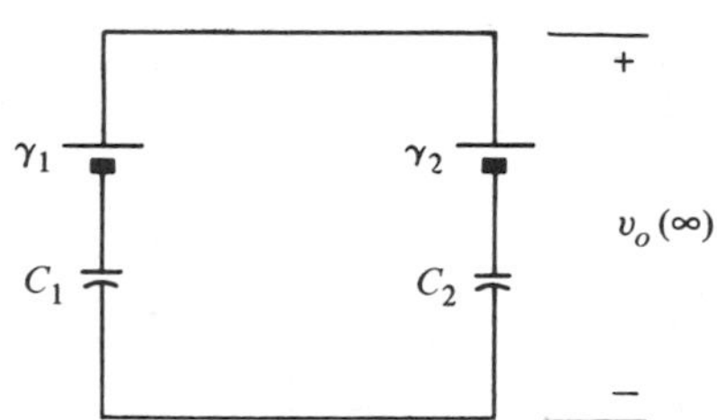

Fig. 6-21

The time constant By inspection of Fig. 6-20, we see that

$$\tau = RC_{\text{eq}} = R\frac{C_1 C_2}{C_1 + C_2}$$

The output voltage

$$\begin{aligned} v_o(t) &= v_o(\infty) + [v_o(0^+) - v_o(\infty)]e^{-t/\tau} \\ &= \frac{\gamma_1 C_1 + \gamma_2 C_2}{C_1 + C_2} + \left[\gamma_1 - \frac{\gamma_1 C_1 + \gamma_2 C_2}{C_1 + C_2}\right] e^{-t/[RC_1C_2/(C_1+C_2)]} \\ &= \frac{\gamma_1 C_1 + \gamma_2 C_2}{C_1 + C_2} + (\gamma_1 - \gamma_2)\frac{C_2}{C_1 + C_2} e^{-t/[RC_1C_2/(C_1+C_2)]} \qquad (t > 0) \quad \text{Ans.} \end{aligned}$$

For $C_1 = C_2$ and $\gamma_2 = -3\gamma_1$, the expression for $v_o(t)$ simplifies to

$$\begin{aligned} v_o(t) &= \frac{\gamma_1 C_1 - 3\gamma_1 C_1}{C_1 + C_1} + (\gamma_1 + 3\gamma_1)\frac{C_1}{C_1 + C_1} e^{-t/[RC_1C_1/2C_1]} \\ &= -\gamma_1 + 2\gamma_1 e^{-t/(RC_1/2)} \end{aligned}$$

This $v_o(t)$ is sketched in Fig. 6-22.

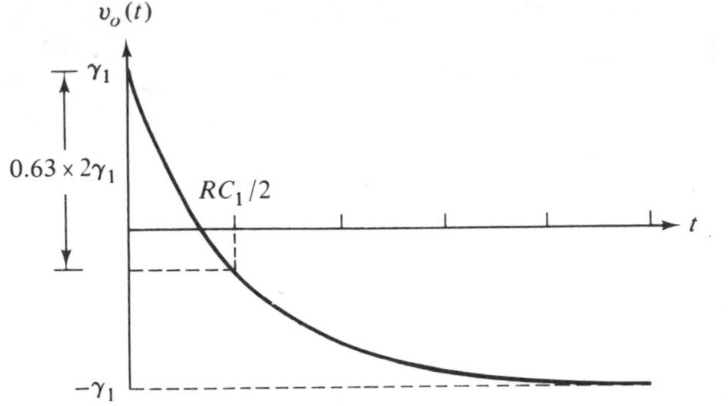

Fig. 6-22

Example 6-11

In Fig. 6-23 the currents in the inductors at $t = 0^-$ are as shown. Obtain the expression for $i(t)$.

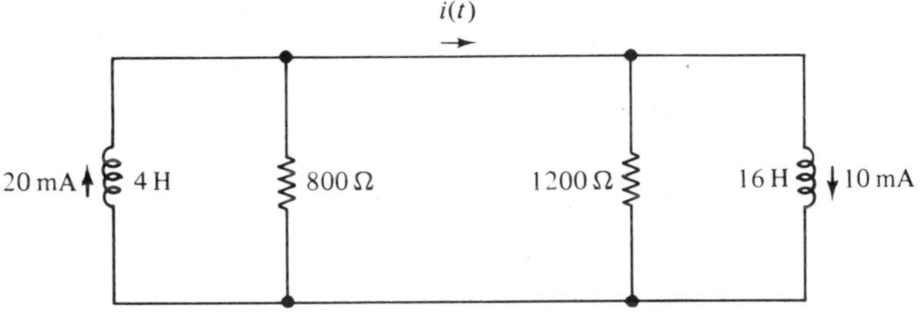

Fig. 6-23

Solution.

Determination of τ Referring to Fig. 6-24(a), we have

$$\tau = \frac{L_{eq}}{R_{eq}} = \frac{(4 \times 16)/(4 + 16)}{(800 \times 1200)/(1800 + 1200)} = \frac{1}{150} \text{ seconds}$$

Determination of $i(0^+)$ We replace the inductors with current sources (representing the initial values) and redraw the circuit as in Fig. 6-24(b). By superposition, we obtain

$$i(0^+) = 20\left(\frac{800}{800 + 1200}\right) + 10\left(\frac{1200}{800 + 1200}\right) = 14 \text{ mA}$$

Determination of $i(\infty)$ The voltage across both inductors is zero [since $v_L(\infty) = 0$]. Consequently, the voltage across the resistors—and hence the currents through the resistors—is zero. So we can remove the resistors (open-circuit them) without affecting the $t = \infty$ conditions. We then redraw the circuit as in Fig. 6-24(c), where the initial conditions are represented as dc current sources across the inductors. Although the inductors act like short circuits, we do not replace them with short circuits in this case, in

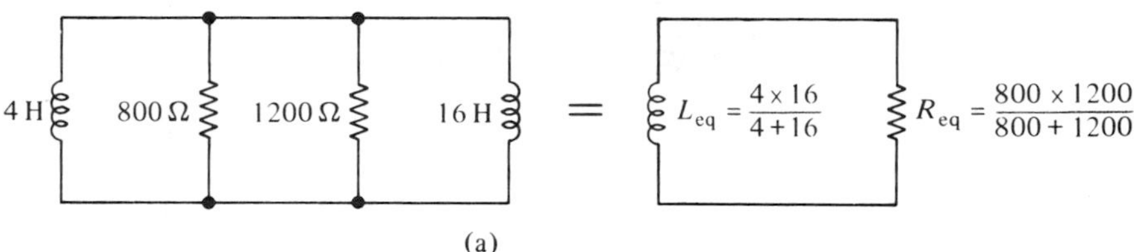

(a)

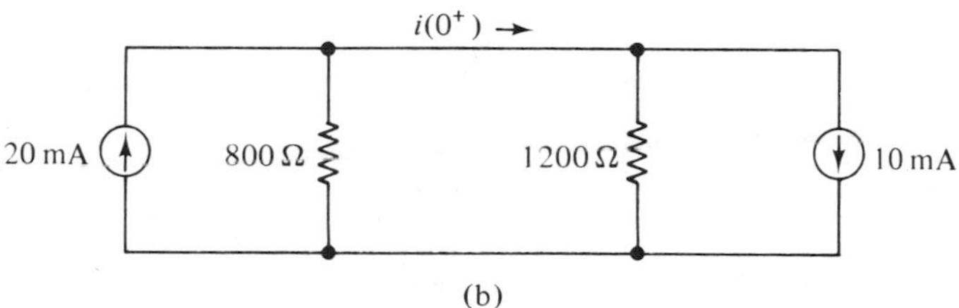

(b)

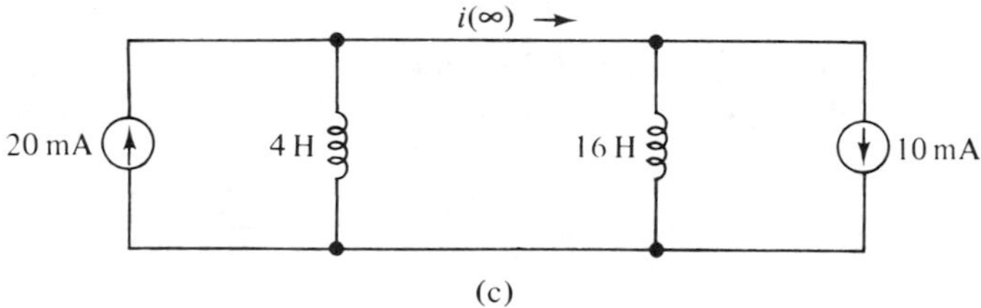

(c)

Fig. 6-24

order to see how the currents divide (between the two short circuits arising from inductors). By superposition, we obtain

$$i(\infty) = 20\left(\frac{4}{4 + 16}\right) + 10\left(\frac{16}{4 + 16}\right) = 12 \text{ mA}$$

Determination of $i(t)$

$$\begin{aligned} i(t) &= i(\infty) + [i(0^+) - i(\infty)]e^{-t/\tau} \\ &= 12 + (14 - 12)e^{-t/(1/150)} \\ &= 12 + 2e^{-150t} \qquad (t > 0) \quad \text{Ans.} \end{aligned}$$

Example 6-12

Two independent step sources and one initial-voltage source excite the network of Fig. 6-25. Obtain $v_o(t)$.

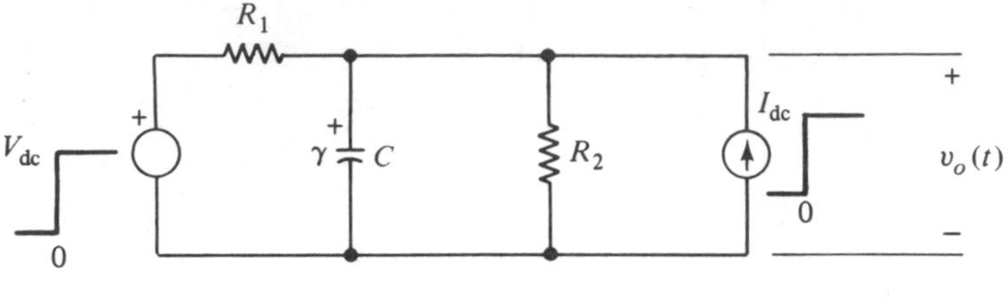

Fig. 6-25

Solution.

Determination of τ By inspection of Fig. 6-25 (with sources reduced to zero), we see that

$$\tau = R_{eq}C = \frac{R_1R_2}{R_1 + R_2}C$$

Determination of $v_o(0^+)$ Figure 6-25 shows that the output voltage is the same as the voltage across the capacitor. Since this voltage cannot jump, it will stay at its $t = 0^-$ value, which is γ. So

$$v_o(0^+) = \gamma$$

Determination of $v_o(0^+)$ Figure 6-25 shows that the output voltage is the same as the voltage across the capacitor. Since this voltage cannot jump, it will stay at its $t = 0^-$ value, which is γ. So

$$v_o(\infty) = V_{dc}\left(\frac{R_2}{R_1 + R_2}\right) + I_{dc}\left(\frac{R_1R_2}{R_1 + R_2}\right)$$

Determination of $v_o(t)$

$$\begin{aligned} v_o(t) &= v_o(\infty) + [v_o(0^+) - v_o(\infty)]e^{-t/\tau} \\ &= V_{dc}\left(\frac{R_2}{R_1 + R_2}\right) + I_{dc}\left(\frac{R_1R_2}{R_1 + R_2}\right) \\ &+ \left[\gamma - V_{dc}\left(\frac{R_2}{R_1 + R_2}\right) - I_{dc}\left(\frac{R_1R_2}{R_1 + R_2}\right)\right]e^{-t/[CR_1R_2/(R_1+R_2)]} \qquad (t \geq 0) \quad \text{Ans.} \end{aligned}$$

6-8 GENERATION OF HIGH VOLTAGE AND CURRENT SURGES FROM INITIAL CONDITIONS

High voltage surges can be generated from initial currents in inductors. High current surges can be generated from initial voltages across capacitors.

Consider the generation of a high voltage surge. A circuit that produces such a voltage is given in Fig. 6-26(a). Assume that the switch has been kept in the closed position for a sufficiently long time to establish a current of V/r through the inductor. This means that the switch has been kept closed for at least $5\tau_0 = 5L/r$ seconds. At $t = 0$ the switch is opened, and we have the circuit shown in Fig. 6-26(b).

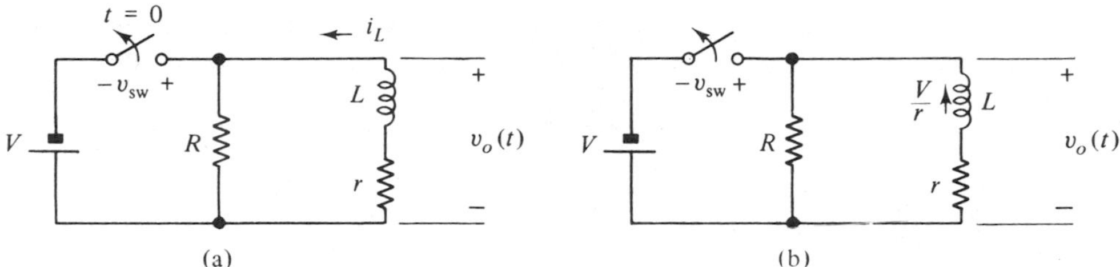

Fig. 6-26

At $t = 0^+$ the current through the inductor is still V/r (it cannot change instantaneously). Because the switch is open, all this current must flow through R. Therefore

$$v_o(0^+) = \frac{V}{r}R$$

$$v_{sw}(0^+) = v_o(0^+) - (-V) = V\left(1 + \frac{R}{r}\right)$$

Since the current in the LrR loop eventually drops to zero (because the voltage across the inductor is zero at $t = \infty$) with a time constant of $\tau = L/(R + r)$, the output voltage and the voltage across the switch eventually become

$$v_o(\infty) = 0, \qquad v_{sw}(\infty) = V$$

Consequently, we can write $v_o(t)$ and $v_{sw}(t)$ as

$$\left.\begin{aligned} v_o(t) &= V\frac{R}{r}e^{-t/\tau} \\ v_{sw}(t) &= V\left(1 + \frac{R}{r}e^{-t/\tau}\right) \end{aligned}\right\} \quad (t > 0) \qquad \text{(6-36)}$$

These voltages are sketched in Fig. 6-27.

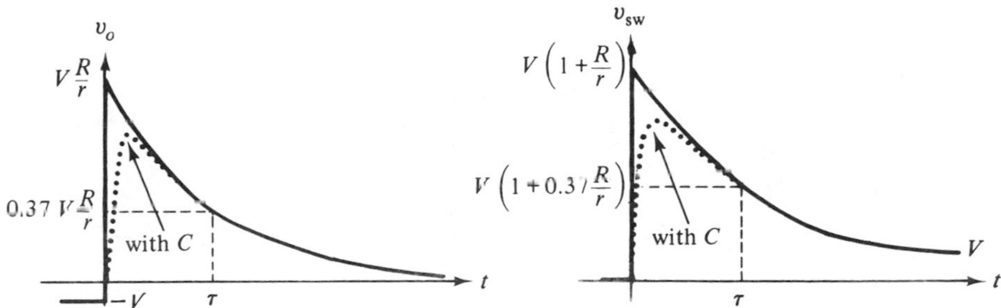

Fig. 6-27

As the R/r ratio is made larger, the values of the voltages at $t = 0^+$ become larger. For instance, if $V = 50$ V, $R = 10$ kΩ, and $r = 100$ Ω, then

$$v_o(0^+) = 5000 \text{ V}, \qquad v_{sw}(0^+) = 5050 \text{ V}$$

and these large voltages are generated by using only a 50 V source. Had we chosen $R = 100$ kΩ instead of 10 kΩ, we would have obtained

$$v_o(0^+) = 50{,}000 \text{ V}, \qquad v_{sw}(0^+) = 50{,}050 \text{ V}$$

Such high voltages across the switch terminals cause arcing when the switch is opened. To minimize or prevent arcing, a capacitor can be connected across the switch terminals. Because the voltage across the capacitor cannot jump, neither v_o nor v_{sw} can jump at $t = 0$. Instead, these voltages rise rapidly as shown by the dotted curves of Fig. 6-27. The smaller the capacitor is made, the more rapidly the voltages change. With the capacitor in the circuit, there is no discontinuity in the voltage curves at $t = 0$. However, the peak voltages are lower in value. The circuit with a capacitor across the switch terminals is a second-order system and must be solved accordingly.

The initial energy stored in the inductor is $\frac{1}{2}L\rho^2 = \frac{1}{2}L(V/r)^2$, where ρ is the initial current in the inductor. Because r is small, it takes a long time $(5\tau_0 = 5L/r)$ to establish this energy in the inductor. However, once the switch is opened at $t = 0$, the energy is rapidly dissipated, mainly in the large resistor R [within a period of $5\tau_1 = 5L/(R + r) = (5L/r)/(1 + R/r)$]. Since $\tau_1 \ll \tau_0$, large amounts of instantaneous power (rate of change of energy) are developed, while very little power is demanded from the voltage source V, which supplies all the energy.

Next, the generation of a high current surge is demonstrated by the circuit in Fig. 6-28(a). Assume that the switch has been kept in the open position for a sufficiently long time to establish the voltage of V across the capacitor. This means that the switch has been kept open for at least $5\tau_0 = 5RC$ seconds. At $t = 0$ the switch is closed, and we have the circuit of Fig. 6-28(b) with an initial voltage of V across the capacitor.

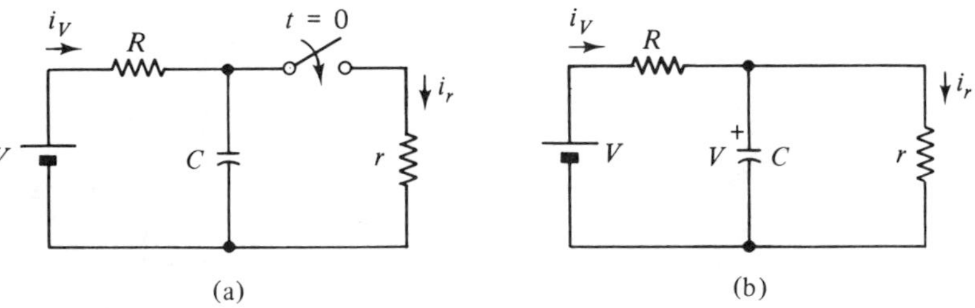

Fig. 6-28

At $t = 0^+$ the voltage across the capacitor is still V (it cannot change instantaneously). Because the switch is closed, this voltage appears across r. Therefore the currents through the two resistors are given by

$$i_r(0^+) = \frac{V}{r}, \qquad i_V(0^+) = \frac{V - V}{R} = 0$$

As $t \to \infty$ the capacitor current approaches zero, and we can determine the currents by taking the capacitor completely out of the circuit.

$$i_r(\infty) = i_V(\infty) = \frac{V}{R + r}$$

The changes occur with a time constant of

$$\tau = \frac{Rr}{R + r}C$$

Consequently, we can write $i_r(t)$ and $i_V(t)$ as

$$\left.\begin{aligned} i_r(t) &= \frac{V}{R + r} + \left(\frac{V}{r} - \frac{V}{R + r}\right)e^{-t/\tau} = \frac{V}{R + r}\left(1 + \frac{R}{r}e^{-t/\tau}\right) \\ i_V(t) &= \frac{V}{R + r}(1 - e^{-t/\tau}) \end{aligned}\right\} \quad (t > 0) \qquad (6\text{-}37)$$

These currents are sketched in Fig. 6-29.

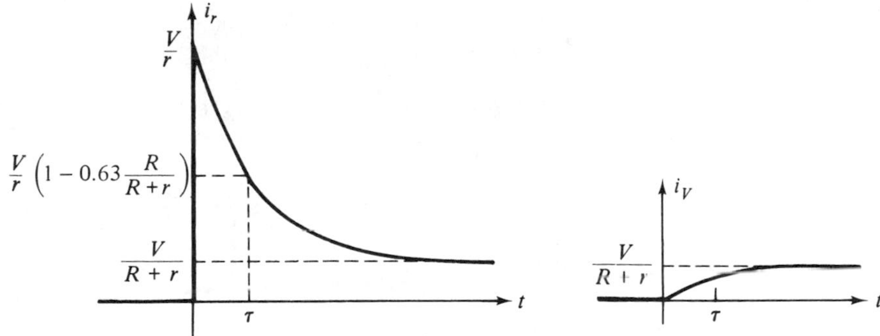

Fig. 6-29

The smaller r is made, the larger the initial surge of current through the load r becomes. For instance, if $V = 50$ V, $R = 10$ KΩ, and $r = 10$ Ω, then

$$i_r(0^+) = 5 \text{ A}, \qquad (i_V)_{\max} \cong 5 \text{ mA}$$

Thus a peak current of 5 A is generated, while the battery delivers no more than 5 mA.

The initial energy stored in the capacitor is $\frac{1}{2}C\gamma^2 = \frac{1}{2}CV^2$. Because R is large, it takes a long time ($5\tau_0 = 5RC$) to establish this energy in the capacitor. Once the switch is closed at $t = 0$, however, the energy is rapidly dissipated, mainly in the small resistor r [within a period of $5\tau_1 = 5[rR/(r + R)]C = 5RC/(1 + R/r)$]. Since $\tau_1 \ll \tau_0$, large amounts of instantaneous power are developed, while very little power is demanded from the voltage source V, which supplies all the energy.

6-9 PULSE EXCITATION OF FIRST-ORDER SYSTEMS

A pulse has the waveform shown in Fig. 6-30(a). Its amplitude is A and its width δ. A pulse can be represented as the sum of two step functions: one with amplitude A occurring at $t = 0$ and another with amplitude $-A$ occurring at $t = \delta$. This decomposition is shown in Fig. 6-30(b). Thus a network that is excited with a pulse can be considered as being excited by two equal but opposite polarity step functions that are applied δ seconds apart. To obtain the response, we need *calculate only* the response due to the first step function. The response to the second step function, being the negative and delayed version of the first response, can be written down without calculation. The response itself is, by superposition, *the sum of the two step function responses*.

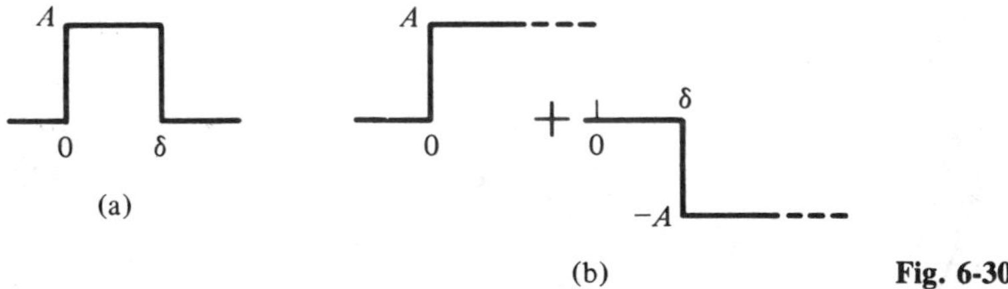

Fig. 6-30

Example 6-13

Obtain the pulse response of the network shown in Fig. 6-31 and sketch it.

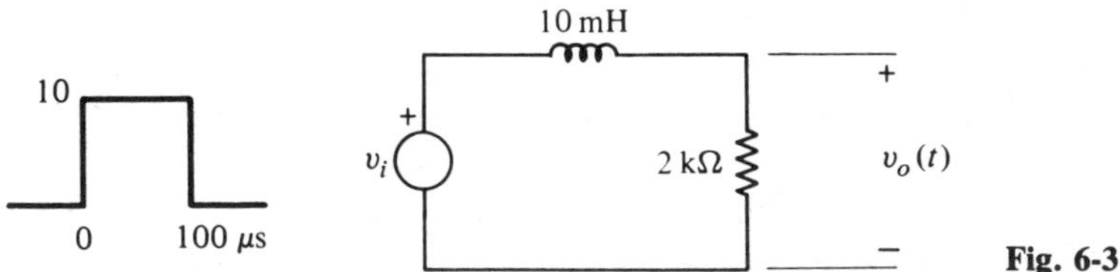

Fig. 6-31

Solution.

Method 1 Decompose the input pulse into the sum of two step voltages: one of amplitude 10 V occurring at $t = 0$ and the other of amplitude -10 V occurring at $t = 100\ \mu s$. We can, therefore. draw the circuit as in Fig. 6-32, where the pulse source is

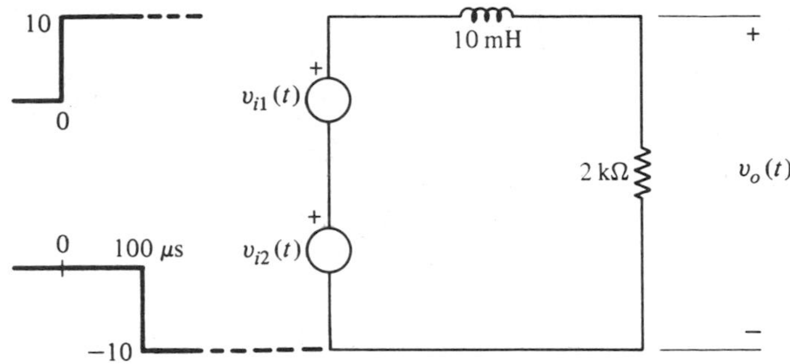

Fig. 6-32

represented by two step voltage sources, v_{i1} and v_{i2}, connected in series. Apply the principle of superposition to obtain $v_o(t)$.

$$v_o(t) = v_{o1}(t) + v_{o2}(t)$$

Voltage $v_{o1}(t)$ is caused by input $v_{i1}(t)$, while $v_{i2}(t)$ is held zero. By inspection of the circuit, we see that $v_{o1}(0^+) = 0$ (because the current through L cannot jump) and $v_{O1}(\infty) = 10$ (because the voltage across L is zero at $t = \infty$). So

$$v_{o1}(t) = 10(1 - e^{-t/\tau}) \qquad (t > 0)$$

Voltage $v_{o2}(t)$ is caused by input $v_{i2}(t)$, while $v_{i1}(t)$ is held at zero. For $t < 100\ \mu\text{s}$, $v_{i2}(t) = 0$, and hence $v_{o2}(t) = 0$. For $t > 100\ \mu\text{s}$, $v_{o2}(t)$ is the same as $v_{o1}(t)$ with two exceptions: it is the negative of $v_{o1}(t)$, and it is delayed by 100 μs. Mathematically, this time delay can be accounted for by replacing t with $(t - 10^{-4})$. Thus

$$v_{o2}(t) = \begin{cases} 0, & t < 100\ \mu\text{s} \\ -10[1 - e^{-(t-10^{-4})/\tau}], & t > 100\ \mu\text{s} \end{cases}$$

Using the expressions for $v_{o1}(t)$ and $v_{o2}(t)$, the output can be written

$$v_o(t) = \begin{cases} 10(1 - e^{-t/\tau}), & 0 < t < 100\ \mu\text{s} \\ 10(1 - e^{-t/\tau}) - 10[1 - e^{-(t-10^{-4})/\tau}] = 10(e^{10^{-4}/\tau} - 1)e^{-t/\tau}, & t > 100\ \mu\text{s} \end{cases} \quad \text{Ans.}$$

where $$\tau = \frac{L}{R} = \frac{10 \times 10^{-3}}{2 \times 10^3} = 5 \times 10^{-6}\ \text{s} = 5\mu\text{s}$$

In Fig. 6-33, $v_{o1}(t)$, $v_{o2}(t)$, and $v_o(t)$ are sketched vs. t. Note that $v_{o2}(t)$ can be sketched by sliding the $v_{o1}(t)$ curve 100 μs to the right and then inverting it.

Method 2 Instead of decomposing v_i into two waveforms, we can express it as a *single* waveform described mathematically by *two different functions, spanning two different time intervals*. Thus

$$v_i(t) = \begin{cases} 10, & 0 < t < 100\ \mu\text{s} \\ 0, & t > 100\ \mu\text{s} \end{cases}$$

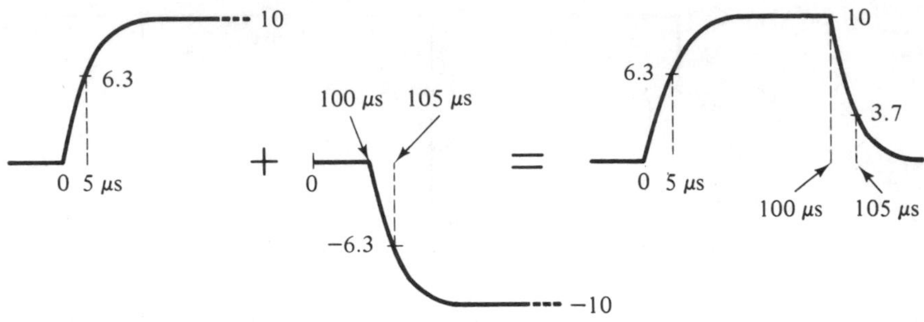

Fig. 6-33

During the first 100 μs the applied voltage is 10 V, and the circuit can be represented as in Fig. 6-34(a). So, as in method 1, we have

$$v_o(t) = 10(1 - e^{-t/\tau}) \qquad (0 < t < 100\ \mu\text{s}) \quad \text{Ans.}$$

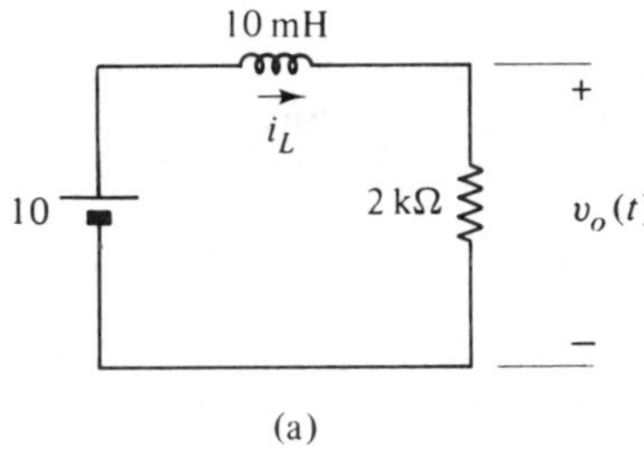

(a)

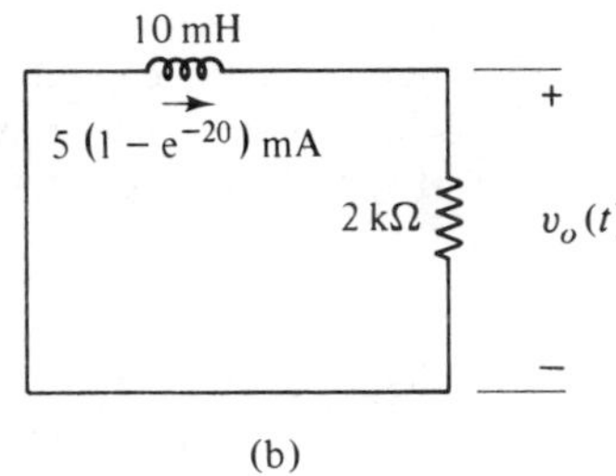

(b)

Fig. 6-34

where $\tau = 5\ \mu$s. At $t = 100^-\ \mu$s the output voltage is

$$v_o(100^-\ \mu\text{s}) = 10(1 - e^{-100/5}) = 10(1 - e^{-20})$$

Correspondingly, at $t = 100^-\ \mu$s the current through the resistor, and hence the current through the inductor, is

$$i_L(100^-\ \mu\text{s}) = \frac{10(1 - e^{-20})}{2} = 5(1 - e^{-20})$$

At $t = 100\ \mu$s the input drops to zero. Thus, for $t > 100\ \mu$s, we have the circuit of Fig. 6-34(b) to solve. Note that the inductor carries $5(1 - e^{-20})$ mA of initial current for this part of operation. This current, which is established during the preceding time interval by the circuit of Fig. 6-34(a), serves as the tie-in between the two circuits. By inspection of Fig. 6-34(b), we see that

$$v_o(100^+\ \mu\text{s}) = 5(1 - e^{-20})\ \text{mA} \times 2\ \text{k}\Omega = 10(1 - e^{-20})$$

$$v_o(\infty) = 0$$

Hence

$$v_o(t) = 10(1 - e^{-20})e^{-(t-10^{-4})/\tau} = 10(e^{10^{-4}/\tau} - 1)e^{-t/\tau} \quad (t > 100\ \mu\text{s}) \quad \text{Ans.}$$

where $(t - 10^{-4})$, instead of t, is used to designate that time is being counted from 100 μs onward for this part of the problem.

The two parts of the solution and the complete solution are shown graphically in Fig. 6-35.

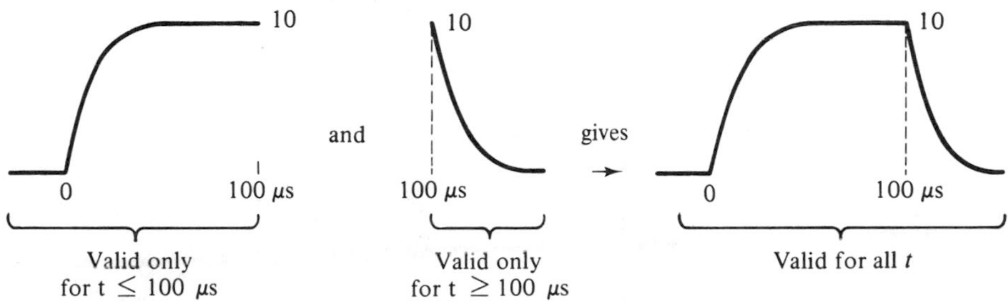

Fig. 6-35

Example 6-14

In Fig. 6-36 the time constant of the RC circuit is much larger than the pulse width. Obtain $v_o(t)$ and sketch it.

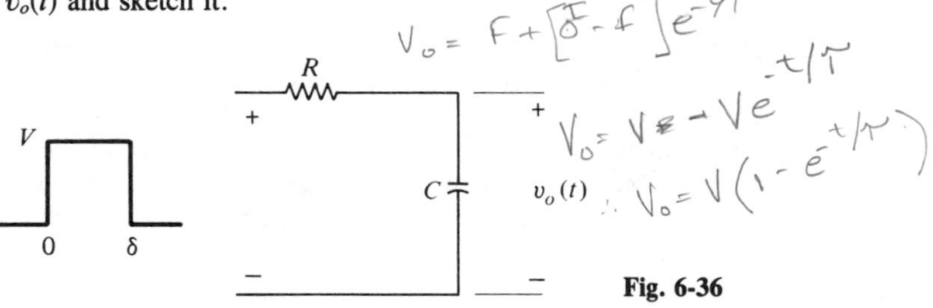

Fig. 6-36

Solution. For t between 0 and δ, the input is held at V volts, and the voltage across the capacitor builds up according to

$$v_o(t) = V(1 - e^{-t/RC}) \qquad (0 \leq t \leq \delta) \tag{6-38}$$

Since $\delta \ll RC$, we can approximate $e^{-t/RC}$ with the first two terms of the power series expansion—that is,

$$e^{-t/RC} \cong 1 - \frac{t}{RC} \qquad \left(\frac{t}{RC} \ll 1\right)$$

So Eq. (6-38) can be simplified to

$$v_o(t) \cong V\left[1 - \left(1 - \frac{t}{RC}\right)\right] = V\frac{t}{RC} \qquad \left(\frac{t}{RC} \ll 1, 0 \leq t \leq \delta\right) \tag{6-39}$$

Thus as long as $t \ll RC$, the voltage across the capacitor builds up linearly. Just before the pulse terminates, this voltage attains the value of

$$v_o(\delta) \cong V\frac{\delta}{RC}$$

As shown in Fig. 6-37(a), this voltage acts as the initial voltage across the capacitor for the remaining period ($t > \delta$). The voltage across the capacitor then decays exponentially to zero with $\tau = RC$.

$$v_o(t) = V\frac{\delta}{RC}e^{-(t-\delta)/RC} \qquad (t \geq \delta)$$

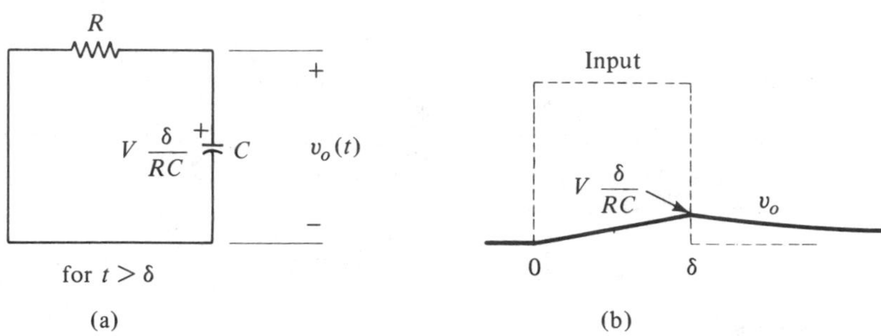

Fig. 6-37

The output voltage is sketched in Fig. 6-37(b). Because the time constant is large in comparison to the pulse width, the voltage cannot change much during this interval. (Recall that the longer the time constant, the longer it takes for changes to run their full range.) Consequently, the output cannot attain any significant level. Immediately after $t = \delta$ the decay can be approximated again with a straight line. However, as t becomes larger, the exponential nature of the curve becomes apparent.

6-10 SQUARE WAVE EXCITATION

A square wave has the waveform shown in Fig. 6-38. Its average value may be zero as shown, or the whole wave may have a dc level, thus shifting the waveform up or down. The wave may also be unsymmetrical; that is, the positive portion may be narrower than the negative portion or vica versa. The time interval T, called the *period* of the square wave, represents the time for one cycle of the waveform.

A square wave can be decomposed into a succession of step functions occurring in alternate directions and in $T/2$-second intervals. All step functions, except the first, are $2V$ volts high. The first step is V volts high. Six such step functions are shown in Fig. 6-38. The square wave can also be thought of as a succession of pulses occurring every T seconds.

Because of our ability to decompose the square wave as indicated, the square wave response of a network can be obtained by summing the individual step function responses.

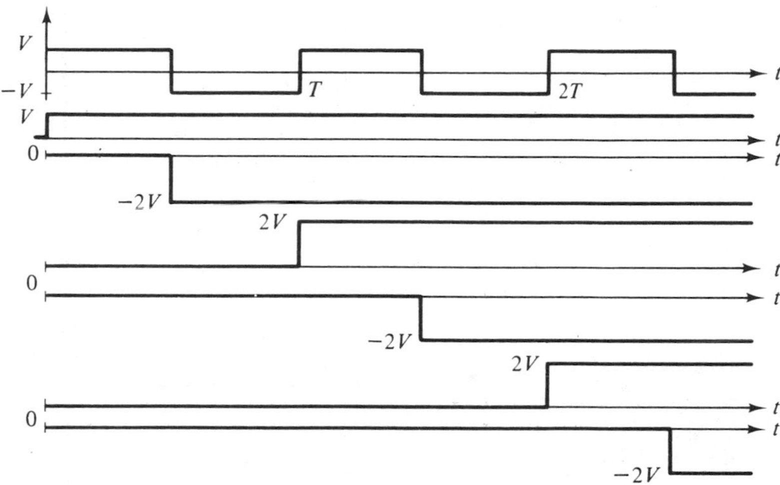

Fig. 6-38

Example 6-15

A symmetric square wave is applied to the network of Fig. 6-39 at $t = 0$. Sketch the output if

(a) $RC \ll \frac{T}{2}$.

(b) $RC = \frac{T}{2}$.

(c) $RC \gg \frac{T}{2}$.

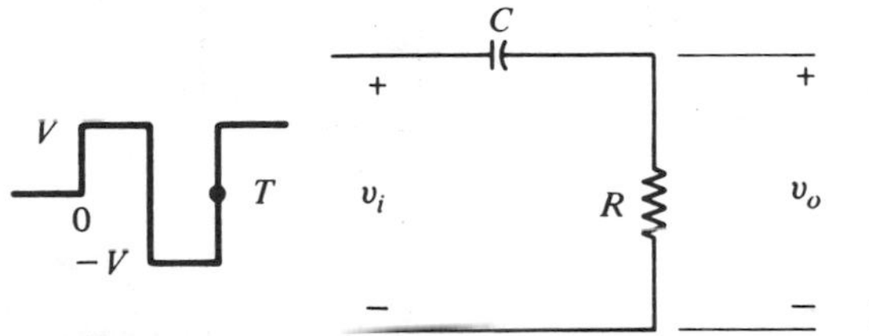

Fig. 6-39

Solution.

(a) Since the time constant of the circuit is much less than the half-period, the waveform *reaches the steady-state value of zero within each half-period*. Furthermore, when *the input jumps, the output jumps* by the same amount because the capacitor voltage remains invariant during the jump. As a result, we obtain the output voltage waveform shown in Fig. 6-40(a).

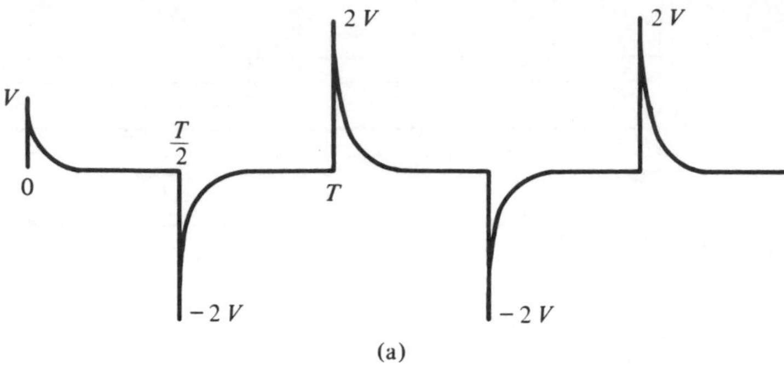

(a)

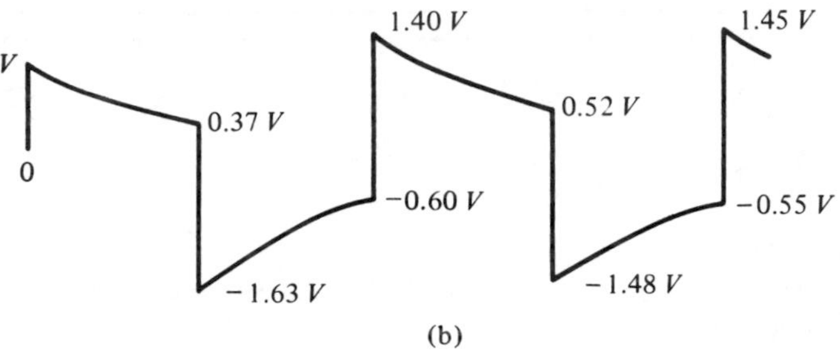

(b)

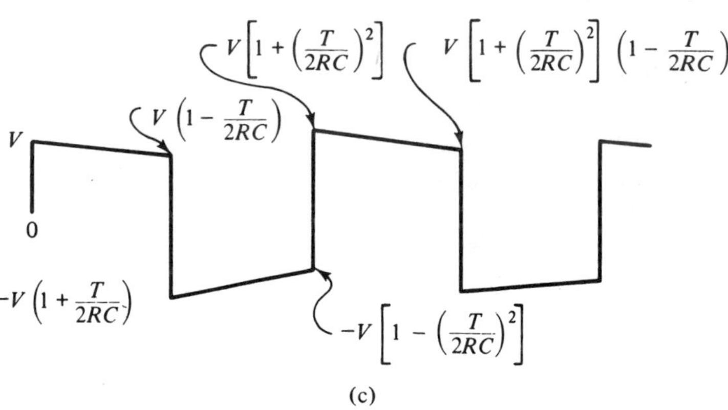

(c)

Fig. 6-40

(b) Since the time constant of the circuit equals the half-period, 63% of the change is completed within the half-period. The result is the waveform shown in Fig. 6-40(b). The various peak amplitudes are calculated as shown on the top of page 309. After about five time constants ($5RC = 2.5T$), the output reaches steady state, and the waveform becomes periodic.

Time	Value of v_o	Method used for calculation
0^+	V	Inputs jumps up by V
$\frac{T^-}{2}$	$V(1 - 0.63) = 0.37V$	Voltage changes by 63%
$\frac{T^+}{2}$	$0.37V - 2V = -1.63V$	Input jumps down by $2V$
T^-	$-1.63V(1 - 0.63) = -0.60V$	Voltage changes by 63%
T^+	$-0.60V + 2V = 1.40V$	Input jumps up by $2V$
$\frac{3T^-}{2}$	$1.40V(1 - 0.63) = 0.52V$	Voltage changes by 63%
$\frac{3T^+}{2}$	$0.52V - 2V = -1.48V$	Input jumps down by $2V$
$2T^-$	$-1.48V(1 - 0.63) = -0.55V$	Voltage changes by 63%
$2T^+$	$-0.55V + 2V = 1.45V$	Input jumps up by $2V$

(c) Since the time constant of the circuit is much larger than the half-period, the exponential decay can be approximated as

$$e^{-t/RC} \cong 1 - \frac{t}{RC}$$

which when evaluated for $t = T/2$ gives

$$e^{-T/2RC} \cong 1 - \frac{T}{2RC}$$

The resulting waveform is shown in Fig. 6-40(c). The various peak amplitudes are evaluated as shown below. After about five time constants, the waveform becomes periodic; that is, it repeats itself regularly.

Time	Value of v_o	Method used for calculation
0^+	V	Input jumps up by V
$\frac{T^-}{2}$	$V\left(1 - \frac{T}{2RC}\right)$	Voltage decays linearly
$\frac{T^+}{2}$	$V\left(1 - \frac{T}{2RC}\right) - 2V = -V\left(1 + \frac{T}{2RC}\right)$	Input jumps down by $2V$
T^-	$-V\left(1 + \frac{T}{2RC}\right)\left(1 - \frac{T}{2RC}\right) = -V\left[1 - \left(\frac{T}{2RC}\right)^2\right]$	Voltage decays linearly
T^+	$-V\left[1 - \left(\frac{T}{2RC}\right)^2\right] + 2V$	
	$= V\left[1 + \left(\frac{T}{2RC}\right)^2\right]$	Voltage jumps up by $2V$
$\frac{3T^-}{2}$	$V\left[1 + \left(\frac{T}{2RC}\right)^2\right]\left(1 - \frac{T}{2RC}\right)$	Voltage decays linearly

Example 6-16

Steady state has been reached in Fig. 6-41.

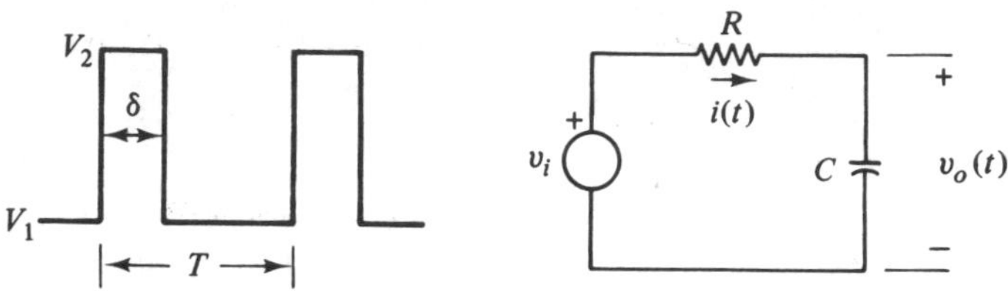

Fig. 6-41

(a) Sketch $v_o(t)$.

(b) What is the average value of the current waveform?

(c) What is the average value of $v_o(t)$?

(d) Let $V_1 = 0$ and $RC \gg T$. Show that $v_o(t)$ is almost constant and proportional to the frequency of the square wave.

Solution.

(a) The input stays at the V_2 level for δ seconds and at the V_1 level for $(T - \delta)$ seconds. Had the input stayed at the V_2 level all the time, the output voltage (being the voltage across a capacitor) would have eventually reached V_2 volts. Had the input stayed at the V_1 level all the time, the output voltage would have eventually leveled off at V_1 volts. So *in the steady state the output voltage would stay between the V_1 and V_2 levels* as shown in Fig. 6-42. When the input is at V_2, the output tends exponentially toward V_2. When the input is at V_1, the output tends exponentially toward V_1.

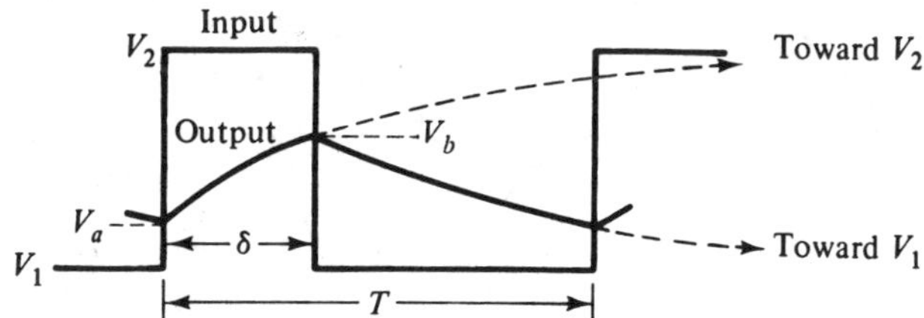

Fig. 6-42

(b) The average value of the current waveform must be zero. If this were not the case, the average value of the current by itself would have caused a linearly rising component in the output voltage; that is,

$$v_o\Big|_{\text{due to } i_{\text{av}}} = \frac{1}{C}\int_0^t i_{\text{av}}\, dt' = \frac{1}{C} i_{\text{av}} \int_0^t dt' = \frac{i_{\text{av}}}{C} t$$

Since such a component cannot be present in the output voltage (see Fig. 6-42), $i_{\text{av}} = 0$.

(c) The output can be written as

$$v_o(t) = v_i(t) - Ri(t)$$

Taking the average value of both sides, we obtain

$$[v_o(t)]_{av} = [v_i(t)]_{av} - [Ri(t)]_{av}$$

Since $[i(t)]_{av} = 0$, we have

$$[v_o(t)]_{av} = [v_i(t)]_{av} = \frac{1}{T}\int_0^T v_i(t)\,dt$$

Either by performing the integration or by inspection of the input waveform, we see that its average value is

$$[v_o(t)]_{av} = \frac{V_2\delta + V_1(T - \delta)}{T} = V_1 + (V_2 - V_1)\frac{\delta}{T} \quad \text{Ans.}$$

(d) If $RC \gg T$, $v_o(t)$ changes very little during the δ and $(T - \delta)$ intervals. For all practical purposes, $v_o(t)$ is constant. From the discussion of (c) we know that this constant is the average value of the input square wave. Hence, using $V_1 = 0$, we obtain

$$v_o(t) \cong V_2\left(\frac{\delta}{T}\right) = k_1\left(\frac{\delta}{T}\right)$$

where $k_1 = V_2$. Thus if the amplitude V_2 is held constant, a dc instrument connected at the output terminals will give a reading proportional to the duty cycle (width-to-period ratio) of the square wave. (Such a circuit can be used to measure the dwell angle in the ignition system of cars.) Since $1/T = f$, we can write $v_o(t)$ also as

$$v_o(t) \cong V_2\,\delta f = k_2 f$$

where $k_2 = V_2\delta$. So if the amplitude V_2 and the width δ are held constant, a dc instrument connected at the output terminals will give a reading proportional to the frequency of the square wave. (Such a circuit can be used to determine the engine rpm.)

Example 6-17

Obtain the expressions for V_a and V_b shown in Fig. 6-42. Discuss the results.

Solution. As shown in Fig. 6-42, the steady-state output voltage, being the voltage across a capacitor, is a continuous function of time and varies between the two unknown voltages V_a and V_b. Assume the input changes from V_1 to V_2 at $t = 0$. For $0 < t < \delta$, the input is held at the V_2 level. Hence, the circuit can be represented as shown in Fig. 6-43(a). Note that the initial voltage across the capacitor is V_a, which is the first unknown voltage to be determined. Also observe that the output would reach the final value of V_2 if the input were held at the V_2 level long enough. Using these initial and final values, the expression for the output can be written

$$v_o(t) = V_2 + (V_a - V_2)e^{-t/RC}, \qquad 0 \le t \le \delta \tag{6-40}$$

As shown in Fig. 6-42, when $t = \delta$, $v_o(t) = V_b$. Hence,

$$V_b = V_2 + (V_a - V_2)e^{-\delta/RC}$$

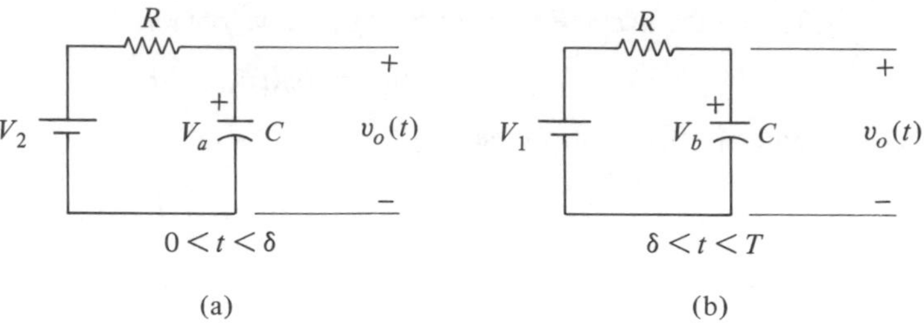

Fig. 6-43

which can be rearranged as

$$V_a e^{-\delta/RC} - V_b = V_2(e^{-\delta/RC} - 1) \tag{6-41}$$

At $t = \delta$, the input changes from V_2 back to V_1. For $\delta < t < T$, the input is held at the V_1 level. Hence the circuit can be represented as shown in Fig. 6-43(b). This time the capacitor voltage starts with the initial value of V_b, which is the second unknown voltage to be determined, and tends toward the final value of V_1. Hence the expression for the output voltage can again easily be determined.

$$v_o(t) = V_1 + (V_b - V_1)e^{-(t-\delta)/RC}, \qquad \delta \le t \le T \tag{6-42}$$

Figure 6-42 shows that when $t = T$, $v_o(t) = V_a$. Hence,

$$V_a = V_1 + (V_b - V_1)e^{-(T-\delta)/RC}$$

which can be rearranged as

$$V_a - V_b e^{-(T-\delta)/RC} = V_1(1 - e^{-(T-\delta)/RC}) \tag{6-43}$$

Solving Eqs. (6-41) and (6-43) simultaneously, the expressions for the two unknown voltages V_a and V_b are obtained.

$$V_a = \frac{V_1(1 - e^{-(T-\delta)/RC}) - V_2(e^{-T/RC} - e^{-(T-\delta)/RC})}{1 - e^{-T/RC}} \tag{6-44a}$$

$$V_b = \frac{V_1(e^{-\delta/RC} - e^{-T/RC}) - V_2(e^{-\delta/RC} - 1)}{1 - e^{-T/RC}} \tag{6-44b}$$

If the two time intervals, δ and $(T - \delta)$, are more than five time constants long, then all exponentials in Eqs. (6-44) can be replaced with zero, in which case V_a and V_b become V_1 and V_2, respectively. This result is to be expected, since during each interval the circuit is given enough time to reach the steady-state value determined by the corresponding input level.

On the other hand, if the two time intervals are very much less than the time constant, then all exponentials in Eqs. (6-44) can be replaced with the first two terms of the power-series expansions ($e^{-x} \cong 1 - x$), in which case we obtain

$$V_a \cong V_b \cong V_1\left(1 - \frac{\delta}{T}\right) + V_2\frac{\delta}{T} \tag{6-45}$$

Since the beginning and end values are the same, $V_a = V_b$, the output does not change in either time interval, that is, it stays constant at the value given by Eq. (6-45). It should be noted that this value represents the average value of the input. Thus, if the time constant is large enough, ($RC \gg \delta$, $RC \gg T - \delta$), the output voltage is a dc voltage which represents the average value of the input square wave.

6-11 SUMMARY

When an *RLC* network is excited by a voltage or current source, responses are produced throughout the network. The waveform of a particular response depends on the excitation waveform as well as on the network itself. The part of the response that is related to the excitation is called the *forced* response. The part of the response that is related to the network is called the *natural* response. The natural response waveform depends on the poles of the network. If the network poles are on the negative real axis, the natural response is composed of damped exponentials. If the network poles are complex and in the left half-plane, the natural response is composed of exponentially damped sine waves. In either case, because of the damped exponentials, the natural response eventually vanishes.

A first-order network is characterized by a single pole. The *step response* of first-order networks with a pole on the negative real axis is the sum of a constant and a damped exponential. It can be obtained by determining (by inspection of the network) the initial ($t = 0^+$) and final ($t = \infty$) values of the response and the time constant. The initial value is calculated by noting that the current through an inductor and the voltage across a capacitor cannot jump. Hence at $t = 0^+$ the inductor is replaced by a current source representing the initial current in the inductor, and the capacitor is replaced by a voltage source representing the initial voltage across the capacitor. When the initial conditions are zero, the inductor is replaced by an open circuit and the capacitor by a short circuit. The final value is calculated by noting that the voltage across the inductor and the current though the capacitor are zero. So at $t = \infty$ the inductor is replaced with a short circuit and the capacitor with an open circuit. The time constant is calculated by killing all dc sources and reducing the network to a single loop consisting of an equivalent resistor and an equivalent capacitor or inductor. The time constant is either $R_{eq}C_{eq}$ or L_{eq}/R_{eq}.

A pulse of width δ can be regarded as the sum of two step functions of equal amplitude but opposite polarity, occurring δ seconds apart. A square wave of period T can be thought of as the sum of alternate polarity step functions, occurring every $T/2$ seconds. Alternatively, the square wave can be considered a succession of pulses occurring every T seconds. The pulse or square wave response of a network can be calculated from the step response of the same network.

A large voltage spike can be generated by suddenly dumping the energy stored in an inductor into a large resistor. And suddenly dumping the energy stored in a capacitor into a small resistor generates a large current spike.

PROBLEMS

6-1. For the networks shown in Fig. 6-44, obtain the natural and forced parts of the time-domain responses that are indicated by a question mark. All inputs are applied at $t = 0$. If the separation into the two parts is not possible, obtain the output.

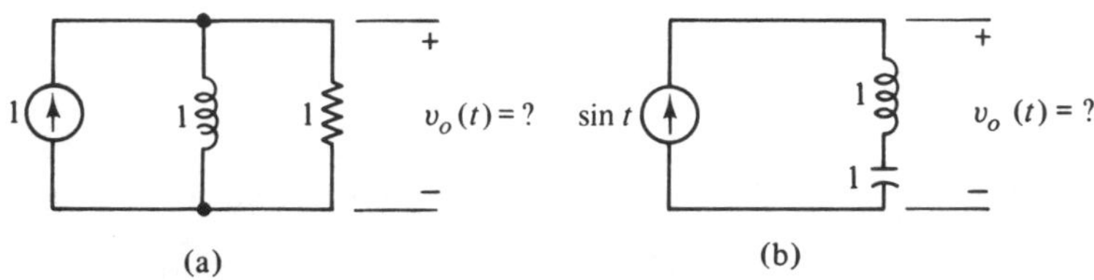

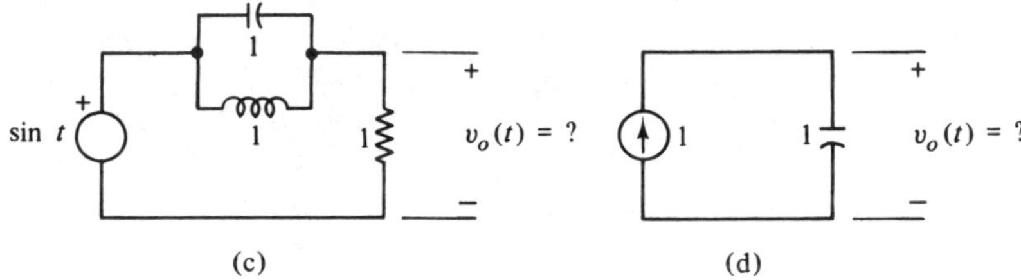

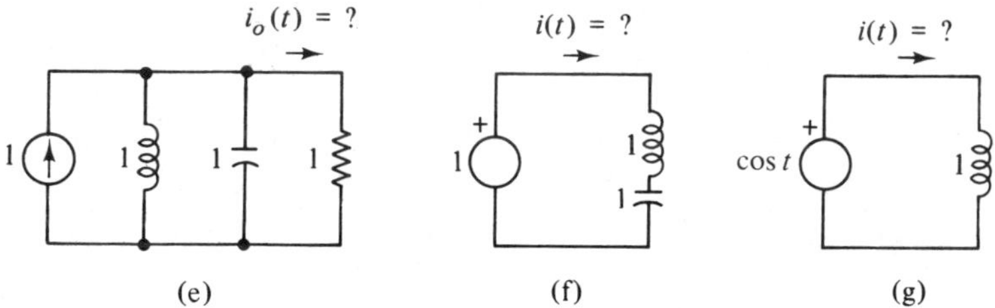

Fig. 6-44

6-2. In Fig. 6-45 obtain the responses indicated by a question mark.

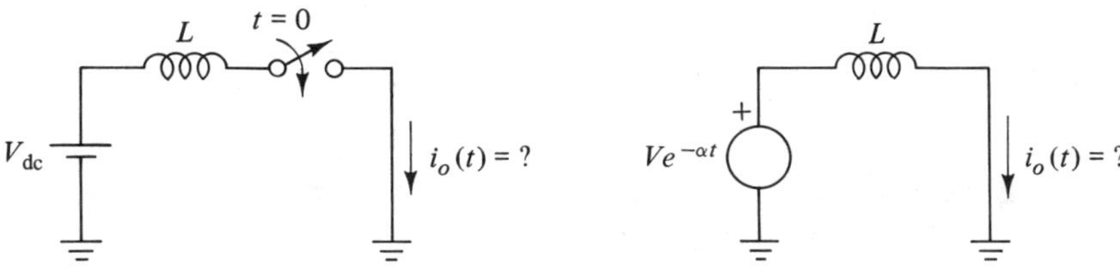

Fig. 6-45

6-3. In Fig. 6-46 the poles of $T(s)$ are in the left half-plane. What is the steady-state response?

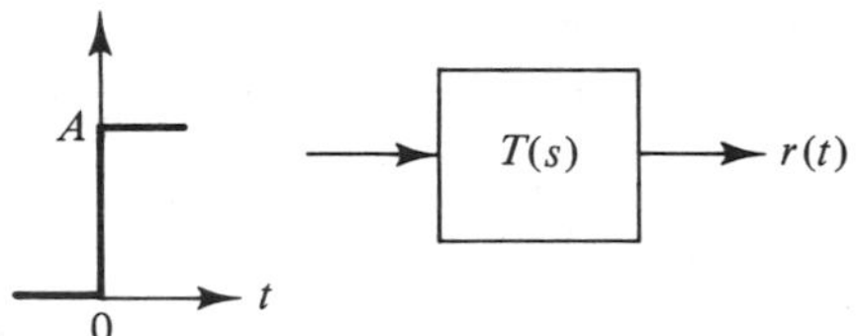

Fig. 6-46

6-4. In Fig. 6-47 what is the effect of a on the response?

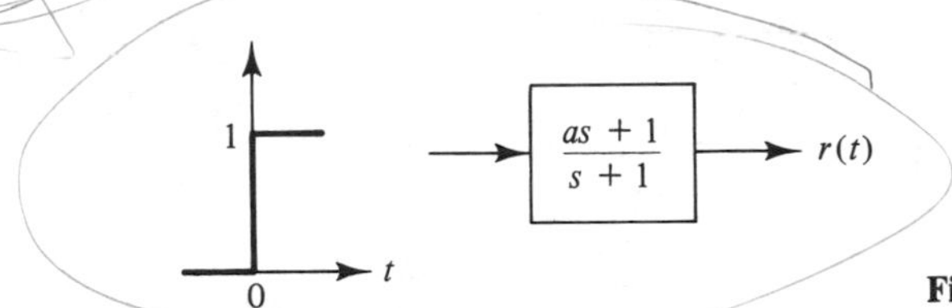

Fig. 6-47

6-5. Using Laplace transformation, obtain the step response of the circuits shown in Fig. 6-48 and sketch the result, indicating important levels and time values.

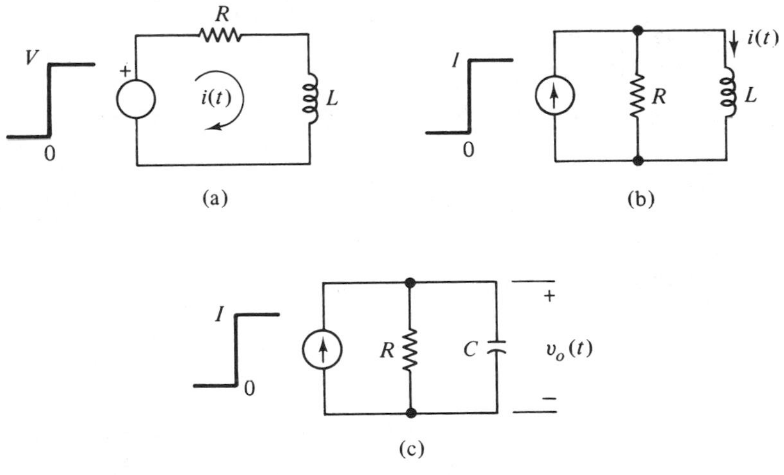

Fig. 6-48

6-6. A step-voltage source has 50 kΩ internal resistance. A 5-foot-long, open-ended cable is used to carry this voltage to its destination. If the capacitance of the cable is 30 pF/ft, how long will it take for the voltage at the end of the cable to reach the final value? (1 pF = 10^{-12} F).

6-7. For the circuits shown in Fig. 6-49, obtain the responses designated by a question mark.

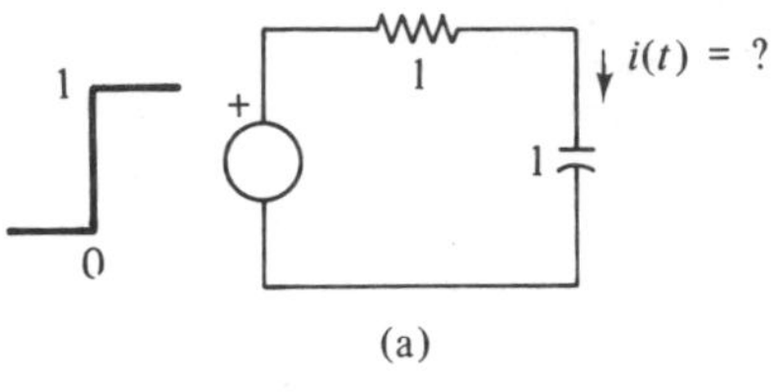

(a)

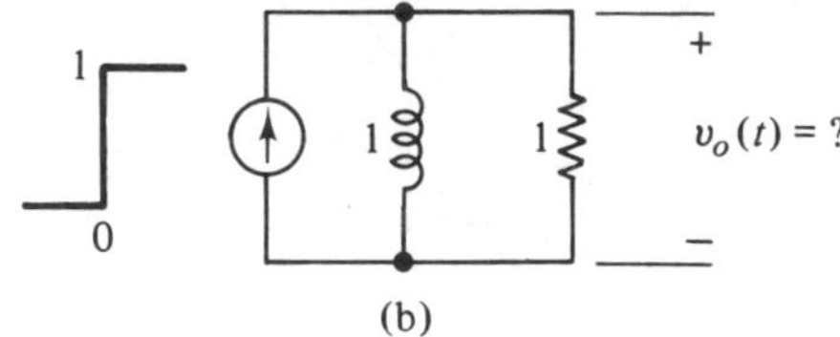

(b)

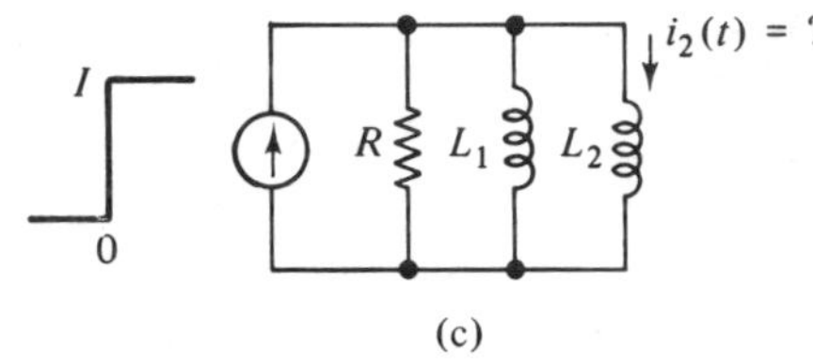

(c)

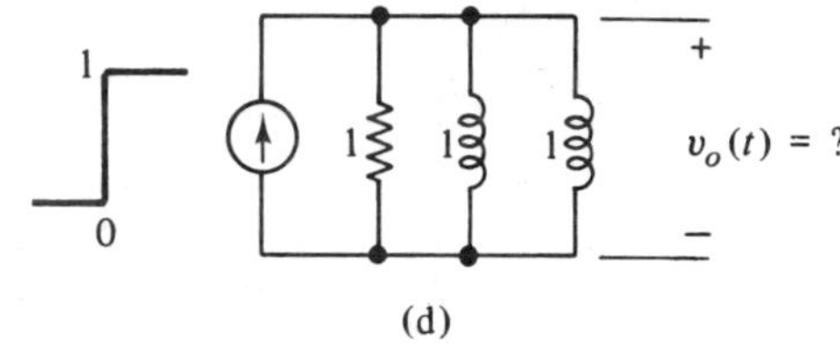

(d)

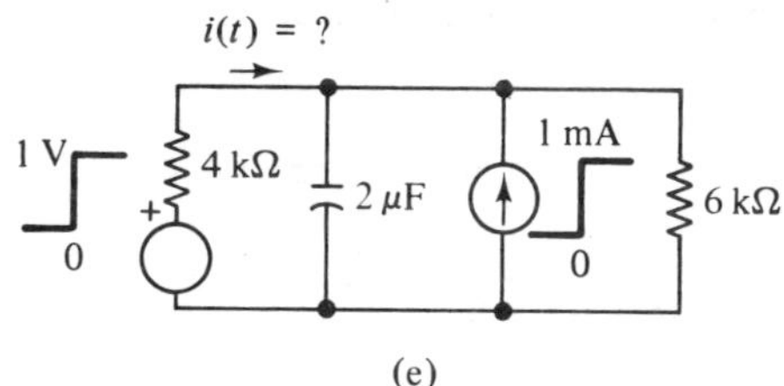

(e)

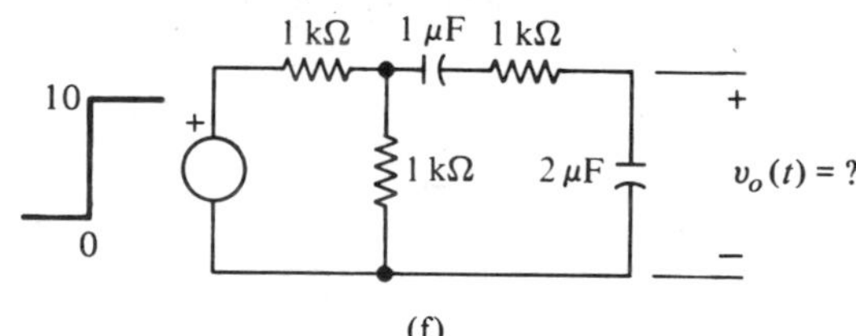

(f)

Fig. 6-49

6-8. For the circuit shown in Fig. 6-50 obtain $i(t)$.

6-9. For the circuit shown in Fig. 6-51 obtain $v_o(t)$.

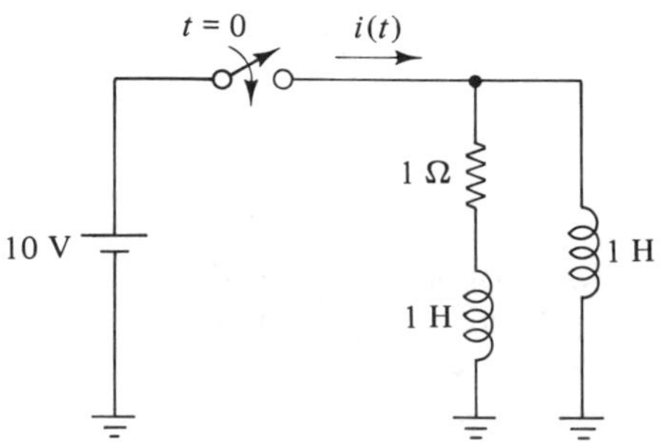

Fig. 6-50

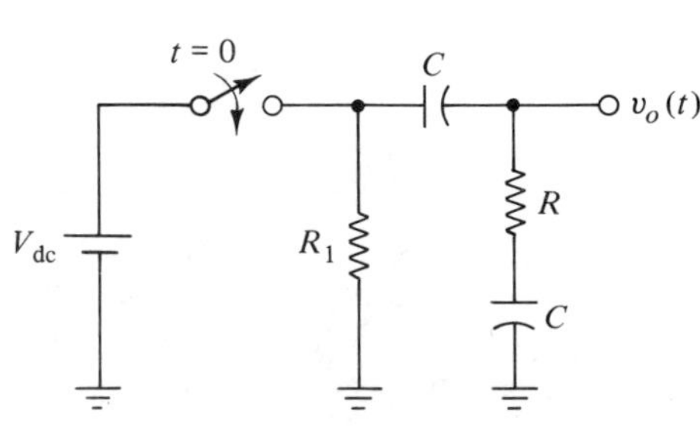

Fig. 6-51

6-10. (**a**) For the circuit shown in Fig. 6-52, obtain the expression for $v(t)$.
(**b**) Simplify the expression obtained in (a) for $R = 0$.

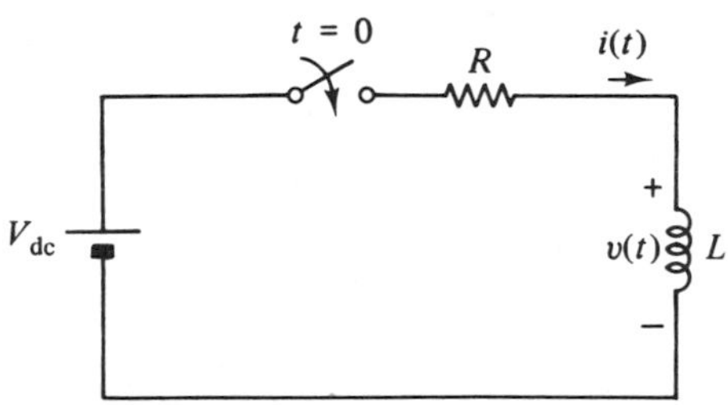

Fig. 6-52

6-11. (**a**) Obtain the expressions for $v(t)$ and $i(t)$ for the circuit shown in Fig. 6-53.
(**b**) Simplify the expressions obtained in (a) for $R = \infty$.

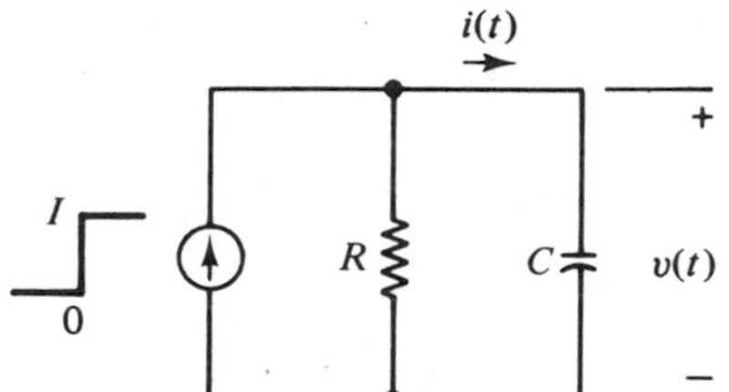

Fig. 6-53

6-12. For the circuits shown in Fig. 6-54, sketch the designated responses. Give the values of various levels and times.

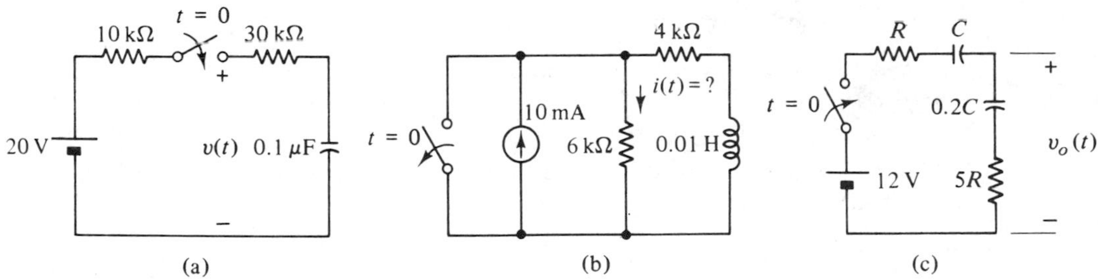

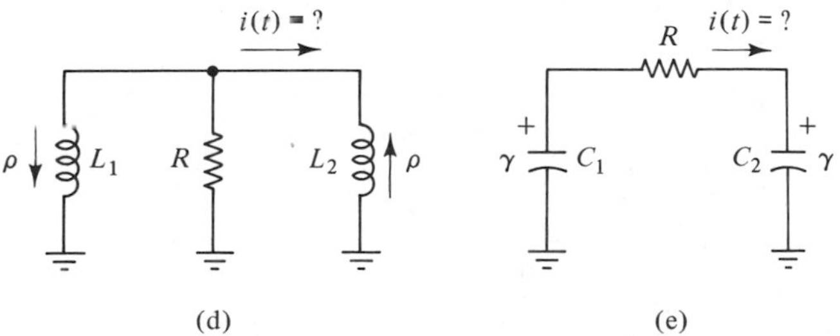

Fig. 6-54

6-13. The responses shown in Fig. 6-55 are from first-order systems. Obtain the expressions for $r(t)$.

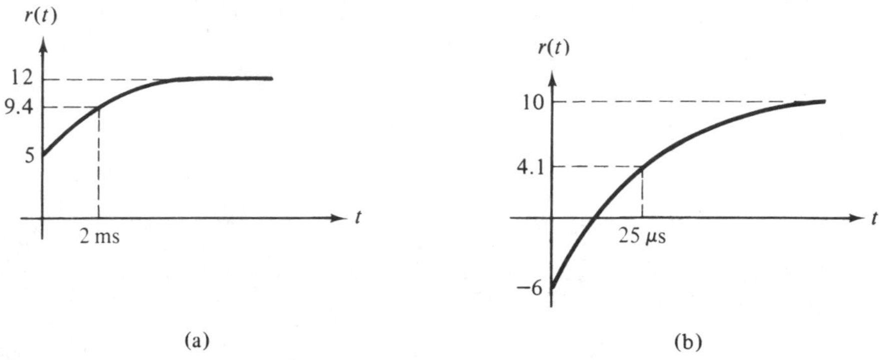

Fig. 6-55

6-14. The unit-step response of a system is shown in Fig. 6-56. The time constant is $1/c$ seconds. What is $T(s)$?

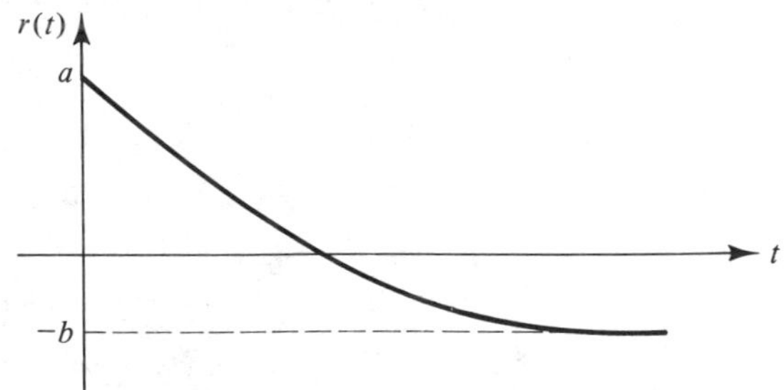

Fig. 6-56

6-15. For the response indicated in Fig. 6-57, obtain by inspection the initial and final values. Also give the time constant.

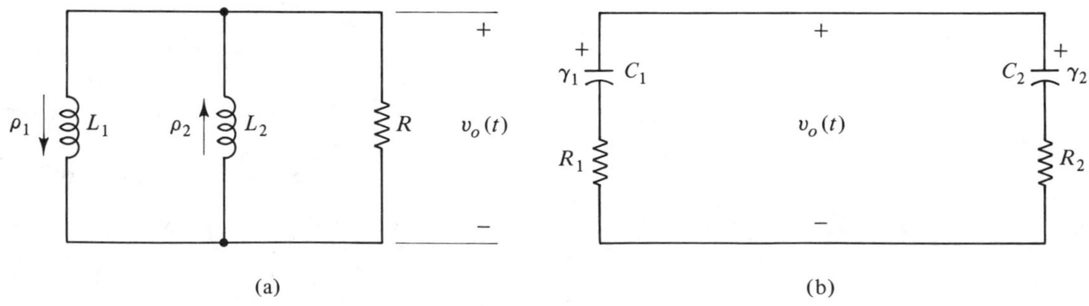

Fig. 6-57

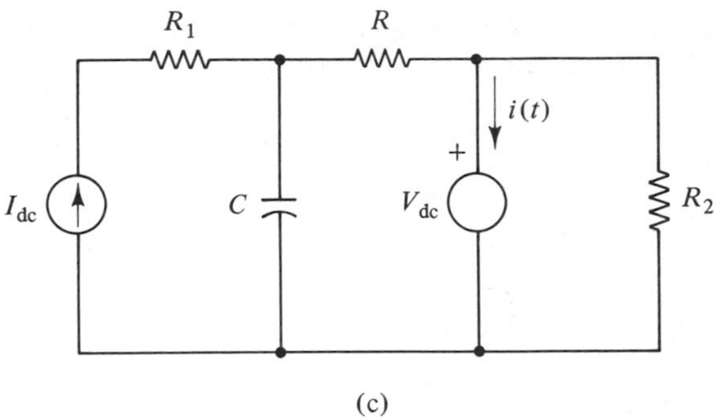

(c)

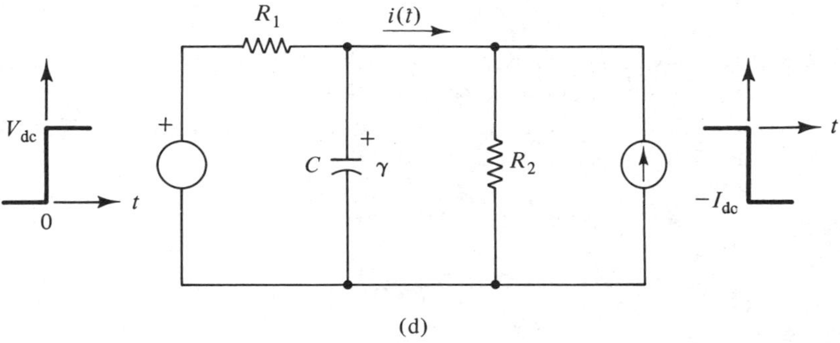

(d)

Fig. 6-57 (*cont.*)

6-16. The circuit shown in Fig. 6-58 is at steady state with both switches closed. Find $v_o(0^+)$ if at $t = 0$

(a) s_1 is opened. **(b)** s_2 is opened.
(c) both s_1 and s_2 are opened.

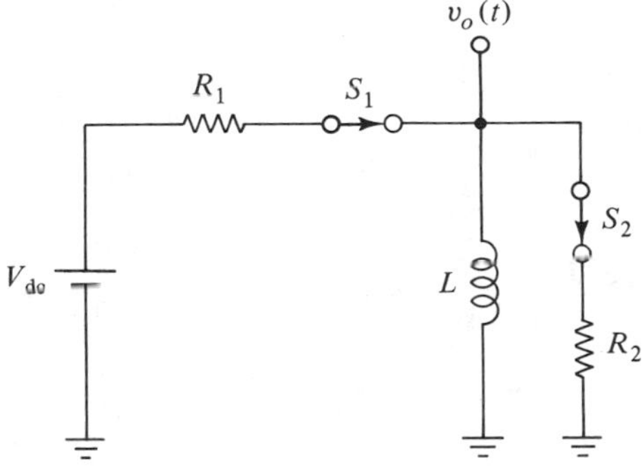

Fig. 6-58

6-17. (**a**) For the circuit shown in Fig. 6-59, obtain $v_o(t)$ and sketch it.
(**b**) What happens to the curve in (a) when $\alpha \to \infty$?

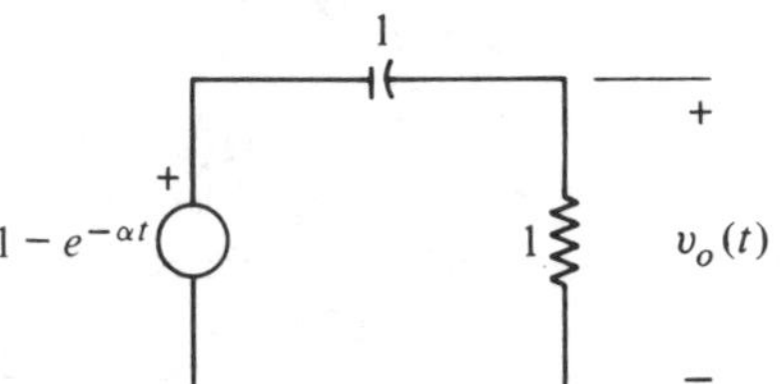

Fig. 6-59

6-18. The input to the circuit of Fig. 6-59 is changed to the unit-ramp function $v_i(t) = t$. Sketch $v_i(t)$ and $v_o(t)$ on the same set of axes.

6-19. The circuit shown in Fig. 6-60 is at steady state when at $t = 0$ the switch is closed. Find the expression for $v_o(t)$ and $i_o(t)$.

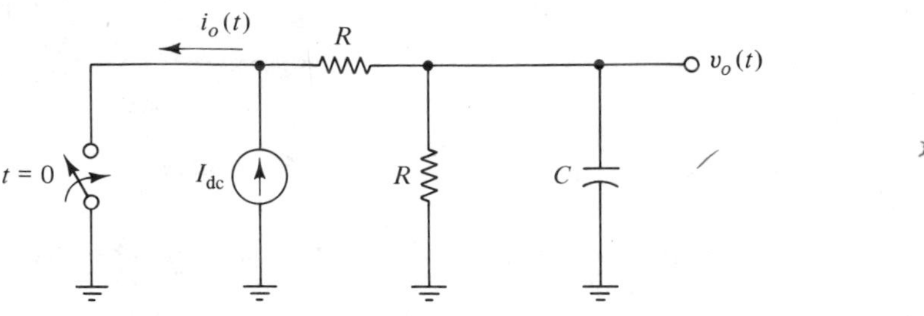

Fig. 6-60

6-20. In Fig. 6-61, obtain for $t > 0$ the expressions for the responses indicated.

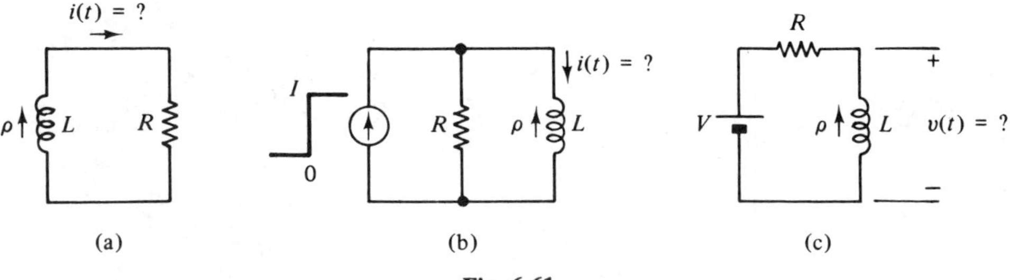

Fig. 6-61

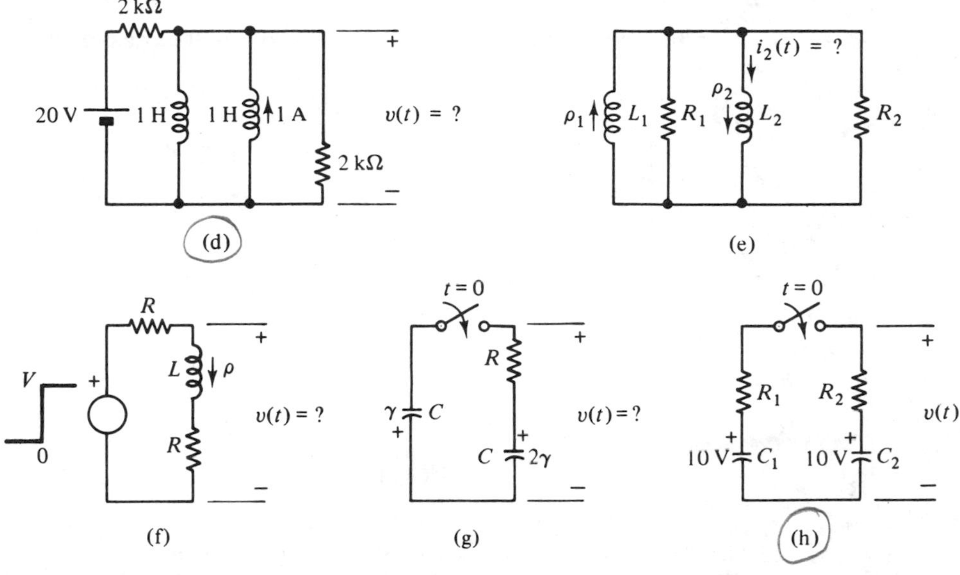

Fig. 6-61 (*cont.*)

6-21. Sketch the indicated responses for the circuits shown in Fig. 6-62. The circuits are at steady state before the switches are opened or closed.

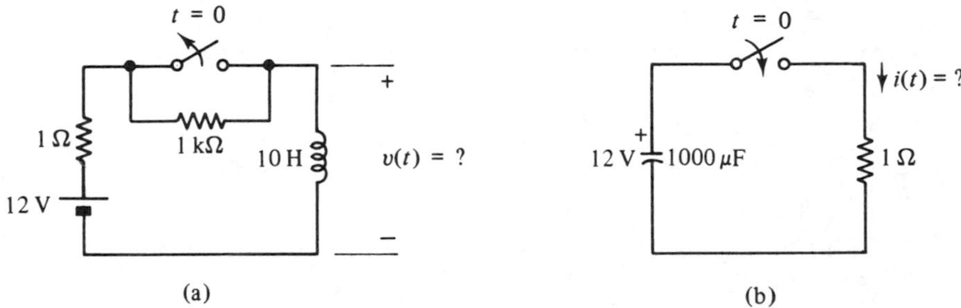

Fig. 6-62

6-22. In Fig. 6-63 the circuit is at steady state. Obtain the expression for $v_o(t)$ after the switch is opened at $t = 0$.

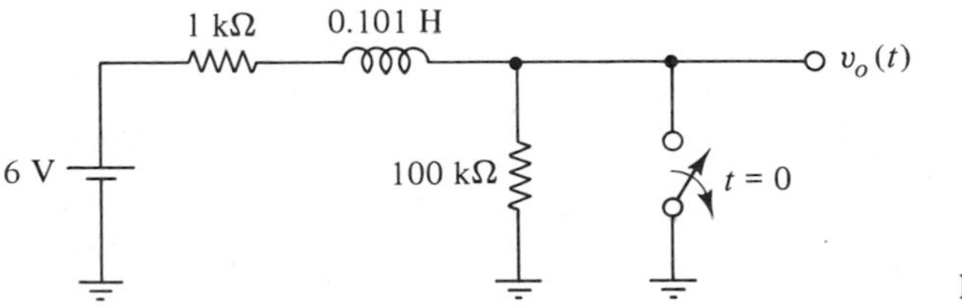

Fig. 6-63

6-23. As shown in Fig. 6-64, one of the inductors carries an initial current of ρ; the other doesn't. Similarly, one of the capacitors has an initial voltage of γ; the other doesn't have any. Find $i(0^+)$, $v(0^+)$, $i(\infty)$, and $v(\infty)$.

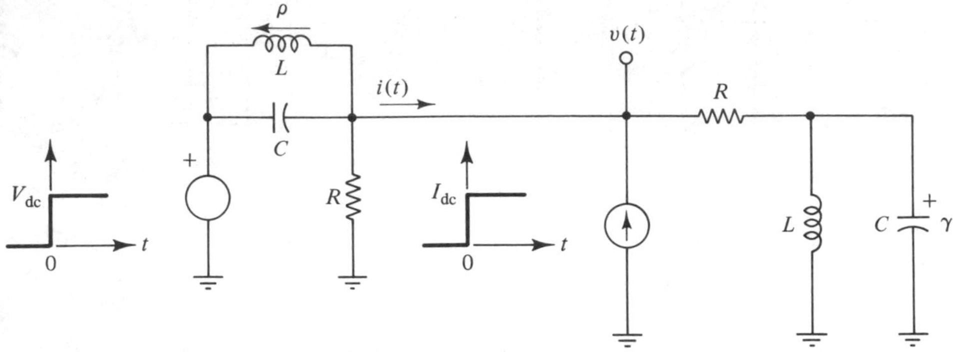

Fig. 6-64

6-24. Given a dc source V_{dc}, two resistors R_1 and R_2 ($R_2 > R_1$), a switch and an inductor. Connect these elements such that a positive voltage spike greater than V_{dc} is generated upon the opening of the switch. What is the amplitude of the spike? Give at least two different circuits.

6-25. In Fig. 6-65 steady state prevails when at $t = 0$ the switch is opened. Obtain the expression for $v_o(t)$.

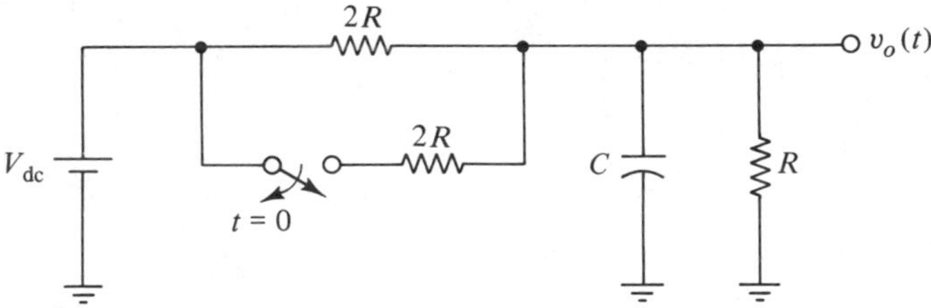

Fig. 6-65

6-26. The circuits shown in Fig. 6-66 are at steady state when at $t = 0$ the switch opens. Obtain $v_o(t)$.

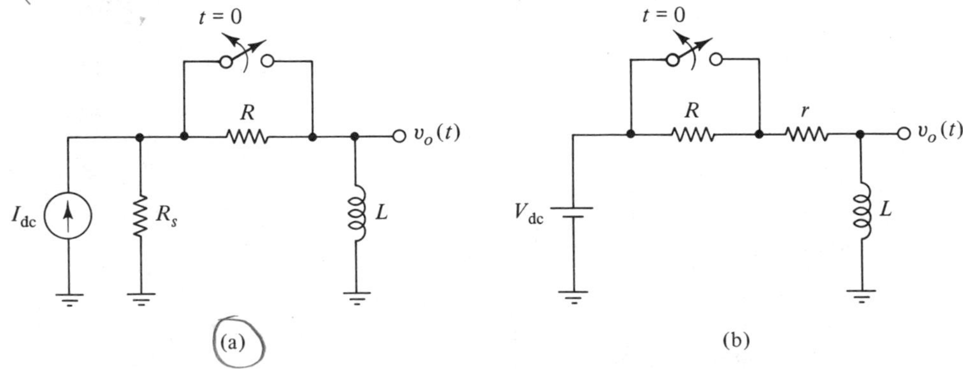

Fig. 6-66

6-27. Refer to Fig. 6-67. At $t = 0$ the switch is closed. It is kept in the closed position until steady state is reached. Then the switch is opened. Assume $R \gg r$. Sketch $i(t)$ and $v(t)$ vs. t. Give values.

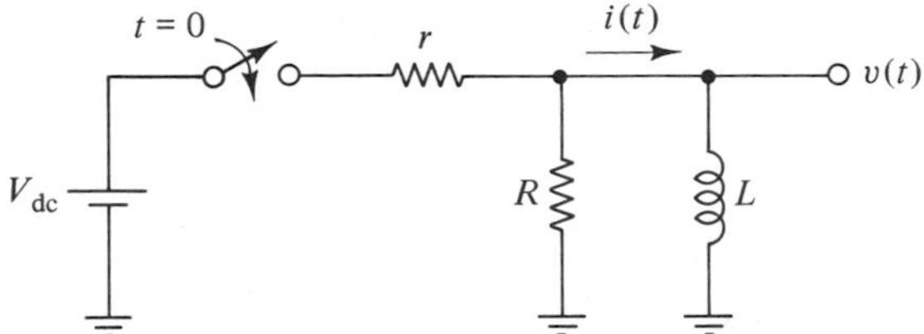

Fig. 6-67

6-28. In Fig. 6-68 what is the final value of $v(t)$?

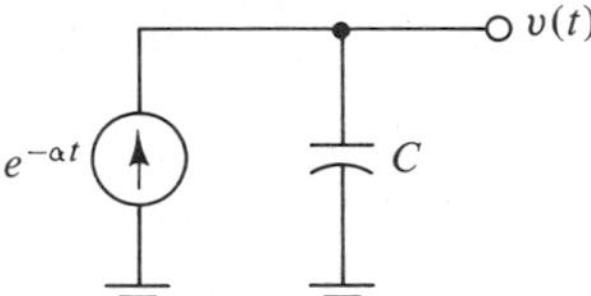

Fig. 6-68

6-29. For the circuit shown in Fig. 6-69 sketch $v_o(t)$. When is this voltage zero?

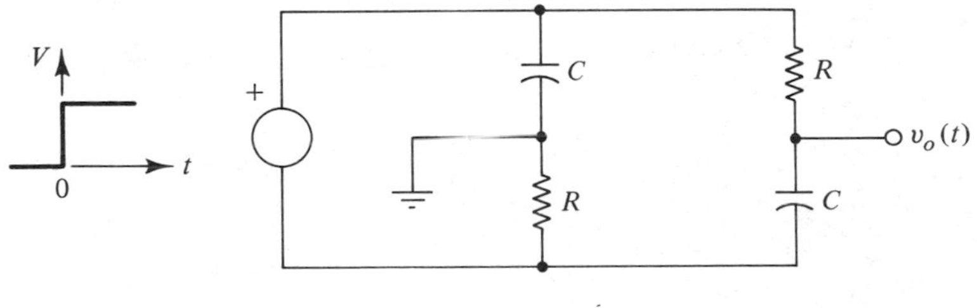

Fig. 6-69

6-30. The circuits shown in Fig. 6-70 are at steady state when at $t = 0$ the indicated jump change in the input occurs. Sketch the output vs. t. Give values.

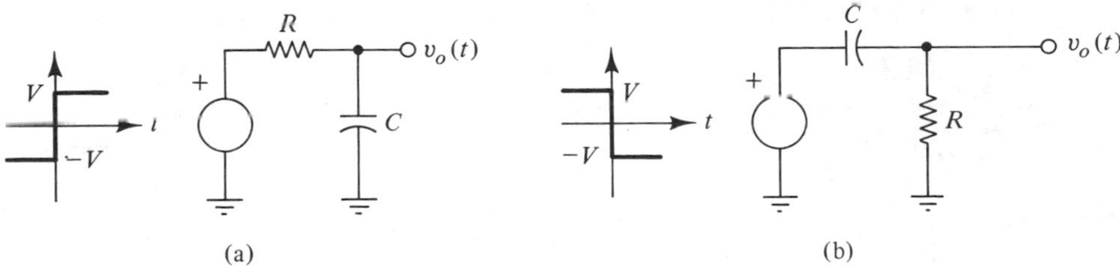

Fig. 6-70

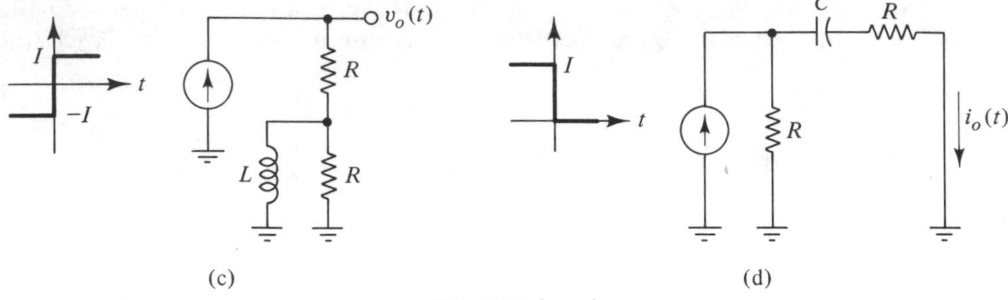

Fig. 6-70 (*cont.*)

6-31. The circuit of Fig. 6-71 is at steady state when at $t = 0$ the input changes from V_1 to $-V_2$ as shown. Obtain the expression for $v_{o1}(t)$ and $v_{o2}(t)$.

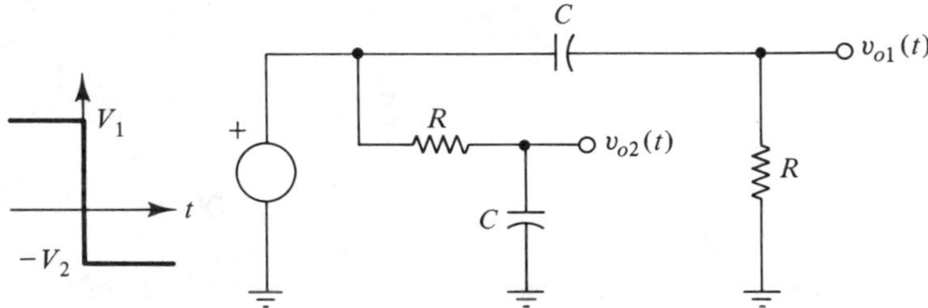

Fig. 6-71

6-32. In Fig. 6-72 the switch is periodically closed for t_1 seconds and opened for t_2 seconds.

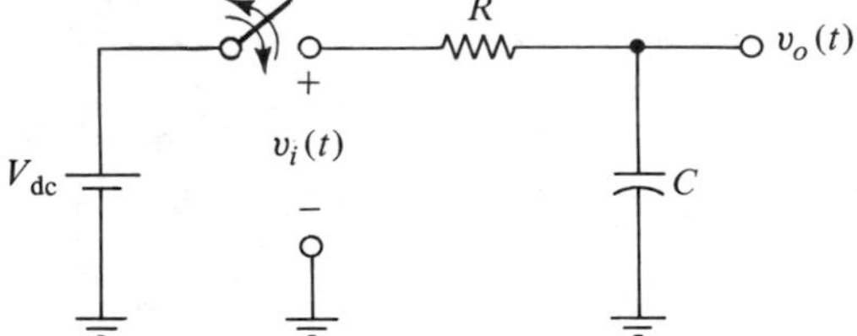

Fig. 6-72

(a) Sketch $v_o(t)$ for several cycles of switch operation.
(b) Will there be a steady-state value?
(c) Sketch $v_i(t)$.

6-33. Refer to Fig. 6-73.

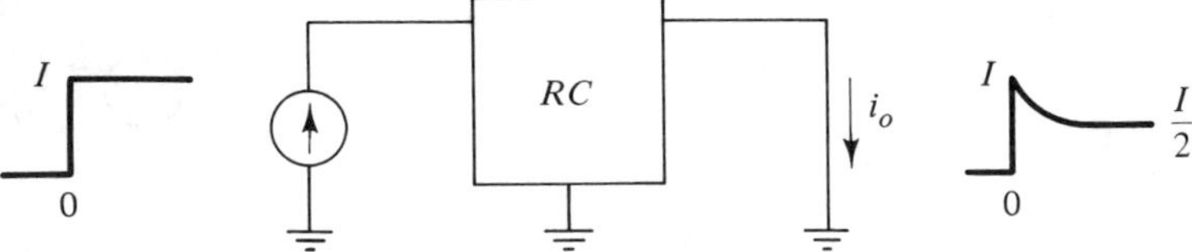

Fig. 6-73

(**a**) What *RC* circuit must be placed between the input and output terminals to produce the desired i_o response? Give circuit diagram and element values.
(**b**) Repeat (a) if the circuit is to be *RL*.

6-34. Refer to Fig. 6-74. What *RL* networks will produce the desired response?

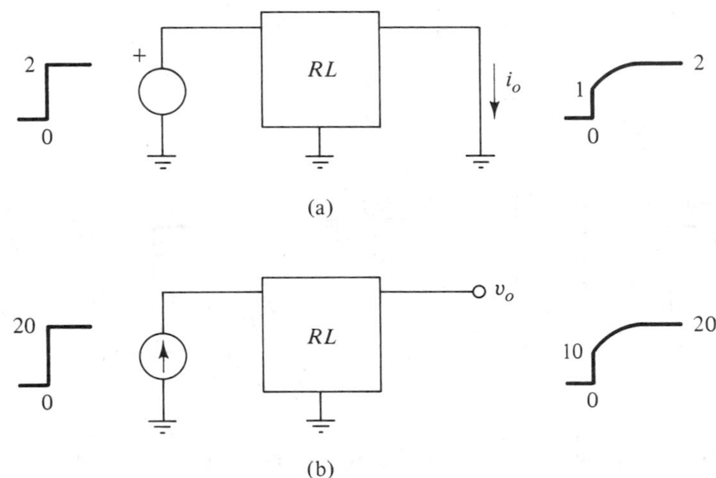

Fig. 6-74

6-35. In Fig. 6-75 the input to the box is a 10 V step. What is in the box if the output voltage is the waveform given in (a)? in (b)?

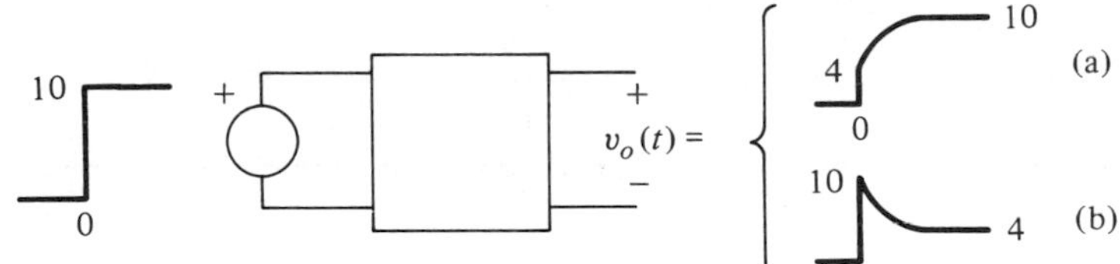

Fig. 6-75

6-36. In Fig. 6-76 the switch is closed and opened periodically. Sketch the steady-state output waveform for one cycle of operation.

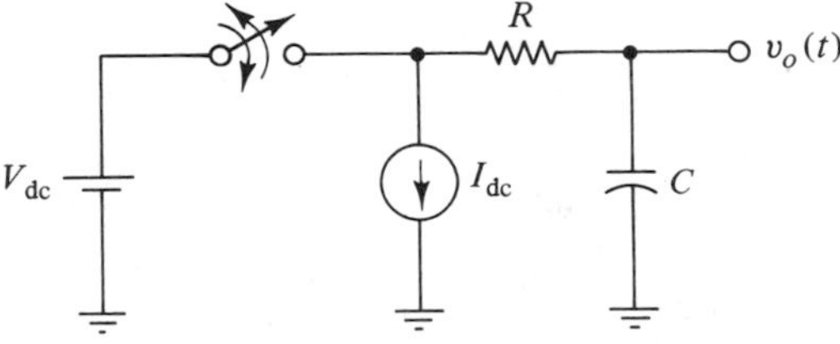

Fig. 6-76

6-37. Obtain the pulse response of the networks shown in Fig. 6-77 and sketch them.

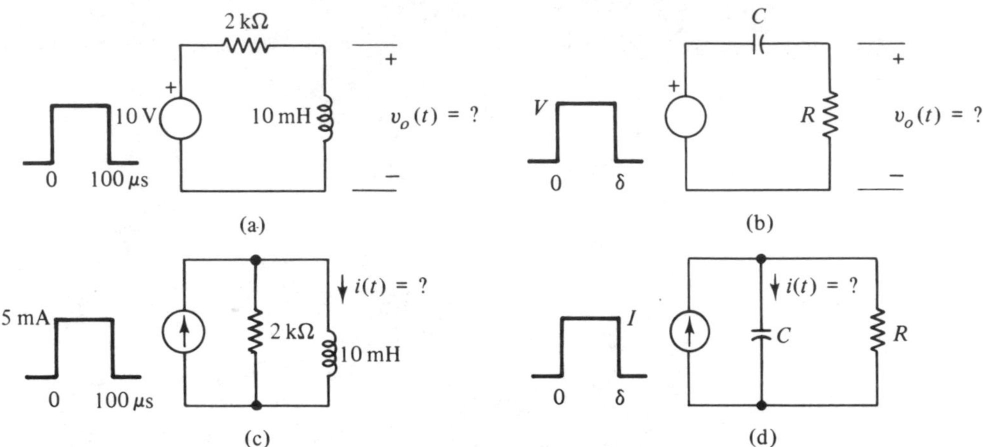

Fig. 6-77

6-38. For the network shown in Fig. 6-78, sketch $i(t)$ and $v(t)$ vs. t for
(a) $\delta \gg L/R$; **(b)** $\delta = L/R$; **(c)** $\delta \ll L/R$.

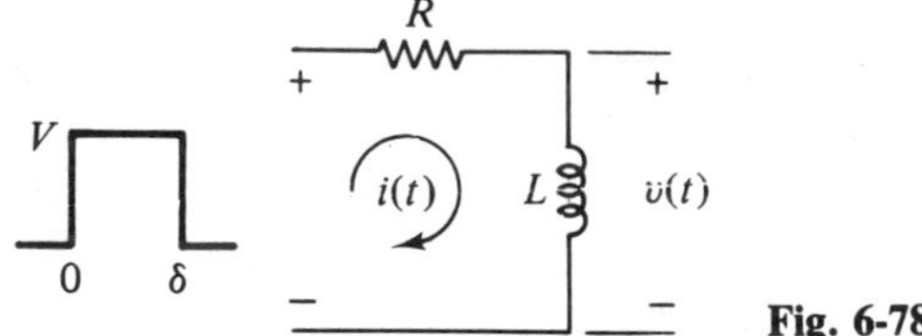

Fig. 6-78

6-39. Sketch the waveforms indicated by a question mark for the circuits shown in Fig. 6-79.

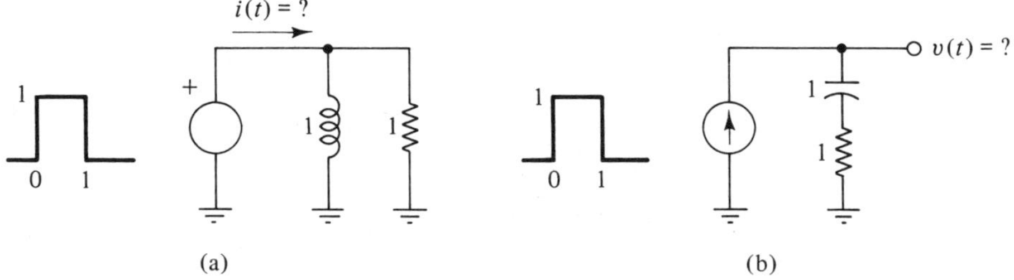

Fig. 6-79

6-40. For the network shown in Fig. 6-80, obtain the expression for $v_o(t)$ and sketch it. The circuit is at steady state when the input changes. Assume $\tau \ll \delta$.

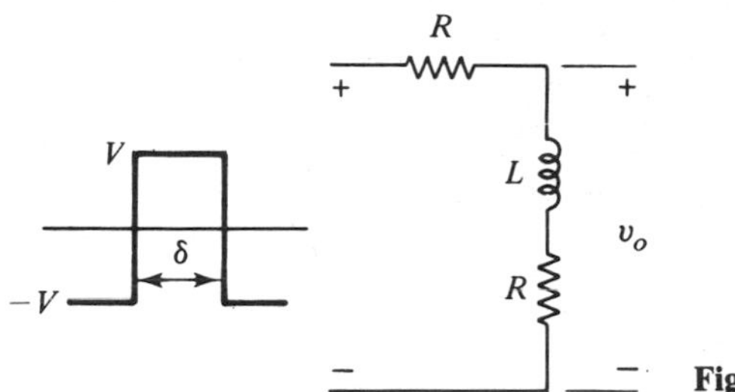

Fig. 6-80

6-41. For the circuit shown in Fig. 6-81 steady state prevails. For $t > 0$ the input changes as indicated. Sketch the output waveform. Give values.

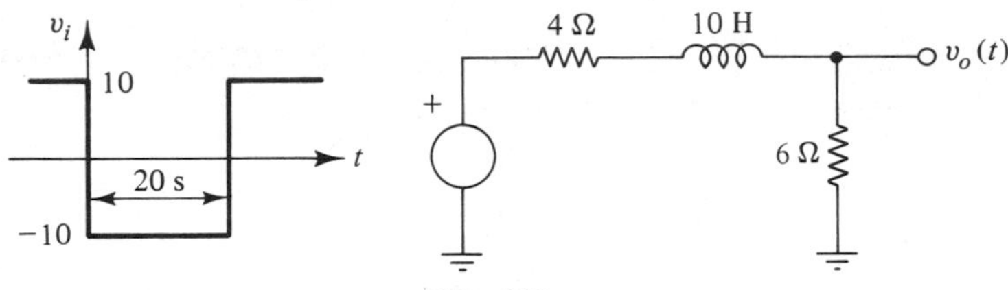

Fig. 6-81

6-42. For the circuit shown in Fig. 6-82 obtain the expression for $v_o(t)$. Assume the circuit is at steady state when the input changes at $t = 0$.

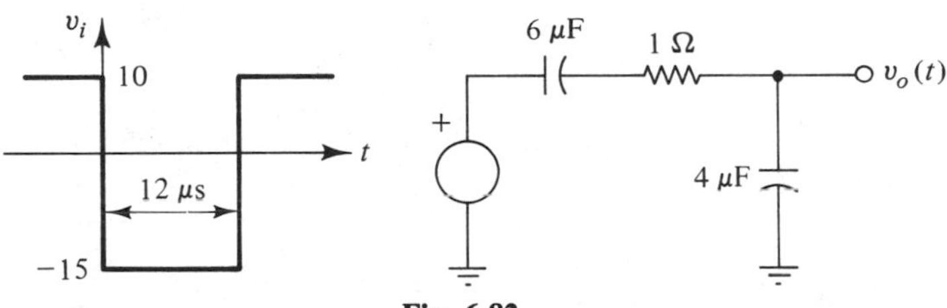

Fig. 6-82

6-43. The circuit of Fig. 6-83 is driven by the i_1 and i_2 waveforms shown. Sketch the output waveform. Give values.

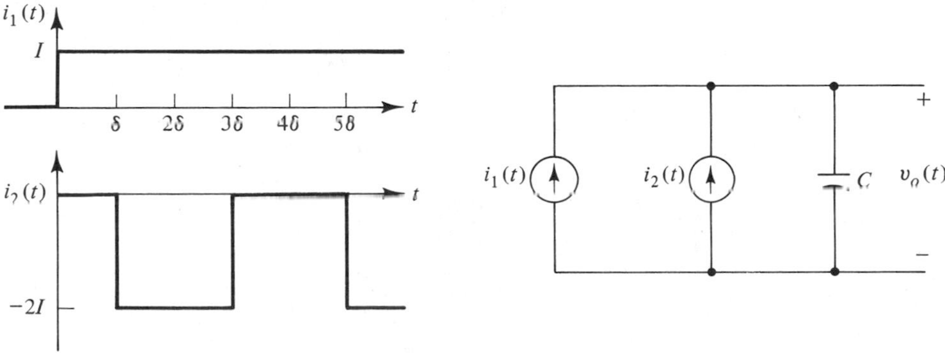

Fig. 6-83

6-44. For the network shown in Fig. 6-84 sketch $v_o(t)$ vs. t. Assume that $T = 5RC$.

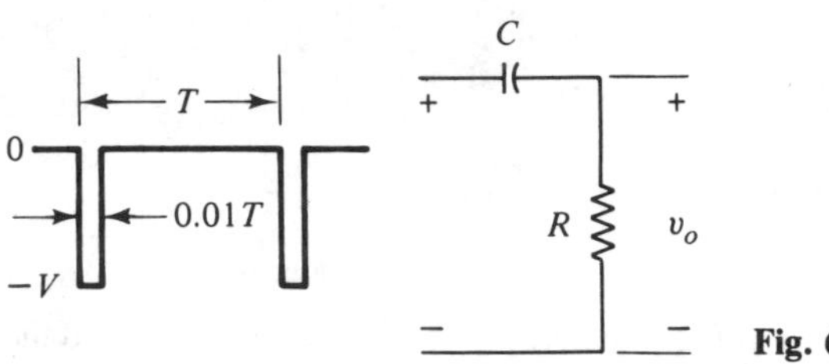

Fig. 6-84

6-45. A square wave is applied to the network of Fig. 6-85 at $t = 0$. Sketch the output if (**a**) $RC \ll T/2$; (**b**) $RC = T/2$; (**c**) $RC \gg T/2$.

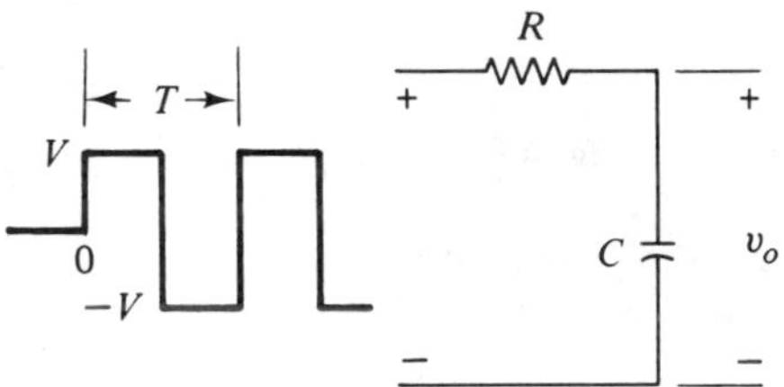

Fig. 6-85

6-46. For the two different periodic input waveforms shown in Fig. 6-86 sketch the output waveform.

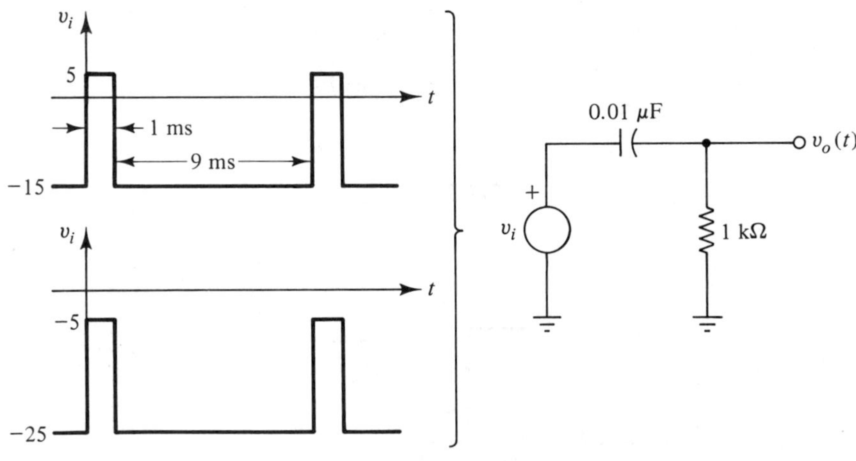

Fig. 6-86

6-47. For the circuit shown in Fig. 6-87 sketch as accurately as possible the steady-state output waveform. The input is periodic.

6-48. Repeat Prob. 6-47 if the level of the input is shifted up by 12 V.

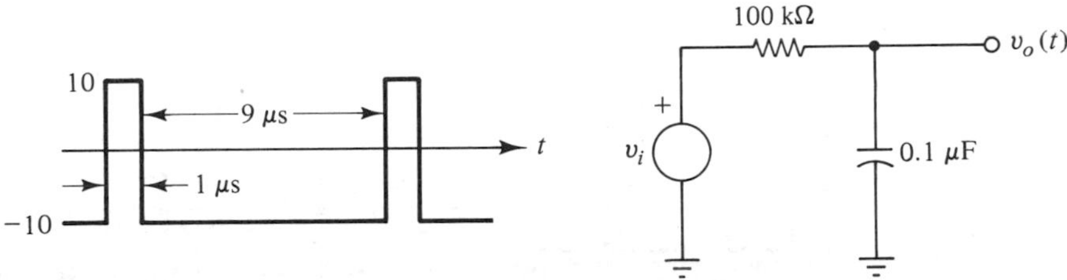

Fig. 6-87

6-49. Refer to Fig. 6-88. The input is periodic. Steady state prevails. Sketch the output waveform for

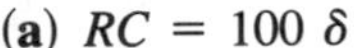

(**a**) $RC = 100\ \delta$ (**b**) $RC = 0.01\delta$

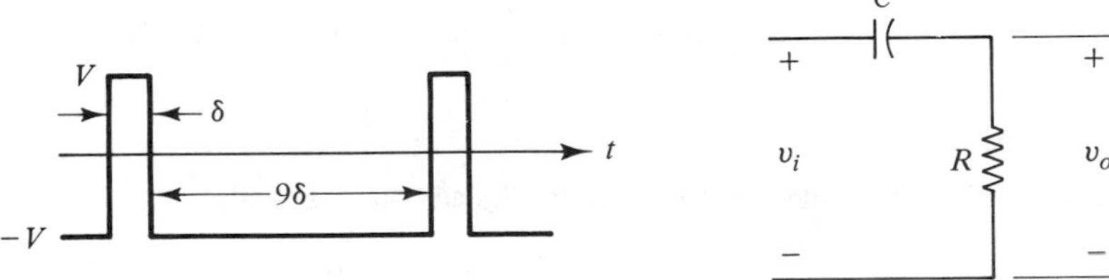

Fig. 6-88

6-50. In Fig. 6-89 assume the time constant to be very much larger than the period of the input waveform. Sketch the steady-state output waveform. Give value(s).

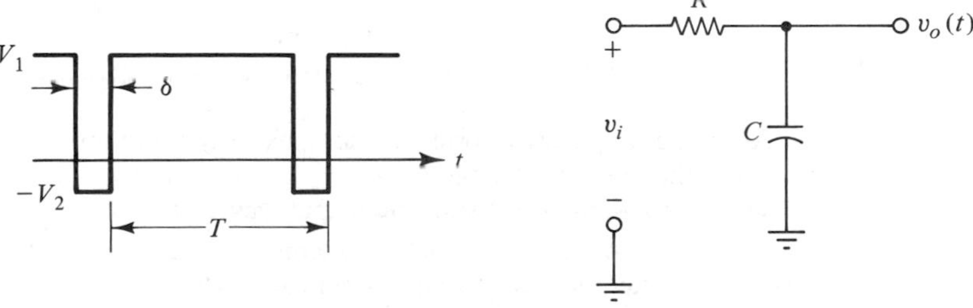

Fig. 6-89

6-51. In Fig. 6-90 the input is periodic. Steady state prevails.

(**a**) Without making any assumptions, sketch the output waveform. Do not calculate any values.

(**b**) Assume the time constant is very much larger than the period of the waveform. Sketch the output waveform. Give values.

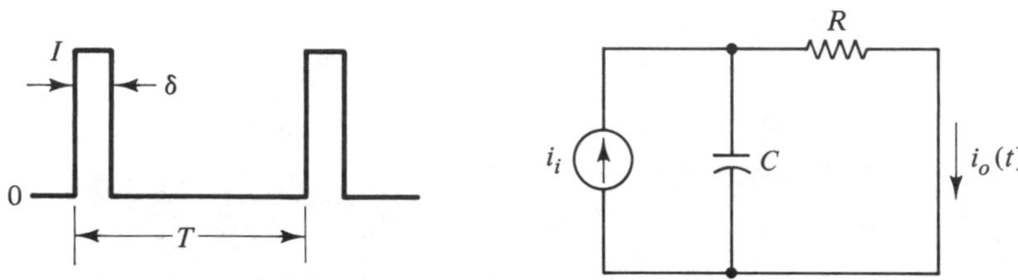

Fig. 6-90

6-52. Derive Eqs. (6-44).

6-53. Show that Eqs. (6-44) reduce to

$$V_a = -V_b = V_1 \frac{1 - e^{-T/2RC}}{1 + e^{-T/2RC}} \quad \text{if } V_2 = -V_1 \quad \text{and} \quad \delta = \frac{T}{2}.$$

6-54. Derive Eq. (6-45).

6-55. In Fig. 6-91 the input is periodic. Steady state prevails.

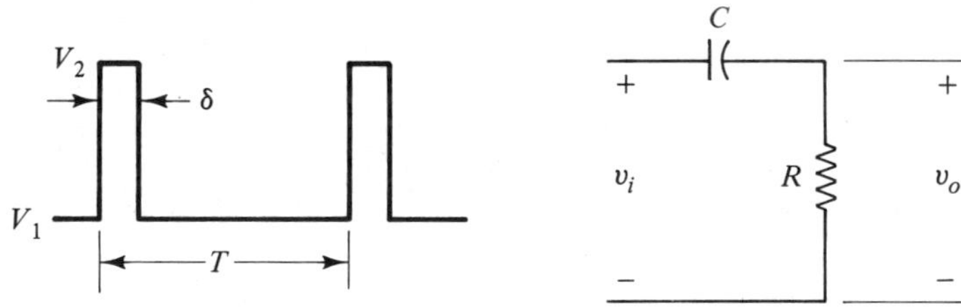

Fig. 6-91

(**a**) Sketch the output waveform. Do not make any assumptions.

(**b**) Obtain the value of the output voltage at $t = 0^+$ and $t = \delta^-$.

(**c**) What is the average value of the output waveform?

6-56. A square-wave voltage source has an internal resistance of R_0 ohms. A series RC network is connected across its output terminals. What is the waveform at the output of the signal generator? Give values. Assume the time constant involved is much less than the half-period of the square wave.

6-57. In Fig. 6-92 the input equivalent circuit of an oscilloscope is shown. The oscilloscope is connected to a circuit which has the Thévenin equivalent representation shown.

(a) Sketch the steady-state output waveforms for both switch positions. Assume the period T of the input waveform is short in comparison to the time constant τ involved.

(b) Repeat (a) if $T \gg \tau$.

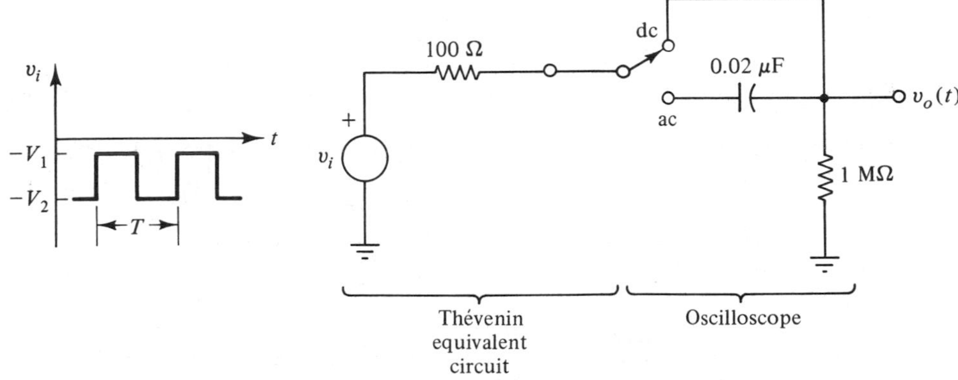

Fig. 6-92

CHAPTER 7

STEP RESPONSE OF SECOND-ORDER SYSTEMS

Second-order linear systems are characterized by second-order differential equations. When transformed, these equations yield transfer functions that are ratios of two polynomials. Since the resulting denominator polynomial is of second degree, second-order systems can be alternatively characterized as two-pole systems. Numerous *RL*, *RC*, and *RLC* networks in common use possess two poles. Such networks are frequently subjected to step function excitations. Step inputs are also widely used for testing. Consequently, it is important to understand and learn how to interpret the step response of second-order systems.

7-1 CHARACTERIZATION OF THE STEP RESPONSE OF SECOND-ORDER SYSTEMS

Second-order systems are two-pole systems. Therefore the denominator polynomial of the transfer function (as well as the input impedance or admittance function) is of second degree. In the general case the numerator polynomial is also of second degree. As a result, $T(s)$ can be written

$$T(s) = \frac{a_2 s^2 + a_1 s + a_0}{s^2 + b_1 s + b_0} \tag{7-1}$$

where the coefficients a and b are real numbers that depend on the R's, L's, and C's of the network.

The values of s that make the *denominator of* $T(s)$ *zero* are the *poles* of $T(s)$, which are obtained by setting the denominator polynomial equal to zero and solving for the roots of the resulting equation by the quadratic formula—that is,

$$s^2 + b_1 s + b_0 = 0$$

$$s = \frac{-b_1 \pm \sqrt{b_1^2 - 4b_0}}{2} \tag{7-2}$$

One pole is at

$$s = p_1 = \frac{-b_1 + \sqrt{b_1^2 - 4b_0}}{2}$$

The other pole is at

$$s = p_2 = \frac{-b_1 - \sqrt{b_1^2 - 4b_0}}{2}$$

The values of s that make the *numerator* of $T(s)$ zero are the *zeros* of $T(s)$. They are obtained by setting the numerator polynomial equal to zero and solving for the two roots:

$$a_2 s^2 + a_1 s + a_0 = 0$$

$$s = \frac{-a_1 \pm \sqrt{a_1^2 - 4a_0 a_2}}{2a_2} \tag{7-3}$$

One zero is at

$$s = z_1 = \frac{-a_1 + \sqrt{a_1^2 - 4a_0 a_2}}{2a_2}$$

The other zero is at

$$s = z_2 = \frac{-a_1 - \sqrt{a_1^2 - 4a_0 a_2}}{2a_2}$$

In the s plane, the locations of the zeros are marked with O's.

Instead of the a and b coefficients, we can use the poles and zeros to describe $T(s)$. Equation (7-1) can then be alternatively expressed as

$$T(s) = \frac{a_2(s - z_1)(s - z_2)}{(s - p_1)(s - p_2)} \tag{7-4}$$

The poles and zeros are functions of the R's, L's, and C's of the network.

Consider, for instance, the network shown in Fig. 7-1. The transfer function is I_o/I_i and can be calculated by the current-divider rule.

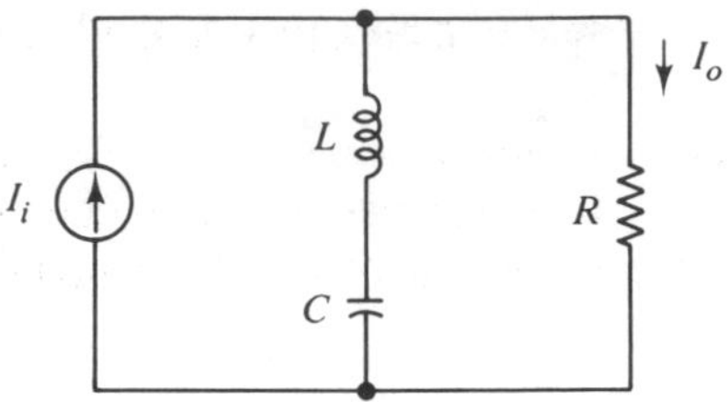

Fig. 7-1

$$I_o = I_i\left[\frac{sL + (1/sC)}{sL + (1/sC) + R}\right] = I_i\left[\frac{s^2 + (1/LC)}{s^2 + s(R/L) + (1/LC)}\right]$$

$$T = \frac{I_o}{I_i} = \frac{s^2 + (1/LC)}{s^2 + s(R/L) + (1/LC)} = \frac{a_2 s^2 + a_1 s + a_0}{s^2 + b_1 s + b_0}$$

where $\quad a_2 = 1, \quad a_1 = 0, \quad a_0 = \dfrac{1}{LC}, \quad b_1 = \dfrac{R}{L}, \quad b_0 = \dfrac{1}{LC}$

The poles are at

$$p_{1,2} = \frac{-b_1 \pm \sqrt{b_1^2 - 4b_0}}{2} = -\frac{R}{2L} \pm \sqrt{\left(\frac{R}{2L}\right)^2 - \frac{1}{LC}}$$

The zeros are at

$$z_{1,2} = \frac{-a_1 \pm \sqrt{a_1^2 - 4a_0 a_2}}{2a_2} = \pm j\sqrt{\frac{a_0}{a_2}} = \pm j\frac{1}{\sqrt{LC}}$$

The step response of a second-order *RLC* network depends on the position of the poles and zeros of $T(s)$. Since there are only two transfer function poles, either both are real or they form a complex-conjugate pair in the left half-plane. Therefore the resulting *natural* response is either the sum of two exponentials (two real axis poles) or a damped sinusoidal wave (complex-conjugate poles). In either case, the *forced* response is a step function whose amplitude depends on the input step amplitude and the transfer function of the network.

In Fig. 7-2 the general second-order system is shown by a block diagram. The input, a unit step, is shown on the left. Its Laplace transform is $1/s$. The output is on the right. The block diagram with the input shown is a schematic representation of the following *frequency-domain* equation:

$$R(s) = \frac{1}{s}T(s) \tag{7-5}$$

That is, the output $R(s)$ is obtained by multiplying the input $1/s$ with the transfer function $T(s)$ (shown within the block). The two special forms of $T(s)$, also shown in Fig. 7-2, characterize $T(s)$ further in terms of real axis poles (at $-\alpha_1$ and $-\alpha_2$) and complex-conjugate poles (at $-\alpha \pm j\beta$).

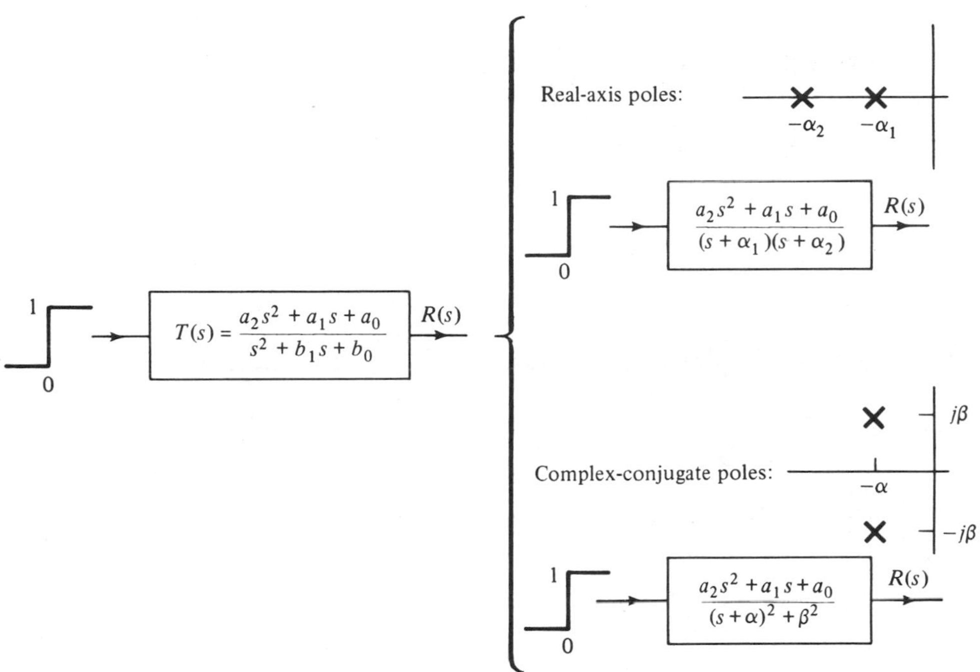

Fig. 7-2

7-2 STEP RESPONSE WHEN POLES ARE ON THE NEGATIVE REAL AXIS

We now determine the unit-step response of second-order systems that have poles on the negative real axis. (See Fig. 7-2.) The transfer function is described by

$$T(s) = \frac{a_2 s^2 + a_1 s + a_0}{(s + \alpha_1)(s + \alpha_2)}$$

Since the input is a unit-step function, it is characterized by $1/s$. The resulting frequency-domain response is

$$R(s) = \frac{1}{s}\frac{a_2 s^2 + a_1 s + a_0}{(s + \alpha_1)(s + \alpha_2)} \tag{7-6}$$

Its partial-fraction expansion for $\alpha_1 \neq \alpha_2$ is

$$R(s) = \frac{K_0}{s} + \frac{K_1}{s + \alpha_1} + \frac{K_2}{s + \alpha_2}$$

$$\text{where } K_0 = sR(s)\bigg|_{s=0} = \frac{a_0}{\alpha_1\alpha_2} = T(0)$$

$$K_1 = (s + \alpha_1)R(s)\bigg|_{s=-\alpha_1} = \frac{a_2\alpha_1^2 - a_1\alpha_1 + a_0}{(-\alpha_1)(-\alpha_1 + \alpha_2)}$$

$$K_2 = (s + \alpha_2)R(s)\bigg|_{s=-\alpha_2} = \frac{a_2\alpha_2^2 - a_1\alpha_2 + a_0}{(-\alpha_2)(-\alpha_2 + \alpha_1)}$$

Thus

$$R(s) = \frac{a_0}{\alpha_1\alpha_2}\frac{1}{s} + \frac{1}{\alpha_2 - \alpha_1}\left[\left(\frac{a_2\alpha_1^2 - a_1\alpha_1 + a_0}{-\alpha_1}\right)\left(\frac{1}{s + \alpha_1}\right) - \left(\frac{a_2\alpha_2^2 - a_1\alpha_2 + a_0}{-\alpha_2}\right)\left(\frac{1}{s + \alpha_2}\right)\right]$$

Then we can take the inverse transform and obtain

$$r(t) = \frac{a_0}{\alpha_1\alpha_2} + \frac{1}{\alpha_2 - \alpha_1}\left[\left(\frac{a_2\alpha_1^2 - a_1\alpha_1 + a_0}{-\alpha_1}\right)e^{-\alpha_1 t} - \left(\frac{a_2\alpha_2^2 - a_1\alpha_2 + a_0}{-\alpha_2}\right)e^{-\alpha_2 t}\right] \qquad (\alpha_2 \neq \alpha_1, \quad t > 0) \qquad \text{(7-7)}$$

This equation gives the response for $t > 0$. The response for $t < 0$ is zero, because the system is assumed to be dead, and there is no input until $t = 0$. (Nonzero initial conditions are treated later.)

At $t = 0^+$ the response is

$$r(0^+) = \frac{a_0}{\alpha_1\alpha_2} + \frac{1}{\alpha_2 - \alpha_1}\left(\frac{a_2\alpha_1^2 - a_1\alpha_1 + a_0}{-\alpha_1} - \frac{a_2\alpha_2^2 - a_1\alpha_2 + a_0}{-\alpha_2}\right)$$

$$= a_2 = T(s)\bigg|_{s=\infty} \qquad \text{(7-8)}$$

So the transfer function evaluated at $s = \infty$, $T(\infty)$, determines the initial ($t = 0^+$) value of the response. If $a_2 \neq 0$, the response at $t = 0$ jumps from 0 to a_2. If $a_2 = 0$, the response is continuous at $t = 0$, and Eq. (7-7) is true also for $t = 0$.

Since the poles are on the negative real axis, the response at $t = \infty$ reduces to

$$r(\infty) = \frac{a_0}{\alpha_1\alpha_2} = T(s)\bigg|_{s=0} \qquad \text{(7-9)}$$

The transfer function evaluated at $s = 0$, $T(0)$, determines the final ($t = \infty$) value of the response. As Eq. (7-7) shows, the response is the sum of three terms (waveforms):

1. A dc term characterized by

$$\frac{a_0}{\alpha_1 \alpha_2}$$

2. An exponential term characterized by

$$\frac{1}{\alpha_2 - \alpha_1}\left(\frac{a_2\alpha_1^2 - a_1\alpha_1 + a_0}{-\alpha_1}\right)e^{-\alpha_1 t}$$

which has a time constant of $\tau_1 = 1/\alpha_1$ seconds.

3. Another exponential term characterized by

$$\frac{-1}{\alpha_2 - \alpha_1}\left(\frac{a_2\alpha_2^2 - a_1\alpha_2 + a_0}{-\alpha_2}\right)e^{-\alpha_2 t}$$

which has a time constant of $\tau_2 = 1/\alpha_2$ seconds.

These three waveforms combine to produce a variety of response waveforms, depending on the a coefficients and the pole locations.

7-3 STEP RESPONSE WHEN $T_0 = \dfrac{a_0}{(s + \alpha_1)(s + \alpha_2)}$

A second-order transfer function with a constant numerator and *negative* real axis poles is represented in block diagram form in Fig. 7-3(a). $T_0(s)$ is described by

$$T_0(s) = \frac{a_0}{(s + \alpha_1)(s + \alpha_2)} = \frac{a_0}{s^2 + s(\alpha_1 + \alpha_2) + \alpha_1\alpha_2} \tag{7-10}$$

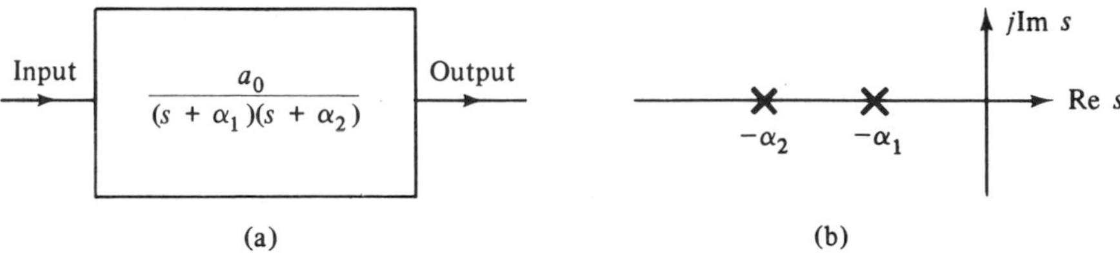

Fig. 7-3

Since a_0 is constant, it acts merely as a scale factor between input and output. There is no loss of generality if we let a_0 equal the constant coefficient in the denominator polynomial—that is, $a_0 = \alpha_1\alpha_2$.

$$T_0(s) = \frac{\alpha_1\alpha_2}{(s + \alpha_1)(s + \alpha_2)} = \frac{\alpha_1\alpha_2}{s^2 + s\underbrace{(\alpha_1 + \alpha_2)}_{b_1} + \underbrace{\alpha_1\alpha_2}_{b_0}} \tag{7-11}$$

The poles of $T(s)$ are sketched in Fig. 7-3(b). The pole at $-\alpha_1$ is nearer to the origin than the pole at $-\alpha_2$. Note that b_1 (coefficient of the s term in the denominator polynomial) represents the negative sum of the two poles, whereas b_0 (the constant term in the denominator polynomial) represents the product of the poles.

The *unit-step response* of $T_0(s)$ is readily obtained from Eq. (7-7) by letting $a_2 = a_1 = 0$ and $a_0 = \alpha_1\alpha_2$.

$$r(t) = 1 + \frac{1}{\alpha_2 - \alpha_1}(\alpha_1 e^{-\alpha_2 t} - \alpha_2 e^{-\alpha_1 t}), \qquad (\alpha_2 \neq \alpha_1, \quad t \geq 0) \tag{7-12}$$

The initial and final values of $r(t)$ are

$$r(0) = 0, \qquad r(\infty) = 1$$

Regardless of the values of α_1 and α_2, the response starts at zero and ends at one. Furthermore, the response starts out horizontally at $t = 0$ because the slope of $r(t)$ is zero at $t = 0$ as shown below.

$$r'(t) = \frac{1}{\alpha_2 - \alpha_1}(-\alpha_1\alpha_2 e^{-\alpha_2 t} + \alpha_1\alpha_2 e^{-\alpha_1 t}) \qquad (\alpha_2 \neq \alpha_1, \quad t \geq 0)$$

$$r'(0) = 0$$

Instead of expressing the response in terms of the pole positions ($-\alpha_1$ and $-\alpha_2$), it can just as well be expressed in terms of the time constants (τ_1 and τ_2). Substituting $\tau_1 = 1/\alpha_1$ and $\tau_2 = 1/\alpha_2$ in Eq. (7-12), we obtain

$$r(t) = 1 + \frac{1}{\tau_1 - \tau_2}(\tau_2 e^{-t/\tau_2} - \tau_1 e^{-t/\tau_1}) \tag{7-13}$$

We can obtain a better understanding of the nature of the response if it is written as the sum of three responses.

$$r(t) = r_1(t) + r_2(t) + r_3(t)$$

where

$$r_1(t) = 1$$

$$r_2(t) = \frac{1}{\left(\dfrac{\tau_1}{\tau_2} - 1\right)} e^{-t/\tau_2}$$

$$r_3(t) = -\frac{\left(\dfrac{\tau_1}{\tau_2}\right)}{\left(\dfrac{\tau_1}{\tau_2} - 1\right)} e^{-t/\tau_1}$$

The forced or steady-state part of the response is represented by $r_1(t)$. The natural or transient part of the response is $r_2(t) + r_3(t)$.Since $\tau_1 > \tau_2$, the amplitude of the exponential representing $r_2(t)$ is smaller than that of $r_3(t)$. Furthermore, $r_2(t)$, having the smaller time constant, vanishes faster than $r_3(t)$. The three waveforms together with their sum representing $r(t)$ are shown in Fig. 7-4 for $\tau_1/\tau_2 > 2$. (For $1 < \tau_1/\tau_2 < 2$ the amplitudes of both exponentials are greater than 1.)

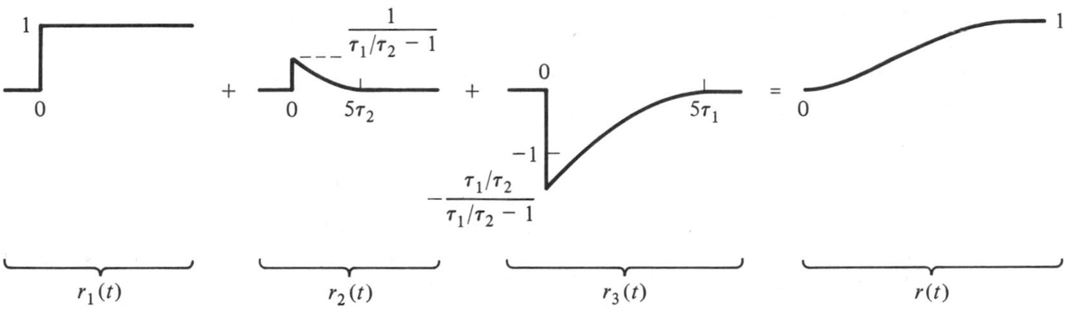

Fig. 7-4

If the poles are coincident, $-\alpha_1 = -\alpha_2 = -\alpha$, Eq. (7-12) becomes indeterminate. Amplitudes of $r_2(t)$ and $r_3(t)$ become ∞ and $-\infty$, respectively, while their time constants become identical. In this situation the unit-step response can be calculated as follows:

$$R(s) = \frac{1}{s}T(s) = \frac{1}{s}\frac{\alpha^2}{(s+\alpha)^2} = \frac{K_1}{s} + \frac{K_2}{(s+\alpha)^2} + \frac{K_3}{s+\alpha}$$

$$K_1 = \left.\frac{\alpha^2}{(s+\alpha)^2}\right|_{s=0} = 1$$

$$K_2 = \left.\frac{\alpha^2}{s}\right|_{s=-\alpha} = -\alpha$$

$$K_3 = \left.\frac{d}{ds}\left(\frac{\alpha^2}{s}\right)\right|_{s=-\alpha} = \left.-\frac{\alpha^2}{s^2}\right|_{s=-\alpha} = -1$$

$$R(s) = \frac{1}{s} - \frac{\alpha}{(s+\alpha)^2} - \frac{1}{s+\alpha}$$

$$r(t) = 1 - \alpha t e^{-\alpha t} - e^{-\alpha t} = 1 - \frac{t}{\tau}e^{-t/\tau} - e^{-t/\tau} \tag{7-14}$$

Alternatively this result can be obtained by applying l'Hospital's Rule to Eq. (7-13).

On the other hand, if the poles are widely separated, then $\tau_1 \gg \tau_2$. In this case the $\tau_2 e^{-t/\tau_2}$ term in Eq. (7-13) can be neglected for $t \geq 5\tau_2$, and Eq. (7-14) simplifies to

$$r(t) \cong 1 - e^{-t/\tau_1}, \qquad t \geq 5\tau_2 \tag{7-15}$$

Two observations are noteworthy about this result. First it is independent of τ_2 which implies that the position of the pole farthest away from the origin of the s-plane has no noticeable effect on the response. [In Fig. 7-4 $r_2(t)$ will have a small amplitude and will vanish fast.] Second, it contains only one time constant, namely τ_1, which implies that we are dealing with a first-order system. [In Fig. 7-4 the $r_3(t)$ waveform will dominate over the $r_2(t)$ waveform.] So, if the poles are widely separated, then except for $0 \leq t \leq 5\tau_2$, solely the pole at $-\alpha_1$ governs the response, and therefore the second-order system can be approximated with a first-order system using the dominant pole at $-\alpha_1$.

$$T_0(s) = \left.\frac{\alpha_1 \alpha_2}{(s + \alpha_1)(s + \alpha_2)}\right|_{\alpha_2 \gg \alpha_1} \cong \frac{\alpha_1}{s + \alpha_1}$$

In this case, if the second-order response given by Eq. (7-14) and its first-order approximation given by Eq. (7-15) are plotted on the same set of axes, the two curves will fall on top of each other except for t near 0. At $t = 0^+$, the exact expression has a slope of 0, whereas the approximation starts out with a slope of $1/\tau_1 = \alpha_1$. Soon thereafter, the two curves merge.

Example 7-1

In second-order system one pole $(-\alpha_1)$ is fixed at -1 and the other $(-\alpha_2)$ is varied from -1 to $-\infty$. What is the effect of the second pole (the one at $-\alpha_2$) on the unit-step response?

Solution. At one extreme, we have $\alpha_2 = 1$. The poles are coincident, and the response is given by Eq. (7-14).

$$r(t) = 1 - (1 + t)e^{-t}, \qquad \alpha_2 = \alpha_1 = 1 \tag{7-16}$$

This equation is plotted in Fig. 7-5. The response is quite "sluggish"—that is, it takes a long time to reach steady state. This is because it takes longer for te^{-t} to vanish than e^{-t}.

At the other extreme, we have $\alpha_2 = \infty$. The separation between the poles is infinite, and the response is entirely dominated by the pole at $-\alpha_1 = -1$ and is given by Eq. (7-15) as

$$r(t) = 1 - e^{-t}, \qquad \alpha_2 = \infty, \qquad \alpha_1 = 1 \tag{7-17}$$

This equation is also plotted in Fig. 7-5. It reaches steady state in the shortest possible time, namely $t = 5\tau_1 = 5$ seconds. All other response curves corresponding to $1 < \alpha_2 < \infty$ fall between the two curves given in Fig. 7-5. They are given by

$$r(t) = 1 + \frac{1}{\alpha_2 - 1}(e^{-\alpha_2 t} - \alpha_2 e^{-t}) = 1 + \frac{1}{1 - \tau_2}(\tau_2 e^{-t/\tau_2} - e^{-t})$$

The middle curve in Fig. 7-5 is a plot of this equation for $\alpha_2 = 10\alpha_1 = 10$. Note that except for t very small, this curve is identical with the curve for $\alpha_2 = \infty$. It is interesting to note that as α_2 is increased from $10\alpha_1$ to ∞, all response curves crowd between the middle curve and the one immediately next to it on the left, which is to say that

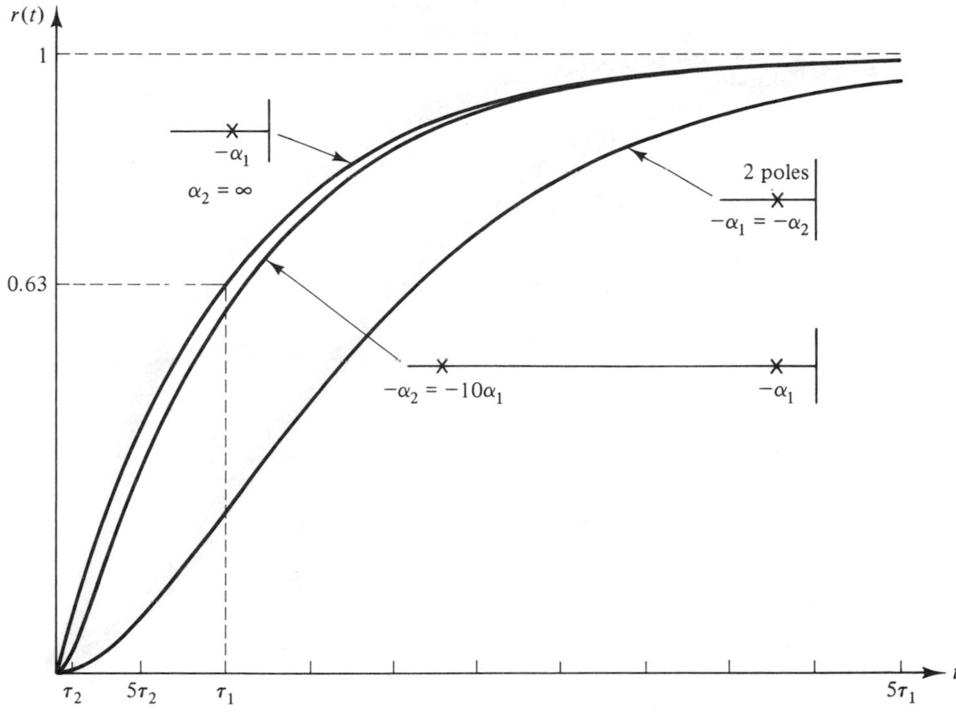

Fig. 7-5

once the poles are widely separated, the pole nearest to the origin determines the response waveform. Stated still differently, the two systems described by

$$T_1(s) = \frac{\alpha_1}{s + \alpha_1} \qquad \text{and} \qquad T_2(s) = \frac{\alpha_1 \alpha_2}{(s + \alpha_1)(s + \alpha_2)}$$

have practically the same step response as long as $\alpha_2 > 10\alpha_1$.

Example 7-2

Refer to Fig. 7-6 and let $T = V_o/V_i$.

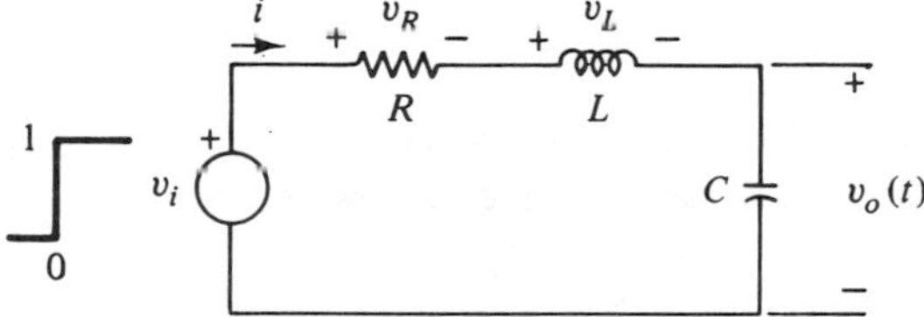

Fig. 7-6

(a) Obtain the transfer function poles.
(b) What condition must be satisfied in order to have real axis poles?

(c) Obtain the initial and final values of the response by inspection of the network.
(d) Discuss the step response if $R \gg 2\sqrt{L/C}$.

Solution.

(a)
$$V_o = V_i \frac{1/sC}{R + sL + (1/sC)} = V_i \frac{1/LC}{s^2 + s(R/L) + (1/LC)}$$

$$T_o = \frac{V_o}{V_i} = \frac{1/LC}{s^2 + s(R/L) + (1/LC)}$$

To obtain the poles, solve for the roots of

$$s^2 + s\frac{R}{L} + \frac{1}{LC} = 0$$

$$s = -\frac{R}{2L} \pm \sqrt{\left(\frac{R}{2L}\right)^2 - \frac{1}{LC}}$$

$$\left.\begin{aligned} p_1 &= -\alpha_1 = -\frac{R}{2L} + \sqrt{\left(\frac{R}{2L}\right)^2 - \frac{1}{LC}} \\ p_2 &= -\alpha_2 = -\frac{R}{2L} - \sqrt{\left(\frac{R}{2L}\right)^2 - \frac{1}{LC}} \end{aligned}\right\} \quad \text{Ans.}$$

Note that

$$p_1 + p_2 = -\frac{R}{L}, \qquad p_1 p_2 = \frac{1}{LC}$$

(b) In order to have real axis poles, the term within the square root (the discriminant) must not be negative.

$$\left(\frac{R}{2L}\right)^2 - \frac{1}{LC} \geq 0, \qquad \frac{R}{2L} \geq \frac{1}{\sqrt{LC}}$$

$$R \geq 2\sqrt{\frac{L}{C}} \quad \text{Ans.}$$

(c) The output voltage is across the capacitor. At $t = 0^-$ the voltage across the capacitor is zero (there is no initial voltage). Since the voltage across the capacitor cannot take a jump, it will still be zero at $t = 0^+$. Hence

$$v_o(0) = 0 \quad \text{Ans.}$$

As $t \to \infty$, all changes in the circuit have already taken place; consequently, all derivatives are zero. It follows that the voltage across the inductor

$$v_L = L\frac{di}{dt}$$

and the current through the capacitor

$$i = C\frac{dv_o}{dt}$$

are both zero. So

$$v_o(\infty) = 1 - \underbrace{i(\infty)R}_{0} - \underbrace{v_L(\infty)}_{0} = 1 \quad \text{Ans.}$$

(d) The expression for the poles can be rearranged as follows.

$$p_{1,2} = -\frac{R}{2L} \pm \sqrt{\left(\frac{R}{2L}\right)^2 - \frac{1}{LC}} = -\frac{R}{2L}\left[1 \mp \sqrt{1 - \left(\frac{2}{R}\sqrt{\frac{L}{C}}\right)^2}\right]$$

Since $(2/R)\sqrt{L/C} \ll 1$, we make use of $\sqrt{1-x} \cong 1 - (1/2)x$ and obtain

$$\sqrt{1 - \left(\frac{2}{R}\sqrt{\frac{L}{C}}\right)^2} \cong 1 - \frac{1}{2}\left(\frac{2}{R}\sqrt{\frac{L}{C}}\right)^2 = 1 - \frac{2L}{R^2C}$$

Therefore

$$p_{1,2} \cong -\frac{R}{2L}\left[1 \mp \left(1 - \frac{2L}{R^2C}\right)\right]$$

$$p_1 \cong -\frac{R}{2L}\left[1 - \left(1 - \frac{2L}{R^2C}\right)\right] = -\frac{1}{RC}$$

$$p_2 \cong -\frac{R}{2L}\left[1 + \left(1 - \frac{2L}{R^2C}\right)\right] = -\frac{R}{L}\left(1 - \frac{L}{R^2C}\right) \cong -\frac{R}{L}$$

We note that one pole is strictly determined by the RC portion of the network (as if L were 0) and that the other pole is strictly determined by the RL portion of the network (as if C were 0). Furthermore, if we form the ratio of the poles

$$\frac{p_2}{p_1} = \frac{-R/L}{-1/RC} = R^2\frac{C}{L} \gg 4$$

we see that the poles are widely separated. The pole nearer to the origin, $-1/RC$, is dominant and hence is mainly responsible for the waveform of the response. In fact, we can ignore the other pole altogether and treat the network simply as an RC network (with $L = 0$). The resulting response is that of a first-order system with $\tau = RC$.

Example 7-3

Refer to the network of Fig. 7-7.

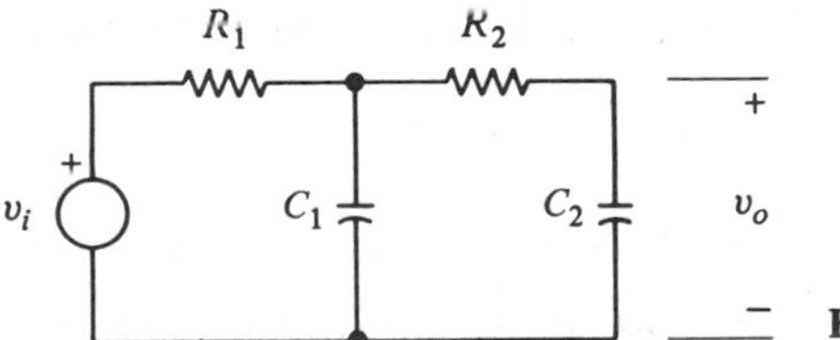

Fig. 7-7

(a) Obtain the transfer function.

(b) Show that no matter what values are chosen for the R's and C's, the poles are always on the negative real axis and distinct.

(c) Adjust the R's and C's to put poles at -1 and -2.

(d) If the input is a step voltage that is V volts high, obtain $v_o(0)$ and $v_o(\infty)$ by inspection of the network.

Solution.

(a) To obtain the transfer function, redraw the network in the Thévenin equivalent form as shown in Fig. 7-8(a) and use the voltage-divider rule.

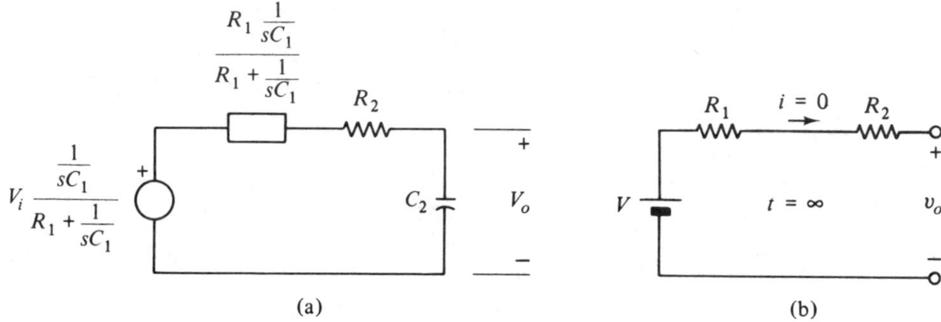

Fig. 7-8

$$V_o = \left[V_i \frac{1/sC_1}{R_1 + (1/sC_1)}\right]\left[\frac{1/sC_2}{\dfrac{R_1(1/sC_1)}{R_1 + (1/sC_1)} + R_2 + (1/sC_2)}\right]$$

$$T = \frac{V_o}{V_i} = \left(\frac{1}{sR_1C_1 + 1}\right)\left[\frac{1/sC_2}{R_1/(sR_1C_1 + 1) + R_2 + (1/sC_2)}\right]$$

$$T = T_o = \frac{1}{s^2R_1R_2C_1C_2 + s(R_1C_1 + R_2C_2 + R_1C_2) + 1} \quad \text{Ans.}$$

(b) The poles are at

$$p_{1,2} = \frac{-(R_1C_1 + R_2C_2 + R_1C_2) \pm \sqrt{(R_1C_1 + R_2C_2 + R_1C_2)^2 - 4R_1R_2C_1C_2}}{2R_1R_2C_1C_2}$$

If the poles are to be on the real axis and distinct, the discriminant must be greater than zero.

$$(R_1C_1 + R_2C_2 + R_1C_2)^2 - 4R_1R_2C_1C_2 > 0$$

$$(R_1C_1 + R_2C_2)^2 + 2R_1C_2(R_1C_1 + R_2C_2) + (R_1C_2)^2 - 4R_1R_2C_1C_2 > 0$$

Combining the last term with the first squared term, we obtain

$$(R_1C_1 - R_2C_2)^2 + 2R_1C_2(R_1C_1 + R_2C_2) + (R_1C_2)^2 > 0$$

Since all the terms on the left-hand side are positive, the inequality is unconditionally satisfied. Consequently, there are two distinct *real* axis poles. Since the radical is less than $(R_1C_1 + R_2C_2 + R_1C_2)$, $p_{1,2}$ is always negative. So both poles are on the *negative real* axis for all combinations of resistor and capacitor values.

(c) There are four unknown elements from which to choose (R_1, R_2, C_1, C_2) and only two equations to satisfy ($p_1 = -1$ and $p_2 = -2$). We can, therefore, arbitrarily choose $R_1C_1 = R_2C_2$.

$$p_{1,2} = \frac{-R_1C_1[2 + (R_1/R_2)] \pm \sqrt{(R_1C_1)^2[2 + (R_1/R_2)]^2 - 4(R_1C_1)^2}}{2(R_1C_1)^2}$$

$$= \frac{-[2 + (R_1/R_2)] \pm \sqrt{(R_1/R_2)^2 + 4(R_1/R_2)}}{2R_1C_1}$$

The sum of the two roots must equal minus three : $(-1) + (-2) = -3$. Their product must equal two: $(-1)(-2) = 2$. So we have

$$p_1 + p_2 = -\frac{2 + (R_1/R_2)}{R_1C_1} = -3$$

$$p_1p_2 = \frac{1}{(R_1C_1)^2} = 2$$

Eliminating R_1C_1 between these two equations gives

$$2 + \frac{R_1}{R_2} = \frac{3}{\sqrt{2}}, \qquad \frac{R_1}{R_2} = \frac{3}{\sqrt{2}} - 2 = 0.121$$

Choose R_2 arbitrarily as 100 kΩ. Then

$$R_1 = 0.121 \times R_2 = 12.1 \text{ k}\Omega$$

Since $(R_1C_1)^2 = \frac{1}{2}$ and $R_1C_1 = R_2C_2$, we have

$$C_1 = \frac{1}{\sqrt{2}\,R_1} = \frac{1}{\sqrt{2} \times 12.1 \times 10^3} = 58.5\ \mu\text{F}$$

$$C_2 = \frac{R_1C_1}{R_2} = \frac{1}{\sqrt{2}\,R_2} = \frac{1}{\sqrt{2} \times 10^5} = 7.07\ \mu\text{F}$$

The element values are

$$R_1 = 12.1 \text{ k}\Omega, \qquad R_2 = 100 \text{ k}\Omega, \qquad C_1 = 58.5\ \mu\text{F}, \qquad C_2 = 7.07\ \mu\text{F}$$

(d) The input jumps V volts at $t = 0$. The output is across a capacitor that has zero initial voltage. Since the voltage across a capacitor cannot jump, we have

$$v_o(0^+) = v_o(0^-) = v_o(0) = 0 \quad \text{Ans.}$$

At $t = \infty$ all changes have taken place, and so both capacitor currents are zero. The capacitors can be taken out of the circuit without affecting the final value of any voltage or any current in the network. The result is Fig. 7-8(b), from which we see that

$$v_o(\infty) = V \quad \text{Ans.}$$

Example 7-4

The input and output of a network described by $T(s)$ are shown in Fig. 7-9.

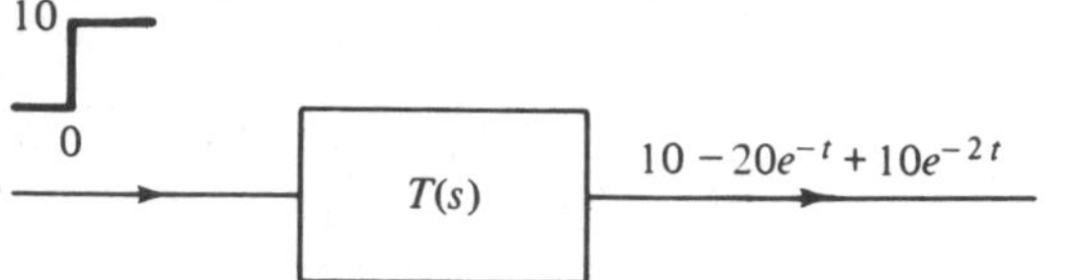

Fig. 7-9

(a) What is $T(s)$?
(b) Obtain a network that is characterized by this $T(s)$.

Solution.

(a) The input and output in the frequency domain are

$$\left(\frac{10}{s}\right) \quad \text{and} \quad \left(\frac{10}{s} - \frac{20}{s+1} + \frac{10}{s+2}\right)$$

Since $T(s)$ is output/input, we obtain

$$T(s) = \frac{10/s - 20/(s+1) + 10/(s+2)}{10/s} = 1 - \frac{2s}{s+1} + \frac{s}{s+2}$$

$$= \frac{2}{(s+1)(s+2)} = \frac{2}{s^2 + 3s + 2} \quad \text{Ans.}$$

(b) Suppose that we visualize $T(s)$ as representing the voltage division between two impedances as shown in Fig. 7-10(a). Then

$$T(s) = \frac{V_o}{V_i} = \frac{Z_2}{Z_1 + Z_2} = \frac{2}{s^2 + 3s + 2} \tag{7-18}$$

Term-by-term comparison gives

$$Z_2 = 2, \qquad Z_1 = 3s + s^2$$

We recognize Z_2 as the impedance of a 2Ω resistor. The impedance Z_1 is the sum (series connection) of two impedances: $3s$ and s^2. We recognize $3s$ as the impedance of a 3 H inductor. However, we do not know of any element that has an impedance of s^2. So even though a mathematical solution to the problem is obtained, the solution is not physically realizable. We simply cannot build the circuit with *RLC* elements. We return to Eq. (7-18) and see whether we can rearrange $T(s)$ differently. For example, we can divide the numerator and the denominator of the transfer function by s and then make the term-by-term comparison.

$$\frac{Z_2}{Z_1 + Z_2} = \frac{(2/s)}{(s+3) + (2/s)}$$

$$Z_2 = \frac{2}{s} = \frac{1}{sC}, \qquad Z_1 = s + 3 = sL + R$$

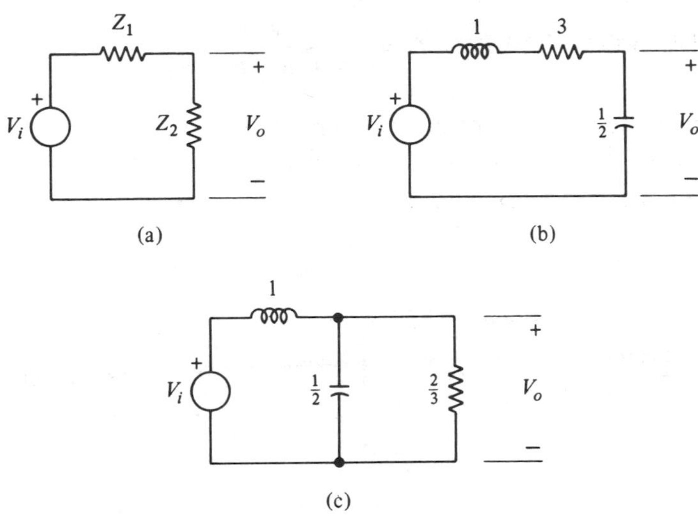

Fig. 7-10

We see that Z_2 and Z_1 are both realizable with *RLC* elements. We can use a $\frac{1}{2}$ F capacitor to realize Z_2 and a 1 H inductor connected in series with a 3 Ω resistor to realize Z_1. The resulting network is shown in Fig. 7-10(b).

For another solution to the problem we divide the numerator and the denominator of the transfer function with $(s + 3)$ and then we compare.

$$\frac{Z_2}{Z_1 + Z_2} = \frac{2/(s + 3)}{(s) + [2/(s + 3)]}$$

$$Z_2 = \frac{2}{s + 3}$$

$$Y_2 = \frac{s + 3}{2} = s\frac{1}{2} + \frac{3}{2} = sC + \frac{1}{R}$$

$$Z_1 = s = sL$$

Hence Z_1 represents the impedance of a 1 H inductor. The admittance Y_2, being the sum of two admittances, represents the parallel connection of two elements: a $\frac{1}{2}$ F capacitor and a $\frac{2}{3}$ Ω resistor. The resulting network is shown in Fig. 7-10(c).

Either the network of Fig. 7-10(b) or the network of Fig. 7-10(c) gives the desired transfer function and, therefore, produces the desired output if a 10 V step is applied at the input. As this example shows, the solution is not unique. Indeed, we can construct other networks that produce the same transfer function. The element values of the *RC* network of Example 7-2 and the element values of the *RL* network of Problem 7-5 can be adjusted to produce the same response. (See Problem 7-8.)

7-4 STEP RESPONSE WHEN $T_1 = \dfrac{a_1 s}{(s + \alpha_1)(s + \alpha_2)}$

A second-order transfer function with a zero at the origin ($s = 0$) and with *negative* real axis poles is presented in block diagram form in Fig. 7-11(a). $T_1(s)$ is described by

$$T_1(s) = \frac{a_1 s}{(s + \alpha_1)(s + \alpha_2)} = \frac{a_1 s}{s^2 + s(\alpha_1 + \alpha_2) + \alpha_1 \alpha_2} \tag{7-19}$$

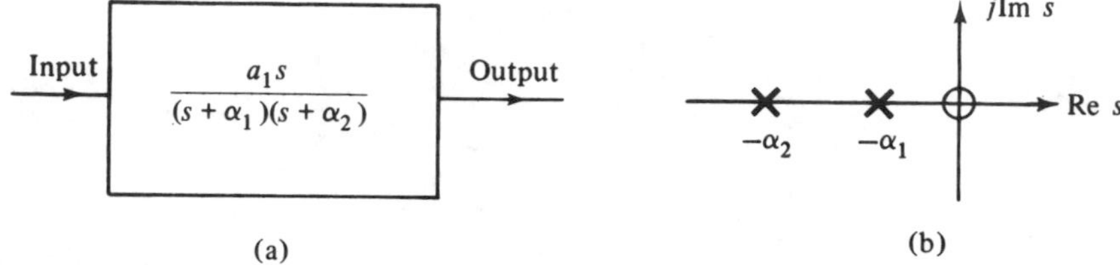

Fig. 7-11

Since a_1 is constant, it acts merely as a scale factor between input and output. Without loss of generality, we can let a_1 equal the coefficient of s in the denominator polynomial.

$$T_1(s) = \frac{(\alpha_1 + \alpha_2)s}{(s + \alpha_1)(s + \alpha_2)} = \frac{(\alpha_1 + \alpha_2)s}{s^2 + s(\alpha_1 + \alpha_2) + \alpha_1 \alpha_2} \tag{7-20}$$

The poles and the zero of $T_1(s)$ are sketched in Fig. 7-11(b).

The *unit-step response* of $T_1(s)$ is obtained from Eq. (7-7) by letting $a_2 = a_0 = 0$ and $a_1 = \alpha_1 + \alpha_2$.

$$r(t) = \frac{\alpha_1 + \alpha_2}{\alpha_2 - \alpha_1}(e^{-\alpha_1 t} - e^{-\alpha_2 t}) \qquad (\alpha_2 \neq \alpha_1, \quad t > 0) \tag{7-21}$$

The initial and final values of $r(t)$ are

$$r(0) = 0, \qquad r(\infty) = 0$$

Regardless of the values of α_1 and α_2, the response starts at zero and ends at zero. Consequently, at some value of time, the response peaks. To find this time, we differentiate $r(t)$ with respect to t and set the result to zero.

$$r'(t) = \frac{\alpha_1 + \alpha_2}{\alpha_2 - \alpha_1}(-\alpha_1 e^{-\alpha_1 t} + \alpha_2 e^{-\alpha_2 t})\bigg|_{t = t_{\max}} = 0$$

$$-\alpha_1 e^{-\alpha_1 t_{\max}} + \alpha_2 e^{-\alpha_2 t_{\max}} = 0$$

$$\frac{\alpha_2}{\alpha_1} = e^{(\alpha_2 - \alpha_1)t_{\max}}$$

$$t_{\max} = \frac{\ln(\alpha_2/\alpha_1)}{\alpha_2 - \alpha_1} \tag{7-22}$$

Using $t_{\max}$, we can determine the maximum value attained by the response

$$r_{\max} = r(t_{\max}) = \frac{\alpha_1 + \alpha_2}{\alpha_2 - \alpha_1}(e^{-\alpha_1 t_{\max} - e^{-\alpha_2 t_{\max}}}) \tag{7-23}$$

$$r_{\max} = \left(1 + \frac{\alpha_2}{\alpha_1}\right)\left(\frac{\alpha_2}{\alpha_1}\right)^{[1/(\alpha_1/\alpha_2 - 1)]} \tag{7-24}$$

The response can easily be plotted for specific values of α_1 and α_2. However, to see how α_1 and α_2 affect the step response of $T(s)$, it is better to plot $r(t)$ vs. t by using the ratio of pole positions α_2/α_1 as a parameter.

In order to see what happens if the larger pole $(-\alpha_2)$ is held constant while the smaller pole $(-\alpha_1)$ is moved closer to the origin, we rearrange Eq. (7-21) as follows.

$$r(t) = \left(\frac{\alpha_2/\alpha_1 + 1}{\alpha_2/\alpha_1 - 1}\right)[e^{-(\alpha_1/\alpha_2)(\alpha_2 t)} - e^{-(\alpha_2 t)}] \tag{7-25}$$

Since α_2 is constant, we let $\alpha_2 t = t'$ and use the α_2/α_1 ratio as a parameter.

$$r(t') = \left(\frac{\alpha_2/\alpha_1 + 1}{\alpha_2/\alpha_1 - 1}\right)[e^{-(\alpha_1/\alpha_2)t'} - e^{-t'}] \qquad (t' = \alpha_2 t) \tag{7-26}$$

Equation (7-26) is plotted in Fig. 7-12 for $\alpha_2/\alpha_1 = 1.01$ (poles close to each other) and for $\alpha_2/\alpha_1 = 10$ (poles far apart). The closer $-\alpha_1$ is brought to the origin (the larger the α_2/α_1 ratio), the longer it takes for the response to die out.

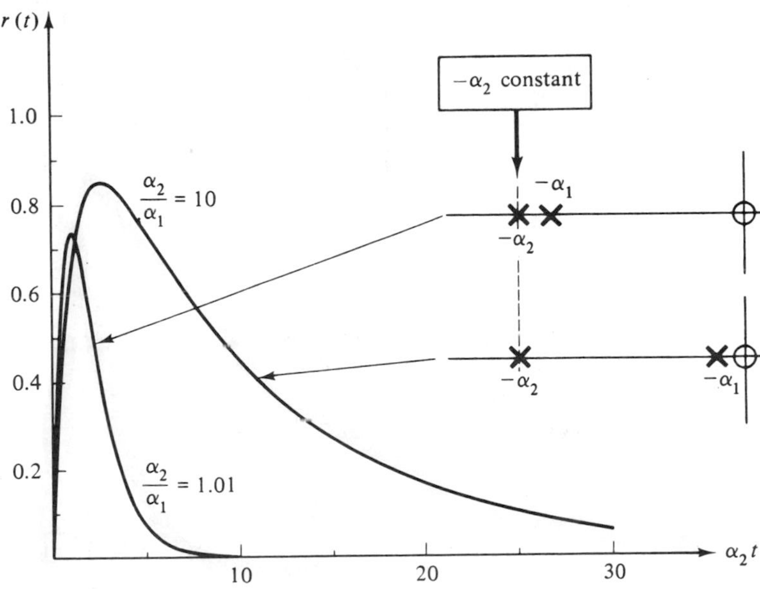

Fig. 7-12

We obtain a better understanding of how these step response curves are shaped if we study the individual terms of the response.

$$r(t) = \underbrace{\frac{(\alpha_2/\alpha_1 + 1)}{(\alpha_2/\alpha_1 - 1)}e^{-\alpha_1 t}}_{r_1(t)} + \underbrace{\frac{-(\alpha_2/\alpha_1 + 1)}{(\alpha_2/\alpha_1 - 1)}e^{-\alpha_2 t}}_{r_2(t)} \tag{7-27}$$

The first term of the response, $r_1(t)$, is a decaying exponential that has a time constant of $1/\alpha_1$. The second term of the response, $r_2(t)$, is also a decaying exponential. Its time constant is $1/\alpha_2$. The exponentials have equal amplitudes but are opposite in sign. The larger the α_2/α_1 ratio, the longer it will take for $r_1(t)$ to decay relative to $r_2(t)$. Indeed, if $\alpha_2/\alpha_1 \gg 1$, the response for $t > 5/\alpha_2$ is, for all practical purposes, $r_1(t)$. This is shown in the response curve of Fig. 7-13. Compare the dashed curve, which represents $r_1(t)$, with the solid curve, which represents $r(t)$. Because the poles are far apart, the amplitude of each term is almost unity. Since $r_2(t)$ vanishes before $r_1(t)$ changes appreciably from unity, the peak value of the response is very close to unity. From the response of Fig. 7-13 we see that, except when t is very small, the shape of the response is determined by the pole nearer the origin (the pole at $-\alpha_1$). See also Fig. 7-12.

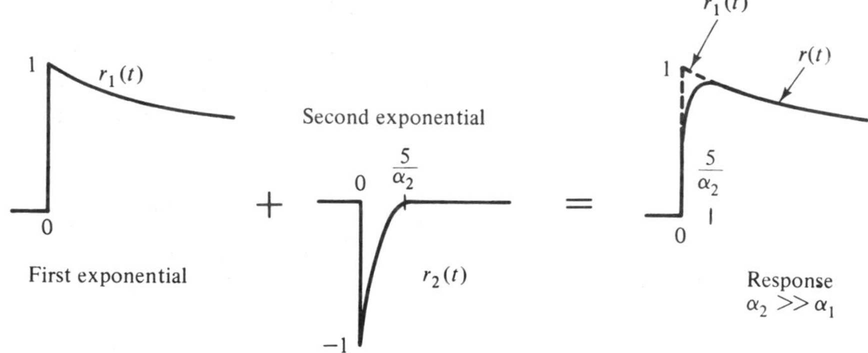

Fig. 7-13

Example 7-5

Refer to Fig. 7-14. This network is identical with the network of Example 7-1 except that the output is taken across the resistor rather than across the capacitor.

(a) Show that V_o/V_i is T_1.

(b) Discuss the step response if $R \gg 2\sqrt{L/C}$.

Solution.

(a)

$$V_o = V_i\frac{R}{sL + (1/sC) + R} = V_i\frac{(R/L)s}{s^2 + s(R/L) + (1/LC)}$$

$$\frac{V_o}{V_i} = \frac{(R/L)s}{s^2 + (R/L)s + (1/LC)} = T_1 \quad \text{Ans.}$$

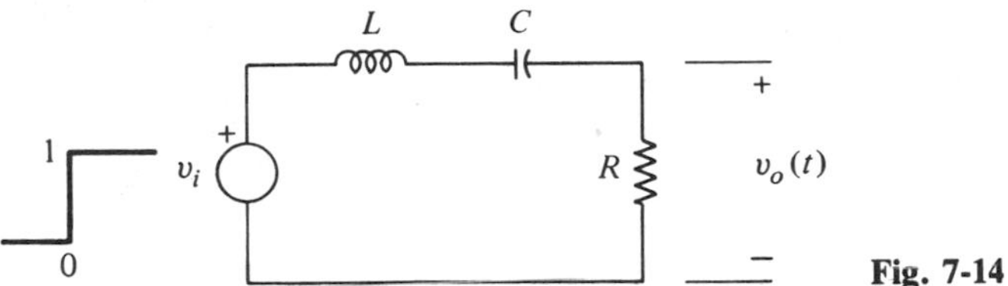

Fig. 7-14

(b) The two poles of $T_1(s)$ are at

$$p_{1,2} = -\frac{R}{2L} \pm \sqrt{\left(\frac{R}{2L}\right)^2 - \frac{1}{LC}} = -\frac{R}{2L}\left[1 \mp \sqrt{1 - \left(\frac{2}{R}\sqrt{\frac{L}{C}}\right)^2}\right]$$

Since $(2/R)\sqrt{L/C} \ll 1$ (or $R\sqrt{C/L} \gg 2$), the poles are widely separated, and we can approximate their positions by

$$p_1 \cong -\frac{1}{RC} = -\alpha_1$$

$$p_2 \cong -\frac{R}{L} = -\alpha_2$$

[See Example 7-2(d).]

Since

$$\frac{\alpha_2}{\alpha_1} = \left(R\sqrt{\frac{C}{L}}\right)^2 \gg 4$$

the expression for the response, given by Eq. (7-27), can be approximated as

$$r(t) = \left(\frac{\alpha_2/\alpha_1 + 1}{\alpha_2/\alpha_1 - 1}\right)(e^{-\alpha_1 t} - e^{-\alpha_2 t}) \cong e^{-\alpha_1 t} - e^{-\alpha_2 t}$$

$$r(t) \cong e^{-t/RC} - e^{-(R/L)t} \tag{7-28}$$

The first exponential decays with a time constant of $\tau_1 = RC$. The second exponential decays with a time constant of $\tau_2 = L/R$. The condition

$$R \gg 2\sqrt{\frac{L}{C}}$$

can be restated as

$$R^2 \gg 4\frac{L}{C}, \qquad \underbrace{RC}_{\tau_1} \gg 4\underbrace{\frac{L}{R}}_{\tau_2}$$

It takes much longer for the first exponential to decay than the second exponential. We can, therefore, readily sketch Eq. (7-28) as in Fig. 7-15. If we study the response, we see that it is initially controlled by the *LR* portion of the circuit. (We can just as easily replace the capacitor with a short circuit, since the voltage across it is negligible.) However, after $5L/R$, the response is controlled by the *RC* portion of the circuit. (We can then replace the inductor with a short circuit, since the voltage across it is negligible.)

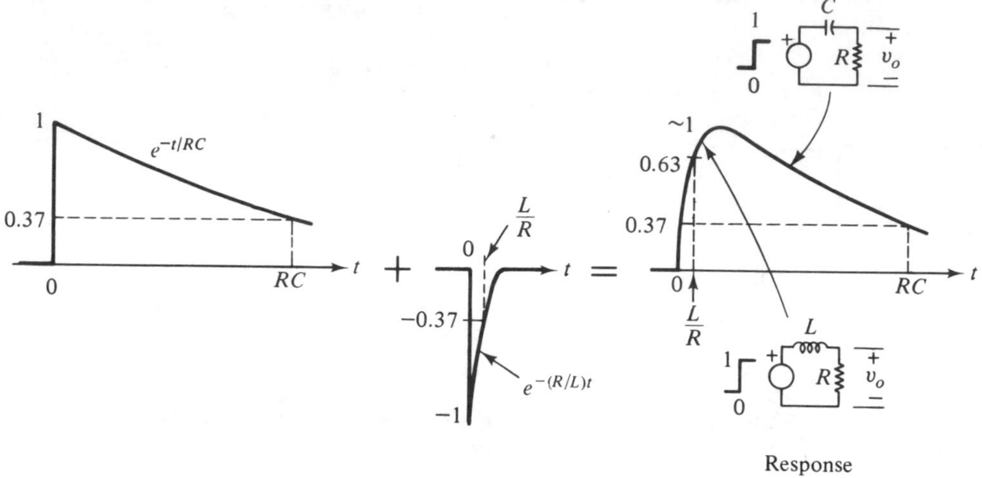

Fig. 7-15

Example 7-6

Sketch the step response of the network shown in Fig. 7-16.

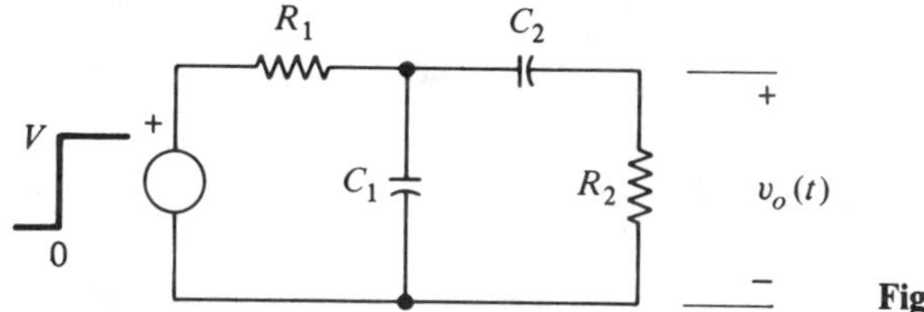

Fig. 7-16

Solution. At $t = 0^+$ both capacitor voltages are zero. So, for this instant alone, the network can be redrawn as in Fig. 7-17(a), from which we see that $v_o(0^+) = 0$. At $t = \infty$ both capacitor currents are zero. Therefore, for $t = \infty$, the network can be redrawn as in Fig. 7-17(b), from which we see that $v_o(\infty) = 0$.

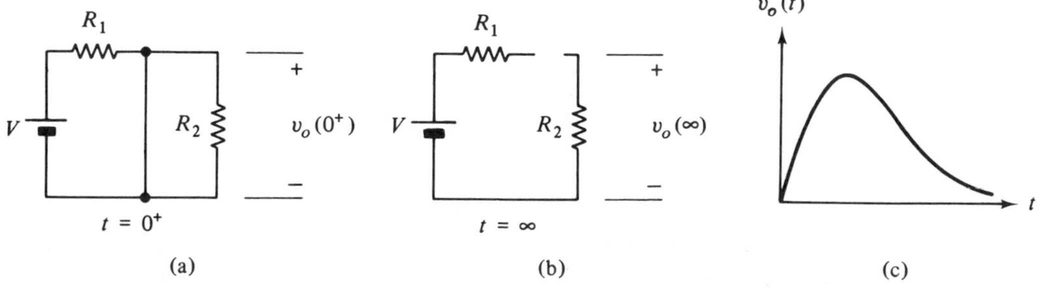

Fig. 7-17

The response starts at zero and ends at zero. In between, it is governed by the difference of two exponentials, since the two poles of the network are on the negative real axis (see Problem 7-13). Hence the response can be sketched as in Fig. 7-17(c).

Example 7-7

What network(s) produces the step response shown in Fig. 7-18?

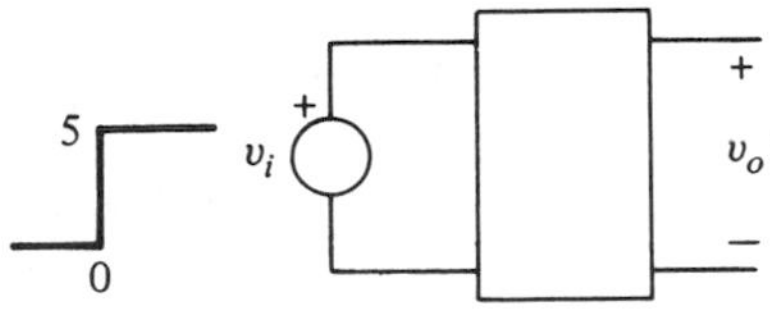

$$v_o(t) = \frac{15}{\sqrt{5}}\left\{e^{-[(3-\sqrt{5})/2]t} - e^{-[(3+\sqrt{5})/2]t}\right\}$$

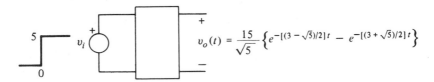

Fig. 7-18

Solution. The input and the output are given, which means that we can determine the transfer function that characterizes the network.

$$\text{Input} = V_i = \frac{5}{s}$$

$$\text{Output} = V_o = \frac{15}{\sqrt{5}}\left[\frac{1}{s+(3-\sqrt{5})/2} - \frac{1}{s+(3+\sqrt{5})/2}\right]$$

$$= \frac{15}{[s+(3-\sqrt{5})/2][s+(3+\sqrt{5})/2]} = \frac{15}{s^2+3s+1}$$

$$T(s) = \frac{\text{Output}}{\text{Input}} = \frac{V_o}{V_i} = \frac{15}{s^2+3s+1}\,\frac{s}{5} = \frac{3s}{s^2+3s+1}$$

We now write V_o/V_i as

$$\frac{V_o}{V_i} = \frac{Z_2}{Z_1+Z_2} = \frac{3s}{s^2+3s+1}$$

Direct comparison gives $Z_1 = s^2+1$ and $Z_2 = 3s$. Since Z_1 is not realizable with *RLC* elements, we try a different rearrangement of V_o/V_i. For example, first we divide the numerator and denominator by $3s$ *or* by s^2+1 and then make the term-by-term comparison as shown below.

$$\frac{3s}{s^2+3s+1} =$$

Divide by $3s$ →

$$\frac{\overbrace{1}^{Z_2}}{\underbrace{s\frac{1}{3}+\frac{1}{s3}}_{Z_1}+\underbrace{1}_{Z_2}}$$

$Z_1 = s\dfrac{1}{3} + \dfrac{1}{s3}$

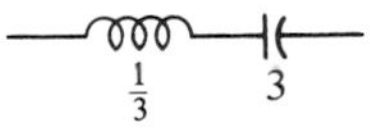

$Z_2 = 1$

Divide by (s^2+1) →

$$\frac{\overbrace{\dfrac{3s}{s^2+1}}^{Z_2}}{\underbrace{1}_{Z_1}+\underbrace{\dfrac{3s}{s^2+1}}_{Z_2}}$$

$Z_1 = 1$

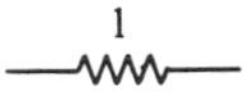

$Z_2 = \dfrac{3s}{s^2+1}$ $\left(Y_2 = s\dfrac{1}{3} + \dfrac{1}{s3}\right)$

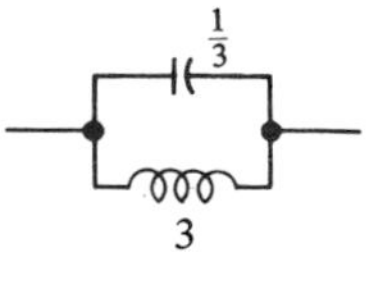

The first development results in the circuit of Fig. 7-19(a); the second gives the circuit of Fig. 7-19(b).

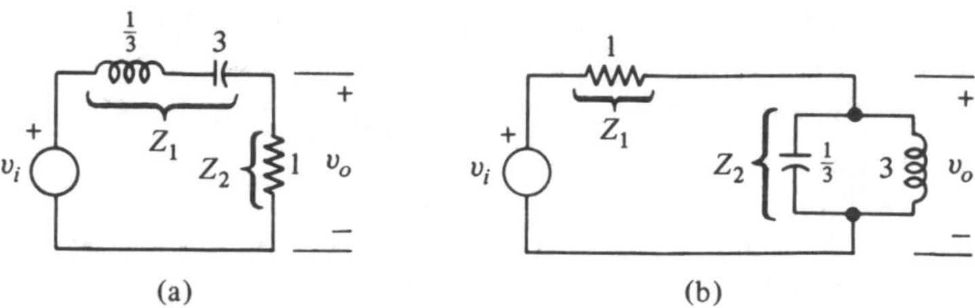

Fig. 7-19

7-5 STEP RESPONSE WHEN $T_2 = \dfrac{a_2 s^2}{(s + \alpha_1)(s + \alpha_2)}$

A second-order transfer function with two zeros at the origin ($s = 0$) and with *negative* real axis poles is represented in block diagram form in Fig. 7-20(a). $T_2(s)$ is described by

$$T_2(s) = \frac{a_2 s^2}{(s + \alpha_1)(s + \alpha_2)} = \frac{a_2 s^2}{s^2 + s(\alpha_1 + \alpha_2) + \alpha_1 \alpha_2} \tag{7-29}$$

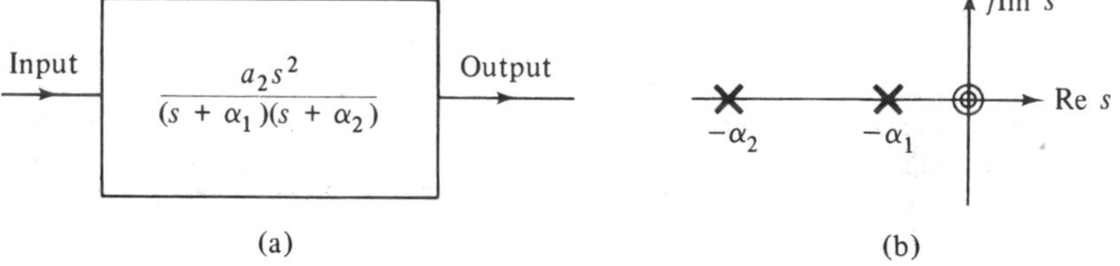

Fig. 7-20

Since a_2 is constant, it acts merely as a scale factor between input and output. Without loss of generality, we can let a_2 equal the coefficient of s^2 in the denominator polynomial and obtain

$$T_2(s) = \frac{s^2}{(s + \alpha_1)(s + \alpha_2)} = \frac{s^2}{s^2 + s(\alpha_1 + \alpha_2) + \alpha_1 \alpha_2} \tag{7-30}$$

The poles and zeros of $T_2(s)$ are sketched in Fig. 7-20(b).

The *unit-step response* of $T_2(s)$ is obtained from Eq. (7-7) by letting $a_1 = a_0 = 0$ and $a_2 = 1$.

$$r(t) = \frac{1}{\alpha_2 - \alpha_1}(\alpha_2 e^{-\alpha_2 t} - \alpha_1 e^{-\alpha_1 t}) \qquad (\alpha_2 \neq \alpha_1, \quad t > 0) \tag{7-31}$$

The initial and final values of the response are

$$r(0^+) = 1, \qquad r(\infty) = 0$$

Regardless of the values of α_1 and α_2, the response starts at one and ends at zero. It becomes zero also at $t = t_0$.

$$r(t_0) = \frac{1}{\alpha_2 - \alpha_1}(\alpha_2 e^{-\alpha_2 t_0} - \alpha_1 e^{-\alpha_1 t_0}) = 0$$

$$\frac{\alpha_2}{\alpha_1} = e^{(\alpha_2 - \alpha_1)t_0}$$

$$t_0 = \frac{\ln(\alpha_2/\alpha_1)}{\alpha_2 - \alpha_1} \tag{7-32}$$

For $t > t_0$ the response is negative and goes through a minimum. To obtain the time when the minimum occurs, as well as the corresponding minimum value of the response, we proceed as follows.

$$r'(t) = \frac{1}{\alpha_2 - \alpha_i}(-\alpha_2^2 e^{-\alpha_2 t} + \alpha_1^2 e^{-\alpha_1 t})\bigg|_{t=t_{\min}} = 0$$

$$-\alpha_2^2 e^{-\alpha_2 t_{\min}} + \alpha_1^2 e^{-\alpha_1 t_{\min}} = 0$$

$$\left(\frac{\alpha_2}{\alpha_1}\right)^2 = e^{(\alpha_2 - \alpha_1)t_{\min}}$$

$$t_{\min} = \frac{2\ln(\alpha_2/\alpha_1)}{\alpha_2 - \alpha_1} \tag{7-33}$$

$$r_{\min} = r(t_{\min}) = \frac{1}{\alpha_2 - \alpha_1}(\alpha_2 e^{-\alpha_2 t_{\min}} - \alpha_1 e^{-\alpha_1 t_{\min}}) \tag{7-34}$$

$$r_{\min} = -\left(\frac{\alpha_1}{\alpha_2}\right)^{(\alpha_1 + \alpha_2)/(\alpha_2 - \alpha_1)} \tag{7-35}$$

We note that the minimum value occurs at twice the time the response crosses the time axis—that is, $t_{\min} = 2t_0$.

To see what happens to the response as the larger pole $(-\alpha_2)$ is varied while the smaller pole $(-\alpha_1)$ is held constant, we rearrange Eq. (7-31) as

$$r(t') = \left(\frac{1}{1 - \alpha_1/\alpha_2}\right) e^{-(\alpha_2/\alpha_1)(\alpha_1 t)} - \left(\frac{1}{\alpha_2/\alpha_1 - 1}\right) e^{(\alpha_1 t)} \tag{7-36}$$

Since α_1 is constant, we let $\alpha_1 t = t'$ and use the α_2/α_1 ratio as a parameter to obtain

$$r(t') = \left(\frac{1}{1 - \alpha_1/\alpha_2}\right) e^{-(\alpha_2/\alpha_1)t'} - \left(\frac{1}{\alpha_2/\alpha_1 - 1}\right) e^{-t'} \qquad (t' = \alpha_1 t) \tag{7-37}$$

Equation (7-37) is plotted in Fig. 7-21 for $\alpha_2/\alpha_1 = 1.01$ and 10. Note, in particular, the crossing of the time axis and the minimum value that follows.

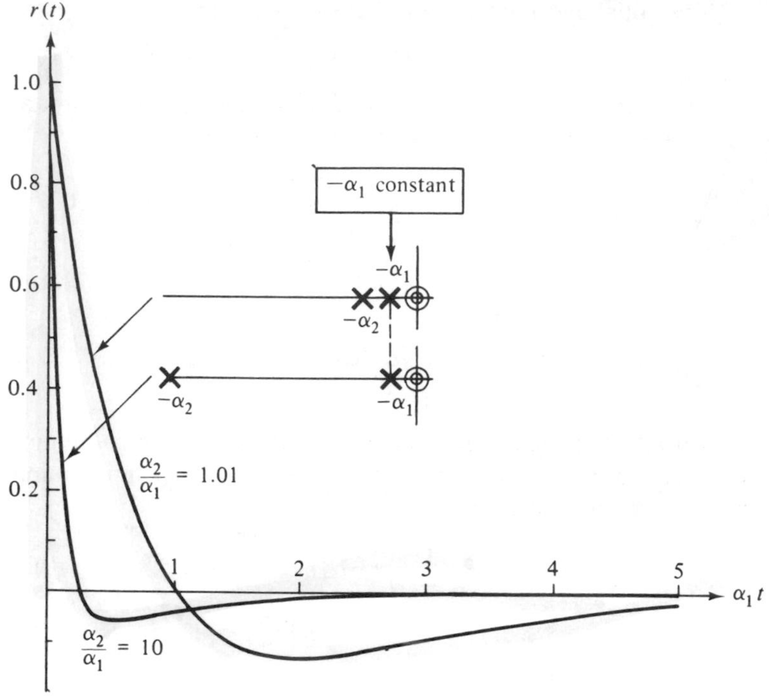

Fig. 7-21

A better insight as to how these response curves are generated can be gained by looking at the individual components of the response. Equation (7-31) can be written

$$r(t) = \underbrace{\left(\frac{1}{1 - \alpha_1/\alpha_2}\right)e^{-\alpha_2 t}}_{r_1(t)} + \underbrace{\left(\frac{-1}{\alpha_2/\alpha_1 - 1}\right)e^{-\alpha_1 t}}_{r_2(t)} \tag{7-38}$$

The first term of the response, $r_1(t)$, is an exponential with time constant $1/\alpha_2$. The second term, $r_2(t)$, is an exponential with time constant $1/\alpha_1$. For $\alpha_2 > \alpha_1$, the amplitude of $r_1(t)$ is positive

$$\left(\frac{1}{1 - \alpha_1/\alpha_2} > 0\right)$$

and the amplitude of $r_2(t)$ is negative

$$\left(\frac{-1}{\alpha_2/\alpha_1 - 1} < 0\right)$$

Furthermore, $r_2(t)$, which has the larger time constant, decays more slowly than $r_1(t)$. Consequently, the response eventually becomes negative. As the α_2/α_1 ratio is increased from unity (the poles are separated farther from each other), both amplitudes ($t = 0^+$ values of the individual components) decrease in magnitude, but their difference is always unity. The larger α_2/α_1 is, the longer $r_2(t)$ lingers relative to $r_1(t)$.

Example 7-8

Show that by adjusting element values, it is possible to make the step response of the two networks shown in Fig. 7-22 identical.

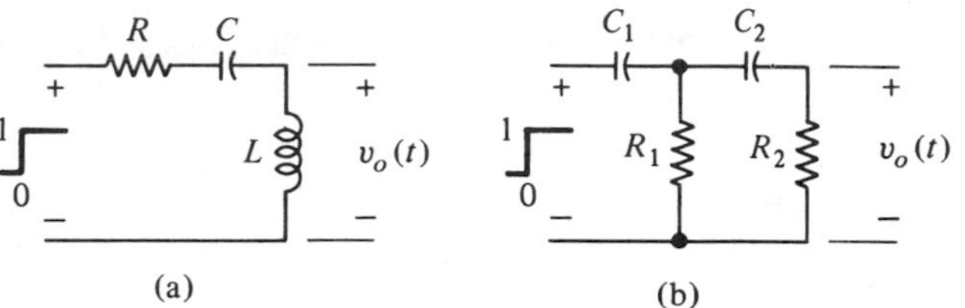

Fig. 7-22

Solution. If the step responses of the two networks are to be identical, then their transfer functions must be identical. The two transfer functions are

$$T_{RLC} = \frac{s^2}{s^2 + s(R/L) + 1/LC} = T_2(s)$$

$$T_{RC} = \frac{s^2}{s^2 + s(1/R_1C_1 + 1/R_2C_2 + 1/R_2C_1) + 1/R_1R_2C_1C_2} = T_2(s)$$

Matching the coefficients of the various powers of s in the denominator polynomial, we have

$$\frac{R}{L} = \frac{1}{R_1C_1} + \frac{1}{R_2C_2} + \frac{1}{R_2C_1} \tag{7-39a}$$

$$\frac{1}{LC} = \frac{1}{R_1R_2C_1C_2} \tag{7-39b}$$

Suppose that the RC network is given—that is, R_1, R_2, C_1, C_2 are fixed—and we are to determine the components of the RLC network. There are two equations: Eq. (7-39a) and Eq. (7-39b). There are three unknown components: R, L, C. So we can arbitrarily pick one of the components, say L. Then R and C are calculated from

$$\left.\begin{aligned} R &= L\left(\frac{1}{R_1C_1} + \frac{1}{R_2C_2} + \frac{1}{R_2C_1}\right) \\ C &= \frac{R_1R_2C_1C_2}{L} \end{aligned}\right\} \text{Ans.}$$

7-6 STEP RESPONSE WHEN $T = \dfrac{a_2 s^2 + a_1 s + a_0}{(s + \alpha_1)(s + \alpha_2)}$

Let us summarize what we have learned about the unit-step response of three special kinds of second-order functions with negative real axis poles. The results are represented in Fig. 7-23. The responses are obtained from

$$r_i(t) = \mathcal{L}^{-1}\left\{\frac{1}{s}T_i\right\} \qquad (i = 0, 1, 2)$$

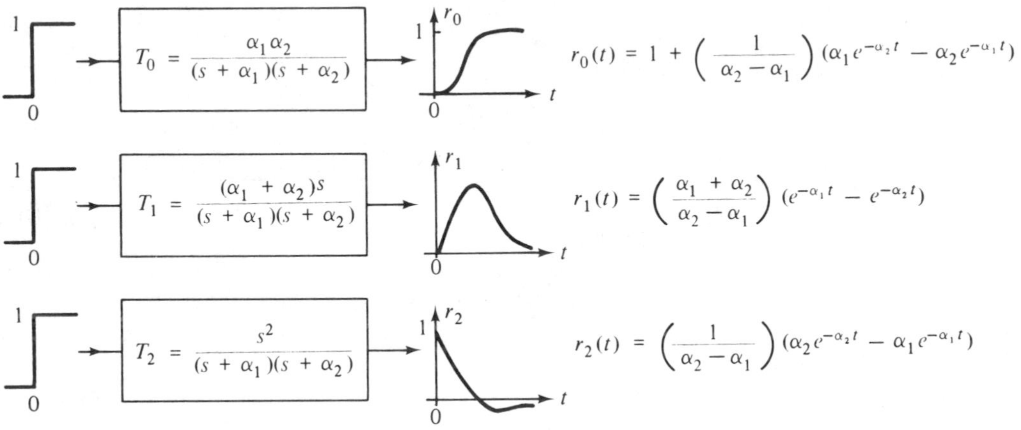

$$T_0 = \frac{\alpha_1 \alpha_2}{(s + \alpha_1)(s + \alpha_2)} \qquad r_0(t) = 1 + \left(\frac{1}{\alpha_2 - \alpha_1}\right)(\alpha_1 e^{-\alpha_2 t} - \alpha_2 e^{-\alpha_1 t})$$

$$T_1 = \frac{(\alpha_1 + \alpha_2)s}{(s + \alpha_1)(s + \alpha_2)} \qquad r_1(t) = \left(\frac{\alpha_1 + \alpha_2}{\alpha_2 - \alpha_1}\right)(e^{-\alpha_1 t} - e^{-\alpha_2 t})$$

$$T_2 = \frac{s^2}{(s + \alpha_1)(s + \alpha_2)} \qquad r_2(t) = \left(\frac{1}{\alpha_2 - \alpha_1}\right)(\alpha_2 e^{-\alpha_2 t} - \alpha_1 e^{-\alpha_1 t})$$

Fig. 7-23

We note that T_1 and T_0 are related by

$$T_1 = \left(\frac{\alpha_1 + \alpha_2}{\alpha_1 \alpha_2}\right) s T_0 \tag{7-40a}$$

If we wish to obtain T_1 from T_0, we must first scale T_0 by

$$\frac{\alpha_1 + \alpha_2}{\alpha_1 \alpha_2}$$

and then multiply it by s. Consequently, the corresponding frequency-domain unit-step responses $R_1(s)$ and $R_0(s)$ are related by

$$\underbrace{R_1(s)}_{\frac{1}{s}T_1} = \left(\frac{\alpha_1 + \alpha_2}{\alpha_1 \alpha_2}\right) s \underbrace{R_0(s)}_{\frac{1}{s}T_0}$$

which results in

$$r_1(t) = \left(\frac{\alpha_1 + \alpha_2}{\alpha_1 \alpha_2}\right) \mathcal{L}^{-1}\{sR_0(s)\} \tag{7-40b}$$

Section 5-2 showed that

$$\mathcal{L}\left\{\frac{dr_0}{dt}\right\} = sR_0(s) - r_0(0^+)$$

Since $r_0(0^+) = 0$ (see Fig. 7-23), we have

$$\mathcal{L}\left\{\frac{dr_0}{dt}\right\} = \{sR_0(s)\}, \qquad \frac{dr_0}{dt} = \mathcal{L}^{-1}\{sR_0(s)\}$$

which when substituted in Eq. (7-40b) gives

$$r_1(t) = \left(\frac{\alpha_1 + \alpha_2}{\alpha_1 \alpha_2}\right) \frac{d}{dt}[r_0(t)] \tag{7-40c}$$

So if given only the $r_0(t)$ vs. t curve, we can obtain the $r_1(t)$ vs. t curve by graphical differentiation and scaling. Note, in particular, that in Fig. 7-23 the maximum value of $r_1(t)$ occurs when the slope of $r_0(t)$ is maximum.

Similarly, T_2 and T_1 are related by

$$T_2 = \left(\frac{1}{\alpha_1 + \alpha_2}\right) sT_1 \tag{7-41a}$$

Consequently, the step response of T_2 is obtainable from the step response of T_1 through the operations of scaling and differentiation.

$$r_2(t) = \left(\frac{1}{\alpha_1 + \alpha_2}\right) \frac{d}{dt}[r_1(t)] \qquad [\text{given } r_1(0^+) = 0] \tag{7-41b}$$

The $r_2(t)$ curve in Fig. 7-23 can be obtained by graphical differentiation and scaling of the $r_1(t)$ curve. Note in this figure that $r_2(t)$ is zero where $r_1(t)$ is maximum. The general second-order system with negative real axis poles can be written

$$T(s) = \frac{a_2 s^2 + a_1 s + a_0}{(s + \alpha_1)(s + \alpha_2)} \tag{7-42a}$$

$$T(s) = \frac{a_2 s^2}{(s + \alpha_1)(s + \alpha_2)} + \frac{a_1 s}{(s + \alpha_1)(s + \alpha_2)} + \frac{a_0}{(s + \alpha_1)(s + \alpha_2)} \tag{7-42b}$$

$$T(s) = a_2 T_2(s) + \frac{a_1}{\alpha_1 + \alpha_2} T_1(s) + \frac{a_0}{\alpha_1 \alpha_2} T_0(s) \tag{7-42c}$$

It follows that the unit-step response of $T(s)$ can be expressed as

$$r(t) = a_2 r_2(t) + \frac{a_1}{\alpha_1 + \alpha_2} r_1(t) + \frac{a_0}{\alpha_1 \alpha_2} r_0(t) \tag{7-43}$$

Thus we can obtain a variety of response waveforms by combining the three basic waveforms shown in Fig. 7-23 with different signs and scale factors that are determined by the a coefficients. Although it is instructive to realize that the step response of $T(s)$ can be viewed as a combination of step responses arising from T_2, T_1, and T_0, it is not always necessary to delineate the individual components, since the response is, after all terms are combined, *the sum of a constant and two exponentials*—that is,

$$r(t) = \underbrace{A}_{\substack{\text{Forced}\\ \text{part}}} + \underbrace{Be^{-\alpha_1 t} + Ce^{-\alpha_2 t}}_{\substack{\text{Natural}\\ \text{part}}} \qquad \alpha_2 \neq \alpha_1 \tag{7-44}$$

Using the results of Eq. (7-40c) and Eq. (7-41b), we can also express Eq. (7-43) as

$$r(t) = \frac{1}{\alpha_1 \alpha_2}\left(a_2 \frac{d^2 r_0}{dt^2} + a_1 \frac{dr_0}{dt} + a_0 r_0\right)$$

Hence the response can be thought as the basic $r_0(t)$ response plus its derivatives with the a coefficients acting as weighting factors in the summation.

Example 7-9

Discuss the unit-step response of the network shown in Fig. 7-24.

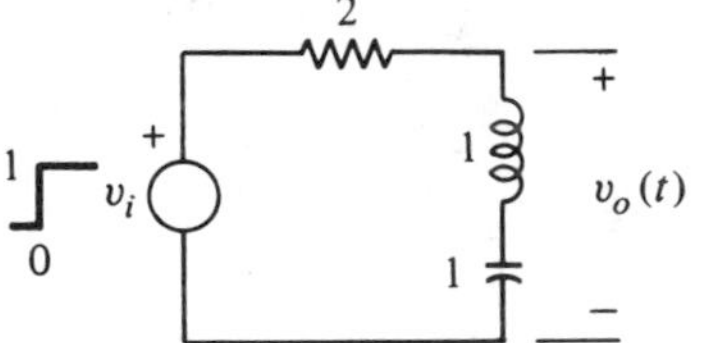

Fig. 7-24

Solution. We first obtain the transfer function and then decompose it into its component parts.

$$T = \frac{V_o}{V_i} = \frac{s + (1/s)}{s + (1/s) + 2} = \frac{s^2 + 1}{s^2 + 2s + 1} = \frac{s^2 + 1}{(s + 1)^2}$$

$$= \underbrace{\frac{s^2}{(s + 1)^2}}_{T_2} + \underbrace{\frac{1}{(s + 1)^2}}_{T_0} = T_2 + T_0$$

The unit-step response is obtained from

$$R(s) = \frac{1}{s}T = \frac{s}{(s + 1)^2} + \frac{1}{s(s + 1)^2}$$

Expanding the individual terms into partial fractions gives

$$R(s) = \underbrace{\left[\frac{1}{s + 1} - \frac{1}{(s + 1)^2}\right]}_{R_2} + \underbrace{\left[\frac{1}{s} - \frac{1}{s + 1} - \frac{1}{(s + 1)^2}\right]}_{R_0}$$

Using Table 5-1, we obtain the inverse transform

$$r(t) = (e^{-t} - te^{-t}) + (1 - e^{-t} - te^{-t}) = \underbrace{e^{-t}(1 - t)}_{r_2(t)} + \underbrace{[1 - e^{-t}(1 + t)]}_{r_0(t)} = \underbrace{1 - 2te^{-t}}_{r(t)}$$

$r_2(t)$ is from the T_2 portion of T. It is plotted in Fig. 7-25(a). $r_0(t)$ is from the T_0 portion of T. It is plotted in Fig. 7-25(b). $r(t)$ is the response. It is the sum of $r_2(t)$ and $r_0(t)$. It is plotted in Fig. 7-25(c). The output jumps 1 V at $t = 0$; then it dips and goes back up to 1 V. By directly combining the T_2 and T_0 responses, we can generate a new waveform.

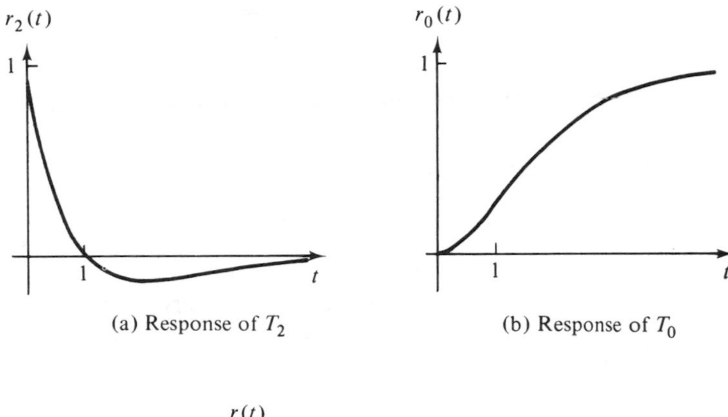

(a) Response of T_2 (b) Response of T_0

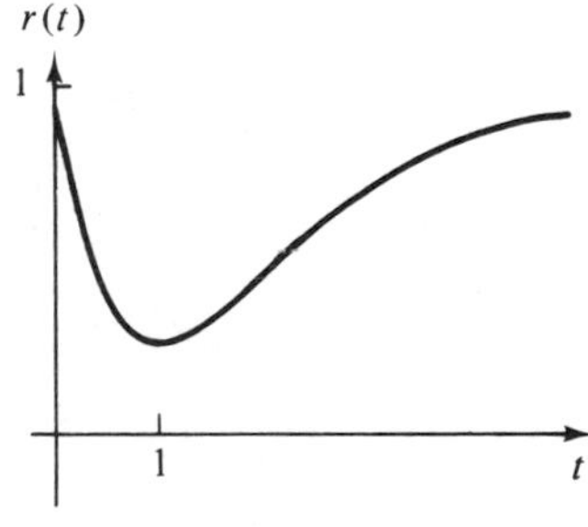

(c) Response of T

Fig. 7-25

Example 7-10

Refer to Fig. 7-26.

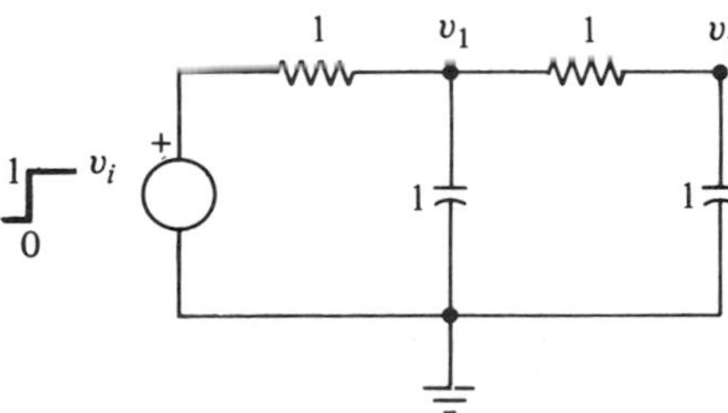

Fig. 7-26

(a) Obtain V_2/V_i, V_1/V_i, and the poles.
(b) Express the two transfer functions in terms of the T functions given in Fig. 7-23.
(c) Obtain $v_2(t)$ and $v_1(t)$ if the input is a unit step as shown.
(d) Plot $v_2(t)$ and $v_1(t)$ vs. t. Discuss results.

Solution.

(a) From the result of Example 7-3(a) we have

$$\frac{V_2}{V_i} = \frac{1}{s^2 + 3s + 1} \quad \text{Ans.}$$

From Fig. 7-26 we see that $$V_2 = V_1 \frac{1/s}{1 + (1/s)} = V_1 \frac{1}{s+1}$$

Consequently, $$V_1 = V_2(s + 1)$$

$$\frac{V_1}{V_i} = \frac{V_2}{V_i}(s + 1) = \frac{s + 1}{s^2 + 3s + 1} \quad \text{Ans.}$$

The poles of the transfer functions are obtained from $s^2 + 3a + 1 = 0$

$$p_{1,2} = \frac{-3 \pm \sqrt{5}}{2}$$

$$p_1 = \frac{-3 + \sqrt{5}}{2} = -\alpha_1, \qquad p_2 = \frac{-3 - \sqrt{5}}{2} = -\alpha_2 \quad \text{Ans.}$$

Note that $\alpha_1 \alpha_2 = 1$, $\quad \alpha_2 - \alpha_1 = \sqrt{5}$, $\quad \alpha_1 + \alpha_2 = 3$

(b) In comparing

$$\frac{V_2}{V_i} = \frac{1}{s^2 + 3s + 1} \quad \text{and} \quad \frac{V_1}{V_i} = \frac{s}{s^2 + 3s + 1} + \frac{1}{s^2 + 3s + 1}$$

to the transfer functions presented in Fig. 7-23, we see that

$$\frac{V_2}{V_i} = T_0, \qquad \frac{V_1}{V_i} = \frac{1}{3}T_1 + T_0 \quad \text{Ans.}$$

(c) Using the responses represented in Fig. 7-23, we obtain $v_2(t)$.

$$v_2(t) = r_0(t) = 1 + \left(\frac{1}{\alpha_2 - \alpha_1}\right)(\alpha_1 e^{-\alpha_2 t} - \alpha_2 e^{-\alpha_1 t})$$

$$= 1 + \frac{1}{\sqrt{5}}\left[\frac{3 - \sqrt{5}}{2} e^{-[(3+\sqrt{5})/2]t} - \frac{3 + \sqrt{5}}{2} e^{-[(3-\sqrt{5})/2]t}\right] \quad \text{Ans.}$$

Since $$V_1 = V_2(s + 1) = V_2 + sV_2$$

we have

$$v_1(t) = v_2(t) + \frac{d}{dt}[v_2(t)]$$

$$= \left\{1 + \frac{1}{\sqrt{5}}\left[\frac{3 - \sqrt{5}}{2}e^{-[(3+\sqrt{5}/2]t} - \frac{3 + \sqrt{5}}{2}e^{-[(3-\sqrt{5}/2]t}\right]\right\}$$

$$+ \frac{1}{\sqrt{5}}[-e^{-[(3+\sqrt{5}/2]t} + e^{-[(3-\sqrt{5}/2]t}]$$

$$v_1(t) = 1 - \frac{1}{2\sqrt{5}}[(\sqrt{5} + 1)e^{-[(3-\sqrt{5}/2]t} + (\sqrt{5} - 1)e^{-[(3+\sqrt{5}/2]t}] \quad \text{Ans.}$$

Alternatively, we can use the result of Fig. 7-23 to obtain $v_1(t)$.

$$v_1(t) = \frac{1}{3}r_1(t) + r_0(t)$$

$$= \frac{1}{3}\left[\frac{\alpha_1 + \alpha_2}{\alpha_2 - \alpha_1}(e^{-\alpha_1 t} - e^{-\alpha_2 t})\right] + \left[1 + \left(\frac{1}{\alpha_2 - \alpha_1}\right)(\alpha_1 e^{-\alpha_2 t} - \alpha_2 e^{-\alpha_1 t})\right]$$

$$= 1 - \frac{1}{2(\alpha_2 - \alpha_1)}\left[\frac{2(2\alpha_2 - \alpha_1)}{3}e^{-\alpha_1 t} + \frac{2(\alpha_2 - 2\alpha_1)}{3}e^{-\alpha_2 t}\right]$$

$$= 1 - \frac{1}{2\sqrt{5}}[(\sqrt{5} + 1)e^{-[(3-\sqrt{5}/2]t} + (\sqrt{5} - 1)e^{-[(3+\sqrt{5}/2]t}] \quad \text{Ans.}$$

(d) $v_2(t)$ and $v_1(t)$ are plotted in Fig. 7-27. While the input jumps to unity at $t = 0$, $v_1(t)$ reaches unity at a later time. It takes still longer for $v_2(t)$ to reach unity. Even though $v_1(t)$ and $v_2(t)$ are not step functions, we may think of them as being delayed "versions" of the input signal. As the input signal propagates from left to right, the first capacitor voltage, $v_1(t)$, starts building up toward unity. This voltage, in turn, causes the second capacitor voltage, $v_2(t)$, to build up toward unity. Since $v_2(t)$ comes after $v_1(t)$ in the network, $v_2(t)$ is delayed more than $v_1(t)$. Indeed, had we added another resistor and capacitor on the right, the voltage across the third capacitor would have been delayed even further. However, the system would then no longer be second order. It would be third order (three capacitors).

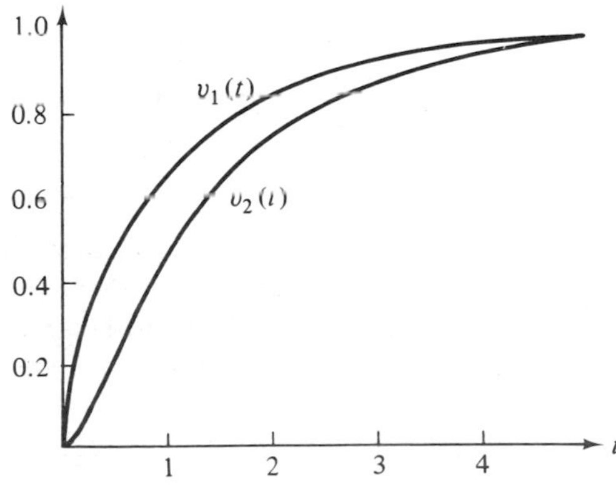

Fig. 7-27

COMPENSATED ATTENUATORS

Attenuators are widely used in voltmeters, oscilloscopes, and other electronic instruments. The basic voltage attenuator, as discussed in Section 2 of Chapter 2, consists of two resistors connected in such a way that a voltage-divider circuit is formed. See Fig. 7-28(a). Its transfer function is

$$T_a(s) = \frac{R_2}{R_1 + R_2} = \frac{1}{1 + \dfrac{R_1}{R_2}} \tag{7-45}$$

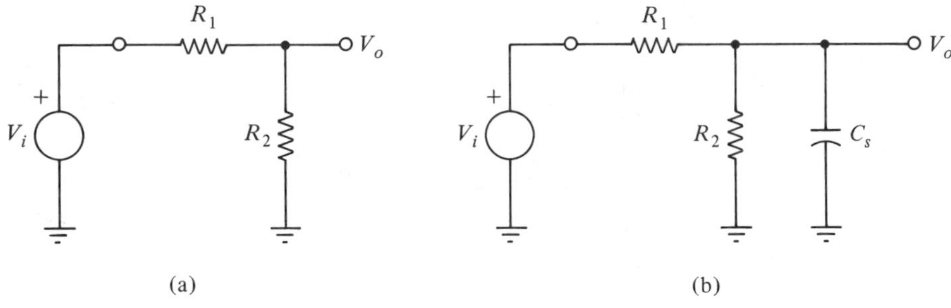

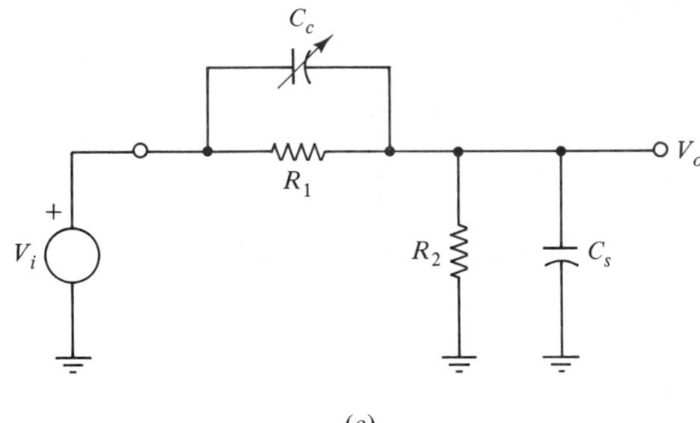

Fig. 7-28

By the appropriate selection of the R_1/R_2 ratio, various attenuation factors can be achieved. For example if $R_1/R_2 = 9$, the attenuation factor is $1/10$. This would complete the design if the input voltage were just constant (dc). However, if the input voltage changes, as it does when it is a step function, other factors must be considered. One of these is shown in Fig. 7-28(b). (For still other factors refer to Examples 7-11 and 7-12.) As signals are carried from one location to another, stray capacitances are inevitably picked up by the circuit wiring. Also the input impedance of the circuit to which the attenuated signal is taken for further processing may be capacitive. These undesirable and yet unavoidable capacitances are lumped together and modeled as C_s shunting the resistor R_2. As a result, the transfer function is no longer just a constant which represents the desired attenuation factor. It also contains a modifying factor which is a function of s.

$$T_b(s) = \underbrace{\left(\frac{1}{1 + \dfrac{R_1}{R_2}}\right)}_{\substack{\text{desired} \\ \text{attenuation}}} \underbrace{\left(\frac{\dfrac{1}{R_\parallel C_s}}{s + \dfrac{1}{R_\parallel C_s}}\right)}_{\substack{\text{modifying} \\ \text{factor}}}, \qquad R_\parallel = \frac{R_1 R_2}{R_1 + R_2} \tag{7-46}$$

As a consequence, a unit-step input does not produce an attenuated step output. Rather the output builds up exponentially toward the desired attenuation level with a time constant of $\tau_b = R_\parallel C_s$.

$$r(t) = \left(\frac{1}{1 + \dfrac{R_1}{R_2}}\right)(1 - e^{-t/(R_\parallel C_s)}) \tag{7-47}$$

The smaller τ_b, the more the output looks like the attenuated version of the input. This requires that the $R_\parallel C_s$ product be made as small as possible. By making both R_1 and R_2 small while holding their ratio R_2/R_1 constant, $R_\parallel$ can be made small. However, these resistors cannot be made too small, since the input voltage source can only supply a limited amount of current. In particular, for a V-volt step input, the source must be capable of supplying a current of V/R_1 at $t = 0^+$. (For $V = 10$ volts and $R_1 = 50\ \Omega$, this current would be 0.2 A. Most laboratory instruments cannot supply this critical current demand.) There is also a limit on how small C_s can be made. It is governed by circuit layout and the input capacitance of the following circuit.

After all is done to minimize the $R_\parallel C_s$ product, the step response of the attenuator may still not meet design specifications. In that case the transition time between the initial and final values can be further reduced by connecting a "speed-up" capacitor C_c across R_1. The result is the compensated attenuator shown in Fig. 7-28(c). Its transfer function is found as follows:

$$T_c(s) = \frac{Z_2}{Z_1 + Z_2}$$

where

$$Z_1 = \frac{R_1 \dfrac{1}{sC_c}}{R_1 + \dfrac{1}{sC_c}}, \qquad Z_2 = \frac{R_2 \dfrac{1}{sC_s}}{R_2 + \dfrac{1}{sC_s}}$$

$$T_c(s) = \left(\frac{1}{1 + \frac{C_s}{C_c}}\right)\frac{\left(s + \frac{1}{R_1C_c}\right)}{\left[s + \left(\frac{R_1 + R_2}{R_1R_2}\right)\left(\frac{1}{C_c + C_s}\right)\right]} \tag{7-48}$$

This transfer function can be rendered independent of s and hence made constant by cancelling the pole at $-[(R_1 + R_2)/R_1R_2][1/(C_c + C_s)]$ with the zero at $-(1/R_1C_c)$. Thus, we have

$$\left(\frac{R_1 + R_2}{R_1R_2}\right)\left(\frac{1}{C_c + C_s}\right) = \frac{1}{R_1C_c}$$

which simplifies to

$$C_c = C_s\left(\frac{R_2}{R_1}\right) \tag{7-49}$$

In a properly compensated attenuator C_c is adjusted to the value given by Eq. (7-49), in which case

$$T_c(s) = \frac{1}{1 + \frac{C_s}{C_c}} = \frac{1}{1 + \frac{R_1}{R_2}} \tag{7-50}$$

The corresponding unit-step response is shown in Fig. 7-29. Note that the output is the exact attenuated version of the input. If C_c is adjusted to a lower value than that given by Eq. (7-50), then the attenuator is *undercompensated*. Initially the output jumps to a lower value and then exponentially builds up to the desired value. On the other hand, if C_c is adjusted to a higher value, then the attenuator is *overcompensated*. Initially the output jumps to a higher value and then exponentially decays to the desired value. Whether over- or undercompensated, the exponential changes occur with a time constant of $R_\|(C_s + C_c)$, as can be seen from Eq. (7-48).

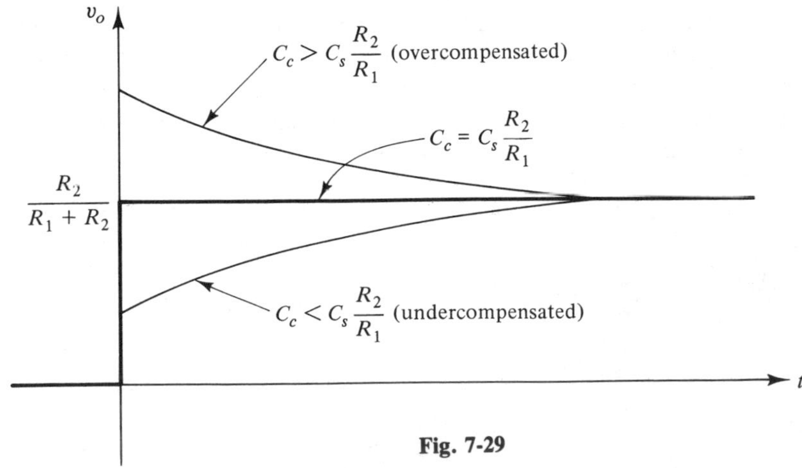

Fig. 7-29

Figure 7-29 shows that the output voltage jumps at $t = 0$. It jumps to $C_c/(C_c + C_s)$. See Problem 7-33. Since C_s is across the output, infinite current must flow through the capacitor to make its voltage jump in zero time! The same infinite current must also flow through C_c to make its voltage jump to $C_s/(C_c + C_s)$. The two capacitor voltage jumps, of course, add up to unity, which corresponds to the jump at the input. Since no real source can supply infinite current, the response of the compensated attenuator, in practice, will not quite be as shown in Fig. 7-29. As the following example shows, the internal resistance of the source, which so far has been assumed to be zero, puts a limit on the current that is available.

Example 7-11

A step-voltage source with an internal resistance of R ohms is shown in Fig. 7-30. This voltage is attenuated by a factor of 10 by the $89R$-$10R$ resistive attenuator shown.

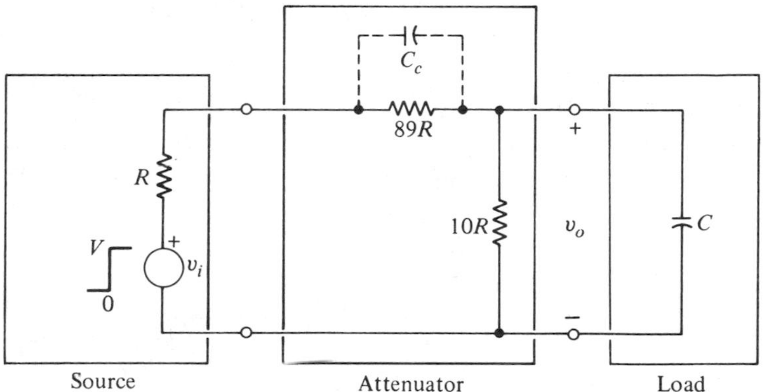

Fig. 7-30

(a) Show that the output is no longer a 10 : 1 attenuated version of the source voltage if the output is loaded by C.

(b) Show that the degradation in the output waveform caused by C can be reduced considerably by adding a compensating capacitor C_c (shown with dashed lines). Let $C_c = C/8.9$. The resulting attenuator is called a compensated attenuator.

Solution.

(a) With $C_c = 0$, the transfer function is

$$\frac{V_o}{V_i} = \frac{\dfrac{10R(1/sC)}{10R + (1/sC)}}{90R + \dfrac{10R(1/sC)}{10R + (1/sC)}} = \frac{1}{10}\frac{1/(9RC)}{s + 1/(9RC)}$$

This is a first-order transfer function. If the input is a step V volts high, the output is

$$V_o = \frac{V}{s}\frac{1}{10}\left[\frac{1/(9RC)}{s + 1/(9RC)}\right] = \frac{V}{10}\left[\frac{1}{s} - \frac{1}{s + 1/(9RC)}\right]$$

$$v_o(t) = \frac{V}{10}[1 - e^{-(t/9RC)}] \tag{7-51}$$

If the capacitive load is taken off ($C = 0$), the output jumps to $V/10$, which is the desired goal. However, because of C, the output builds up exponentially toward $V/10$ with a time constant of $9RC$. Hence the output is not a 10 : 1 attenuated version of the input step. Only after the capacitor current drops to zero [$t > 5(9RC)$] do we obtain the desired attenuation.

(b) With C_c included, the transfer function is

$$\frac{V_o}{V_i} = \frac{\dfrac{10R(1/sC)}{10R + (1/sC)}}{R + \dfrac{89R(1/sC_c)}{89R + (1/sC_c)} + \dfrac{10R(1/sC)}{10R + (1/sC)}}$$

$$= \frac{1}{10}\left[\frac{89sRC_c + 1}{8.9s^2R^2CC_c + sR(9C + 9.79C_c) + 1}\right]$$

This is a second-order system. However, as shown below, it *reduces to a first-order system, through pole-zero cancellation,* if C_c is chosen to equal $C/8.9$.

$$\frac{V_o}{V_i} = \frac{1}{10}\left(\frac{10sRC + 1}{s^2R^2C^2 + s\,10.1RC + 1}\right)$$

$$= \frac{1}{10}\frac{\cancel{(10sRC + 1)}}{\cancel{(10sRC + 1)}(0.1sRC + 1)} = \frac{1}{10}\left(\frac{1}{0.1sRC + 1}\right)$$

$$\frac{V_o}{V_i} = \frac{1}{10}\left[\frac{10/RC}{s + (10/RC)}\right]$$

To obtain the output, we let $V_i = V/s$.

$$V_o = \frac{V}{s}\frac{1}{10}\left[\frac{10/RC}{s + (10/RC)}\right] = \frac{V}{10}\left[\frac{1}{s} - \frac{1}{s + (10/RC)}\right]$$

$$v_o(t) = \frac{V}{10}[1 - e^{-t/(RC/10)}] \tag{7-52}$$

Now we compare the step response of the two first-order systems. The one with no compensating capacitor is given by Eq. (7-51). The one with the appropriately chosen capacitor is given by Eq. (7-52).

$$v_o(t) = \frac{V}{10}(1 - e^{-t/9RC}) \qquad (C_c = 0)$$

$$v_o(t) = \frac{V}{10}(1 - e^{-t/0.1RC}) \qquad \left(C_c = \frac{C}{8.9}\right)$$

Although both responses are exponential (rather than step functions), the response with the compensating capacitor has a time constant 90 times smaller than the response with no compensating capacitor. Thus it will reach the steady-state value of $V/10$ volts 90 times faster, which means that it will look more like the attenuated version of the input. This situation is shown in Fig. 7-31.

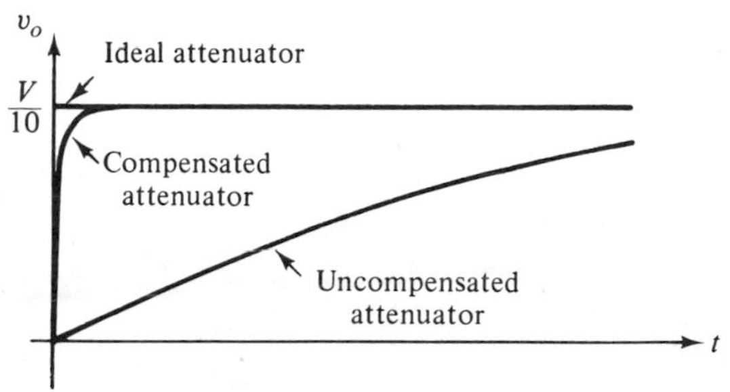

Fig. 7-31

It is interesting to note that the condition

$$C_c = \frac{C}{8.9}$$

can be written

$$89RC_c = 10RC$$

which shows that compensation is achieved when the resistance-capacitance products of the two individual parallel sections in Fig. 7-30 are made equal. (See also Problem 7-31.)

Example 7-12

In Fig. 7-32 the voltage source is capable of delivering up to 100 mA of current. If the input is a 10 V step, what is the output?

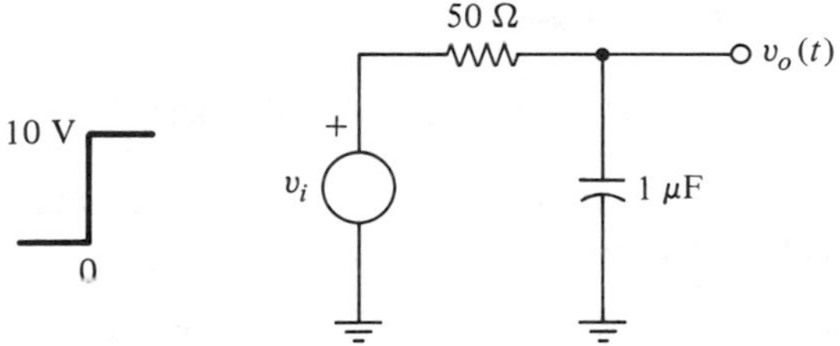

Fig. 7-32

Solution. At $t = 0^+$ the output voltage, being the voltage across a capacitor, is still 0. Hence the voltage source is asked to deliver initially a current of 10 V/50 Ω = 200 mA. But it cannot do so! It can provide a maximum of only 100 mA. What then happens depends on the particular design used in the construction of the voltage source. Here, we will assume that, being current limited, the voltage source will not work as intended but rather become a 100 mA current source as shown in Fig. 7-33(a). Since the current through the capacitor is constant, the voltage across it will build up linearly.

$$v_o(t) = \frac{1}{C}\int_0^t i(t')\,dt' = \frac{1}{1 \times 10^6}\int_0^t 0.1\,dt' = 10^5 t$$

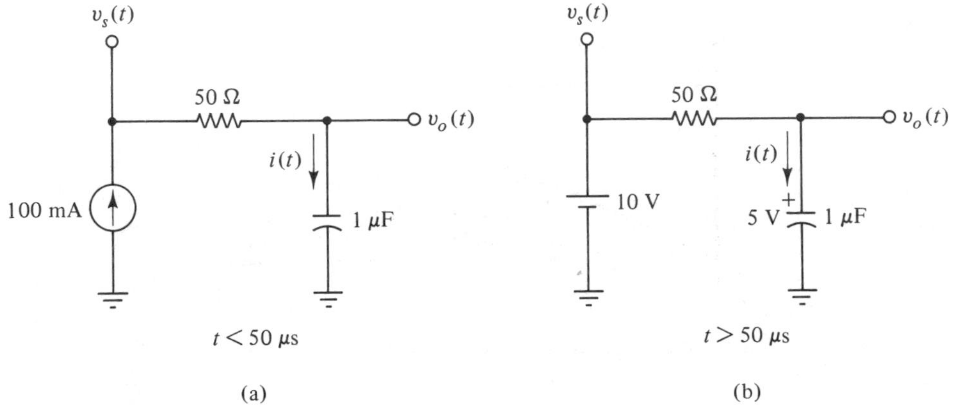

Fig. 7-33

In the meantime the voltage across the source will develop according to

$$v_s(t) = i(t)R + v_o(t) = 5 + 10^5 t$$

Note that this voltage starts out with 5 V and then linearly rises. At $t = 5 \times 10^{-5} = 50\ \mu s$, the capacitor and source voltage reach 5 V and 10 V, respectively. If now the source were to revert back to its normal mode of operation as a voltage source, it will be able to supply the ensuing current demand while maintaining 10 V across itself. The situation is as shown in Fig. 7-33(b). Note the 5 V across the capacitor. The current $i(t)$ is then given by

$$i(t) = 100\, e^{-(t-50\times10^{-6})/(50\times10^{-6})}\ \text{mA}, \qquad t > 50\ \mu s$$

which being equal to or less than 100 mA is well within the capability of the voltage source.

With initial and final values of 5 V and 10 V, respectively, the expression for the output voltage can readily be obtained.

$$v_o(t) = 10 - 5e^{\,(t-50\times10^{-6}/(50\times10^{-6})}, \qquad t \geq 50\ \mu s$$

Because of the inability of the voltage source to meet the demands placed by this particular load, the output voltage will not be a single exponential but rather a linear curve followed by an exponential as shown in Fig. 7-34. To keep the discussion on the source limitations simple, a first-order RC circuit is used in this example. Similar techniques can be used to obtain the responses of second- and higher-order systems.

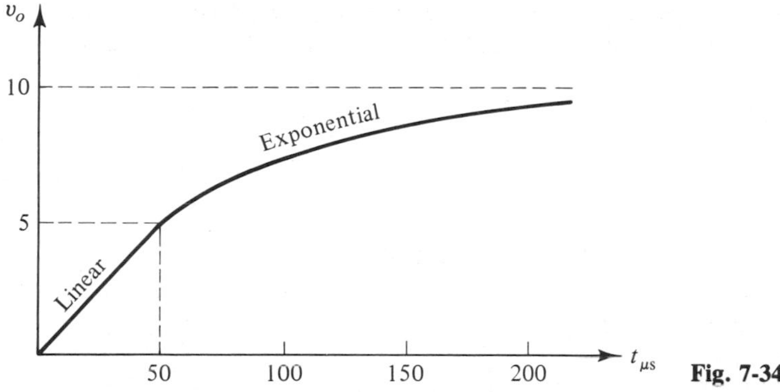

Fig. 7-34

7-7 STEP RESPONSE WITH COMPLEX-CONJUGATE POLES

Consider next the unit-step response of second-order systems that have left half-plane, complex-conjugate poles. (See Fig. 7-2.) The transfer function is described by

$$T(s) = \frac{a_2 s^2 + a_1 s + a_0}{(s + \alpha)^2 + \beta^2} \tag{7-53}$$

where $-\alpha$ is the real part of the poles and the $\pm\beta$ are the imaginary parts.

The unit-step response is obtained from

$$R(s) = \frac{1}{s} \frac{a_2 s^2 + a_1 s + a_0}{(s + \alpha)^2 + \beta^2} \tag{7-54}$$

After some manipulation (see Problem 7-37), Eq. (7-54) can be decomposed into

$$\begin{aligned} R(s) &= \frac{a_0}{\alpha^2 + \beta^2} \frac{1}{s} + \left(a_2 - \frac{a_0}{\alpha^2 + \beta^2}\right)\left[\frac{(s + \alpha)}{(s + \alpha)^2 + \beta^2}\right] \\ &\quad + \frac{1}{\beta}\left(a_1 - \alpha \frac{a_0}{\alpha^2 + \beta^2} - a_2 \alpha\right)\left[\frac{\beta}{(s + \alpha)^2 + \beta^2}\right] \end{aligned}$$

Using Table 5-1, we obtain $r(t)$.

$$\begin{aligned} r(t) &= \frac{a_0}{\alpha^2 + \beta^2} + \left(a_2 - \frac{a_0}{\alpha^2 + \beta^2}\right) e^{-\alpha t} \cos \beta t \\ &\quad + \frac{1}{\beta}\left(a_1 - \frac{\alpha a_0}{\alpha^2 + \beta^2} - a_2 \alpha\right) e^{-\alpha t} \sin \beta t \qquad (\beta \neq 0,\ t > 0) \end{aligned} \tag{7-55}$$

This equation gives the response for $t > 0$. The response for $t < 0$ is zero, because the system is assumed to be dead, and the input is zero. (Initial conditions are treated later.)

At $t = 0^+$ the response is

$$r(0^+) = \frac{a_0}{\alpha^2 + \beta^2} + \left(a_2 - \frac{a_0}{\alpha^2 + \beta^2}\right) = a_2 = T(s)\Big|_{s=\infty} \tag{7-56}$$

Thus the initial value of the response is determined by $T(\infty)$.

If $a_2 \neq 0$, the response at $t = 0$ jumps from zero to a_2. If $a_2 = 0$, the response is zero and hence continuous at $t = 0$.

At $t = \infty$ the response is

$$r(\infty) = \frac{a_0}{\alpha^2 + \beta^2} = T(s)\Big|_{s=0} \tag{7-57}$$

Therefore the final value of the response is determined by $T(0)$.

The general form of the response is

$$r(t) = A + Be^{-\alpha t}\cos\beta t + Ce^{-\alpha t}\sin\beta t \qquad (t > 0) \tag{7-58}$$

which can be regrouped as

$$r(t) = A + e^{-\alpha t}(B\cos\beta t + C\sin\beta t)$$

$$r(t) = A + \sqrt{B^2 + C^2}e^{-\alpha t}\sin\left(\beta t + \tan^{-1}\frac{B}{C}\right) \qquad (t > 0) \tag{7-59a}$$

$$r(t) = A + \sqrt{B^2 + C^2}e^{-\alpha t}\cos\left(\beta t - \tan^{-1}\frac{C}{B}\right) \qquad (t > 0) \tag{7-59b}$$

Since $\alpha > 0$, we see that the response consists of a constant and a damped sinusoid. The time constant associated with the exponential is $1/\alpha$. So after five time constants ($t > 5/\alpha$) the response is almost equal to A. (If α were zero, the response would be the sum of a constant and a sinusoid. If α were negative, the response would be the sum of a constant and an exponentially growing sinusoid.)

7-8 STEP RESPONSE WHEN $T_0 = \dfrac{(\alpha^2 + \beta^2)}{(s + \alpha)^2 + \beta^2}$

A second-order transfer function with a constant numerator and left half-plane, complex-conjugate poles is represented in block diagram form in Fig. 7-35(a). $T_0(s)$ is described by

$$T_0(s) = \frac{(\alpha^2 + \beta^2)}{(s + \alpha)^2 + \beta^2} = \frac{\alpha^2 + \beta^2}{s^2 + 2\alpha s + \alpha^2 + \beta^2} \tag{7-60}$$

The poles of $T_0(s)$ are shown in Fig. 7-35(b). Note that $\sqrt{\alpha^2 + \beta^2}$ represents the distance of the poles from the origin.

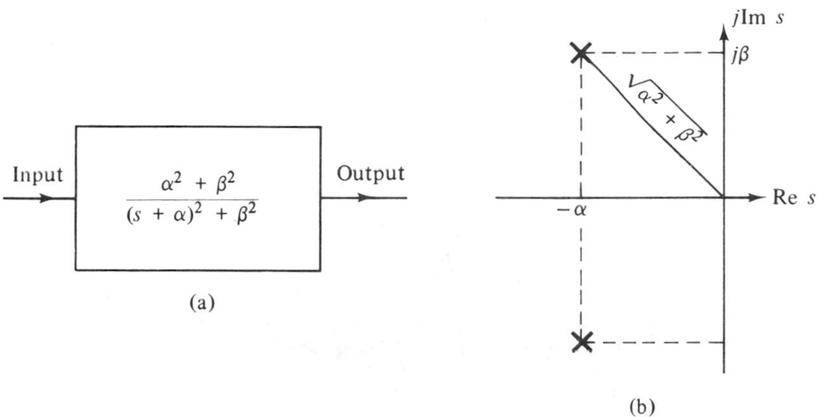

Fig. 7-35

The unit-step response of $T_0(s)$ is obtained by letting $a_2 = a_1 = 0$ and $a_0 = \alpha^2 + \beta^2$ in Eq. (7-55).

$$r(t) = 1 - e^{-\alpha t}\left(\cos \beta t + \frac{\alpha}{\beta} \sin \beta t\right) \qquad (\beta \neq 0, \qquad t \geq 0) \qquad \text{(7-61)}$$

The initial and final values of the response are

$$r(0) = 0, \qquad r(\infty) = 1 \qquad (\alpha > 0)$$

Regardless of the complex pole positions, the response starts at zero and ends at one. Furthermore, the response starts out horizontally because $r'(0) = 0$, as can be seen by differentiating $r(t)$ with respect to t and letting $t = 0$.

The step response of $T_0(s)$ can be studied in several ways. We can, for example, keep α constant at some value and vary β to see how the response is affected. To make the resulting response curves as general as possible, we rearrange Eq. (7-61) as follows.

$$r(t) = 1 - e^{-(\alpha t)}\left\{\cos\left[\left(\frac{\beta}{\alpha}\right)(\alpha t)\right] + \left(\frac{\alpha}{\beta}\right) \sin\left[\left(\frac{\beta}{\alpha}\right)(\alpha t)\right]\right\} \qquad \text{(7-62)}$$

Since α is constant, we can use (αt) as the independent variable. Since β/α always appears as a ratio, we can use it as a parameter to show the effect of β variation. Equation (7-62) is plotted in Fig. 7-36, which also shows the pole locations.

As illustrated, the larger the β/α ratio, the more cycles of ringing the sine wave undergoes before it is damped out. Stated differently, the frequency of ringing is higher. If $\alpha/\beta \ll 1$, the amplitude envelope for all practical purposes is given by $1 \pm e^{-\alpha t}$.

Suppose that instead of keeping α constant while we vary β, we keep $\sqrt{\alpha^2 + \beta^2}$ constant while we vary the β/α ratio. To study the effects of this kind of variation, we must rearrange Eq. (7-61) differently.

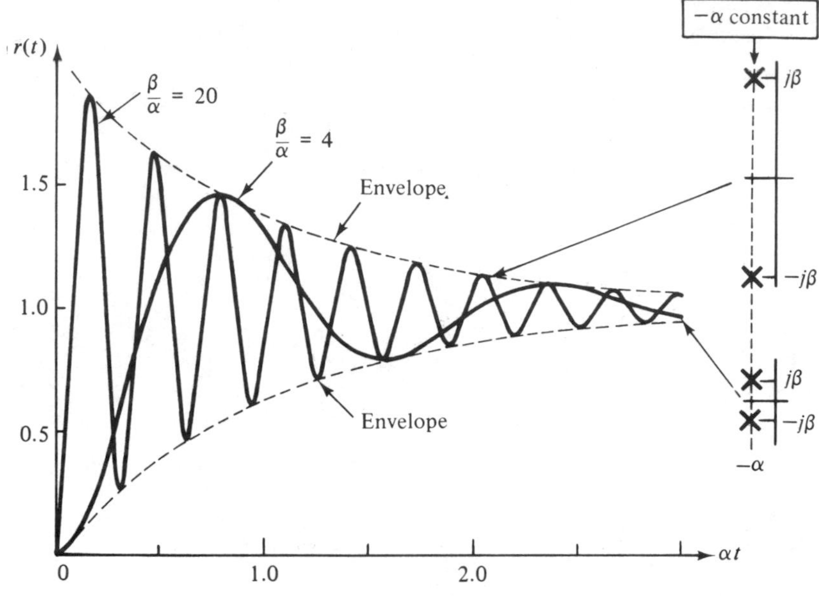

Fig. 7-36

$$r(t) = 1 - e^{-(\alpha/\sqrt{\alpha^2+\beta^2})(\sqrt{\alpha^2+\beta^2}t)}\left\{\cos\left[\frac{\beta}{\sqrt{\alpha^2+\beta^2}}(\sqrt{\alpha^2+\beta^2}t)\right] + \left(\frac{\alpha}{\beta}\right)\sin\left[\frac{\beta}{\sqrt{\alpha^2+\beta^2}}(\sqrt{\alpha^2+\beta^2}t)\right]\right\}$$

$$r(t') = 1 - e^{-(1/\sqrt{1+(\beta/\alpha)^2})t'}\left[\cos\left(\frac{1}{\sqrt{1+(\alpha/\beta)^2}}t'\right) + \left(\frac{\alpha}{\beta}\right)\sin\left(\frac{1}{\sqrt{1+(\alpha/\beta)^2}}t'\right)\right] \qquad (t' = \sqrt{\alpha^2+\beta^2}t) \tag{7-63}$$

Since $\sqrt{\alpha^2 + \beta^2}$ is kept constant, we can plot Eq. (7-63) as a function of t' (rather than t) without distorting the time axis. Again, the β/α ratio is used as a parameter. The results are shown in Fig. 7-37. Note that as β/α is varied while $\sqrt{\alpha^2 + \beta^2}$ is held constant, the poles move on a circle of radius $\sqrt{\alpha^2 + \beta^2}$.

As β/α varies from 20 to 4, the imaginary part of the poles hardly varies (see pole diagram). However, the real part varies almost 5 : 1. The $\beta/\alpha = 4$ curve is damped five times faster than the $\beta/\alpha = 20$ curve, whereas the frequency of ringing remains about the same in both cases. If β/α is lowered further, the curve is damped out faster while the frequency of ringing, β, becomes lower. In conclusion, if we want the system to ring a great deal, the β/α ratio must be made high; that is, the poles must be placed close to the imaginary axis. Alternatively stated, a ringing step response implies poles close to the imaginary axis.

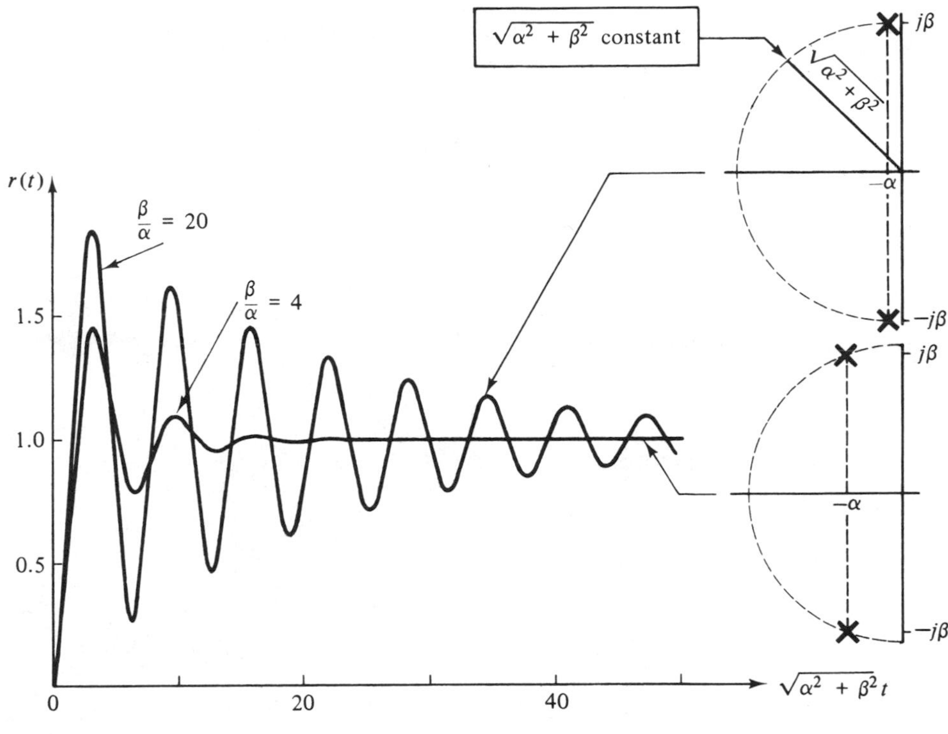

Fig. 7-37

Example 7-13

Refer to the network of Fig. 7-38.

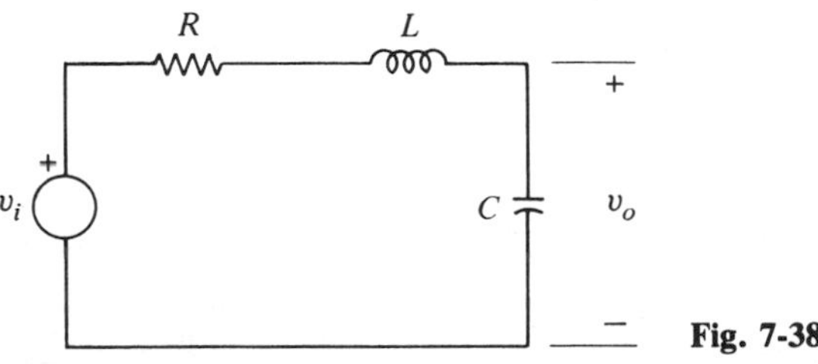

Fig. 7-38

(a) In order for the poles to be complex, what condition must be satisfied? Obtain α, β, and $\sqrt{\alpha^2 + \beta^2}$.

(b) The input is a step function. What element must be varied to obtain the curves displayed in Fig. 7-36? What element must be varied to obtain the curves displayed in Fig. 7-37?

Solution

(a) This network is the same as in Example 7-2. The transfer function is

$$\frac{V_o}{V_i} = \frac{1/LC}{s^2 + s(R/L) + (1/LC)}$$

The poles are at

$$p_{1,2} = -\frac{R}{2L} \pm \sqrt{\left(\frac{R}{2L}\right)^2 - \frac{1}{LC}} \tag{7-64}$$

If the poles are to be complex, the discriminant must be negative—that is,

$$\left(\frac{R}{2L}\right)^2 - \frac{1}{LC} < 0$$

which simplifies to

$$R < 2\sqrt{\frac{L}{C}} \quad \text{Ans.} \tag{7-65}$$

To show the complex nature of the poles, we write Eq. (7-64) as

$$p_{1,2} = -\frac{R}{2L} \pm j\sqrt{\frac{1}{LC} - \left(\frac{R}{2L}\right)^2} = -\alpha \pm j\beta \tag{7-66}$$

Thus

$$\alpha = \frac{R}{2L}, \qquad \beta = \sqrt{\frac{1}{LC} - \left(\frac{R}{2L}\right)^2}, \qquad \sqrt{\alpha^2 + \beta^2} = \frac{1}{\sqrt{LC}} \quad \text{Ans.}$$

(b) The curves of Fig. 7-36 are obtained by varying β while α is held constant. Since $\alpha = R/2L$, it can be held constant by keeping both R and L (or the R/L ratio) constant. β can then be varied by changing C.
The curves of Fig. 7-37 are obtained by varying the β/α ratio while $\sqrt{\alpha^2 + \beta^2}$ is held constant. Since $\sqrt{\alpha^2 + \beta^2} = \sqrt{1/LC}$, it can be held constant by keeping both L and C (or the LC product) constant. The β/α ratio can then be varied by changing R.

Example 7-14

Refer to the network of Fig. 7-39.

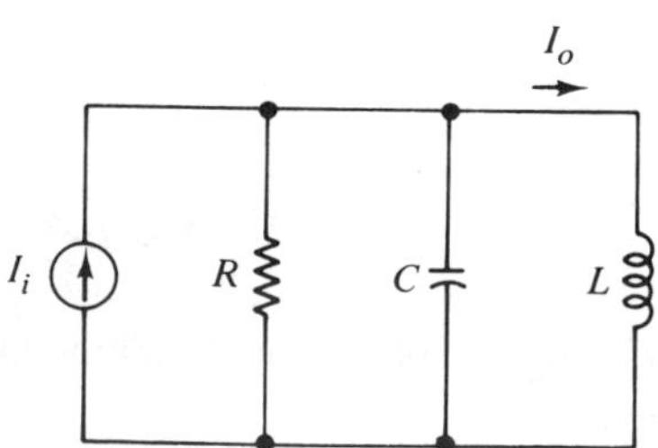

Fig. 7-39

(a) Obtain I_o/I_i.

(b) Determine the poles for $R = \frac{1}{10}\sqrt{L/C}$, $R = \frac{1}{2}\sqrt{L/C}$, and $R = 10\sqrt{L/C}$ and plot the corresponding unit-step responses.

Solution

(a)

$$I_o = I_i \frac{\dfrac{R(1/sC)}{R + (1/sC)}}{\dfrac{R(1/sC)}{R + (1/sC)} + sL} = I_i \frac{\dfrac{R}{sRC + 1}}{\dfrac{R}{sRC + 1} + sL}$$

$$\frac{I_o}{I_i} = \frac{1/LC}{s^2 + s(1/RC) + (1/LC)} \quad \text{Ans.}$$

(b) The poles are obtained from

$$s^2 + s\frac{1}{RC} + \frac{1}{LC} = 0$$

$$p_{1,2} = -\frac{1}{2RC} \pm \sqrt{\left(\frac{1}{2RC}\right)^2 - \frac{1}{LC}} \tag{7-67a}$$

$$p_{1,2} = -\frac{1}{2RC} \pm j\sqrt{\frac{1}{LC} - \left(\frac{1}{2RC}\right)^2} \tag{7-67b}$$

where Eq. (7-67a) is used if $R \le \frac{1}{2}\sqrt{L/C}$ and Eq. (7-67b) is used if $R \ge \frac{1}{2}\sqrt{L/C}$. For $R = \frac{1}{10}\sqrt{L/C}$, the poles are on the real axis, and we have from Eq. (7-67a)

$$p_{1,2} = -\frac{1}{2 \times (1/10)\sqrt{(L/C)}C} \pm \sqrt{\left(\frac{1}{2 \times (1/10)\sqrt{(L/C)}C}\right)^2 - \frac{1}{LC}}$$

$$= -\frac{5}{\sqrt{LC}} \pm \sqrt{\frac{25}{LC} - \frac{1}{LC}} = \frac{1}{\sqrt{LC}}(-5 \pm 2\sqrt{6})$$

The corresponding unit-step response is obtained from Eq. (7-12) with

$$\alpha_1 = \frac{1}{\sqrt{LC}}(5 - 2\sqrt{6}) \quad \text{and} \quad \alpha_2 = \frac{1}{\sqrt{LC}}(5 + 2\sqrt{6}) \tag{7-68}$$

$$i_o(t) = 1 + \frac{1}{4\sqrt{6}}[(5 - 2\sqrt{6})e^{-[(5+2\sqrt{6})/\sqrt{LC}]t} - (5 + 2\sqrt{6})e^{-[(5-2\sqrt{6})/\sqrt{LC}]t}]$$

For $R = \frac{1}{2}\sqrt{L/C}$, the discriminant in Eq. (7-67) is zero, and we have both poles in the same location on the negative real axis.

$$p_{1,2} = -\frac{1}{2 \times (1/2)\sqrt{(L/C)}C} = -\frac{1}{\sqrt{LC}}$$

The corresponding unit-step response is obtained from the answer to Problem 7-2 with $\alpha = 1/\sqrt{LC}$:

$$i_o(t) = 1 - \left(1 + \frac{1}{\sqrt{LC}}t\right)e^{-t/\sqrt{LC}} \tag{7-69}$$

For $R = 10\sqrt{L/C}$, the poles are complex conjugates, and we have from Eq. (7-67b)

$$p_{1,2} = -\frac{1}{2 \times 10\sqrt{(L/C)}C} \pm j\sqrt{\frac{1}{LC} - \left[\frac{1}{2 \times 10\sqrt{(L/C)}C}\right]^2}$$

$$= -\frac{1}{20\sqrt{LC}} \pm j\sqrt{\frac{1}{LC} - \frac{1}{400LC}} \cong \frac{1}{\sqrt{LC}}\left(-\frac{1}{20} \pm j\right)$$

The corresponding unit-step response is obtained from Eq. (7-61) with

$$\alpha = \frac{1}{20\sqrt{LC}} \text{ and } \beta \cong \frac{1}{\sqrt{LC}}$$

$$i_o(t) = 1 - e^{-t/(20\sqrt{LC})}\left(\cos\frac{t}{\sqrt{LC}} + \frac{1}{20}\sin\frac{t}{\sqrt{LC}}\right) \tag{7-70}$$

So, depending on the resistance value, the response is governed by (7-68), (7-69), or (7-70). The responses given by these three equations are plotted in Fig. 7-40. Note that the response reacts much faster (gets up to the 1 A level sooner) if the poles are complex. However, the response overshoots and rings before it settles at the final value.

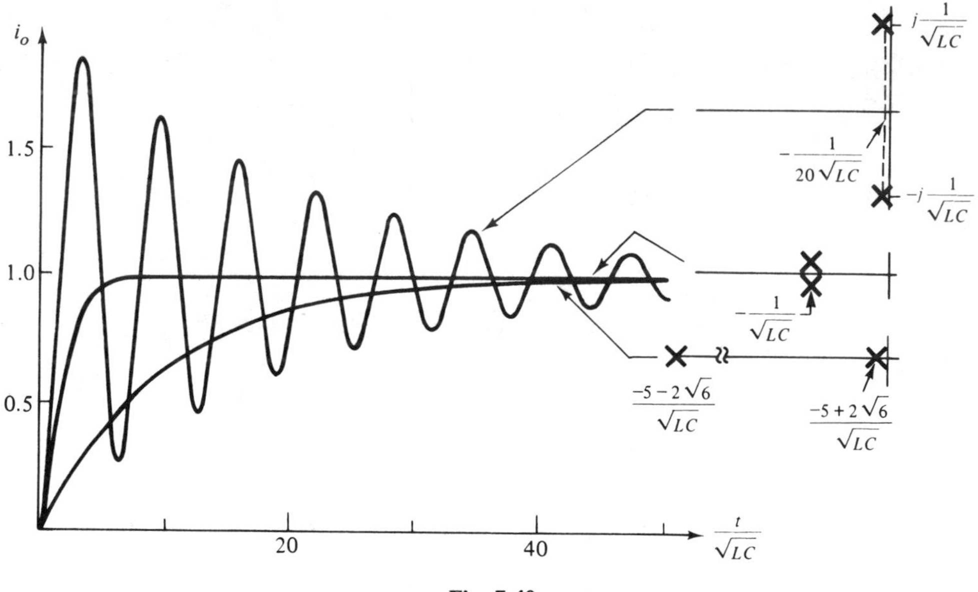

Fig. 7-40

7-9 STEP RESPONSE WHEN $T_1 = \frac{2\alpha s}{(s+\alpha)^2 + \beta^2}$

A second-order transfer function with a zero at the origin and with left half-plane complex poles is presented in block diagram form in Fig. 7-41(a). $T_1(s)$ is described by

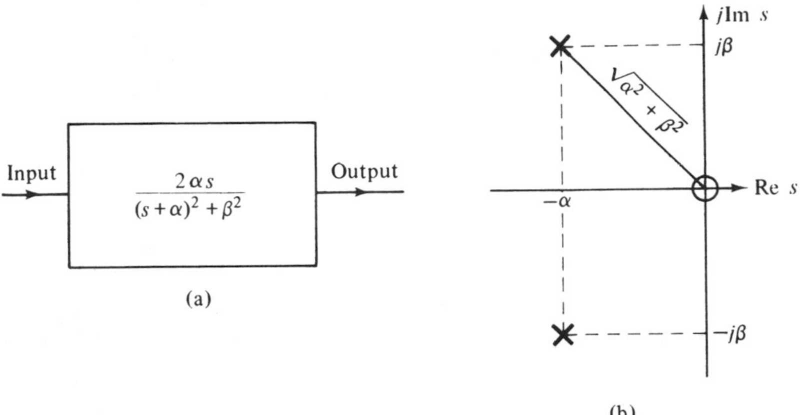

Fig. 7-41

$$T_1(s) = \frac{2\alpha s}{(s+\alpha)^2+\beta^2} = \frac{2\alpha s}{s^2+2\alpha s+\alpha^2+\beta^2} \tag{7-71}$$

The zero and the poles of $T_1(s)$ are shown in Fig. 7-41(b).

The unit-step response of $T_1(s)$ is obtained by letting $a_2 = a_0 = 0$ and $a_1 = 2\alpha$ in Eq. (7-55).

$$r(t) = \frac{2\alpha}{\beta}e^{-\alpha t}\sin\beta t \qquad (\beta \neq 0, \qquad t \geq 0) \tag{7-72}$$

The initial and final values of the response are

$$r(0) = 0, \qquad r(\infty) = 0 \qquad (\alpha > 0)$$

Regardless of the complex pole positions, the response starts and ends at zero.

To plot the unit-step response of $T_1(s)$, we can rearrange Eq. (7-72) as

$$r(t') = 2\left(\frac{\alpha}{\beta}\right)e^{-t'}\sin\left(\frac{\beta}{\alpha}\right)t' \qquad (t' = \alpha t) \tag{7-73a}$$

or

$$r(t') = 2\left(\frac{\alpha}{\beta}\right)e^{-t'/\sqrt{1+(\beta/\alpha)^2}}\sin\frac{t'}{\sqrt{1+(\alpha/\beta)^2}} \qquad (t' = \sqrt{\alpha^2+\beta^2}t) \tag{7-73b}$$

Equation (7-73a) is plotted in Fig. 7-42(a), and Eq. (7-73b) in Fig. 7-42(b). In both plots, β/α is used as a parameter. As these curves indicate, the larger the β/α ratio, the more the step response of $T_1(s)$ rings before it dies out completely.

Example 7-15

When a unit-step voltage is applied to a network, we want the output voltage to be

$$v_o(t) = 2e^{-t}\sin t$$

Design the network.

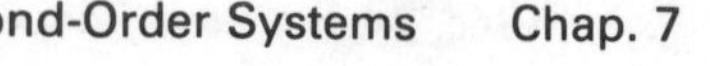

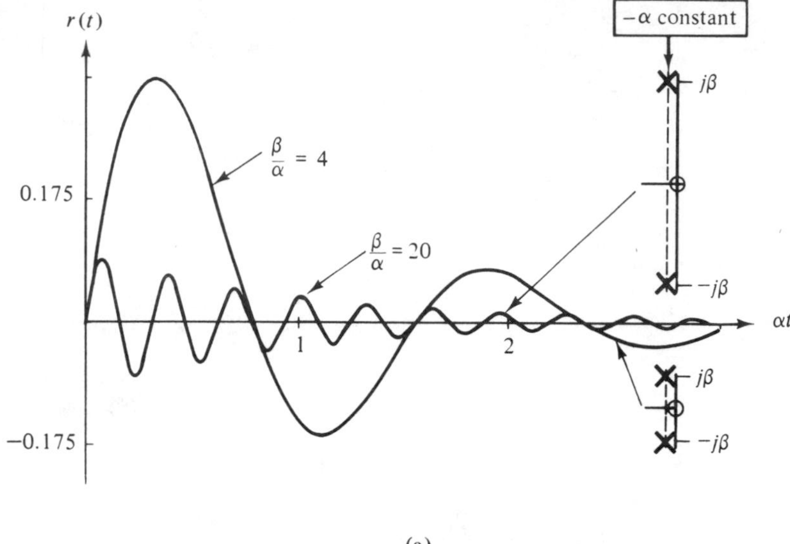
r(t)
−α constant
jβ
β/α = 4
0.175
β/α = 20
−jβ
1
2
αt
jβ
−jβ
−0.175

(a)

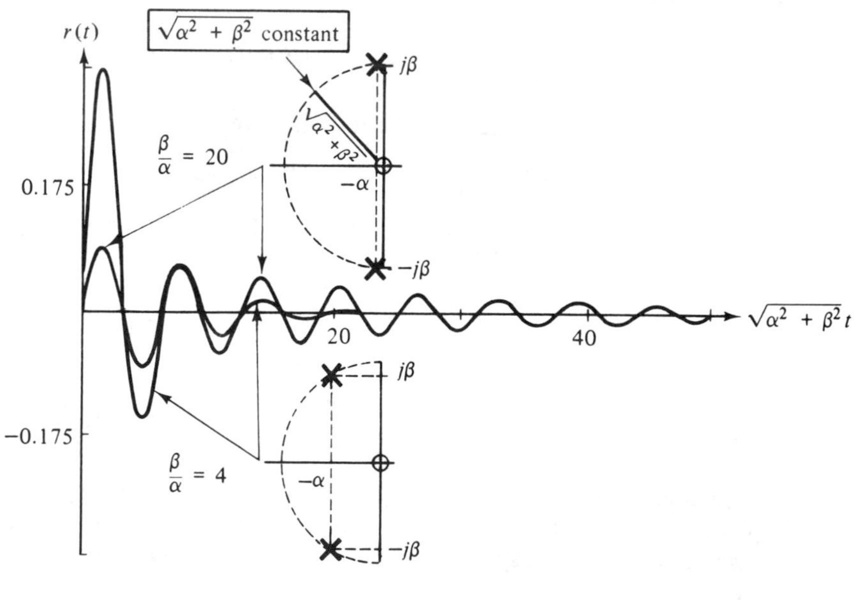
r(t)
√(α² + β²) constant
jβ
β/α = 20
0.175
−α
−jβ
20
40
√(α² + β²) t
jβ
−0.175
β/α = 4
−α
−jβ

(b)

Fig. 7-42

Solution. From the given input and output we can determine the transfer function.

$$V_i = \frac{1}{s}$$

$$V_o = \mathcal{L}\{2e^{-t} \sin t\} = \frac{2}{(s+1)^2 + 1}$$

$$T = \frac{V_o}{V_i} = \frac{2s}{s^2 + 2s + 2} = T_1$$

Alternatively, we could have compared the given output to Eq. (7-72) and recognized that it is the response of $T_1(s)$ given by Eq. (7-71) with $\alpha = \beta = 1$.

We now realize $T_1(s)$ by using the voltage-divider rule between two impedances Z_1 and Z_2 as shown in Fig. 7-43(a).

$$\frac{2s}{s^2 + 2s + 2} = \frac{Z_2}{Z_1 + Z_2} \tag{7-74}$$

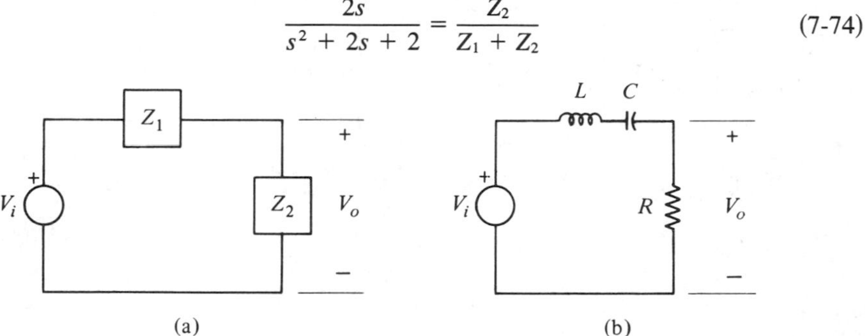

Fig. 7-43

To obtain identifiable impedances, let us divide the numerator and denominator of T_1 by $2s$. (We could just as well divide by ks, where k is a positive number.)

$$\frac{V_o}{V_i} = \frac{2s/2s}{[(s^2 + 2)/2s] + (2s/2s)} = \frac{\overbrace{1}^{Z_2}}{\underbrace{[s(1/2) + (1/s)]}_{Z_1} + \underbrace{1}_{Z_2}}$$

We see that

$$Z_1 = s\frac{1}{2} + \frac{1}{s}$$

is the series combination of a $\frac{1}{2}$ H inductor with a 1 F capacitor, wheras $Z_2 = 1$ is realizable with a 1 Ω resistor. Thus we can design the network as in Fig. 7-43(b) with $L = \frac{1}{2}$, $C = 1$, and $R = 1$.

The design is not unique. We could have divided the numerator and denominator just as well by $(s^2 + 2)$ and then obtained another network that produces exactly the same response (see Problem 7-46).

7-10 STEP RESPONSE WHEN $T_2 = \dfrac{s^2}{(s+\alpha)^2+\beta^2}$

Figure 7-44(a) represents a block diagram of a second-order transfer function with two zeros at the origin and with left half-plane complex poles. $T_2(s)$ is described by

$$T_2(s) = \frac{s^2}{(s+\alpha)^2+\beta^2} = \frac{s^2}{s^2+2\alpha s+\alpha^2+\beta^2} \tag{7-75}$$

The zeros and poles of $T_2(s)$ are shown in Fig. 7-44(b).

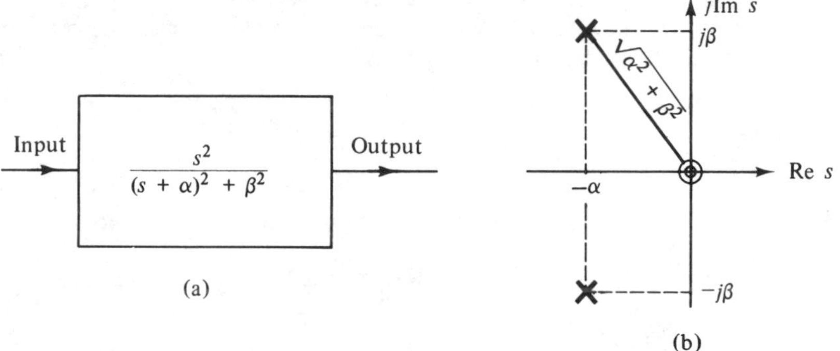

Fig. 7-44

The unit-step response of $T_2(s)$ is obtained by letting $a_2 = 1$ and $a_1 = a_0 = 0$ in Eq. (7-55).

$$r(t) = e^{-\alpha t}\left(\cos \beta t - \frac{\alpha}{\beta}\sin \beta t\right) \qquad (\beta \neq 0, \quad t > 0) \tag{7-76}$$

The initial and final values of the response are

$$r(0^+) = 1, \qquad r(\infty) = 0$$

Regardless of the complex pole positions, the response starts at one and ends at zero.

The response can be plotted in many ways, depending on what is kept constant and what is varied. Two possible ways of representing the response curves are based on the following rearrangements of Eq. (7-76).

$$r(t') = e^{-t'}\left[\cos\left(\frac{\beta}{\alpha}\right)t' - \left(\frac{\alpha}{\beta}\right)\sin\left(\frac{\beta}{\alpha}\right)t'\right] \qquad (t' = \alpha t) \tag{7-77a}$$

$$r(t') = e^{-t'/\sqrt{1+(\beta/\alpha)^2}}\left[\cos\frac{t'}{\sqrt{1+(\alpha/\beta)^2}} - \left(\frac{\alpha}{\beta}\right)\sin\frac{t'}{\sqrt{1+(\alpha/\beta)^2}}\right]$$
$$(t' = \sqrt{\alpha^2+\beta^2}\,t) \tag{7-77b}$$

Equation (7-77a) is plotted in Fig. 7-45(a) and Eq. (7-77b) in Fig. 7-45(b). In both plots, β/α is used as a parameter.

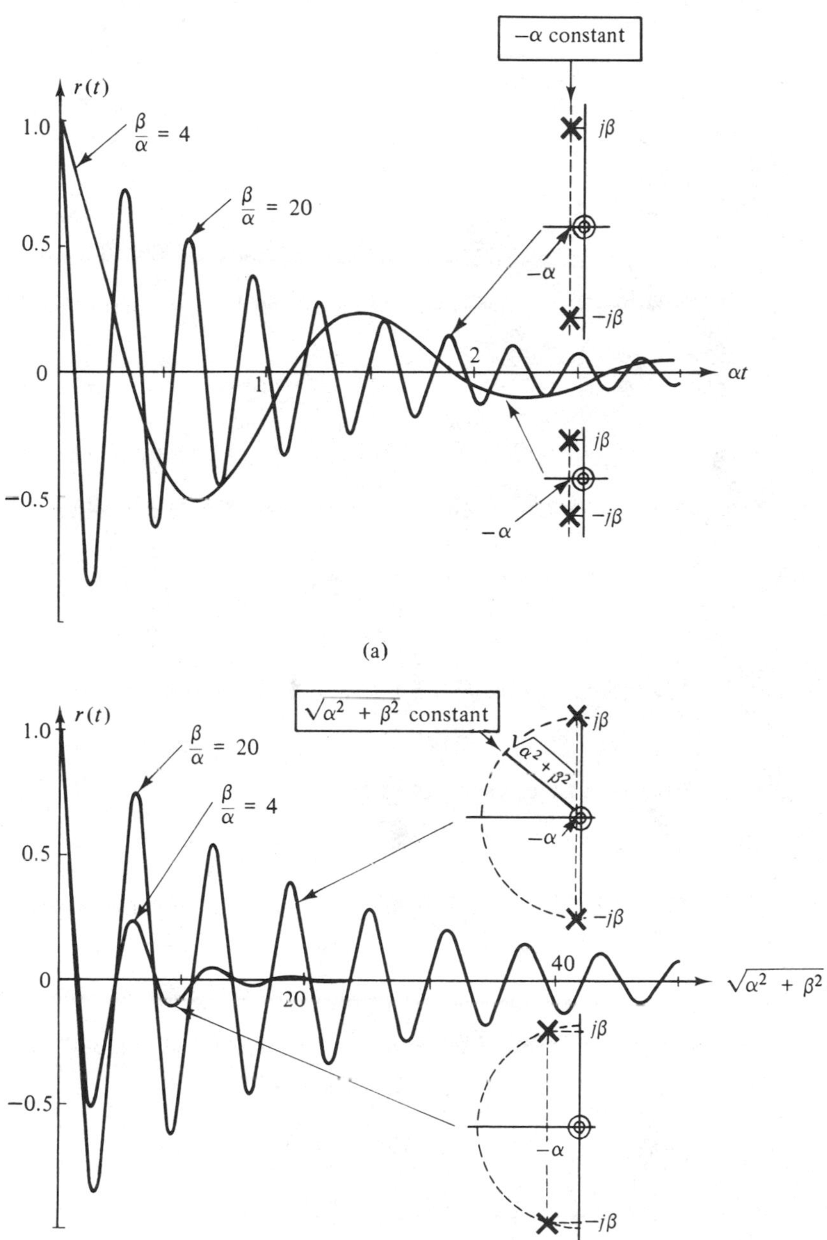

(b)

Fig. 7-45

Example 7-16

Sketch the unit-step response of the network shown in Fig. 7-46 for $R \gg 2\sqrt{L/C}$ and $R = 0$.

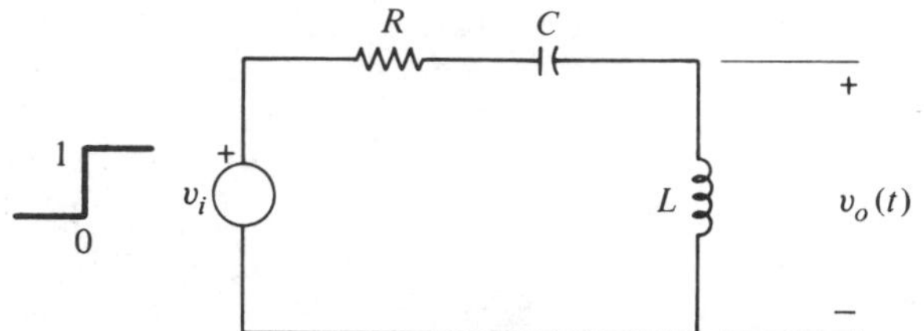

Fig. 7-46

Solution. To see the effect of R, we calculate the transfer function and the poles.

$$\frac{V_o}{V_i} = \frac{s^2}{s^2 + s(R/L) + (1/LC)}$$

$$p_{1,2} = -\frac{R}{2L} \pm \sqrt{\left(\frac{R}{2L}\right)^2 - \frac{1}{LC}} = -\frac{R}{2L} \pm j\sqrt{\frac{1}{LC} - \left(\frac{R}{2L}\right)^2}$$

For $R \gg 2\sqrt{L/C}\,(4L/R^2C \ll 1)$, the poles can be approximated by

$$p_{1,2} \cong -\frac{R}{2L} \pm \frac{R}{2L}\left(1 - \frac{2L}{R^2C}\right) \cong \begin{cases} -\dfrac{1}{RC} \cong 0 \\ -\dfrac{R}{L} \end{cases}$$

The poles are on the real axis, and the response is given by Eq. (7-31) with $\alpha_1 \cong 0$ and $\alpha_2 = R/L$.

$$v_o(t) \cong e^{-(R/L)t} \tag{7-78a}$$

For $R = 0$ the poles are given by

$$p_{1,2} = \pm j\frac{1}{\sqrt{LC}}$$

The poles are on the imaginary axis, and the response is given by Eq. (7-76) with $\alpha = 0$ and $\beta = 1/\sqrt{LC}$.

$$v_o(t) = \cos\frac{t}{\sqrt{LC}} \tag{7-78b}$$

The two responses given by (7-78) are sketched in Fig. 7-47. The response waveform

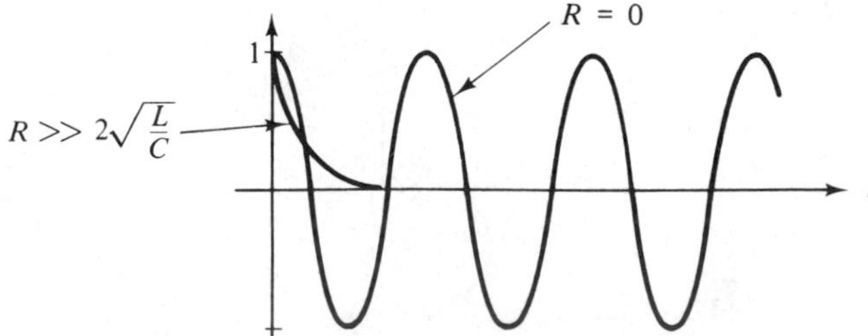

Fig. 7-47

changes drastically from an exponential to a cosine wave as R is changed from a very large value to zero.

7-11 STEP RESPONSE WHEN $T = \dfrac{a_2 s^2 + a_1 s + a_0}{(s+\alpha)^2 + \beta^2}$

Let us summarize what we have learned about the unit-step response of three special kinds of second-order functions that have left half-plane, complex-conjugate poles. The results appear in Fig. 7-48.

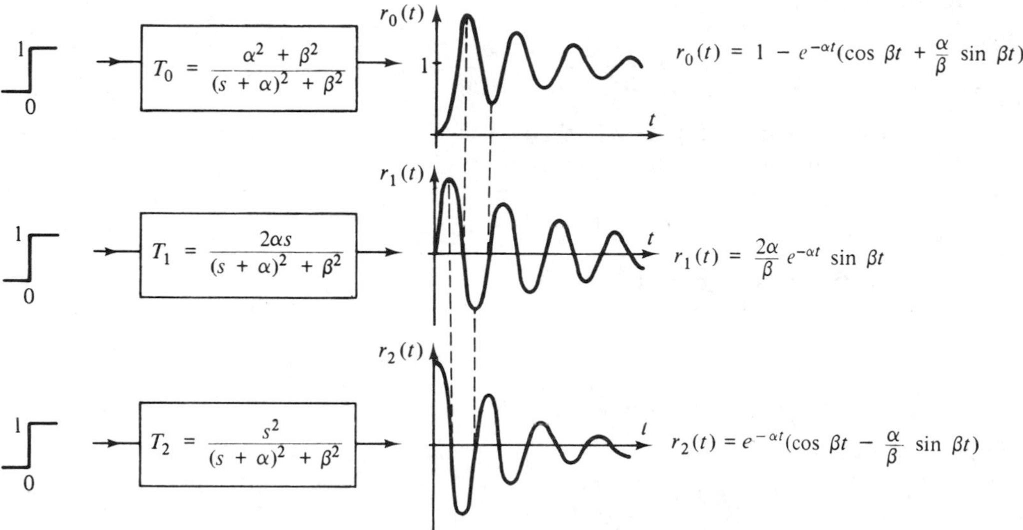

Fig. 7-48

The transfer functions and responses are related by

$$T_2 = \frac{1}{2\alpha} s T_1 = \frac{1}{\alpha^2 + \beta^2} s^2 T_0 \tag{7-79a}$$

$$r_2(t) = \frac{1}{2\alpha}\frac{d}{dt}[r_1(t)] = \frac{1}{\alpha^2 + \beta^2}\frac{d^2}{dt^2}[r_0(t)] \tag{7-79b}$$

If we examine the response curves in Fig. 7-48 carefully, we see that the $r_1(t)$ curve can be obtained by differentiating the $r_0(t)$ curve [note that $r_1(t) = 0$ when $r_0(t)$ is a relative maximum or minimum]. Similarly, the $r_2(t)$ curve can be obtained by differentiating the $r_1(t)$ curve [note that $r_2(t) = 0$ when $r_1(t)$ is a relative maximum or minimum].

The general second-order system with complex poles can be written

$$T(s) = \frac{a_2 s^2 + a_1 s + a_0}{(s + \alpha)^2 + \beta^2}$$

$$T(s) = a_2 T_2(s) + \frac{a_1}{2\alpha} T_1(s) + \frac{a_0}{\alpha^2 + \beta^2} T_0(s) \tag{7-80}$$

The unit-step response of $T(s)$ can then be expressed as

$$r(t) = a_2 r_2(t) + \frac{a_1}{2\alpha} r_1(t) + \frac{a_0}{\alpha^2 + \beta^2} r_0(t) \tag{7-81}$$

This response can also be stated entirely in terms of $r_0(t)$ by making use of the results of Eq. (7-79). Thus

$$r(t) = \frac{1}{\alpha^2 + \beta^2}\left(a_2 \frac{d^2 r_0}{dt^2} + a_1 \frac{dr_0}{dt} + a_0 r_0\right)$$

It is clear from Eq. (7-81) that a variety of response waveforms can be obtained by combining (with appropriate scaling) the three basic response curves shown in Fig. 7-48.

Example 7-17

Plot the unit-step response of

$$T = \frac{s^2 + k}{s^2 + 0.1s + 1}$$

for $k = 0$, $k = 1$, and $k = 2$.

Solution. Referring to Fig. 7-48, we see that

$$T = T_2 + kT_0$$

$$\begin{aligned} r(t) &= r_2(t) + kr_0(t) \\ &= e^{-\alpha t}\left(\cos \beta t - \frac{\alpha}{\beta} \sin \beta t\right) + k\left[1 - e^{-\alpha t}\left(\cos \beta t + \frac{\alpha}{\beta} \sin \beta t\right)\right] \\ &= k + e^{-\alpha t}\left[(1 - k)\cos \beta t - \frac{\alpha}{\beta}(1 + k) \sin \beta t\right] \end{aligned}$$

where

$$\alpha = \frac{0.1}{2} = \frac{1}{20}, \qquad \beta = \sqrt{1 - \alpha^2} \cong 1$$

Thus we have

$$r(t) = k + e^{-t/20}\left[(1 - k) \cos t - \frac{1}{20}(1 + k) \sin t\right]$$

This equation is plotted in Fig. 7.49. As we increase k from 0, the basic T_2-type response is altered by the addition of more T_0-type response. All three responses start at one but end at different values, as determined by k. Since $\pm j\sqrt{k}$ represent the zeros of

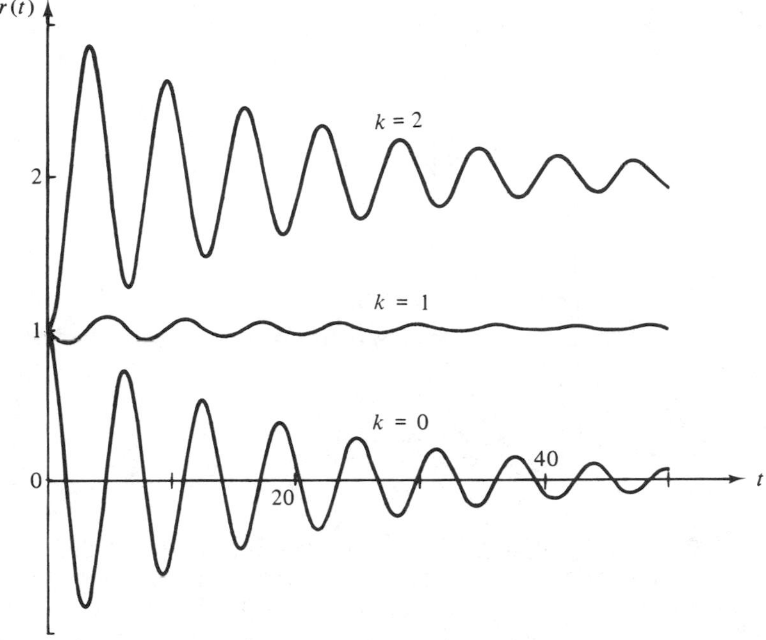

Fig. 7-49

T, the three curves of Fig. 7-49 show how the response is affected by the position of the zeros.

7-12 RESPONSE DUE TO INITIAL CONDITIONS

Initial conditions represent currents in inductors and voltages across capacitors at $t = 0^-$. Since these currents and voltages are continuous functions of time, it can just as well be said that initial conditions are currents in inductors and voltages across capacitors at $t = 0$ or, for that matter, at $t = 0^+$. As is done in the preceding chapter, initial conditions can be treated as step-function sources applied at $t = 0$. For instance, an inductor with an initial current ρ can be treated as a separate step-current source of amplitude ρ across an inductor having no initial current, as shown in Fig. 7 50(a). A capacitor with an initial voltage γ can be treated as a separate step-voltage source of amplitude γ in series with a capacitor having no initial voltage, as shown in Fig. 7.50(b). It should be emphasized that the *equivalence is valid only at terminals 1–1′* for $t \geq 0$. Thus in the equivalent representation of Fig. 7-50(a), the current through the original inductor is not i' but i_L, which is equal to $(i' - \rho)$ by Kirchhoff's Current Law. Similarly, in the equivalent representation of Fig. 7-50(b), the voltage across the original capacitor is not v'; it is $v_c = v' + \gamma$ by Kirchhoff's Voltage Law.

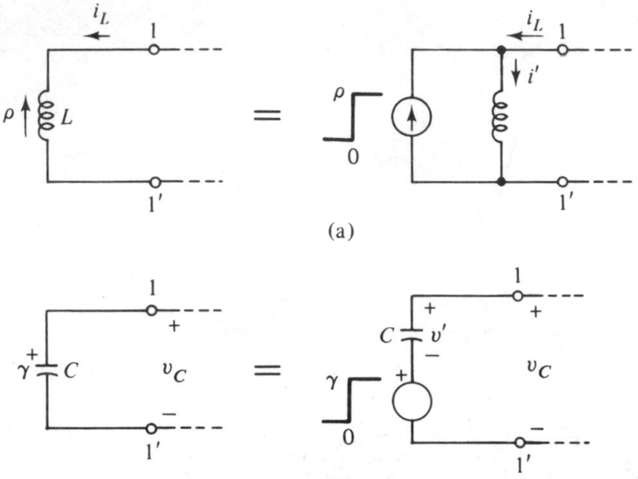

(a)

(b)

Fig. 7-50

To see how initial conditions are handled, let us calculate in the network of Fig. 7-51(a) responses due to the initial current in the inductor and the initial voltage across the capacitor. First, we redraw the network as in Fig. 7-51(b), indicating equivalent step excitations. Then we use the principle of superposition to obtain $I(s)$ and $V(s)$.

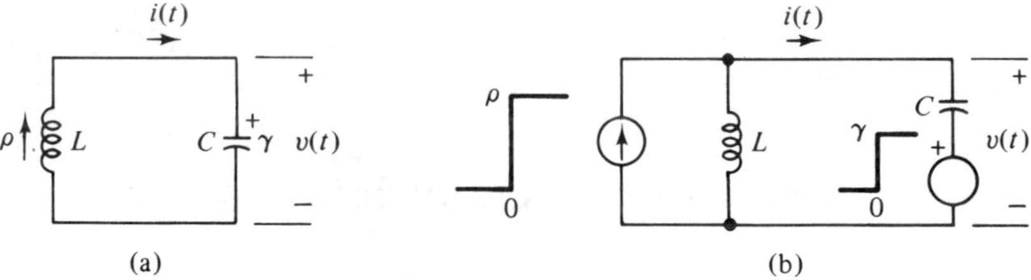

(a) (b)

Fig. 7-51

$$I(s) = \left(\frac{\rho}{s}\right)\left[\frac{sL}{sL + (1/sC)}\right] + \left(\frac{-\gamma}{s}\right)\left[\frac{1}{sL + (1/sC)}\right] = \frac{\rho s - (\gamma/L)}{s^2 + (1/LC)} \tag{7-82a}$$

$$V(s) = \left(\frac{\rho}{s}\right)\left[\frac{sL(1/sC)}{sL + (1/sC)}\right] + \left(\frac{\gamma}{s}\right)\left[\frac{sL}{sL + (1/sC)}\right] = \frac{\rho/C + \gamma s}{s^2 + (1/LC)} \tag{7-82b}$$

We can rearrange Eq. (7-82) and use Table 5-1 to obtain the time-domain responses.

$$I(s) = \rho\left[\frac{s}{s^2 + (1/LC)}\right] - \gamma\sqrt{\frac{C}{L}}\left(\frac{1/\sqrt{LC}}{s^2 + (1/LC)}\right]$$

$$V(s) = \rho\sqrt{\frac{L}{C}}\left[\frac{1/\sqrt{LC}}{s^2 + (1/LC)}\right] + \gamma\left[\frac{s}{s^2 + (1/LC)}\right]$$

$$i(t) = \rho \cos \frac{t}{\sqrt{LC}} - \gamma \sqrt{\frac{C}{L}} \sin \frac{t}{\sqrt{LC}} \tag{7-83a}$$

$$v(t) = \rho \sqrt{\frac{L}{C}} \sin \frac{t}{\sqrt{LC}} + \gamma \cos \frac{t}{\sqrt{LC}} \tag{7-83b}$$

Note that $i(0) = \rho$ (current through inductor cannot jump) and $v(0) = \gamma$ (voltage across capacitor cannot jump). As a result, the initial current in the inductor, if acting alone, causes a voltage that is a sine wave (starts with zero). On the other hand, the initial voltage across the capacitor, if acting alone, causes a voltage that is a cosine wave (starts with γ).

The energy stored in the inductor at any time t is

$$w_L(t) = \frac{1}{2} L[i(t)]^2 = \frac{1}{2} L\left(\rho \cos \frac{t}{\sqrt{LC}} - \gamma \sqrt{\frac{C}{L}} \sin \frac{t}{\sqrt{LC}}\right)^2 \tag{7-84}$$

$$w_L(t) = \frac{1}{2} L\rho^2 \cos^2 \frac{t}{\sqrt{LC}} - \rho\gamma\sqrt{LC} \sin \frac{t}{\sqrt{LC}} \cos \frac{t}{\sqrt{LC}} + \frac{1}{2} C\gamma^2 \sin^2 \frac{t}{\sqrt{LC}} \tag{7-85}$$

The energy stored in the capacitor at any time t is

$$w_C(t) = \frac{1}{2} C[v(t)]^2 = \frac{1}{2} C\left(\rho \sqrt{\frac{L}{C}} \sin \frac{t}{\sqrt{LC}} + \gamma \cos \frac{t}{\sqrt{LC}}\right)^2 \tag{7-86}$$

$$w_C(t) = \frac{1}{2} L\rho^2 \sin^2 \frac{t}{\sqrt{LC}} + \rho\gamma\sqrt{LC} \sin \frac{t}{\sqrt{LC}} \cos \frac{t}{\sqrt{LC}} + \frac{1}{2} C\gamma^2 \cos^2 \frac{t}{\sqrt{LC}} \tag{7-87}$$

To obtain the total energy in the network at any time t, we sum the two energies.

$$w(t) = w_L(t) + w_C(t) = \frac{1}{2} L\rho^2 + \frac{1}{2} C\gamma^2 \tag{7-88}$$

Equation (7-88) states that the sum of the energies stored in the inductor and in the capacitor is constant at all times. This constant represents the sum of the two *initial* energies. Indeed, such a result is to be expected, since there is no place in which energy can be dissipated (there are no resistors). Furthermore, it can be shown that whenever the energy in the inductor reaches a maximum value, the energy in the capacitor is zero and vice versa (see Problem 7-65). Thus energy is transferred back and forth without loss between the inductor and the capacitor.

In practice, it is not possible to have such perpetual transfer of energy between the inductor and capacitor because of the inevitable losses associated with actual (nonideal) elements. The effect of losses can be accounted for (modeled) by the addition of a resistance in parallel with the network as shown in Fig. 7-52.

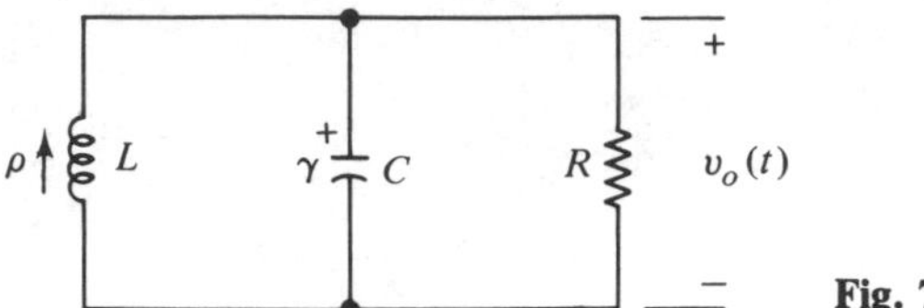

Fig. 7-52

If the losses are small ($R \gg (1/2)\sqrt{L/C}$), the voltage response can be approximated by (see Problem 7-66)

$$v_o(t) \cong e^{-t/2RC}\left(\rho\sqrt{\frac{L}{C}}\sin\frac{t}{\sqrt{LC}} + \gamma\cos\frac{t}{\sqrt{LC}}\right) \tag{7-89}$$

which states that

$$\underbrace{\text{Voltage with losses present}}_{\text{Eq. (7-89)}} \cong e^{-t/2RC} \times \underbrace{\text{Voltage with no losses}}_{\text{Eq. (7-83b)}}$$

The sinusoidal voltage across the network decays exponentially with a time constant of $2RC$.

Example 7-18

Obtain v_o(t) in Fig. 7-53.

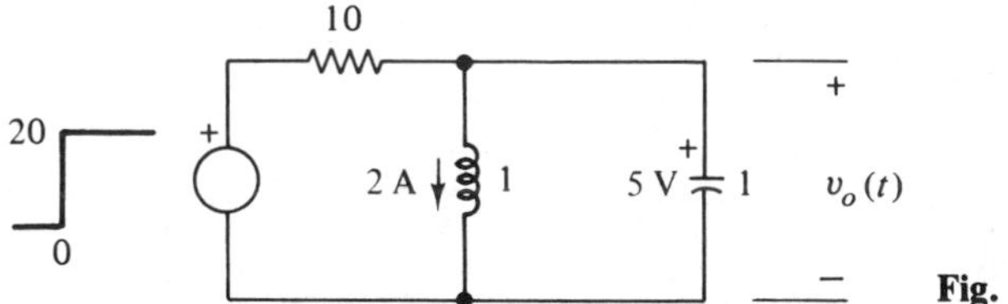

Fig. 7-53

Solution. When the 20 V-10 Ω combination is converted to its Norton equivalent form and when the initial current in the inductor is designated as a current source, Fig. 7-53 can be redrawn as in Fig. 7-54(a). We can simplify the circuit further by combining the two current sources and obtaining Fig. 7-54(b), which is the same as

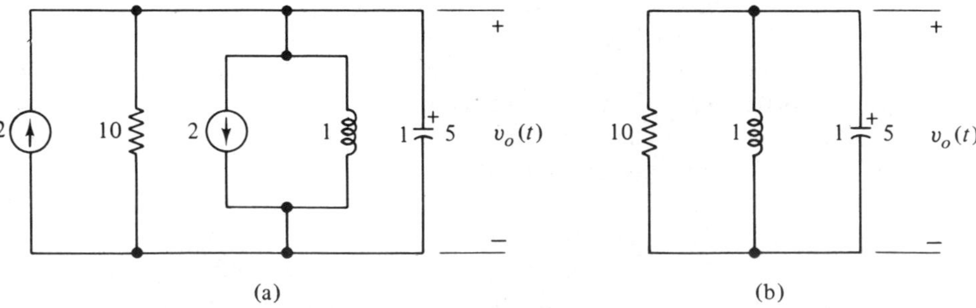

Fig. 7-54

Fig. 7-52 with $\rho = 0$. Since $R \gg (1/2)\sqrt{L/C}$ $(10 \gg 1/2)$, we can use Eq. (7-89) to obtain

$$v_o(t) \cong 5e^{-t/20} \cos t \quad \text{Ans.}$$

Example 7-19

In Fig. 7-55 the switch has been in the closed position for a long time. At $t = 0$ it is opened.

(a) Determine the initial and final values of v_o by inspection of the circuit.

(b) Calculate the output voltage.

(c) Simplify the expression for the output voltage for $R \ll 2\sqrt{L/C}$ and sketch it.

(d) $V = 12$ volts, $R = 1\ \Omega$, $L = 10$ mH, and $C = 1\ \mu$F. What is $v_o(t)$? Discuss results.

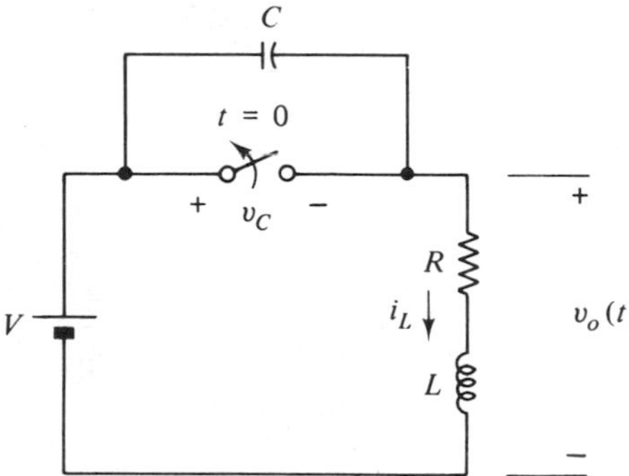

Fig. 7-55

Solution.

(a) *Conditions at $t = 0^-$* are illustrated in Fig. 7-56(a). Because the switch is closed, $v_C(0^-) = 0$. Because the circuit is at steady state, $v_L(0^-) = 0$. Hence $v_R(0^-) = V$, and $i_L(0^-) = i_R(0^-) = V/R$.

Conditions at $t = 0^+$ are illustrated in Fig. 7-56(b). Because the capacitor voltage cannot jump, $v_C(0^+) = v_C(0^-) = 0$ So for this instant alone, the capacitor can be replaced with a short circuit. As a result,

$$v_o(0^+) = V \quad \text{Ans.}$$

[Because the current through the inductor cannot jump, $i_L(0^+) = i_L(0^-) = V/R$. So for this instant alone, the inductor can be replaced with a current source.]

Conditions at $t = \infty$ are illustrated in Fig. 7-56(c). Because the capacitor current is zero, the capacitor can be replaced with an open circuit. Because the inductor voltage is zero, the inductor can be replaced with a short circuit. As a result,

$$v_o(\infty) = 0 \quad \text{Ans.}$$

(b) To calculate $v_o(t)$, we draw the circuit as in Fig. 7-56(d), showing the initial inductor current as a current source. Using superposition, we obtain $V_o(s)$.

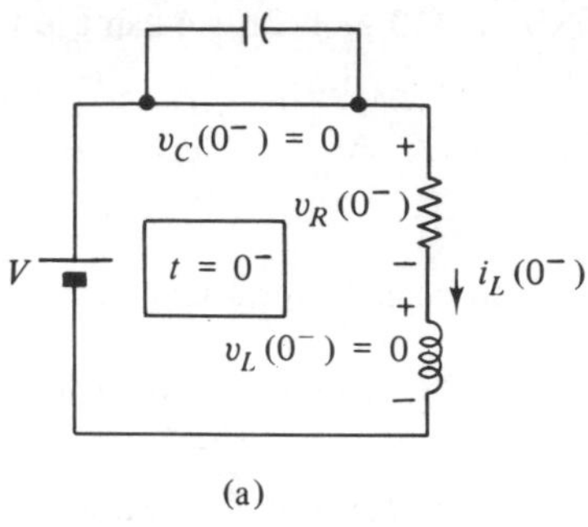

(a)

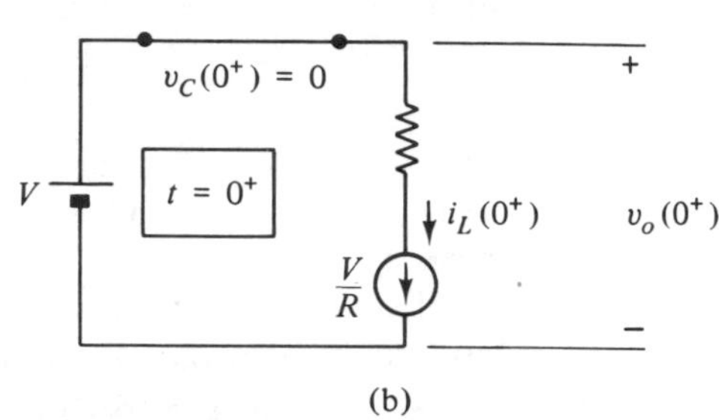

(b)

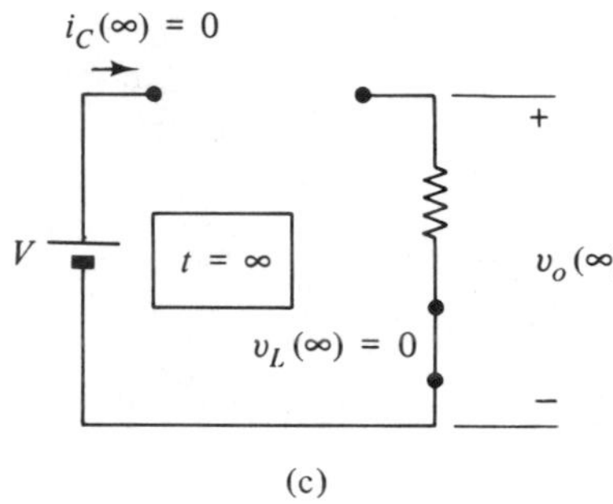

(c)

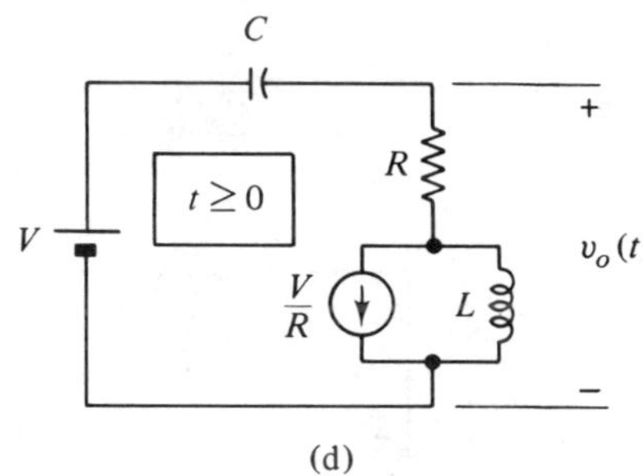

(d)

Fig. 7-56

$$V_o = \left(\frac{V}{s}\right)\left[\frac{sL + R}{sL + R + (1/sC)}\right] - \left(\frac{V/R}{s}\right)\left[\frac{sL}{sL + R + (1/sC)}\right]\left(\frac{1}{sC}\right)$$

$$= \left(\frac{V}{s}\right)\left\{\underbrace{\left[\frac{s^2}{s^2 + s(R/L) + (1/LC)}\right]}_{T_2} + \underbrace{\left[\frac{s(R/L)}{s^2 + s(R/L) + (1/LC)}\right]}_{T_1}\right\}$$

$$- \left(\frac{V/R}{s}\right)\left(\frac{L}{RC}\right)\underbrace{\left[\frac{s(R/L)}{s^2 + s(R/L) + (1/LC)}\right]}_{T_1} \tag{7-90}$$

Using the results presented in Fig. 7-48, we find

$$v_o(t) = Ve^{-\alpha t}\left[\cos \beta t + \frac{\alpha}{\beta}\left(1 - \frac{2L}{R^2C}\right)\sin \beta t\right] \qquad (t \geq 0) \quad \text{Ans.} \quad (7\text{-}91)$$

where
$$\alpha = \frac{R}{2L}, \qquad \beta = \sqrt{\frac{1}{LC} - \left(\frac{R}{2L}\right)^2}$$

(c) For $R \ll 2\sqrt{L/C}$, $\beta \cong 1/\sqrt{LC}$. As a result, Eq. (7-91) can be approximated as

$$v_o(t) \cong Ve^{-(R/2L)t}\left(\cos\frac{t}{\sqrt{LC}} + \frac{R}{2}\sqrt{\frac{C}{L}}\sin\frac{t}{\sqrt{LC}} - \frac{1}{R}\sqrt{\frac{L}{C}}\sin\frac{t}{\sqrt{LC}}\right)$$

$$v_o(t) \cong -\frac{V}{R}\sqrt{\frac{L}{C}}e^{-(R/2L)t}\sin\frac{t}{\sqrt{LC}} \qquad (t \geq 0) \quad \text{Ans.} \tag{7-92}$$

This waveform is sketched in Fig. 7-57 (solid curve). For all practical purposes, the first minimum is

$$-\frac{V}{R}\sqrt{\frac{L}{C}} \tag{7-93}$$

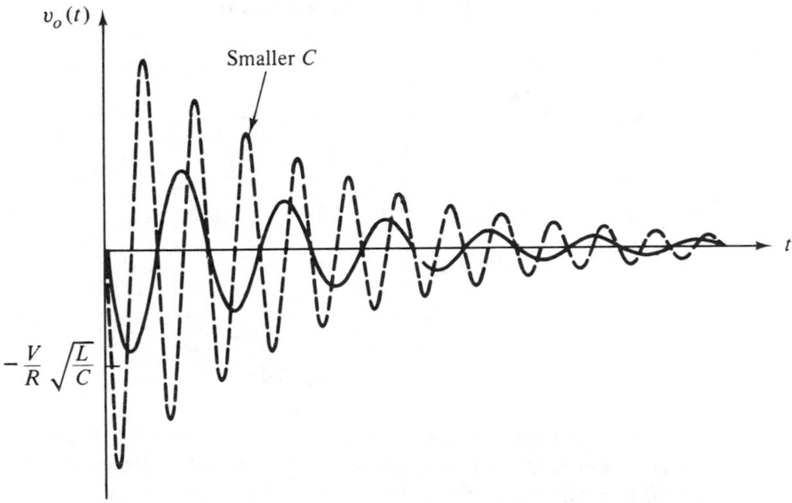

Fig. 7-57

Note that the smaller C is made, the larger this first negative swing becomes and the higher the frequency (dashed curve) becomes.

(d) For $V = 12$, $R = 1$, $L = 0.01$, and $C = 10^{-6}$ we have

$$\alpha = \frac{R}{2L} = \frac{1}{0.02}$$

$$\beta = \sqrt{\frac{1}{LC} - \left(\frac{R}{2L}\right)^2} = \sqrt{10^8 - 2.5 \times 10^3} \cong 10^4$$

$$v_o(t) \cong -1200e^{-t/0.02}\sin 10^4 t \quad \text{Ans.}$$

So by using no more than a 12 V battery to energize the circuit, we achieve a 1200 V negative peak. If we change C from 10^{-6} F to 0.01×10^{-6} F, the negative peak becomes 12,000 V. Since the voltage across the switch (see Fig. 7-55) is

$$v_{sw}(t) = V - v_o(t) \cong -v_o(t)$$

the same high voltage will also appear across the terminals of the switch. In practice, such high voltages cause severe arcing at the contacts of the switch when it opens. (Basically, this circuit represents part of the automobile ignition system with the points serving as the switch.)

Example 7-19

In Fig. 7-58 S_1 is periodically closed for t_{ON} seconds and opened for t_{OFF} seconds. While S_1 is closed, S_2 is opened and vice versa. Steady state prevails. A large enough inductor is used to assure that the current through it stays practically constant during the two switching intervals. Similarly a large enough capacitor is used to assure that the voltage across it stays practically constant. The load on the circuit is designated by R_L. Obtain the output voltage and the inductor current.

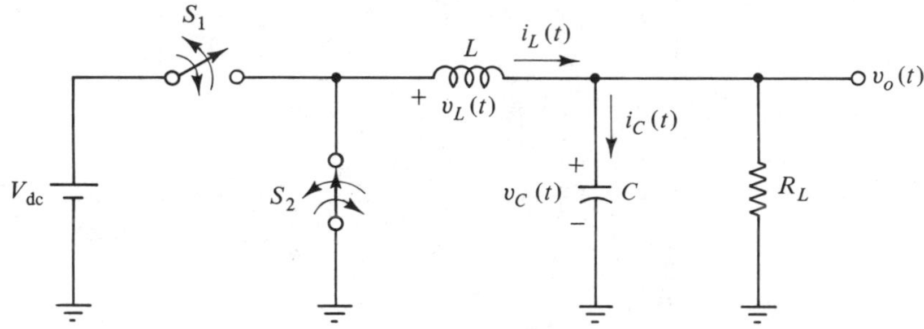

Fig. 7-58

Solution. Consider first the t_{ON} period when S_1 is closed and S_2 opened. Since the current through the inductor is practically constant, replace the inductor with a current source I_L as shown in Fig. 7-59(a). Since the voltage across the capacitor is practically constant, replace the capacitor with a voltage source V_C as shown in Fig. 59(a). From the equivalent circuit representation it can be seen that

$$v_L = V_{dc} - V_C \tag{7-94a}$$

$$i_C = I_L - \frac{V_C}{R_L} \tag{7-94b}$$

Since V_{dc}, V_C, and I_L are all constants, neither v_L nor i_C changes during the t_{ON} interval. This is shown in Fig. 7-59(c).

Consider next the t_{OFF} period when S_1 is opened and S_2 closed. Since the inductor still maintains its current and the capacitor its voltage, we can draw the circuit of Fig. 7-59(b). From this equivalent circuit representation it can be seen that

$$v_L = -V_C \tag{7-95a}$$

$$i_C = I_L - \frac{V_C}{R_L} \tag{7-95b}$$

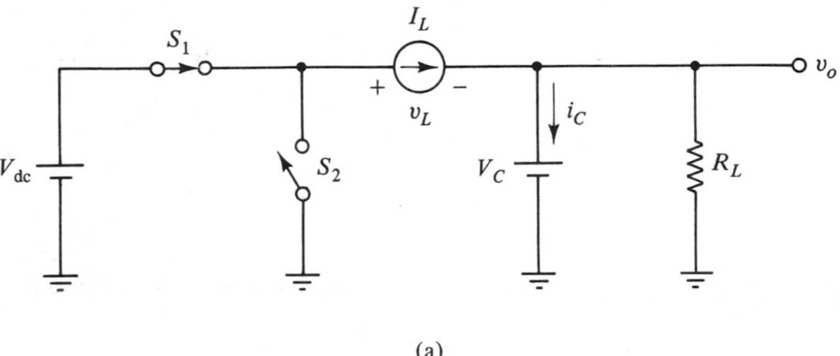
I_L
S_1
v_o
+
−
v_L
i_C
V_{dc}
S_2
V_C
R_L

(a)

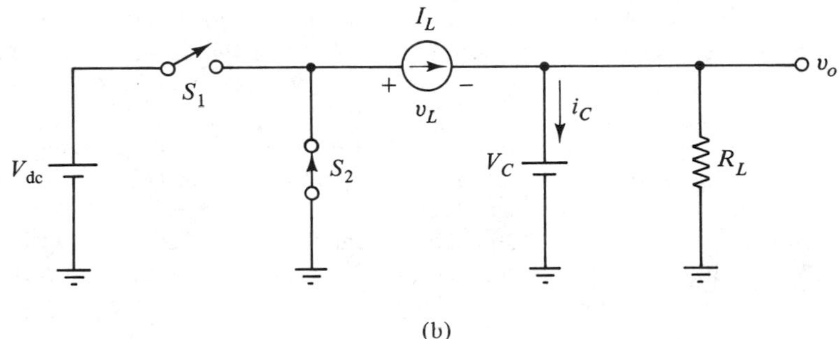
I_L
v_o
+
−
S_1
v_L
i_C
V_{dc}
S_2
V_C
R_L

(b)

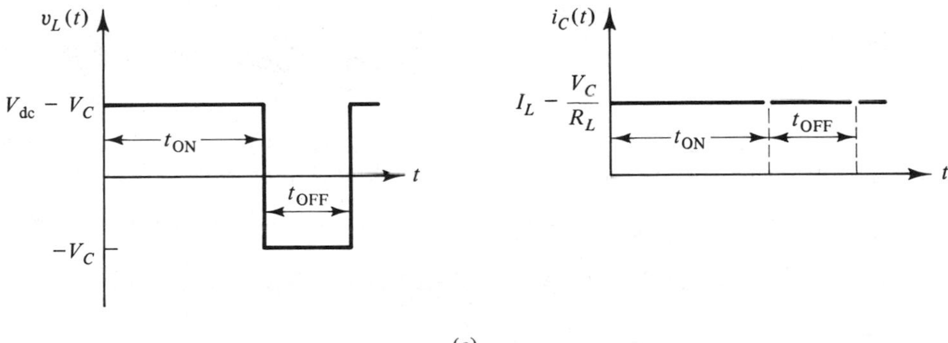
$v_L(t)$
$V_{dc} - V_C$
t_{ON}
t
t_{OFF}
$-V_C$
$i_C(t)$
$I_L - \frac{V_C}{R_L}$
t_{ON}
t_{OFF}
t

(c)

Fig. 7-59

These equations show that v_L and i_C don't change (are constant) during the t_{OFF} interval also. Hence the second half of $v_L(t)$ and $i_C(t)$ waveforms can be drawn as shown in Fig. 7-59(c).

Now we use a key argument: *the average value of the voltage across the inductor must be zero*. If this were not the case, the current through the inductor couldn't have stayed constant. (Any dc component of voltage would produce an ever linearly rising or falling component of current in the inductor, thereby contradicting the initial assumption that the inductor current is constant.) From Fig. 7-59(c) we obtain the average value of v_L and set it equal to zero.

$$(v_L)_{av} = \frac{(V_{dc} - V_C)t_{ON} - V_C t_{OFF}}{t_{ON} + t_{OFF}} = 0$$

$$V_C = \frac{V_{dc}}{1 + \dfrac{t_{OFF}}{t_{ON}}} \qquad \text{Ans.} \tag{7-96}$$

Note that by changing the t_{OFF}/t_{ON} ratio, we can obtain any desired dc output voltage that is less than the input voltage V_{dc}. This principle is widely used in switched-mode power supply designs to down-convert a given dc voltage. (A transister is used for S_1 and a diode for S_2.)

Another key argument gives us the value of I_L: *The average value of the current through the capacitor must be zero*. If this were not the case, the voltage across the capacitor wouldn't have stayed constant. (Any dc current component would produce an ever linearly rising or falling component of voltage across the capacitor, thereby contradicting the initial assumption that the capacitor voltage is constant.) From Fig. 7-59(c) we obtain the average value of i_C and set it equal to zero.

$$(i_C)_{av} = I_L - \frac{V_C}{R_L} = 0$$

$$I_L = \frac{V_C}{R_L} = \frac{V_{dc}}{R_L} \frac{1}{1 + \dfrac{t_{OFF}}{t_{ON}}} \qquad \text{Ans.} \tag{7-97}$$

This equation allows us to find the value of the inductor current I_L for any load current V_{dc}/R_L. Refer to Problem 7-78 for the determination of the size of L and C.

7-13 PULSE RESPONSE OF SECOND-ORDER SYSTEMS

Two equal but opposite polarity step functions occurring δ seconds apart form a pulse of width δ. When such a pulse excites a second-order system, it produces a response that is the sum of two equal but opposite polarity step responses that are displaced in time. Therefore if the step response is known, the pulse response can easily be constructed.

Example 7-20

In Fig. 7-60, $R \gg (1/2)\sqrt{L/C}$.

(a) Obtain the pulse response.
(b) Sketch the pulse response for $\delta \gg 2RC$ and $\delta = 2\pi\sqrt{LC}$.

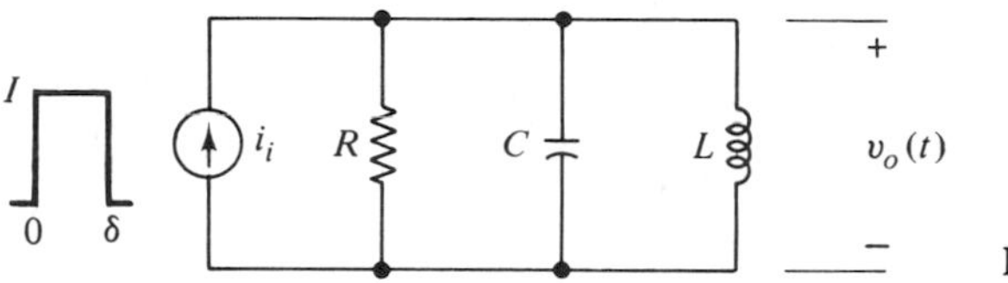

Fig. 7-60

Solution.

(a) The input impedance is

$$\frac{V_o}{I_i} = \frac{s(1/C)}{s^2 + s(1/RC) + (1/LC)}$$

Since

$$R \gg \frac{1}{2}\sqrt{\frac{L}{C}}$$

the poles are complex and we can obtain the unit-step response from Fig. 7-48. Note that the input impedance must be divided by R so that it conforms with the standard forms for which the answers are given. For a step I units high the response is

$$v_o(t) = IRr_1(t) = IR\frac{2\alpha}{\beta}e^{-\alpha t}\sin\beta t \tag{7-98}$$

where

$$\alpha = \frac{1}{2RC}, \qquad \beta = \sqrt{\frac{1}{LC} - \left(\frac{1}{2RC}\right)^2} \cong \frac{1}{\sqrt{LC}}$$

The excitation is the sum of two step functions. The first step function is of amplitude $I\sqrt{L/C}$ and occurs at $t = 0$. The second is of amplitude $-I\sqrt{L/C}$ and occurs at $t = \delta$. The resulting step responses are obtained by using Eq. (7-98).

$$v_{o1}(t) = I\sqrt{\frac{L}{C}}e^{-t/2RC}\sin\frac{t}{\sqrt{LC}} \qquad (t \geq 0)$$

$$v_{o2}(t) = -I\sqrt{\frac{L}{C}}e^{-(t-\delta)/2RC}\sin\frac{t-\delta}{\sqrt{LC}} \qquad (t \geq \delta)$$

For $t < \delta$, only $v_{o1}(t)$ exists. For $t > \delta$, both $v_{o1}(t)$ and $v_{o2}(t)$ exist. Thus

$$v_o(t) = \begin{cases} I\sqrt{\frac{L}{C}}e^{-t/2RC}\sin\frac{t}{\sqrt{LC}} & (0 \leq t \leq \delta) \\ I\sqrt{\frac{L}{C}}e^{-t/2RC}\sin\frac{1}{\sqrt{LC}} - I\sqrt{\frac{L}{C}}e^{-(t-\delta)/2RC}\sin\frac{t-\delta}{\sqrt{LC}} & (t \geq \delta) \end{cases} \quad \text{Ans.}$$

(7-99)

Even though the input jumps at both $t = 0$ and $t = \delta$, the output, being the voltage across a capacitor, is a continuous function of time. For this reason equality signs are included in the time-interval designations.

(b) The waveform given by Eq. (7-99) decays with a time constant of $\tau = 2RC$. If the pulse width δ is made much larger than τ, the waveform due to the step occurring at $t = 0$ will have sufficient time to decay completely to zero before the second step occurs at $t = \delta$. As a result, we obtain the output sketched in Fig. 7-61(a). On the other hand, if the pulse terminates at $\delta = 2\pi\sqrt{LC}$, the output is as shown in Fig. 7-61(b). Since at $t = \delta$ we have

$$\sin \frac{t}{\sqrt{LC}}\bigg|_{t=\delta} = \sin \frac{\delta}{\sqrt{LC}} = \sin 2\pi$$

we see that exactly one cycle (2π radians) of the first sinusoidal ringing is completed before the input drops to zero and initiates the second sinusoidal ringing. Because the first ringing has decayed only slightly at the end of δ seconds (see the individual waveforms drawn within the bracket), the two waveforms are almost equal in magnitude but opposite in sign for $t > \delta$, thereby canceling each other almost completely. The larger R is made, the more perfect the cancellation becomes and the more the output looks like one cycle of a sine wave. It should be clear that if $\delta = 4\pi\sqrt{LC}$, we would obtain two cycles of a sine wave.

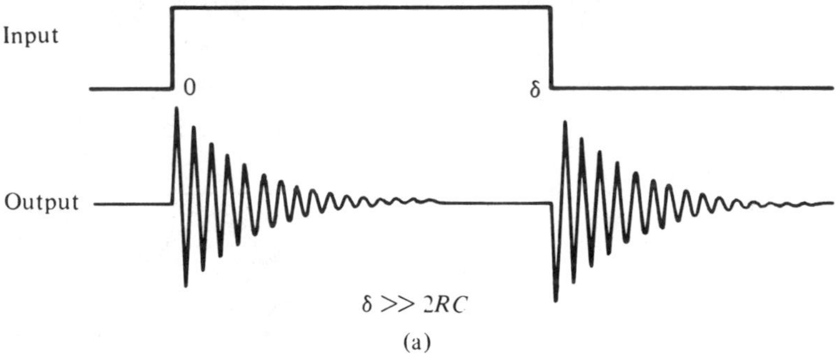

(a)

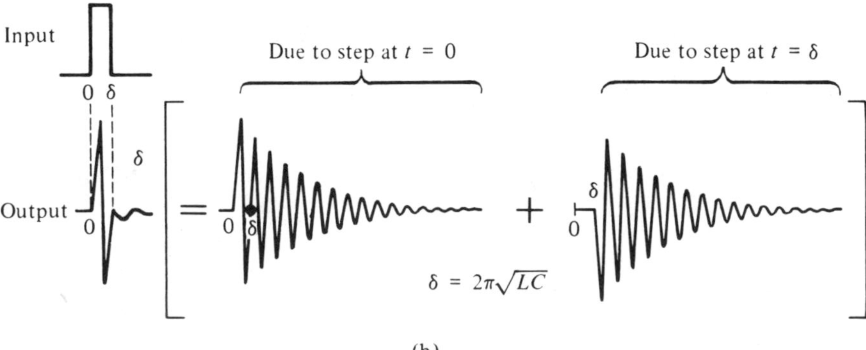

(b)

Fig. 7-61

7-14 SQUARE WAVE RESPONSE OF SECOND-ORDER SYSTEMS

A square wave initiated at $t = 0$ can be regarded as a series of alternate-polarity step functions occurring in a periodic fashion. Alternatively, the square wave can be thought of as a series of pulses occurring in periodic fashion. Consequently, when the step function or pulse response of a system is known, its square wave response can be constructed.

Example 7-21

In Fig. 7-62, $R \gg (1/2)\sqrt{L/C}$.

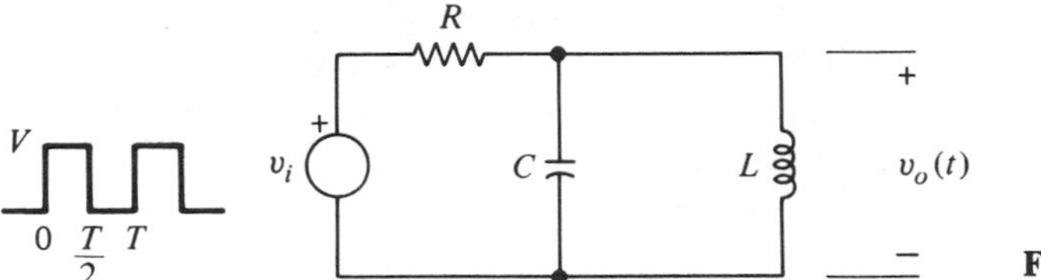

Fig. 7-62

(a) The input is a square wave as shown. Obtain the response.

(b) Sketch the square wave response for $T \gg RC$ and $T = 2\pi\sqrt{LC}$.

(c) Assume that $T = 2\pi\sqrt{LC}$ and steady state prevails. Obtain the expression for $v_o(t)$ for $T \ll 4RC$.

Solution.

(a) Convert the voltage-source-resistance combination to a current-source-resistance combination as in Fig. 7-63. The network then becomes identical with the network of Example 7-20. Since the current input can be considered as a current *pulse* of amplitude V/R and width $T/2$ occurring every T seconds, we can use Eq. (7-99) to obtain the output.

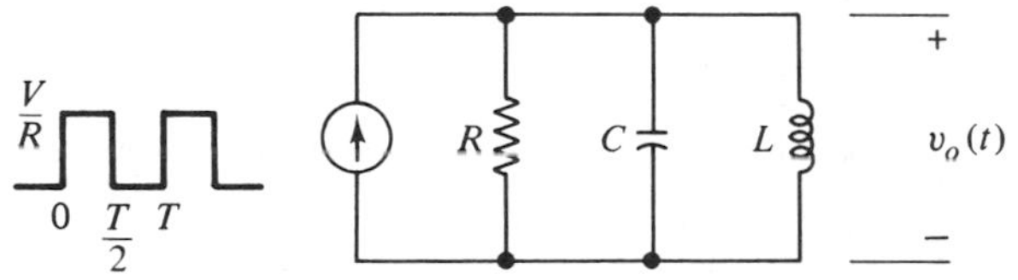

Fig. 7-63

$$v_o(t) = \frac{V}{R}\sqrt{\frac{L}{C}}e^{-t/2RC}\sin\frac{t}{\sqrt{LC}} = v_{o1}(t) \qquad \left(0 \le t \le \frac{T}{2}\right)$$

$$= v_{o1}(t) - \frac{V}{R}\sqrt{\frac{L}{C}}e^{-(t-T/2)/2RC}\sin\frac{t - T/2}{\sqrt{LC}} = v_{o2}(t) \qquad \left(\frac{T}{2} \le t \le T\right)$$

$$= v_{o2}(t) + \frac{V}{R}\sqrt{\frac{L}{C}}e^{-(t-T)/2RC}\sin\frac{t - T}{\sqrt{LC}} = v_{o3}(t) \qquad \left(T \le t \le \frac{3T}{2}\right)$$

$$= v_{o3}(t) - \frac{V}{R}\sqrt{\frac{L}{C}}e^{-(t-3T/2)/2RC}\ sin\ \frac{t - 3T/2}{\sqrt{LC}} = v_{o4}(t) \qquad \left(\frac{3T}{2} \leq t \leq 2T\right)$$

$$= v_{o4}(t) + \cdots \quad \text{Ans.} \tag{7-100}$$

(b) As Eq. (7-100) shows, the response is a sum of alternate-polarity step responses occurring $T/2$ seconds apart. How the sum looks depends, therefore, on how much the damped sinusoidal response has decayed in $T/2$ seconds. For instance, if $T \gg RC$, we obtain Fig. 7-64(a), which shows that the response due to the step occurring at $t = 0$ has completely decayed before the next step occurring at $t = T/2$ strikes. On the other hand, if $T = 2\pi\sqrt{LC}$, only half a cycle of sine wave goes by before the next step arrives. Thus each new damped sine wave that starts is in step with the damped sine waves initiated by the previous steps. As a result, the response grows as shown in Fig. 7-64(b). The smaller the losses—that is, the larger R—the more the response builds up initially in a linear fashion. However, because of losses, the growth eventually levels off and the response becomes an almost pure sine wave. This is a remarkable result. Even though *the input is a square wave, the output is nearly a sine wave*. This result occurs because the input rein-

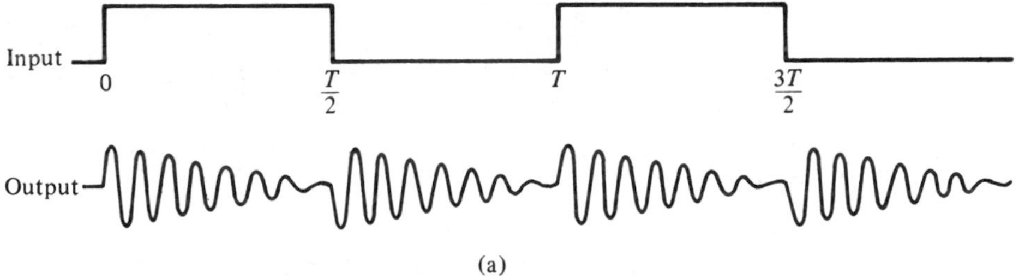

(a)

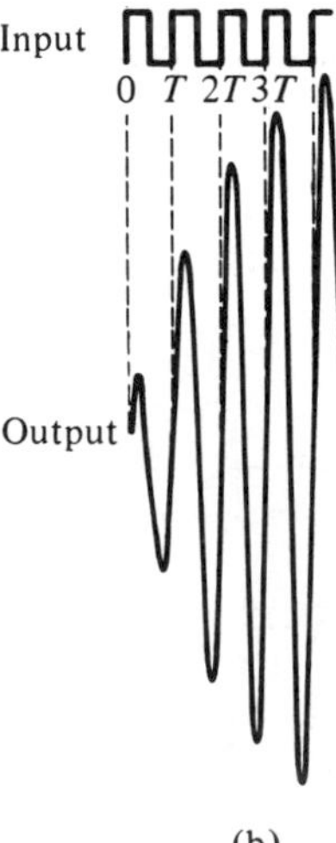

(b)

Fig. 7-64

forces the natural behavior of the network at the correct times and makes up for the losses that have occurred during the previous half-cycle of operation. Indeed, this correct reinforcing action is manifested whenever the square wave period is an odd multiple of the period of the damped sine wave generated by the network—that is, $T = n2\pi\sqrt{LC}$ (n odd). (See Problems 7-88 and 7-90.)

(c) The waveform shown in Fig. 7-64(b) for $T = 2\pi\sqrt{LC}$ will eventually stop growing in amplitude. This is when steady state is reached. For steady-state waveform calculation assume that $t = 0$ occurs when the input jumps up by V volts. This step initiates a response given by

$$\frac{V}{R}\sqrt{\frac{L}{C}}e^{-t/2RC}\sin\frac{t}{\sqrt{LC}} = \frac{V}{R}\sqrt{\frac{L}{C}}e^{-t/2RC}\sin\frac{2\pi}{T}t, \qquad t \geq 0$$

The response due to the previous jump of $-V$ volts occurring $T/2$ seconds earlier is

$$-\frac{V}{R}\sqrt{\frac{L}{C}}e^{-[t+(T/2)]/2RC}\sin\frac{2\pi}{T}\left(t+\frac{T}{2}\right), \qquad t \geq -\frac{T}{2}$$

This response can be written as

$$-\frac{V}{R}\sqrt{\frac{L}{C}}e^{-[t+(T/2)]/2RC}\sin\left(\frac{2\pi}{T}t+\pi\right) = \frac{V}{R}\sqrt{\frac{L}{C}}e^{-[t+(T/2)]/2RC}\sin\frac{2\pi}{T}t, \qquad t \geq -\frac{T}{2}$$

Similarly, the response due to the step of V volts occurring at $t = -T$ is given by

$$\frac{V}{R}\sqrt{\frac{L}{C}}e^{-(t+T)/2RC}\quad\sin\frac{2\pi}{T}(t+T) = \frac{V}{R}\sqrt{\frac{L}{C}}e^{-(t+T)/2RC}\sin\left(\frac{2\pi}{T}t+2\pi\right)$$

$$= \frac{V}{R}\sqrt{\frac{L}{C}}e^{-(t+T)/2RC}\sin\frac{2\pi}{T}t, \qquad t \geq -T$$

Summing the responses due to all the steps occurring at $t = 0$ and previously gives us

$$v_o(t) = \frac{V}{R}\sqrt{\frac{L}{C}}e^{-t/2RC}\sin\frac{2\pi}{T}t(1 + e^{-T/4RC} + e^{-2T/4RC} + e^{-3T/4RC} + e^{-4T/4RC} + \cdots)$$

$$0 \leq t \leq \frac{T}{2} \qquad \text{(7-101)}$$

Note that this expression is valid only for $t \geq 0$ (thus including all the responses initiated at $t = 0$ and previously) but not for $t > T/2$ (thus excluding the responses that would be initiated by the alternate polarity steps occuring at $t = T/2$ and thereafter). The parenthetical term in Eq. (7-101) is an infinite series that can be summed and written in closed form according to

$$1 + x + x^2 + x^3 + \cdots = \frac{1}{1-x}, \qquad x^2 < 1$$

Hence with $x = e^{-T/4RC}$, Eq. (7-101) can be written as

$$v_o(t) = \frac{\frac{V}{R}\sqrt{\frac{L}{C}}}{1 - e^{-T/4RC}} e^{-t/2RC} \sin \frac{2\pi}{T}t, \qquad 0 \leq t \leq \frac{T}{2} \tag{7-102}$$

If it were not for the exponential damping factor ($e^{-t/2RC}$), the output waveform would be a sine wave of amplitude

$$\frac{\frac{V}{R}\sqrt{\frac{L}{C}}}{1 - e^{-T/4RC}} \tag{7-103}$$

Since the exponential damping factor starts with 1 and at $t = 0$ and ends with $e^{-T/4RC}$ half a cycle later, it will affect the waveform. In particular, the slope of $v_o(t)$ at $t = 0$ will be different from the magnitude of the slope at $t = T/2$, thus destroying the symmetry of the sine wave. However, if $T \ll 4RC$, then

$$e^{-T/4RC} \cong 1 - \frac{T}{4RC} \cong 1 \tag{7-104}$$

in which case the exponential term can be replaced with 1 as long as $0 \leq t \leq T/2$. Similarly, using Eq. (7-104), the denominator of Eq. (7-103) can be replaced with $T/4RC$. The end result is

$$v_o(t) \cong \frac{\frac{V}{R}\sqrt{\frac{L}{C}}}{\frac{T}{4RC}} \sin \frac{2\pi}{T}t = \frac{2V}{\pi} \sin \frac{2\pi}{T}t, \qquad 0 \leq t \leq \frac{T}{2} \tag{7-105}$$

It should be clear that succeeding alternate polarity steps occuring at $T/2$, T, $3T/2$, etc, would produce alternate polarity half sine waves. When put all together, we obtain

$$v_o(t) \cong \frac{2V}{\pi} \sin \frac{2\pi}{T}t, \qquad 0 \leq t \tag{7-106}$$

Thus the input square wave of period T is converted to an output sine wave of the same period.

7-15 SUMMARY

The step response of second-order systems is either the sum of two exponentials arising from two negative real axis poles or a damped sine wave arising from a pair of left half-plane, complex-conjugate poles. The numerator polynomial, $a_2s^2 + a_1s + a_0$, determines how the response starts and ends. If $a_2 = 0$, the response starts at zero; otherwise it jumps at $t = 0$. If $a_0 = 0$, the response ends at zero; otherwise it levels off at a nonzero dc value, which represents the forced response of the system.

How fast a system reacts to the forcing action of the input depends on the pole positions. The farther away the poles are from the origin, the more rapidly steady state is reached. In the case of widely separated, negative real axis poles, the response waveform is, for all practical purposes, determined by the pole nearer the origin; this pole is called the dominant pole. When the poles are complex and the β/α ratio is high, the response rings for quite awhile.

The pulse or square wave response of a system can easily be obtained from its step response. The nature of the response waveform can be controlled by adjusting the pulse width δ or square wave period T.

PROBLEMS

7-1. Obtain the coefficients a and b and the poles and zeros of the transfer function associated with the network shown in Fig. 7-65.

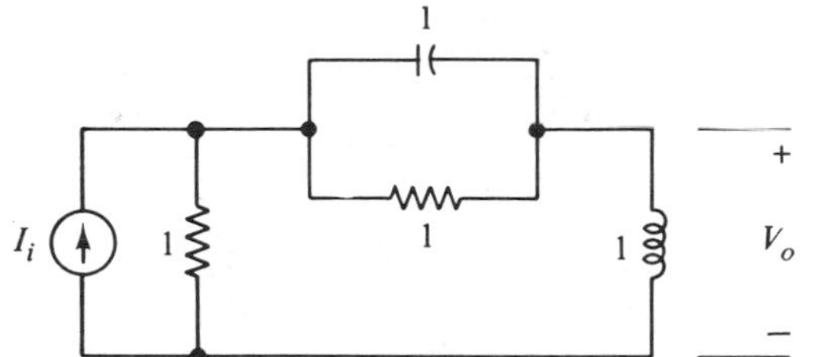

Fig. 7-65

7-2. Show that Eq. (7-12) becomes indeterminate for $\alpha_2 = \alpha_1$. The use l'Hospital's rule to evaluate $r(t)$ for $\alpha_2 = \alpha_1 = \alpha$.

7-3. The equation

$$r(t) = 1 + \frac{1}{\alpha_2 - \alpha_1}(\alpha_1 e^{-\alpha_2 t} - \alpha_2 e^{-\alpha_1 t})$$

has three independent variables: t, α_1, and α_2. In this equation α_1 will be kept constant and α_2 varied. Without selecting any specific values for α_1 and α_2, how would you graph the $r(t)$ curve, using only one parameter?

7-4. Refer to Fig. 7-66 and let $T = V_o/V_i$.

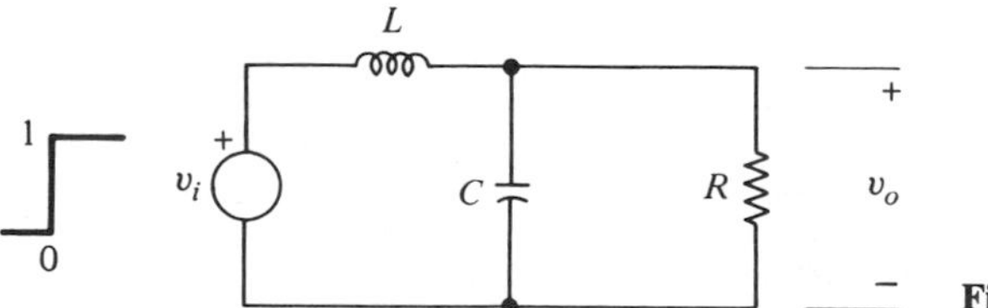

Fig. 7-66

(a) Obtain T.

(b) What condition must be satisfied in order to have real axis poles?

(c) What element varies the position of the poles without affecting their geometric mean?

(**d**) What element varies the position of the poles without affecting their arithmetic mean?

(**e**) Obtain the initial and final values of $v_o(t)$ by inspection of the network.

7-5. Show that the network of Fig. 7-67 realizes

$$T_o = \frac{\alpha_1 \alpha_2}{(s + \alpha_1)(s + \alpha_2)}$$

and that its poles are always on the negative real axis.

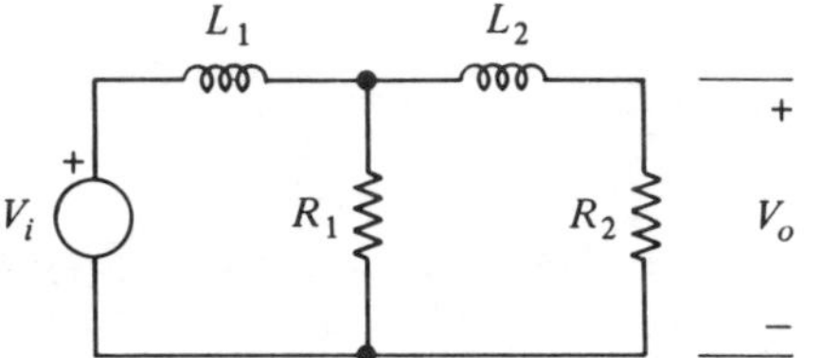

Fig. 7-67

7-6. Show that the network of Fig. 7-68 realizes

$$T = \frac{H}{s^2 + b_1 s + b_0}$$

where H is a constant and that it includes the networks of Figs. 7-6 and 7-66 as special cases.

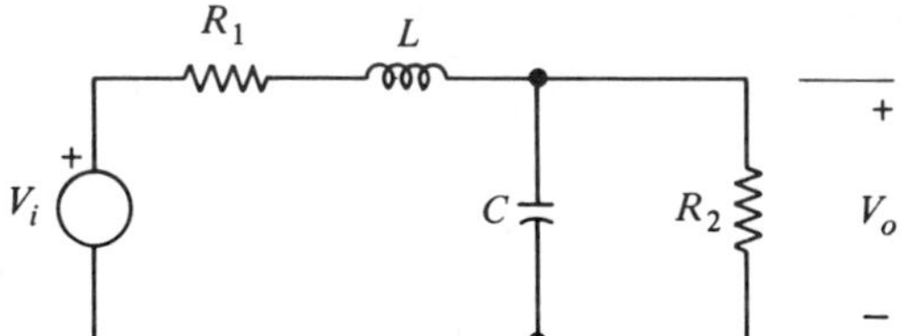

Fig. 7-68

7-7. The input and output of the network are shown in Fig. 7-69. Obtain the element values.

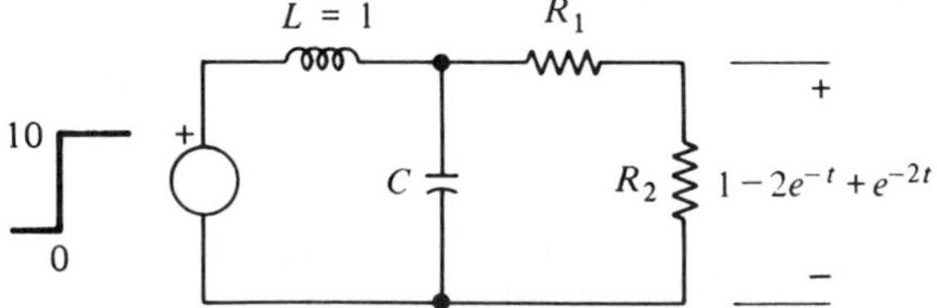

Fig. 7-69

7-8. Adjust the element values of the two networks shown in Fig. 7-70 to produce a response of $10 - 20e^{-t} + 10e^{-2t}$ when excited by a 10 V step.

7-9. In Fig. 7-71 the system is at steady state when at t = 0 the input switches from 1 to −1 as shown. Obtain $r(t)$.

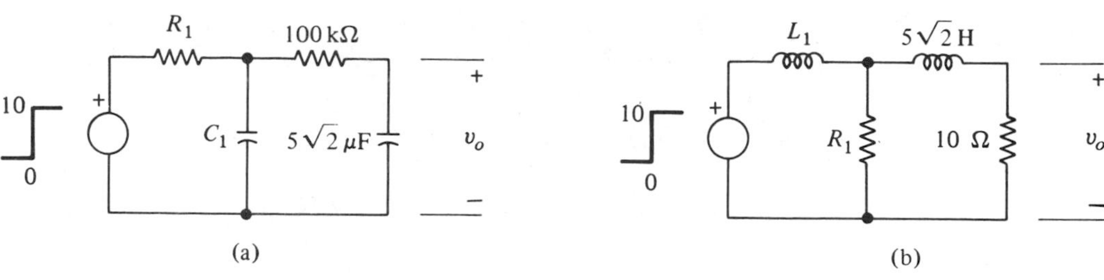

Fig. 7-70

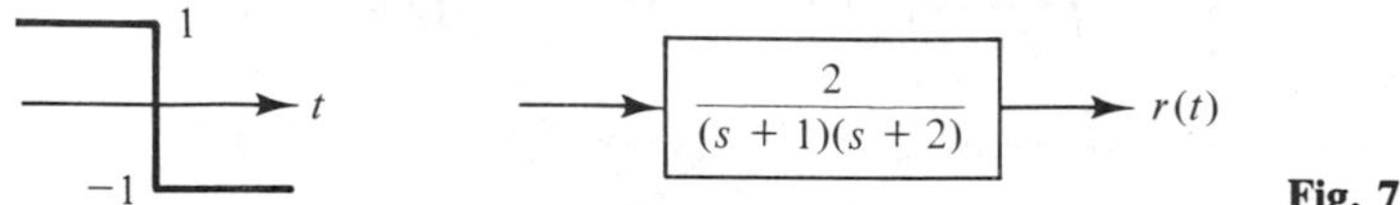

Fig. 7-71

7-10. Derive Eq. (7-24).

7-11. Given $T_1(s) = 2\alpha s/(s + \alpha)^2$, what is the unit-step response?

7-12. Sketch $e^{-10t} - e^{-t}$. Be accurate without the use of a computer.

7-13. Show that both poles of the network shown in Fig. 7-72 are on the negative real axis.

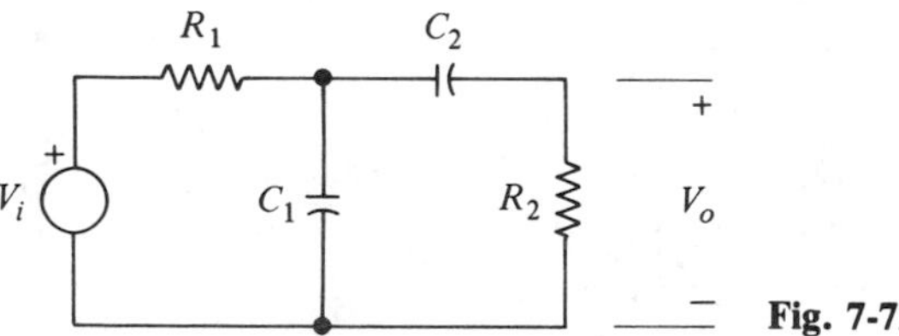

Fig. 7-72

7-14. Show that the networks of Fig. 7-73 produce $T_1(s)$.

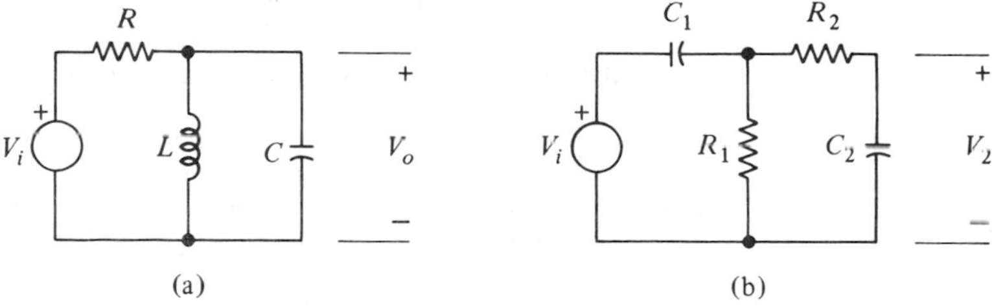

Fig. 7-73

7-15. Sketch the step response of the network shown in Fig. 7-74.

7-16. The input and the output of the network in Fig. 7-75 are as given. Obtain the element values.

7-17. Derive Eq. (7-35).

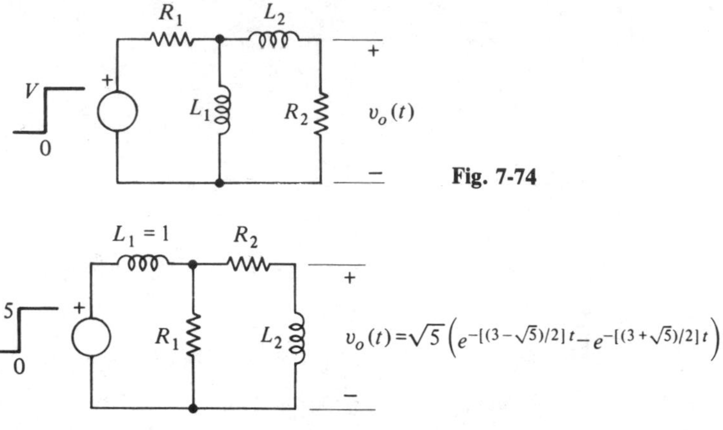

Fig. 7-74

Fig. 7-75

7-18. Given $T_2(s) = s^2/(s + \alpha)^2$, obtain the unit-step response.

7-19. Given the RL network of Fig. 7-76(a), adjust the R and the C of the RLC network of Fig. 7-76(b) so that the step responses of the two networks are identical as shown.

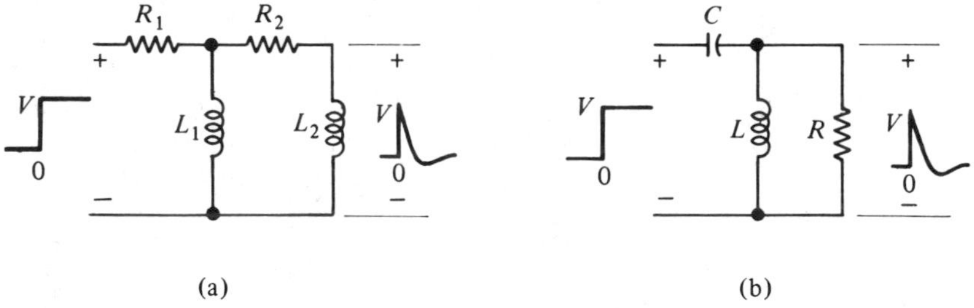

Fig. 7-76

7-20. In Fig. 7-77, the input and output are as shown. What is in the box?

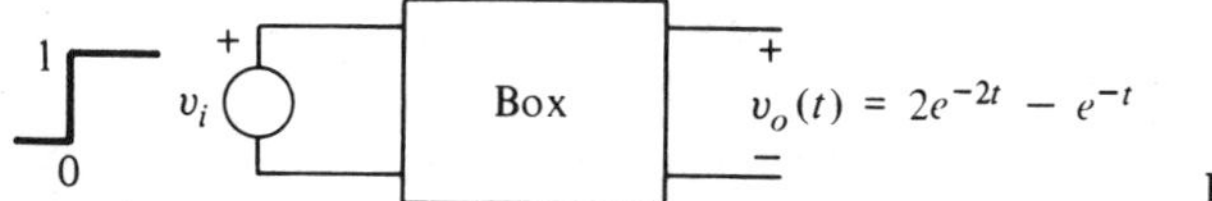

Fig. 7-77

7-21. Show that T_2 and T_0 are related by

$$T_2 = \frac{1}{\alpha_1 \alpha_2} s^2 T_0$$

and then obtain the step response of T_2 directly from the step response of T_0 through appropriate operations.

7-22. The unit-step response of $T_1(s) = b_2/(s^2 + sb_1 + b_0)$ is $x(t)$. What is the unit-step response of

$$T_2(s) = \frac{a_2 s^2 + a_1 s + a_0}{s^2 + sb_1 + b_0}\ ?$$

Give the answer in terms of $x(t)$.

7-23. The unit-step response of $T_1(s) = 2s/(s^2 + s + 1)$ is $y(t)$. What is the unit-step response of

$$T_2(s) = \frac{3s^2 + s + 2}{s^2 + s + 1}\ ?$$

Give the answer in terms of $y(t)$.

7-24. The unit-step response of $T_1(s) = a_1 s/D(s)$ is $r(t)$ with $r(0^+) = 0$. What is the unit-step response of

$$T_2(s) = \frac{a_2 s^2 + a_0}{D(s)}\ ?$$

7-25. What network is in the box shown in Fig. 7-78?

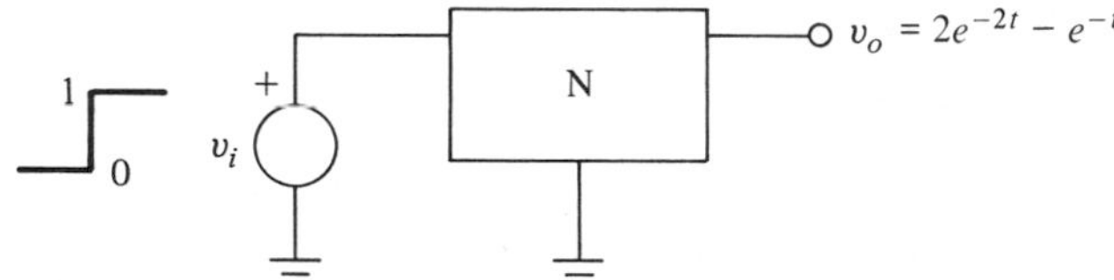

Fig. 7-78

7-26. Sketch the following functions.

(a) $\dfrac{1}{\alpha_2 - \alpha_1}(\alpha_1 e^{-\alpha_2 t} - \alpha_2 e^{-\alpha_1 t})$

(b) $\dfrac{1}{\alpha_2 - \alpha_1}(\alpha_1 e^{-\alpha_1 t} - \alpha_2 e^{-\alpha_2 t})$

7-27. The unit-step response of $T(s)$ is $r(t)$ with $r(0^+) = 0$. What is the unit-step response of

$$T(s)\left(\frac{a_2 s^2 + a_1 s + a_0}{s}\right)\ ?$$

7-28. By inspection of the network of Fig. 7-79, obtain $v_o(0^-)$, $v_o(0^+)$, and $v_o(\infty)$. The initial conditions are zero.

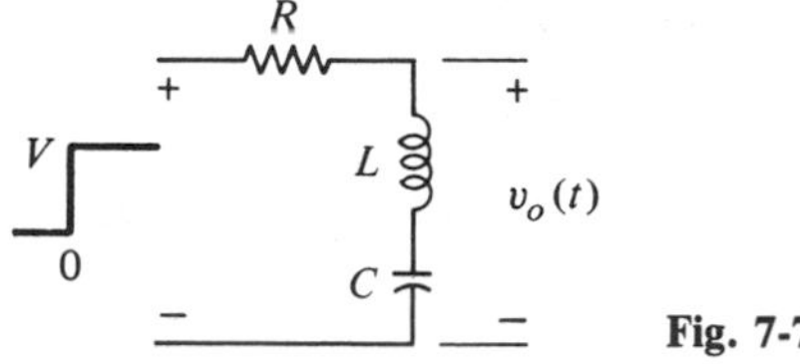

Fig. 7-79

7-29. Given $T_1 = \dfrac{s}{s^2 + 2s + 1}$,

(a) Obtain the unit-step response of T_1.
(b) Show that the function

$$T = \frac{s^2 - 2s + 1}{s^2 + 2s + 1}$$

can be expressed in terms of T_1 as

$$T = \left(s - 2 + \frac{1}{s}\right)T_1$$

(c) Using the results of (a) and (b), obtain the unit-step response of T.

7-30. Show that the network of Fig. 7-80 produces a continuous transition between the $v_1(t)$ and $v_2(t)$ curves given in Fig. 7-27.

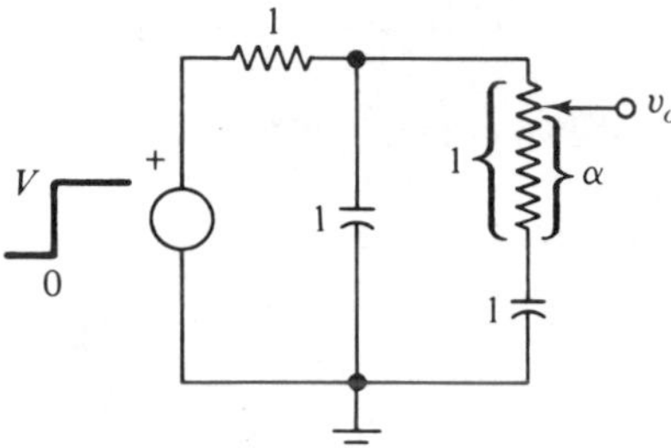

Fig. 7-80

7-31. (a) Show that the transfer functions of the two networks shown in Fig. 7.81 are identical if $R_1C_1 = R_2C_2$.
(b) Since the network of Fig. 7-81(a) is a first-order system, its step response can be written by inspection (by using initial and final values plus the time constant). Obtain the step response if the input jumps V volts at $t = 0$.
(c) Using the results of (a) and (b), obtain the step response of the attenuator network given in Example 7-11.

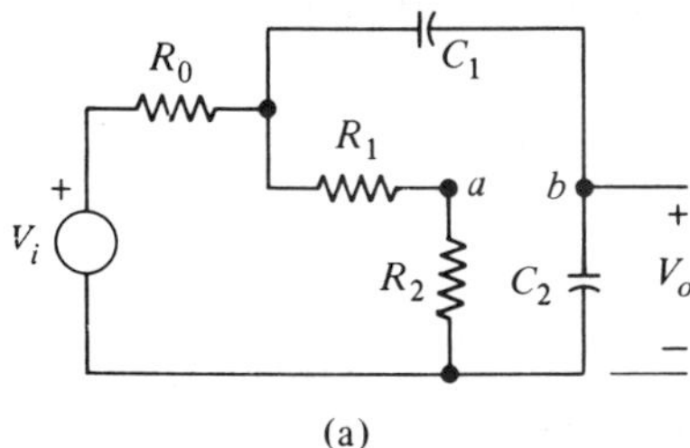

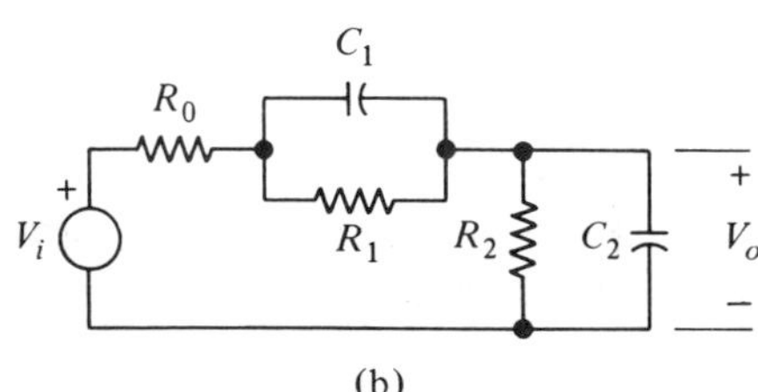

Fig. 7-81

7-32. In Fig. 7-82 R_o represents the equivalent resistance of the source. The R_1R_2 combination represents an attenuator. The stray capacitance across R_2 is designated by C_s. The input is a step function.
(a) Assume $C_c = 0$. What is the time constant associated with the response?
(b) The compensating capacitor C_c is adjusted such that $R_1C_c = R_2C_s$ is satisfied. What is the new time constant? What is the improvement over the result of (a)?

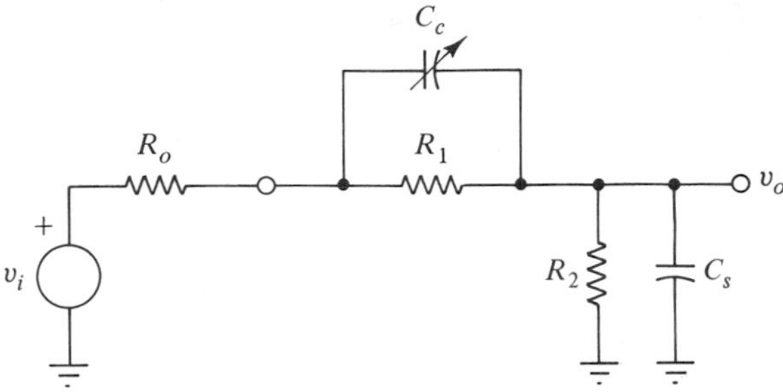

Fig. 7-82

7-33. Obtain the unit-step response of the attenuator shown in Fig. 7-28(c). Do not assume that it is properly compensated. By comparing the $t = 0^+$ and $t = \infty$ values of the response obtain the condition for proper compensation.

7-34. Oscilloscopes are used to observe waveforms in circuits. However, the very act of connecting the oscilloscope changes the circuit, and hence has an effect on the waveform under measurement. Suppose the Thévenin equivalent circuit at a point of measurement is representable as shown in Fig. 7-83(a).

(**a**) The input of the oscilloscope is modeled by the *RC* network shown in Fig. 7-83(b). It is connected directly to the terminals of the circuit of Fig. 7-83(a). What will be the v_o waveform at the input of the oscilloscope?

(**b**) To minimize the loading presented by the oscilloscope, a probe is used in conjunction with the oscilloscope as shown in Fig. 7-83(c). The capacitance C_P of the probe is adjusted to $C/9$, where C is the capacitance of the scope. What is the input impedance Z_i of the probe-scope combination? What simpler circuit model can be used to represent it?

(**c**) The probe-scope combination is connected to the terminals of the circuit of Fig. 7-83(a) for measurement. What will be the v_o waveform at the input of the oscilloscope? Assume $R_s \ll 10R$.

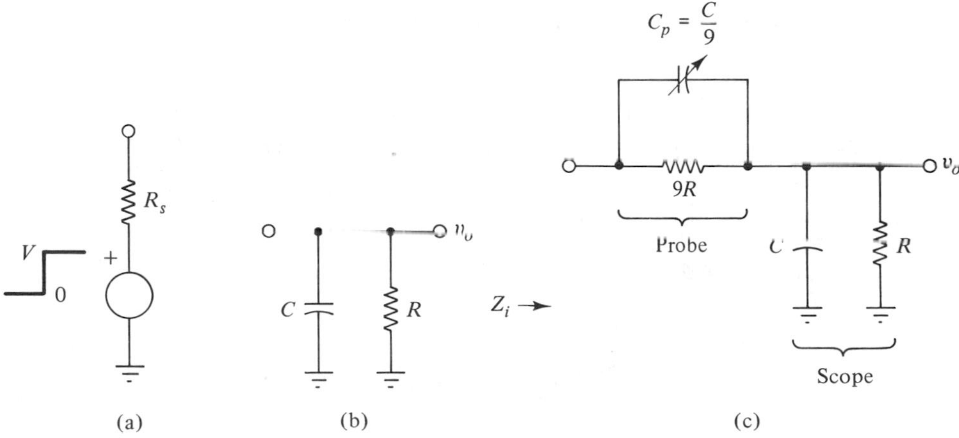

Fig. 7-83

7-35. Obtain the expression for $v_o(t)$ in Fig. 7-84.

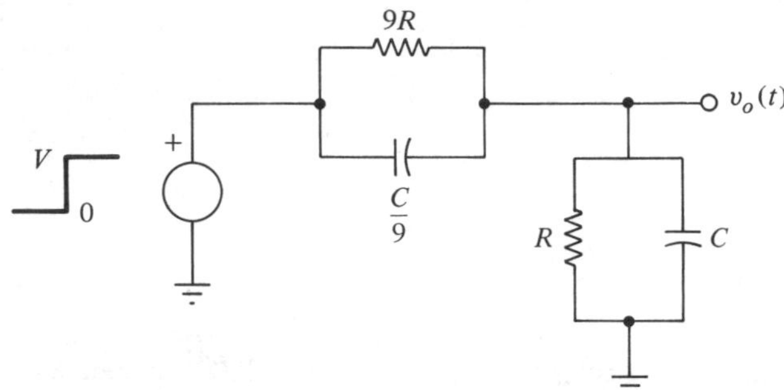

Fig. 7-84

7-36. Obtain the expression for $v_o(t)$ in Fig. 7-85.

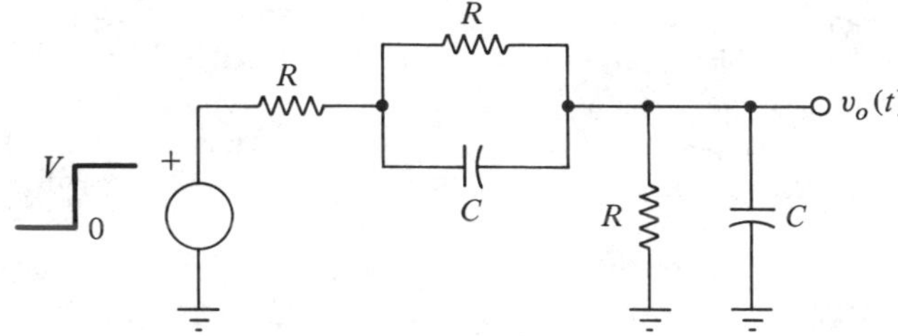

Fig. 7-85

7-37. Staring with Eq. (7-54), derive Eq. (7-55).

7-38. Equation (7-61) is indeterminate for $\beta = 0$. Use 1'Hospital's rule to obtain $r(t)$ for $\beta = 0$.

7-39. Let $\beta = j\lambda$ in Eq. (7-61) and show that it can be manipulated to result in Eq. (7-12). What is α_1? α_2?

7-40. Sketch $1 - e^{-2t} \cos 2t$. Be accurate without the use of a computer.

7-41. When a unit step voltage is applied to a network, we want the output voltage to be

$$v_o(t) = 1 - e^{-t}(\cos t + \sin t)$$

This voltage is to be taken across a resistor. Design the network.

7-42. Refer to Fig. 7-86.

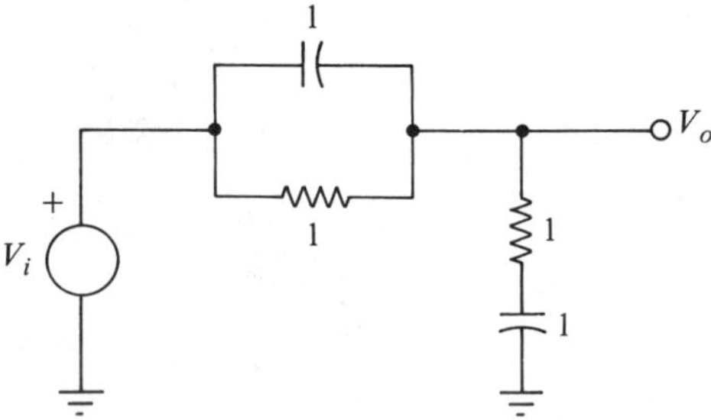

Fig. 7-86

(**a**) Obtain the transfer function.
(**b**) Obtain the poles and zeros of the transfer function.

7-43. Refer to Fig. 7-87.

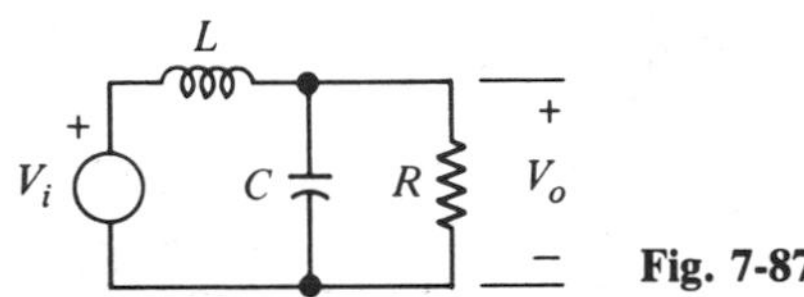

Fig. 7-87

(**a**) For what values of R are the poles complex?
(**b**) R is such that the poles are complex. Discuss the step response as R is increased further from its present value.

7-44. In Fig. 7-88 steady state prevails when at $t = 0$ the input switches from $+1$ to -1 as shown.

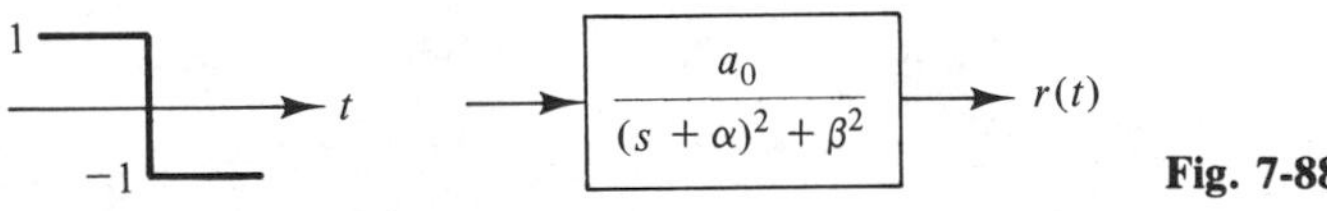

Fig. 7-88

(**a**) What is $r(0^-)$?
(**b**) Sketch $r(t)$ vs. t.

7-45. In Fig. 7-89 what is in the box?

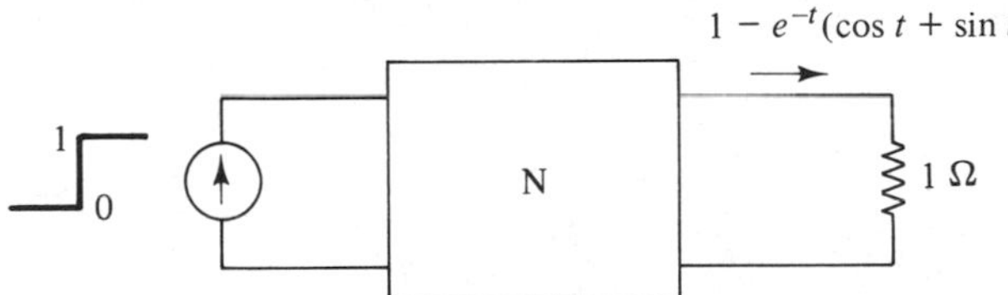

Fig. 7-89

7-46. Design another network that meets the requirements of Example 7-15.

7-47. Show that it is possible to produce the various response curves shown in Fig. 7-42 by varying a single element in the network of Fig. 7-90. Consider changing the β/α ratio both at constant α and at constant $\sqrt{\alpha^2 + \beta^2}$.

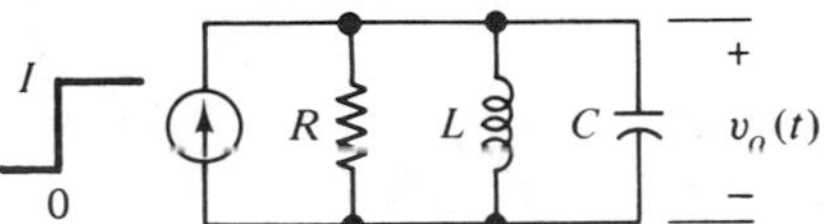

Fig. 7-90

7-48. In Fig. 7-91 what is in the box?

7-49. Refer to Fig. 7-92.
(**a**) Assume the poles are on the real axis. What is $r(t)$?
(**b**) Assume the poles are complex. What is $r(t)$?

7-50. Obtain the unit-ramp response of the system shown in Fig. 7-93.

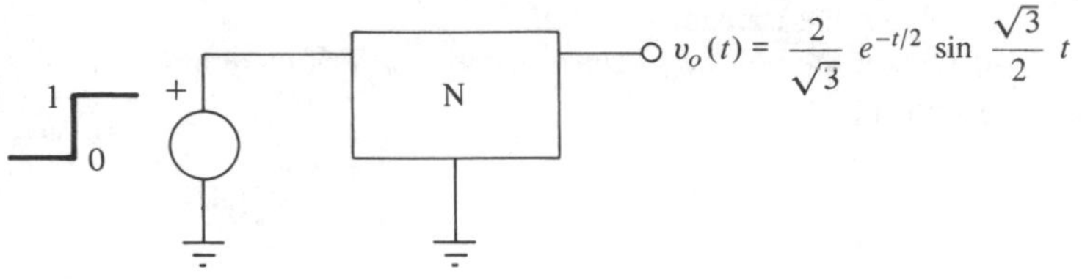

$$v_o(t) = \frac{2}{\sqrt{3}} e^{-t/2} \sin \frac{\sqrt{3}}{2} t$$

Fig. 7-91

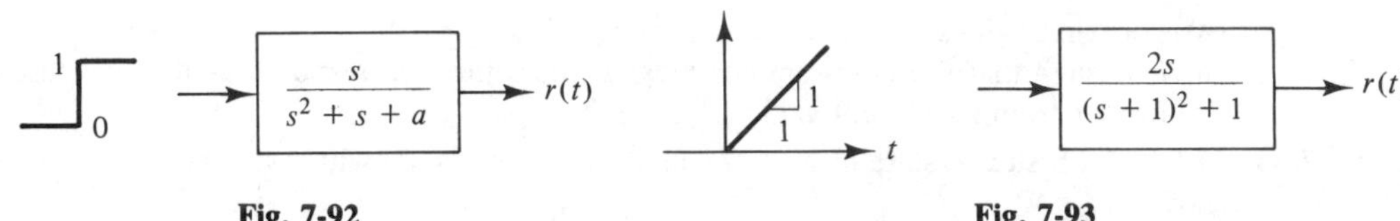

Fig. 7-92 Fig. 7-93

7-51. The system is at steady state in Fig. 7-94 when at $t = 0$ the input switches from -1 to $+1$ as shown.
(**a**) Find $y(0^-)$ and $x(0^-)$.
(**b**) Obtain the approximate expressions for $y(t)$ and $x(t)$ if δ is very small.
(**c**) Plot y vs. x.

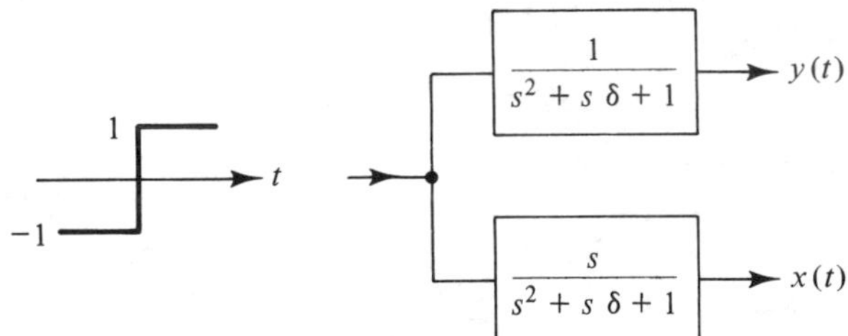

Fig. 7-94

7-52. Design a network that will produce $v_o(t) = (2/\sqrt{3})e^{-t/2} \sin (\sqrt{3}/2)t$ upon being excited by a unit-step voltage.

7-53. Obtain a realization for $V_o/V_i = 2\alpha s/[(s + \alpha)^2 + \beta^2]$.

7-54. Sketch the unit-step response of the network shown in Fig. 7-95 for $R \ll (1/2)\sqrt{L/C}$ and $R \gg (1/2)\sqrt{L/C}$.

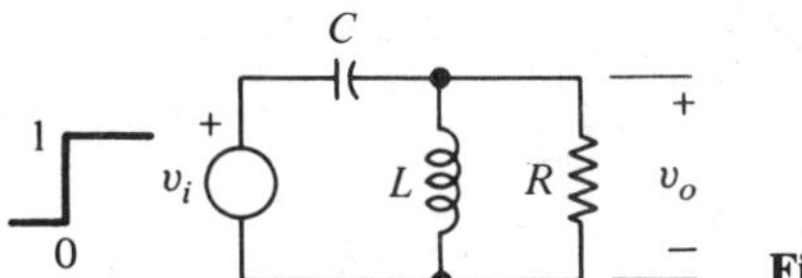

Fig. 7-95

7-55. Refer to Fig. 7-48. Starting with the given $r_0(t)$, obtain $r_1(t)$ and $r_2(t)$ through differentiation and appropriate scaling.

7-56. In Fig. 7-96, obtain the response as a function of the potentiometer setting a, and sketch it for $a = 0$, $a = 0.5$, and $a = 1$.

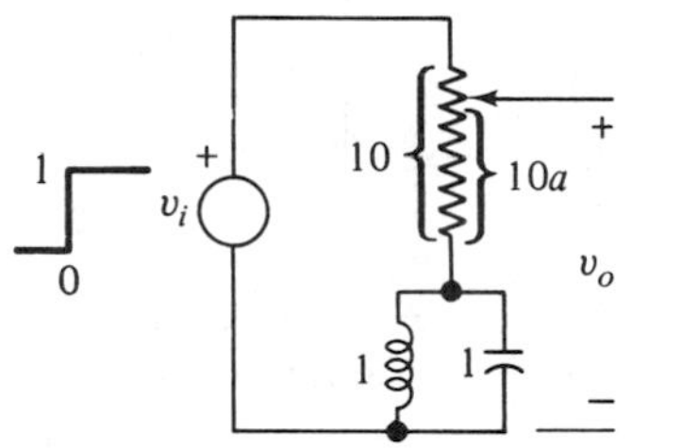

Fig. 7-96

7-57. Refer to Fig. 7-97.

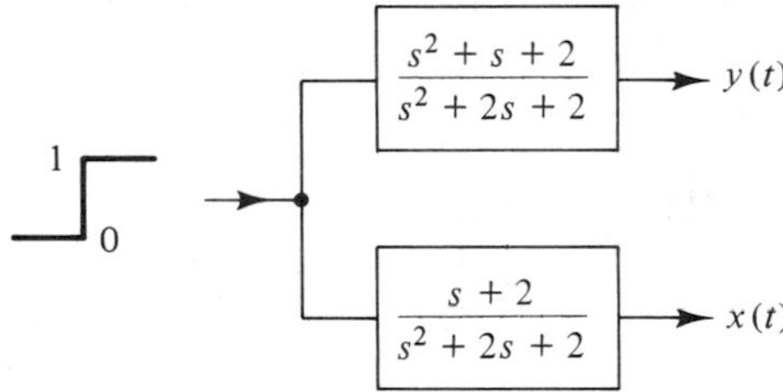

Fig. 7-97

(**a**) Obtain the expressions for $y(t)$ and $x(t)$.
(**b**) Sketch $y(t)$ vs. $x(t)$.

7-58. Refer to Fig. 7-98.

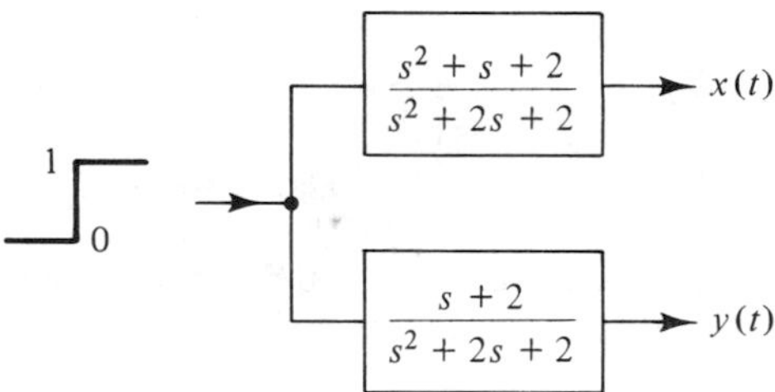

Fig. 7-98

(**a**) Obtain the expressions for $y(t)$ and $x(t)$.
(**b**) Sketch $y(t)$ vs. $x(t)$.

7-59. Obtain the unit-step response of $2(s^2 + 1)/(s^2 + 2s + 2)$.

7-60. The unit-step response of $T(s)$ is $r(t)$. It is also known that $r(0^+) = 0$. What is the unit-step response of $(s + 1)T(s)$?

7-61. Obtain the unit-step response of $(s^2 + s)/(s^2 + 2s + 2)$.

7-62. What is the unit-step response of $\alpha_1\alpha_2\alpha_3/[(s + \alpha_1)(s + \alpha_2)(s + \alpha_3)]$? Assume $\alpha_1 < \alpha_2 < \alpha_3$ and $\alpha_2 \gg \alpha_1$. What does the result indicate?

7-63. The poles of the network shown in Fig. 7-99 are on the real axis. Sketch the waveforms for $i_R(t)$, $i_L(t)$, and $i_C(t)$.

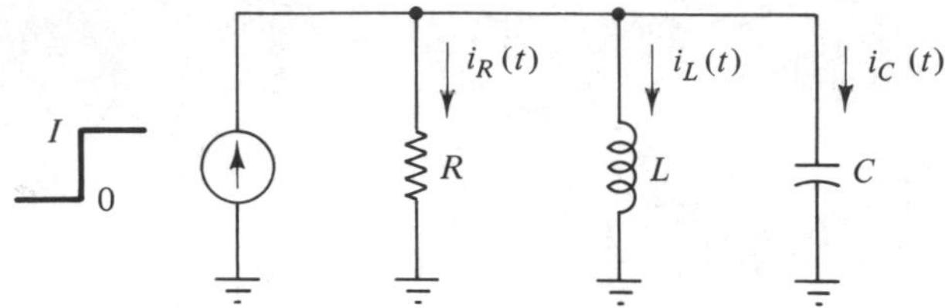

Fig. 7-99

7-64. The system is described by $(a_2s^2 + a_1s + a_0)/(s^2 + b_1s + 10)$.
(**a**) If $b_1 = 11$, how long does it take for $r(t)$ to reach steady state?
(**b**) Repeat (a) for $b_1 = 2$.

7-65. In Fig. 7-100, show that whenever the energy in the inductor is maximum, the energy in the capacitor is zero and vice versa. Furthermore, show that the maximum value of energy stored in the inductor equals the maximum value of energy stored in the capacitor.

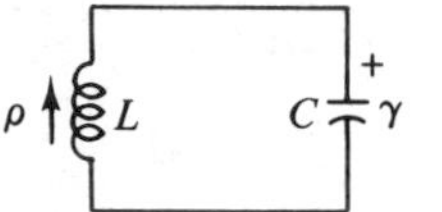

Fig. 7-100

7-66. Derive Eq. (7-89).

7-67. The losses in the network of Fig. 7-101 are small ($R \ll 2\sqrt{L/C}$). Obtain the approximate expression for $i(t)$. Compare it with the lossless case ($R = 0$).

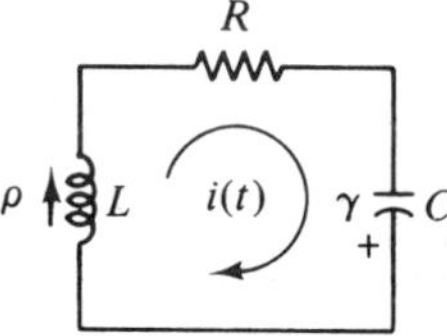

Fig. 7-101

7-68. The circuit of Fig. 7-102 is at steady state. At $t = 0$ the switch opens. Sketch the energies stored in the capcitor $\omega_C(t)$ and inductor $\omega_L(t)$ vs. t. Give significant values.

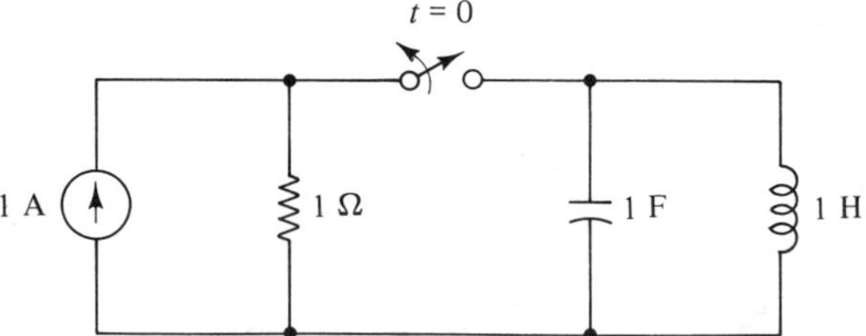

Fig. 7-102

7-69. The circuits shown in Fig. 7-103 are at steady state when at $t = 0$ the switch positions are changed as shown. Obtain the expression for $v_o(t)$.

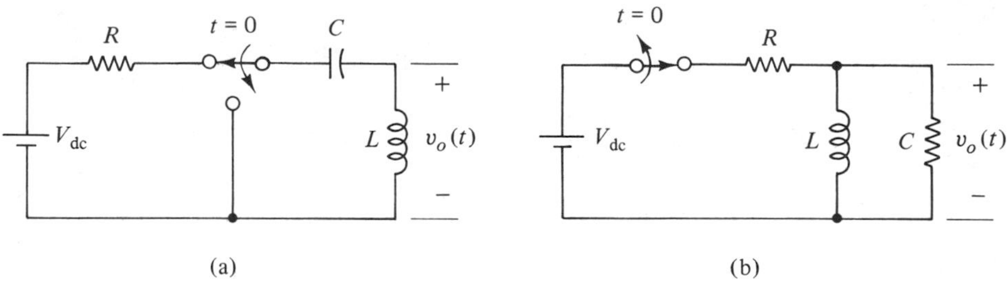

Fig. 7-103

7-70. In Fig. 7-104 the switch is opened at $t = 0$. Find $i(t)$.

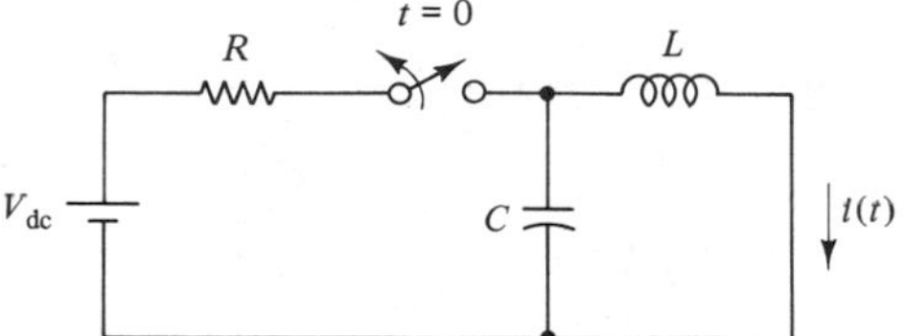

Fig. 7-104

7-71. In Fig. 7-105 the network is at steady state when the input switches from V_2 to V_1 as shown.

(**a**) In order for the circuit to have complex poles, what conditions must be satisfied?

(**b**) Assume the poles are complex. Sketch $i(t)$ vs. t.

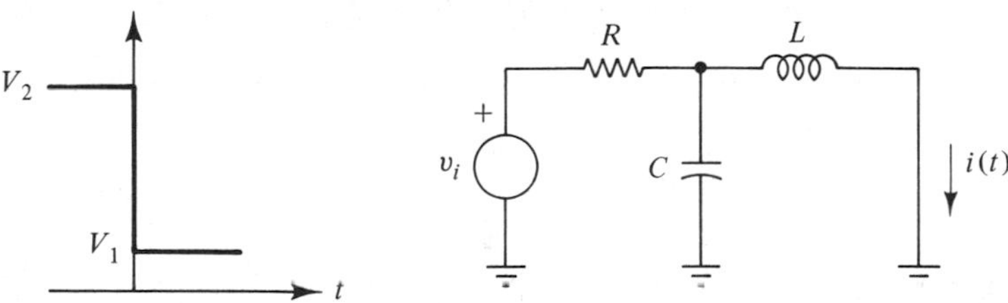

Fig. 7-105

7-72. For the networks shown in Fig. 7-106, calculate the indicated responses.

7-73. In Fig. 7-107, the switch has been in the closed position for some time; that is, steady-state conditions prevail.

(**a**) What are the initial conditions?

(**b**) At $t = 0$ the switch is opened. Obtain the expression for $v(t)$.

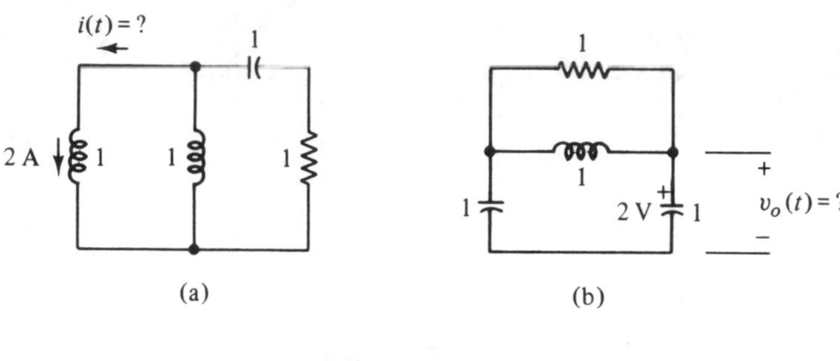

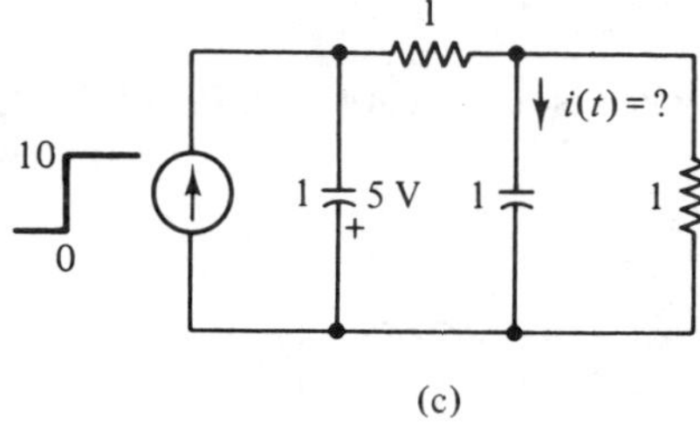

Fig. 7-106

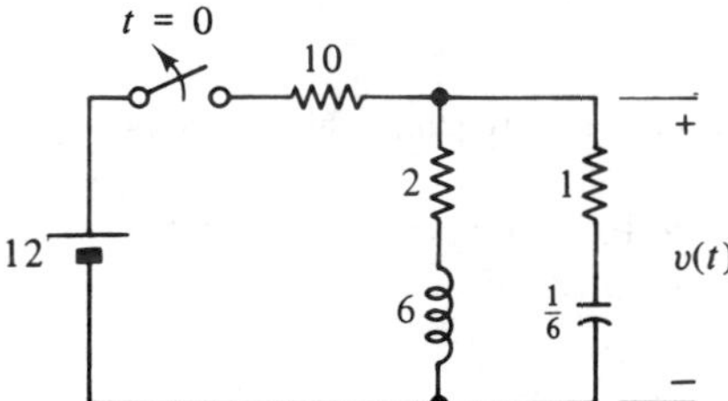

Fig. 7-107

7-74. By inspection of the networks of Fig. 7-108, obtain the indicated response values at $t = 0^+$ and $t = \infty$.

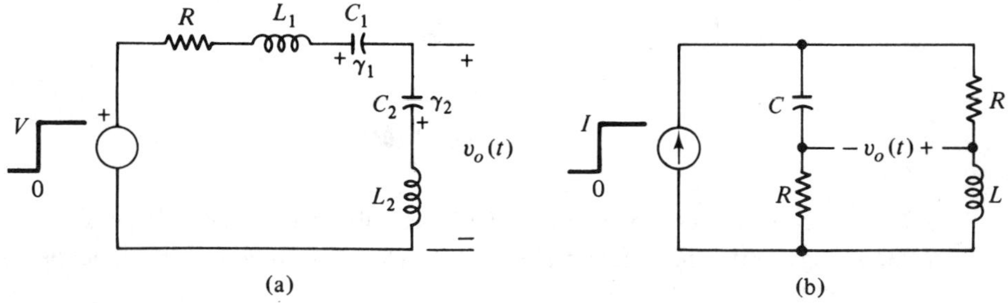

Fig. 7-108

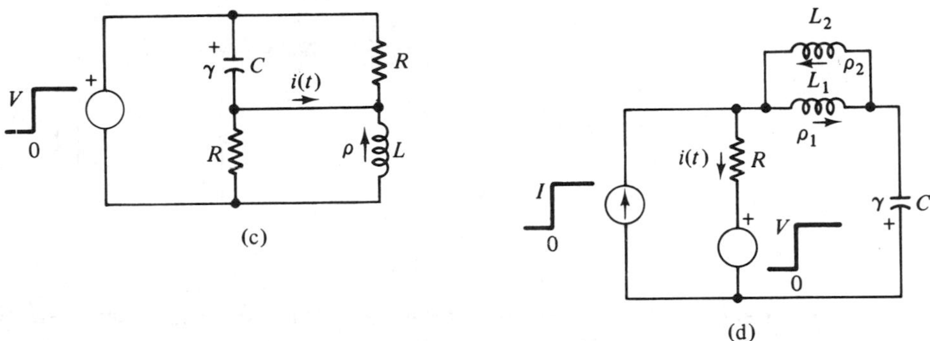

Fig. 7-108 (cont.)

7-75. In Fig. 7-109 obtain $i(0^+)$ and $i(\infty)$.

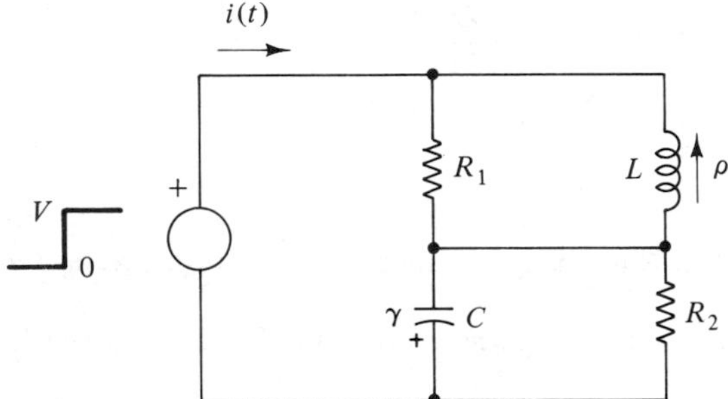

Fig. 7-109

7-76. In Fig. 7-110, the network is at steady state when the switch opens at $t = 0$. Find $v_o(0^+)$ and $v_o(\infty)$.

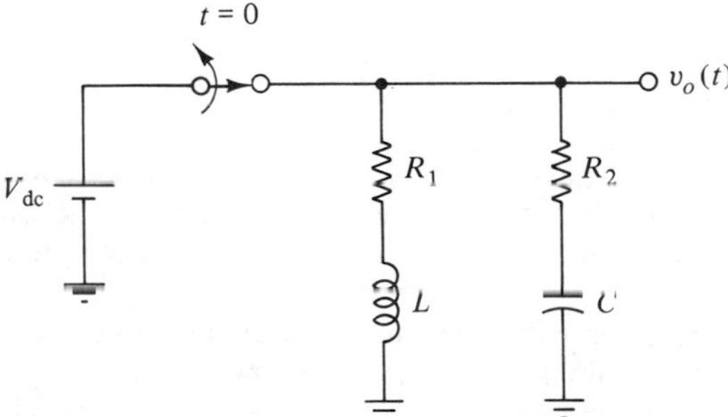

Fig. 7-110

7-77. In Fig. 7-111 the network is at steady state when the input switches from $-V$ to $+V$. Find $i(0^+)$.

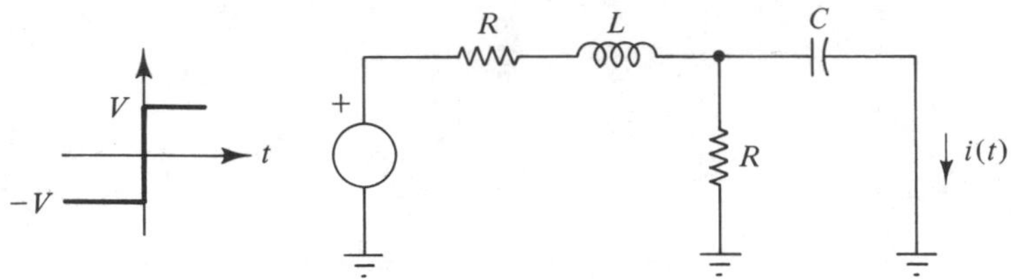

Fig. 7-111

7-78. In Fig. 7-112 the network is at steady state. At $t = 0$ the input current switches from I to 0 as shown. Find $v_1(0^+)$ and $v_2(0^+)$.

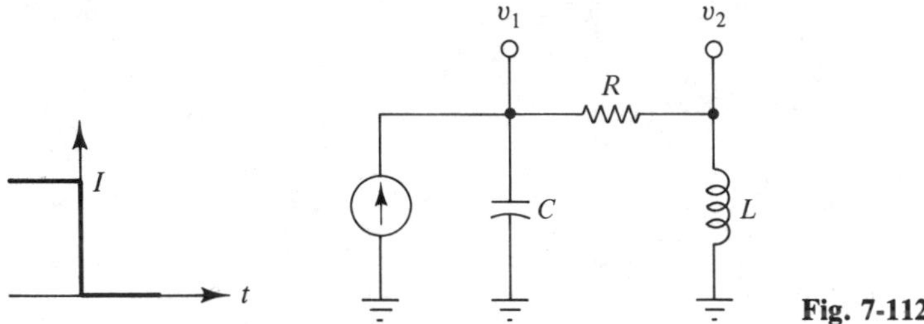

Fig. 7-112

7-79. Refer to Example 7-19.

(**a**) If the current through L is to change no more than 1% of its average value, how large should L be?

(**b**) If the voltage across C is to change no more than 1% of its average value, how large should C be?

7-80. For the problem discussed in Example 7-20, sketch $v_o(t)$ for $\delta = \pi\sqrt{LC}$.

7-81. Refer to Fig. 7-113.

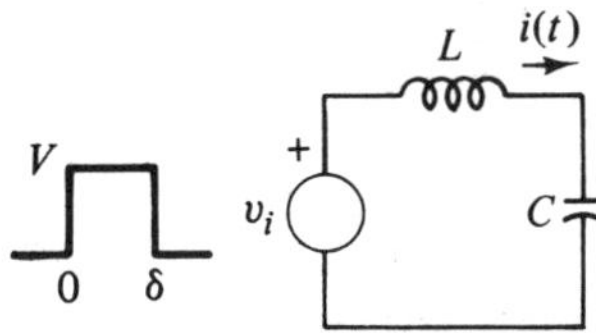

Fig. 7-113

(**a**) Obtain $i(t)$ by decomposing the input into the sum of two step functions.

(**b**) What is the current through the inductor and the voltage across the capacitor at $t = \delta$?

(**c**) Alternatively, the current for $t \geq \delta$ can be obtained by using the current and voltage evaluated in (b) as initial conditions and by noting that $v_i = 0$ for $t > \delta$. Show that the expression for current for $t \geq \delta$ obtained by this method is the same as in (a).

7-82. In Fig. 7-114, what must the pulse width δ be in order to produce as output a single peak $2V$ volts high?

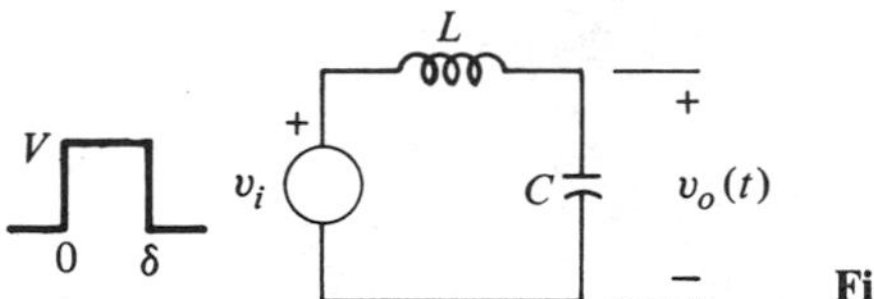

Fig. 7-114

7-83. Refer to Fig. 7-114.
(**a**) Assume $\delta = \infty$. Obtain the expression for $v_o(t)$.
(**b**) What must be δ if the output is to contain only one cycle of a sinusoidal wave?

7-84. Refer to Fig. 7-115.

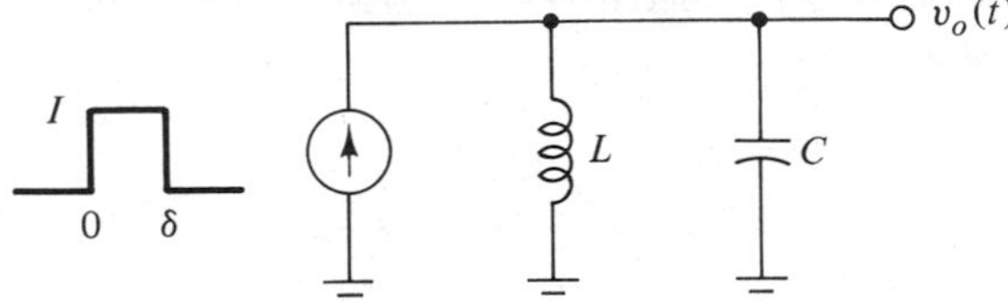

Fig. 7-115

(**a**) Obtain the expression for $v_o(t)$.
(**b**) Sketch $v_o(t)$ for $\delta = 4\pi\sqrt{LC}$.

7-85. In Fig. 7-116 a five-cycle sinusoidal output voltage is to be produced by the π ms wide input current pulse shown. What should be the value of C?

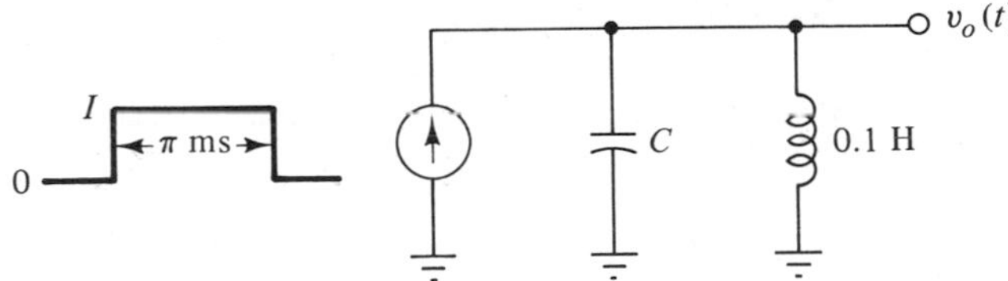

Fig. 7-116

7-86. Refer to Fig. 7-117.

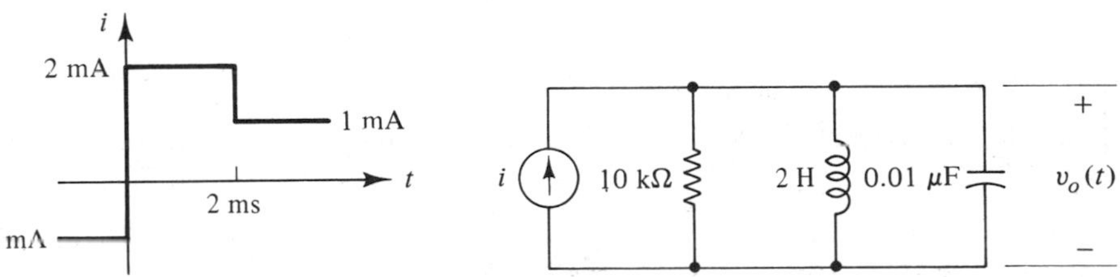

Fig. 7-117

(**a**) What is the system time constant?
(**b**) The system is at steady state at $t = 0^-$. Obtain the value of $v_o(t)$ at $t = 0^-$, 0^+, 2^+ms, and 3 ms.

7-87. In Fig. 7-118, sketch the output current for $\delta = 2\pi\sqrt{LC}$.

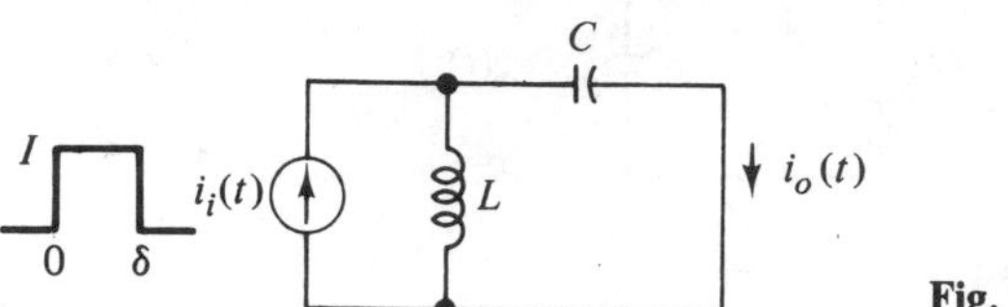

Fig. 7-118

7-88. In Fig. 7-119, a step voltage is applied to the upper network at $t = 0$. An equal but opposite step is applied to the lower network at $t = \pi\sqrt{LC}$. The output of the first network is summed with the output of the second network to produce $v_o(t)$. Obtain the expression for $v_o(t)$ and sketch it.

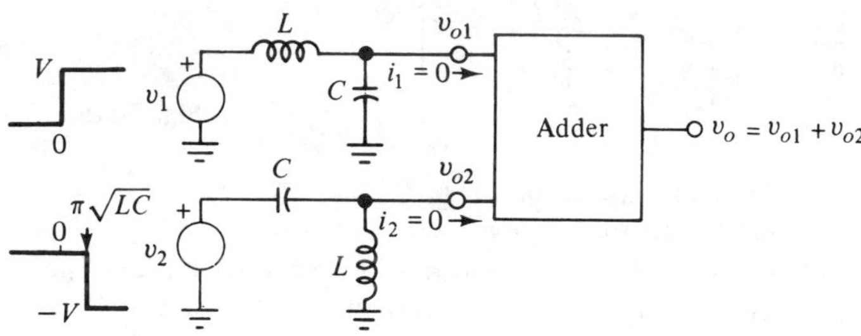

Fig. 7-119

7-89. In Fig. 7-120, a pulse is applied to three networks described by transfer functions T_a, T_b, and T_c. After studying the responses, what can you say about the characteristics of the transfer functions?

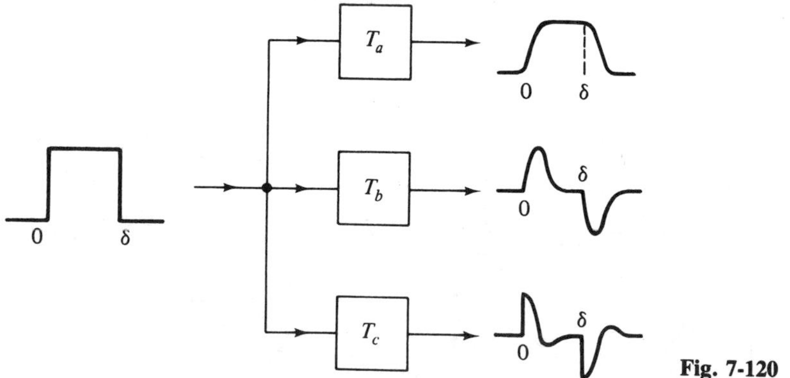

Fig. 7-120

7-90. Refer to Example 7-21. Sketch the response for $T = 6\pi\sqrt{LC}$.

7-91. Refer to Example 7-21. Sketch the response for $T = 4\pi\sqrt{LC}$.

7-92. Show that the current waveform in Fig. 7-121 builds up with time if $T = n2\pi\sqrt{LC}$ (n odd). Sketch the $i(t)$ vs. t curve for $n = 1$ and $n = 3$.

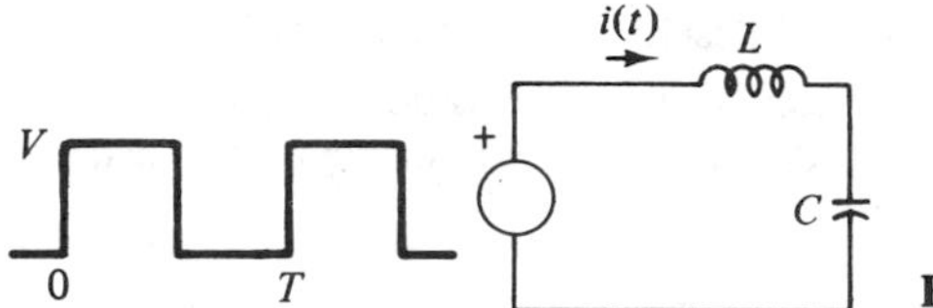

Fig. 7-121

7-93. In Fig. 7-122, the input has been at the $-A$ level for a sufficiently long time so that steady-state conditions prevail. At $t = 0$ the input jumps to A. Obtain the expressions for a, b, and c outputs and sketch them. Assume a large β/α ratio.

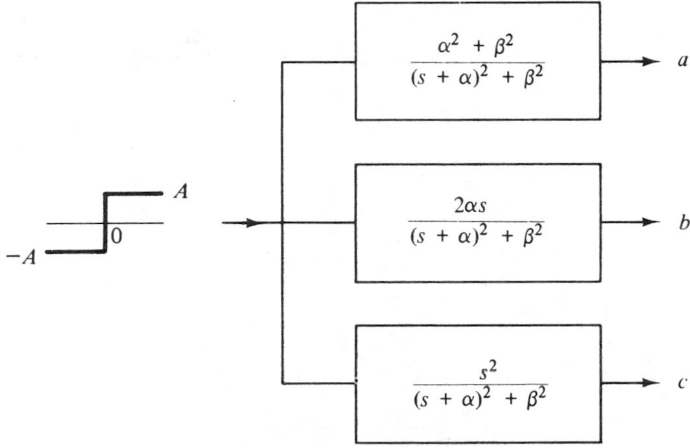

Fig. 7-122

7-94. In Fig. 7-123, the β/α ratio is such that the x and y outputs ring quite awhile. The input changes after all the ringings have died out ($T/2 > 5/\alpha$).

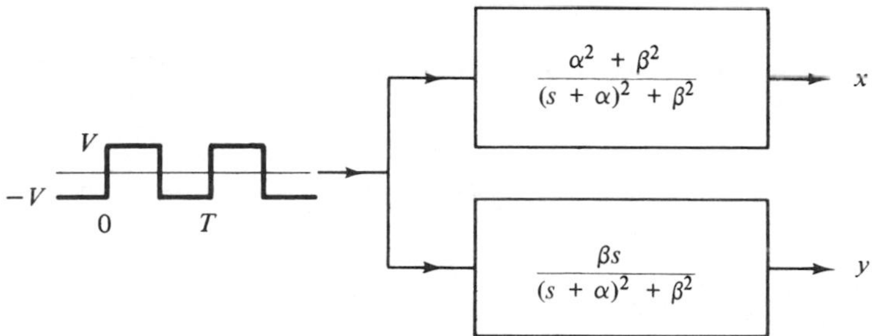

Fig. 7-123

(**a**) Obtain x and y. Assume that the input changes from $-V$ to $+V$ (or $+V$ to $-V$) and that thc output reaches steady state before the input changes again.
(**b**) x and y outputs are connected to the horizontal and vertical amplifiers of an oscilloscope. Sketch the display and describe it mathematically.

7-95. In. Fig. 7-124, sketch the steady state $v_{o1}(t)$ and $v_{o2}(t)$ outputs. Assume the period of the square wave is very much larger than any of the time constants involved.

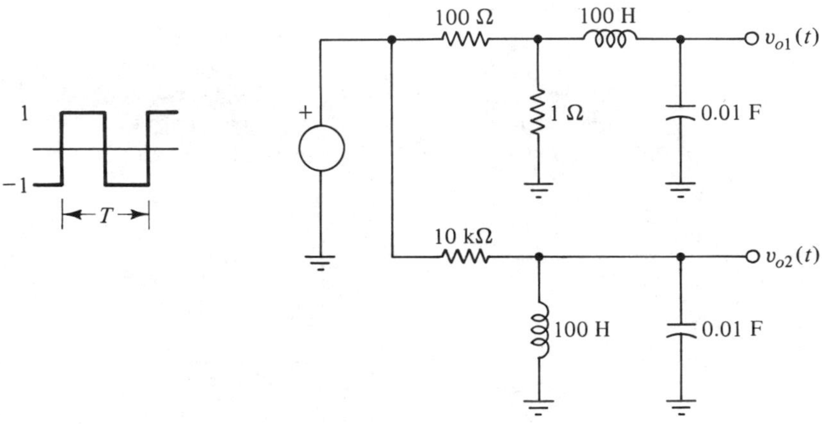

Fig. 7-124

CHAPTER 8

THE SINUSOIDAL RESPONSE

The sine wave is one of the most widely encountered and used waveforms in electrical engineering. Easily generated by ac machines, it is distributed by transmission lines and brought to our homes to run a variety of appliances. In addition, it is generated by laboratory oscillators and used to test the performance of circuits. Mathematically, the sine wave is described by a simple function that, on differentiation or integration, yields a sinusoidal function. As a result, a sinusoidal current through an inductor or a capacitor produces a sinusoidal voltage across the inductor $[v = L(di/dt)]$ or capacitor $[v = (1/C) \int i \, dt]$. Furthermore, the sum of two or more sine waves of the same frequency is also a sine wave. Consequently, when Kirchhoff's laws are applied to sum sinusoidal currents or voltages, the unknown variables can easily be determined.

Because the sine wave is important and simple to deal with, a great deal of knowledge, theoretical as well as experimental, exists about sinusoidally excited networks. In this chapter we learn how to calculate the sinusoidal steady-state response of *RLC* networks.

8-1 THE SINUSOIDAL WAVE

The sinusoidal wave is expressed mathematically by

$$A \sin (2\pi ft + \theta) = A \sin (\omega t + \theta) = A \sin \left(\frac{2\pi}{T}t + \theta\right) \tag{8-1}$$

where A = amplitude or peak value of sine wave
f = frequency of sine wave in hertz
ω = angular frequency of sine wave in radians per second
T = period of sine wave in seconds
θ = phase angle of sine wave in radians
$T = 1/f$
$\omega = 2\pi f$

The sinusoidal wave is sketched in Fig. 8-1, where the amplitude A represents the peak value of the sine wave. The frequency f represents the number of cycles of sine wave contained in one second. The unit for frequency is *hertz,* which is abbreviated Hz. (One Hz is the same as *one cycle per second.*) Since each cycle contains 2π radians of angle, $2\pi f$ represents the total angle (in radians) that is covered each second. So $2\pi f = \omega$ represents the *angular frequency* measured *in radians per second* (rad/s). One radian is $180/\pi$ degrees.

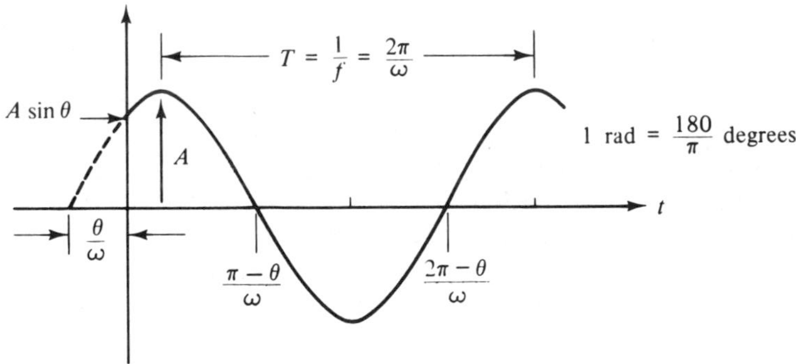

Fig. 8-1

The reciprocal of frequency is *the period T,* which represents the time in seconds for completing one cycle of operation. Thus $T = 1/f$.

The angle θ is called the *phase angle* of the sine wave and is measured in radians. θ represents the angle (the argument) of the sine wave when $t = 0$. When $\theta = 0$, Eq. (8-1) becomes a sine wave. When $\theta = \pi/2$, it becomes a cosine wave—that is,

$$A \sin \left(\omega t + \frac{\pi}{2}\right) = A \cos \omega t$$

In general, regardless of the value of θ, the waveform shown in Fig. 8-1 is called a sinusoidal wave or, briefly, a sine wave. In dealing with circuits, time is taken as the independent variable. Therefore the sine wave is drawn by using t (rather than the angle) as the abscissa.

A sine wave is completely specified if three constants are given: A, f, θ, or A, ω, θ, or A, T, θ.

8-2 THE SINUSOIDAL RESPONSE

Let $T(s)$ represent the transfer function (or input impedance or input admittance) of a linear system shown in Fig. 8-2. The excitation is a sine wave. We wish to obtain the response $r(t)$. To relate the output to the input, we go into the frequency domain and write

$$R(s) = T(s)\mathscr{L}\{A \sin (\omega + \theta)\} \tag{8-2}$$

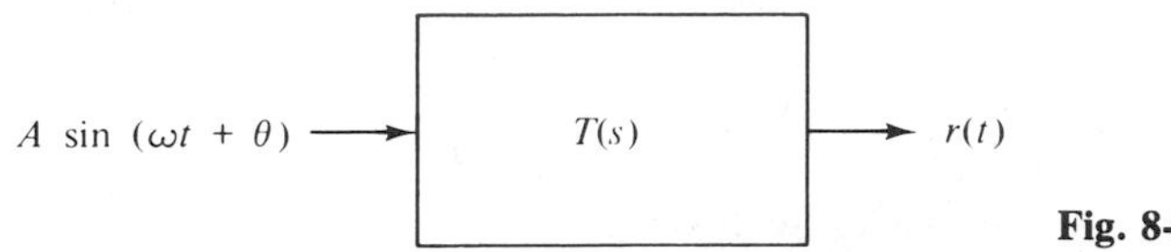

Fig. 8-2

Since

$$A \sin (\omega t + \theta) = A \cos \theta \sin \omega t + A \sin \theta \cos \omega t$$

we have

$$\mathscr{L}\{A \sin (\omega t + \theta)\} = A \cos \theta\left(\frac{\omega}{s^2 + \omega^2}\right) + A \sin \theta\left(\frac{s}{s^2 + \omega^2}\right)$$

Equation (8-2) can then be written

$$R(s) = T(s)\left(\frac{\omega A \cos \theta + sA \sin \theta}{s^2 + \omega^2}\right) \tag{8-3}$$

In order to take the inverse transformation, we must expand $R(s)$ in partial fractions. Doing so requires that we know *all* the poles of $R(s)$. Equation (8-3) shows the *two poles of* $R(s)$ that are due to the *excitation* (forcing) function. These poles are on the imaginary axis and are located at $s = \pm j\omega$. As we vary the frequency of the sine wave, we vary the poles of excitation up or down the imaginary axis. It is important to form a clear picture of the change initiated in the time domain (vary the frequency of the oscillator) to the corresponding change caused in the frequency domain (pole movement along the imaginary axis). The higher the frequency of the sine wave, the more distant is the conjugate pair of poles from the origin.

The remaining poles of $R(s)$ are contained in $T(s)$, which represents the system. These poles produce the natural part of the response. [It is assumed that $T(s)$

does not have any poles that are coincident with the poles of excitation.] We can therefore partition Eq. (8-3) as

$$R(s) = \underbrace{R_n(s)}_{\substack{\text{Natural part}\\ \text{due to poles}\\ \text{of } T(s)}} + \underbrace{R_f(s)}_{\substack{\text{Forced part}\\ \text{due to poles}\\ \text{of excitation}}}$$

$$R(s) = R_n(s) + \underbrace{\left(\frac{K}{s - j\omega} + \frac{K^*}{s + j\omega}\right)}_{R_f(s)} \tag{8-4}$$

where K^* is the conjugate of K. The next step is to take the inverse transform of $R(s)$.

$$r(t) = \underbrace{r_n(t)}_{\text{Natural}} + \underbrace{(Ke^{j\omega t} + K^*e^{-j\omega t})}_{\text{Forced}}$$

Since the sum of two complex-conjugate functions is twice the real part of either function, we have

$$r(t) = r_n(t) + 2 \text{ Re } \{Ke^{j\omega t}\} \tag{8-5}$$

Using Eq. (8-4), we can easily evaluate K.

$$K = (s - j\omega)R(s)\bigg|_{s=j\omega} = \cancel{(s - j\omega)}T(s)\left[\frac{\omega A \cos \theta + sA \sin \theta}{\cancel{(s - j\omega)}(s + j\omega)}\right]\bigg|_{s=j\omega}$$

$$= T(j\omega)\left(\frac{\omega A \cos \theta + j\omega A \sin \theta}{2j\omega}\right) = \frac{1}{2}T(j\omega)\left(\frac{A \cos \theta + jA \sin \theta}{j}\right)$$

Next, all the terms in K are converted to the exponential form.

$$K = \frac{1}{2}|T(j\omega)|e^{j\theta_T}\left[\frac{Ae^{j\theta}}{e^{j(\pi/2)}}\right] = \frac{1}{2}A|T(j\omega)|e^{j[\theta+\theta_T-(\pi/2)]} \tag{8-6}$$

where $|T(j\omega)|$ = magnitude of $T(j\omega)$

θ_T = angle of $T(j\omega)$

Substituting (8-6) into (8-5) gives

$$r(t) = r_n(t) + 2 \text{ Re } \left\{\frac{1}{2}A|T(j\omega)|e^{j[\omega t+\theta+\theta_T-(\pi/2)]}\right\}$$

$$= r_n(t) + A|T(j\omega)| \text{ Re } \{e^{j[\omega t+\theta+\theta_T-(\pi/2)]}\}$$

$$= r_n(t) + A|T(j\omega)| \cos\left(\omega t + \theta + \theta_T - \frac{\pi}{2}\right)$$

$$r(t) = r_n(t) + \underbrace{A|T(j\omega)| \sin (\omega t + \theta + \theta_T)}_{r_f(t)} \tag{8-7}$$

We have obtained the general solution for sinusoidally excited linear systems. If the system, $T(s)$, is given, $r_n(t)$, as well as $|T(j\omega)|$ and θ_T, can be evaluated to obtain the resulting response.

Example 8-1

At $t = 0$ a sine wave is applied to the network as shown in Fig. 8-3.

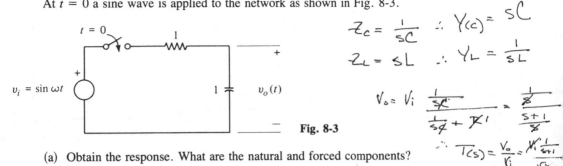

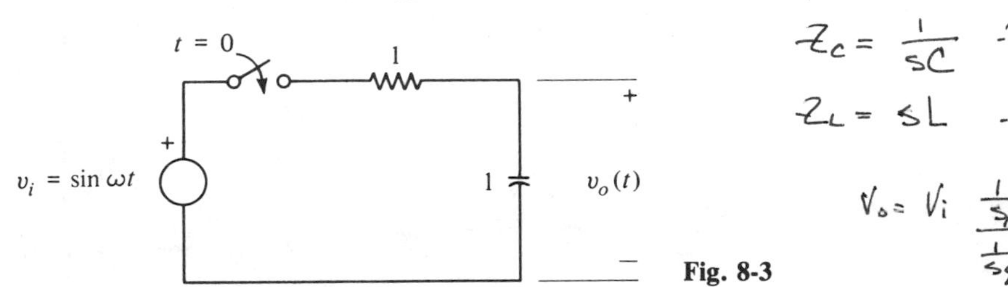

Fig. 8-3

(a) Obtain the response. What are the natural and forced components?

(b) Let $\omega = 10$. Plot the response and its components.

Solution.

(a)

$$V_o(s) = V_i(s)T(s) = \frac{\omega}{s^2 + \omega^2}\left(\frac{1}{s+1}\right) = V_n(s) + V_f(s)$$

$V_n(s)$ is due to the pole of $T(s)$ (natural part), and $V_f(s)$ is due to the poles of excitation (forced part). So

$$V_o(s) = \frac{K}{s+1} + V_f(s)$$

where
$$K = (s+1)V_o(s)\big|_{s=-1} = (s+1)\frac{\omega}{s^2+\omega^2}\frac{1}{(s+1)}\bigg|_{s=-1}$$

$$= \frac{\omega}{s^2+\omega^2}\bigg|_{s=-1} = \frac{\omega}{1+\omega^2}$$

When K is substituted in the expression for $V_o(s)$, we find

$$V_o(s) = \left(\frac{\omega}{1+\omega^2}\right)\frac{1}{s+1} + V_f(s)$$

which on inverse transformation gives

$$v_o(t) = \left(\frac{\omega}{1+\omega^2}\right)e^{-t} + v_f(t)$$

To obtain $v_f(t)$, we use the general formulation given by Eq. 8-7, which requires that we evaluate $|T(j\omega)|$ and θ_T.

$$T(j\omega) = \frac{1}{s+1}\bigg|_{s=j\omega} = \frac{1}{1+j\omega} = \underbrace{\frac{1}{\sqrt{1+\omega^2}}}_{|T(j\omega)|}e^{j\overbrace{(-\tan^{-1}\omega)}^{\theta_T}}$$

Then

$$v_f(t) = |T(j\omega)| \sin(\omega t + \theta_T) = \frac{1}{\sqrt{1+\omega^2}} \sin(\omega t - \tan^{-1}\omega)$$

The response and its parts are given by

$$\left.\begin{aligned} v_o(t) &= \frac{\omega}{1+\omega^2} e^{-t} + \frac{1}{\sqrt{1+\omega^2}} \sin(\omega t - \tan^{-1}\omega) \\ v_n(t) &= \frac{\omega}{1+\omega^2} e^{-t} \\ v_f(t) &= \frac{1}{\sqrt{1+\omega^2}} \sin(\omega t - \tan^{-1}\omega) \end{aligned}\right\} \text{Ans.}$$

Note that

$$\begin{aligned} v_o(0) &= \frac{\omega}{1+\omega^2} + \frac{1}{\sqrt{1+\omega^2}} \sin(-\tan^{-1}\omega) \\ &= \frac{\omega}{1+\omega^2} - \frac{1}{\sqrt{1+\omega^2}} \sin(\tan^{-1}\omega) \\ &= \frac{\omega}{1+\omega^2} - \frac{1}{\sqrt{1+\omega^2}} \frac{\omega}{\sqrt{1+\omega^2}} = 0 \end{aligned}$$

This zero initial value is to be expected, since the output voltage, being the voltage across a capacitor, cannot jump.

(b) For $\omega = 10$, $v_o(t)$, $v_n(t)$, and $v_f(t)$ become

$$\begin{aligned} v_o(t) &= \frac{10}{101} e^{-t} + \frac{1}{\sqrt{101}} \sin(10t - \tan^{-1} 10) \\ v_n(t) &= \frac{10}{101} e^{-t} \\ v_f(t) &= \frac{1}{\sqrt{101}} \sin(10t - \tan^{-1} 10) \end{aligned}$$

These waveforms are plotted in Fig. 8-4. Since the time constant associated with the exponential is 1 second (due to pole at $s = -1$), the natural response dies out in 5 seconds.

The period of the sine wave is

$$T = \left.\frac{2\pi}{\omega}\right|_{\omega=10} = 0.2\pi$$

So it takes about eight cycles of the sine wave ($8 \times 0.2\pi \cong 5$ seconds) before the response settles down completely. Thereafter the response is indistinguishable from the forced component of the response. In electronic circuits the natural component of the response frequently vanishes in milliseconds or less. Unless care is taken to trigger the sweep of the oscilloscope at the same time as the input sine

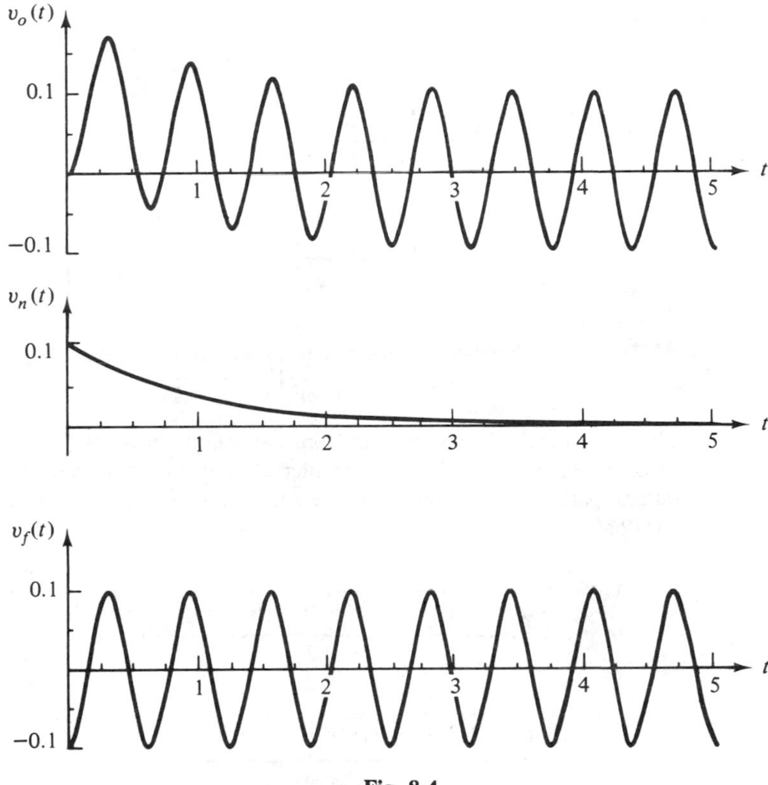

Fig. 8-4

wave is applied, the natural part of the solution is not seen and the display is a pure sine wave. This situation creates the erroneous impression that when the input is a sine wave, so is the output. Yet only after the natural part of the response has vanished is this result true.

Example 8-2

At $t = 0$ a sine wave is applied to the network shown in Fig. 8-5.

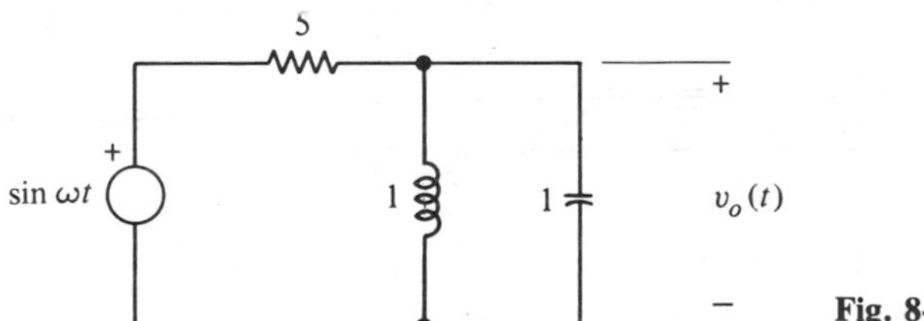

Fig. 8-5

(a) Obtain the response.

(b) Plot the response for $\omega = 0.25$ and $\omega = 4$. Discuss the results.

Solution.

(a)

$$V_o(s) = V_i(s)T(s)$$

$$V_i(s) = \frac{\omega}{s^2 + \omega^2}$$

$$T(s) = \frac{\dfrac{s \times 1/s}{s + 1/s}}{\left(5 + \dfrac{s \times 1/s}{s + 1/s}\right)} = \frac{0.2s}{s^2 + 0.2s + 1}$$

$$V_o(s) = \left(\frac{\omega}{s^2 + \omega^2}\right)\left(\frac{0.2s}{s^2 + 0.2s + 1}\right)$$

The part of the response arising from the excitation poles ($\pm j\omega$) can be calculated by using Eq. (8-7), and so we consider this part of the response later. To obtain the natural part of the response, we use the partial-fraction expansion for the poles of $T(s)$ only.

$$V_o(s) = \underbrace{\frac{0.2s}{(s + 0.1 - j\sqrt{0.99})(s + 0.1 + j\sqrt{0.99})}}_{s^2 + 0.2s + 1}\left(\frac{\omega}{s^2 + \omega^2}\right)$$

$$= \underbrace{\frac{K}{s + 0.1 - j\sqrt{0.99}} + \frac{K^*}{s + 0.1 + j\sqrt{0.99}}}_{\substack{\text{Due to poles of} \\ \text{network at} \\ -0.1 \pm j\sqrt{0.99}}} + \underbrace{V_f(s)}_{\substack{\text{Due to poles of} \\ \text{excitation at} \\ \pm j\omega}}$$

where $$K = \frac{0.2s}{s + 0.1 + j\sqrt{0.99}}\left(\frac{\omega}{s^2 + \omega^2}\right)\Bigg|_{s=-0.1+j\sqrt{0.99}}$$

$$= \left[\frac{0.2(-0.1 + j\sqrt{0.99})}{-0.1 + j\sqrt{0.99} + 0.1 + j\sqrt{0.99}}\right]\left[\frac{\omega}{(-0.1 + j\sqrt{0.99})^2 + \omega^2}\right]$$

$$= \frac{0.1(\sqrt{99} + j)}{\sqrt{99}}\left[\frac{\omega}{(\omega^2 - 0.98) - j0.2\sqrt{0.99}}\right]$$

$$= \underbrace{\frac{\omega/\sqrt{99}}{\sqrt{(\omega^2 - 0.98)^2 + 0.0396}}}_{|K|} e^{\overbrace{j\{tan^{-1}(1\sqrt{99}) - tan^{-1}[-0.2\sqrt{0.99}/(\omega^2 - 0.98)]\}}^{\theta_K}} \tag{8-8}$$

When the inverse transform of $V_o(s)$ is taken, the result is

$$v_o(t) = [Ke^{(-0.1+j\sqrt{0.99})t} + \text{conjugate}] + v_f(t)$$

$$= 2\ \text{Re}\ \{Ke^{(-0.1+j\sqrt{0.99})t}\} + v_f(t)$$

$$= 2\ \text{Re}\ \{|K|e^{[-0.1t+j(\sqrt{0.99}t+\theta_K)]}\} + v_f(t)$$

$$= 2|K|e^{-0.1t} \text{ Re } \{e^{j(\sqrt{0.99}t+\theta_K)}\} + v_f(t)$$

$$= 2|K|e^{-0.1t} \cos(\sqrt{0.99}\, t + \theta_K) + v_f(t)$$

$$= \frac{(2\omega/\sqrt{99})e^{-0.1t}}{\sqrt{(\omega^2 - 0.98)^2 + 0.0396}} \cos\left[\sqrt{0.99}\, t + \tan^{-1}\left(\frac{1}{\sqrt{99}}\right) + \tan^{-1}\left(\frac{0.2\sqrt{0.99}}{\omega^2 - 0.98}\right)\right] + v_f(t) \qquad (8\text{-}9)$$

The next step is to calculate the forced component of the response, which means that we need to evaluate $T(j\omega)$ and use Eq. (8-7).

$$T(s)\Big|_{s=j\omega} = \frac{0.2s}{s^2 + 0.2s + 1}\Big|_{s=j\omega} = \frac{j0.2\omega}{(1 - \omega^2) + j0.2\omega}$$

$$= \underbrace{\frac{0.2\omega}{\sqrt{(1 - \omega^2)^2 + 0.04\omega^2}}}_{|T(j\omega)|} e^{\overbrace{j\{(\pi/2) - \tan^{-1}[0.2\omega/(1-\omega^2)]\}}^{}}$$

with the exponent labelled θ_T.

$$v_f(t) = |T(j\omega)| \sin(\omega t + \theta_T)$$

$$= \frac{0.2\omega}{\sqrt{(1 - \omega^2)^2 + 0.04\omega^2}} \sin\left(\omega t + \frac{\pi}{2} - \tan^{-1}\frac{0.2\omega}{1 - \omega^2}\right)$$

$$= \frac{0.2\omega}{\sqrt{(1 - \omega^2)^2 + 0.04\omega^2}} \cos\left(\omega t - \tan^{-1}\frac{0.2\omega}{1 - \omega^2}\right)$$

So the response is

$$v_o(t) = \frac{(2\omega/\sqrt{99})e^{-0.1t}}{\sqrt{(\omega^2 - 0.98)^2 + 0.0396}} \cos\left[\sqrt{0.99}\, t + \tan^{-1}\left(\frac{1}{\sqrt{99}}\right) + \tan^{-1}\left(\frac{0.2\sqrt{0.99}}{\omega^2 - 0.98}\right)\right]$$

$$+ \frac{0.2\omega}{\sqrt{(1 - \omega^2)^2 + 0.04\omega^2}} \cos\left(\omega t - \tan^{-1}\frac{0.2\omega}{1 - \omega^2}\right)$$

$$= \frac{0.2\omega}{\sqrt{\omega^4 - 1.96\omega^2 + 1}} \left\{\frac{10}{\sqrt{99}} e^{-0.1t} \cos\left[\sqrt{0.99}\, t + \tan^{-1}\left(\frac{1}{\sqrt{99}}\right) + \tan^{-1}\left(\frac{0.2\sqrt{0.99}}{\omega^2 - 0.98}\right)\right] + \cos\left[\omega t - \tan^{-1}\left(\frac{0.2\omega}{1 - \omega^2}\right)\right]\right\} \quad \text{Ans.} \qquad (8\text{-}10)$$

(b) The response is plotted in Fig. 8-6 for sine wave frequencies of $\omega = 0.25$ and $\omega = 4$ rad/s. These frequencies are forced on the network by the excitation. Then there is the frequency of the damped sine wave, representing the natural frequency of the network. This frequency does not change with the excitation. It stays constant at $\beta = \sqrt{0.99} \cong 1$ rad/s. The corresponding period in seconds is

$$\frac{2\pi}{\beta} \cong 6.3$$

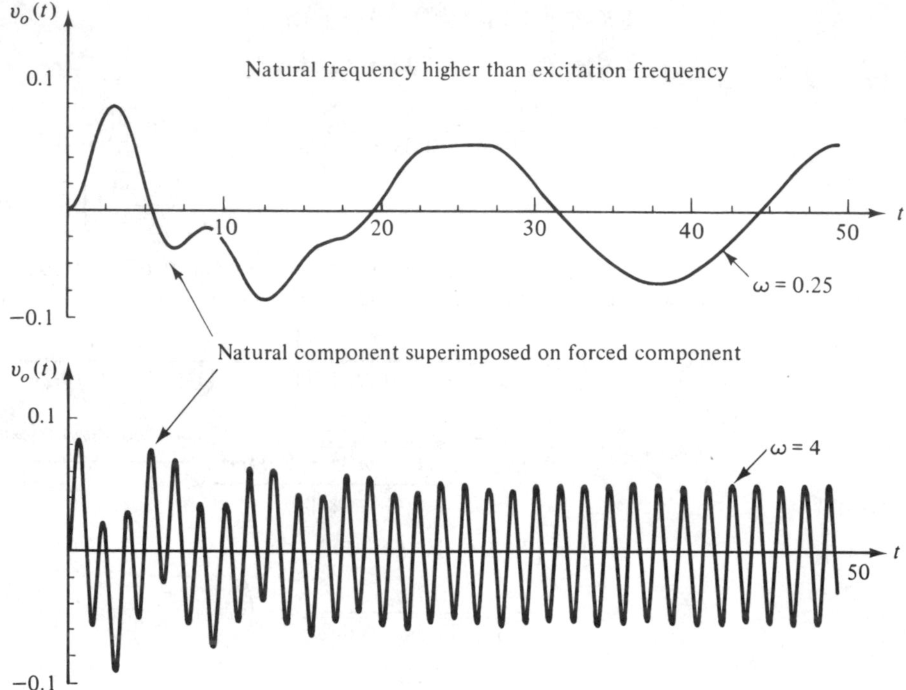

Fig. 8-6

A careful study of the two curves in Fig. 8-6 shows clearly this *damped* sine wave superimposed on the forced component of the response. After five time constants ($5 \times 1/\alpha = 50$ seconds) the forced component stands out. The output voltage is then a sine wave whose frequency is dictated by the input sine wave frequency (0.25 rad/s for the upper curve and 4 rad/s for the lower curve).

Note that the responses shown in Fig. 8-6 start out at zero—that is, $v_o(0) = 0$. This result is to be expected, since the output voltage, being the voltage across a capacitor, maintains its initial ($t = 0^-$) value, which is zero.

Example 8-3

In Fig. 8-7, when θ is chosen appropriately, the natural part of the response can be made zero. Find the θ and the resulting response.

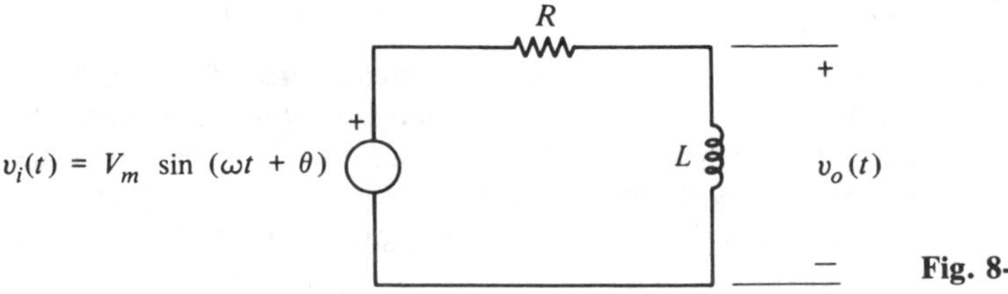

Fig. 8-7

Solution. To see how the natural part of the response can be made zero, we calculate $V_o(s)$.

$$V_o(s) = V_i(s)\left(\frac{sL}{sL + R}\right) = V_m\left(\frac{\omega \cos \theta + s \sin \theta}{s^2 + \omega^2}\right)\left(\frac{sL}{sL + R}\right)$$

$$= \frac{V_m \sin \theta(s + \omega \operatorname{ctn} \theta)s}{(s^2 + \omega^2)(s + R/L)}$$

The pole at $s = -R/L$ is responsible for the natural part of the response. However, if we make

$$\omega \operatorname{ctn} \theta = \frac{R}{L}$$

the zero at $s = -\omega \operatorname{ctn} \theta$ cancels the pole at $s = -R/L$. Thus the natural response term becomes eliminated. The output then simplifies to

$$V_o(s) = V_m \sin \theta \left(\frac{s}{s^2 + \omega^2}\right), \qquad v_o(t) = (V_m \sin \theta) \cos \omega t$$

To obtain this result, the angle θ should be chosen so that ctn $\theta = R/\omega L$. Refer to Fig. 8-8(a). From the figure we see that

$$\sin \theta = \frac{\omega L}{\sqrt{R^2 + \omega^2 L^2}}$$

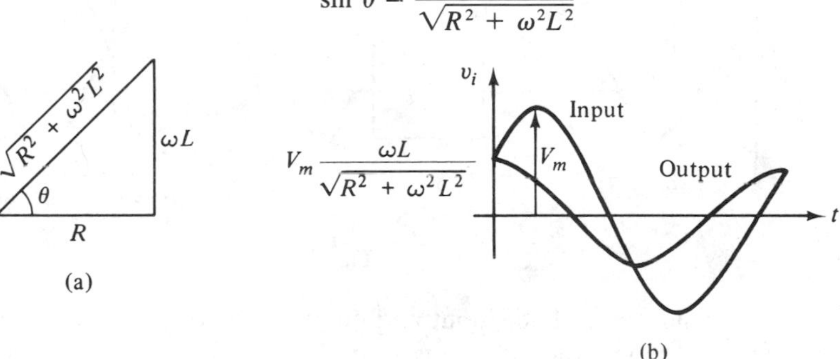

Fig. 8-8

So the output can be expressed as

$$v_o(t) = V_m \frac{\omega L}{\sqrt{R^2 + \omega^2 L^2}} \cos \omega t \quad \text{Ans.}$$

Thus if the input sine wave is caught on its way up at the point shown in Fig. 8-8(b) (as it is applied to the network at $t = 0$), the output will be due to the forcing action of the input only. Note that at $t = 0$ the input and output have the same value, which they must, since the current through the inductor—and hence the voltage across the resistor—is zero at that instant.

8-3 THE SINUSOIDAL STEADY-STATE RESPONSE

When a sine wave $A \sin(\omega t + \theta)$ is applied to a linear system described by $T(s)$, the response is given by Eq. (8-7), which is reproduced here for convenience.

$$r(t) = r_n(t) + A|T(j\omega)| \sin(\omega t + \theta + \theta_T) \tag{8-11}$$

If *all* the poles of $T(s)$ are *in the left half-plane,* the natural response, $r_n(t)$, is the sum of damped exponentials or exponentially damped sine waves (see Fig. 6-3). Consequently, these waveforms will eventually vanish. As a result, $r_n(t)$ is also called the *transient* part of the response. The response *then* becomes identical with the forced response, which is a sine wave of the same frequency as the input. When this situation occurs, we say that the response is in *steady state*—no transient waveform is present to make the output look different from the input waveform. Steady state is reached after $5\tau_{\max}$, where $\tau_{\max}$ represents the time constant $(1/\alpha)$ associated with the pole (or poles for a complex-conjugate pair) of $T(s)$ closest to the imaginary axis. The steady-state response is shown in Fig. 8-9, where the subscript ss stands for steady state. We could just as well use the subscript *f*, meaning forced. In this case, the steady-state response is the same as the forced response.

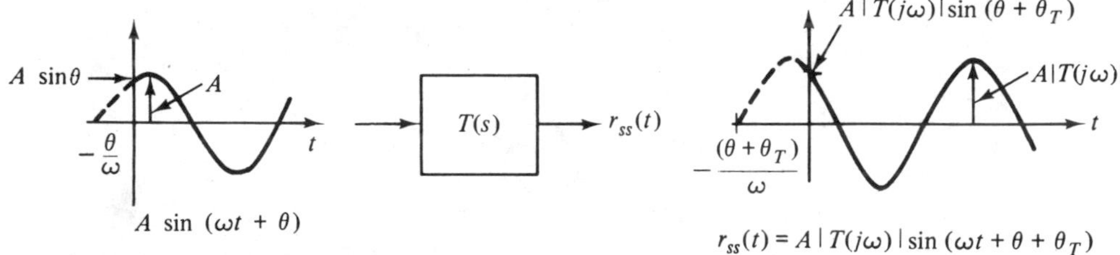

Fig. 8-9

In steady state, both input and output waveforms are sine waves *of the same frequency*. The input amplitude is A, and the output amplitude is $A|T(j\omega)|$. The input phase is θ, and the output phase is $\theta + \theta_T$. As the sine wave goes through the system, it undergoes a *change in amplitude* and a *change in phase*. The amount of change depends solely on the magnitude and angle of $T(j\omega)$, which, in turn, depends on the system, $T(s)$, and the input frequency, ω. As the frequency is changed, both $|T(j\omega)|$ and θ_T change. Consequently, the response depends on the frequency of the sine wave.

We now can formulate a systematic procedure for calculating the steady-state response.

1. From the network, calculate $T(s)$. [If the response is an input function, such as the input current or input voltage, calculate the input admittance $Y(s)$ or input impedance $Z(s)$.] Since $T(s)$ is independent of the input waveform, it is calculated by using the general designation $V_i(s)$ or $I_i(s)$ for the input.

2. Evaluate $T(s)$ for $s = j\omega$, where ω is the frequency (in rad/s) of the input sine wave.
3. Obtain the magnitude and angle of $T(j\omega)$: $|T(j\omega)|$ and θ_T.
4. Write the steady-state response as

$$r_{ss}(t) = A|T(j\omega)| \sin (\omega t + \theta + \theta_T) \tag{8-12}$$

where A and θ represent the input amplitude and phase. If the input is given as a cosinusoidal wave, simply replace sin with cos in Eq. (8-12).

Example 8-4

What is the steady-state output voltage in Fig. 8-10?

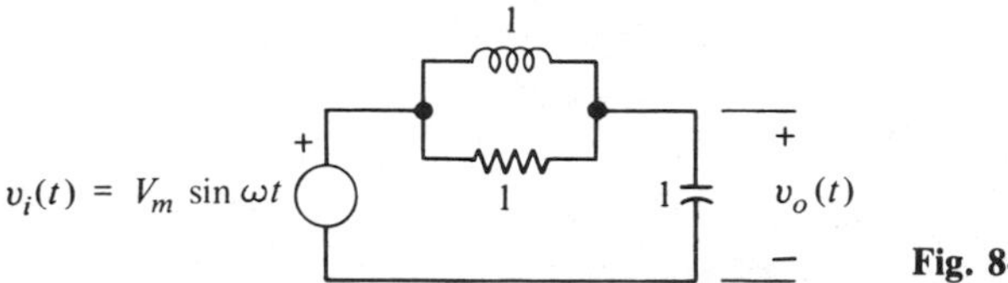

Fig. 8-10

Solution To calculate $v_{oss}(t)$, we need to find $T(s)$ first. From Fig. 8-10 we see that

$$T(s) = \frac{V_o(s)}{V_i(s)} = \frac{Z_2}{Z_1 + Z_2} = \frac{1/s}{(s \times 1)/(s+1) + 1/s} = \frac{s+1}{s^2+s+1}$$

Next, we evaluate $T(s)$ for $s = j\omega$ and find the resulting magnitude and angle.

$$T(j\omega) = \left.\frac{s+1}{s^2+s+1}\right|_{s=j\omega} = \frac{1+j\omega}{(1-\omega^2)+j\omega} = \frac{\sqrt{1+\omega^2}\,e^{j\tan^{-1}\omega}}{\sqrt{(1-\omega^2)^2+\omega^2}\,e^{j\tan^{-1}[\omega/(1-\omega^2)]}}$$

$$= \underbrace{\frac{\sqrt{1+\omega^2}}{\sqrt{(1-\omega^2)^2+\omega^2}}}_{|T(j\omega)|}\, e^{\overbrace{j\{\tan^{-1}\omega - \tan^{-1}[\omega/(1-\omega^2)]\}}^{}}$$

$$\theta_T$$

The input amplitude and phase are V_m and 0 radians, respectively. Hence the steady-state output voltage is

$$v_{oss}(t) = V_m|T(j\omega)| \sin (\omega t + \theta_T)$$

$$= V_m\sqrt{\frac{\omega^2+1}{\omega^4-\omega^2+1}} \sin \left(\omega t + \tan^{-1}\omega - \tan^{-1}\frac{\omega}{1-\omega^2}\right) \quad \text{Ans.}$$

Example 8-5

In Fig. 8-11, obtain the steady-state value of the input current.

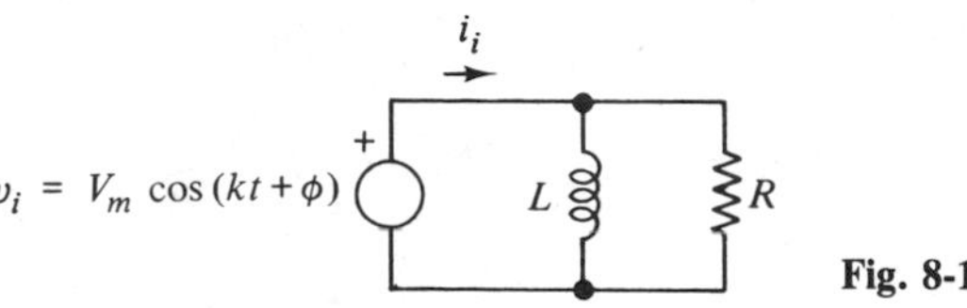

Fig. 8-11

Solution Since the response is the input current, here we work with the input function and not the transfer function.

$$\frac{\text{Response}}{\text{Excitation}} = \frac{I_i(s)}{V_i(s)} = Y_i(s) = \frac{1}{R} + \frac{1}{sL} = \frac{sL + R}{sLR}$$

The input frequency is k rad/s. So we evaluate $Y_i(s)$ for $s = jk$.

$$Y_i(jk) = \left.\frac{sL + R}{sLR}\right|_{s=jk} = \frac{jkL + R}{jkLR}$$

$$|Y_i(jk)| = \frac{\sqrt{R^2 + k^2L^2}}{kLR}$$

$$\theta_{Y_i} = \tan^{-1}\frac{kL}{R} - \frac{\pi}{2}$$

The steady-state response is given by

$$\begin{aligned} i_{iss}(t) &= V_m|Y_i(jk)| \cos\,(kt + \phi + \theta_{Y_i}) \\ &= V_m\frac{\sqrt{R^2 + k^2L^2}}{kLR} \cos\left(kt + \phi + \tan^{-1}\frac{kL}{R} - \frac{\pi}{2}\right) \\ &= V_m\frac{\sqrt{R^2 + k^2L^2}}{kLR} \sin\left(kt + \phi + \tan^{-1}\frac{kL}{R}\right) \quad \text{Ans.} \end{aligned}$$

Example 8-6

What is the forced part of the output current in Fig. 8-12?

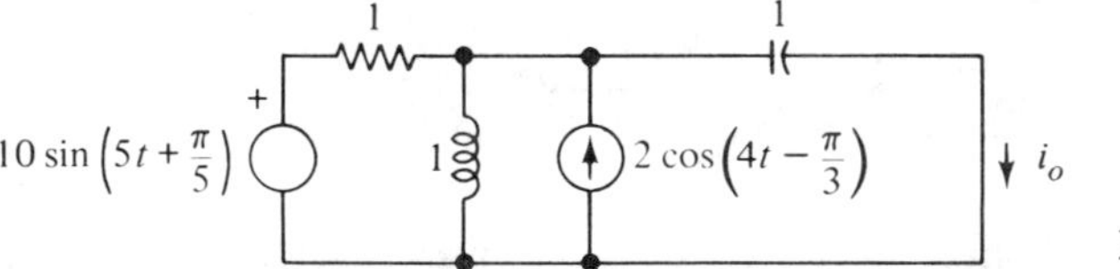

Fig. 8-12

Solution Since there are two sources exciting the network, there are two transfer functions, one for each input. Therefore we use superposition to obtain the forced (steady-state) part of the output current.

When the voltage source is turned on and the current source turned off, we have the circuit shown in Fig. 8-13(a). The output and input are related by

$$T_1(s) = \frac{I_{o1}(s)}{V_i(s)} = \frac{\left(\dfrac{s}{s + 1/s}\right)}{\left(1 + \dfrac{s \times 1/s}{s + 1/s}\right)} = \frac{s^2}{s^2 + s + 1}$$

The frequency of the voltage source is 5 rad/s. So we evaluate $T_1(s)$ for $s = j5$.

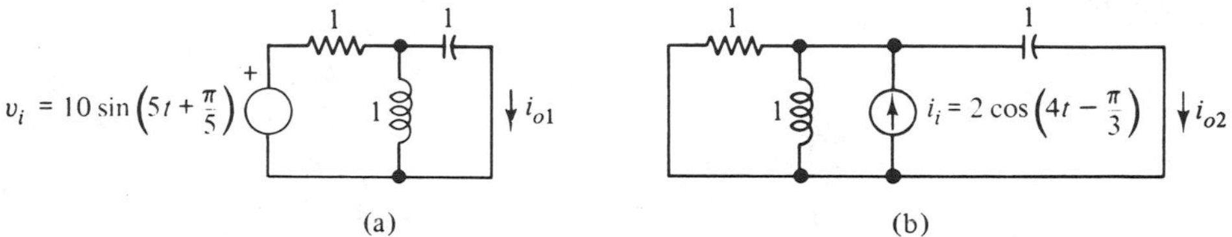

Fig. 8-13

$$T_1(j5) = \left.\frac{s^2}{s^2+s+1}\right|_{s=j5} = \frac{-25}{(1-25)+j5} = \frac{25}{24-j5}$$

$$= \frac{25}{\sqrt{601}}e^{j[-\tan^{-1}(-5/24)]} = \underbrace{\frac{25}{\sqrt{601}}}_{|T_1(j5)|}e^{j\overbrace{\tan^{-1}(5/24)}^{\theta_{T1}}}$$

The input is a sine wave of amplitude 10 and phase $\pi/5$. Thus the resulting forced component of the output current is

$$i_{o1f}(t) = \frac{250}{\sqrt{601}}\sin\left(5t+\frac{\pi}{5}+\tan^{-1}\frac{5}{24}\right)$$

When the current source is turned on and the voltage source turned off, we have the circuit shown in Fig. 8-13(b). The output and input are related by

$$T_2(s) = \frac{I_{o2}(s)}{I_i(s)} = \frac{(s\times 1)/(s+1)}{(s\times 1)/(s+1)+1/s} = \frac{s^2}{s^2+s+1}$$

The frequency of the current source is 4 rad/s. So we evaluate $T_2(s)$ for $s = j4$.

$$T_2(j4) = \left.\frac{s^2}{s^2+s+1}\right|_{s=j4} = \frac{-16}{(1-16)+j4} = \frac{16}{15-j4}$$

$$= \frac{16}{\sqrt{241}}e^{j[-\tan^{-1}(-4/15)]} = \underbrace{\frac{16}{\sqrt{241}}}_{|T_2(j4)|}e^{j\overbrace{\tan^{-1}(4/15)}^{\theta_{T2}}}$$

The input is a cosine wave of amplitude 2 and phase $-\pi/3$. The resulting forced component of the output current is therefore

$$i_{o2f}(t) = \frac{32}{\sqrt{241}}\cos\left(4t-\frac{\pi}{3}+\tan^{-1}\frac{4}{15}\right)$$

By superposition, the forced part of the output current is

$$i_{of}(t) = i_{o1f}(t) + i_{o2f}(t)$$

$$= \frac{250}{\sqrt{601}}\sin\left(5t+\frac{\pi}{5}+\tan^{-1}\frac{5}{24}\right) + \frac{32}{\sqrt{241}}\cos\left(4t-\frac{\pi}{3}+\tan^{-1}\frac{4}{15}\right) \quad \text{Ans.}$$

8-4 PHASORS

In the sinusoidal steady state, input and output are given by

$$\begin{aligned} &\textit{Input:} \quad A \sin(\omega t + \theta) \\ &\textit{Output:} \quad A|T(j\omega)| \sin(\omega t + \theta + \theta_T) \end{aligned} \tag{8-13}$$

Or if the input is stated in the cosine form, we have

$$\begin{aligned} &\textit{Input:} \quad A \cos(\omega t + \theta) \\ &\textit{Output:} \quad A|T(j\omega)| \cos(\omega t + \theta + \theta_T) \end{aligned} \tag{8-14}$$

Note that input and output frequencies are the same. Furthermore, the input and output are written either as sine functions or as cosine functions. The system does not alter the frequency or the nature of the function, which means that it is superfluous to carry this infomation in the calculations. The amplitude and phase are altered, however, and so it is necessary to keep track of these changes. We do so by comparing the input with the output as follows.

Since $\sin \phi = \operatorname{Im}\{e^{j\phi}\}$, we can write Eq. (8-13) as

$$i(t) = \operatorname{Im}\{Ae^{j(\omega t+\theta)}\}, \qquad o(t) = \operatorname{Im}\{A|T(j\omega)|e^{j(\omega t+\theta+\theta_T)}\}$$

where $o(t)$ represents the output and $i(t)$ the input (not to be confused with current). Rearranging these results, we have

$$i(t) = \operatorname{Im}\{(Ae^{j\theta})e^{j\omega t}\}, \qquad o(t) = \operatorname{Im}\{(Ae^{j\theta})[T(j\omega)]e^{j\omega t}\}$$

where $T(j\omega) = |T(j\omega)|e^{j\theta_T}$

Both input and output can be expressed in similar format if we write

$$i(t) = \operatorname{Im}\{\mathbf{I}e^{j\omega t}\}, \qquad o(t) = \operatorname{Im}\{\mathbf{O}e^{j\omega t}\} \tag{8-15}$$

where

$$\mathbf{I} = Ae^{j\theta}, \qquad \mathbf{O} = (Ae^{j\theta})T(j\omega) \tag{8-16}$$

Had we expressed the input and the output as cosine waves rather than sine waves, Eq. (8-15) would have come out in terms of the real rather than imaginary parts. However, (8-16) would have stayed the same.

From Eq. (8-16) we see that

$$\mathbf{O} = \mathbf{I}T(j\omega) \tag{8-17}$$

which is a familiar equation—namely,

$$\text{Output} = \text{Input} \times \text{Transfer function}$$

In Eq. (8-17) the input and output are *complex functions carrying only amplitude and phase information*. For emphasis, we point this fact out by writing input and output as

$$\mathbf{I} = \underbrace{A}_{\substack{\text{Input}\\\text{amplitude}}} \times \underbrace{e^{j\theta}}_{\substack{\text{Input}\\\text{phase}}} \tag{8-18}$$

$$\mathbf{O} = (Ae^{j\theta})T(j\omega) = (Ae^{j\theta})[|T(j\omega)|e^{j\theta_T}] = \underbrace{A|T(j\omega)|}_{\substack{\text{Output}\\\text{amplitude}}} \times \underbrace{e^{j(\theta+\theta_T)}}_{\substack{\text{Output}\\\text{phase}}} \tag{8-19}$$

Once the amplitude and phase information is known, the time-domain waveform for the input or output can be written

$$\text{Amplitude} \times \sin(\omega t + \text{phase})$$

or

$$\text{Amplitude} \times \cos(\omega t + \text{phase})$$

Henceforth, unless otherwise specified, we will use the sine form.

Conversely, we can represent any sine or cosine wave in the form

$$\text{Amplitude} \times e^{j\text{phase}} \tag{8-20}$$

and call this abbreviated representation a *phasor*. Thus a phasor is a complex number that represents a sinusoidal wave. By this definition, **I** and **O** are phasors; they carry amplitude and phase informtion only. To distinguish them from other variables, phasors are indicated with boldface type. So the phasor.

$$\mathbf{A} = Ae^{j\theta}$$

has an amplitude (magnitude) of A and a phase (angle) of θ. (Although not specifically indicated, it is understood that the frequency of the sinusoidal wave is ω.)

The transfer function $T(j\omega)$ is *not* a phasor. It does not represent a sine wave. However, $T(j\omega)$ is a function of the complex-frequency variable $j\omega$, and therefore it has a magnitude and an angle. When a phasor is multiplied with $T(j\omega)$, the result is another phasor whose amplitude and phase are dependent on the magnitude and angle of $T(j\omega)$.

There are many equivalent designations for a phasor. They are given below.

$$\mathbf{A} = \begin{cases} Ae^{j\theta} & \text{(exponential form)} \\ A(\cos\theta + j\sin\theta) & \text{(rectangular form)} \\ A\underline{/\theta} & \text{(polar form)} \end{cases}$$

When the three forms are compared, it is clear that

$$e^{j\theta} = \cos\theta + j\sin\theta = \underline{/\theta}$$

Although familiar with the equivalence

$$e^{j\theta} = \cos\theta + j\sin\theta$$

we see for the first time the symbolic equivalence

$$e^{j\theta} = \underline{/\theta}$$

From now on *when we see* $\underline{/\theta}$, *we can replace it with* $e^{j\theta}$ *or* $\cos\theta + j\sin\theta$. Alternatively, we can carry out operations by using $\underline{/\theta}$ directly. For instance, we can easily obtain the following results.

$$(\underline{/\theta_1})(\underline{/\theta_2}) = (e^{j\theta_1})(e^{j\theta_2}) = e^{j(\theta_1+\theta_2)} = \underline{/\theta_1 + \theta_2}$$

$$\frac{\underline{/\theta_1}}{\underline{/\theta_2}} = \frac{e^{j\theta_1}}{e^{j\theta_2}} = e^{j(\theta_1-\theta_2)} = \underline{/\theta_1 - \theta_2}$$

It follows that

$$(\underline{/\theta_1})(\underline{/\theta_2}) = \underline{/\theta_1 + \theta_2}, \qquad \frac{\underline{/\theta_1}}{\underline{/\theta_2}} = \underline{/\theta_1 - \theta_2}$$

Operations like multiplication and division are easily performed by using the exponential or polar form of phasors or complex numbers. On the other hand, addition and subtraction require that the phasors or complex numbers be given in rectangular form. Mixed operations require the conversion of one form to another. The relationship between the forms is given in Fig. 8-14, where the phasor **A** is designated with a point in the complex plane. The magnitude of **A** is the distance A measured from the point to the origin. The phase of **A** is the angle θ measured counterclockwise from the real axis as shown. The real part of **A** is the distance A_r, measured along the real axis. The imaginary part of **A** is the distance A_i measured along the imaginary axis. From this figure we obtain the following conversion rules.

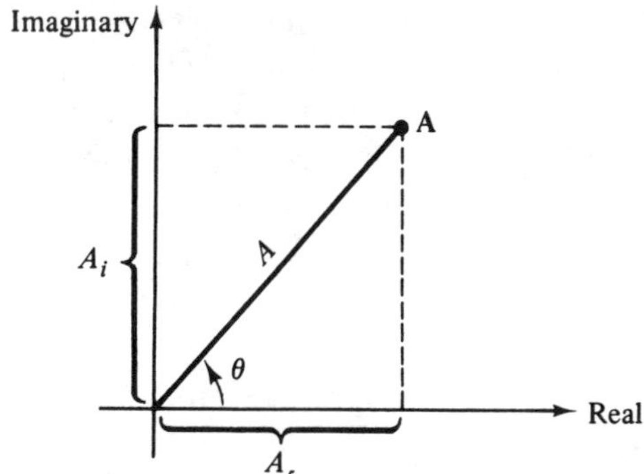

Fig. 8-14

1. If the phasor is given in exponential or polar form and we wish to convert it to rectangular form, we use

$$Ae^{j\theta} = A\underline{/\theta} = \underbrace{A\cos\theta}_{A_r} + j\underbrace{A\sin\theta}_{A_i}$$

2. If the phasor is given in rectangular form and we wish to convert it to polar or exponential form, we use

$$A_r + jA_i = \underbrace{\sqrt{A_r^2 + A_i^2}}_{A} \;\Big/\overbrace{\tan^{-1}\frac{A_i}{A_r}}^{\theta} = Ae^{j\theta}$$

These conversion rules also apply to complex numbers. The product of a complex number with a phasor is a phasor.

Example 8-7

Given

$$x(t) = A \sin\left(\omega t + \frac{\pi}{3}\right), \qquad y(t) = B \cos\left(\omega t - \frac{7\pi}{6}\right)$$

(a) Obtain **X**, **Y**, and **X** + **Y**.

(b) Let **P** = **X**/[$C(-1 + j)$], where C is a real number. Evaluate **P** and $p(t)$.

Solution.

(a) We express both $x(t)$ and $y(t)$ as sine waves. Then we obtain their amplitudes and phases to form the phasors.

$$x(t) = A \sin\left(\omega t + \frac{\pi}{3}\right)$$

$$y(t) = B \cos\left(\omega t - \frac{7\pi}{6}\right) = B \sin\left(\omega t - \frac{7\pi}{6} + \frac{\pi}{2}\right) = B \sin\left(\omega t - \frac{2\pi}{3}\right)$$

$$\mathbf{X} = A \Big/\frac{\pi}{3}, \qquad \mathbf{Y} = B \Big/ -\frac{2\pi}{3} \quad \text{Ans.}$$

To form the sum, we must first convert each phasor into the rectangular form.

$$\mathbf{X} = A\Big/\frac{\pi}{3} = A \cos\frac{\pi}{3} + jA \sin\frac{\pi}{3} = \frac{A}{2} + j\frac{A\sqrt{3}}{2}$$

$$\mathbf{Y} = B\Big/-\frac{2\pi}{3} = B \cos\left(-\frac{2\pi}{3}\right) + jB \sin\left(-\frac{2\pi}{3}\right) = -\frac{B}{2} - j\frac{B\sqrt{3}}{2}$$

$$\mathbf{X} + \mathbf{Y} = \left(\frac{A}{2} + j\frac{A\sqrt{3}}{2}\right) + \left(-\frac{B}{2} - j\frac{B\sqrt{3}}{2}\right)$$

$$= \frac{1}{2}(A - B) + j\frac{\sqrt{3}}{2}(A - B)$$

$$= \frac{1}{2}(A - B)(1 + j\sqrt{3}) \quad \text{Ans.}$$

This answer can also be expressed in polar form.

$$\mathbf{X} + \mathbf{Y} = \frac{1}{2}(A - B)\sqrt{1^2 + (\sqrt{3})^2} \Big/\tan^{-1}\frac{\sqrt{3}}{1} = (A - B)\Big/\frac{\pi}{3} \quad \text{Ans.}$$

(b)
$$\mathbf{P} = \frac{\mathbf{X}}{C(-1+j)} = \frac{A\underline{/\frac{\pi}{3}}}{C\sqrt{1^2+1^2}\,\underline{/\tan^{-1}\frac{1}{-1}}} = \frac{A\underline{/\frac{\pi}{3}}}{C\sqrt{2}\,\underline{/\pi - \frac{\pi}{4}}}$$
$$= \frac{A}{C\sqrt{2}}\underline{/\frac{\pi}{3} - \left(\pi - \frac{\pi}{4}\right)}$$
$$= \frac{A}{C\sqrt{2}}\underline{/-\frac{5}{12}\pi} \quad \text{Ans.}$$

This answer can also be expressed in rectangular form.

$$\mathbf{P} = \frac{A}{C\sqrt{2}}\left[\cos\left(-\frac{5\pi}{12}\right) + j\sin\left(-\frac{5\pi}{12}\right)\right]$$
$$= \frac{A}{C\sqrt{2}}\left(\cos\frac{5\pi}{12} - j\sin\frac{5\pi}{12}\right) \quad \text{Ans.}$$

Using the magnitude and angle given in the polar representation, we obtain $p(t)$.

$$p(t) = \frac{A}{C\sqrt{2}}\sin\left(\omega t - \frac{5\pi}{12}\right) \quad \text{Ans.}$$

When phasors are used, it is understood that operation is at a single frequency. *We cannot perform operations with two phasors that are related to two different frequencies.* Thus if $\mathbf{X}_1 = A + jB$ at frequency ω_1 and $\mathbf{X}_2 = C + jD$ at frequency ω_2, then

$$\mathbf{X}_1 + \mathbf{X}_2 \neq (A + C) + j(B + D)$$

However, we can use superposition *in the time domain* and obtain

$$x_1(t) + x_2(t) = \sqrt{A^2 + B^2}\sin\left(\omega_1 t + \tan^{-1}\frac{B}{A}\right)$$
$$+ \sqrt{C^2 + D^2}\sin\left(\omega_2 t + \tan^{-1}\frac{D}{C}\right)$$

8-5 VOLTAGES AND CURRENTS AS PHASORS

In networks, voltage and current sources are used as input. In Fig. 8-15(a) the network N is composed of R, L, and C elements and is excited with a *single, independent, sinusoidal voltage source,* which is represented by the phasor $\mathbf{V}_i$. Three responses, also designated by phasors, are shown: the input current $\mathbf{I}_i$, the output

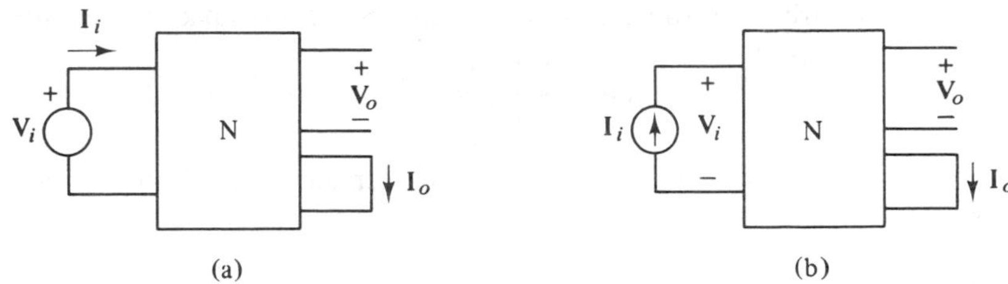

Fig. 8-15

voltage $\mathbf{V}_o$, and the output current $\mathbf{I}_o$. The responses are related to the input by the input admittance, the voltage transfer function, and the transadmittance function—all evaluated at $s = j\omega$, where ω represents the frequency of the sine wave in radians per second.

$$\mathbf{I}_i = \mathbf{V}_i Y(j\omega) \tag{8-21a}$$

$$\mathbf{V}_o = \mathbf{V}_i T_V(j\omega) \tag{8-21b}$$

$$\mathbf{I}_o = \mathbf{V}_i T_Y(j\omega) \tag{8-21c}$$

The network in Fig. 8-15(b) is excited by a *single, independent, sinusoidal current source,* which is represented by the phasor $\mathbf{I}_i$. Three responses, designated by phasors $\mathbf{V}_i$, $\mathbf{V}_o$, and $\mathbf{I}_o$ are shown. These responses are related to the input impedance, the transimpedance function, and the current transfer function, evaluated at $s = j\omega$.

$$\mathbf{V}_i = \mathbf{I}_i Z(j\omega) \tag{8-22a}$$

$$\mathbf{V}_o = \mathbf{I}_i T_Z(j\omega) \tag{8-22b}$$

$$\mathbf{I}_o = \mathbf{I}_i T_I(j\omega) \tag{8-22c}$$

The sets of equations given by Eqs. (8-21) and (8-22) are specific forms of the general result

$$\textbf{Response} = \textbf{Excitation} \times T(j\omega) \tag{8-23}$$

where $T(j\omega)$ is taken in the broad sense to represent any input or transfer function.

Because it is no longer necessary to use the complex-frequency variable s, input and transfer functions are expressed directly as a function of $j\omega$. Thus we have $Z(j\omega)$ or $Y(j\omega)$ and $T(j\omega)$. *The $j\omega$ designation inherently assumes that sinusoidal steady state is under consideration.* On the other hand, $Z(s)$ or $Y(s)$ and $T(s)$ are used for the general characterization, which is applicable for any kind of input waveform that is Laplace transformable and results in solutions that give *both* the *forced* as well as the *natural response*.

For sinusoidal steady-state calculations we can write the impedance and admittance of an inductor as

$$Z_L(j\omega) = j\omega L, \qquad Y_L(j\omega) = \frac{1}{j\omega L} = \frac{-j}{\omega L} \tag{8-24}$$

Similarly, the impedance and admittance of a capacitor become

$$Z_C(j\omega) = \frac{1}{j\omega C} = \frac{-j}{\omega C}, \qquad Y_C(j\omega) = j\omega C \tag{8-25}$$

To see how phasors are used, consider the network of Fig. 8-16. We wish to find I_o.

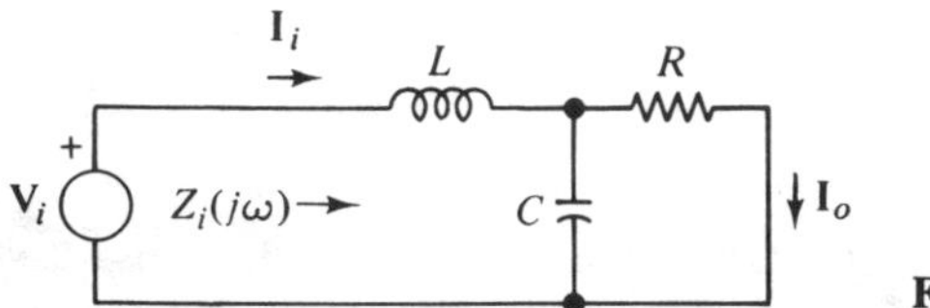

Fig. 8-16

The voltage source $\mathbf{V}_i$ sees the input impedance $Z_i(j\omega)$, which is given by

$$Z_i(j\omega) = j\omega L + \frac{R(1/j\omega C)}{R + (1/j\omega C)}$$

The input current $\mathbf{I}_i$ is obtained from

$$\mathbf{I}_i = \frac{\mathbf{V}_i}{Z_i(j\omega)} = \frac{\mathbf{V}_i}{j\omega L + \dfrac{R(1/j\omega C)}{R + (1/j\omega C)}}$$

The output current $\mathbf{I}_o$ is obtained by current division.

$$\mathbf{I}_o = \mathbf{I}_i \frac{1/j\omega C}{R + (1/j\omega C)} = \left[\frac{\mathbf{V}_i}{j\omega L + \dfrac{R(1/j\omega C)}{R + (1/j\omega C)}}\right]\left[\frac{1/j\omega C}{R + (1/j\omega C)}\right]$$

$$= \left[\frac{\mathbf{V}_i}{j\omega L + R/(j\omega RC + 1)}\right]\left(\frac{1}{j\omega RC + 1}\right) = \mathbf{V}_i \underbrace{\frac{1}{R(1 - \omega^2 LC) + j\omega L}}_{T(j\omega)} \tag{8-26}$$

Putting $T(j\omega)$ in magnitude and angle form, we have

$$\mathbf{I}_o = \mathbf{V}_i\left[\frac{1}{\sqrt{R^2(1 - \omega^2 LC)^2 + \omega^2 L^2}}\right] \angle -\tan^{-1}\frac{\omega L}{R(1 - \omega^2 LC)} \tag{8-27}$$

Equation (8-27) gives the output current in phasor form. It possesses all the information about the output current at steady state. Thus if

$$v_i(t) = V_m \sin(\omega t + \theta)$$

then

$$\mathbf{V}_i = V_m \angle \theta$$

and

$$\mathbf{I}_o = V_m\underline{/\theta}\left[\frac{1}{\sqrt{R^2(1-\omega^2LC)^2+\omega^2L^2}}\right]\underline{\Big/-\tan^{-1}\frac{\omega L}{R(1-\omega^2LC)}}$$

$$= \frac{V_m}{\sqrt{R^2(1-\omega^2LC)^2+\omega^2L^2}}\underline{\Big/\theta-\tan^{-1}\frac{\omega L}{R(1-\omega^2LC)}}$$

$$i_{oss}(t) = \frac{V_m}{\sqrt{R^2(1-\omega^2LC)^2+\omega^2L^2}}\sin\left[\omega t+\theta-\tan^{-1}\frac{\omega L}{R(1-\omega^2LC)}\right] \quad (8\text{-}28)$$

In ac steady-state analysis it suffices to give the answer in phasor form as in Eq. (8-27). It is not necessary to convert the answer to the time-domain form. However, it should be realized that oscilloscopes display time-domain waveforms—not phasors (although special instruments can be constructed to display magnitude and phase characteristics). With a little practice we can look at the phasor [Eq. (8-27)] and see in our minds the corresponding time-domain waveform [Eq. (8-28)] without going through the intermediate steps of the transformation.

It should be clear that we could just as well have solved for the steady-state response without resorting to phasors. As is done in Section 8-3, we calculate the transfer function $T(s)$, which in this case is a transadmittance function (I_o/V_i), and evaluate it for $s = j\omega$. Then we have

$$T(s) = \frac{I_o(s)}{V_i(s)} = \underbrace{\left[\frac{1}{sL+\dfrac{R(1/sC)}{R+(1/sC)}}\right]}_{\dfrac{1}{Z_i(s)}}\underbrace{\left[\frac{1/sC}{R+(1/sC)}\right]}_{\text{Current division}} = \frac{1/(sRC+1)}{sL+R/(sRC+1)}$$

$$= \frac{1}{R+s^2LCR+sL}$$

$$T(j\omega) = \frac{1}{R(1-\omega^2LC)+j\omega L}$$

Once $T(j\omega)$ is obtained, the steady-state response is easy to calculate. The magnitude and angle of $T(j\omega)$ modify the amplitude and phase of the input sine wave according to

$$i_{oss}(t) = V_m|T(j\omega)|\sin(\omega t+\theta+\theta_T) \quad (8\text{-}29)$$

Although this latter approach is more direct and simpler to use, the use of phasors is widely accepted; it is unnecessary to know Laplace transformation in order to calculate the sinusoidal steady-state response.

To become more familiar with phasors, consider the network shown in Fig. 8-17. We wish to calculate $\mathbf{V}_o$.

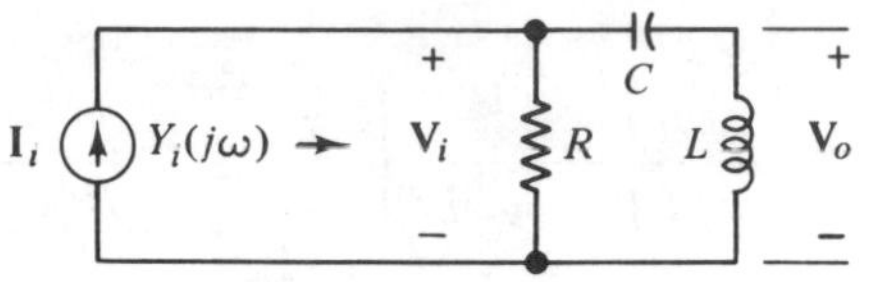

Fig. 8-17

The current source $\mathbf{I}_i$ sees the input admittance $Y_i(j\omega)$, which is given by

$$Y_i(j\omega) = \frac{1}{R} + \frac{1}{(1/j\omega C) + j\omega L}$$

The input voltage V_i is obtained from

$$\mathbf{V}_i = \mathbf{I}_i Z_i(j\omega) = \mathbf{I}_i \frac{1}{Y_i(j\omega)} = \frac{\mathbf{I}_i}{\dfrac{1}{R} + \dfrac{1}{(1/j\omega C) + j\omega L}}$$

$$= \mathbf{I}_i \frac{1}{1/R + j\omega C/(1 - \omega^2 LC)} = I_i \frac{R(1 - \omega^2 LC)}{(1 - \omega^2 LC) + j\omega RC}$$

$$= \mathbf{I}_i \frac{R(1 - \omega^2 LC)}{\sqrt{(1 - \omega^2 LC)^2 + \omega^2 R^2 C^2}} \Big/ -\tan^{-1} \frac{\omega RC}{1 - \omega^2 LC}$$

To obtain the output voltage, we use the voltage-divider rule.

$$\mathbf{V}_o = \mathbf{V}_i \left[\frac{j\omega L}{(1/j\omega C) + j\omega L}\right] = \mathbf{V}_i \left(\frac{-\omega^2 LC}{1 - \omega^2 LC}\right)$$

$$= \left[\mathbf{I}_i \frac{R(1 - \omega^2 LC)}{\sqrt{(1 - \omega^2 LC)^2 + \omega^2 R^2 C^2}} \Big/ -\tan^{-1} \frac{\omega RC}{1 - \omega^2 LC}\right] \left(\frac{-\omega^2 LC}{1 - \omega^2 LC}\right)$$

$$= \mathbf{I}_i \frac{-\omega^2 LCR}{\sqrt{(1 - \omega^2 LC)^2 + \omega^2 R^2 C^2}} \Big/ -\tan^{-1} \frac{\omega RC}{1 - \omega^2 LC}$$

Example 8-8

Refer to Fig. 8-18.

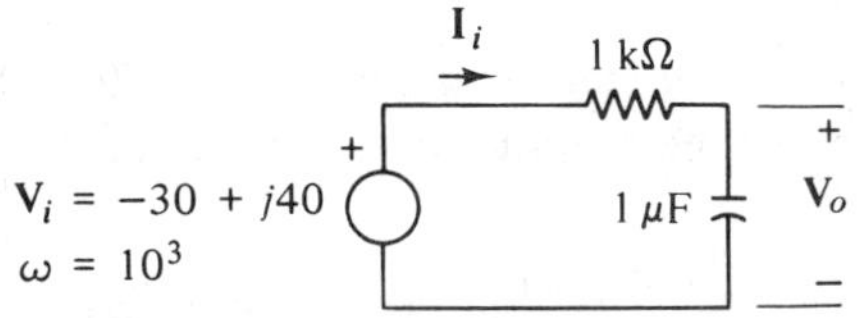

Fig. 8-18

(a) Obtain $\mathbf{I}_i$ and $\mathbf{V}_o$. Give answers in magnitude and angle form.

(b) Obtain $v_i(t)$, $i_{iss}(t)$, and $v_{oss}(t)$.

Solution.

(a) Using $\omega = 10^3$, we have

$$\mathbf{I}_i = \frac{\mathbf{V}_i}{R + (1/j\omega C)} = \frac{-30 + j40}{10^3 + 1/(j10^3 \times 10^{-6})}$$

$$= \frac{-30 + j40}{10^3(1 - j)} = \frac{\sqrt{30^2 + 40^2}}{10^3\sqrt{1^2 + 1^2}} \angle \tan^{-1}\frac{40}{-30} - \tan^{-1}\frac{-1}{1}$$

$$= 25\sqrt{2} \times 10^{-3} \angle \frac{5}{4}\pi - \tan^{-1}\frac{4}{3} \quad \text{Ans.}$$

$$\mathbf{V}_o = \mathbf{I}_i \frac{1}{j\omega C} = \mathbf{I}_i \frac{1}{j10^3 \times 10^{-6}} = \mathbf{I}_i 10^3 \angle -\frac{\pi}{2}$$

$$= 25\sqrt{2} \angle \frac{3}{4}\pi - \tan^{-1}\frac{4}{3} \quad \text{Ans.}$$

(b)

$$\mathbf{V}_i = -30 + j40 = 50 \angle \pi - \tan^{-1}\frac{4}{3}$$

$$v_i(t) = 50 \sin\left(10^3 t + \pi - \tan^{-1}\frac{4}{3}\right) \quad \text{Ans.}$$

$$\mathbf{I}_i = 25\sqrt{2} \times 10^{-3} \angle \frac{5}{4}\pi - \tan^{-1}\frac{4}{3}$$

$$i_{iss}(t) = 25\sqrt{2} \times 10^{-3} \sin\left(10^3 t + \frac{5}{4}\pi - \tan^{-1}\frac{4}{3}\right) \quad \text{Ans.}$$

$$\mathbf{V}_o = 25\sqrt{2} \angle \frac{3}{4}\pi - \tan^{-1}\frac{4}{3}$$

$$v_{oss}(t) = 25\sqrt{2} \sin\left(10^3 t + \frac{3}{4}\pi - \tan^{-1}\frac{4}{3}\right) \quad \text{Ans.}$$

Example 8-9

(a) In Fig. 8-19, show that signals $\mathbf{V}_1$ and $\mathbf{V}_2$ are 90° out of phase.

(b) $\mathbf{V}_1$ is connected to the x input and $\mathbf{V}_2$ to the y input of an oscilloscope. What will the oscilloscope display, and how does this display change with frequency?

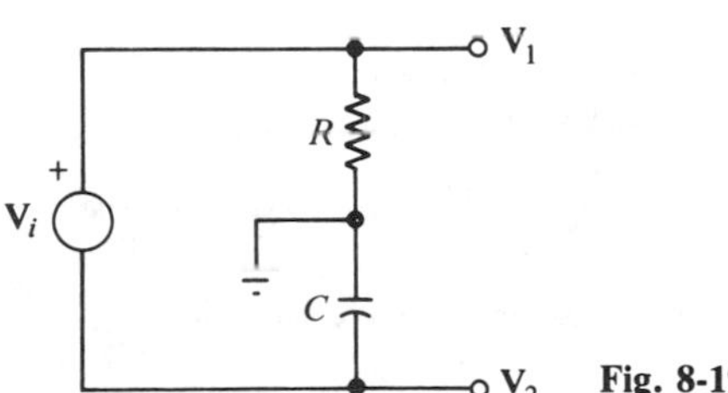

Fig. 8-19

Solution.

(a) By inspection of the circuit, we obtain $\mathbf{V}_1$ and $\mathbf{V}_2$.

$$\mathbf{V}_1 = \mathbf{V}_i \frac{R}{R + (1/j\omega C)} = \mathbf{V}_i \frac{j\omega RC}{j\omega RC + 1}$$

$$= \mathbf{V}_i \frac{\omega RC}{\sqrt{1 + \omega^2 R^2 C^2}} \Big/ \frac{\pi}{2} - \tan^{-1} \omega RC$$

$$\mathbf{V}_2 = -\mathbf{V}_i \frac{1/j\omega C}{R + (1/j\omega C)} = -\mathbf{V}_i \frac{1}{j\omega RC + 1}$$

$$= \mathbf{V}_i \frac{1}{\sqrt{1 + \omega^2 R^2 C^2}} \Big/ \pi - \tan^{-1} \omega RC$$

Let the phase of $\mathbf{V}_i$ be θ. Then the phase of $\mathbf{V}_1$ and $\mathbf{V}_2$ are given by

$$\theta_1 = \theta + \frac{\pi}{2} - \tan^{-1} \omega RC, \qquad \theta_2 = \theta + \pi - \tan^{-1} \omega RC$$

The phase difference between $\mathbf{V}_2$ and $\mathbf{V}_1$ is

$$\theta_2 - \theta_1 = \frac{\pi}{2} \text{rad} = 90° \quad \text{Ans.}$$

(b) Let V_m and θ be the amplitude and phase of the input sine wave. The x and y inputs of the oscilloscope are

$$x(t) = v_{1ss}(t) = V_m \frac{\omega RC}{\sqrt{1 + \omega^2 R^2 C^2}} \sin \left(\omega t + \theta + \frac{\pi}{2} - \tan^{-1} \omega RC \right)$$

$$= V_m \frac{\omega RC}{\sqrt{1 + \omega^2 R^2 C^2}} \cos (\omega t + \theta - \tan^{-1} \omega RC)$$

$$y(t) = v_{2ss}(t) = V_m \frac{1}{\sqrt{1 + \omega^2 R^2 C^2}} \sin (\omega t + \theta + \pi - \tan^{-1} \omega RC)$$

$$= -V_m \frac{1}{\sqrt{1 + \omega^2 R^2 C^2}} \sin (\omega t + \theta - \tan^{-1} \omega RC)$$

To see what kind of a curve the oscilloscope will display, we eliminate t between the x and y signals as follows.

$$\frac{x}{V_m(\omega RC/\sqrt{1 + \omega^2 R^2 C^2})} = \cos (\omega t + \theta - \tan^{-1} \omega RC)$$

$$\frac{y}{V_m(1/\sqrt{1 + \omega^2 R^2 C^2})} = -\sin (\omega t + \theta - \tan^{-1} \omega RC)$$

Since $\sin^2 \phi + \cos^2 \phi = 1$, we have

$$\left(\frac{x}{V_m \omega RC/\sqrt{1 + \omega^2 R^2 C^2}} \right)^2 + \left(\frac{y}{V_m/\sqrt{1 + \omega^2 R^2 C^2}} \right)^2 = 1$$

This is the equation of an ellipse with x-axis intercepts at

$$\pm V_m \frac{\omega RC}{\sqrt{1 + \omega^2 R^2 C^2}}$$

and y-axis intercepts at

$$\pm V_m \frac{1}{\sqrt{1 + \omega^2 R^2 C^2}}$$

As the frequency of the sine wave is increased, the x-axis intercepts become larger and the y-axis intercepts smaller. As a result, the display changes from a vertically oriented figure to a horizontally oriented one. For $\omega = 1/RC$ the x-axis and y-axis intercepts are equal, and the ellipse degenerates into a circle (provided that the vertical and horizontal amplifiers of the oscilloscope have the same gain setting). These results, which are shown in Fig. 8-20, lead us to the following conclusion: when two sinusoidal waves that are 90° apart in phase are connected to the x and y inputs of an oscilloscope, *the resulting display is an ellipse*. (The circle is a special case of an ellipse.)

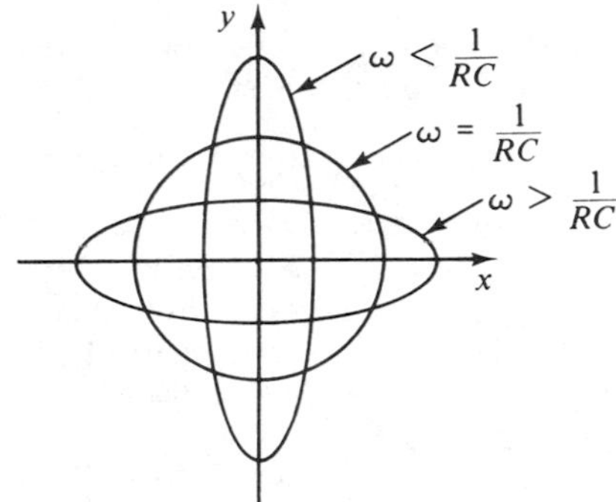

Fig. 8-20

Example 8-10

(a) In Fig. 8-21 R is varied from zero to infinity. Compare the amplitude and phase of voltages $\mathbf{V}_1$ and $\mathbf{V}_o$.

(b) $\mathbf{V}_1$ is connected to the x input and $\mathbf{V}_o$ to the y input of an oscilloscope. Discuss the resulting display and the effect of the ωRC product on the display.

(c) Generalize the results presented in (b) for two sinusoidal waves that are ϕ radians apart in phase.

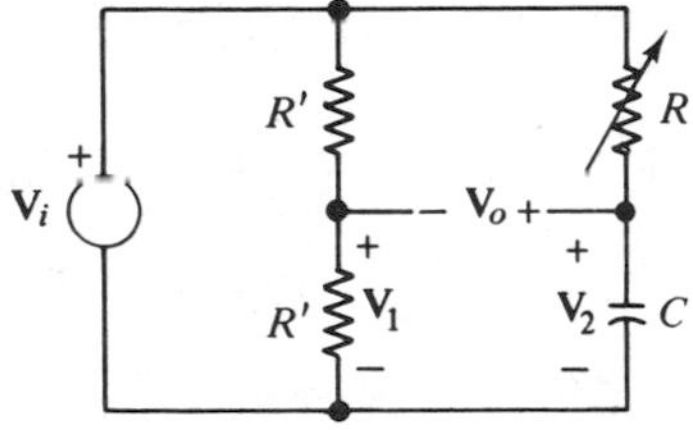

Fig. 8-21

Solution

(a) From Fig. 8-21 we see that

$$\mathbf{V}_0 = \mathbf{V}_2 - \mathbf{V}_1 = \mathbf{V}_i \frac{1/j\omega C}{R + (1/j\omega C)} - \mathbf{V}_i \frac{R'}{R' + R'}$$

$$= \mathbf{V}_i\left(\frac{1}{j\omega RC + 1} - \frac{1}{2}\right) = \mathbf{V}_i \frac{1}{2}\left(\frac{1 - j\omega RC}{1 + j\omega RC}\right)$$

$$= \mathbf{V}_i \frac{1}{2} \frac{\sqrt{1 + \omega^2R^2C^2}\,\underline{/\tan^{-1} - \omega RC}}{\sqrt{1 + \omega^2R^2C^2}\,\underline{/\tan^{-1} \omega RC}} = \mathbf{V}_i \frac{1}{2}\underline{/-2\tan^{-1}\omega RC}$$

We now compare $\mathbf{V}_1$ with $\mathbf{V}_0$. Let $\mathbf{V}_i = V_m\underline{/\theta}$.

$$\mathbf{V}_1 = \mathbf{V}_i \frac{1}{2}\underline{/0} = \frac{1}{2} V_m\underline{/\theta} \tag{8-30a}$$

$$\mathbf{V}_0 = \mathbf{V}_i \frac{1}{2}\underline{/-2\tan^{-1}\omega RC} = \frac{1}{2} V_m\underline{/\theta - 2\tan^{-1}\omega RC} \tag{8-30b}$$

Both voltages have a peak value of $\frac{1}{2}V_m$ (where V_m is the peak value of the input voltage). However, the two voltages differ in phase by

$$\theta_1 - \theta_0 = \theta - \theta_0 = 2\tan^{-1}\omega RC$$

When $\omega RC = 0$, the phase difference is 0°. When $\omega RC = 1$, the phase difference is 90°. When $\omega RC = \infty$, the phase difference is 180°. So depending on the ωRC product, the phase difference can be anywhere from 0 to 180°.

As shown in Fig. 8-22(a), a phase difference of $(\theta_1 - \theta_0)$ results in a time difference of $(\theta_1 - \theta_0)/\omega$ seconds between the two sine waves.

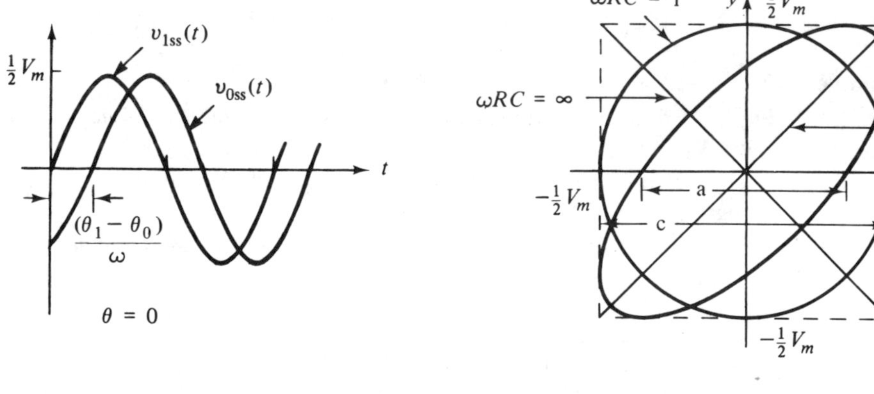

Fig. 8-22

(b) From $\mathbf{V}_1$ and $\mathbf{V}_0$ [see Eq. (8-30)] we obtain $v_{1ss}(t)$ and $v_{0ss}(t)$.

$$\begin{aligned} v_{1ss}(t) &= \tfrac{1}{2}V_m \sin(\omega t + \theta) = x(t) \\ v_{0ss}(t) &= \tfrac{1}{2}V_m \sin(\omega t + \theta - 2\tan^{-1}\omega RC) = y(t) \end{aligned} \tag{8-31}$$

We note that maximum and minimum x and y deflections are $\pm\frac{1}{2}V_m$. In other words, the y vs. x curve is contained within a square. See Fig. 8-22(b).

When $\omega RC = 0$, we have

$$y = x$$

which is a straight line with unity slope going through the origin. This is the display when the two sine waves are *in* phase. When $\omega RC = 1$, we have

$$x = \tfrac{1}{2}V_m \sin(\omega t + \theta)$$

$$y = \frac{1}{2}V_m \sin\left(\omega t + \theta - \frac{\pi}{2}\right) = -\frac{1}{2}V_m \cos(\omega t + \theta)$$

Eliminating t between these two equations, we obtain

$$x^2 + y^2 = (\tfrac{1}{2}V_m)^2$$

which represents a circle of radius $\frac{1}{2}V_m$, centered at the origin. This is the display when the two sine waves are 90° out of phase.

When $\omega RC = \infty$, we have

$$x = \tfrac{1}{2}V_m \sin(\omega t + \theta)$$

$$y = \tfrac{1}{2}V_m \sin(\omega t + \theta - \pi) = -\tfrac{1}{2}V_m \sin(\omega t + \theta)$$

$$y = -x$$

which represents a straight line of slope -1 going through the origin. This is the display when the two sine waves are 180° out of phase.

Thus as the phase difference between the two sine waves is increased from 0 to 180°, the display changes from a straight line with positive slope to a straight line with negative slope. In between these extremes the display is governed by the equation

$$x^2 - 2xy \cos(2 \tan^{-1} \omega RC) + y^2 = [\tfrac{1}{2}V_m \sin(2 \tan^{-1} \omega RC)]^2 \qquad (8\text{-}32)$$

which represents a rotated ellipse (see Problem 8-35). The rotation angle is 45° if the phase difference is between 0 and 90°. See Fig. 8-22(b). The rotation angle is $-45°$ if the phase difference is between 90 and 180°. The ellipse degenerates into a circle when the phase difference is 90° and into a straight line when the phase difference is 0° or 180°. As Eq. (8-32) shows, the phase difference is governed by 2 $\tan^{-1} \omega RC$. So as ωRC is increased from zero to infinity, the display goes through the following forms: a straight line with $+1$ slope, an ellipse at 45°, a circle, an ellipse at $-45°$, and a straight line with -1 slope.

(c) For the general case we have

$$x = A \sin(\omega t + \theta), \qquad y = B \sin(\omega t + \theta + \phi) \qquad (8\text{-}33)$$

where ϕ represents the phase difference between the two sine waves. When t is eliminated between these equations, the result is

$$\left(\frac{x}{A}\right)^2 - 2\left(\frac{x}{A}\right)\left(\frac{y}{B}\right) \cos\phi + \left(\frac{y}{B}\right)^2 = \sin^2\phi \qquad (8\text{-}34)$$

which represents a tilted ellipse (see Problem 8-36). The x- and y-axis intercepts are

$$x_{\text{int}} = \pm A \sin \phi = \pm x_{\max} \sin \phi, \qquad y_{\text{int}} = \pm B \sin \phi = \pm y_{\max} \sin \phi$$

which give

$$\pm \sin \phi = \frac{x_{\text{int}}}{x_{\max}} = \frac{y_{\text{int}}}{y_{\max}} \tag{8-35}$$

This result can be generalized and stated as

$$\sin |\phi| = \frac{\text{midway swing}}{\text{peak-to-peak swing}}$$

The measurements can be taken either horizontally or vertically as shown in Fig. 8-23(a) and (b). Unless ω is low enough for us to see in which direction (clockwise or counterclockwise) the ellipse is generated by the electron beam that forms the oscilloscope display, it is not possible to ascertain whether the x or y signal is ahead by ϕ radians (see Problem 8-35). From a display like the one shown in Fig. 8-23 we can determine only the phase difference.

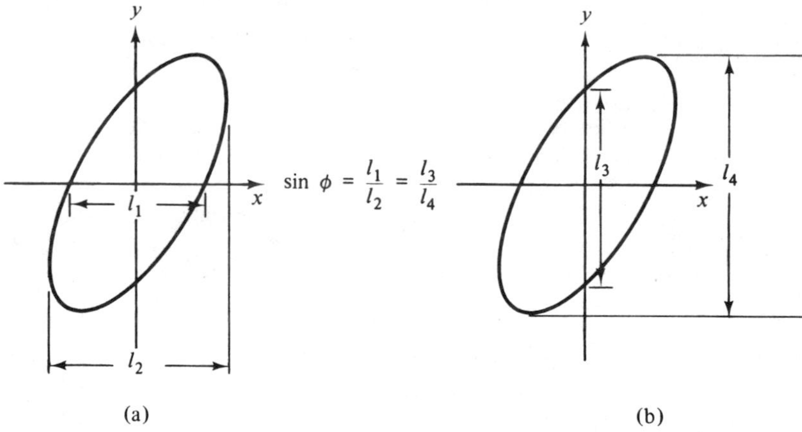

Fig. 8-23

Example 8-11

Obtain the Thévenin equivalent representation of the circuit shown in Fig. 8-24. The equivalent circuit will be used for sinusoidal steady-state calculations.

Solution. First, we represent the input sine wave as a phasor

$$10\sqrt{2} \angle \frac{\pi}{4}$$

Next, noting that $\omega = 2$, we obtain the open-circuit voltage.

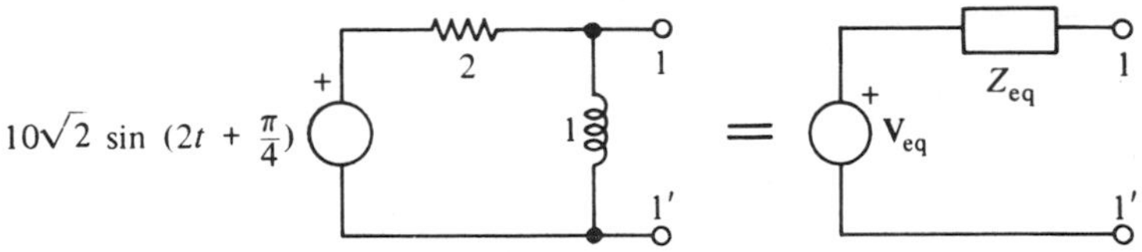

Fig. 8-24

$$\mathbf{V}_{oc} = 10\sqrt{2}\,\underline{/\tfrac{\pi}{4}}\left(\frac{j2}{2+j2}\right) = 10\sqrt{2}\,\underline{/\tfrac{\pi}{4}}\left(\frac{j}{1+j}\right)$$

$$= 10\sqrt{2}\,\underline{/\tfrac{\pi}{4}}\left(\frac{\underline{/\pi/2}}{\sqrt{2}\,\underline{/\pi/4}}\right) = 10\,\underline{/\tfrac{\pi}{2}}$$

The Thévenin equivalent voltage is

$$\mathbf{V}_{eq} = \mathbf{V}_{oc} = 10\,\underline{/\tfrac{\pi}{2}} = 10e^{j\pi/2} = j10 \quad \text{Ans.}$$

Finally, we obtain the equivalent impedance by replacing the source with a short circuit and calculating the impedance seen from terminals 1–1′.

$$Z_{eq} = \frac{(2)(j2)}{2+j2} = \frac{j2}{1+j} = \frac{j2(1-j)}{(1+j)(1-j)}$$

$$= 1 + j = \sqrt{2}e^{j\pi/4} = \sqrt{2}\,\underline{/\tfrac{\pi}{4}} \quad \text{Ans.}$$

8-6 PHASE LAG AND PHASE LEAD

Consider the three sine waves given by

$$s_1 = A \sin \omega t, \qquad s_2 = B \sin(\omega t - \theta), \qquad s_3 = C \sin(\omega t + \theta) \tag{8-36}$$

All three have the same angular frequency ω. The argument of s_2 is θ radians *less* than the argument of s_1. We say that s_2 *lags* s_1 by θ radians. The argument of s_3 is θ radians *more* than the argument of s_1. We say that s_3 *leads* s_1 by θ radians.

Alternatively, Eq. (8-36) can be written

$$s_1 = A \sin \omega t, \qquad s_2 = B \sin \omega(t - t'), \qquad s_3 = C \sin \omega(t + t') \tag{8-37}$$

where $t' = \dfrac{\theta}{\omega}$

The s_1, s_2, and s_3 curves are sketched in Fig. 8-25(a), (b), and (c), respectively. In comparing the three curves, we see that s_2 zero crossings occur t' seconds *after* the s_1 zero crossings. We say that s_2 *lags* s_1 by t' seconds. On the other hand, when s_1 and s_3 are compared, we see that s_3 zero crossings occur t' seconds *before* the s_1 zero crossings. We say that s_3 *leads* s_1 by t' seconds.

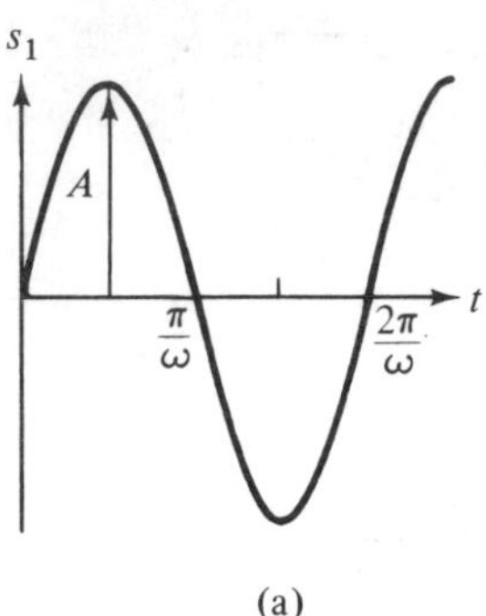

(a)

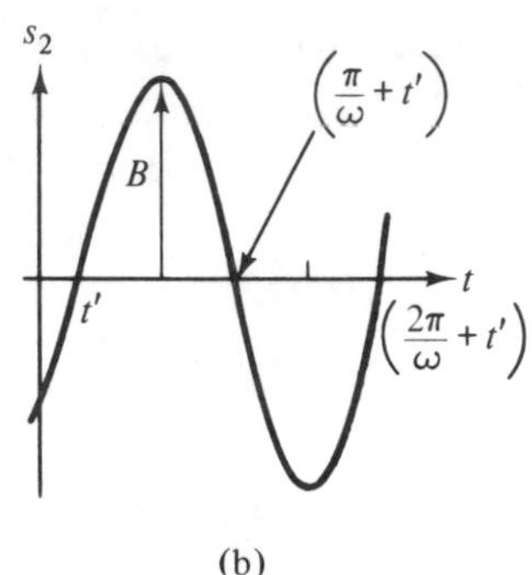

(b)

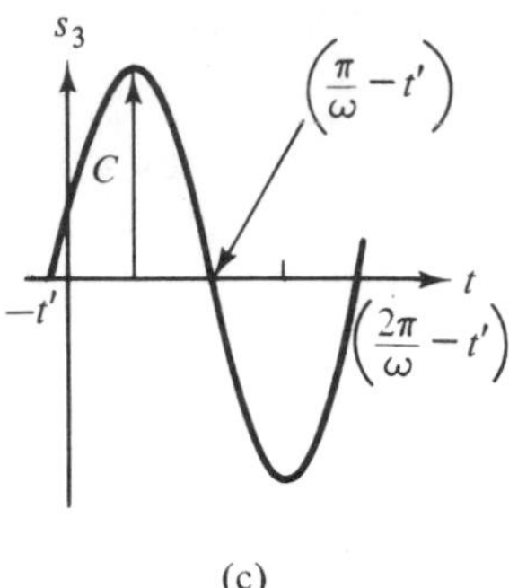

(c)

Fig. 8-25

Lag or lead can be expressed in terms of angle θ [see Eq. (8-36)] or time t' [see Eq. (8-37)]. Whether one curve lags or leads the other depends on the *sign* of the angle following the angle of ωt. A negative sign means lag; a positive sign means lead. For instance, to compare two waves given by

$$s_A = A \sin(\omega t + \theta_1) \qquad (A > 0)$$

$$s_B = B \sin(\omega t - \theta_2) \qquad (B > 0)$$

we express both waves in terms of either lag or lead angles as follows.

$$\left.\begin{aligned} s_A &= A \sin[\omega t - (-\theta_1)] \\ s_B &= B \sin[\omega t - (\theta_2)] \end{aligned}\right\} \quad \text{(lag angles are } -\theta_1 \text{ are } \theta_2\text{)}$$

$$\left.\begin{aligned} s_A &= A \sin[\omega t + (\theta_1)] \\ s_B &= B \sin[\omega t + (-\theta_2)] \end{aligned}\right\} \quad \text{(lead angles are } \theta_1 \text{ and } -\theta_2\text{)}$$

We can then say that s_B lags s_A by $[\theta_2 - (-\theta_1)] = (\theta_2 + \theta_1)$ radians. Alternatively, we can say that s_B leads s_A by $[(-\theta_2) - \theta_1] = -(\theta_2 + \theta_1)$ radians. From these results we see that

$$\text{Lead angle of } -(\theta_2 + \theta_1) = \text{Lag angle of } (\theta_2 + \theta_1)$$

Example 8-12

Given

$$s_1 = A \sin \omega t$$

$$s_2 = B \cos \omega t$$

$$s_3 = C \cos(\omega t - \theta)$$

$$s_4 = -D \sin(\omega t + \psi)$$

$$s_5 = E \sin(-\omega t)$$

The constants A, B, C, D, and E are positive.

(a) How much do signals s_2, s_3, s_4, and s_5 lead s_1?

(b) How much do signals s_1, s_2, s_4, and s_5 lag s_3?
(c) How much does $s_1 + s_2$ lead $-s_4$?

Solution.

(a) Express all signals as sine (or cosine) waves with lead angles.

$$s_1 = A \sin \omega t$$

$$s_2 = B \cos \omega t = B \sin\left[\omega t + \left(\frac{\pi}{2}\right)\right]$$

$$s_3 = C \cos(\omega t - \theta) = C \sin\left[\omega t + \left(\frac{\pi}{2} - \theta\right)\right]$$

$$s_4 = -D \sin(\omega t + \psi) = D \sin[\omega t + (\psi - \pi)]$$

$$s_5 = E \sin(-\omega t) = -E \sin(\omega t) = E \sin[\omega t + (-\pi)]$$

Comparing lead angles, we obtain

s_2 leads s_1 by $\frac{\pi}{2}$

s_3 lead s_1 by $\left(\frac{\pi}{2} - \theta\right)$

s_4 leads s_1 by $(\psi - \pi)$

s_5 leads s_1 by $(-\pi)$

Alternatively, all signals can be expressed as cosine waves and then compared. Thus

$$s_1 = A \sin \omega t = A \cos\left[\omega t + \left(-\frac{\pi}{2}\right)\right]$$

$$s_2 = B \cos \omega t$$

$$s_3 = C \cos(\omega t - \theta) = C \cos[\omega t + (-\theta)]$$

$$s_4 = -D \sin(\omega t + \psi) = D \sin(\omega t + \psi - \pi) = D \cos\left[\omega t + \left(\psi - \frac{3\pi}{2}\right)\right]$$

$$s_5 = E \sin(-\omega t) = E \sin(\omega t - \pi) = E \cos\left[\omega t + \left(-\frac{3\pi}{2}\right)\right]$$

The resulting lead angles are the same as given above. (It should also be clear that an angle of $\pm 2\pi$ radians can be added to any argument without affecting lead or lag relationships.)

(b) Express all signals as cosine (or sine) waves with lag angles.

$$s_1 = A \cos\left[\omega t - \left(\frac{\pi}{2}\right)\right]$$

$$s_2 = B \cos \omega t$$

$$s_3 = C \cos [\omega t - (\theta)]$$

$$s_4 = D \cos \left[\omega t - \left(\frac{3\pi}{2} - \psi\right)\right]$$

$$s_5 = E \cos \left[\omega t - \left(\frac{3\pi}{2}\right)\right]$$

Comparing lag angles, we find

$$s_1 \text{ lags } s_3 \text{ by } \left(\frac{\pi}{2} - \theta\right)$$

$$s_2 \text{ lags } s_3 \text{ by } (-\theta)$$

$$s_4 \text{ lags } s_3 \text{ by } \left(\frac{3\pi}{2} - \psi - \theta\right)$$

$$s_5 \text{ lags } s_3 \text{ by } \left(\frac{3\pi}{2} - \theta\right)$$

(c) First, we express all waves as sine (or cosine) waves.

$$s_1 = A \sin \omega t$$

$$s_2 = B \cos \omega t = B \sin \left(\omega t + \frac{\pi}{2}\right)$$

$$-s_4 = D \sin (\omega t + \psi)$$

Next, we form the sum of s_1 and s_2. We can do so by using trigonometric identities directly on the time-domain waveforms, or we can convert both sine waves into phasor forms, perform the summation of phasors, and then convert the result back to a sine wave. Let us use this latter approach.

$$\mathbf{S}_1 = A\underline{/0}, \quad \mathbf{S}_2 = B\underline{/\frac{\pi}{2}}$$

$$\mathbf{S}_1 + \mathbf{S}_2 = A\underline{/0} + B\underline{/\frac{\pi}{2}}$$

$$= A(\cos 0 + j \sin 0) + B\left(\cos \frac{\pi}{2} + j \sin \frac{\pi}{2}\right) = A + jB$$

$$= \sqrt{A^2 + B^2}\ \underline{/\tan^{-1} \frac{B}{A}}$$

$$s_1 + s_2 = \sqrt{A^2 + B^2} \sin \left(\omega t + \tan^{-1} \frac{B}{A}\right)$$

Now we compare the phase angle of $s_1 + s_2$, $(\tan^{-1} B/A)$, with the phase angle of $-s_4$, (ψ). Therefore $s_1 + s_2$ leads $-s_4$ by

$$\tan^{-1} \left(\frac{B}{A}\right) - \psi \quad \text{Ans.}$$

Example 8-13

Show that in the network of Fig. 8-26 the current leads the input voltage, whereas the output voltage lags it.

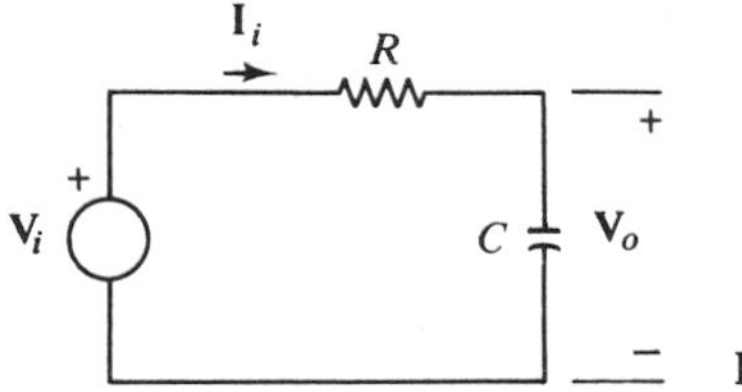

Fig. 8-26

Solution.

$$\mathbf{I}_i = \frac{\mathbf{V}_i}{R + (1/j\omega C)} = \mathbf{V}_i \frac{j\omega C}{1 + j\omega RC} = \mathbf{V}_i \frac{\omega C}{\sqrt{1 + \omega^2 R^2 C^2}} \angle \frac{\pi}{2} - \tan^{-1} \omega RC$$

We see then that the phase of $\mathbf{I}_i$ is

$$\frac{\pi}{2} - \tan^{-1} \omega RC$$

radians ahead of the phase of $\mathbf{V}_i$. Depending on the value of the ωRC product, this lead angle is between $\pi/2$ and 0 radians.

$$\mathbf{V}_o = \mathbf{I}_i \frac{1}{j\omega C} = \mathbf{V}_i \frac{1}{1 + j\omega RC} = \mathbf{V}_i \frac{1}{\sqrt{1 + \omega^2 R^2 C^2}} \angle -\tan^{-1} \omega RC$$

The phase of $\mathbf{V}_o$ is $\tan^{-1} \omega RC$ radians behind the phase of $\mathbf{V}_i$. This lag angle is between 0 and $\pi/2$ radians.

The resulting phase relations are shown in Fig. 8-27. Either from the expressions for $\mathbf{I}_i$ and $\mathbf{V}_o$ or from Fig. 8-27 we see that, regardless of the value of ωRC, $i_{ss}(t)$ *leads* $v_{oss}(t)$ by $\pi/2$ radians.

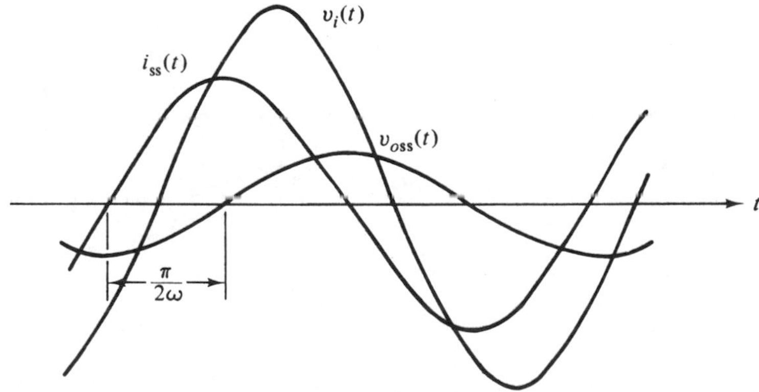

Fig. 8-27

The voltage across the resistor, being $\mathbf{I}_i R$, is in phase with the current. So the voltage across the capacitor lags the voltage across the resistor by $\pi/2$ radians.

Example 8-14

Show that in Fig. 8-28 the output voltage leads or lags the input voltage, depending on the position of the potentiometer.

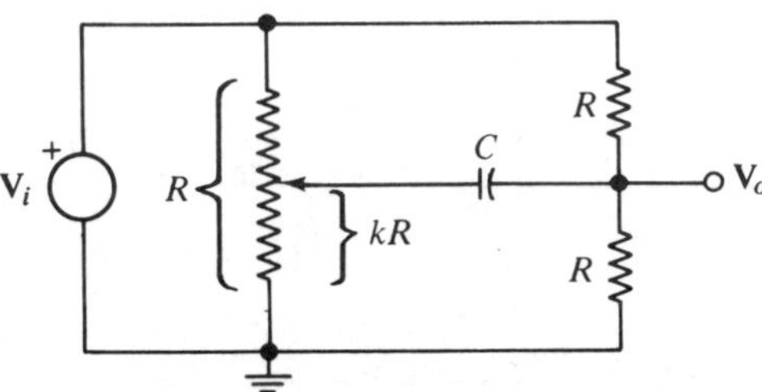

Fig. 8-28

Solution. Redraw the network as in Fig. 8-29(a). Then obtain the Thévenin equivalent circuits to the left of p and to the right of q and redraw the resulting circuit as in Fig. 8-29(b). Inspection of Fig. 8-29(b) shows that

$$\mathbf{V}_o = \frac{k\mathbf{V}_i \dfrac{R}{2} + \dfrac{\mathbf{V}_i}{2}\left[k(1-k)R + \dfrac{1}{j\omega C}\right]}{k(1-k)R + \dfrac{1}{j\omega C} + \dfrac{R}{2}} = \mathbf{V}_i \frac{1}{2}\left\{\frac{1 + j\omega RCk(2-k)}{1 + j\omega RC[(1/2) + k(1-k)]}\right\}$$

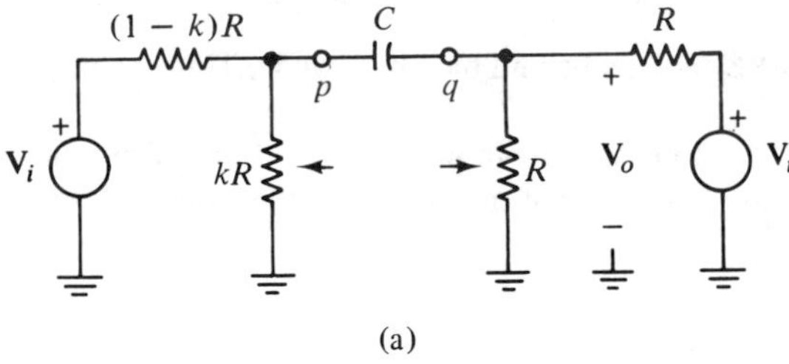

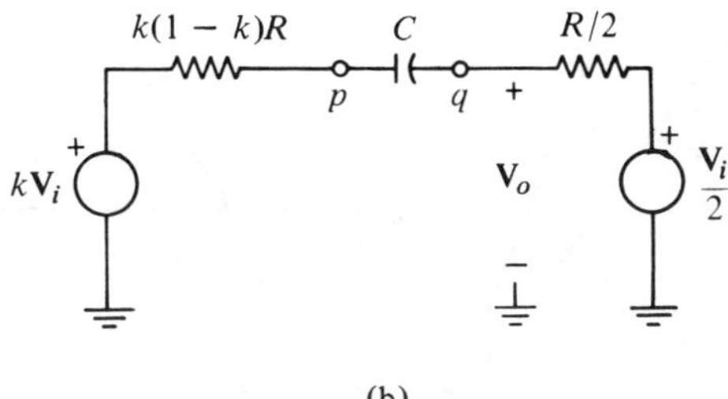

Fig. 8-29

Let θ_i *and* θ_o represent the phase angles of $\mathbf{V}_i$ and $\mathbf{V}_o$, respectively. The phase difference between the input and output sine waves is

$$\theta_o - \theta_i = \tan^{-1} \omega RCk(2 - k) - \tan^{-1} \left\{ \omega RC \left[\frac{1}{2} + k(1 - k) \right] \right\} \qquad (8\text{-}38)$$

When $k = 0$, we have the situation illustrated in Fig. 8-30(a). The resulting phase difference is

$$\theta_o - \theta_i = -\tan^{-1} \frac{\omega RC}{2} \qquad (8\text{-}39)$$

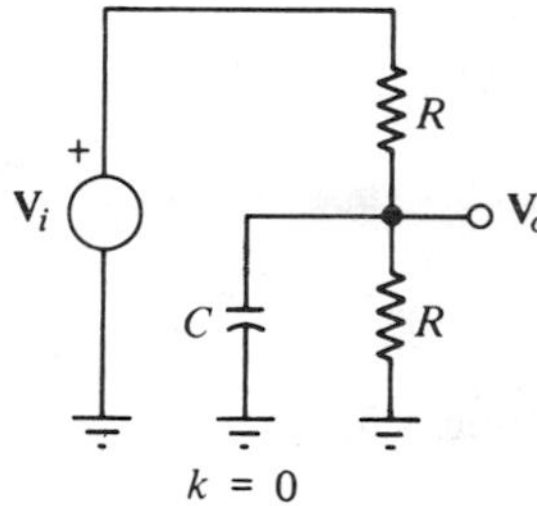

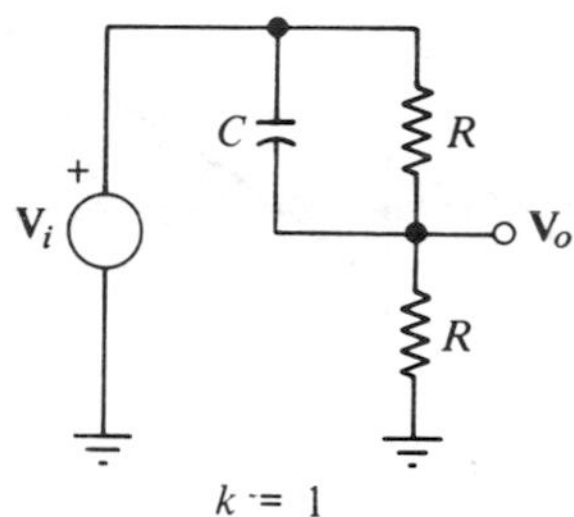

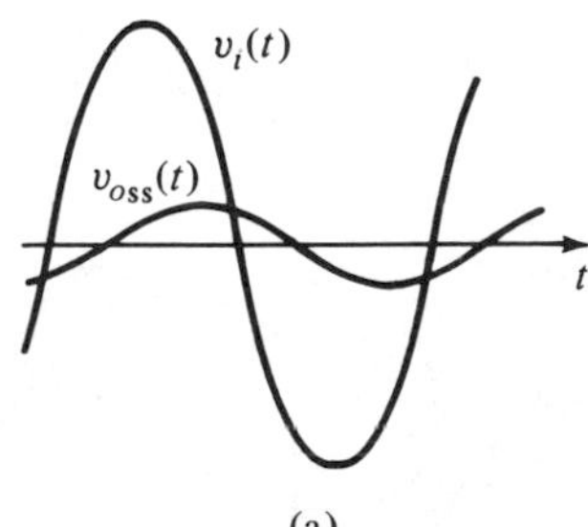

(a)

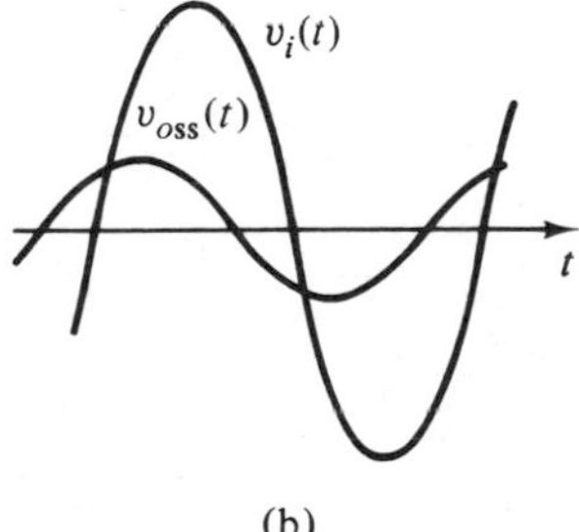

(b)

Fig. 8-30

which is a negative angle between 0 and $-90°$ (the value being determined by the ωRC product). Consequently, the output lags the input as shown. When $k = 1$, we have the situation illustrated in Fig. 8-30(b). The resulting phase difference is

$$\theta_o - \theta_i = \tan^{-1} \omega RC - \tan^{-} \left(\frac{\omega RC}{2} \right) \qquad (8\text{-}40)$$

which is a positive angle between 0 and 19.47° (the actual value being determined by the ωRC product). So the output leads the input as shown. When $k = 0.5$,

$$\theta_o - \theta_i = \tan^{-1} \tfrac{3}{4}\omega RC - \tan^{-1} \tfrac{3}{4}\omega RC = 0$$

Therefore input and output are in phase. We see that as k is varied from zero to one, $\theta_o - \theta_i$ varies from a negative value (output lags input) to a positive value (output leads input). This phase difference is plotted in Fig. 8-31 as a function of k for $\omega RC = 1$. The shape of the curve changes about the $k = 0.5$ point if the ωRC product is changed from one to another value.

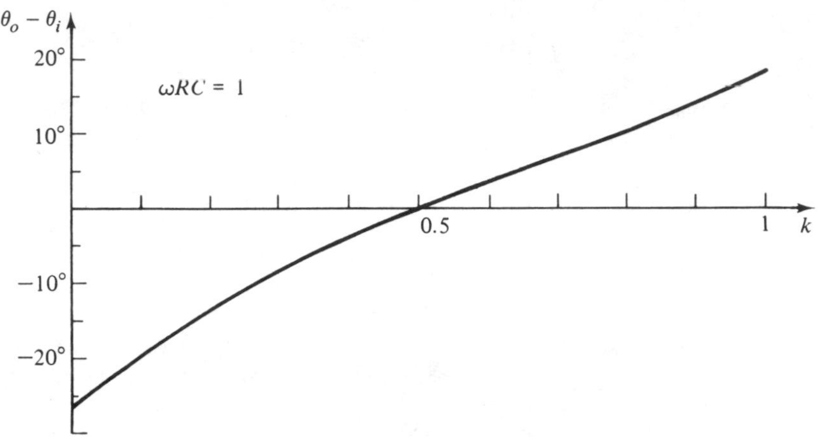

Fig. 8-31

Example 8-15

In Fig. 8-32, show that, regardless of frequency, $\mathbf{V}_{o1}$ and V_{o2} are in phase.

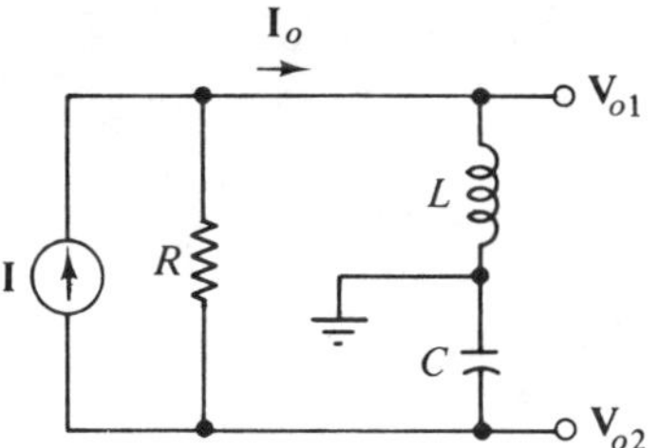

Fig. 8-32

Solution.

$$\mathbf{V}_{o1} = \mathbf{I}_o j\omega L = \mathbf{I}_o \omega L \,\angle \frac{\pi}{2}$$

$$\mathbf{V}_{o2} = -\mathbf{I}_o\left(\frac{1}{j\omega C}\right) = \mathbf{I}_o\left(\frac{j}{\omega C}\right) = \mathbf{I}_o\left(\frac{1}{\omega C}\right)\angle \frac{\pi}{2}$$

The angle of $\mathbf{V}_{o1}$ is the same as the angle of $\mathbf{V}_{o2}$. So $\mathbf{V}_{o1}$ and V_{o2} are in phase regardless of frequency.

8-7 LARGE CURRENTS AND VOLTAGES WITH SMALL INPUTS

Consider the parallel *RLC* network in Fig. 8-33, which receives its excitation from a sinusoidal source contained in N. The four currents shown are related to the input voltage $\mathbf{V}$ by

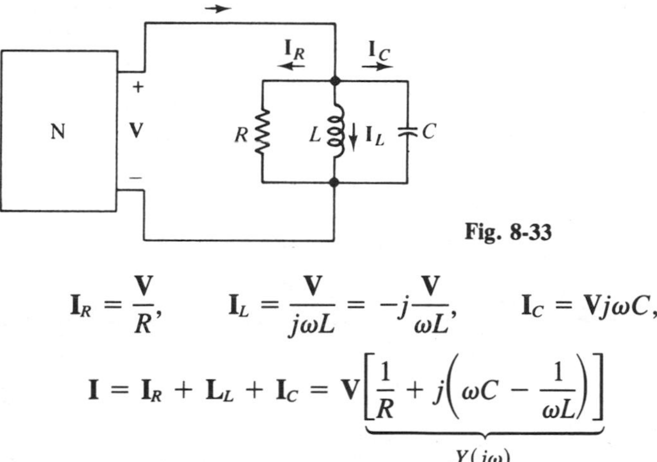

Fig. 8-33

$$\mathbf{I}_R = \frac{\mathbf{V}}{R}, \qquad \mathbf{I}_L = \frac{\mathbf{V}}{j\omega L} = -j\frac{\mathbf{V}}{\omega L}, \qquad \mathbf{I}_C = \mathbf{V}j\omega C,$$

$$\mathbf{I} = \mathbf{I}_R + \mathbf{L}_L + \mathbf{I}_C = \mathbf{V}\underbrace{\left[\frac{1}{R} + j\left(\omega C - \frac{1}{\omega L}\right)\right]}_{Y(j\omega)}$$

where $Y(j\omega)$ is the input admittance of the *RLC* circuit.

The peak value of the input current **I** is

$$I_m = V_m|Y(j\omega)| = V_m\sqrt{\left(\frac{1}{R}\right)^2 + \left(\omega C - \frac{1}{\omega L}\right)^2} \tag{8-41}$$

where V_m represents the peak value of the input voltage **V**. As shown by Eq. (8-41), the peak current I_m depends on the frequency ω. It is *large* at low frequencies because $1/\omega L$ is large. It is *large* at high frequencies because ωC is large. It achieves its minimum value of

$$(I_m)_{\min} = \frac{V_m}{R} \tag{8-42}$$

when

$$\omega = \frac{1}{\sqrt{LC}}$$

The frequency dependence of I_m is shown in Fig. 8-34(a), which is obtained by sketching Eq. (8-41) vs. ω. Suppose that we adjust the frequency of the source inside N to $\omega = 1/\sqrt{LC}$. At this frequency the expressions for the currents and the input impedance simplify to

$$\mathbf{I}_R = \frac{\mathbf{V}}{R}, \qquad \mathbf{I}_L = -j\frac{\mathbf{V}}{\omega L} = -j\sqrt{\frac{C}{L}}\mathbf{V}$$

$$\mathbf{I}_C = \mathbf{V}j\omega C = j\sqrt{\frac{C}{L}}\mathbf{V}, \qquad \mathbf{I} = \frac{\mathbf{V}}{R}$$

$$Z = \frac{1}{Y} = R$$

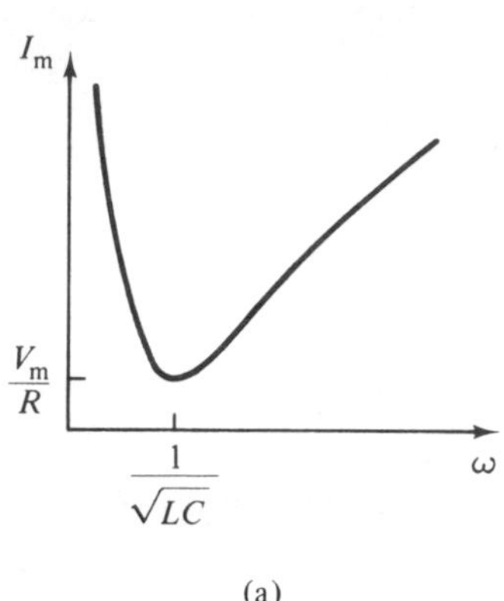

(a)

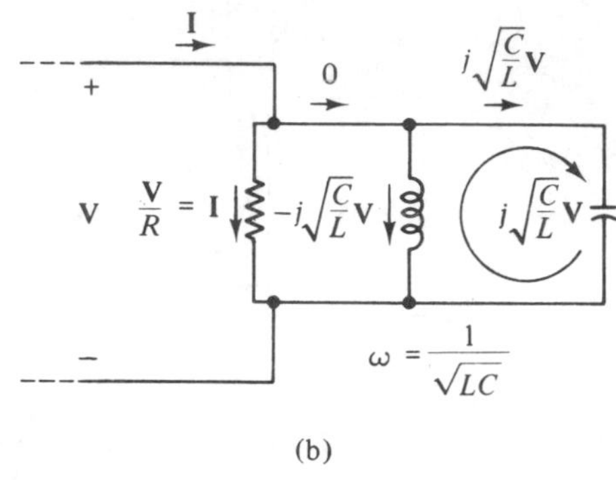

(b)

Fig. 8-34

The relationship between the various currents can be seen in Fig. 8-34(b). Note that the current through the inductor

$$-j\sqrt{\frac{C}{L}}\mathbf{V}$$

is 180° out of phase with the current through the capacitor

$$j\sqrt{\frac{C}{L}}\mathbf{V}$$

Furthermore, they are equal to magnitude, which means that their sum is zero and also that the current fed to the *LC* portion of the network is zero. Nonetheless, the inductive and capacitive branches carry current. We can think of this current as a circulating current in the *LC* loop as shown. All of the input current **I** goes through the resistor. If this resistor is infinite, the input current is also zero. We end up with the interesting situation of having current in the *LC* loop with zero input current. Although seemingly strange at first, it should be realized that here we are dealing with sinusoidal steady-state conditions. Prior to this time (before steady state prevails) current is coming into the *LC* circuit, and thus energy is being delivered to the inductor and capacitor. After steady state is reached, this energy is sent back and forth between the inductor and capacitor, since there is no resistance associated with this loop to dissipate any of it. In practice, because of inevitable losses, this situation is impossible. However, it is possible to have *large currents in the inductor and capacitor with a relatively small* current coming into the parallel *LC* network.

Consider next the *RLC* network shown in Fig. 8-35. This network is excited by a sinusoidal source within N. The four voltages shown are related to the input current **I** by

$$\mathbf{V}_R = R\mathbf{I}$$

$$\mathbf{V}_L = j\omega L\mathbf{I}$$

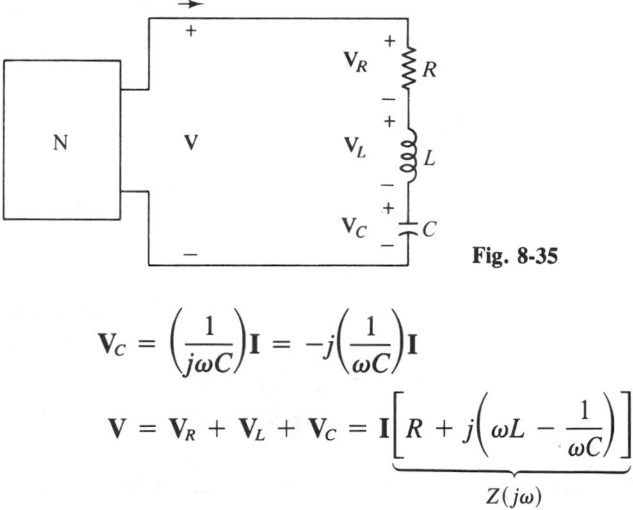

Fig. 8-35

$$\mathbf{V}_C = \left(\frac{1}{j\omega C}\right)\mathbf{I} = -j\left(\frac{1}{\omega C}\right)\mathbf{I}$$

$$\mathbf{V} = \mathbf{V}_R + \mathbf{V}_L + \mathbf{V}_C = \mathbf{I}\underbrace{\left[R + j\left(\omega L - \frac{1}{\omega C}\right)\right]}_{Z(j\omega)}$$

where $Z(j\omega)$ is the input impedance of the RLC circuit.

The peak value of the input voltage $\mathbf{V}$ is

$$V_m = I_m|Z(j\omega)| = I_m\sqrt{R^2 + \left(\omega L - \frac{1}{\omega C}\right)^2}$$

where I_m represents the peak value of the input current $\mathbf{I}$. The peak voltage V_m is large at low frequencies (because of $1/\omega C$) and at high frequencies (because of ωL). It achieves its minimum value of

$$(V_m)_{\min} = I_m R \tag{8-43}$$

when

$$\omega = \frac{1}{\sqrt{LC}}$$

the frequency dependence of V_m is sketched in Fig. 8-36(a). At $\omega = 1/\sqrt{LC}$ the voltages and the input impedance are given by

$$\mathbf{V}_R = R\mathbf{I}, \qquad V_L = j\omega L\mathbf{I} = j\sqrt{\frac{L}{C}}\mathbf{I}$$

$$\mathbf{V}_C = -j\frac{1}{\omega C}\mathbf{I} = -j\sqrt{\frac{L}{C}}\mathbf{I}, \qquad \mathbf{V} = R\mathbf{I}$$

$$Z = R$$

The various voltages are shown in Fig. 8-36(b). Note that the voltage across the inductor

$$j\sqrt{\frac{L}{C}}\mathbf{I}$$

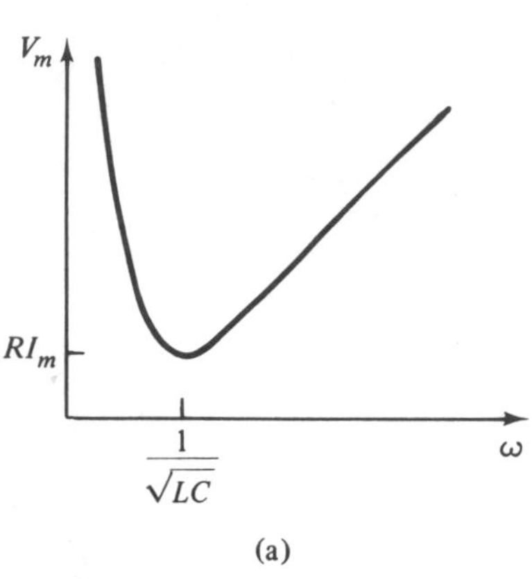

(a)

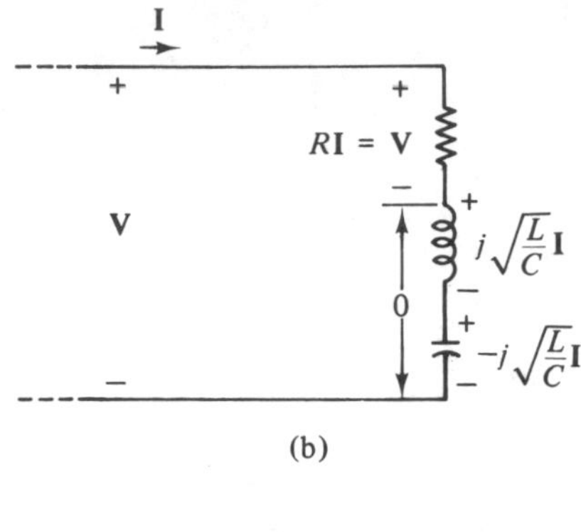

(b)

Fig. 8-36

is 180° out of phase with the voltage across the capacitor.

$$-j\sqrt{\frac{L}{C}}\,\mathbf{I}$$

Moreover, they are equal in magnitude. As a result, their sum is zero, and thus there is no voltage across the LC portion of the network even though there is voltage across the L and across the C. All of the input voltage, $\mathbf{V}$, appears across the resistor. If $R = 0$, the voltage across the resistor is zero and so the input voltage is zero. We then have a situation in which there are voltages across the L and the C while the voltage across the LC combination is zero. Energy is transferred back and forth between L and C without any loss. In practice, because of inevitable losses associated with actual L's and C's, the voltage across the LC combination is not zero. However, we can obtain *large inductor and capacitor voltages with a relatively small input voltage across the series LC network.*

8-8 POWER RELATIONSHIPS IN AC CIRCUITS

The instantaneous power delivered to a two-terminal circuit (see Fig. 8-37) is given by

$$p(t) = v(t)i(t) \tag{8-44}$$

$i(t)$ + $v(t)$ − RLC and sources

Fig. 8-37

If all the excitations are sinusoidal and of the same frequency, then both $v(t)$ and $i(t)$ are sinusoidal in the steady state. So we can express them, in general, as

$$v(t) = V_m \sin(\omega t + \theta_V), \qquad i(t) = I_m \sin(\omega t + \theta_I) \tag{8-45}$$

where θ_V and θ_I are the phase angles of the voltage and current waveforms. The instantaneous power in the steady state is given by

$$p(t) = V_m I_m \sin(\omega t + \theta_V) \sin(\omega t + \theta_I) \tag{8-46}$$

Since

$$\sin A \sin B = \tfrac{1}{2}[\cos(A - B) - \cos(A + B)]$$

we can write Eq. (8-46) as

$$p(t) = \tfrac{1}{2} V_m I_m [\cos(\theta_V - \theta_I) - \cos(2\omega t + \theta_V + \theta_I)] \tag{8-47}$$

In ac circuits the average power is of more interest than the instantaneous power. Since $p(t)$ in Eq. (8-47) is periodic with period π/ω, we average $p(t)$ over one period of operation. (We could just as easily average over a time interval of $k\pi/\omega$, where k is an integer; the result will be the same.)

$$\begin{aligned} p_{av} &= \frac{\omega}{\pi} \int_0^{\pi/\omega} p(t)\, dt = \frac{\omega}{\pi} \int_0^{\pi/\omega} \frac{1}{2} V_m I_m [\cos(\theta_V - \theta_I) - \cos(2\omega t + \theta_V + \theta_I)]\, dt \\ &= \frac{1}{2} V_m I_m \frac{\omega}{\pi} \cos(\theta_V - \theta_I) \int_0^{\pi/\omega} dt - \frac{1}{2} V_m I_m \frac{\omega}{\pi} \int_0^{\pi/\omega} \cos(2\omega t + \theta_V + \theta_I)\, dt \end{aligned} \tag{8-48}$$

When evaluated, the first and second integrals give π/ω and 0, respectively. Then Eq. (8-48) reduces to

$$p_{av} = \tfrac{1}{2} V_m I_m \cos(\theta_V - \theta_I) \tag{8-49}$$

This is an important result. It states that in the sinusoidal steady state the average power delivered is one-half the product of the maximum voltage, the maximum current, and the cosine of the phase difference between the voltage and current waveforms. Because $\cos(\theta_V - \theta_I)$ plays a key role in the determination of the average power, it is given a special name—*power factor*. Thus

$$\text{PF} = \cos(\theta_V - \theta_I)$$

$$p_{av} = \tfrac{1}{2} V_m I_m \,\text{PF} \tag{8-50}$$

If the power factor is zero, the average power delivered to the circuit is zero. This situation occurs when voltage and current are 90° out of phase $[(\theta_V - \theta_I) = \pi/2]$. See Fig. 8-38(a). Note that the instantaneous power, which is the product of the voltage with the current, is alternately positive and negative. So for half the time, power is received by the circuit; during the other half, power is sent out by the circuit. Consequently, the circuit absorbs energy over $T/4$ seconds and

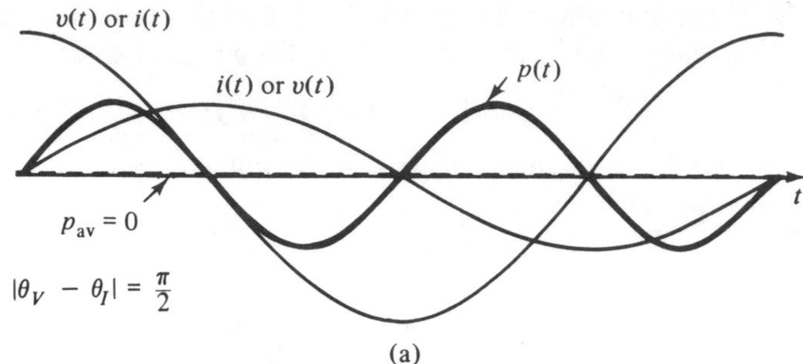

(a)

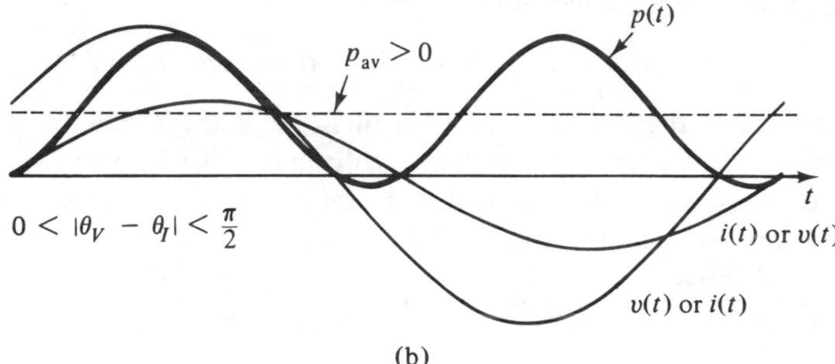

(b)

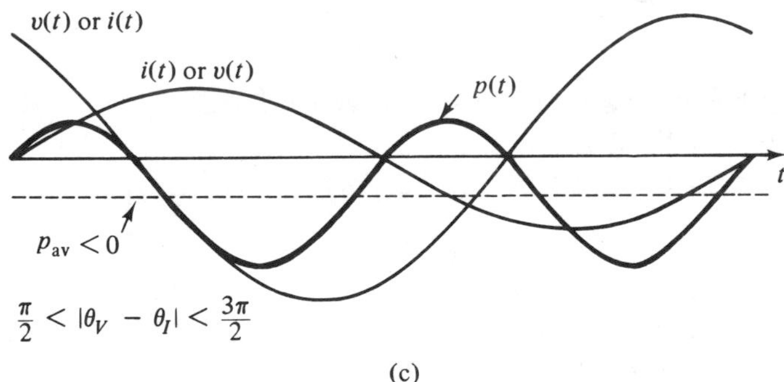

(c)

Fig. 8-38

then completely returns this absorbed energy over the next $T/4$ seconds. (T is the period of the voltage or current waveform.)

If the phase difference between the voltage and current is between $-90°$ and $90°$, the situation illustrated in Fig. 8-38(b) occurs. The instantaneous power curve is again periodic, but it has a positive average value. Therefore the circuit absorbs energy.

If the phase difference between the voltage and current is between $90°$ and $270°$, the situation illustrated in Fig. 8-38(c) occurs. Here the average power is negative, and the circuit actually delivers (sends out) energy.

When the current leads the voltage, the power factor is considered leading. When the current lags the voltage, the power factor is considered lagging. (It is not possible, from PF alone, to ascertain which waveform is leading or lagging.)

At home we receive power through transmission lines at constant V_m; that is, the peak value of the supplied voltage does not vary. The average power consumed varies during the day, depending on the number of electrical appliances in use at a given time. The current that comes in on the lines is obtained from Eq. (8-50) as

$$I_m = \frac{2p_{av}}{V_m \text{PF}}$$

Since the current is inversely proportional to the power factor, the lower the PF, the greater the amount of current needed to meet the power demand. On the other hand, if PF is unity, the least current is needed to provide power. This situation is desirable because transmission-line power losses, which are proportional to the square of the line current, are then minimized. In those industrial applications in which power is demanded at a low power factor, the utilities company may require that the power factor be brought close to unity by special devices in order to provide a requested amount of power with less current and hence with lower line losses.

Since superposition does not apply to power, we cannot make power calculations in multiple-source problems by considering one source at a time. However, *superposition does apply to voltages and currents,* and so we can calculate them by taking one source at a time. Then by using total values of currents and voltages, we can determine the power.

Example 8-16

Calculate the average power delivered to a sinusoidally excited (a) resistor, (b) capacitor.

Solution.

(a) Let the voltage across the resistor be

$$v(t) = V_m \sin(\omega t + \theta)$$

Then the current through the resistor is

$$i(t) = \frac{v(t)}{R} = \underbrace{\frac{V_m}{R}}_{I_m} \sin(\omega t + \theta)$$

Since the phase difference between the voltage and current is 0°, the power factor is

$$\text{PF} = \cos 0° = 1$$

So the average power delivered to the resistor is

$$p_{av} = \frac{1}{2}V_m I_m = \frac{1}{2}I_m^2 R = \frac{1}{2}\frac{V_m^2}{R} \quad \text{Ans.}$$

(b) Let the voltage across the capacitor be

$$v(t) = V_m \sin(\omega t + \theta)$$

Then the current through the capacitor is

$$i(t) = C\frac{dv(t)}{dt} = \omega C V_m \cos(\omega t + \theta) = \underbrace{\omega C V_m}_{I_m} \sin\left(\omega t + \theta + \frac{\pi}{2}\right)$$

Since the phase difference between the voltage and current is 90°, the power factor is

$$\text{PF} = \cos 90° = 0$$

Hence the average power delivered to the capacitor is

$$p_{av} = 0$$

Example 8-17

In Fig. 8-39, what is the average power delivered by the source?

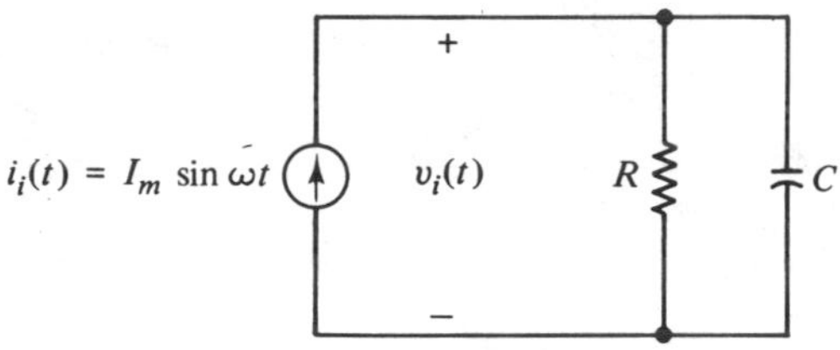

Fig. 8-39

Solution. In order to determine the phase difference between the input current and the input voltage, we calculate the phasor voltage across the input in terms of the phasor current.

$$\mathbf{V}_i = \mathbf{I}_i Z_i(j\omega) = \mathbf{I}_i\left[\frac{R(1/j\omega C)}{R + (1/j\omega C)}\right] = \mathbf{I}_i\left(\frac{R}{j\omega RC + 1}\right)$$

$$\mathbf{V}_i = \mathbf{I}_i \frac{R}{\sqrt{1 + (\omega RC)^2}} \angle -\tan^{-1} \omega RC \tag{8.51}$$

From Eq. (8-51) we see that the phase of the voltage is the phase of the current plus $(-\tan^{-1} \omega RC)$. Thus the magnitude of the phase difference is $\tan^{-1} \omega RC$. To find the cosine of this angle, we refer to Fig. 8-40.

$$\text{PF} = \cos\theta = \frac{1}{\sqrt{1 + (\omega RC)^2}}$$

From Eq. (8-51) we see that the maximum value of the input voltage is

$$V_m = I_m \frac{R}{\sqrt{1 + (\omega RC)^2}}$$

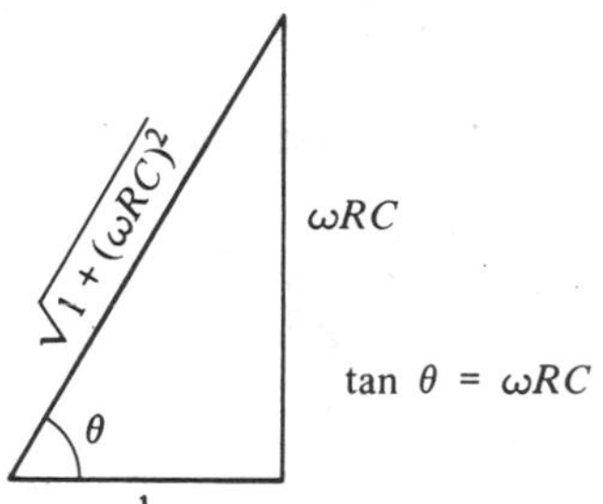

Fig. 8-40

Hence the average power is

$$p_{av} = \frac{1}{2}V_m I_m \text{ PF} = \frac{1}{2}I_m^2 \frac{R}{\sqrt{1+(\omega RC)^2}}\frac{1}{\sqrt{1+(\omega RC)^2}}$$

$$= \frac{1}{2}I_m^2\left[\frac{R}{1+(\omega RC)^2}\right], = \frac{1}{2}\frac{V_m^2}{R} \quad \text{Ans.}$$

Note that

$$p_{av} = \begin{cases} \frac{1}{2}I_m^2 R, & C = 0 \quad \text{(resistive circuit: PF = 1)} \\ 0, & R = \infty \quad \text{(capacitive circuit: PF = 0)} \end{cases}$$

Example 8-18

A load with lagging power factor of $1/\sqrt{2}$ draws 11.5 kW of power when connected across the 115 $\sqrt{2}$ V peak, 60 Hz line.

(a) What is the line current? Assume that the input voltage has zero phase.

(b) A 3260 μF capacitor is connected across the load to improve the overall power factor (make it higher). What is the resulting line current? Compare it to (a).

(c) What size capacitor will bring the overall PF to unity? What is the resulting line current?

Solution.

(a) Since we know p_{av}, V_m, and PF, we can calculate I_m from

$$p_{av} = \frac{1}{2}V_m I_m \text{ PF}$$

$$I_m = \frac{2p_{av}}{V_m \text{ PF}} = \frac{2 \times 11.5 \times 10^3}{115\sqrt{2} \times 1/\sqrt{2}} = 200 \text{ A}$$

Since the PF of the load is

$$\text{PF} = \cos\theta_L = \frac{1}{\sqrt{2}} \quad \text{(lagging)}$$

we know that the phase of the load current relative to the line voltage is

$$\theta_L = -\frac{\pi}{4}$$

Therefore the load current is given by

$$\mathbf{I}_L = 200\angle -\frac{\pi}{4} \qquad \text{Ans.}$$

(b) When the capacitor is connected across the load, we have the situation illustrated in Fig. 8-41. The capacitor current is given by

$$\mathbf{I}_C = \mathbf{V}_l j\omega C = 115\sqrt{2} \times 2\pi \times 60 \times 3260 \times 10^{-6}\angle\frac{\pi}{2} = 200\angle\frac{\pi}{2}$$

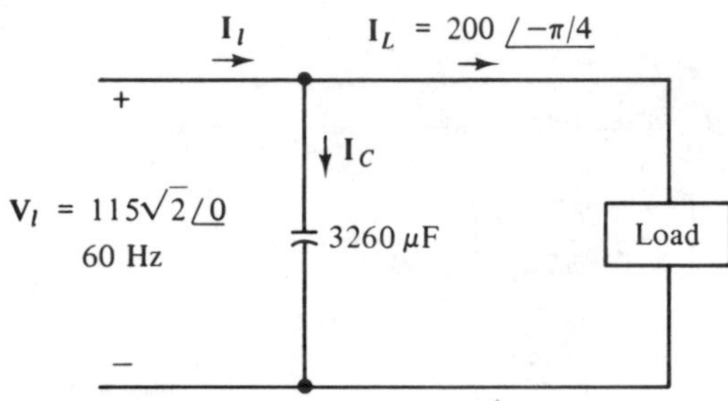

Fig. 8-41

So the line current is

$$\mathbf{I}_l = \mathbf{I}_C + \mathbf{I}_L = 200\angle\frac{\pi}{2} + 200\angle -\frac{\pi}{4}$$

$$= 200\left(\angle\frac{\pi}{2} + \angle -\frac{\pi}{4}\right) = 200(e^{j\pi/2} + e^{-j\pi/4})$$

$$= 200\left[\left(\cos\frac{\pi}{2} + j\sin\frac{\pi}{2}\right) + \left(\cos\left(-\frac{\pi}{4}\right) + j\sin\left(-\frac{\pi}{4}\right)\right)\right]$$

$$= 200\left[(j) + \left(\frac{1}{\sqrt{2}} - j\frac{1}{\sqrt{2}}\right)\right] = 200\left[\frac{1}{\sqrt{2}} + j\left(\frac{\sqrt{2}-1}{\sqrt{2}}\right)\right]$$

$$= 200\sqrt{\frac{1}{2} + \frac{(\sqrt{2}-1)^2}{2}}\angle\tan^{-1}(\sqrt{2}-1)$$

$$= 200\sqrt{2-\sqrt{2}}\angle\tan^{-1} 0.4142 = 153\angle\frac{\pi}{8}$$

Thus the addition of the capacitor changes the line current from

$$200\angle -\frac{\pi}{4} \quad \left(\text{PF} = \cos\frac{\pi}{4} = 0.707 \text{ lagging}\right)$$

to

$$153\angle\frac{\pi}{8} \quad \left(\text{PF} = \cos\frac{\pi}{8} = 0.924 \text{ leading}\right) \qquad \text{Ans.}$$

We see that there is considerable reduction in line current (from 200 to 153), while the same amount of power (11.5 kW) is still supplied to the load.

(c) The load draws lagging current (relative to line voltage), and the capacitor draws leading current. In (b) the combination draws leading current, which indicates that we have improved the power factor more than necessary. Therefore we can use a *smaller* capacitor and bring the overall power factor to unity, thereby acquiring 11.5 kW of power from the line at minimum line current.

We obtain the correct size of the capacitor by calculating the line current and making its phase 0° (so that it is in phase with the input voltage). From Fig. 8-41 we have

$$\mathbf{I}_l = \mathbf{I}_C + \mathbf{I}_L = 115\sqrt{2}\, j\omega C + 200 \angle -\frac{\pi}{4}$$

$$= 115\sqrt{2}\, j2\pi \times 60C + 200\left[\cos\left(-\frac{\pi}{4}\right) + j\sin\left(-\frac{\pi}{4}\right)\right]$$

$$= j13{,}800\pi\sqrt{2}C + 200\left(\frac{1}{\sqrt{2}} - j\frac{1}{\sqrt{2}}\right)$$

$$= 100\sqrt{2} + j\sqrt{2}(13{,}800\pi C - 100)$$

To make the phase of the line current 0, we set the imaginary part to zero and solve for C.

$$13{,}800\pi C - 100 = 0$$

$$C = \frac{1}{138\pi}\text{F} = 2300\ \mu\text{F} \quad \text{Ans.}$$

The resulting line current is

$$I_l = 100\sqrt{2} = 141.42 \quad \text{Ans.}$$

This current represents the smallest line current at which 11.5 kW of power can be supplied to the load.

8-9 POWER IN TERMS OF *R*(ω) AND *G*(ω)

When the terminal variables are sinusoidal, the average power delivered to a linear, two-terminal network is

$$p_{av} = \tfrac{1}{2}V_m I_m \cos\theta \tag{8-52}$$

where V_m = peak value of voltage
I_m = peak value of current
θ = phase difference between voltage and current

If there are no sources within the network, the terminal variables are related by

$$\mathbf{V} = \mathbf{I}Z(j\omega) \tag{8-53}$$

where $Z(j\omega)$ is the input impedance of the network. See Fig. 8-42(a). Since $Z(j\omega)$ is complex, it can be represented as a point in the complex plane as shown in Fig. 8-42(b). This point can be expressed in polar or rectangular form as

$$Z(j\omega) = |Z(j\omega)|\underline{/\theta_Z(\omega)} \tag{8-54}$$

$$Z(j\omega) = R(\omega) + jX(\omega) \tag{8-55}$$

where $|Z(j\omega)|$ = magnitude of $Z(j\omega)$
$\theta_Z(\omega)$ = angle of $Z(j\omega)$
$R(\omega)$ = real (resistive) part of $Z(j\omega)$
$X(\omega)$ = imaginary (reactive) part of $Z(j\omega)$

From Fig. 8-42(b) we see that

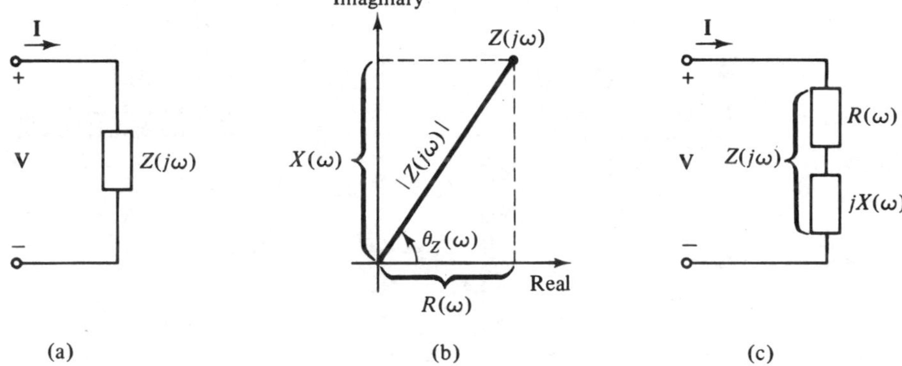

Fig. 8-42

$$R(\omega) = |Z(j\omega)| \cos \theta_Z \tag{8-56}$$

$$X(\omega) = |Z(j\omega)| \sin \theta_Z \tag{8-57}$$

$$|Z(j\omega)|^2 = R^2(\omega) + X^2(\omega) \tag{8-58}$$

$$\theta_Z = \tan^{-1} \frac{X(\omega)}{R(\omega)} \tag{8-59}$$

As the input frequency is varied, the position of $Z(j\omega)$ in the complex plane changes. Consequently, the magnitude, angle, real part, and imaginary part of $Z(j\omega)$ assume new values.

Using the polar form, Eq. (8-53) can be rewritten to show the magnitude and angle relationship between the input voltage and current. The ω dependence of Z, being understood, is henceforth left out.

$$\underbrace{V_m\angle\theta_V}_{\mathbf{V}} = \underbrace{(I_m\angle\theta_I)}_{\mathbf{I}}\underbrace{(|Z|\angle\theta_Z)}_{\mathbf{Z}} \tag{8-60}$$

$$V_m\angle\theta_V = I_m|Z|\angle\theta_I + \theta_Z$$

Equating magnitude and angles, we obtain

$$V_m = I_m|Z| \tag{8-61}$$

$$\theta_V = \theta_I + \theta_Z$$

or

$$\theta_V - \theta_I = \theta_Z = \theta \tag{8-62}$$

Using Eqs. (8-61) and (8-62), we can express the average power, given by Eq. (8-52), in terms of the input impedance.

$$p_{av} = \tfrac{1}{2}V_m I_m \cos\theta = \tfrac{1}{2}I_m^2|Z|\cos\theta_Z \tag{8-63}$$

Since $|Z|\cos\theta_Z = R(\omega)$, Eq. (8-63) simplifies to

$$p_{av} = \tfrac{1}{2}I_m^2 R(\omega) \tag{8-64}$$

Thus the real part of the impedance, $R(\omega)$, determines the power absorbed by the impedance. The imaginary part of the impedance, $X(\omega)$, does not absorb any power. These important results can also be easily obtained from Fig. 8-42(c), where $Z(j\omega) = R(\omega) + jX(\omega)$ is represented as the series combination of $R(\omega)$ with $jX(\omega)$. The power supplied to $Z(j\omega)$ must be used up by the components within the network. So the sum of powers delivered to $R(\omega)$ and $jX(\omega)$ must equal p_{av}.

$$p_{av} = p_R + p_X$$

$$p_{av} = \tfrac{1}{2}V_{mR}I_m\cos\theta_R + \tfrac{1}{2}V_{mX}I_m\cos\theta_X \tag{8-65}$$

Since $R(\omega)$ is real, $\theta_R = 0$. Since $jX(\omega)$ is purely imaginary, $\theta_X = 90°$. As a result, Eq. (8-65) simplifies to

$$p_{av} = \tfrac{1}{2}V_{mR}I_m = \tfrac{1}{2}[I_m R(\omega)]I_m = \tfrac{1}{2}I_m^2 R(\omega)$$

In this development we used the input impedance to relate the input current to the input voltage. We could just as well have used the input admittance, as shown in Fig. 8-43(a).

$$Y(j\omega) = |Y(j\omega)|\angle\theta_Y(\omega) = G(j\omega) + jB(\omega)$$

where $|Y(j\omega)|$ = magnitude of $Y(j\omega)$
$\theta_Y(\omega)$ = angle of $Y(j\omega)$
$G(\omega)$ = real part of $Y(j\omega)$
$B(\omega)$ = imaginary part of $Y(j\omega)$

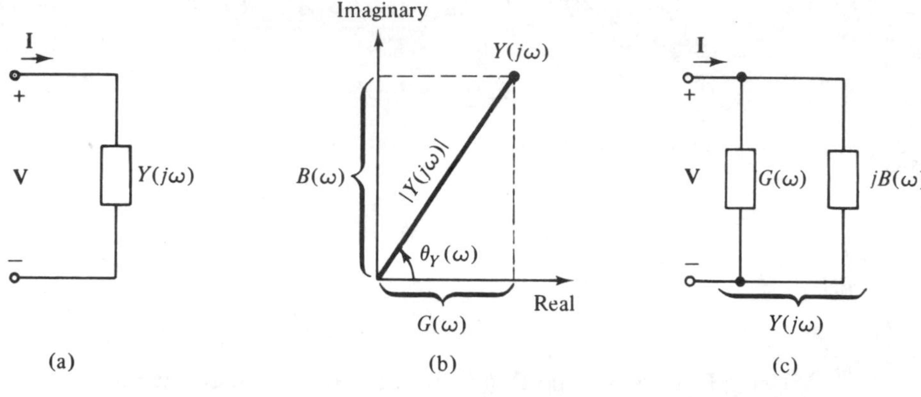

Fig. 8-43

The relationship among the various variables is shown in Fig. 8-43(b). The equivalent representation of $Y(j\omega)$ as the parallel connection of $G(\omega)$ with $jB(\omega)$ is shown in Fig. 8-43(c).

It is left as a problem at the end of the chapter to show that the average power delivered to $Y(j\omega)$ can be expressed as

$$p_{av} = \tfrac{1}{2}V_m^2|Y| \cos \theta_Y = \tfrac{1}{2}V_m^2 G(\omega) \tag{8-66}$$

We can use either Eq. (8-64) or Eq. (8-66) to calculate the average power delivered to an RLC network. The equation involving $R(\omega)$ is simpler to use if the elements within the network are connected in series. On the other hand, the equation involving $G(\omega)$ is simpler to use if the elements are connected in parallel.

If there are sinusoidal sources within the network, the input variables are no longer related by the input impedance or admittance. In this case, in order to calculate the average input power, we must resort to the general formulation given by Eq. (8-52).

Example 8-19

In Fig. 8-44, obtain

(a) $Z(j\omega)$, $|Z(j\omega)|$, $\theta_Z(\omega)$, $R(\omega)$, and $X(\omega)$.

(b) the average power delivered to the R_1R_2L network.

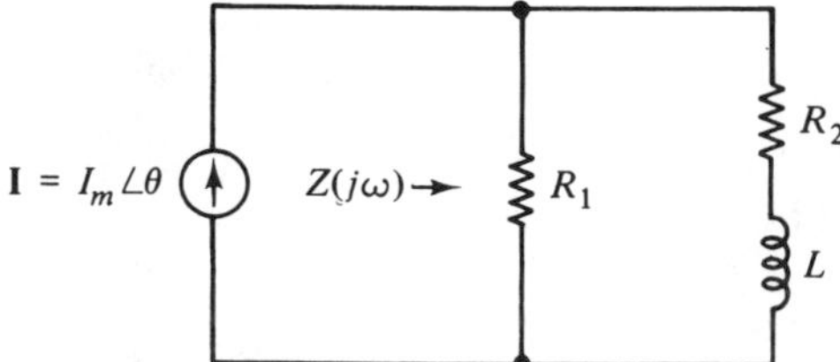

Fig. 8-44

Solution.

(a) To obtain $|Z(j\omega)|$ and $\theta_Z(\omega)$, we put the numerator and denominator of $Z(j\omega)$ in polar form.

$$Z(j\omega) = \frac{R_1\sqrt{R_2^2 + \omega^2L^2} \angle \tan^{-1}\dfrac{\omega L}{R_2}}{\sqrt{(R_1 + R_2)^2 + \omega^2L^2} \angle \tan^{-1}\dfrac{\omega L}{R_1 + R_2}}$$

$$= \frac{R_1\sqrt{R_2^2 + \omega^2L^2}}{\sqrt{(R_1 + R_2)^2 + \omega^2L^2}} \angle \tan^{-1}\frac{\omega L}{R_2} - \tan^{-1}\frac{\omega L}{R_1 + R_2}$$

$$\left.\begin{aligned} |Z(j\omega)| &= \frac{R_1\sqrt{R_2^2 + \omega^2L^2}}{\sqrt{(R_1 + R_2)^2 + \omega^2L^2}} \\ \theta_Z(\omega) &= \tan^{-1}\frac{\omega L}{R_2} - \tan^{-1}\frac{\omega L}{R_1 + R_2} \end{aligned}\right\} \text{Ans.}$$

To obtain $R(\omega)$ and $X(\omega)$, we put $Z(j\omega)$ in real and imaginary parts form: $R(\omega) + jX(\omega)$. We do so by multiplying the numerator and denominator of $Z(j\omega)$ with the complex conjugate of the denominator.

$$Z(j\omega) = \frac{R_1(R_2 + j\omega L)}{(R_1 + R_2) + j\omega L} \times \frac{(R_1 + R_2) - j\omega L}{(R_1 + R_2) - j\omega L}$$

$$= \frac{R_1[R_2(R_1 + R_2) + \omega^2L^2 + j\omega LR_1]}{(R_1 + R_2)^2 + \omega^2L^2}$$

$$R(\omega) = \frac{R_1[R_2(R_1 + R_2) + \omega^2L^2]}{(R_1 + R_2)^2 + \omega^2L^2}, \qquad X(\omega) = \frac{\omega LR_1^2}{(R_1 + R_2)^2 + \omega^2L^2} \quad \text{Ans.}$$

(b) The average power delivered to the R_1R_2L network is

$$p_{\text{av}} = \frac{1}{2}I_m^2R(\omega) = \frac{1}{2}I_m^2\frac{R_1[R_2(R_1 + R_2) + \omega^2L^2]}{(R_1 + R_2)^2 + \omega^2L^2} \quad \text{Ans.}$$

8-10 MAXIMUM POWER TRANSFER

A nonideal voltage source delivering power to a load is shown in Fig. 8-45(a). We can represent the source impedance in terms of its real and imaginary parts as

$$Z_s(j\omega) - R_s(\omega) + jX_s(\omega)$$

Similarly, the load impedance can be represented by

$$Z_L(j\omega) = R_L(\omega) + jX_L(\omega)$$

Using these equivalent representations for the source and load impedances, Fig. 8-45(a) can be redrawn as in part (b). As is the case with most sources, the source

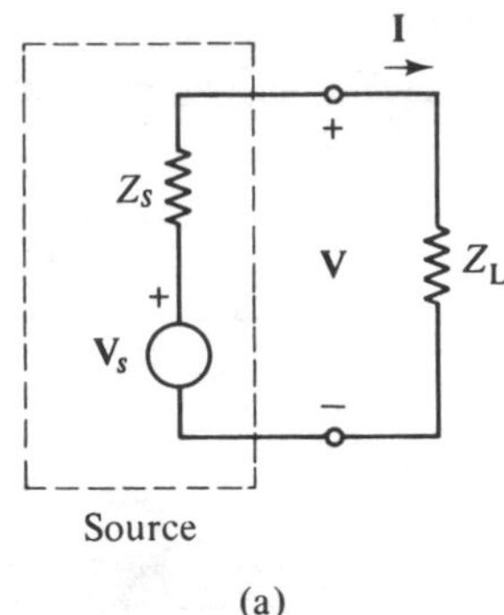

(a)

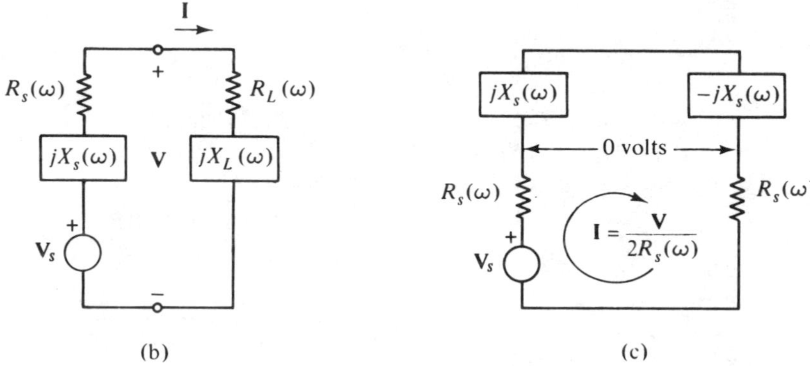

(b) (c)

Fig. 8-45

impedance cannot be adjusted. We now ask: What is the maximum power that this source is capable of delivering, and under what condition does this occur?

Stated differently, for *fixed* $\mathbf{V}_s$ and Z_s, what Z_L would receive the most power from the source, assuming that the real and imaginary parts of $Z_L(j\omega)$ *can be independently adjusted*?

To answer, we refer to Fig. 8-45(b) and calculate the average power delivered to the load Z_L as follows.

$$p_{av} = \frac{1}{2} I_m^2 R_L(\omega)$$

$$\mathbf{I} = \frac{\mathbf{V}}{R_s(\omega) + jX_s(\omega) + R_L(\omega) + jX_L(\omega)} = \frac{\mathbf{V}}{[R_s(\omega) + R_L(\omega)] + j[X_s(\omega) + X_L(\omega)]}$$

$$I_m = \frac{V_m}{\sqrt{[R_s(\omega) + R_L(\omega)]^2 + [X_s(\omega) + X_L(\omega)]^2}}$$

$$p_{av} = \frac{1}{2} \frac{V_m^2 R_L(\omega)}{[R_s(\omega) + R_L(\omega)]^2 + [X_s(\omega) + X_L(\omega)]^2} \tag{8-67}$$

As for adjusting the imaginary part $X_L(\omega)$ of the load, we see by inspection of Eq. (8-67) that p_{av} attains its maximum value when

$$X_L(\omega) = -X_s(\omega) \tag{8-68}$$

which results in

$$p_{av} = \frac{1}{2}V_m^2 \frac{R_L(\omega)}{[R_s(\omega) + R_L(\omega)]^2} \tag{8-69}$$

As Section 3-8 shows, this p_{av} can be further maximized by making

$$R_L(\omega) = R_s(\omega) \tag{8-70}$$

Thus the source delivers to the load the maximum power of

$$(p_{av})_{max} = \frac{1}{8}\frac{V_m^2}{R_s(\omega)} \tag{8-71}$$

when the load impedance is adjusted to the complex conjugate of the source impedance; that is,

$$Z_L(j\omega) = R_s(\omega) - jX_s(\omega) \tag{8-72}$$

When this condition is satisfied, we say that the load is matched to the source. Since $R_s(\omega) = R_L(\omega)$, as much power is lost in the source impedance as is delivered to the load.

When the load is matched to the source, the current in the circuit [see Fig. 8-45(b)] is given by

$$\mathbf{I} = \frac{\mathbf{V}}{R_s(\omega) + R_L(\omega) + j[X_s(\omega) + X_L(\omega)]}\Bigg|_{\substack{R_L(\omega)=R_s(\omega)\\ X_L(\omega)=-X_s(\omega)}} = \frac{\mathbf{V}}{2R_s(\omega)}$$

which shows that the source $\mathbf{V}$ sees an impedance of $2R_s(\omega)$. The imaginary components of the load and source impedances cancel each other out. As a result, if we redraw Fig. 8-45(b) as in part (c), we see that the voltage across the imaginary components of the network is zero (even though the voltage across the individual imaginary components is not zero).

If the load impedance had been fixed and if we had the liberty of adjusting the source impedance, then, as shown by Eq. (8-67), the load would have received maximum power if $X_s(\omega) = -X_L(\omega)$. The resulting power would have been

$$p_{av} = \frac{1}{2}\frac{V_m^2 R_L(\omega)}{[R_s(\omega) + R_L(\omega)]^2}$$

As this equation shows, the smaller $R_s(\omega)$ is made, the more power the load receives. Indeed, the load would receive the most power if we could make $R_s(\omega) = 0$.

Example 8-20

A voltage source has an internal impedance of $R + j\omega L$.

(a) To obtain the maximum power out of this source, what load impedance must be connected across the source?

(b) What is the maximum power that can be delivered by this source?

Solution.

(a) The source delivers maximum power when it sees a load impedance that is the complex conjugate of its source impedance. So

$$Z_L(j\omega) = R - j\omega L$$

We can write this Z_L as

$$Z_L(j\omega) = R + \frac{\omega L}{j} = R + \frac{1}{j\omega C} \quad \text{Ans.}$$

where $\dfrac{1}{\omega C} = \omega L$
which when solved for C gives

$$C = \frac{1}{\omega^2 L}$$

The resulting network is shown in Fig. 8-46.

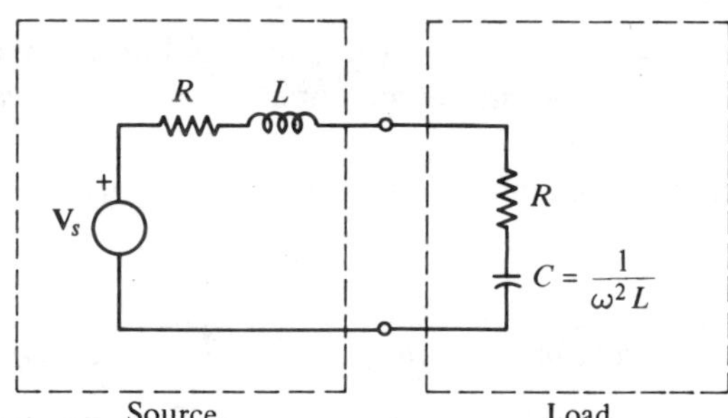

Fig. 8-46

(b) When the load is matched to the source, the source delivers maximum power. From Eq. (8-71) this power is

$$(p_{av})_{max} = \frac{1}{8}\frac{V_m^2}{R} \quad \text{Ans.}$$

Where V_m represents the peak value of $\mathbf{V}_s$.

Example 8-21

Maximum power is to be taken out of the network shown in Fig. 8-47. What load Z_L must be connected across it, and what is the power delivered to this load?

Solution. We first obtain the Thévenin equivalent of the network as seen by the load Z_L. The result is Fig. 8-48(a). If maximum power is to be drawn out of the network, Z_L must be the complex conjugate of the impedance of the RC network. Thus

$$Z_{RC}(j\omega) = \frac{R(1/j\omega C)}{R + (1/j\omega C)}$$

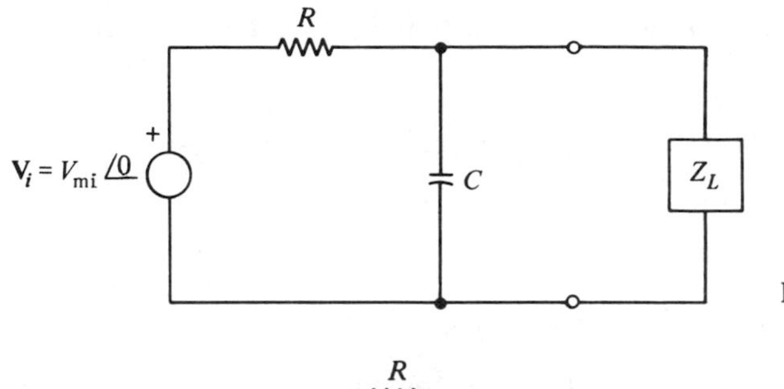

Fig. 8-47

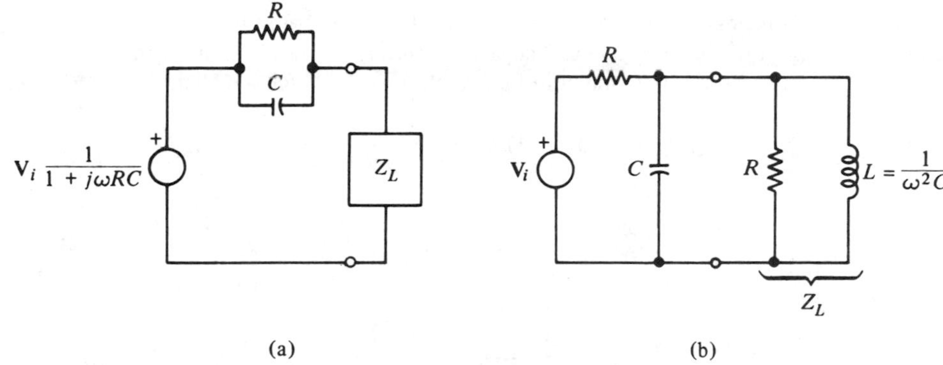

Fig. 8-48

$$\begin{aligned} Z_L(j\omega) &= Z_{RC}(j\omega)\big|_{j \text{ replaced by } -j} = Z_{RC}(-j\omega) \\ &= \frac{R(1/-j\omega C)}{R + (1/-j\omega C)} = \frac{Rj(1/\omega C)}{R + j(1/\omega C)} = \frac{Rj\omega L}{R + j\omega L} \end{aligned} \tag{8-73}$$

where

$$\omega L = \frac{1}{\omega C}, \qquad L = \frac{1}{\omega^2 C}$$

We see from Eq. (8-73) that Z_L represents the impedance of a resistor R connected in parallel with an inductor L. The resulting network is shown in Fig. 8-48(b).

In order to determine the power delivered to the load, we must calculate $R_L(\omega)$, which is the real part of the load impedance $Z_L(j\omega)$. From Eq. (8-73) we obtain

$$Z_L(j\omega) = \frac{jR}{\omega RC + j} = \frac{jR}{\omega RC + j} \times \frac{\omega RC - j}{\omega RC - j} = \underbrace{\frac{R}{1 + \omega^2 R^2 C^2}}_{R_L(\omega)} + j\underbrace{\frac{R^2 C}{1 + \omega^2 R^2 C^2}}_{X_L(\omega)}$$

$$R_L(\omega) = \frac{R}{1 + \omega^2 R^2 C^2}$$

The expression for maximum power is

$$(p_{\text{av}})_{\max} = \frac{1}{8}\frac{V_m^2}{R_L(\omega)}$$

where V_m represents the peak value of the Thévenin equivalent voltage facing Z_L—that is,

$$V_m = \text{peak value of} \left(\frac{\mathbf{V}_i}{1 + j\omega RC}\right) = \frac{V_{mi}}{\sqrt{1 + \omega^2 R^2 C^2}}$$

Then

$$(p_{\text{av}})_{\text{max}} = \frac{1}{8}\left(\frac{V_{mi}^2}{1 + \omega^2 R^2 C^2}\right)\left[\frac{1}{R/(1 + \omega^2 R^2 C^2)}\right] = \frac{1}{8}\frac{V_{mi}^2}{R} \quad \text{Ans.}$$

This answer could have been obtained directly from Fig. 8-48(b) if we realized that the sum of the inductive and capacitive currents is zero. To show this situation explicitly, Fig. 8-48(b) is redrawn in Fig. 8-49(a), from which we obtain

$$\mathbf{I}_{LC} = \mathbf{I}_C + \mathbf{I}_L = \mathbf{V}_{LC}\left(j\omega C + \frac{1}{j\omega L}\right)\bigg|_{L=1/\omega^2 C} = \mathbf{V}_{LC}(j\omega C - j\omega C) = 0$$

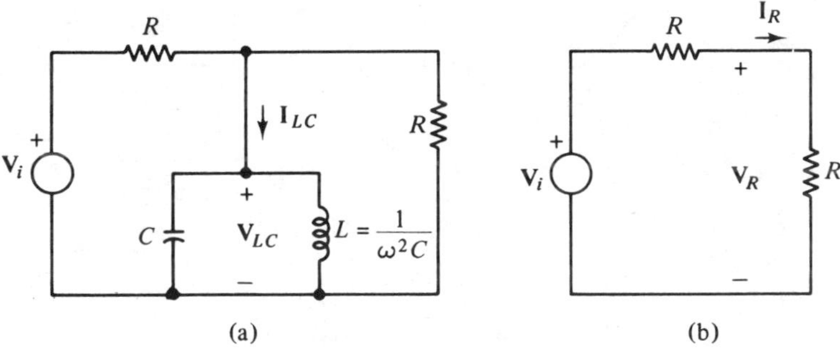

Fig. 8-49

Alternatively stated, the impedance of the LC combination is infinite. So the LC circuit can be taken out altogether and the network drawn as in Fig. 8-49(b). By inspection of this resistive network, we obtain

$$p_{av} = \frac{1}{2}V_{mR}I_{mR} = \frac{1}{2}\frac{V_{mR}^2}{R}$$

where V_{mR} and I_{mR} represent the peak values of $\mathbf{V}_R$ and $\mathbf{I}_R$. Since $\mathbf{V}_R = \mathbf{V}_i/2$, $(V_{mR} = V_{mi}/2)$, we have

$$p_{\text{av}} = \frac{1}{2}\frac{(V_{mi}/2)^2}{R} = \frac{1}{8}\frac{V_{mi}^2}{R} \quad \text{Ans.}$$

8-11 ROOT-MEAN-SQUARE VALUE

In Fig. 8-50 the attention is directed to a resistor in a circuit. As shown, the voltage across it is some arbitrary function of time. The instantaneous power delivered to the resistor is

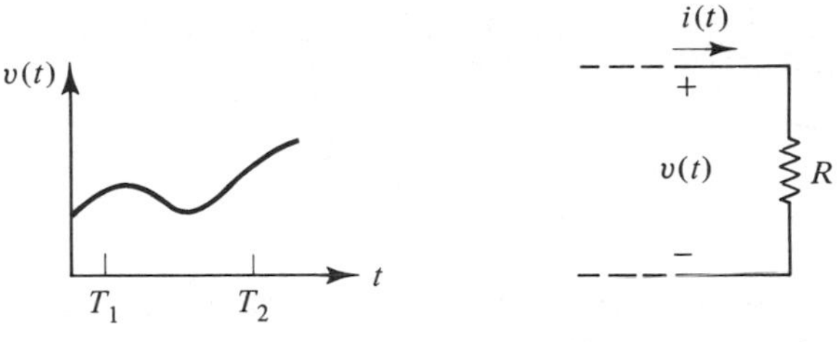

Fig. 8-50

$$p(t) = v(t)i(t) = i^2(t)R = \frac{v^2(t)}{R} \tag{8-74}$$

The average power delivered to the resistor from time T_1 to T_2 is

$$p_{av} = \frac{1}{T_2 - T_1} \int_{T_1}^{T_2} i^2(t)R \, dt \tag{8-75}$$

This result can be written as

$$p_{av} = \left[\sqrt{\frac{1}{T_2 - T_1} \int_{T_1}^{T_2} i^2(t) \, dt} \right]^2 R \tag{8-76}$$

Although this is a more complicated way to express p_{av}, it is in a form that can be interpreted. The term within the bracket is a constant and is in units of amperes. Let us call this fictitious current I_{rms}. Then the average power delivered to the resistor can be written as

$$p_{av} = I_{rms}^2 R \tag{8-77a}$$

where

$$I_{rms} = \sqrt{\frac{1}{T_2 - T_1} \int_{T_1}^{T_2} i^2(t) \, dt} \tag{8-77b}$$

Similarly, we could have started with the other form of $p(t)$, namely $v^2(t)/R$, and arrived at

$$p_{av} = \frac{V_{rms}^2}{R} \tag{8-78a}$$

where

$$V_{rms} = \sqrt{\frac{1}{T_2 - T_1} \int_{T_1}^{T_2} v^2(t) \, dt} \tag{8-78b}$$

Since I_{rms} and V_{rms} are constants, they represent dc values. Equations (8-77a) and (8-77b) tell us that the average power dissipated in a resistor due to an arbitrary current or voltage waveform can be calculated using an equivalent dc current through the resistor or an equivalent dc voltage across it. These equivalent dc values are called root-mean-square (rms) values.

Strictly from a mathematical viewpoint, the rms value of a function of time $s(t)$ is defined by

$$S_{\text{rms}} = \sqrt{\frac{1}{T_2 - T_1} \int_{T_1}^{T_2} s^2(t)\, dt} \tag{8-79}$$

In the rms designation, r stands for the *square root* ($\sqrt{\quad}$), m for the *mean value*

$$\left[\frac{1}{T_2 - T_1} \int_{T_1}^{T_2} (\;)\, dt\right]$$

and s for the *square* of the function $[s^2(t)]$. The averaging is done over a time interval of $(T_2 - T_1)$ seconds. The rms value represents the square root of the average value of the squared function.

For a sinusoidal function

$$s(t) = A \sin(\omega t + \theta)$$

we use the period $T = 2\pi/\omega$ as the averaging interval. The rms value of a sinusoid is then

$$S_{\text{rms}} = \sqrt{\frac{1}{T} \int_0^T s^2(t)\, dt} \tag{8-80}$$

$$= \sqrt{\frac{1}{T} \int_0^T A^2 \sin^2(\omega t + \theta)\, dt}$$

$$S_{\text{rms}} = A\sqrt{\frac{1}{T} \int_0^T \sin^2(\omega t + \theta)\, dt} \tag{8-81}$$

We can either perform the indicated integration or recognize that the average value of the sine-squared function is $\frac{1}{2}$. So Eq. (8-81) becomes

$$S_{\text{rms}} = \frac{A}{\sqrt{2}} \tag{8-82}$$

and we see that the *rms value* of a sine wave is equal to the *peak value* of the sine wave divided by $\sqrt{2}$.

We can now express the average power in a sinusoidally excited network in terms of rms values as follows.

$$p_{\text{av}} = \frac{1}{2} V_m I_m \cos\theta = \frac{V_m}{\sqrt{2}} \frac{I_m}{\sqrt{2}} \cos\theta = V_{\text{rms}} I_{\text{rms}} \cos\theta \tag{8-83}$$

where $V_{\text{rms}} = \dfrac{V_m}{\sqrt{2}}, \qquad I_{\text{rms}} = \dfrac{I_m}{\sqrt{2}}$

In general, a sine wave can be represented in terms of its rms value rather than the peak value.

$$s(t) = A \sin(\omega t + \theta) = \sqrt{2}A_{\text{rms}} \sin(\omega t + \theta)$$

Indeed, instead of using peak values to designate phasors ($A\angle\theta$), we can just as easily use rms values ($A_{\text{rms}}\angle\theta$); then *all voltages and currents* are expressed in terms of their rms values. Throughout the power industry *all calculations and measurements are done by using rms values;* peak values are not even mentioned. For instance, power is supplied to our homes at 115 V. This voltage represents the rms value of the sine wave voltage, although not specifically designated as such. Of course, we can always multiply it by $\sqrt{2}$ to find its peak value: $115\sqrt{2} = 163$ V.

Under sinusoidal excitation voltage and current in a resistor are in phase—that is, $\mathbf{V} = \mathbf{I}R$. So the power factor is unity. We can, therefore, write

$$V_{\text{rms}} = I_{\text{rms}}R$$

$$p_{\text{av}} = V_{\text{rms}}I_{\text{rms}}\,\text{PF} = V_{\text{rms}}I_{\text{rms}} = \frac{V_{\text{rms}}^2}{R} = I_{\text{rms}}^2R \tag{8-84}$$

Under dc excitation, for a resistor, we have

$$V_{\text{dc}} = I_{\text{dc}}R$$

$$p_{\text{av}} = V_{\text{dc}}I_{\text{dc}} = \frac{V_{\text{dc}}^2}{R} = I_{\text{dc}}^2R \tag{8-85}$$

where V_{dc} and I_{dc} represent dc values. By comparing Eq. (8-84) with (8-85), we see that a sinusoidally excited resistor receives as much power as a dc excited resistor if

$$V_{\text{rms}} = V_{\text{dc}} \qquad \text{or} \qquad I_{\text{rms}} = I_{\text{dc}} \tag{8-86}$$

Stated differently, the same power is dissipated in a resistor if the voltage across it is 1 V rms or 1 V dc. Similarly, 1 A rms or 1 A dc current dissipates the same amount of power in the resistor. For this reason, rms values are also called *effective* values. As far as power dissipation is concerned, there is no difference between effective and dc values. This statement is graphically illustrated in Fig. 8-51, using the current in the resistor as a basis for comparison. The relationship is equally valid for voltage.

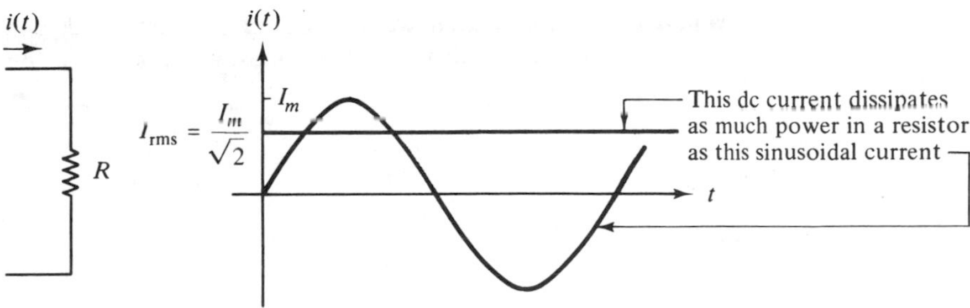

Fig. 8-51

Example 8-22

The periodic current waveform shown in Fig. 8-52 is applied to a resistor.

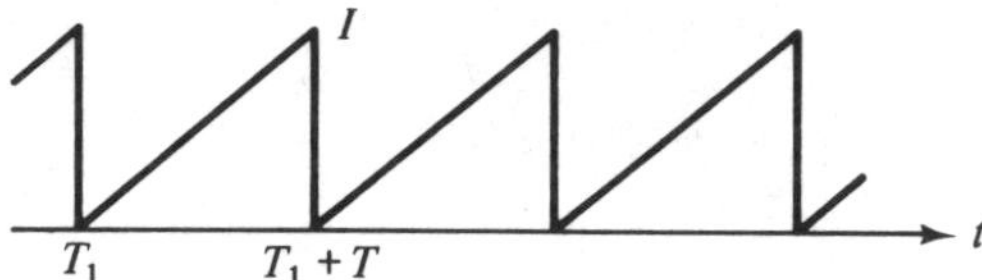

Fig. 8-52

(a) What dc current would produce the same amount of average power dissipation in the resistor?

(b) What sinusoidal current would produce the same amount of average power dissipation in the resistor?

Solution

(a) The instantaneous power dissipated in the resistor is

$$p(t) = v(t)i(t) = i^2(t)R$$

From Fig. 8-52 we have

$$i(t) = \frac{I}{T}(t - T_1) \qquad T_1 < t < T_1 + T$$

Without loss of generality, we can take T_1 as zero and obtain

$$p(t) = \left(\frac{I}{T}t\right)^2 R = \frac{I^2R}{T^2}t^2$$

To find the average power, we integrate over the period T and divide by T.

$$p_{av} = \frac{1}{T}\int_0^T p(t)\,dt = \frac{I^2R}{T^3}\int_0^T t^2\,dt$$

$$p_{av} = \frac{I^2R}{T^3}\frac{t^3}{3}\bigg|_0^T = \frac{I^2R}{3} \tag{8-87}$$

The power dissipated by a dc current I_{dc} in the same resistor would be

$$p_{av} = I_{dc}^2 R \tag{8-88}$$

If the same amount of average power is to be dissipated by the dc current as by the sawtooth current waveform, then Eq. (8-87) must agree with Eq. (8-88). Hence

$$\frac{I^2R}{3} = I_{dc}^2 R$$

which results in

$$I_{dc} = \frac{\text{I}}{\sqrt{3}} \quad \text{Ans.}$$

(b) A sinusoidal current with an rms value equal to the dc current value obtained in (a) would produce the same amount of average power dissipation in the resistor. Thus

$$I_{\text{rms}} = I_{\text{dc}} = \frac{I}{\sqrt{3}} \quad \text{Ans.}$$

The three current waveforms that dissipate the same average power in the resistor are sketched in Fig. 8-53. Note that the frequency of the sine wave is independent of the frequency of the sawtooth wave. Effective values do not depend on frequency.

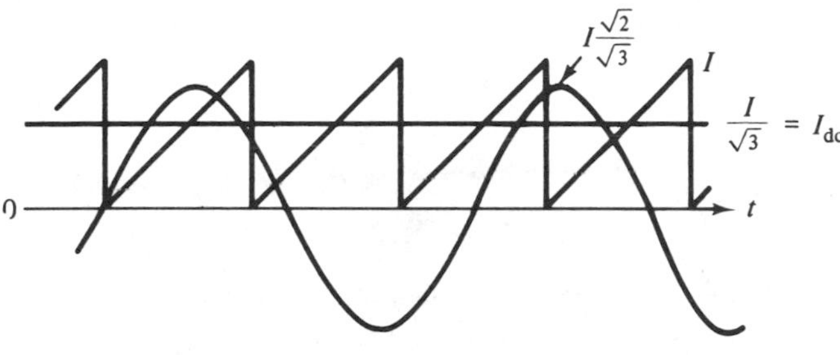

Fig. 8-53

8-12 SUMMARY

When a sine wave excites an *RLC* network, it produces a response that has two distinct parts. One part is due to the poles of the *RLC* network. Because these poles have negative real parts, this part of the response eventually vanishes. The other part is due to the poles of excitation, and so it is a sine wave. This sine wave differs from the input sine wave in both amplitude and phase. The transfer function $T(j\omega)$ accounts for the differences. The magnitude of the transfer function, $|T(j\omega)|$, multiplies the input amplitude to produce the output amplitude. The phase of the transfer function, $\theta_T(\omega)$, adds onto the phase of the input to produce the output phase. Thus if A and θ are the input amplitude and phase, then the output amplitude and phase are $A|T(j\omega)|$ and $[\theta + \theta_T(\omega)]$. When dealing with input functions, the input impedance $Z(j\omega)$ or the input admittance $Y(j\omega)$ is used instead of $T(j\omega)$ to determine the amplitude and phase of the input voltage or input current.

Phasors carry magnitude and phase information that is associated with sine waves. A voltage phasor is designated by the symbol **V** and a current phasor by the symbol **I**. If we are interested in the sinusoidal steady-state response, we can use phasors to manipulate complex numbers and obtain the output voltage or current. Thus if the output phasor is **X** (which can represent either current or voltage), then the corresponding time-domain response is $x(t) = |X| \sin (\omega t + \theta_x)$ or $|X| \cos (\omega t + \theta_x)$, where $|X|$ = magnitude of **X** and θ_x is the angle of **X**. If the input function used is a sine wave, the output is expressed in the sinusoidal format. If the input is given as a cosine wave, the output is expressed in the cosinusoidal format.

The average, steady-state, sinusoidal power delivered to an *RLC* network is $\frac{1}{2}V_m I_m$ PF $= V_{\text{rms}} I_{\text{rms}}$ PF, where the subscript m stands for the peak value and rms stands for the rms value (peak value $= \sqrt{2}$ rms value). The power factor PF is equal to cos θ, where θ represents the phase difference between the current and voltage phasors, determined at the terminals where power is calculated. A leading PF means that the current leads the voltage. A lagging PF means that the current lags the voltage.

Maximum power is delivered by a source with fixed internal impedance when the load impedance is matched to the source impedance. So if the source impedance is $R_s + jX_s$, then the load receives the maximum power available from the source if the load impedance is $Z_L = R_s - jX_s$.

PROBLEMS

8-1. Given $4 \sin (\pi/2)(t - 3)$. Obtain the period and phase of the sine wave.

8-2. The input to a circuit is $A \sin (\omega t + \theta)$. The resulting output is $Be^{-\alpha t} \sin (\beta t + \phi) + Ce^{-\gamma t} + D \sin \delta t + E \cos (\omega t + \phi) + F$. What is the forced part of the output?

8-3. The input in Fig. 8-54 is applied at $t = 0$.

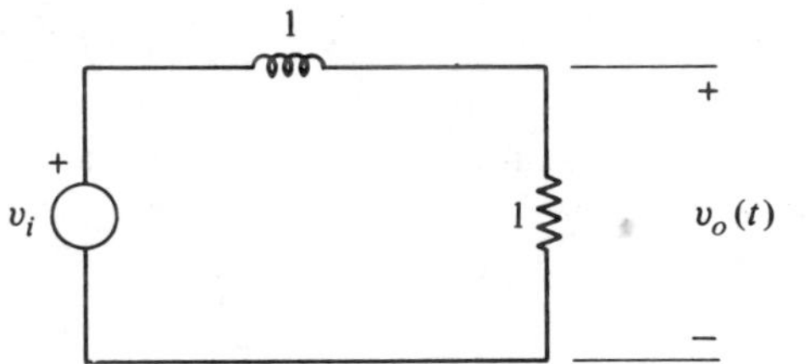

Fig. 8-54

(a) Obtain the response if $v_i = V_m \sin \omega t$.
(b) Obtain the response if $v_i = V_m \cos \omega t$.
(c) The input is $v_i = V_m \sin (\omega t + \theta)$. Show that the response does not have any natural component if θ is chosen appropriately—that is, the input is applied at a precise point on the sine wave. What is the resulting response?

8-4. In Fig. 8-55, obtain the response.

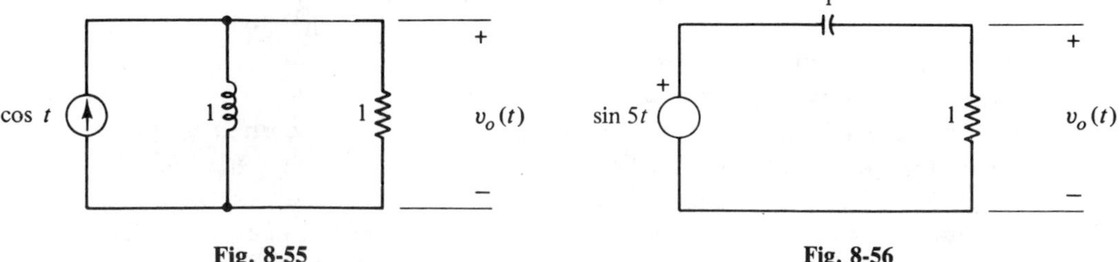

Fig. 8-55

Fig. 8-56

8-5. Calculate $v_o(t)$ in Fig. 8-56.

8-6. For what value of C does the current response in Fig. 8-57 contain no natural component?

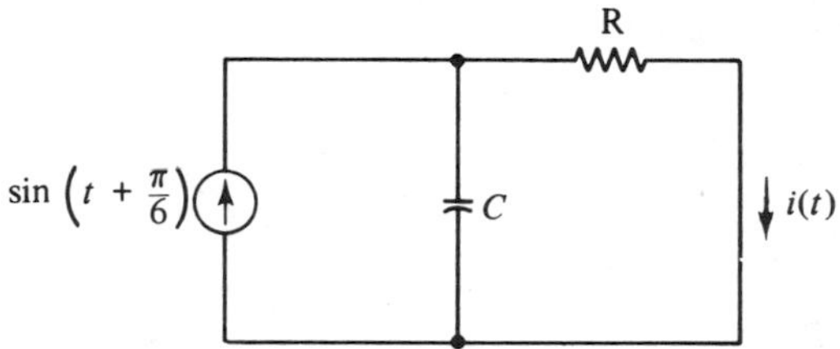

Fig. 8-57

8-7. For what value of ω is the forced response in Fig. 8-58 zero?

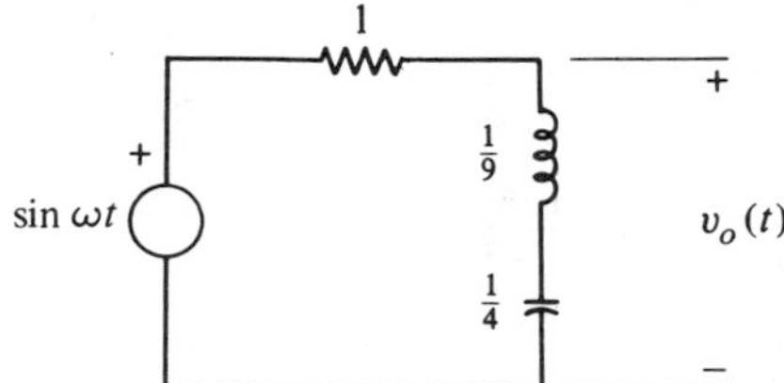

Fig. 8-58

8-8. What value of K in Fig. 8-59 makes the natural response zero?

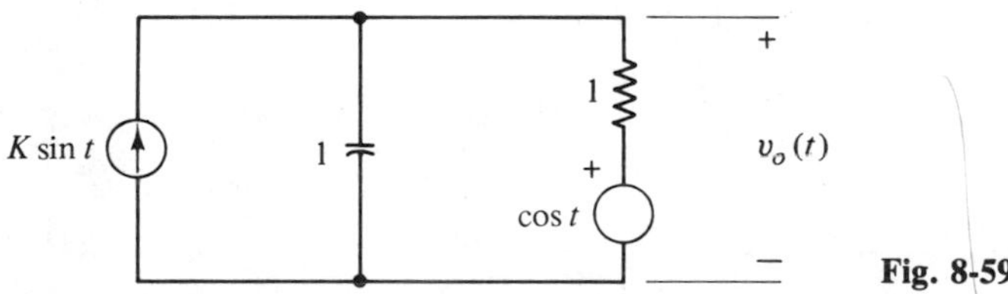

Fig. 8-59

8-9. When θ is chosen appropriately in Fig. 8-60, the natural part of the response can be made zero. Find θ and the resulting response.

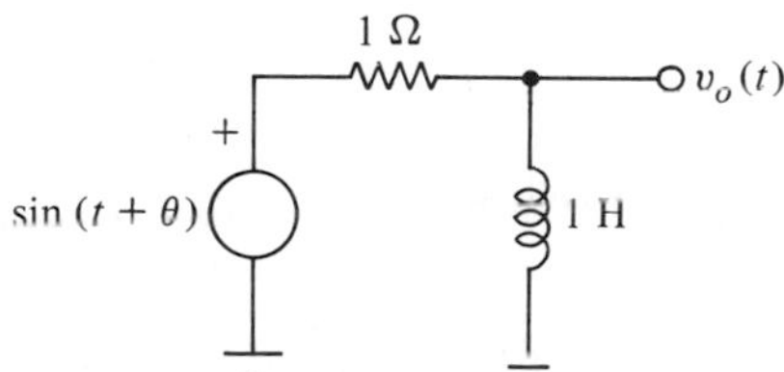

Fig. 8-60

8-10. In Fig. 8-61 the sine wave is applied at $t = 0$. Obtain the expressions for the natural and forced components of $v_o(t)$.

8-11. Sketch the following functions.

(a) $r(t) = \sin t + e^{-0.2t} \sin 10t$

(b) $r(t) = e^{-0.2t} \sin t + \sin 10t$

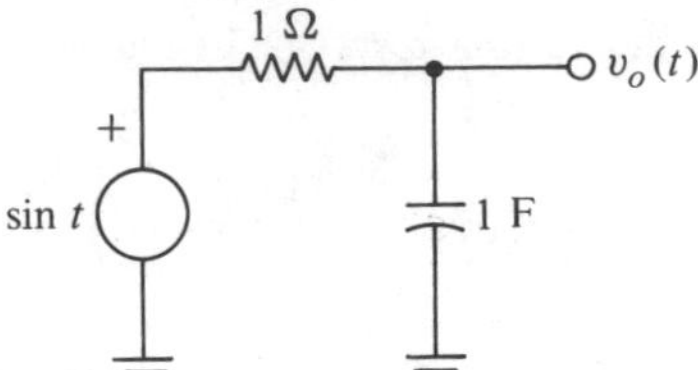

Fig. 8-61

8-12. Refer to Fig. 8-62.

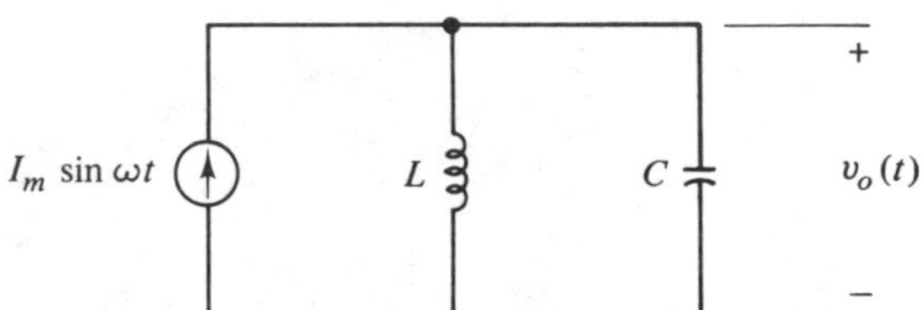

Fig. 8-62

(**a**) Obtain the response.
(**b**) Evaluate the response for $\omega = 1/\sqrt{LC}$.

8-13. For the networks shown in Fig. 8-63, determine how long it will take before the natural response vanishes.

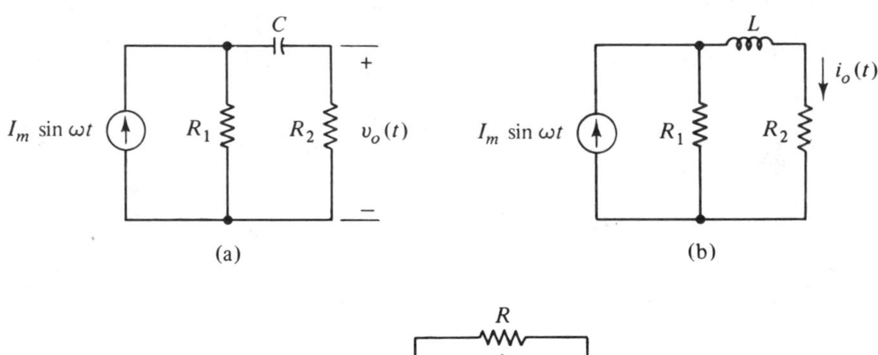

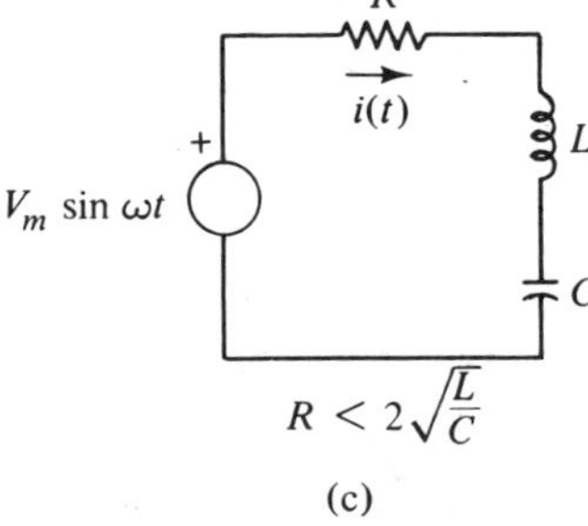

Fig. 8-63

8-14. Evaluate Eq. (8-10) for $t = 0$. Check this answer against the answer obtained by inspection of Fig. 8-5.

8-15. In the circuits shown in Fig. 8-64 the output does not contain any sine wave. What is the frequency?

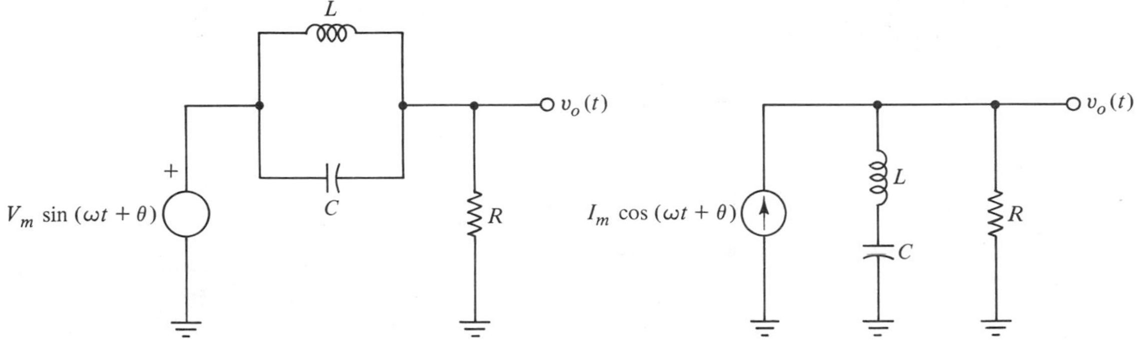

Fig. 8-64

8-16. Refer to Fig. 8-65.

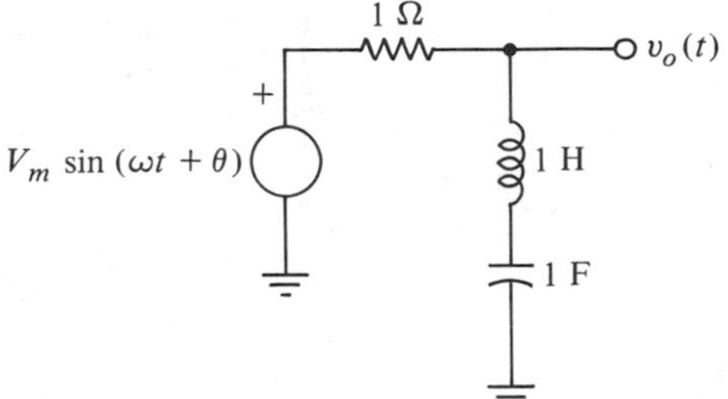

Fig. 8-65

(**a**) What is the transfer function? Present the answer in the form of the ratio of two polynomials arranged in descending powers of s.

(**b**) For what value of ω is the forced component of $v_o(t)$ zero?

8-17. For the circuits shown in Fig. 8-66, calculate the steady-state response of the variables indicated by a question mark.

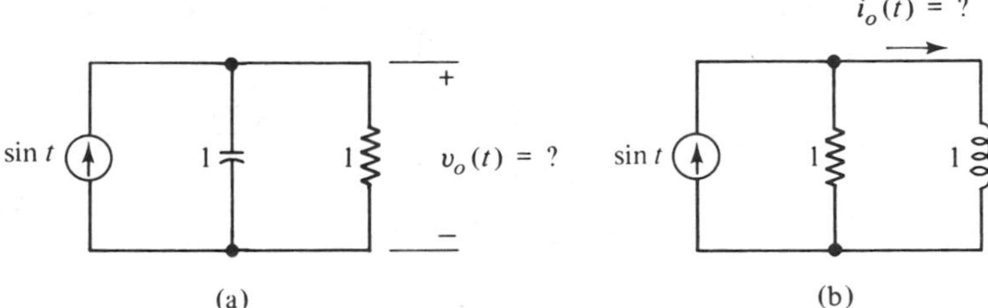

Fig. 8-66

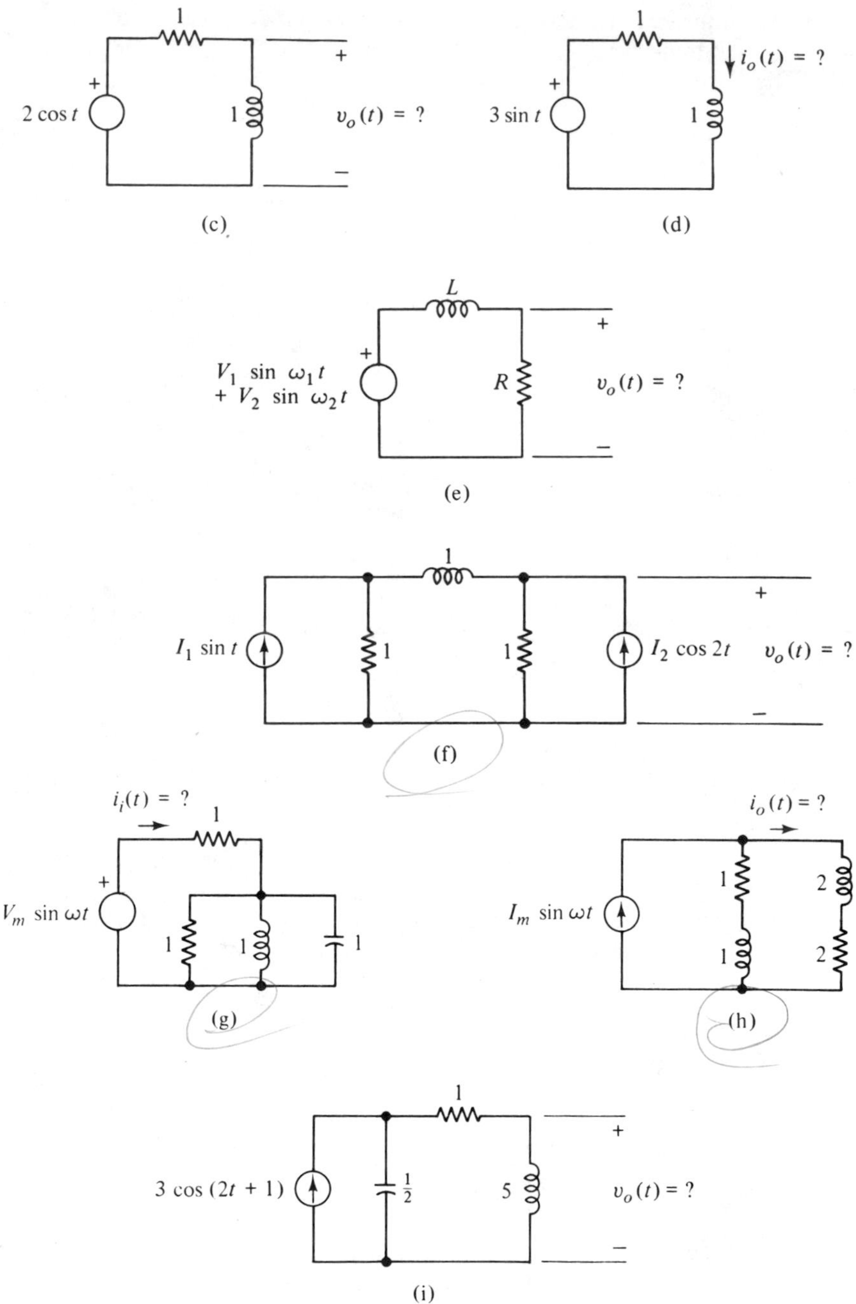
1
+
2 cos t
1
$v_o(t)$ = ?
–
(c)
1
$i_o(t)$ = ?
+
3 sin t
1
(d)
L
+
V_1 sin $\omega_1 t$
+ V_2 sin $\omega_2 t$
R
$v_o(t)$ = ?
–
(e)
1
+
I_1 sin t
1
1
I_2 cos 2t
$v_o(t)$ = ?
–
(f)
$i_i(t)$ = ?
1
+
V_m sin ωt
1
1
1
(g)
$i_o(t)$ = ?
1
2
I_m sin ωt
1
2
(h)
1
+
3 cos (2t + 1)
$\frac{1}{2}$
5
$v_o(t)$ = ?
–
(i)

Fig. 8-66 (*cont.*)

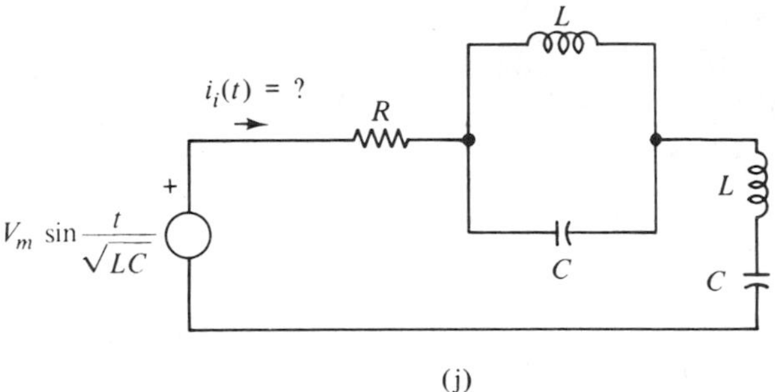

Fig. 8-66 (*cont.*)

8-18. For the systems shown in Fig. 8-67 obtain the steady-state responses.

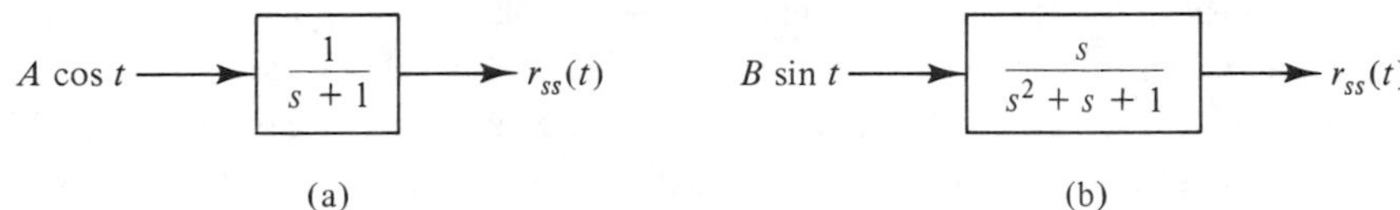

Fig. 8-67

8-19. For the system shown in Fig. 8-68 obtain the steady-state response.

$$\sin t + \cos 2t \longrightarrow \boxed{\frac{s^2+4}{s^2+s+1}} \longrightarrow r_{ss}(t)$$

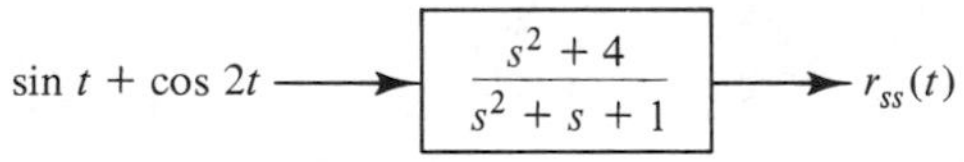

Fig. 8-68

8-20. Given

$$A \sin \omega t + B \cos \omega t = C \sin (\omega t + \theta) = D \cos (\omega t + \phi)$$

Using phasors obtain C, θ, D, and ϕ as a function of A and B.

8-21. Given

$$A_1 \sin (\omega t + \theta_1) + A_2 \sin (\omega t + \theta_2) = A_3 \sin (\omega t + \theta) = A_4 \cos (\omega t + \phi)$$

Using phasors obtain A_3, θ, A_4, and ϕ as a function of A and B.

8-22. In Fig. 8-69 all three currents are sinusoidal but not necessarily in phase. Let I_{m1} and I_{m2} represent the amplitudes of $i_1(t)$ and $i_2(t)$, respectively. What can be said about the amplitude I_{m3} of $i_3(t)$? Be quantitative.

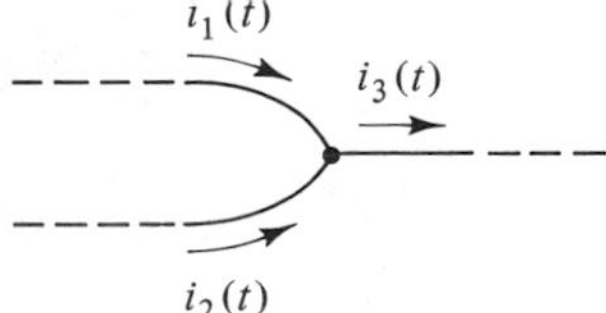

Fig. 8-69

8-23. Given

$$\sqrt{2}\sin\left(t+\frac{\pi}{4}\right)-\cos t+\sqrt{2}\cos\left(t-\frac{\pi}{4}\right)=A\sin(t+\theta)$$

Find A and θ.

8-24. Given $x(t) = A\sin\left(\omega t+\frac{\pi}{6}\right)$

$$y(t) = B\sin\left(\omega t+\frac{2}{3}\pi\right)$$

Obtain **X**, **Y**, **X** + **Y**, and **X** − **Y**, where **X** and **Y** are phasors. Give answers in the format: magnitude /angle.

8-25. Given $x(t) = \sin t$ and $y(t) = \cos t$.

(a) Obtain **X** + **Y**. Express your answer in polar form.

(b) What is the time domain representation of **X** + **Y**?

8-26. Given $s(t) = \sin(3t+\theta)+\cos 3t$. Find **S** in polar form.

8-27. For the circuits in Fig. 8-70 obtain the phasor responses designated by a question mark. The excitation frequency is ω. The excitation amplitude is V_m or I_m, and the phase is 0.

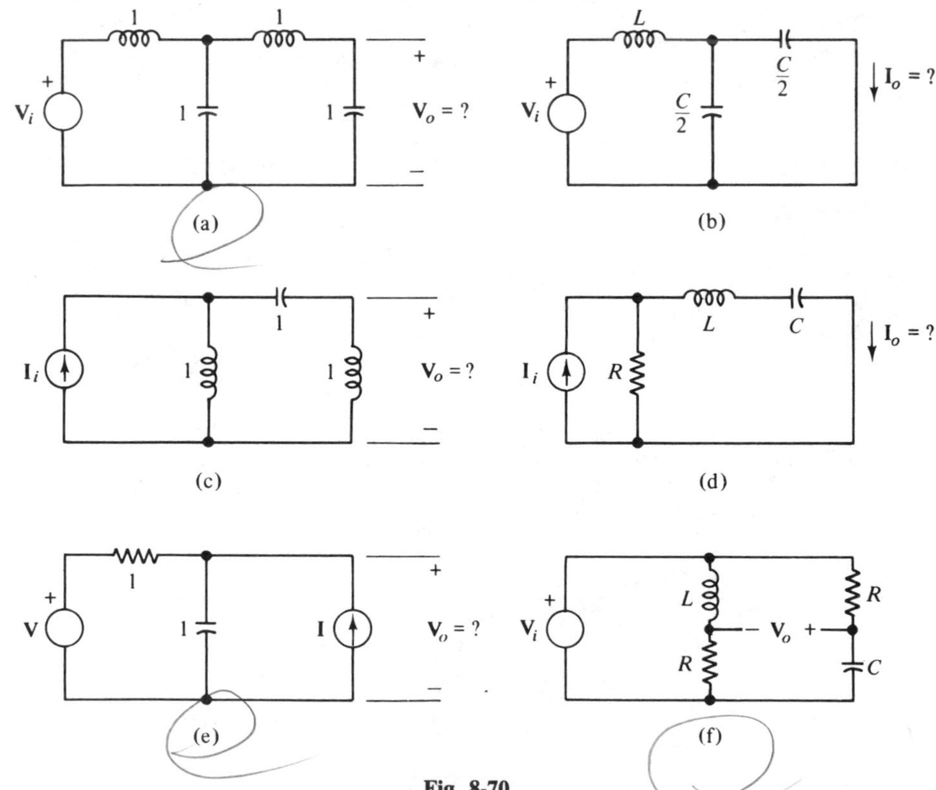

Fig. 8-70

8-28. In Fig. 8-71, obtain the indicated responses in the form: magnitude $\underline{/\text{angle}}$.

Fig. 8-71

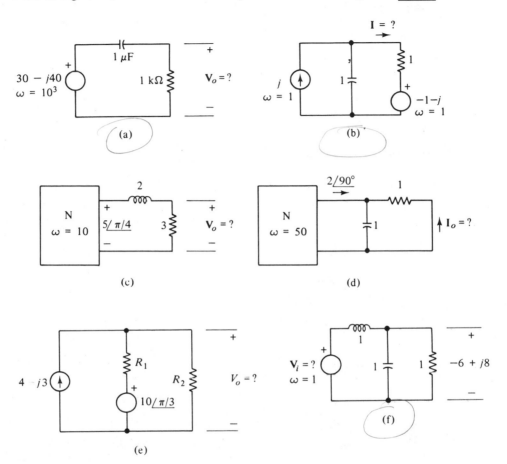

8-29. In Fig. 8-72 what $v_i(t)$ would produce the output voltage shown? Assume $\omega = 1$.

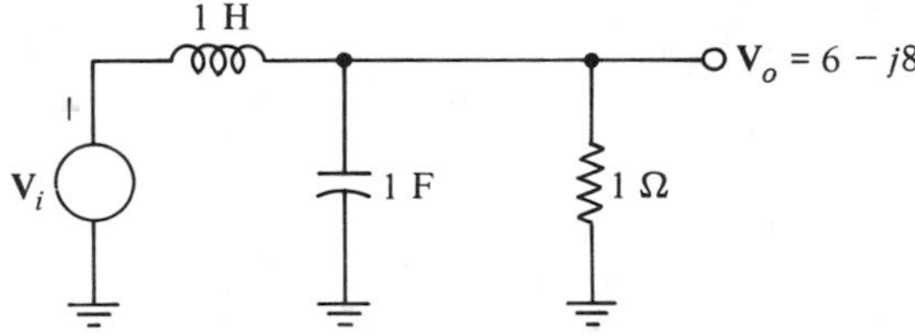

Fig. 8-72

8-30. In Fig. 8-73 both $v_1(t)$ and $v_2(t)$ are sinusoidal with amplitudes 3 V and 4 V, respectively. What is the amplitude of v?

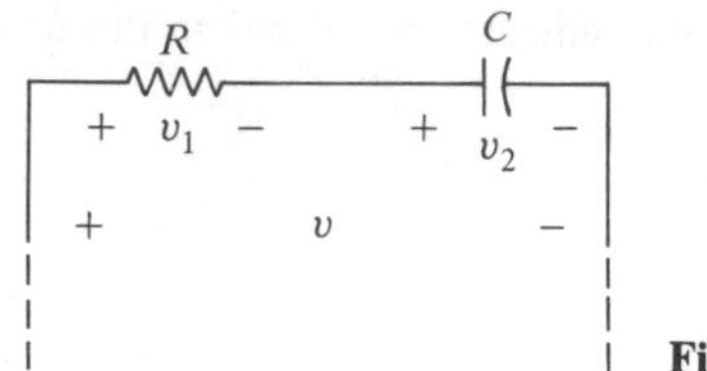

Fig. 8-73

8-31. In Fig. 8-74 both $v_R(t)$ and $v_L(t)$ are sinusoidal with amplitudes of 6 V and 8 V, respectively. What is the amplitude of $v_i(t)$?

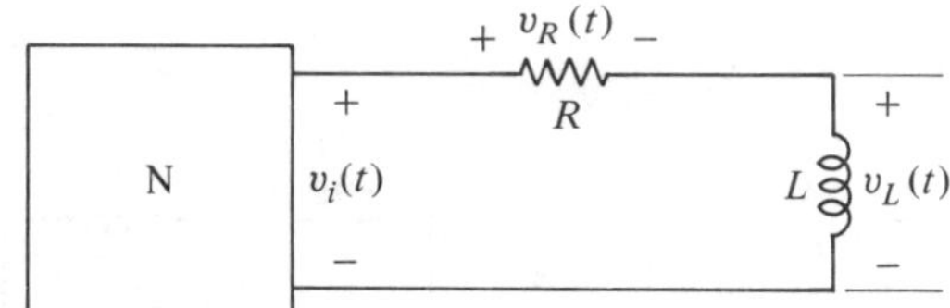

Fig. 8-74

8-32. Refer to Fig. 8-75.

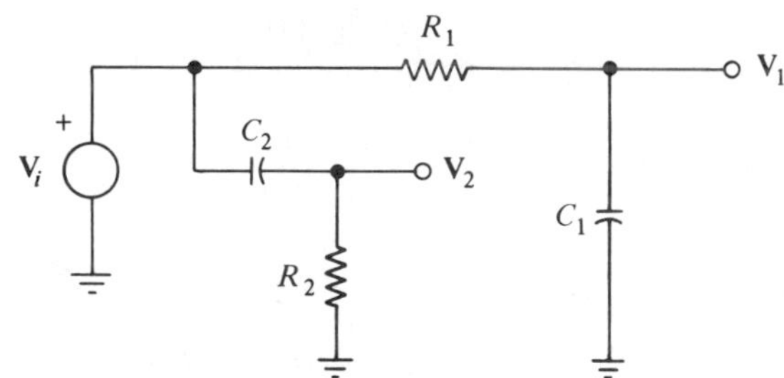

Fig. 8-75

(a) What is the phase difference between $\mathbf{V}_1$ and $\mathbf{V}_2$?
(b) What condition must be satisfied to make the phase difference 90°?
(c) Let $R_1C_1 = R_2C_2$. Connect $\mathbf{V}_1$ to the x input and $\mathbf{V}_2$ to the y input of the oscilloscope. What is the resulting display? How does it vary with ω?

8-33. Show that V_{o1} and V_{o2} in Fig. 8-76 are 90° out of phase, regardless of the frequency.

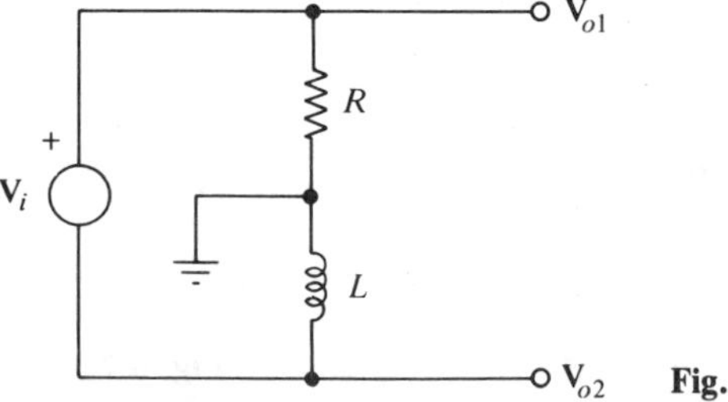

Fig. 8-76

8-34. What condition in Fig. 8-77 must be satisfied to make the phase difference between the two outputs $\pi/2$ radians?

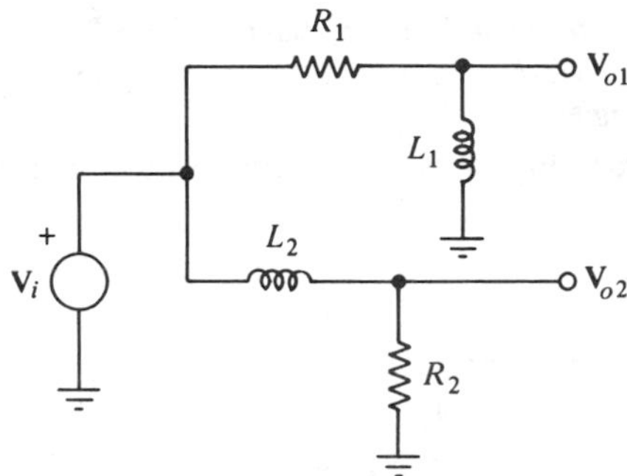

Fig. 8-77

8-35. Derive Eq. (8-32).

8-36. Derive Eq. (8-34).

8-37. The horizontal (x) and vertical (y) signals that are applied to an oscilloscope have the phase relationship shown in Fig. 8-78. Sketch the oscilloscope displays and indicate whether a clockwise or counterclockwise ellipse is generated.

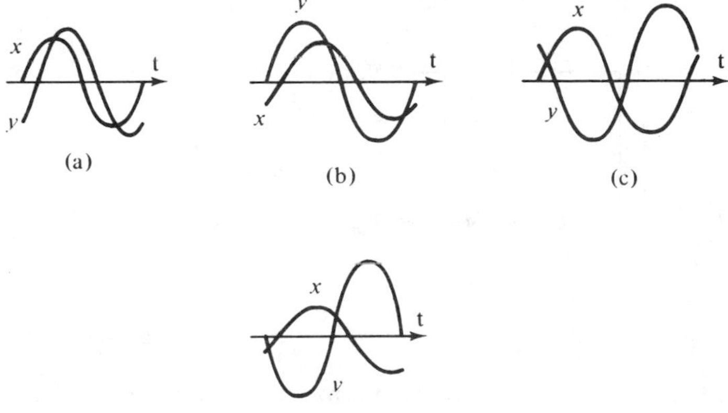

Fig. 8-78

8-38. What is the phase relationship between current and voltage in a (a) resistor? (b) capacitor? (c) inductor?

8-39. Given

$$s_1 = A \cos \omega t, \qquad s_2 = B \cos (\omega t - \theta), \qquad s_3 = -C \cos (\omega t + \psi)$$

where A, B, and C are positive numbers.

(a) State whether s_1 and s_2 lead or lag s_3 and by how much.

(b) How much does s_2 lead s_1?

8-40. Given

$$\mathbf{S}_1 = A\angle{-30^\circ}, \qquad \mathbf{S}_2 = B\angle{-150^\circ}, \qquad \mathbf{S}_3 = C\angle{\pi \text{ radians}}, \qquad \mathbf{S}_4 = -D\angle{0}$$

where A, B, C, and D are positive numbers.

(a) $\mathbf{S}_1$ is the reference. How much do $\mathbf{S}_2$, $\mathbf{S}_3$, and $\mathbf{S}_4$ lag $\mathbf{S}_1$?
(b) How much does $\mathbf{S}_4$ lead $\mathbf{S}_3$?
(c) How much does $\mathbf{S}_3$ lag $\mathbf{S}_1 + \mathbf{S}_2$?

8-41. Show that in the network of Fig. 8-79 the current lags the input voltage, whereas the output voltage leads it.

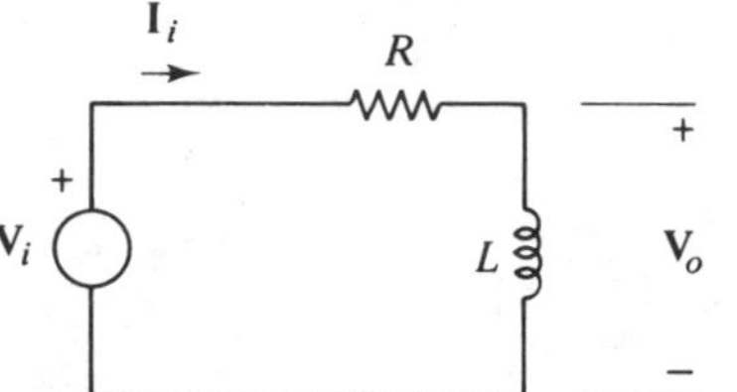

Fig. 8-79

8-42. Sketch Eq. (8-40) as a function of ωRC. For what value of ω is the phase difference maximum? What is the maximum value of the phase difference?

8-43. Refer to Fig. 8-80. At what frequency is $V_{m1} = V_{m2}$? At that frequency what is the phase difference $\theta_1 - \theta_2$?

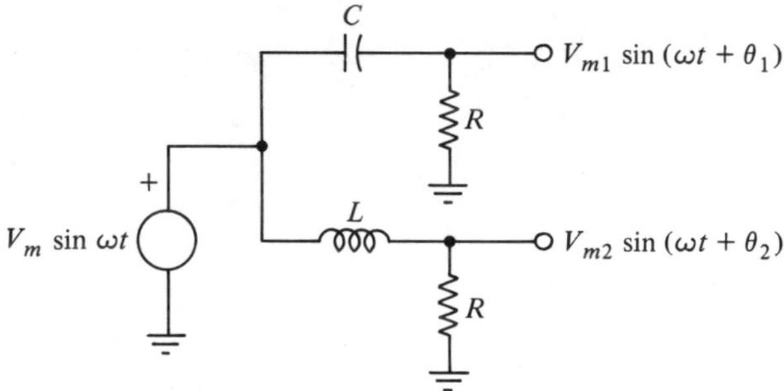

Fig. 8-80

8-44. In Fig. 8-81, k varies between zero and one. Does the output voltage lead or lag the input voltage?

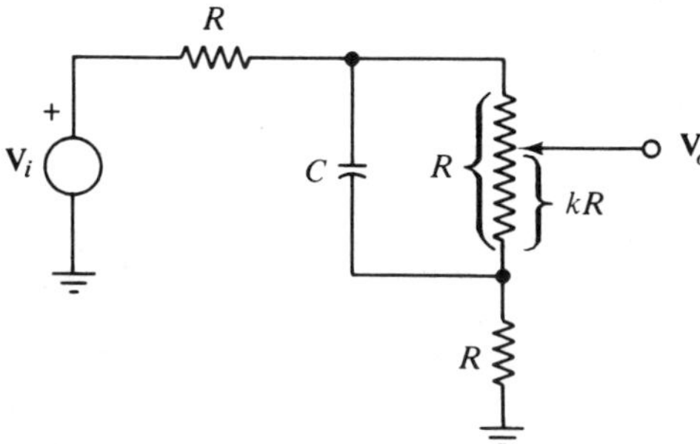

Fig. 8-81

8-45. Derive Eqs. (8-42) and (8-43).

8-46. In Fig. 8-82, $v(t) = V_m \sin(\omega t + \theta)$, and the responses are at steady state.

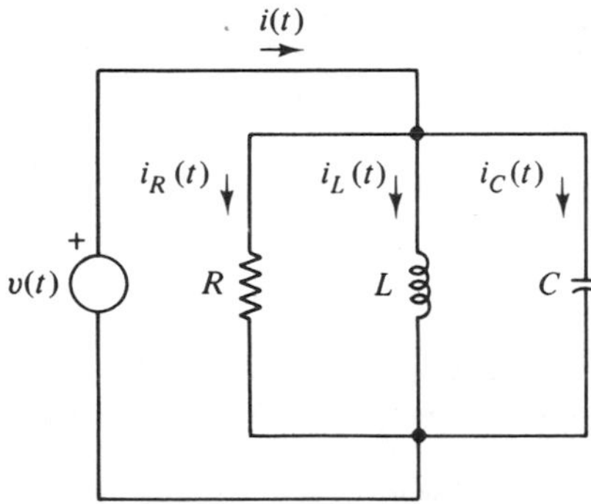

Fig. 8-82

(a) Calculate $i_R(t)$, $i_L(t)$, $i_C(t)$, and $i(t)$.
(b) Sketch I_{mR}, I_{mL}, I_{mC}, and I_m vs. ω.
(c) Obtain the current gain I_{mC}/I_m at $\omega = 1\sqrt{LC}$.

8-47. In Fig. 8-83 $i(t) = I_m \sin \omega t$. In the steady state the output voltage can be written as $v_o(t) = V_m \sin(\omega t + \theta)$. Obtain the expressions for V_m and θ, and sketch them vs. ω. At what frequency does V_m take on its maximum value? What is the phase θ at this frequency?

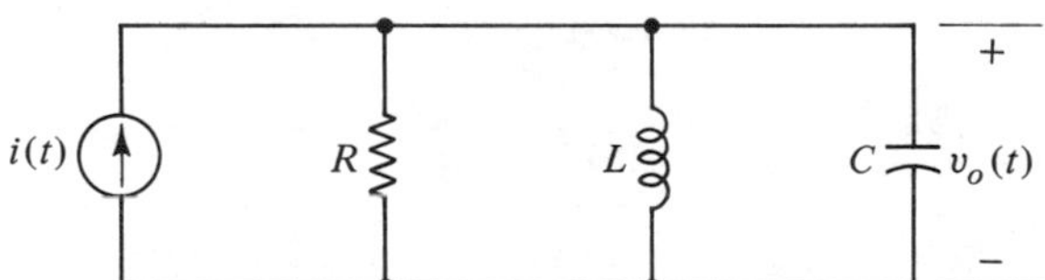

Fig. 8-83

8-48. In Fig. 8-84 $v(t) = V_m \sin \omega t$. In the steady state the input current can be written as $i(t) = I_m \sin(\omega t + \theta)$. Obtain the expressions for I_m and θ and sketch them vs. ω. At what frequency does I_m take on its maximum value. What is the phase at this frequency?

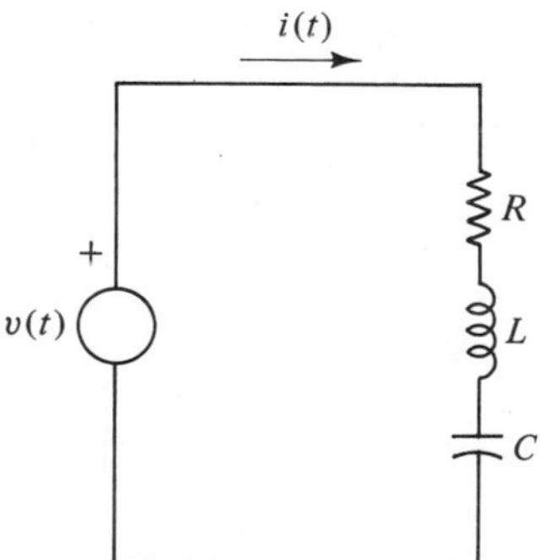

Fig. 8-84

8-49. In Fig. 8-85, $i(t) = I_m \sin(\omega t + \theta)$, and the responses are at steady state.

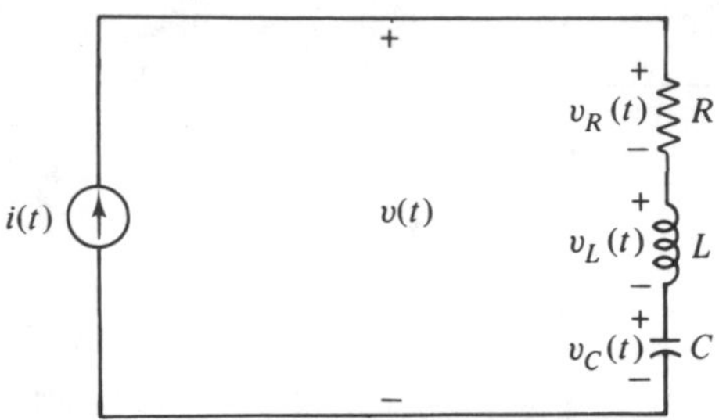

Fig. 8-85

(**a**) Calculate $v_R(t)$, $v_L(t)$, $v_C(t)$, and $v(t)$.
(**b**) Sketch V_{mR}, V_{mL}, V_{mC}, and V_m vs. ω.
(**c**) Obtain the voltage gain V_{mC}/V_m at $\omega = 1/\sqrt{LC}$.

8-50. The input current and voltage to a circuit are given by

$$v_i(t) = V_m \sin(\omega t + \theta) \qquad \text{and} \qquad i_i(t) = I_m \cos(\omega t + \phi)$$

Calculate the average power delivered to the circuit.

8-51. What is the average power input to a sinusoidally excited inductor?

8-52. Show that $\tan^{-1} a/b + \tan^{-1} b/a = \pi/2$.

8-53. Refer to Fig. 8-86. For each circuit, calculate the average power delivered by the source. Also, calculate the average power delivered to the R, L, and C.

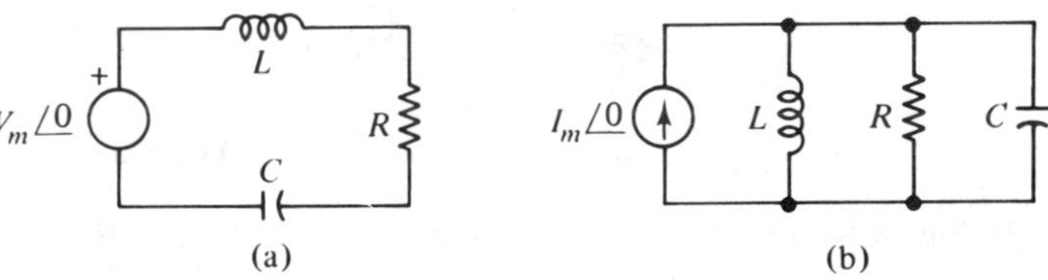

Fig. 8-86

8-54. Obtain the power factors associated with the circuits of Fig. 8-87.

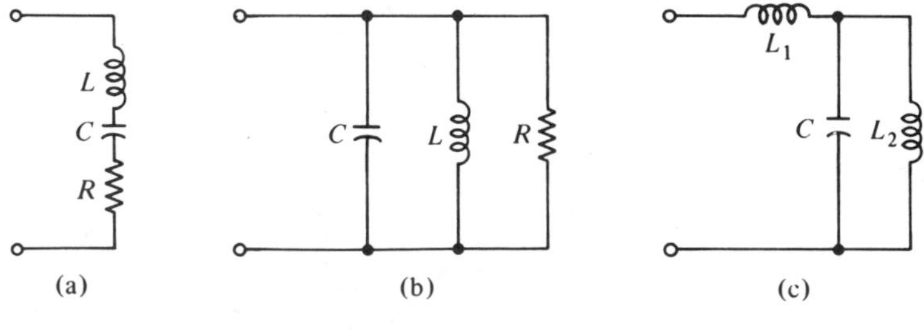

Fig. 8-87

8-55. Refer to Fig. 8-88.

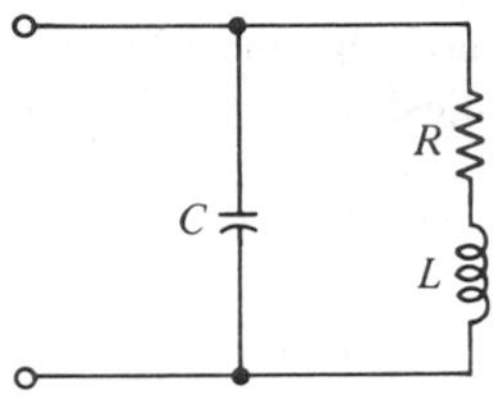

Fig. 8-88

(a) What is the PF associated with the inductive load (the R-L combination)?
(b) What is the PF associated with the capacitive load?
(c) What is the PF associated with the parallel combination?
(d) What size C must be used to make the PF of the combination unity?
(e) At what frequency is the PF of the RLC network unity?

8-56. The following information is given on the nameplate of a motor:

Line volts:	230 V rms
Line frequency:	60 Hz
Line current:	14 A rms
Horsepower:	3 (1 hp = 746 W)

(a) What is the power factor (lagging) of the motor?
(b) What size C must be connected across the input of the motor to bring the PF to unity? What is then the resulting line current?

8-57. Refer to Fig. 8-89.

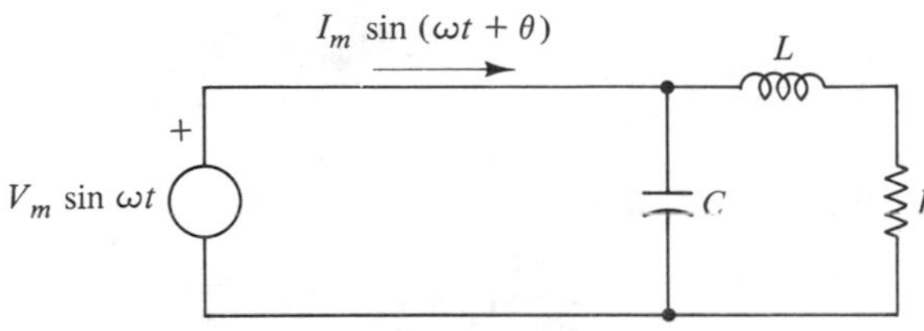

Fig. 8-89

(a) For what value of C is I_m minimum?
(b) What is the resulting I_m and θ?

8-58. Refer to Fig. 8-90. Under what condition is the PF at the input unity? The input voltage has zero phase.

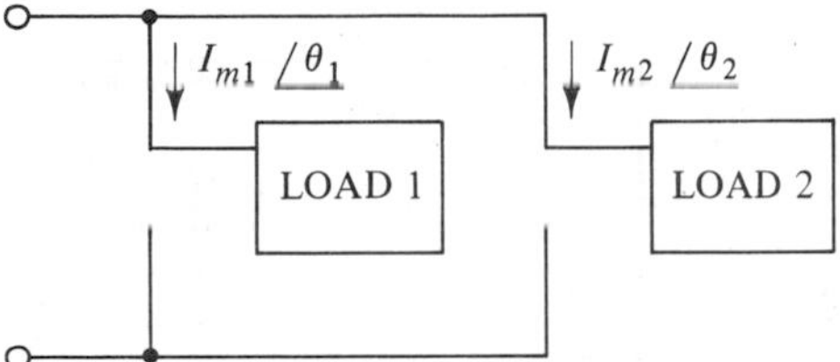

Fig. 8-90

8-59. In Fig. 8-91 the network N draws a current of I_m at the lagging angle θ as shown. The capacitor C is added for power-factor correction.
(a) What is the average power delivered by the input?
(b) What is the average power consumed by N?

(c) For what value of C does the line current i_L have the minimum amplitude?
(d) The capacitor C is adjusted to the value obtained in (c). What is the line current $i_L(t)$?
(e) What is the power factor of the capacitor–N parallel combination?

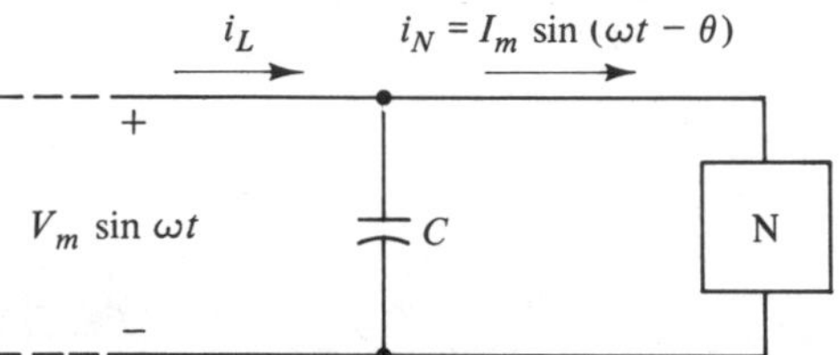

Fig. 8-91

8-60. Refer to Fig. 8-92. When $C = 0$, $i(t) = -I_m \cos \omega t$, what is $i(t)$ when $C \neq 0$?

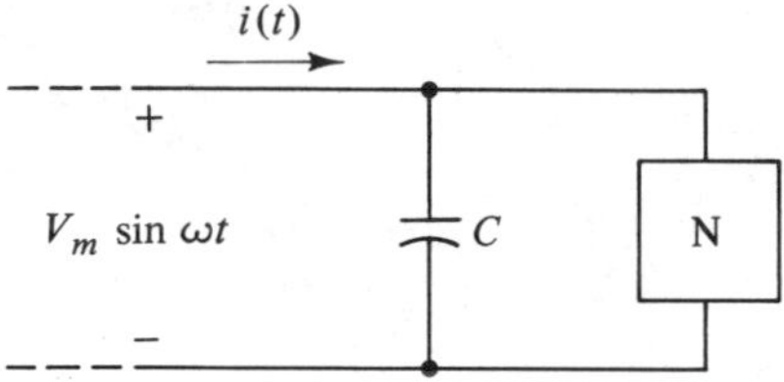

Fig. 8-92

8-61. Refer to Fig. 8-93.

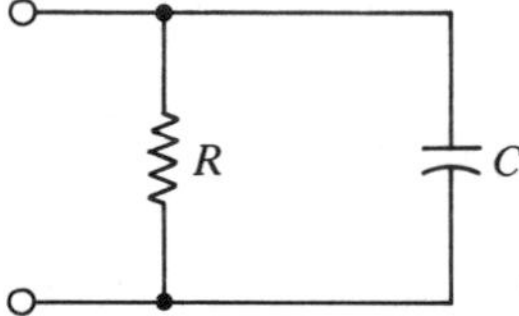

Fig. 8-93

(a) Obtain the PF of the circuit.
(b) What size L must be connected across the input to bring the PF to unity?.

8-62. In Fig. 8-94 the input is sinusoidal. What is the average power delivered to the LC circuit?

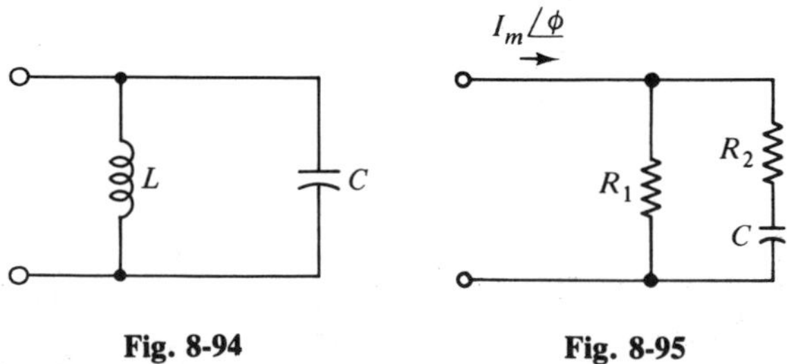

Fig. 8-94 Fig. 8-95

8-63. In Fig. 8-95, obtain $Z(j\omega)$, $|Z(j\omega)|$, θ_Z, $R(\omega)$, $X(\omega)$, and the average power delivered to the R_1R_2C network.

8-64. Derive Eq. (8-66).

8-65. Given

$$Z(j\omega) = |Z|\underline{/\theta_Z} = R + jX$$
$$Y(j\omega) = |Y|\underline{/\theta_Y} = G + jB$$

Express $Y(j\omega)$, $|Y|$, θ_Y, G, and B in terms of $Z(j\omega)$, $|Z|$, θ_Z, R, and X.

8-66. For the networks shown in Fig. 8-96, calculate $Y(j\omega)$, $|Y(j\omega)|$, θ_Y, $G(\omega)$, $B(\omega)$, and the average power delivered to the networks.

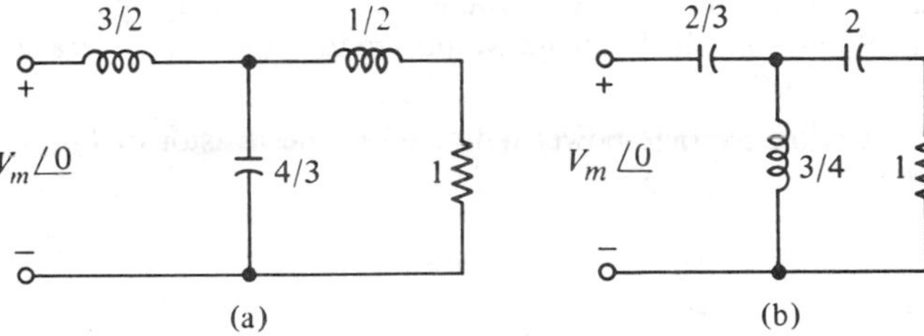

Fig. 8-96

8-67. The periodic voltage waveform shown in Fig. 8-97 is applied to a resistor.

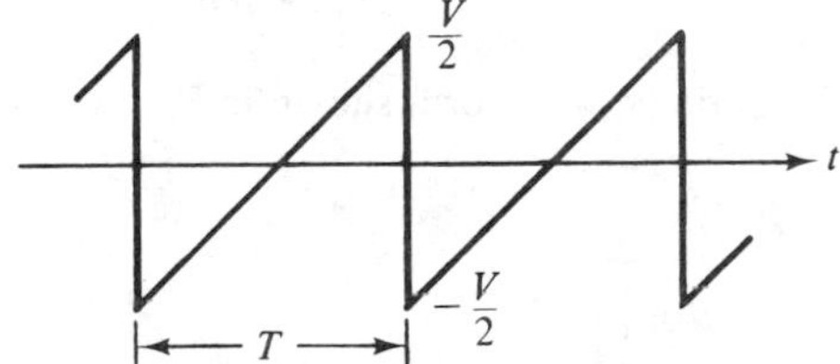

Fig. 8-97

(**a**) What dc voltage would produce the same average power dissipation in the resistor?
(**b**) What sinusoidal voltage would produce the same average power dissipation in the resistor?

8-68. The periodic voltage waveform shown in Fig. 8-98 is applied to a resistor.

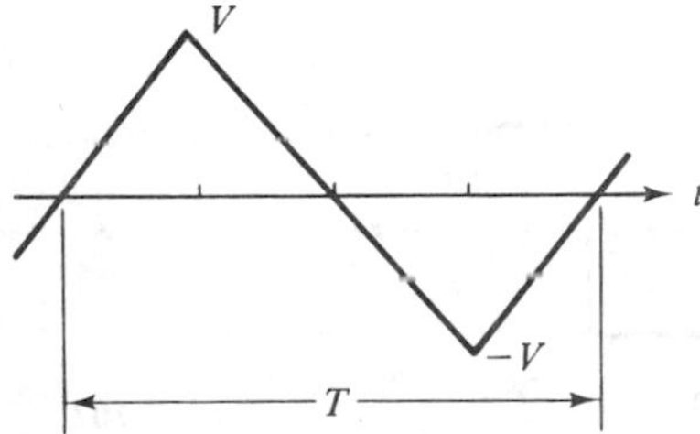

Fig. 8-98

(**a**) What dc voltage would produce the same average power dissipation in the resistor?
(**b**) What sinusoidal voltage would produce the same average power dissipation in the resistor?

8-69. The periodic voltage waveform shown in Fig. 8-99 is applied to a resistor.

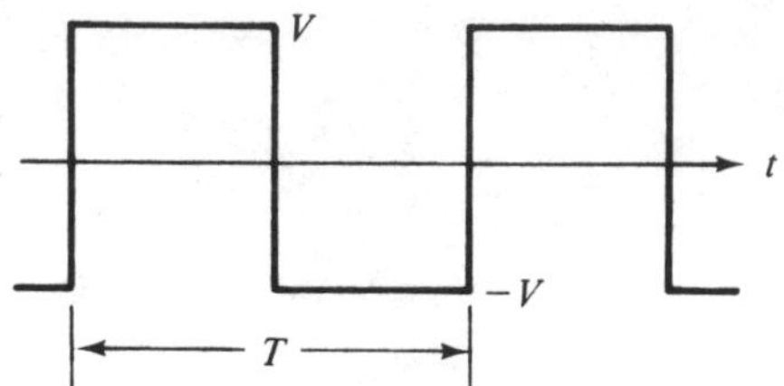

Fig. 8-99

(**a**) What dc voltage would produce the same average power dissipation in the resistor?
(**b**) What sinusoidal voltage would produce the same average power dissipation in the resistor?

8-70. What is the average power delivered to the resistor of Fig. 8-100? The input is periodic.

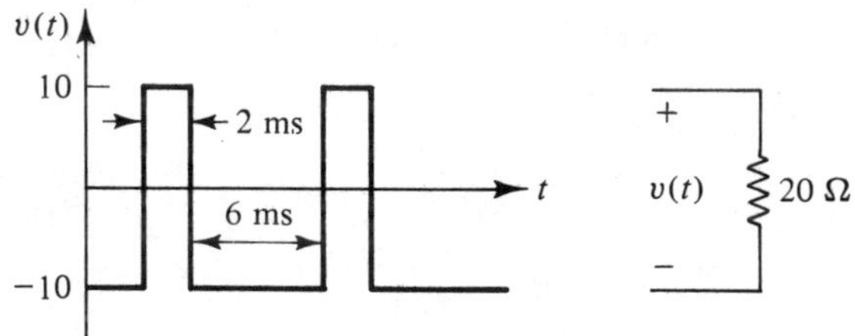

Fig. 8-100

8-71. What is the rms value of the periodic waveform shown in Fig. 8-101?

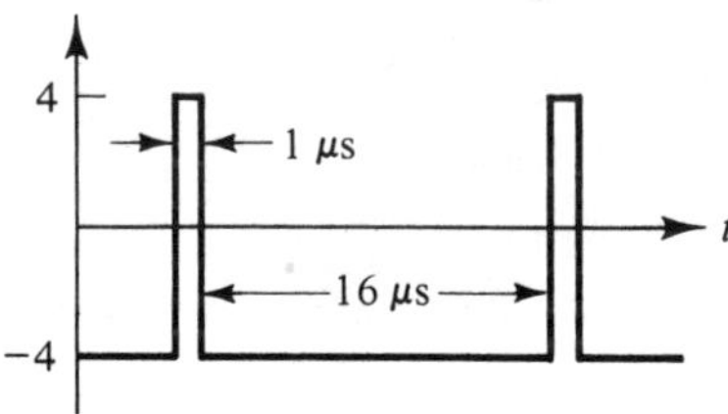

Fig. 8-101

8-72. Refer to Fig. 8-102.

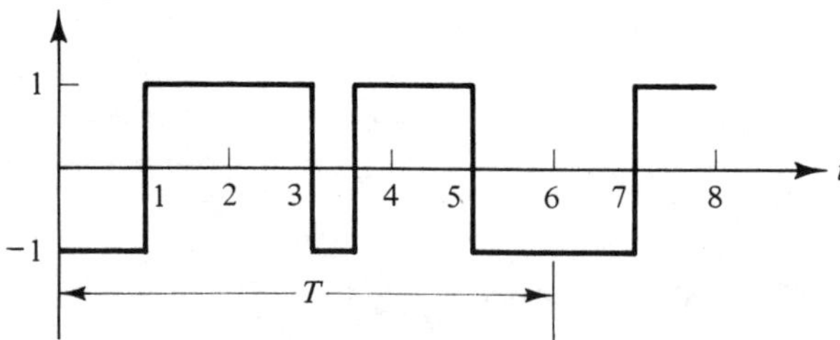

Fig. 8-102

(**a**) The waveform is periodic. What is its rms value?
(**b**) If the waveform represents the voltage across a 10 Ω resistor, what must be the average power rating of the resistor?

8-73. What is the rms value of the periodic waveform shown in Fig. 8-103?

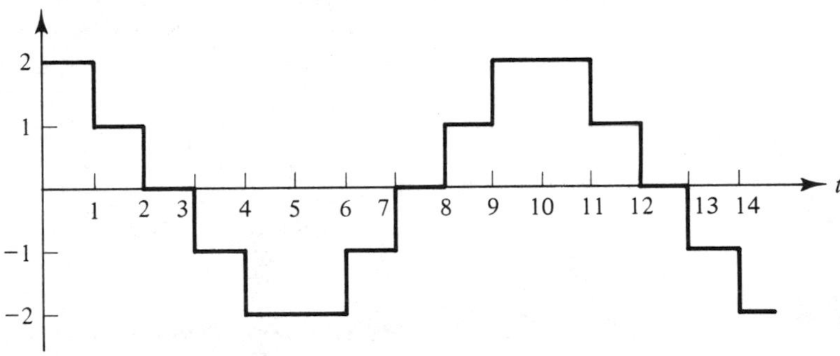

Fig. 8-103

CHAPTER 9

FILTERING WITH FIRST- AND SECOND-ORDER RLC NETWORKS

When we tune a radio to a station or switch a television set to a particular channel, we change part of the circuitry of the receiver so that it amplifies signals with frequencies assigned to that station or channel and attenuates the other incoming signals. When recording very low level physiological signals, we use circuits to reject the undesirable 60 Hz signal that may contaminate the desirable signal. We use crossover networks to separate low- and high-frequency signals and direct them to low- and high-frequency speakers. We use phase-shift networks to produce a specified phase relationship between the input and output sine waves. All these and other networks that alter the amplitude and phase characteristics of sine waves in a prescribed way are called *filters*. In this chapter we discuss the characteristics of some widely used filters and show how they are used in practical applications.

9-1 INPUT-OUTPUT RELATIONSHIP IN A FILTER

An electrical filter is a network that is used to change the amplitude or phase of a sine wave in a prescribed manner, the change depending on the frequency of the sine wave. For instance, a filter may pass sine waves that fall within a band of frequencies and attenuate all others. Or a filter may emphasize low-frequency sine waves over high-frequency sine waves.

Generally, a filter works between a voltage source with internal resistance R_s and a load with resistance R_L. (See Fig. 9-1). These resistive terminations affect the performance of the filter. Therefore the transfer function $T(s) = V_o(s)/V_i(s)$ under loaded conditions is used to characterize the filter. Since we are interested in knowing how a sine wave is altered as it goes through the filter, the input is taken as

$$v_i(t) = V_m \sin(\omega t + \phi) \tag{9-1}$$

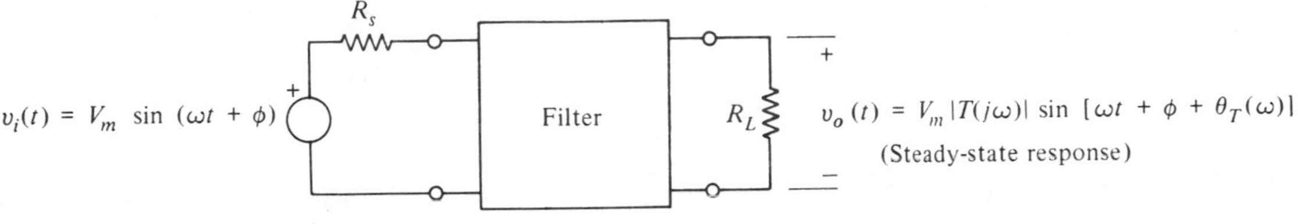

Fig. 9-1

The output in steady state is a sine wave of the same frequency ω, but its amplitude and phase are altered by $T(s)$ as follows.

$$v_o(t) = V_m|T(j\omega)| \sin[\omega t + \phi + \theta_T(\omega)] \tag{9-2}$$

where

$$|T(j\omega)| = \text{magnitude of } T(j\omega)$$
$$\theta_T(\omega) = \text{angle of } T(j\omega)$$
$$T(j\omega) = T(s)\big|_{s=j\omega}$$

Thus the filter changes the amplitude of the sine wave from V_m to $V_m|T(j\omega)|$ and the phase of the sine wave from ϕ to $\phi + \theta_T(\omega)$. Since $|T(j\omega)|$ and $\theta_T(\omega)$ are functions of ω, sine waves of different frequencies will be affected differently as they go through the network. By shaping $|T(j\omega)|$ vs. ω and $\theta_T(\omega)$ vs. ω characteristics, we can filter (discriminate) sine waves according to their frequencies in any manner that we choose.

The idealized magnitude characteristics of four widely used filters are shown in Fig. 9-2. All these filters have a passband and a stopband. Depending on where the bands are, the filters either pass or stop sine waves. If low-frequency sine waves are passed and high-frequency sine waves are stopped, as shown in Fig. 9-2(a), we have a *lowpass filter*. On the other hand, if low frequencies are stopped and high frequencies are passed, as in Fig. 9-2(b), we have a *highpass filter*. In Fig. 9-2(c), we have the characteristics of a *bandpass filter*, whereas Fig. 9-2(d) shows the characteristics of a *bandstop filter*.

All the characteristics shown in Fig. 9-2 are magnitude characteristics. Suppose that we attribute to all filters the phase characteristic given by

$$\theta_T(\omega) = k\pi - \tau_d\omega \tag{9-3}$$

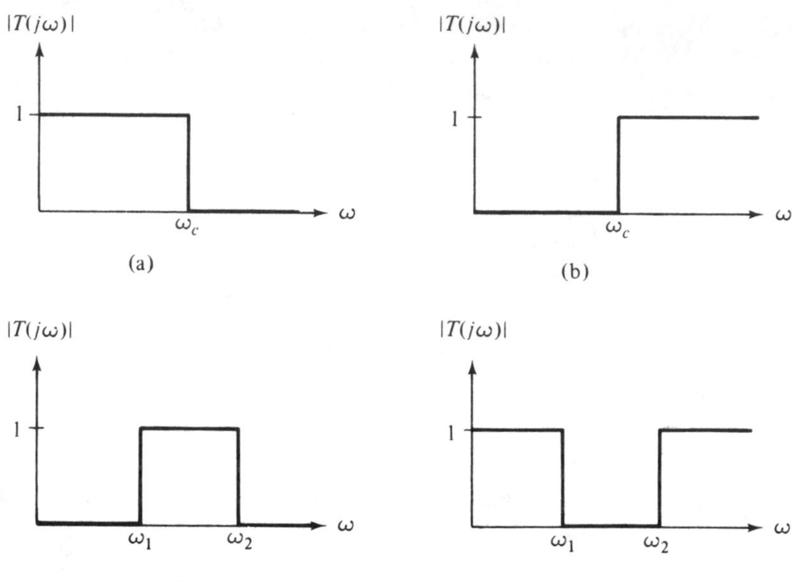

Fig. 9-2

where k is an integer and τ_d is a constant. With both magnitude and phase functions thus specified, we can compare the input and the steady-state output sine waves.

$$v_i(t) = V_m \sin(\omega t + \phi) \tag{9-4a}$$

$$v_o(t) = V_m \sin[\omega t + \phi + \theta_T(\omega)] \qquad \text{(passband)} \tag{9-4b}$$

$$= 0 \qquad \text{(stopband)} \tag{9-4c}$$

Using Eq. (9-3), the expression for the output in the passband can be written

$$v_o(t) = V_m \sin(\omega t + \phi + k\pi - \tau_d \omega) = \pm V_m \sin[\omega(t - \tau_d) + \phi] \tag{9-5}$$

where the + is for k even and the − sign for k odd. Noting that the difference between this output and the input is the replacement of t by $(t - \tau_d)$ and a negative sign for k odd, we conclude that the sine waves that are passed are *all delayed* by τ_d seconds. They are also inverted if k is odd. Otherwise there is no difference between the input and output. This result is based on the presupposition that $\theta_T(\omega) = k\pi - \tau_d\omega$. If the phase characteristic of the filter is not quite as linear as prescribed by Eq. (9-3), then sine waves with different frequencies will emerge from the passband with different amounts of delay. When added to form the output, these sine waves do not reproduce a time-delayed replica of the input. Consequently, distortion results. In order to have distortionless reproduction of a band of sine waves, then, the filter must possess in the passband not only a constant magnitude characteristic but also a linear phase characteristic. Having only a constant magnitude characteristic is not sufficient.

9-2 LOWPASS FILTERS

Lowpass filters are used to pass low-frequency sine waves and attenuate high-frequency sine waves. *The cutoff frequency* ω_c is used to distinguish the passband ($\omega < \omega_c$) from the stopband ($\omega > \omega_c$). The ideal lowpass filter is characterized by the magnitude and phase curves given in Fig. 9-3. The shape of the phase characteristic in the stopband is not important, for the amplitude function there is zero.

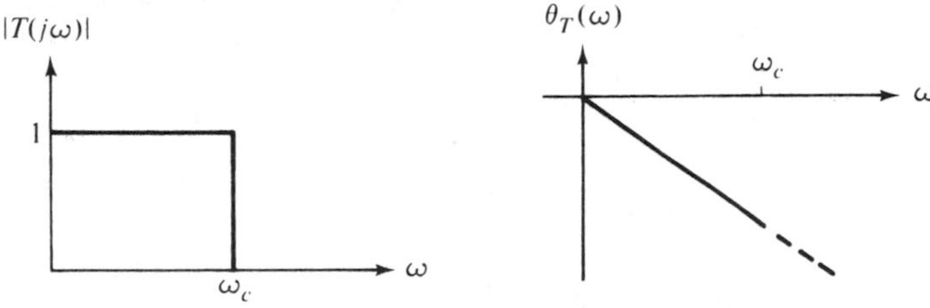

Fig. 9-3

It is *not possible* to produce networks having such idealized lowpass characteristics. In practice, we obtain characteristics that are *approximations* to the ideal. The closer the actual characteristics approach the ideal, the better the approximation. It should be realized, however, that this result can only be achieved by increasing the complexity of the network—that is, we must use additional L's and C's to implement the filter. Doing so, in turn, makes the filter costlier, bulkier, and heavier. Here we discuss only first-order (one-pole) and second-order (two-poles) functions and networks that possess lowpass characteristics.

The First-order Function and First-order Networks

The first-order lowpass function is given by

$$T_1(s) = \frac{\omega_c}{s + \omega_c} = \frac{1}{s/\omega_c + 1} \tag{9-6}$$

To show that it approximates the ideal lowpass characteristics, we let $s = j\omega$ and find the resulting magnitude and phase functions.

$$T_1(j\omega) = \frac{1}{1 + j(\omega/\omega_c)}$$

$$|T_1(j\omega)| = \frac{1}{\sqrt{1 + (\omega/\omega_c)^2}} \tag{9-7a}$$

$$\theta_1(\omega) = -\tan^{-1}\left(\frac{\omega}{\omega_c}\right) \tag{9-7b}$$

These functions are plotted in Fig. 9-4. The magnitude characteristic does not exhibit a sharp drop with frequency to allow a clear distinction between passband and stopband. Nonetheless, we designate as *cutoff frequency that frequency at which the magnitude is* $1/\sqrt{2}$ *times the magnitude at* $\omega = 0$. The reduction in magnitude to 70.7% occurs when $\omega = \omega_c$. Thus the constant ω_c in Eq. (9-6) represents the cutoff frequency. This frequency is also known as the *half-power frequency* because at $\omega = \omega_c$ the power delivered to the load (being proportional to $|T_1(j\omega)^2|$ is half as much as at $\omega = 0$.

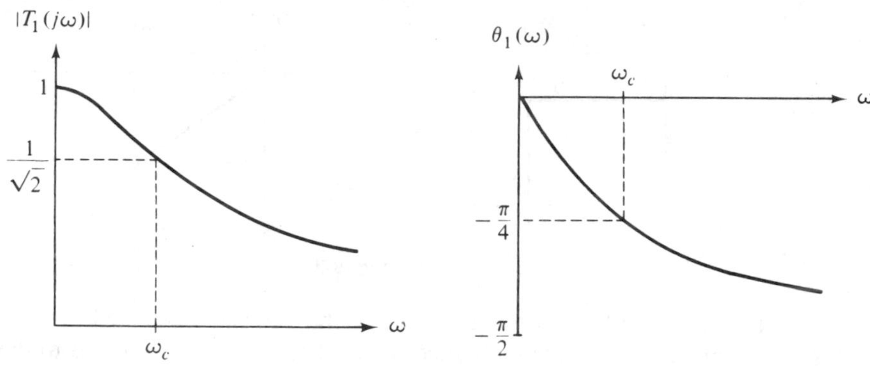

Fig. 9-4

Since all frequencies from zero to ω_c are passed (more or less), ω_c is also called the lowpass *bandwidth*. Since ω_c is given in radians per second, it must be divided by 2π to obtain the cutoff frequency or bandwidth in hertz.

The phase characteristic of $T_1(j\omega)$ approaches $-\pi/2$ radians asymptotically. In the passband ($\omega < \omega_c$), it is fairly linear.

The first-order lowpass function given by Eq. (9-6) is realized (within a scale factor) by the two networks shown in Fig. 9-5. Both networks operate between a resistive source R_s and a resistive load R_L. The networks are described by the transfer function.

$$T(s) = \frac{V_o}{V_i} = \frac{R_L}{R_s + R_L}\frac{\omega_c}{s + \omega_c} \tag{9-8}$$

where

$$\omega_c = \frac{1}{[R_sR_L/(R_s + R_L)]C} \qquad (RC \text{ network})$$

$$\omega_c = \frac{R_s + R_L}{L} \qquad (RL \text{ network})$$

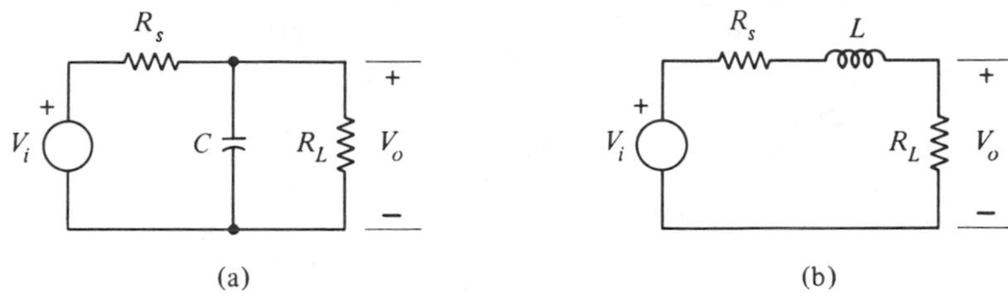

Fig. 9-5

Generally, the source and load resistances are specified, in which case the cutoff frequency is controlled by the capacitor in the network of Fig. 9-5(a) or by the inductor in the network of Fig. 9-5(b).

The scale factor, $R_L/(R_s + R_L)$, does not alter the shape of the lowpass curve, for it affects all frequencies equally. Because it is less than unity, it attenuates the signals in the passband (as well as those in the stopband).

We may find the lowpass approximation presented by the first-order function unacceptable. For instance, we may wish greater attenuation for all frequencies in the stopband or sharper distinction between the passband and the stopband. It then becomes necessary to use a second- or higher-order function.

The Second-order Function and Second-order Networks

Many second-order functions possess lowpass characteristics. These functions differ somewhat in their passband and stopband characteristics. One widely used function is described by

$$T_2(s) = \frac{\omega_c^2}{s^2 + s\sqrt{2}\omega_c + \omega_c^2} \tag{9-9}$$

The associated magnitude and phase functions are obtained by letting $s = j\omega$.

$$T_2(j\omega) = \frac{\omega_c^2}{(\omega_c^2 - \omega^2) + j\omega\sqrt{2}\,\omega_c} = \frac{1}{[1 - (\omega/\omega_c)^2] + j\sqrt{2}(\omega/\omega_c)}$$

$$|T_2(j\omega)| = \frac{1}{\sqrt{[1 - (\omega/\omega_c)^2]^2 + 2(\omega/\omega_c)^2}} = \frac{1}{\sqrt{1 + (\omega/\omega_c)^4}} \tag{9-10a}$$

$$\theta_2(\omega) = -\tan^{-1}\left[\frac{\sqrt{2}(\omega/\omega_c)}{1 - (\omega/\omega_c)^2}\right] \tag{9-10b}$$

These functions are plotted in Fig. 9-6. Note again that the constant ω_c, which designates the frequency at which the magnitude function is $1/\sqrt{2}$ times the magnitude at $\omega = 0$, is used to represent the cutoff frequency or bandwidth. The phase characteristic approaches $-\pi$ radians asymptotically. In the passband, it is fairly linear.

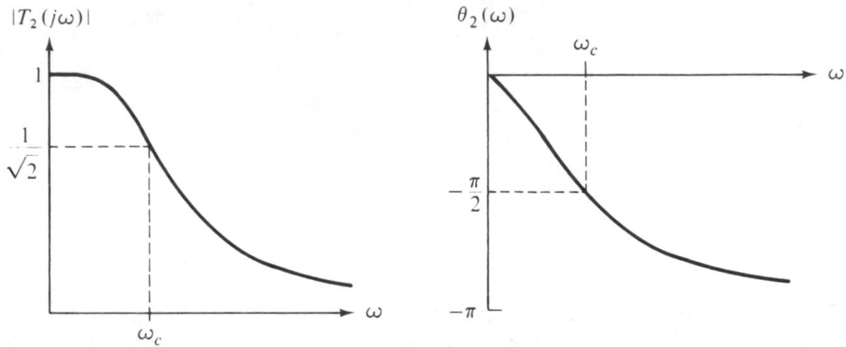

Fig. 9-6

In Fig. 9-7 the magnitude characteristic of this second-order function [Eq. (9-10a)] is compared with that of the first-order function [Eq. (9-7a)]. The second-order function exhibits passband and stopband characteristics that are closer to the ideal than that exhibited by the first-order function. In the passband it is above and in the stopband it is below the first-order curve. So it passes the low frequencies more faithfully, and it provides more attenuation for the high frequencies.

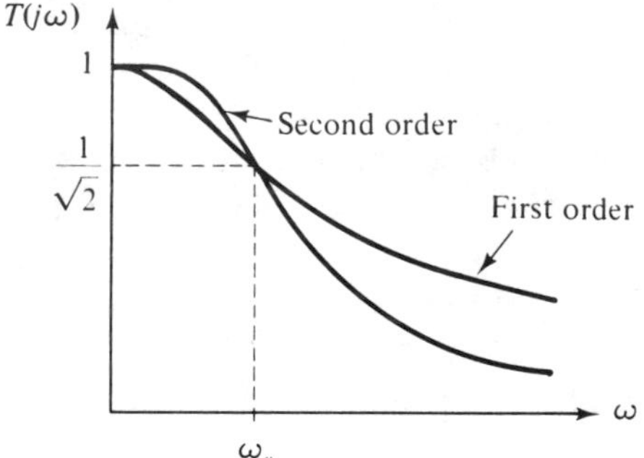

Fig. 9-7

The second-order function given by Eq. (9-9) is realized (within a scale factor) by either network shown in Fig. 9-8. The network of Fig. 9-8(a) is described by

$$\frac{V_o}{V_i} = \left(\frac{R_L}{R_s + R_L}\right)\left[\frac{(1 + R_s/R_L)(1/LC)}{s^2 + s(R_s/L + 1/R_LC) + (1 + R_s/R_L)(1/LC)}\right] \tag{9-11}$$

When Eq. (9-11) is compared coefficient by coefficient with the second-order function given by (9-9), we see that

$$\omega_c^2 = \left(1 + \frac{R_s}{R_L}\right)\frac{1}{LC}, \qquad \sqrt{2}\omega_c = \frac{R_s}{L} + \frac{1}{R_LC} \tag{9-12}$$

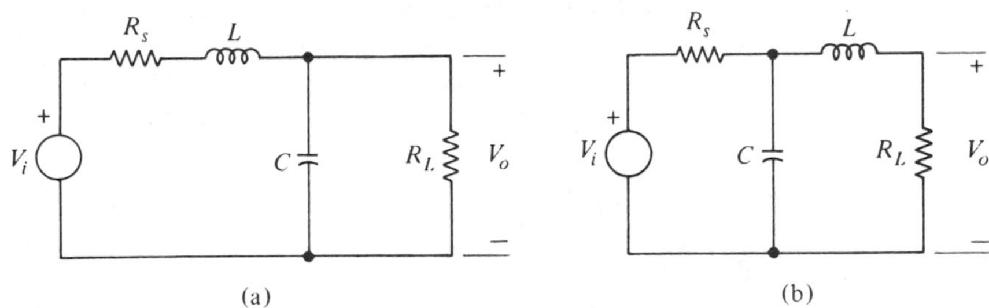

Fig. 9-8

The scale factor, $R_L/(R_s + R_L)$, affects all frequencies equally, and so it does not alter the relative frequency discrimination in any way. In practice, R_s and R_L are usually specified. The desired cutoff frequency ω_c is also specified. The set of equations given by Eq. (9-12) is then simultaneously solved for the L and C in order to achieve the desired lowpass response.

Similarly, the L and C of the network of Fig. 9-8(b) can be adjusted to produce the second-order lowpass transfer function given by Eq. (9-9) with a scale factor of $R_L/(R_s + R_L)$ in front (see Problem 9-3).

In either network the scale factor reduces to unity if $R_s = 0$ or $R_L = \infty$.

Example 9-1

The network of Fig. 9-9 is to be designed as a lowpass filter with $R_s = R_L = R$. The resistance R and the cutoff frequency ω_c are specified.

(a) What are the design equations for the L and C?

(b) $R = 50\ \Omega$, and the cutoff frequency is 1000 Hz. Design the network.

(c) Plot the resulting magnitude characteristic.

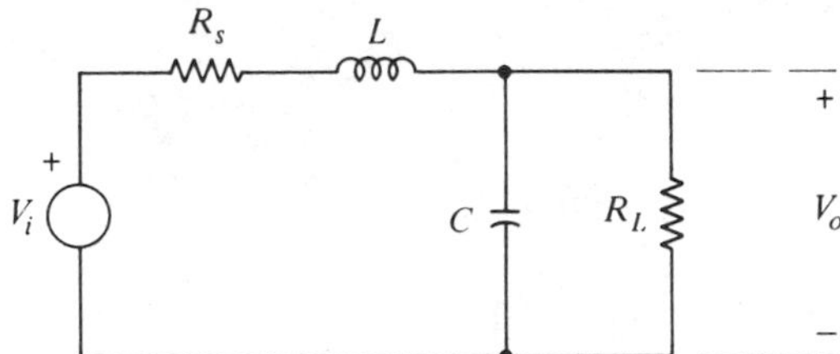

Fig. 9-9

Solution.

(a) From Eq. (9-11) we obtain the network transfer function

$$\frac{V_o}{V_i} = \frac{1}{2}\left[\frac{2/LC}{s^2 + s(R/L + 1/RC) + 2/LC}\right] \tag{9-13}$$

Equation (9-9) gives the desired transfer function

$$T(s) = \frac{\omega_c^2}{s^2 + s\sqrt{2}\omega_c + \omega_c^2} \tag{9-14}$$

The desired function is realized by the network (with a scale factor of $\frac{1}{2}$) if the numerator and denominator coefficients are matched. The result is

$$\omega_c^2 = \frac{2}{LC}, \qquad \sqrt{2}\omega_c = \frac{R}{L} + \frac{1}{RC} \tag{9-15}$$

This set of equations contains four variables: ω_c, R, L, and C. However, ω_c and R are specified and thus are known. So we can solve the two equations simultaneously for the L and C.

We solve the first equation for C and substitute it into the second equation.

$$C = \frac{2}{\omega_c^2 L} \tag{9-16}$$

$$\sqrt{2}\omega_c = \frac{R}{L} + \frac{\omega_c^2 L}{2R}$$

When rearranged, this equation becomes a quadratic equation in L.

$$\left(\frac{\omega_c^2}{2R}\right)L^2 - (\sqrt{2}\omega_c)L + R = 0$$

Solving for L, we have

$$L = \frac{\sqrt{2}\omega_c \pm \sqrt{(\sqrt{2}\omega_c)^2 - 4(\omega_c^2/2R)R}}{2(\omega_c^2/2R)} = \sqrt{2}\,\frac{R}{\omega_c}$$

Using this value of L in Eq. (9-16) results in

$$C = \frac{2}{\omega_c^2(\sqrt{2}R/\omega_c)} = \frac{\sqrt{2}}{\omega_c R}$$

The design equations are

$$L = \sqrt{2}\frac{R}{\omega_c}, \qquad C = \frac{\sqrt{2}}{\omega_c R} \quad \text{Ans.} \tag{9-17}$$

(b) Using $R = 50\ \Omega$ and $\omega_c = 2\pi \times 1000$ in Eq. (9-17), we obtain

$$\left.\begin{aligned} L &= \frac{\sqrt{2} \times 50}{2\pi \times 10^3} = 11.25\text{ mH} \\ C &= \frac{\sqrt{2}}{2\pi \times 10^3 \times 50} = 4.50\ \mu\text{F} \end{aligned}\right\} \text{Ans.}$$

The network with values is shown in Fig. 9-10(a).

(c) Using Eqs. (9-13) and (9-15), we have

$$\frac{V_o}{V_i} = \frac{1}{2}\,\frac{\omega_c^2}{s^2 + s\sqrt{2}\omega_c + \omega_c^2}$$

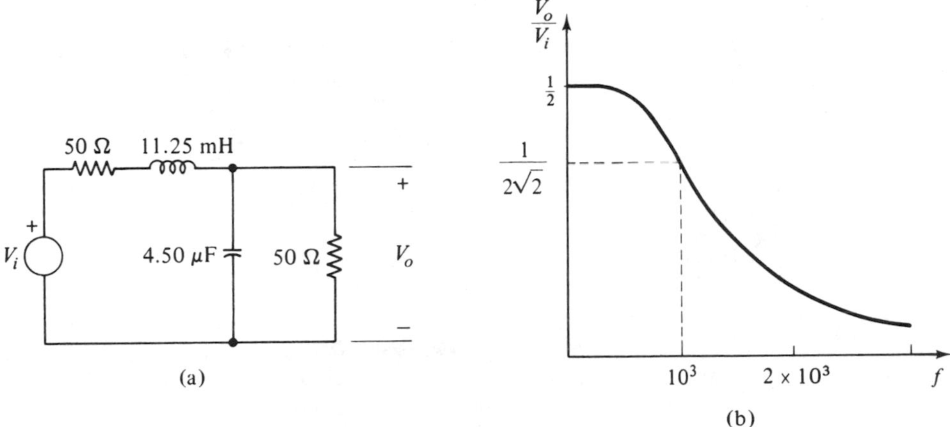

Fig. 9-10

The corresponding magnitude function is

$$\left|\frac{V_o}{V_i}\right|_{s=j\omega} = \left|\frac{1}{2}\frac{\omega_c^2}{(\omega_c^2 - \omega^2) + j\omega\sqrt{2}\omega_c}\right| = \frac{1}{2}\frac{\omega_c^2}{\sqrt{(\omega_c^2 - \omega^2)^2 + 2\omega^2\omega_c^2}}$$

$$= \frac{1}{2}\frac{\omega_c^2}{\sqrt{\omega_c^4 + \omega^4}} = \frac{1}{2}\frac{1}{\sqrt{1 + (\omega/\omega_c)^4}} \tag{9-18}$$

Equation (9-18) is plotted in Fig. 9-10(b).

Example 9-2

As shown in Fig. 9-11, the input to the *RC* network contains a sine wave superimposed on a dc voltage.

(a) Obtain the steady-state output.

(b) Compare the input and output waveforms. Discuss the circuit.

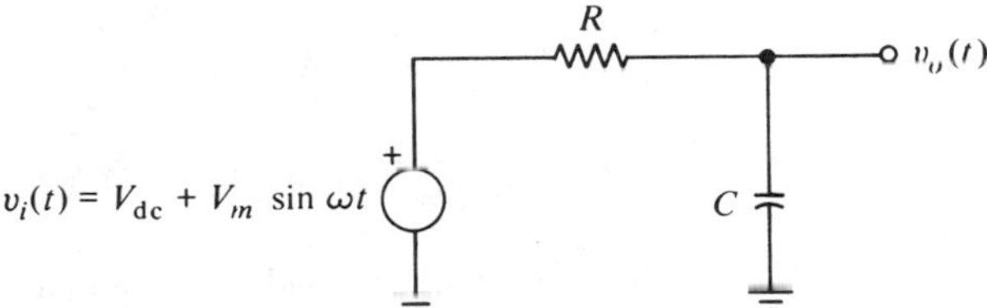

Fig. 9-11

Solution.

(a) Consider one component of the input at a time as shown in Fig. 9-12. The dc portion of the input causes the output eventually to rise to V_{dc}. (When the excitation is constant, the current in an *RC* circuit becomes zero, for all practical purposes, after

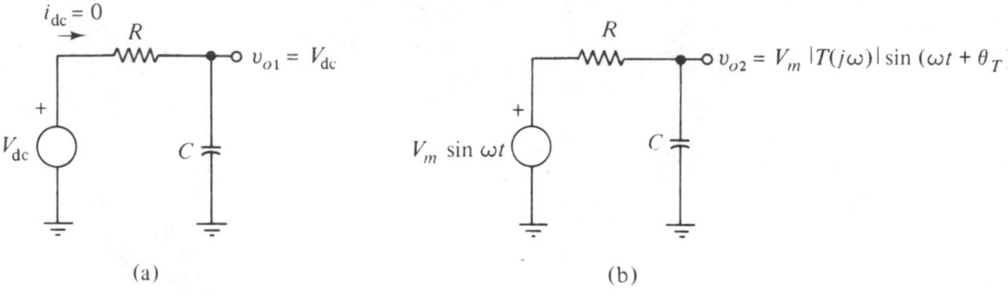

Fig. 9-12

five time constants). The sinusoidal portion of the input causes, in the steady state, a sinusoidal output. By superposition, we have

$$v_o = v_{o1} + v_{o2} = V_{dc} + V_m \left| T(j\omega) \right| \sin(\omega t + \theta_T)$$

where $\left| T(j\omega) \right|$ and θ_T are obtained from

$$T(s) = \frac{1/sC}{R + 1/sC} = \frac{1}{sRC + 1}, \qquad T(j\omega) = \frac{1}{j\omega RC + 1}$$

$$\left| T(j\omega) \right| = \frac{1}{\sqrt{1 + (\omega RC)^2}}, \qquad \theta_T = -\tan^{-1} \omega RC$$

Then

$$v_o(t) = V_{dc} + \frac{V_m}{\sqrt{1 + (\omega RC)^2}} \sin(\omega t - \tan^{-1} \omega RC) \quad \text{Ans.}$$

(b) The input and output waveforms are

$$v_i(t) = V_{dc} + V_m \sin \omega t$$

$$v_o(t) = V_{dc} + \frac{V_m}{\sqrt{1 + (\omega RC)^2}} \sin(\omega t - \tan^{-1} \omega RC)$$

The dc component of both waveforms is the same. However, because the RC network acts as a lowpass filter (with cutoff frequency $\omega_c = 1/RC$), the sine wave component in the output waveform is smaller in amplitude than at the input. As a result, the input and output waveforms differ as shown in Fig. 9-13. By making the cutoff frequency of the filter much smaller than the frequency of the sine wave ($1/RC \ll \omega$), we can attenuate the sine wave by a large amount. Consequently, the output waveform, for all practical purposes, stays at a constant level that represents the dc value of the input. Thus we are able to separate and recover completely the dc component of the input waveform. Alternatively speaking, the circuit detects the average value of the input waveform.

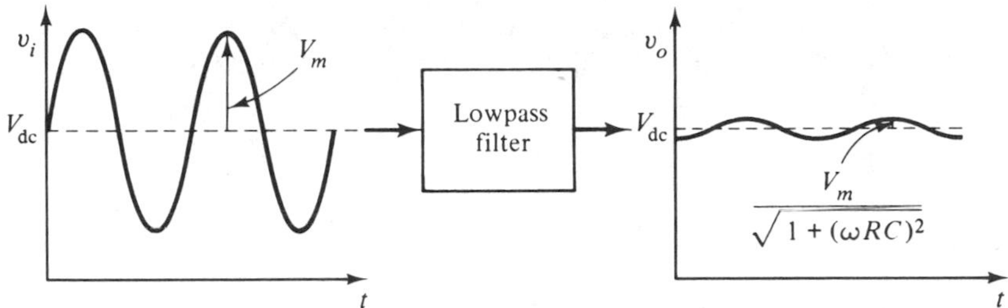

Fig. 9-13

9-3 HIGHPASS FILTERS

Highpass filters are used to stop low-frequency sine waves and pass the high-frequency sine waves. The *cutoff frequency* ω_c is used to distinguish the stopband ($\omega < \omega_c$) from the passband ($\omega > \omega_c$). The ideal highpass filter is characterized by the magnitude and phase curves given in Fig. 9-14. The shape of the phase characteristic in the stopband is not important, since the amplitude function there is zero.

It is *not possible* to produce networks having such idealized highpass characteristics. Rather, networks produce an approximation to the highpass response. The higher the order of the function, the better the approximation that can be made. However, it should be realized that higher-order functions are more difficult to implement in practice, since there are many more components to adjust for proper operation. Here we discuss only first- and second-order functions and networks.

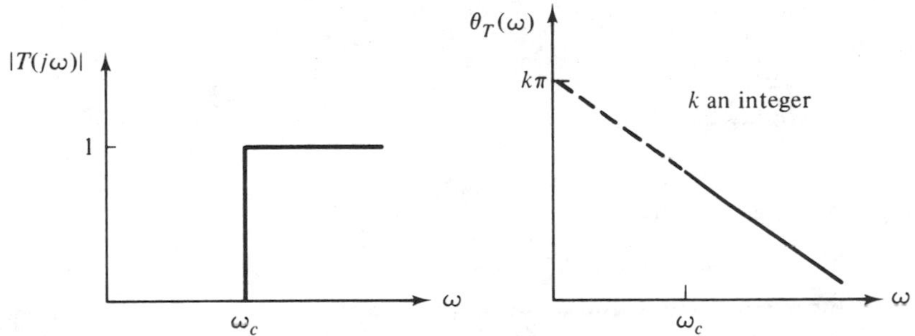

Fig. 9-14

The First-order Function and First-order Networks

The first-order highpass function is given by

$$T_1(s) = \frac{s}{s + \omega_c} = \frac{s/\omega_c}{s/\omega_c + 1} \tag{9-19}$$

To show that it approximates the ideal highpass characteristics, we let $s = j\omega$ and find the resulting magnitude and phase functions.

$$T_1(j\omega) = \frac{j\omega/\omega_c}{j\omega/\omega_c + 1}$$

$$|T_1(j\omega)| = \frac{\omega/\omega_c}{\sqrt{1 + (\omega/\omega_c)^2}} \tag{9-20a}$$

$$\theta_1(\omega) = \frac{\pi}{2} - \tan^{-1}\frac{\omega}{\omega_c} \tag{9-20b}$$

These functions are plotted in Fig. 9-15. The magnitude characteristic does not exhibit a sharp rise with frequency to allow clear distinction between the stopband and passband. Nonetheless, the constant ω_c, which designates the frequency at which the magnitude is $1/\sqrt{2}$ times the magnitude value at infinite frequency, is taken as the cutoff or half-power frequency. Since ω_c is in radians per second, the cutoff frequency in hertz is given by $f_c = \omega_c/2\pi$. The cutoff frequency also represents the bandwidth of rejection.

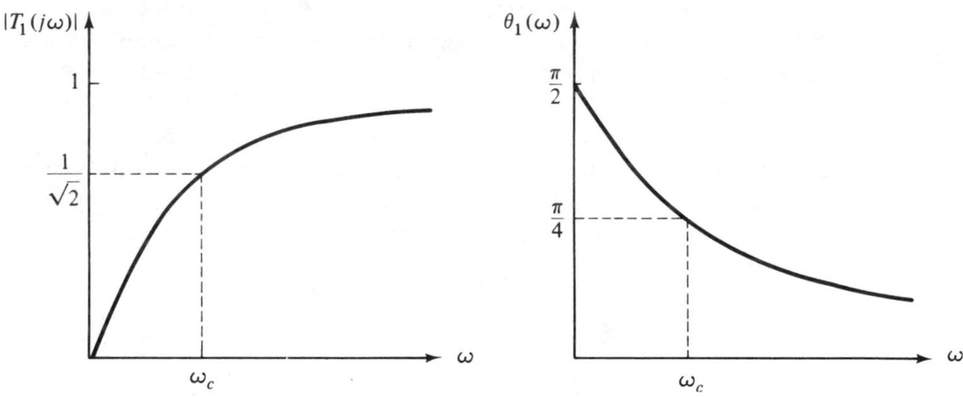

Fig. 9-15

The phase characteristic approaches zero asymptotically. Thus it approximates in the passband the ideal phase curve given in Fig. 9-14 if we take both k and the slope of the ideal curve to be zero.

The first-order highpass function given by Eq. (9-19) is realized (within a scale factor) by the two networks shown in Fig. 9-16. Both networks operate between a resistive source R_s and a resistive load R_L. The networks are described by the transfer function.

$$T(s) = \frac{V_o}{V_i} = \frac{R_L}{R_s + R_L}\left(\frac{s}{s + \omega_c}\right) \tag{9-21}$$

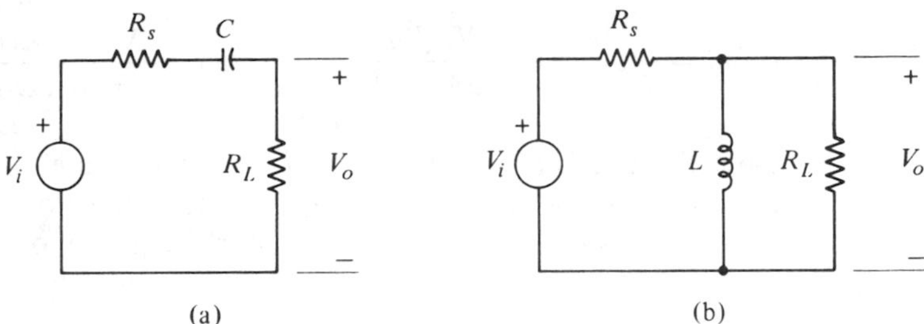

Fig. 9-16

where $\omega_c = \dfrac{1}{(R_s + R_L)C}$ $\quad$ (RC network)

$$\omega_c = \frac{R_s R_L}{R_s + R_L}\frac{1}{L} \quad (RL \text{ network})$$

These expressions for the cutoff frequency are used to determine the value of C [for the network of Fig. 9-16(a)] or the value of L [for the network of Fig. 9-16(b)] to achieve a specified cutoff frequency for given or known source and load resistances.

The scale factor, $R_L/(R_s + R_L)$, affects all frequencies equally. Being less than unity, it attenuates the signals in the passband (as well as those in the stopband).

If the highpass characteristic presented by the first-order function turns out to be a poor approximation to the desired characteristic, using a second- or higher-order function becomes necessary.

The Second-order Function and Second-order Networks

Many second-order functions possess highpass characteristics. These functions differ somewhat in their stopband and passband characteristics. One widely used function is described by

$$T_2(s) = \frac{s^2}{s^2 + s\sqrt{2}\omega_c + \omega_c^2} \tag{9-22}$$

The associated magnitude and phase functions are obtained by letting $s = j\omega$.

$$T_2(j\omega) = \frac{-\omega^2}{(\omega_c^2 - \omega^2) + j\omega\sqrt{2}\omega_c} = \frac{(\omega/\omega_c)^2}{[(\omega/\omega_c)^2 - 1] - j\sqrt{2}(\omega/\omega_c)}$$

$$\left|T_2(j\omega)\right| = \frac{(\omega/\omega_c)^2}{\sqrt{[(\omega/\omega_c)^2 - 1]^2 + 2(\omega/\omega_c)^2}} = \frac{(\omega/\omega_c)^2}{\sqrt{1 + (\omega/\omega_c)^4}} \tag{9-23a}$$

$$\theta_2(\omega) = -\tan^{-1}\frac{-\sqrt{2}(\omega/\omega_c)}{(\omega/\omega_c)^2 - 1} = \pi - \tan^{-1}\frac{\sqrt{2}(\omega/\omega_c)}{1 - (\omega/\omega_c)^2} \qquad \text{(9-23b)}$$

These functions are plotted in Fig. 9-17. We note again that the constant ω_c, which designates the frequency at which the magnitude function is $1/\sqrt{2}$ times the magnitude at $\omega = \infty$, is used to represent the cutoff frequency or the rejection bandwidth. The phase characteristic approaches zero asymptotically.

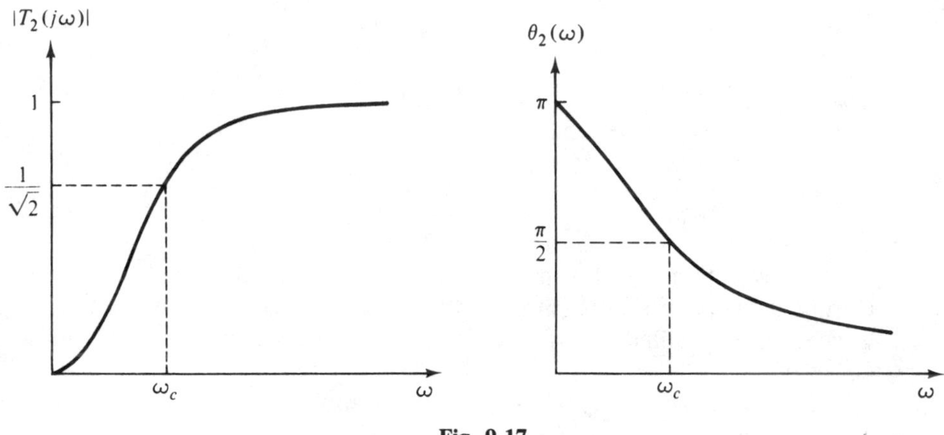

Fig. 9-17

In Fig. 9-18 the magnitude characteristic of the second-order function [Eq. (9-23a)] is compared with that of the first-order function [Eq. (9-20a)]. The second-order curve is below the first-order curve in the stopband (hence it attenuates more), and it is above the first-order curve in the passband (hence it passes better).

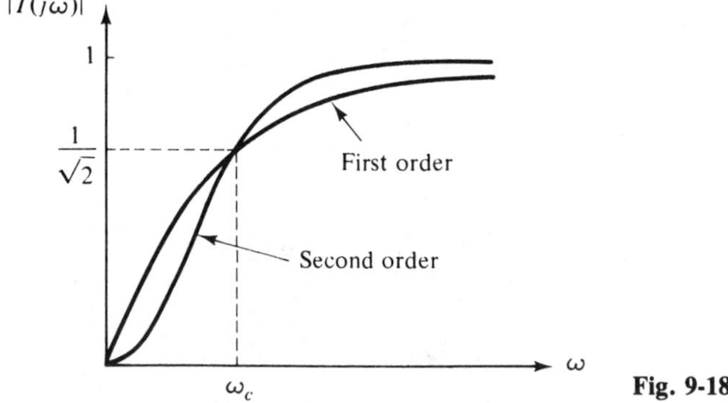

Fig. 9-18

The second-order function given by Eq. (9-22) is realized (within a scale factor) by either network shown in Fig. 9-19.

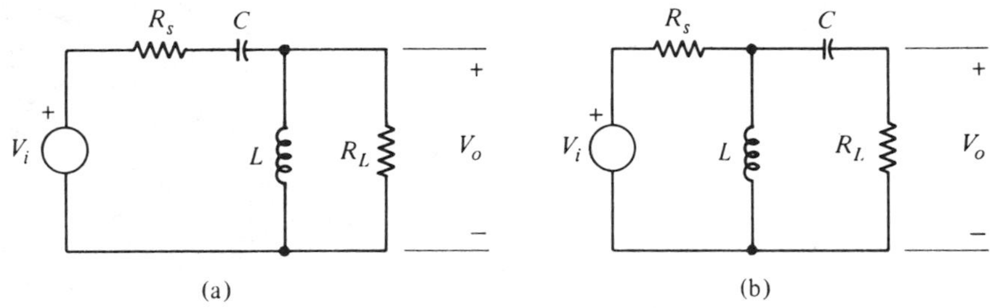

Fig. 9-19

It can be shown (see Problem 9-10) that, for $R_s = R_L = R$, the transfer function of both networks is the same and is given by

$$\frac{V_o}{V_i} = \frac{1}{2}\left[\frac{s^2}{s^2 + s\frac{1}{2}\left(\frac{R}{L} + \frac{1}{RC}\right) + \frac{1}{2LC}}\right] \tag{9-24}$$

We want the transfer function to represent the highpass function given by Eq. (9-22) with a scale factor of $\frac{1}{2}$—that is,

$$\frac{V_o}{V_i} = \frac{1}{2}\left(\frac{s^2}{s^2 + s\sqrt{2}\omega_c + \omega_c^2}\right) \tag{9-25}$$

Matching the coefficients in the denominator polynomial, we obtain

$$\sqrt{2}\omega_c = \frac{1}{2}\left(\frac{R}{L} + \frac{1}{RC}\right), \qquad \omega_c^2 = \frac{1}{2LC} \tag{9-26}$$

Usually R is given and ω_c is specified. L and C, the remaining unknowns, are obtained by solving simultaneously the set of equations given by Eq. (9-26). The result is

$$L = \frac{R}{\sqrt{2}\omega_c}, \qquad C = \frac{1}{\sqrt{2}\omega_c R} \tag{9-27}$$

Thus the design of the filter is completed.

Example 9-3

Design a circuit that removes the dc component of the input voltage waveform while it passes the sinusoidal component. The internal resistance of the source is R_s.

Solution. The circuit must stop the dc voltage and pass the sine wave. So a highpass circuit must be used. A first-order RL or RC circuit can be used for this purpose. The circuits are shown in Fig. 9-20. In the RL circuit of Fig. 9-20(a) the voltage across the inductor due to the dc voltage source is zero (after five time constants from the time the voltage is applied). Thus the steady-state output is due to the ac signal only.

$$v_{oa} = V_m |T_a(j\omega)| \sin\ (\omega t + \theta_a) \tag{9-28}$$

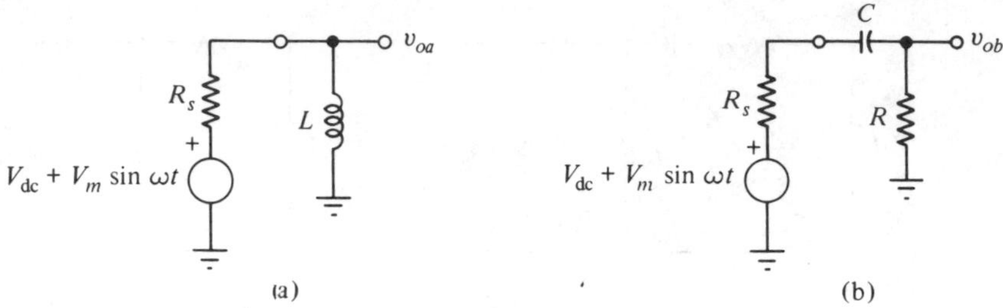

Fig. 9-20

where $$|T_a(j\omega)| = \frac{\omega}{\sqrt{\omega^2 + (R_s/L)^2}}$$

$$\theta_a = \frac{\pi}{2} - \tan^{-1}\frac{\omega L}{R_s}$$

The cutoff frequency of this highpass filter is

$$f_{ca} = \frac{1}{2\pi}\frac{R_s}{L} \quad \text{Hz}$$

For $\omega \gg \omega_{ca}$, $|T_a(j\omega)| \cong 1$ and $\theta_a \cong 0$. So the output is the same as the sinusoidal portion of the input.

In the RC circuit of Fig. 9-20(b) the current through the capacitor due to the dc voltage source is zero (after five time constants from the time the voltage source is applied). As a result, there is no dc voltage across the output resistor. The capacitor blocks the dc. The steady-state output is due to the ac signal only.

$$v_{ob} = V_m|T_b(j\omega)| \sin\ (\omega t + \theta_b) \tag{9-29}$$

where $$|T_b(j\omega)| = \left(\frac{R}{R_s + R}\right)\frac{\omega}{\sqrt{\omega^2 + 1/[(R_s + R)^2C^2]}}$$

$$\theta_b(\omega) = \frac{\pi}{2} - \tan^{-1}[\omega(R_s + R)C]$$

The cutoff frequency is

$$f_{cb} = \frac{1}{2\pi}\frac{1}{(R_s + R)C}$$

For $\omega \gg \omega_{cb}$, $|T_b(j\omega)| \cong R/(R_s + R)$ and $\theta_b \cong 0$. The output then becomes

$$v_{ob} \cong V_m\frac{R}{R_s + R}\sin\ \omega t$$

Because of $R/(R_s + R)$, the passband signals are attenuated by this filter. In either circuit, the cutoff frequency is taken equal to or lower than the smallest frequency expected to be passed by the circuit.

Example 9-4

The circuit of Fig. 9-21 has one input and two outputs. Discuss the operations of the circuit as the frequency of the input signal is varied from low to high values.

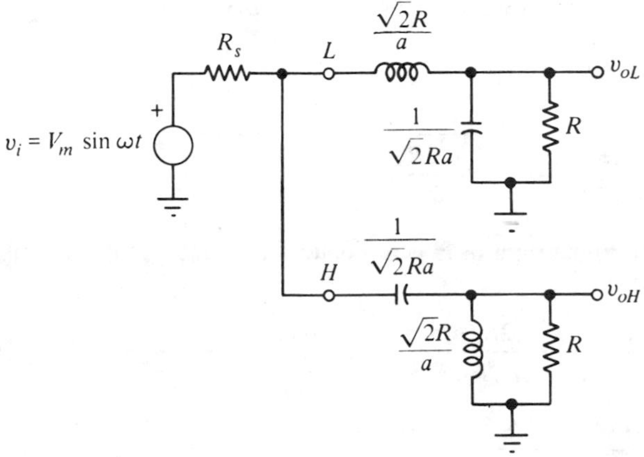

Fig. 9-21

Solution. The transfer function $V_{oL}(s)/V_i(s)$ and $V_{oH}(s)/V_i(s)$ describe the properties of this circuit. The various steps in the calculation of these functions are given in Fig. 9-22.

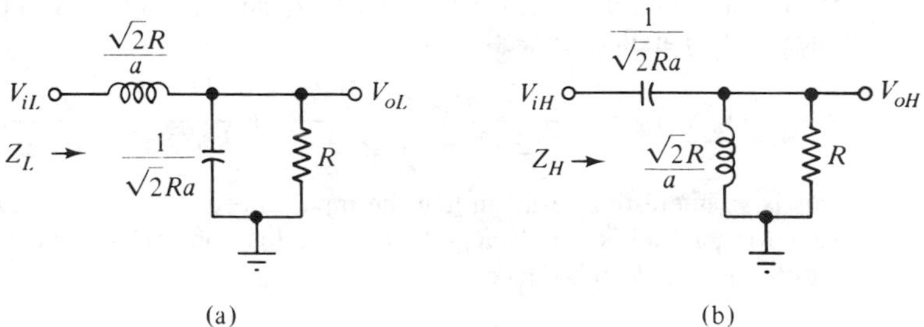

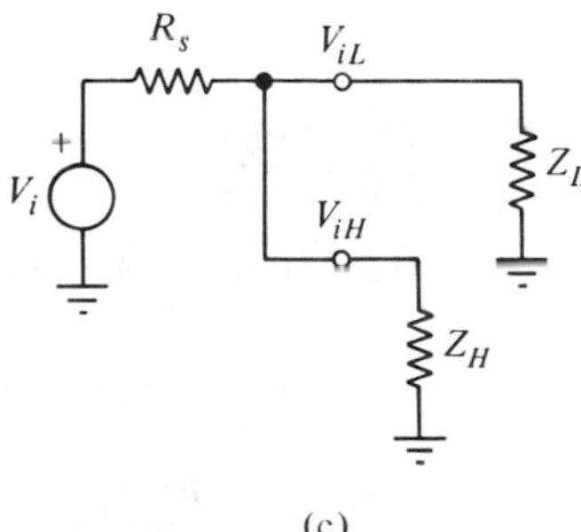

Fig. 9-22

The portion of the circuit to the right of L is reproduced in Fig. 9-22(a). We now calculate the input impedance Z_L and the voltage ratio V_{oL}/V_{iL} for this circuit.

$$Z_L = s\frac{\sqrt{2}R}{a} + \frac{R(\sqrt{2}Ra/s)}{R + (\sqrt{2}Ra/s)} = R\sqrt{2}\left[\frac{s^2 + s\sqrt{2}a + a^2}{a(s + \sqrt{2}a)}\right] \tag{9-30}$$

$$\frac{V_{oL}}{V_{iL}} = \frac{\dfrac{R(\sqrt{2}Ra/s)}{R + (\sqrt{2}Ra/s)}}{\dfrac{R(\sqrt{2}Ra/s)}{R + (\sqrt{2}Ra/s)} + s\dfrac{\sqrt{2}R}{a}} = \frac{a^2}{s^2 + s\sqrt{2}a + a^2} \tag{9-31}$$

The portion of the circuit to the right of H is reproduced in Fig. 9-22(b). From this circuit we calculate Z_H and V_{oH}/V_{iH}.

$$Z_H = \frac{\sqrt{2}Ra}{s} + \frac{s(\sqrt{2}R/a)R}{s(\sqrt{2}R/a) + R} = R\sqrt{2}\left[\frac{s^2 + s\sqrt{2}a + a^2}{s(s\sqrt{2} + a)}\right] \tag{9-32}$$

$$\frac{V_{oH}}{V_{iH}} = \frac{\dfrac{s(\sqrt{2}R/a)R}{s(\sqrt{2}R/a) + R}}{\dfrac{s(\sqrt{2}R/a)R}{s(\sqrt{2}R/a)} + \dfrac{\sqrt{2}Ra}{s}} = \frac{s^2}{s^2 + s\sqrt{2}a + a^2} \tag{9-33}$$

As shown in Fig. 9-22(c), the source sees Z_L and Z_H connected in parallel. The admittance of the parallel connection is

$$Y_L + Y_H = \frac{1}{R\sqrt{2}}\frac{a(s + \sqrt{2}a)}{s^2 + s\sqrt{2}a + a^2} + \frac{1}{R\sqrt{2}}\frac{s(s\sqrt{2} + a)}{s^2 + s\sqrt{2}a + a^2} = \frac{1}{R}$$

This is an interesting result in that the input impedance of the two RLC networks connected in parallel is simply R, which is the load on each circuit. So the input divides between R_s and R to produce

$$V_{iL} = V_{iH} = V_i\frac{R}{R_s + R} \tag{9-34}$$

Since

$$\frac{V_{oL}}{V_i} = \left(\frac{V_{iL}}{V_i}\right)\left(\frac{V_{oL}}{V_{iL}}\right) \qquad \text{and} \qquad \frac{V_{oH}}{V_i} = \left(\frac{V_{iH}}{V_i}\right)\left(\frac{V_{oH}}{V_{iH}}\right)$$

we make use of Eqs. (9-34), (9-31), and (9-33) to obtain the desired transfer functions.

$$\frac{V_{oL}}{V_i} = \frac{R}{R_s + R}\left(\frac{a^2}{s^2 + s\sqrt{2}a + a^2}\right) \tag{9-35}$$

$$\frac{V_{oH}}{V_i} = \frac{R}{R_s + R}\left(\frac{s^2}{s^2 + s\sqrt{2}a + a^2}\right) \tag{9-36}$$

To see how the two outputs vary with frequency, we calculate the two magnitude functions.

$$\left|\frac{V_{oL}}{V_i}\right|_{s=j\omega} = \frac{R}{R_s + R}\frac{1}{\sqrt{1 + (\omega/a)^4}} \tag{9-37}$$

$$\left|\frac{V_{oH}}{V_i}\right|_{s=j\omega} = \frac{R}{R_s + R}\frac{(\omega/a)^2}{\sqrt{1 + (\omega/a)^4}} \tag{9-38}$$

Equation (9-37) represents the response of a lowpass filter with cutoff at $\omega = a$ rad/s [see Eq. (9-10a)]. Equation (9-38) represents the response of a highpass filter with cutoff at $\omega = a$ rad/s [see Eq. (9-23a)]. Hence the circuit of Fig. 9-21 separates the low frequencies from the high frequencies. It channels all frequencies between 0 and $a(0 < \omega < a)$ to the output marked v_{oL}, and it channels all frequencies above $a(\omega > a)$ to the output marked v_{oH}. This action is graphically illustrated in Fig. 9-23. The frequency $a/2\pi$ is appropriately called the *crossover* frequency. This circuit can be used to direct low- and high-frequency audio signals to low- and high-frequency speakers. The load resistances on the filters are the equivalent speaker resistances.

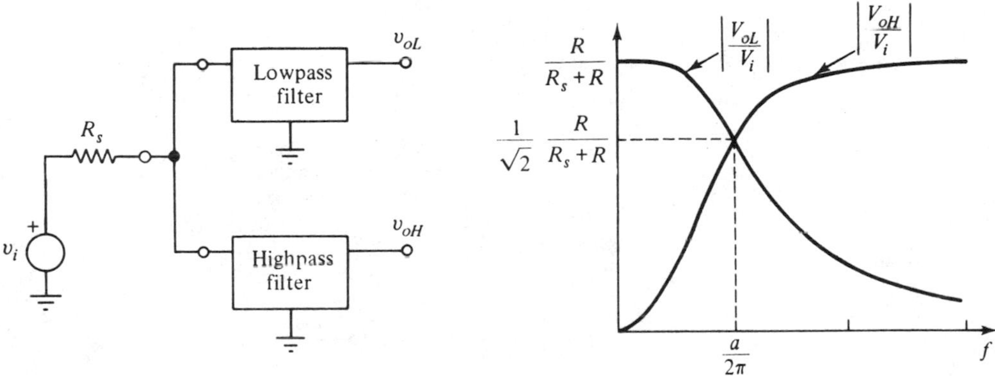

Fig. 9-23

9-4 BANDPASS FILTERS

Bandpass filters are used to pass sine waves that have frequencies falling within a specified band. This band is known as the *bandwidth* of the filter. The ideal bandpass filter is characterized by the magnitude and phase curve given in Fig. 9-24. The bandwidth is $(\omega_2 - \omega_1)$ rad/s.

Using networks it is possible to produce only an approximation to the ideal bandpass characteristics. At least a second-order function—and hence a two-pole network—is required to achieve a bandpass response. Although there are many sec-

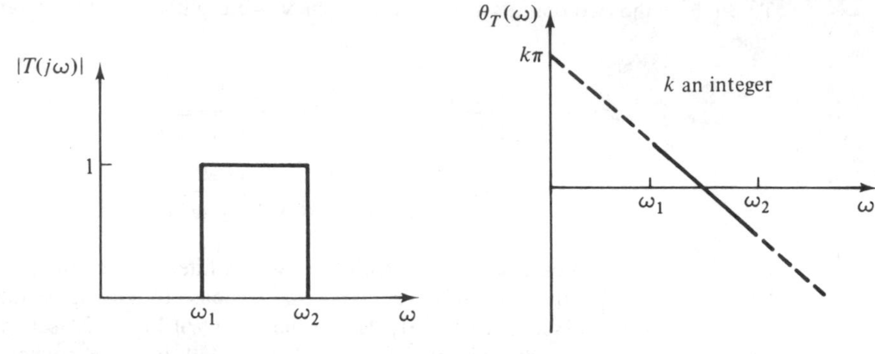

Fig. 9-24

ond- and higher-order functions that can be used, here we discuss the properties of the second-order function given by

$$T(s) = \frac{s\omega_b}{s^2 + s\omega_b + \omega_p^2} \tag{9-39}$$

where ω_b and ω_p are constants.

For $s = j\omega$ we obtain

$$T(j\omega) = \frac{j\omega\omega_b}{(\omega_p^2 - \omega^2) + j\omega\omega_b}$$

$$\left|T(j\omega)\right| = \frac{\omega\omega_b}{\sqrt{(\omega_p^2 - \omega^2)^2 + (\omega\omega_b)^2}} \tag{9-40a}$$

$$\theta_T(\omega) = \frac{\pi}{2} - \tan^{-1}\left(\frac{\omega\omega_b}{\omega_p^2 - \omega^2}\right) \tag{9-40b}$$

The magnitude and phase functions are plotted in Fig. 9-25. The magnitude has a maximum at $\omega = \omega_p$. So the constant ω_p in Eq. (9-39) represents the frequency at which the magnitude curve reaches a maximum.

The *bandwidth* of the bandpass function is defined as *the difference of the two frequencies at which the magnitude is $1/\sqrt{2}$ times the peak magnitude*. These two frequencies, which are also known as half-power frequencies, are designated in Fig. 9-25 as ω_1 and ω_2. It can be shown that the difference of these two frequencies is ω_b—that is,

$$\omega_2 - \omega_1 = \omega_b \tag{9-41}$$

The constant ω_b in Eq. (9-39) thus represents the bandwidth in radians per second.

It can also be shown that $\theta_T(\omega_1) = \pi/4$ and $\theta_T(\omega_2) = -\pi/4$ (see Problem 9-29).

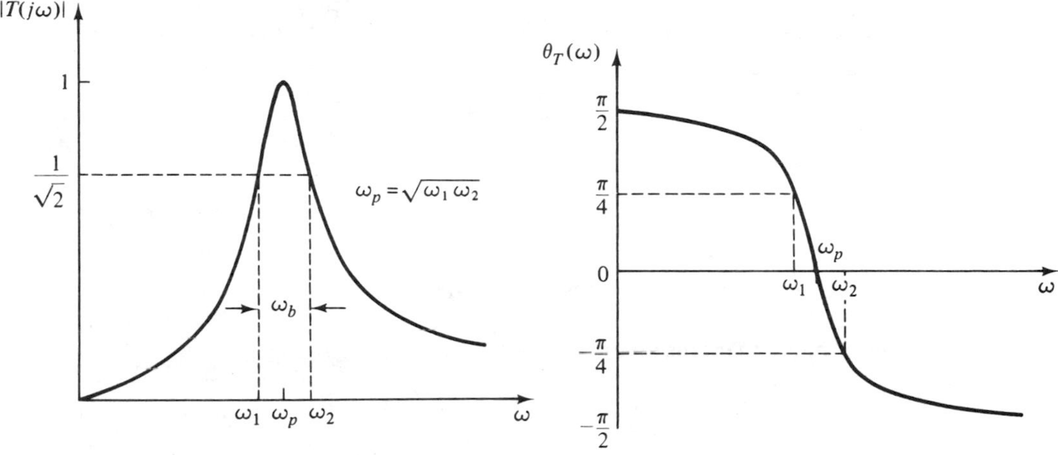

Fig. 9-25

To underscore the significance of the coefficients in the bandpass function, Eq. (9-39) is reproduced here with added descriptions.

$$T(s) = \frac{s\omega_b}{s^2 + \underbrace{s\omega_b}_{\text{Bandwidth}} + \underbrace{(\omega_p)^2}_{\text{Frequency of peak magnitude}}} \tag{9-42}$$

Changing the coefficient of the s^1 term (ω_b) in the denominator polynomial changes the bandwidth of the bandpass characteristic without affecting the frequency at which the peak occurs. The *smaller this coefficient* is made, the smaller the bandwidth and the *more selective* the bandpass curve. On the other hand, changing the constant term in the denominator polynomial (ω_p^2) changes the frequency at which the peak occurs. If this coefficient is made larger, the selectivity curve is moved to the right (to a higher band of frequencies) without altering the bandwidth. The process of changing the frequency of the bandpass curve by changing ω_p is known as *tuning*.

The second-order bandpass function can be realized by the circuits shown in Fig. 9-26. For the circuit of Fig. 9-26(a), we have

$$\frac{V_o}{V_i} = \frac{R_L}{R_s + R_L}\left[\frac{s\dfrac{1}{C}\left(\dfrac{R_s + R_L}{R_sR_L}\right)}{s^2 + s\dfrac{1}{C}\left(\dfrac{R_s + R_L}{R_sR_L}\right) + \dfrac{1}{LC}}\right]$$

$$\frac{V_o}{V_i} = \frac{R_L}{R_s + R_L}\left[\frac{s\omega_b}{s^2 + s\omega_b + \omega_p^2}\right] \tag{9-43a}$$

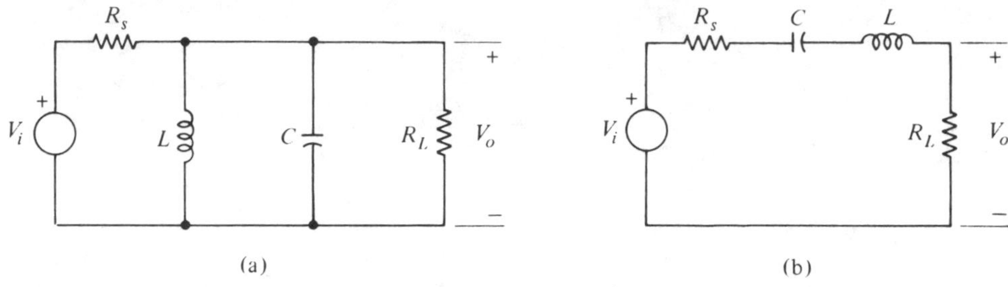

Fig. 9-26

Term-by-term comparison gives

$$\omega_b = \frac{1}{C}\left(\frac{R_s + R_L}{R_s R_L}\right) \tag{9-43b}$$

$$\omega_p = \frac{1}{\sqrt{LC}} \tag{9-43c}$$

In a typical design problem, ω_b and ω_p are specified. Also, R_s and R_L are given. The two remaining element values are obtained by solving Eq. (9-43b) for C and Eq. (9-43c) for L.

$$C = \frac{R_s + R_L}{R_s R_L}\frac{1}{\omega_b} \tag{9-44a}$$

$$L = \frac{1}{\omega_p^2 C} = \frac{R_s R_L}{R_s + R_L}\frac{\omega_b}{\omega_p^2} \tag{9-44b}$$

The circuit of Fig. 9-26(a) is known as the *parallel-resonant* circuit. The frequency at which the output peaks ($\omega = \omega_p = 1/\sqrt{LC}$) is called the *resonant frequency*. At the resonant frequency the transfer function becomes

$$\left.\frac{V_o}{V_i}\right|_{s=j\omega_p} = \frac{R_L}{R_s + R_L}\left[\frac{j\omega_p\omega_b}{-\omega_p^2 + j\omega_p\omega_b + \omega_p^2}\right] = \frac{R_L}{R_s + R_L}$$

This result can be seen directly from Fig. 9-26(a) by recognizing that at the resonant frequency the impedance of the parallel LC circuit is infinite—that is,

$$Z_{LC} = \left.\frac{s(1/C)}{s^2 + 1/LC}\right|_{s=j(1/\sqrt{LC})} = \frac{j(1/\sqrt{LC})(1/C)}{-1/LC + 1/LC} = \infty$$

Therefore the resistive portion of the circuit determines the output.

For the circuit of Fig. 9-26(b), we have

$$\frac{V_o}{V_i} = \frac{R_L}{R_s + R_L}\left[\frac{s(R_s + R_L)/L}{s^2 + s(R_s + R_L)/L + 1/LC}\right] = \frac{R_L}{R_s + R_L}\left(\frac{s\omega_b}{s^2 + s\omega_b + \omega_p^2}\right) \tag{9-45}$$

Term-by-term comparison gives

$$\omega_b = \frac{R_s + R_L}{L} \tag{9-46a}$$

$$\omega_p = \frac{1}{\sqrt{LC}} \tag{9-46b}$$

These equations are used to calculate L and C for given ω_b, ω_p, R_s, and R_L.

The circuit of Fig. 9-26(b) is known as the *series-resonant* circuit. The frequency at which the output peaks ($\omega = \omega_p = 1/\sqrt{LC}$) is called the *resonant frequency*. At the resonant frequency the transfer function becomes

$$\left.\frac{V_o}{V_i}\right|_{s=j\omega_p} = \frac{R_L}{R_s + R_L}$$

This result can be seen directly from Fig. 9-26(b) by recognizing that at the resonant frequency the impedance of the series LC circuit is zero—that is,

$$Z_{LC} = \left.\frac{s^2LC + 1}{sC}\right|_{s=j(1/\sqrt{LC})} = \frac{-1 + 1}{j(1/\sqrt{LC})C} = 0$$

Thus the resistive portion of the circuit determines the output.

Example 9-5

Refer to Fig. 9-27. The inductor is made variable. How does the magnitude curve change with changes in L?

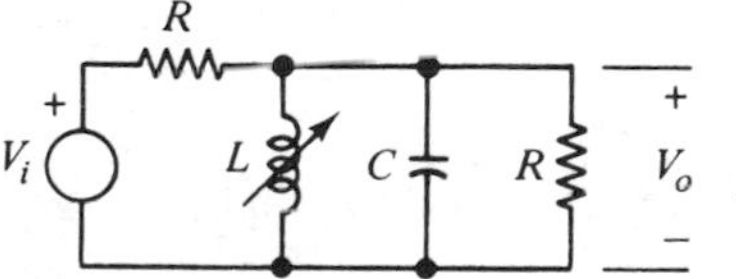

Fig. 9-27

Solution. From Eq. (9-43) we have

$$\frac{V_o}{V_i} = \frac{1}{2}\frac{s\omega_b}{s^2 + s\omega_b + \omega_p^2}$$

where $\omega_b = \dfrac{2}{RC}$, $\qquad \omega_p = \dfrac{1}{\sqrt{LC}}$

The inductor affects ω_p but not ω_b. The peak value of the magnitude is not dependent on L either.

$$\left|\frac{V_o}{V_i}\right|_{\omega=\omega_p} = \frac{1}{2}$$

So as L is varied, the bandpass curve is shifted to the right (smaller L) or left (larger L) at constant bandwidth and constant peak value. The shift for a two-to-one variation in L is shown in Fig. 9-28.

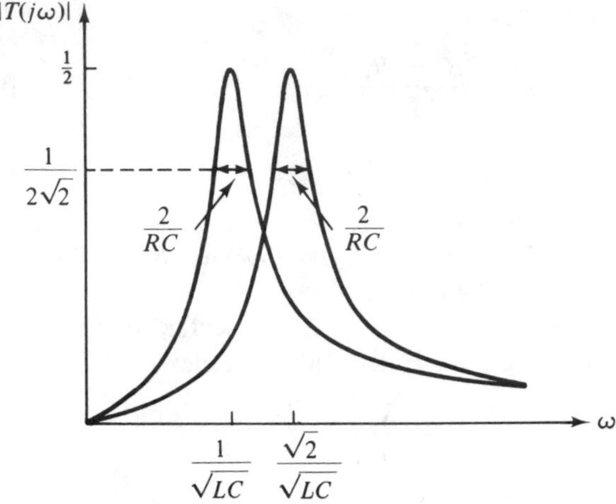

Fig. 9-28

Example 9-6

In the bandpass circuit of Fig. 9-29 $R \ll \frac{1}{2}\sqrt{L/C}$.

(a) Sketch the magnitude characteristic and discuss it.

(b) How are the half-power frequencies related to the pole positions?

Solution.

(a) The transfer function realized by the network is

$$\frac{V_o}{V_i} = \frac{s\dfrac{1}{RC}}{s^2 + s\dfrac{1}{RC} + \dfrac{1}{LC}} \tag{9-47}$$

The poles of the transfer function are given by

$$p_{1,2} = -\frac{1}{2RC} \pm \sqrt{\left(\frac{1}{2RC}\right)^2 - \frac{1}{LC}} = -\frac{1}{2RC}\left(1 \pm \sqrt{1 - \frac{4R^2C}{L}}\right) \tag{9-48}$$

The given constraint, $R \ll \frac{1}{2}\sqrt{L/C}$ can be expressed as

$$\frac{4R^2C}{L} \ll 1 \tag{9-49}$$

Making use of the fact that $\sqrt{1-x} \cong 1 - \frac{1}{2}x$ for $|x| \ll 1$, Eq. (9-48) can be simplified.

$$p_{1,2} \cong -\frac{1}{2RC}\left[1 \pm \left(1 - \frac{2R^2C}{L}\right)\right]$$

$$p_1 \cong -\frac{1}{2RC}\left[1 - \left(1 - \frac{2R^2C}{L}\right)\right] = -\frac{R}{L} \tag{9-50a}$$

$$p_2 \cong -\frac{1}{2RC}\left[1 + \left(1 - \frac{2R^2C}{L}\right)\right] \cong -\frac{1}{RC} \tag{9-50b}$$

Hence the transfer function can be written in factored form as

$$\frac{V_o}{V_i} \cong \frac{s\dfrac{1}{RC}}{\left(s + \dfrac{R}{L}\right)\left(s + \dfrac{1}{RC}\right)} \tag{9-51}$$

The corresponding magnitude function is obtained as follows.

$$\left.\frac{V_o}{V_i}\right|_{s=j\omega} \cong \frac{j\omega\dfrac{1}{RC}}{\left(j\omega + \dfrac{R}{L}\right)\left(j\omega + \dfrac{1}{RC}\right)}$$

$$\left|\frac{V_o}{V_i}\right| \cong \frac{\omega\dfrac{1}{RC}}{\sqrt{\omega^2 + \left(\dfrac{R}{L}\right)^2}\sqrt{\omega^2 + \left(\dfrac{1}{RC}\right)^2}} \tag{9-52}$$

The magnitude characteristic is sketched in Fig. 9-30. The frequency at which the maximum magnitude occurs is obtained from the square root of the constant term in the denominator of Eq. (9-47): $\omega = 1/\sqrt{LC}$. Because $R/L \ll 1/RC$, the poles are widely separated. As a result, the operation of the circuit can be discussed in terms of three distinct frequency ranges.

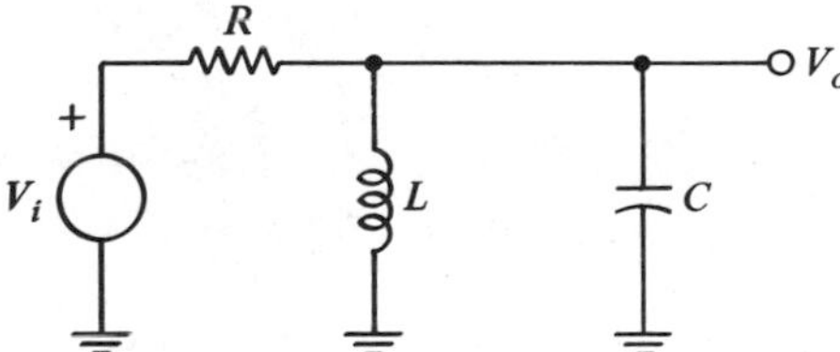

Fig. 9-29

1. For frequencies much less than the center frequency, $\omega \ll 1/\sqrt{LC}$, ω^2 is negligible in comparison to $(1/RC)^2$. Hence Eq. (9-52) can be approximated as

$$\frac{V_o}{V_i} \cong \frac{\omega\dfrac{1}{RC}}{\sqrt{\omega^2 + \left(\dfrac{R}{L}\right)^2}\sqrt{\omega^2 + \left(\dfrac{1}{RC}\right)^2}} \simeq \frac{\omega\dfrac{1}{RC}}{\sqrt{\omega^2 + \left(\dfrac{R}{L}\right)^2}\dfrac{1}{RC}} = \frac{\omega}{\sqrt{\omega^2 + \left(\dfrac{R}{L}\right)^2}} \tag{9-53}$$

This result can be interpreted as follows. If the frequency is low enough, the current taken by the capacitor of Fig. 9-29 is negligible in comparison to the current taken by the inductor. Hence the circuit can be redrawn without the C

as shown in Fig. 9-30. The resulting *RL* network is described by the transfer function

$$\frac{V_o}{V_i} = \frac{sL}{sL + R} = \frac{s}{s + \dfrac{R}{L}} \tag{9-54}$$

which has the magnitude characteristic described by Eq. (9-53).

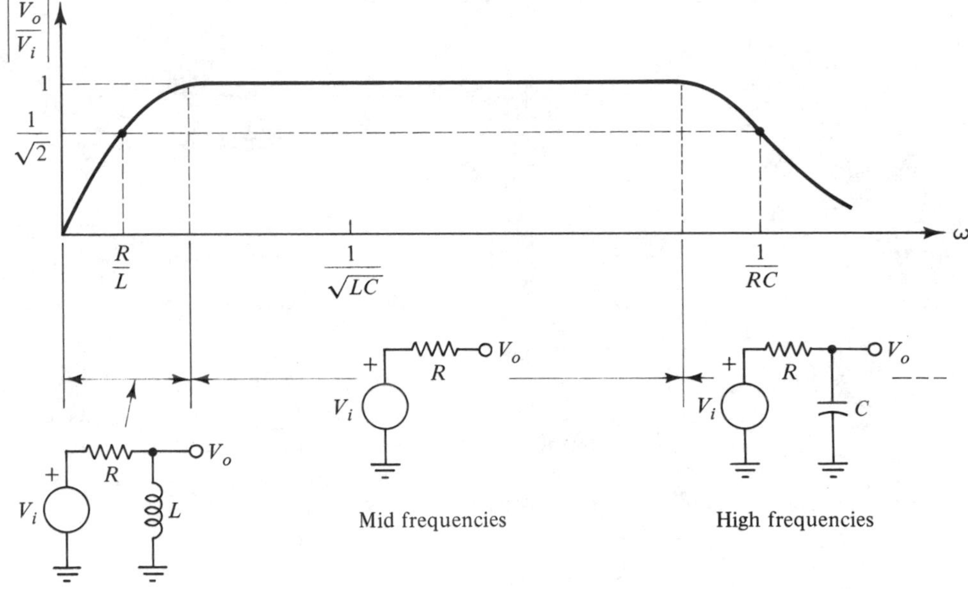

Fig. 9-30

2. For frequencies near $1/\sqrt{LC}$, ω^2 is much greater than $(R/L)^2$ but much less than $(1/RC)^2$. Hence Eq. (9-52) can be approximated as

$$\left|\frac{V_o}{V_i}\right| \cong \frac{\omega\dfrac{1}{RC}}{\sqrt{\omega^2 + \left(\dfrac{R}{L}\right)^2}\sqrt{\omega^2 + \left(\dfrac{1}{RC}\right)^2}} \cong \frac{\omega\dfrac{1}{RC}}{(\omega)\dfrac{1}{RC}} = 1 \tag{9-55}$$

This result can be interpreted as follows. At mid frequencies, the *LC* portion is at or near resonance. Therefore its impedance is infinite or high and practically all of the source voltage appears across it. Hence the circuit of Fig. 2-29 can be redrawn as if the source voltage is facing an open circuit. See Fig. 9-30. The resulting transfer function is

$$\frac{V_o}{V_i} = 1$$

3. For frequencies much greater than the center frequency, $\omega \gg 1/\sqrt{LC}$, ω^2 is much larger than $(R/L)^2$. Hence Eq. (9-52) can be approximated as

$$\frac{V_o}{V_i} \cong \frac{\omega \dfrac{1}{RC}}{\sqrt{\omega^2 + \left(\dfrac{R}{L}\right)^2}\sqrt{\omega^2 + \left(\dfrac{1}{RC}\right)^2}} \cong \frac{\omega \dfrac{1}{RC}}{\omega\sqrt{\omega^2 + \left(\dfrac{1}{RC}\right)^2}} = \frac{\dfrac{1}{RC}}{\sqrt{\omega^2 + \left(\dfrac{1}{RC}\right)^2}} \tag{9-56}$$

This result can be interpreted as follows. If the frequency is high enough, the current taken by the inductor of Fig. 9-29 is negligible in comparison to the current taken by the capacitor. Hence the circuit can be redrawn without the L as shown in Fig. 9-30. The resulting RC network is described by the transfer function

$$\frac{V_o}{V_i} = \frac{\dfrac{1}{sC}}{R + \dfrac{1}{sC}} = \frac{\dfrac{1}{RC}}{s + \dfrac{1}{RC}} \tag{9-57}$$

which has the magnitude characteristic described by Eq. (9-56).

(b) Because the poles are widely separated, the half-power frequencies ω_1 and ω_2 correspond to the magnitude of the poles. This is shown in Fig. 9-31. Stated differently, the imaginary axis intercepts of circles drawn through the poles represent the frequencies at which the magnitude characteristic is $1/\sqrt{2}$ times the peak magnitude.

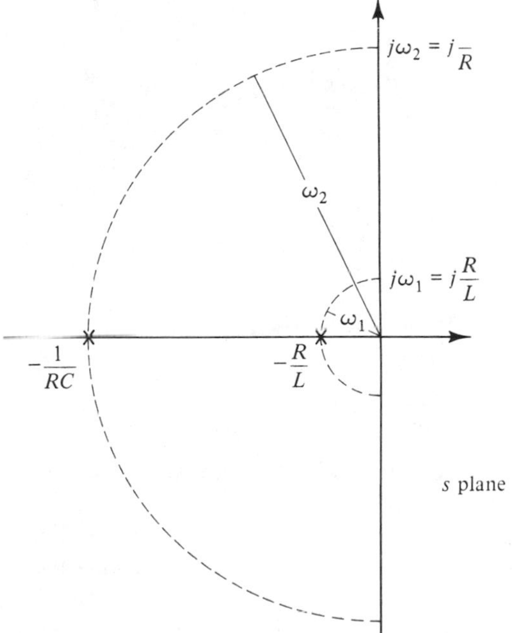

Fig. 9-31

9-5 BANDSTOP FILTERS

Bandstop filters are used to stop sine waves that have frequencies falling within a specified band. This band is known as the *rejection or stop* band. The ideal bandstop filter is characterized by the magnitude and phase curves given in Fig. 9-32. The bandwidth of rejection is $(\omega_2 - \omega_1)$ rad/s. The two passband phase curves ($\omega < \omega_1$ and $\omega > \omega_2$) have the same slope. The shape of the phase curve in the stopband is not important because there is no output in this band.

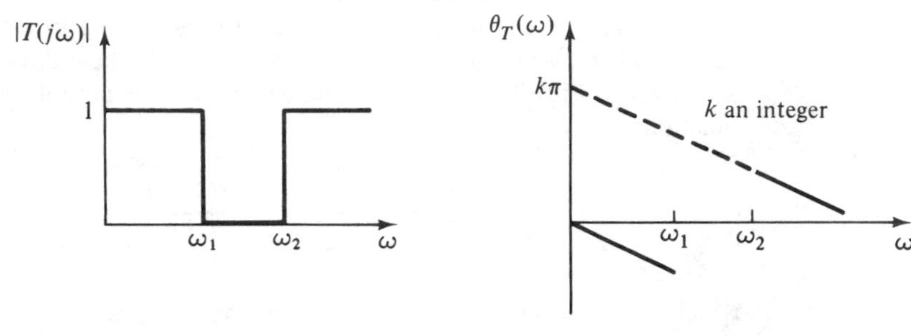

Fig. 9-32

At least a second-order function is required to approximate the ideal characteristics. One such function is

$$T(s) = \frac{s^2 + \omega_r^2}{s^2 + s\omega_b + \omega_r^2} \tag{9-58}$$

where ω_b and ω_r are constants.

For $s = j\omega$ we obtain from Eq. (9-58).

$$T(j\omega) = \frac{\omega_r^2 - \omega^2}{(\omega_r^2 - \omega^2) + j\omega\omega_b} \tag{9-59}$$

$$|T(j\omega)| = \frac{|\omega_r^2 - \omega^2|}{\sqrt{(\omega_r^2 - \omega^2)^2 + (\omega\omega_b)^2}} \tag{9-60a}$$

$$\theta_T(\omega) = -\tan^{-1}\frac{\omega\omega_b}{\omega_r^2 - \omega^2} \qquad (\omega < \omega_r)$$

$$\theta_T(\omega) = \pi - \tan^{-1}\frac{\omega\omega_b}{\omega_r^2 - \omega^2} = \tan^{-1}\frac{\omega\omega_b}{\omega^2 - \omega_r^2} \qquad (\omega > \omega_r) \tag{9-60b}$$

Two equations are given to describe the phase characteristics because the numerator of Eq. (9-59) changes sign as ω exceeds ω_r.

The magnitude and phase functions are plotted in Fig. 9-33. The magnitude is zero at $\omega = \omega_r$. Hence the constant ω_r in Eq. (9-58) represents the frequency of complete rejection.

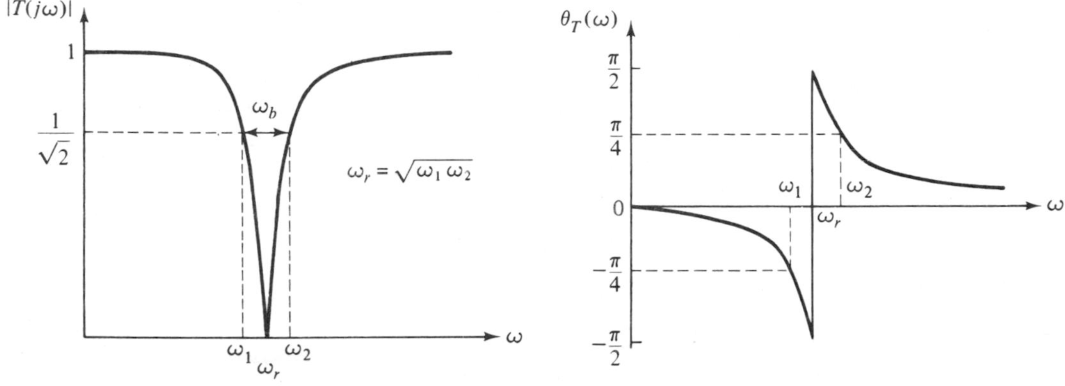

Fig. 9-33

The *bandwidth of rejection* is defined as *the difference of the two frequencies at which the magnitude is* $1/\sqrt{2}$ *times the magnitude at* $\omega = 0$ *and* $\omega = \infty$. These frequencies, which are also known as half-power frequencies, are designated in Fig. 9-33 as ω_1 and ω_2. It can be shown that the difference between the two is ω_b—that is,

$$\omega_2 - \omega_1 = \omega_b \tag{9-61}$$

Thus the constant ω_b in Eq. (9-58) represents the bandwidth of rejection in radians per second.

The phase characteristic jumps π radians at $\omega = \omega_r$. It can be shown that $\theta_T(\omega_1) = -\pi/4$ and $\theta_T(\omega_2) = \pi/4$ (see Problem 9-37).

To underscore the significance of the coefficients in the bandstop function, Eq. (9-58) is reproduced here with added descriptions.

$$T(s) = \frac{s^2 + \overbrace{(\omega_r)}^{\text{Frequency of rejection}}{}^2}{s^2 + s\underbrace{\omega_b}_{\text{Bandwidth of rejection}} + \omega_r^2} \tag{9-62}$$

Changing the coefficient of the s^1 term (ω_b) in the denominator polynomial changes the bandwidth of rejection without affecting the frequency of complete rejection. The smaller ω_b is made, the narrower becomes the band of frequencies that are rejected. Changing the constant term (ω_r^2) in the numerator (and hence denominator) polynomial changes the frequency at which complete rejection occurs without affecting the bandwidth of rejection.

The second-order bandstop function can be realized by the networks shown in Fig. 9-34.

The circuit of Fig. 9-34(a) produces

$$\frac{V_o}{V_i} = \frac{R_L}{R_s + R_L}\left[\frac{s^2 + \dfrac{1}{LC}}{s^2 + s\dfrac{1}{(R_s + R_L)C} + \dfrac{1}{LC}}\right] = \frac{R_L}{R_s + R_L}\left(\frac{s^2 + \omega_r^2}{s^2 + s\omega_b + \omega_r^2}\right) \tag{9-63a}$$

where

$$\omega_b = \frac{1}{(R_s + R_L)C} \tag{9-63b}$$

$$\omega_r = \frac{1}{\sqrt{LC}} \tag{9-63c}$$

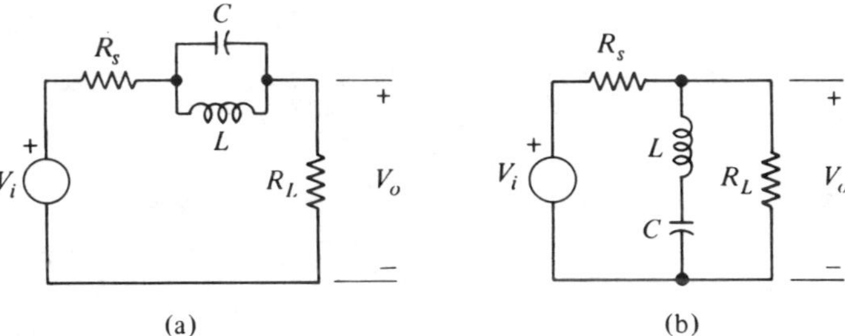

Fig. 9-34

At the rejection frequency ($\omega = \omega_r = 1/\sqrt{LC}$) the impedance of the parallel LC circuit becomes infinite, thereby preventing the signal from reaching the output.

In a typical problem ω_b, ω_r, R_s, and R_L are specified. The two remaining element values are obtained by solving Eq. (9-63b) for C and Eq. (9-63c) for L.

$$C = \frac{1}{(R_s + R_L)\omega_b} \tag{9-64a}$$

$$L = \frac{1}{\omega_r^2 C} = \frac{(R_s + R_L)\omega_b}{\omega_r^2} \tag{9-64b}$$

The circuit of Fig. 9-34(b) produces

$$\frac{V_o}{V_i} = \frac{R_L}{R_s + R_L}\left(\frac{s^2 + \dfrac{1}{LC}}{s^2 + s\dfrac{R_s R_L}{R_s + R_L}\dfrac{1}{L} + \dfrac{1}{LC}}\right) = \frac{R_L}{R_s + R_L}\left(\frac{s^2 + \omega_r^2}{s^2 + s\omega_b + \omega_r^2}\right) \tag{9-65a}$$

where

$$\omega_b = \frac{R_s R_L}{R_s + R_L}\frac{1}{L} \tag{9-65b}$$

$$\omega_r = \frac{1}{\sqrt{LC}} \tag{9-65c}$$

These equations are used to calculate L and C for given ω_b, ω_r, R_s, and R_L.

At the rejection frequency the impedance of the series LC circuit becomes zero, thereby causing the output to become zero also.

Example 9-7

(a) Design a bandstop filter to reject 60 Hz. The bandwidth of rejection is to be 30 Hz. The source and load resistances are 600 Ω.

(b) The input is $10 + 5 \sin 120\pi t$. What is the steady-state output?

Solution.

(a) We use the network of Fig. 9-35 to obtain the desired rejection characteristics. With $R_s = R_L = R$ in Eq. (9-64), we obtain

$$C = \frac{1}{2R\omega_b} = \frac{1}{2 \times 600 \times 2\pi \times 30} = 4.42\ \mu\text{F} \quad \text{Ans.}$$

$$L = \frac{2R\omega_b}{\omega_r^2} = \frac{2 \times 600 \times 2\pi \times 30}{(2\pi \times 60)^2} = 1.59\ \text{H} \quad \text{Ans.}$$

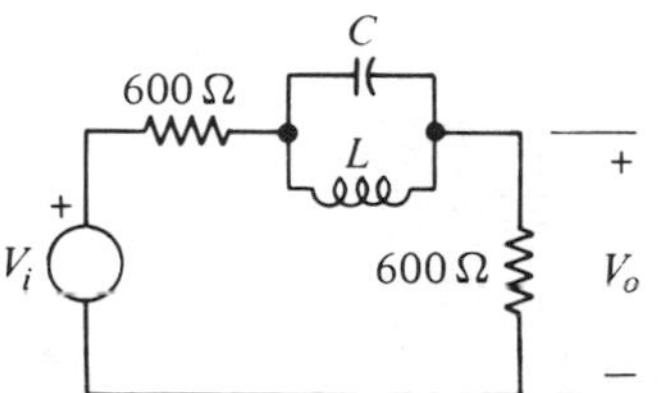

Fig. 9-35

(b) The frequency of the input sine wave is $120\pi/2\pi = 60$ Hz. Since the network is tuned to reject 60 Hz sine waves completely, the output is due to the dc input only. In the steady state the dc voltage across the inductor in Fig. 9-35 is zero. Hence the input dc voltage divides equally between the source and load resistances and results in

$$v_o = \frac{10}{2} = 5\ \text{V} \quad \text{Ans.}$$

9-6 A FILTER WITH LOW-FREQUENCY BOOST OR ATTENUATION

Depending on the potentiometer setting, the filter of Fig. 9-36 can boost or attenuate low frequencies. This characteristic can be demonstrated by plotting the magnitude

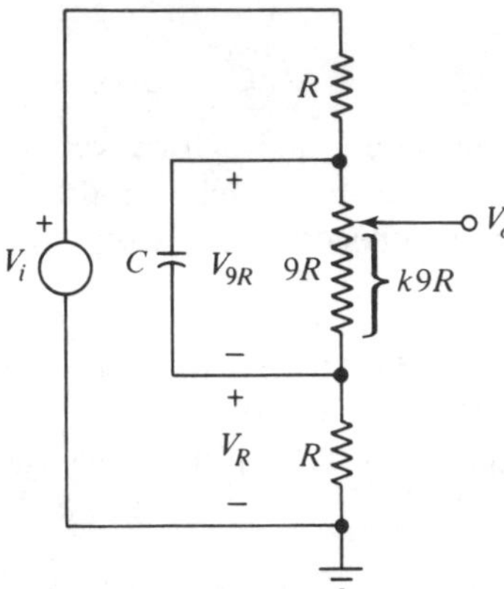

Fig. 9-36

characteristic as a function of frequency, using k as a parameter. The various steps in obtaining this result are shown below.

$$V_o = kV_{9R} + V_R = \left(\frac{k \dfrac{9R}{s9RC + 1} + R}{2R + \dfrac{9R}{s9RC + 1}} \right) V_i$$

$$\frac{V_o}{V_i} = \frac{1}{2} \left[\frac{s + \left(k + \dfrac{1}{9}\right)\dfrac{1}{RC}}{s + \dfrac{11}{18}\dfrac{1}{RC}} \right]$$

$$\left.\frac{V_o}{V_i}\right|_{s=j\omega} = \frac{1}{2} \left[\frac{j\omega + \left(k + \dfrac{1}{9}\right)\dfrac{1}{RC}}{j\omega + \dfrac{11}{18}\dfrac{1}{RC}} \right]$$

$$\left|\frac{V_o}{V_i}\right| = \frac{1}{2} \sqrt{\frac{\left(k + \dfrac{1}{9}\right)^2 + (\omega RC)^2}{\left(\dfrac{11}{18}\right)^2 + (\omega RC)^2}} \tag{9-66}$$

$$\theta = \tan^{-1} \frac{9\omega RC}{9k + 1} - \tan^{-1} \frac{18\omega RC}{11} \tag{9-67}$$

For $k = 0, \frac{1}{2}$, and 1 the magnitude and phase functions simplify to

$$\left.\begin{cases} \left|\dfrac{V_o}{V_i}\right| = \dfrac{1}{2}\sqrt{\dfrac{\left(\dfrac{1}{9}\right)^2 + (\omega RC)^2}{\left(\dfrac{11}{18}\right)^2 + (\omega RC)^2}} \cong \begin{cases} \omega \ll \dfrac{1}{9}\dfrac{1}{RC} & = \dfrac{1}{11} \\ \omega \gg \dfrac{11}{18}\dfrac{1}{RC} & = \dfrac{1}{2} \end{cases} \\ \theta = \tan^{-1} 9\omega RC - \tan^{-1}\dfrac{18\omega RC}{11} \end{cases}\right\} \quad k = 0 \tag{9-68a}$$

$$\left.\begin{cases} \left|\dfrac{V_o}{V_i}\right| = \dfrac{1}{2} \\ \theta = 0 \end{cases}\right\} \quad k = \frac{1}{2} \tag{9-68b}$$

$$\left.\begin{cases} \left|\dfrac{V_o}{V_i}\right| = \dfrac{1}{2}\sqrt{\dfrac{\left(\dfrac{10}{9}\right)^2 + (\omega RC)^2}{\left(\dfrac{11}{18}\right)^2 + (\omega RC)^2}} \cong \begin{cases} \omega \ll \dfrac{11}{18}\dfrac{1}{RC} & = \dfrac{10}{11} \\ \omega \gg \dfrac{10}{9}\dfrac{1}{RC} & = \dfrac{1}{2} \end{cases} \\ \theta = \tan^{-1}\dfrac{9\omega RC}{10} - \tan^{-1}\dfrac{18\omega RC}{11} \end{cases}\right\} \quad k = 1 \tag{9-68c}$$

These functions are plotted in Fig. 9-37. The magnitude characteristics show that for $k > \frac{1}{2}$ low frequencies are boosted, whereas for $k < \frac{1}{2}$ low frequencies are attenuated. For $k = \frac{1}{2}$ the magnitude curve is flat—that is, it passes all frequencies equally well. Regardless of the value of k, all high frequencies are passed equally well. With this filter we can then control the low-frequency characteristics (bass control in a Hi-

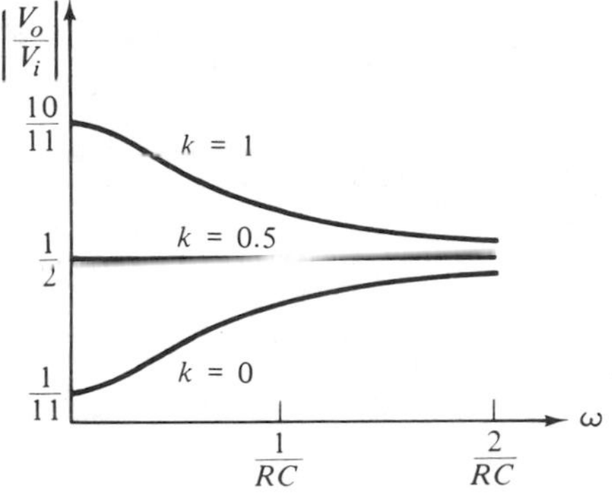

Fig. 9-37

Fi amplifier) without affecting the high-frequency response. (See Problems 9-43 for the opposite effect.)

9-7 DISTORTION INTRODUCED BY FILTERS

Consider the first-order lowpass filter shown in Fig. 9-38. The filter has a cutoff frequency of ω_c rad/s and is designed to eliminate high-frequency noise (unwanted signals). Turning now to signals in the passband, we take an input that is the sum of two sine waves. One sine wave has an amplitude of 1 and frequency of $\frac{1}{3}\omega_c$. The other sine wave has an amplitude of $\frac{1}{4}$ and frequency of ω_c. Whereas the lower-frequency signal is well within the passband, the upper-frequency signal is at the edge of the passband. The input waveform is shown in Fig. 9-39(a). We now calculate the output waveform.

$$\left|T\left(j\frac{1}{3}\omega_c\right)\right| \sin\left[\frac{1}{3}\omega_c t + \theta_T\left(\frac{1}{3}\omega_c\right)\right] + \frac{1}{4}|T(j\omega_c)| \sin\left[\omega_c t + \theta_T(\omega_c)\right] \tag{9-69}$$

where the various magnitude and phase functions are obtained from the given lowpass function as follows.

$$T(s) = \frac{\omega_c}{s + \omega_c} \tag{9-70}$$

$$T(j\omega) = \frac{\omega_c}{j\omega + \omega_c} = \frac{1}{1 + j(\omega/\omega_c)} \tag{9-71}$$

$$|T(j\omega)| = \frac{1}{\sqrt{1 + (\omega/\omega_c)^2}}, \qquad \theta_T(\omega) = -\tan^{-1}\frac{\omega}{\omega_c} \tag{9-72}$$

$$\left|T\left(j\frac{1}{3}\omega_c\right)\right| = \frac{1}{\sqrt{1 + \frac{1}{9}}} = \frac{3}{\sqrt{10}} = 0.949$$

$$\theta_T\left(\frac{1}{3}\omega_c\right) = -\tan^{-1}\frac{1}{3} = -0.322 \text{ radian} \tag{9-73}$$

$$|T(j\omega_c)| = \frac{1}{\sqrt{1+1}} = \frac{1}{\sqrt{2}} = 0.707, \qquad \theta_T(\omega_c) = -\tan^{-1} 1 = -0.785 \text{ radian} \tag{9-74}$$

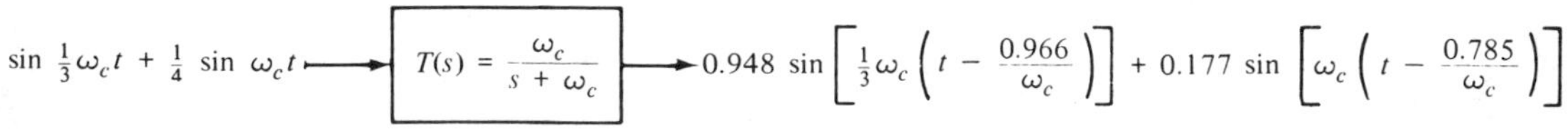

$\sin \frac{1}{3}\omega_c t + \frac{1}{4} \sin \omega_c t$ → $T(s) = \dfrac{\omega_c}{s + \omega_c}$ → $0.948 \sin\left[\frac{1}{3}\omega_c\left(t - \dfrac{0.966}{\omega_c}\right)\right] + 0.177 \sin\left[\omega_c\left(t - \dfrac{0.785}{\omega_c}\right)\right]$

Fig. 9-38

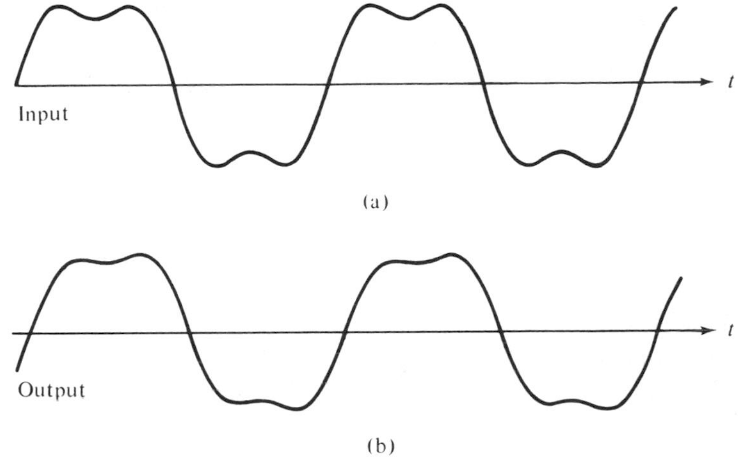

Fig. 9-39

Substitution of Eqs. (9-73) and (9-74) into Eq. (9-69) gives the output signal.

$$0.949 \sin \left(\frac{1}{3} \omega_c t - 0.322\right) + 0.177 \sin (\omega_c t - 0.785) \tag{9-75}$$

The next step is to compare the input and output signals.

$$\text{Input} = \sin \left(\frac{1}{3} \omega_c t\right) + 0.250 \sin (\omega_c t) \tag{9-76}$$

$$\text{Output} = 0.949 \sin \left[\frac{1}{3} \omega_c \left(t - \frac{0.966}{\omega_c}\right)\right] + 0.177 \sin \left[\omega_c \left(t - \frac{0.785}{\omega_c}\right)\right] \tag{9-77}$$

Although both signals are passed by the filter, there are two notable differences. First, the output amplitudes are not in the same ratio as the input amplitudes. The higher-frequency wave, being at the edge of the passband, is attenuated more than the lower-frequency wave (see magnitude characteristic shown in Fig. 9-4). Such unequal treatment of amplitudes in the passband results in *amplitude distortion* of signals. Secondly, the two sine waves are not delayed by the same amount as they come out of the filter. This situation occurs because the phase of the filter is not a linear function of ω but an inverse tangent function. The result is *phase,* or *time-delay, distortion*. Consequently, we have both amplitude and phase, or time-delay, distortion. The output waveform is no longer a scaled and delayed replica of the input waveform but is somewhat distorted as shown in Fig. 9-39(b). Particularly noticeable is the skewed form of the waveform caused by the phase distortion.

All filters introduce a certain amount of distortion for signals in the passband. The amount of distortion that is acceptable depends on the particular application. With a sufficiently high-order filter it is possible to meet most realistic design specifications.

9-8 PHASE CORRECTION

Certain networks do not cause discrimination in magnitude but introduce different amounts of phase shift, depending on frequency. Such networks are described by the transfer function

$$T(s) = \frac{N(s)}{D(s)} = \frac{D(-s)}{D(s)} \tag{9-78}$$

As indicated, the numerator polynomial $N(s)$ is obtained from the denominator polynomial by substituting $-s$ for s. Thus

$$T(j\omega) = \frac{D(-j\omega)}{D(j\omega)} = \frac{P(\omega) - jQ(\omega)}{P(\omega) + jQ(\omega)} \tag{9-79}$$

where $P(\omega)$ and $Q(\omega)$ are, respectively, the real and imaginary parts of $D(j\omega)$. The corresponding magnitude and phase functions are

$$|T(j\omega)| = \frac{\sqrt{P^2(\omega) + Q^2(\omega)}}{\sqrt{P^2(\omega) + Q^2(\omega)}} = 1 \tag{9-80}$$

$$\theta_T = \tan^{-1}\frac{-Q(\omega)}{P(\omega)} - \tan^{-1}\frac{Q(\omega)}{P(\omega)} = -2\tan^{-1}\frac{Q(\omega)}{P(\omega)} \tag{9-81}$$

From Eq. (9-80) we see that all sine waves are passed regardless of their frequency. However, their phases are shifted according to Eq. (9-81).

Functions that affect the phase but not the magnitude of sine waves are called *all-pass* functions. These functions can be used to correct the phase of filter functions so that the overall phase characteristic becomes more linear.

The first-order all-pass function is

$$T(s) = \frac{-s + \alpha}{s + \alpha} \tag{9-82}$$

Its magnitude and phase functions are

$$|T(j\omega)| = 1, \qquad \theta_T(\omega) = -2\tan^{-1}\frac{\omega}{\alpha} \tag{9-83}$$

These functions are plotted in Fig. 9-40.

Two first-order all-pass networks are shown in Fig. 9-41.

These networks realize the transfer function

$$T(s) = -\frac{1}{2}\frac{s - \alpha}{s + \alpha} \tag{9-84}$$

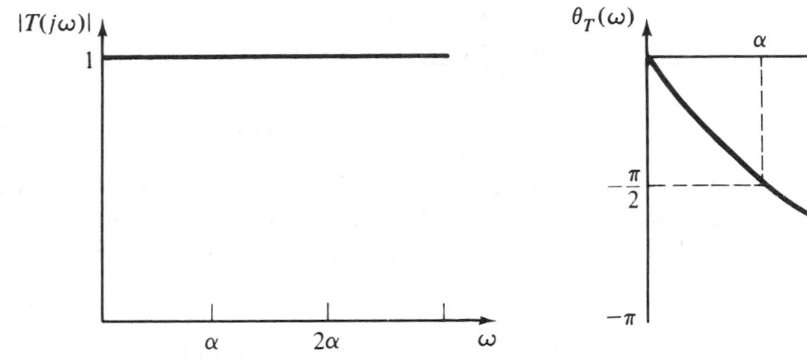

Fig. 9-40

$$\text{where } \alpha = \frac{1}{RC} \qquad (RC \text{ network})$$

$$\alpha = \frac{R}{L} \qquad (RL \text{ network})$$

The resulting magnitude and phase functions are

$$T(j\omega) = \frac{1}{2}, \qquad \theta(\omega) = -2 \tan^{-1} \frac{\omega}{\alpha} \tag{9-85}$$

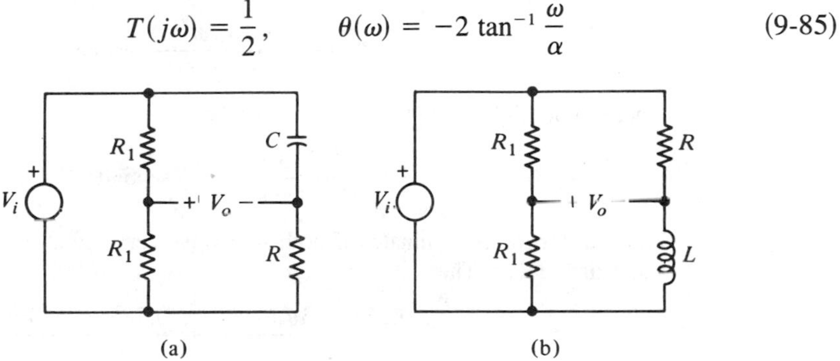

Fig. 9-41

Example 9-8

Obtain the all-pass function that will correct the phase of the lowpass filter discussed in Section 9-7.

Solution. The lowpass filter shown in Fig. 9-38 introduced both amplitude and phase distortion. The phase distortion can be eliminated by using an appropriate all-pass filter. The overall design is shown in block diagram form in Fig. 9-42. The input s_i and the lowpass output s_{o1} are obtained from Eqs. (9-76) and (9-77).

$$s_i = \sin\left(\frac{1}{3}\omega_c t\right) + 0.250 \sin(\omega_c t)$$

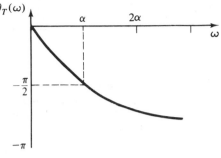

$$s_{o1} = 0.949 \sin\left(\frac{1}{3}\omega_c t - 0.322\right) + 0.177 \sin(\omega_c t - 0.785)$$

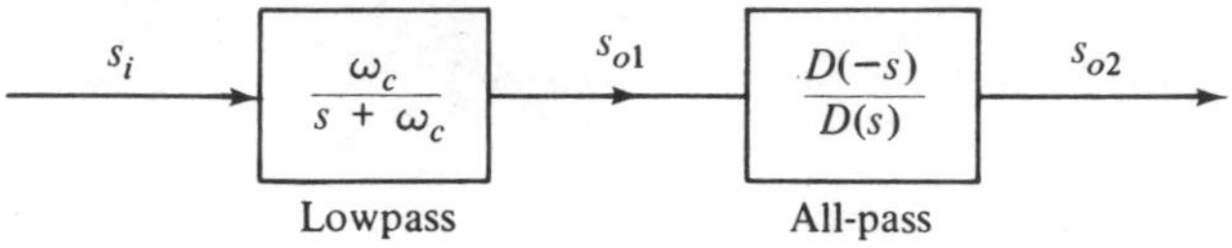

$$s_i \rightarrow \boxed{\frac{\omega_c}{s+\omega_c}} \xrightarrow{s_{o1}} \boxed{\frac{D(-s)}{D(s)}} \xrightarrow{s_{o2}}$$

Lowpass All-pass

Fig. 9-42

The all-pass filter receives s_{o1} as input and produces s_{o2} as output. Except for a possible scale factor k, the amplitudes in s_{o2} are the same as in s_{o1}. The amount of phase shift undergone by each sine wave is determined by the phase $\theta_A(\omega)$ of the all-pass function. Hence

$$s_{o2} = k\left\{0.949 \sin\left[\frac{1}{3}\omega_c t - 0.322 + \theta_A\left(\frac{\omega_c}{3}\right)\right] + 0.177 \sin\left[\omega_c t - 0.785 + \theta_A(\omega_c)\right]\right\} \tag{9-86}$$

$$s_{o2} = k\left(0.949 \sin\left\{\frac{1}{3}\omega_c\left[t - \frac{0.966 - 3\theta_A(\omega_c/3)}{\omega_c}\right]\right\} + 0.177 \sin\left\{\omega_c\left[t - \frac{0.785 - \theta_A(\omega_c)}{\omega_c}\right]\right\}\right) \tag{9-87}$$

Relative to the input, the lower-frequency signal is delayed

$$\frac{0.966 - 3\theta_A(\omega_c/3)}{\omega_c} \text{ seconds} \tag{9-88}$$

whereas the higher-frequency signal is delayed

$$\frac{0.785 - \theta_A(\omega_c)}{\omega_c} \text{ seconds} \tag{9-89}$$

Phase distortion is eliminated if both sine waves emerge at the all-pass output with the same time delay. Thus

$$\frac{0.966 - 3\theta_A(\omega_c/3)}{\omega_c} = \frac{0.785 - \theta_A(\omega_c)}{\omega_c}$$

$$\theta_A(\omega_c) = 3\theta_A\left(\frac{\omega_c}{3}\right) - 0.181 \tag{9-90}$$

Equation (9-90) states that the phase shift introduced by the all-pass function at the frequency of ω_c must be equal to three times the phase shift introduced at the frequency $\omega_c/3$ *minus* 0.181 radians.

A first-order all-pass function cannot meet this demand because of the convex nature of the phase characteristic curve (see Fig. 9-40). We must therefore resort to a second-order all-pass function, which is given by

$$T(s) = k\frac{s^2 - bs + c}{s^2 + bs + c} \tag{9-91a}$$

$$T(j\omega) = k\frac{(c - \omega^2) - j\omega b}{(c - \omega^2) + j\omega b}$$

$$|T(j\omega)| = k \tag{9-91b}$$

$$\theta_A(\omega) = -2\tan^{-1}\frac{b\omega}{c - \omega^2} \tag{9-91c}$$

where b and c are constants that determine the phase characteristics.

Using Eq. (9-91) to evaluate Eq. (9-90), we obtain

$$-2\tan^{-1}\frac{b\omega_c}{c - \omega_c^2} = -6\tan^{-1}\frac{b\omega_c/3}{c - (\omega_c/3)^2} - 0.181 \tag{9-92}$$

We have one equation and two unknowns—namely, b and c. By trial and error, we obtain a solution that satisfies Eq. (9-92). (This solution is not unique.)

$$b = 1.00\omega_c, \qquad c = 0.571\omega_c^2 \tag{9-93}$$

So an all-pass function that meets the desired specifications is

$$T(s) = k\frac{s^2 - s1.00\omega_c + 0.571\omega_c^2}{s^2 + s1.00\omega_c + 0.571\omega_c^2} \tag{9-94}$$

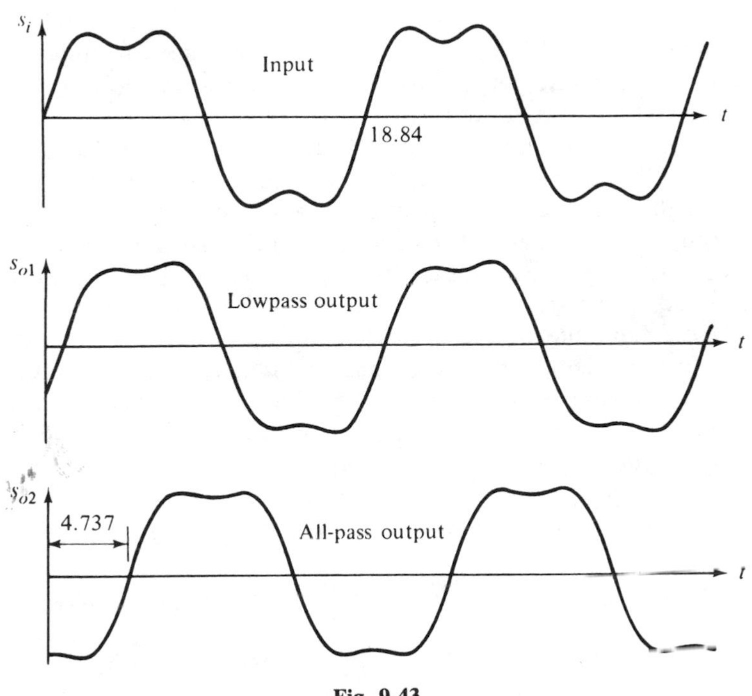

Fig. 9-43

This function can be realized by the *RLC* networks given in Problem 9-45.

With the values of b and c obtained in Eq. (9-93) the resulting time delay can be evaluated by using either Eq. (9-88) or Eq. (9-89).

$$\text{Delay} = \frac{0.785 - \theta_A(\omega_c)}{\omega_c} = \frac{0.785 + 2\tan^{-1}[b\omega_c/(c - \omega_c^2)]}{\omega_c}$$

$$= \frac{0.785 + 2\tan^{-1}[1.00/(0.571 - 1.00)]}{\omega_c} = \frac{4.737}{\omega_c} \tag{9-95}$$

So by using Eq. (9-87), the output can be written

$$s_{o2} = k\left\{0.949 \sin\left[\frac{1}{3}\omega_c\left(t - \frac{4.737}{\omega_c}\right)\right] + 0.177 \sin\left[\omega_c\left(t - \frac{4.737}{\omega_c}\right)\right]\right\} \tag{9-96}$$

To see the improvement in waveform resulting from the elimination of phase distortion, Eq. (9-96) is plotted in Fig. 9-43 (with $k = 1$, $\omega_c = 1$) along with the input and the lowpass output. Note that phase correction results in removal of the skewing present in the lowpass output. However, the output is not quite a delayed replica of the input because of amplitude distortion.

9-9 SUMMARY

Essentially, every *RLC* network is a filter. It produces an output that depends on the frequency of the input sine wave. Each sinusoidal wave is affected differently in amplitude and phase as it goes through the network.

Certain filters are named according to their intended use. A lowpass filter passes low frequencies and rejects high frequencies, whereas a highpass filter does exactly the opposite. A bandpass filter passes only a band of frequencies; a bandstop filter rejects only a band of frequencies. An all-pass filter passes all sine waves while modifying their phase. These filters are described by the following functions and magnitude characteristics.

All these filter functions can be implemented with *RLC* networks.

Ideally, signals in the passband should only be scaled and delayed as they are processed by the network. In practice, the functions that approximate the ideal behavior introduce distortion. Amplitude distortion is caused by the unequal treatment of the amplitudes of the sine waves that are in the passband. Phase distortion results from phase characteristics that are not linear in the passband. In general, signals suffer both amplitude and phase distortion as they emerge from the network.

Lowpass

$$T_1(s) = \frac{\omega_c}{s + \omega_c}$$

$$T_2(s) = \frac{\omega_c^2}{s^2 + s\sqrt{2}\,\omega_c + \omega_c^2}$$

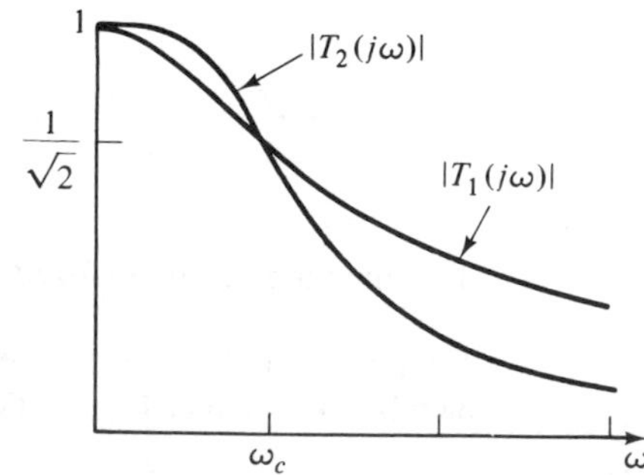

Highpass

$$T_1(s) = \frac{s}{s + \omega_c}$$

$$T_2(s) = \frac{s^2}{s^2 + s\sqrt{2}\,\omega_c + \omega_c^2}$$

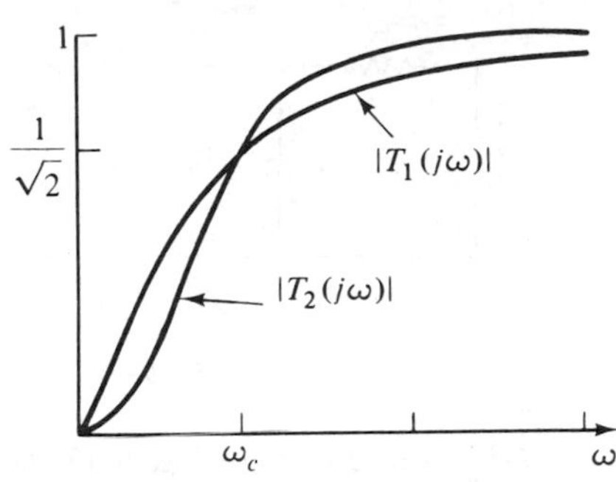

Bandpass

$$T(s) = \frac{s\omega_b}{s^2 + s\omega_b + \omega_p^2}$$

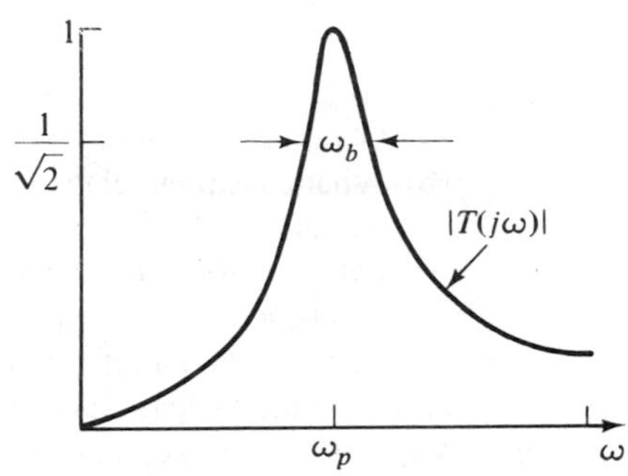

Bandstop

$$T(s) = \frac{s^2 + \omega_r^2}{s^2 + s\omega_b + \omega_r^2}$$

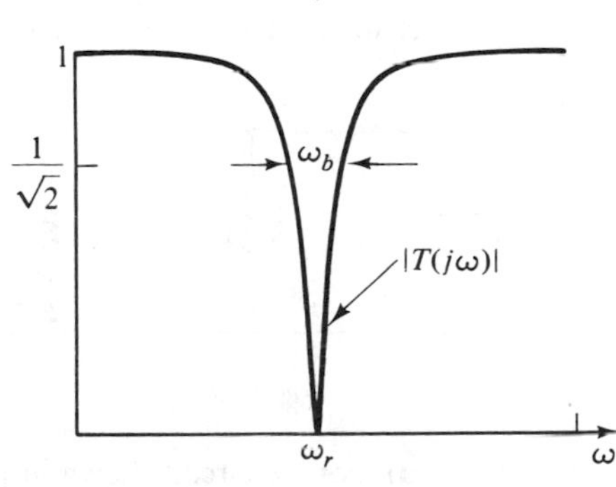

All-pass

$$T(s) = -\frac{s - \alpha}{s + \alpha}$$

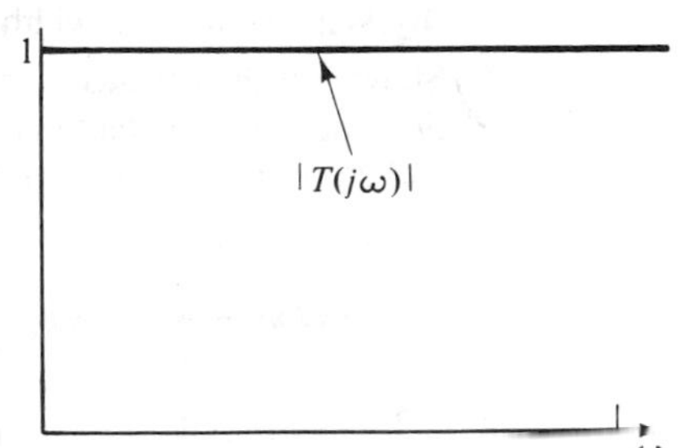

PROBLEMS

9-1. Derive Eq. (9-8).

9-2. For the circuits shown in Fig. 9-44, the cutoff frequency is to be set at 1 k rad/s. Design the filters.

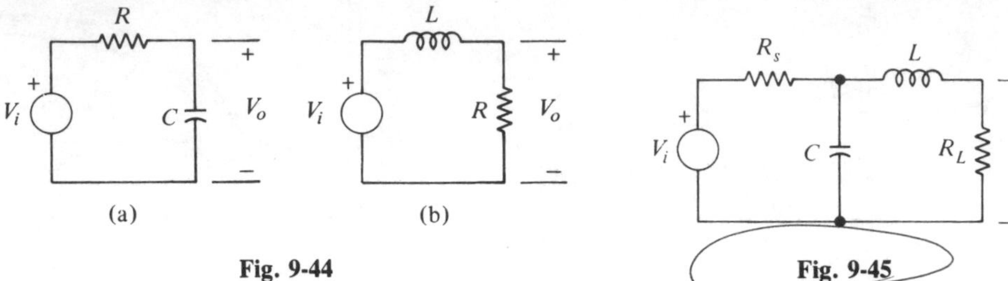

Fig. 9-44

Fig. 9-45

9-3. The network of Fig. 9-45 can be designed to realize the lowpass function given by

$$T(s) = \frac{\alpha\omega_c^2}{s^2 + s\sqrt{2}\omega_c + \omega_c^2}$$

(**a**) Obtain α and ω_c in terms of R_s, R_L, L, and C.
(**b**) What constraint relationship is imposed on the components of the network if it is to realize $T(s)$?
(**c**) Let $R_s = R_L = R$. Obtain the design values for the L and C to achieve a specified cutoff ω_c.

9-4. At ten times the cutoff frequency, compare the attenuation produced by the first- and second-order lowpass functions.

9-5. Show that the transadmittance (I_o/V_i) of the circuit shown in Fig. 9-46 is lowpass in its characteristic. What is the cutoff frequency?

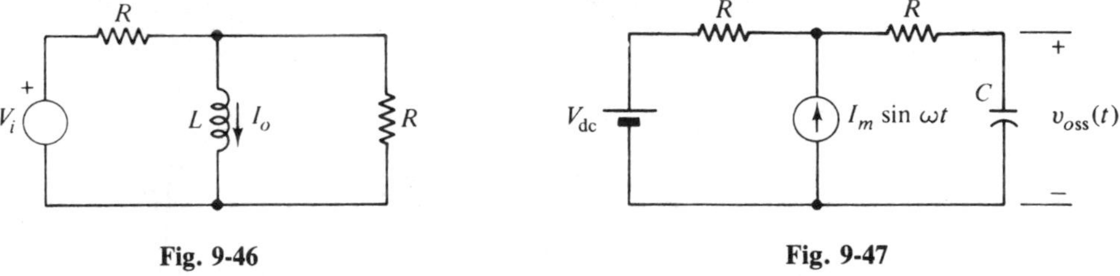

Fig. 9-46

Fig. 9-47

9-6. (**a**) For the circuit shown in Fig. 9-47, obtain the steady-state output voltage.
(**b**) What is the bandwidth associated with the transimpedance function?

9-7. Show that the circuits given in Fig. 9-48 can act as lowpass filters. (The tranfer functions produced by these circuits do not have as sharp a transition between the passband and stopband as the circuits discussed in Fig. 9-8.)

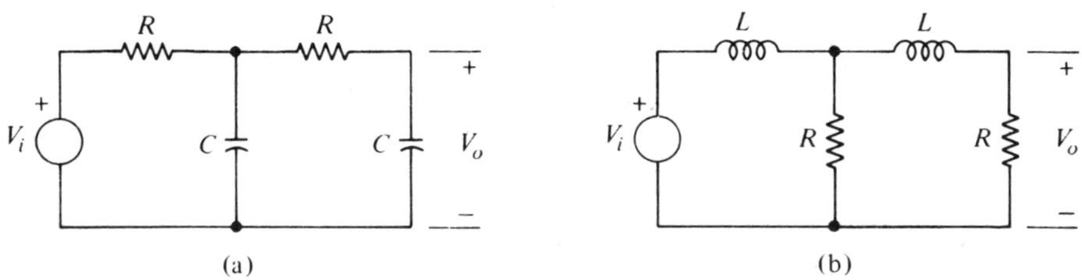

Fig. 9-48

9-8. For the circuit shown in Fig. 9-49, obtain the steady-state output.

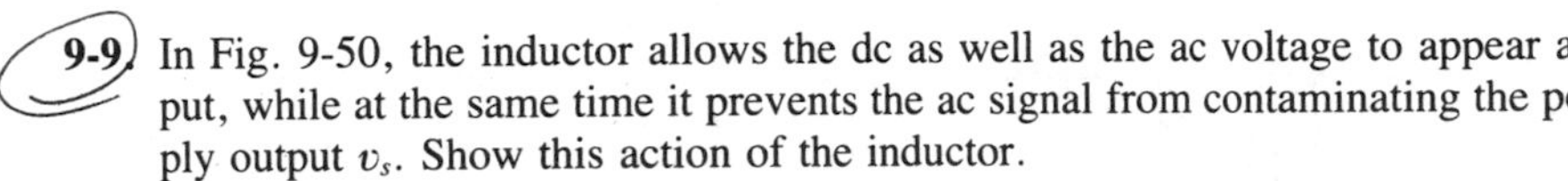

9-9. In Fig. 9-50, the inductor allows the dc as well as the ac voltage to appear at the output, while at the same time it prevents the ac signal from contaminating the power supply output v_s. Show this action of the inductor.

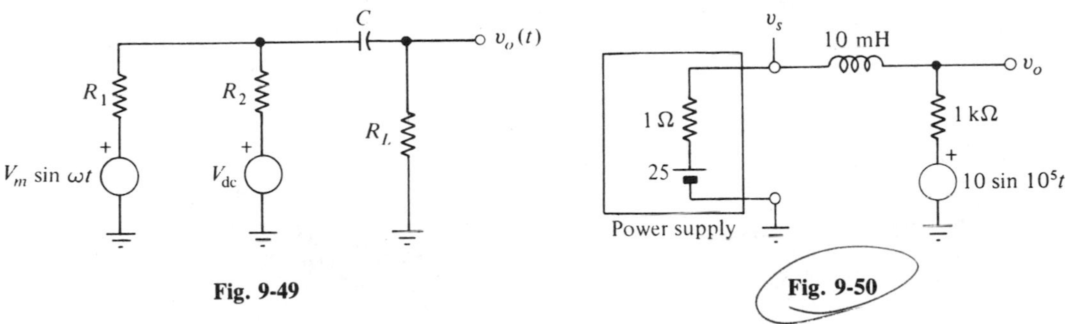

Fig. 9-49 **Fig. 9-50**

9-10. The b and c values in $T(s) = c/(s^2 + bs + c)$ are such that $T(s)$ is a lowpass function different from the one given by Eq. (9-9). What is its bandwidth?

9-11. Derive Eq. (9-24).

9-12. Derive Eq. (9-27).

9-13. Refer to Fig. 9-51.

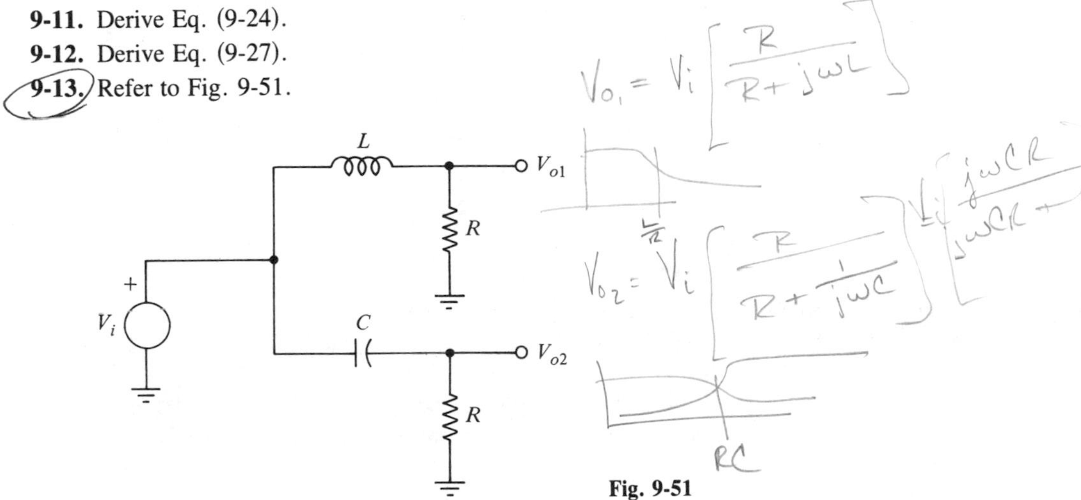

Fig. 9-51

(**a**) Using the same set of axes, sketch the magnitude characteristics associated with the two outputs. Give values.

(**b**) What condition must be satisfied if the cutoff frequencies of the two transfer functions are to be the same?

9-14. What are the two cutoff frequencies associated with the two outputs shown in Fig. 9-52?

9-15. Refer to Fig. 9-53.

(**a**) What condition must be satisfied to make Z_i independent of s? What is the resulting Z_i?

(**b**) With the condition in (a) satisfied, obtain the two transfer functions associated with the two outputs. What is the crossover frequency?

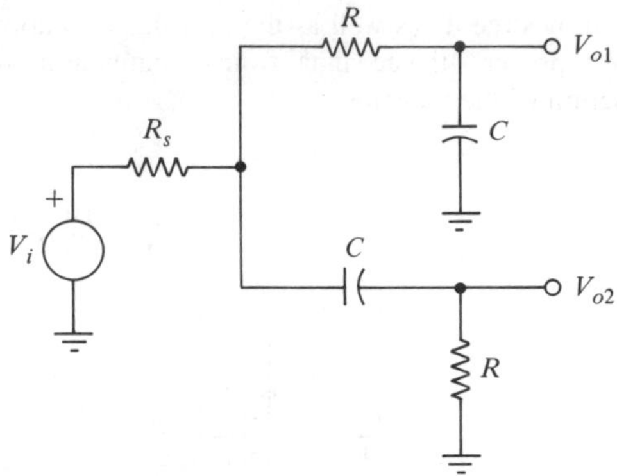

Fig. 9-52

9-16. In Fig. 9-53, $R_s = R = 1\ \Omega$, $L = 1$ H, C = 1 F, and $v_i(t) = V_m \sin \omega t$.

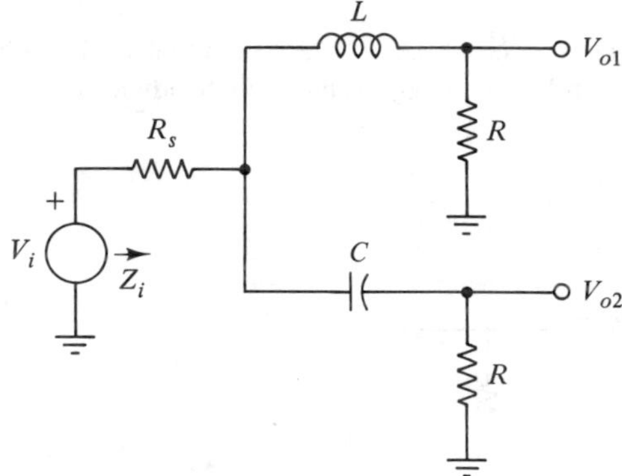

Fig. 9-53

(**a**) Steady state prevails. Obtain the expressions for $v_{o1}(t)$ and $v_{o2}(t)$.
(**b**) How would the results of (a) change if all individual impedances were multiplied by the constant k?
(**c**) How would the results of (a) change if L and C were divided by the constant ω_c?

9-17. The input circuit of oscilloscopes is represented in Fig. 9-54. The input impedance of the amplifier is infinite.

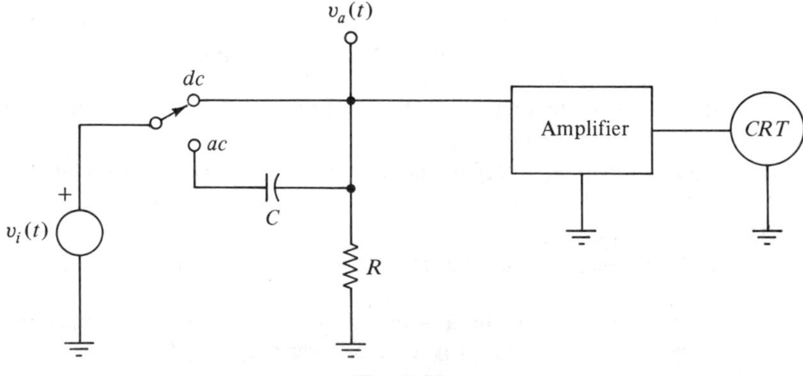

Fig. 9-54

(**a**) Explain the function of the ac/dc switch.
(**b**) The switch is in the ac position. What must be the frequency of the input sine wave if it is to pass unattenuated?

9-18. In Fig. 9-54 $v_i(t) = 10(1 + \sin 5t)$, $C = 0.2\ \mu\text{F}$, and $R = 1\ \text{M}\Omega$. Sketch the steady-state $v_a(t)$ for both switch positions.

9-19. Refer to Fig. 9-55.

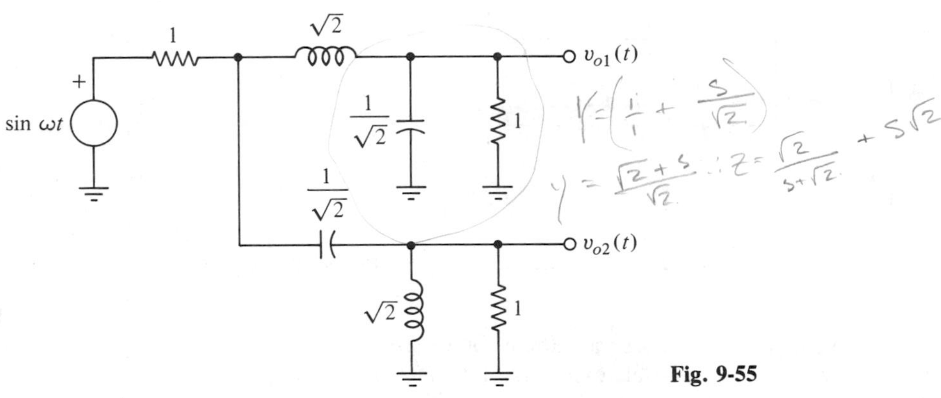

Fig. 9-55

(**a**) What impedance does the source see?
(**b**) Steady state prevails. Obtain $v_{o1}(t)$ and $v_{o2}(t)$.

9-20. In Fig. 9-56 choose the element values such that

$$\frac{V_{o1}}{I_i} = \frac{s^2}{s^2 + s + 1}, \qquad \frac{V_{o2}}{I_i} = \frac{1}{s^2 + s + 1}$$

are realized.

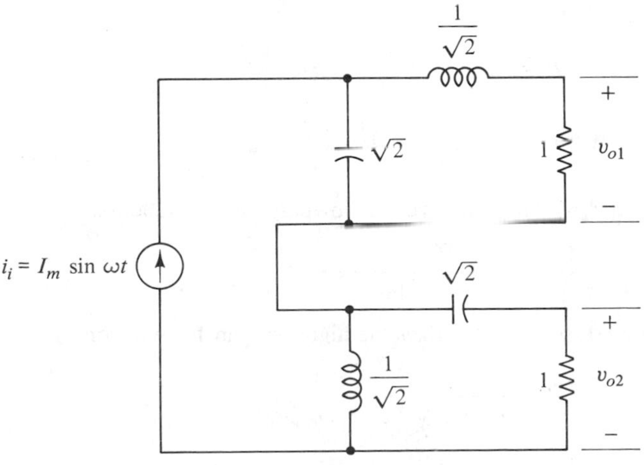

Fig. 9-56

9-21. Refer to Fig. 9-57.

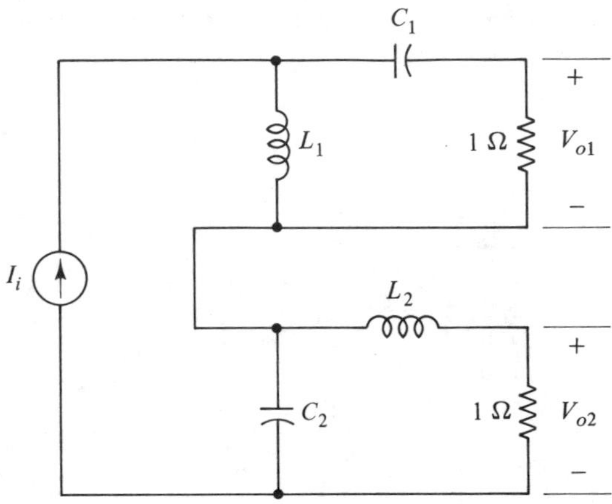

Fig. 9-57

(**a**) What impedance does the current source see?

(**b**) Obtain the steady-state expression for $v_{o1}(t)$ and $v_{o2}(t)$.

9-22. Refer to Fig. 9-58.

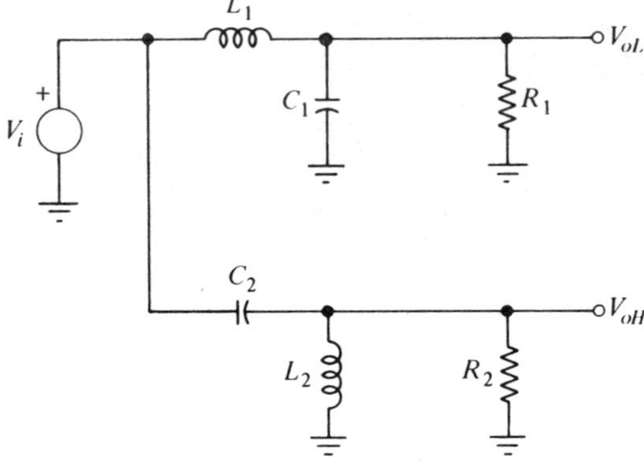

Fig. 9-58

(**a**) Design the upper network so that it realizes the lowpass transfer function:

$$\frac{V_{oL}}{V_i} = \frac{\omega_c^2}{s^2 + s\sqrt{2}\omega_c + \omega_c^2}$$

(**b**) Design the lower network so that it realizes the highpass transfer function:

$$\frac{V_{oH}}{V_i} = \frac{s^2}{s^2 + s\sqrt{2}\omega_c + \omega_c^2}$$

9-23. Show that the circuits given in Fig. 9-59 can act as highpass filters. (The transfer functions produced by these circuits do not have as sharp a transition between the stopband and passband as the circuits discussed in Fig. 9-19.)

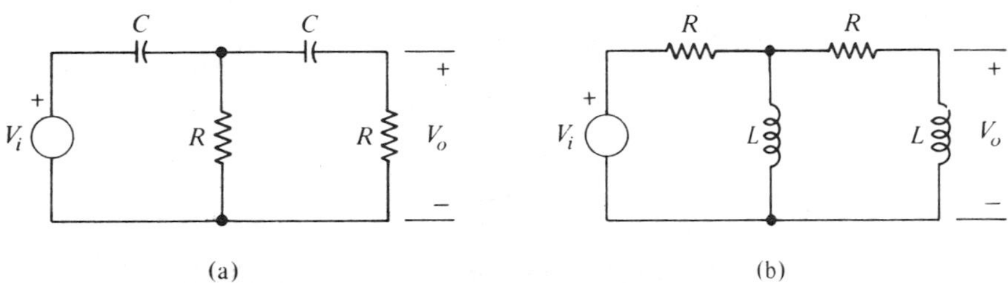

Fig. 9-59

9-24. In Fig. 9-60, $v_i(t) = V_{dc} + V_{m1} \sin \omega_1 t + V_{m2} \sin \omega_2 t$ where $\omega_1 \ll 1/RC \ll \omega_2$. Steady state prevails. Sketch the output voltage. Give values.

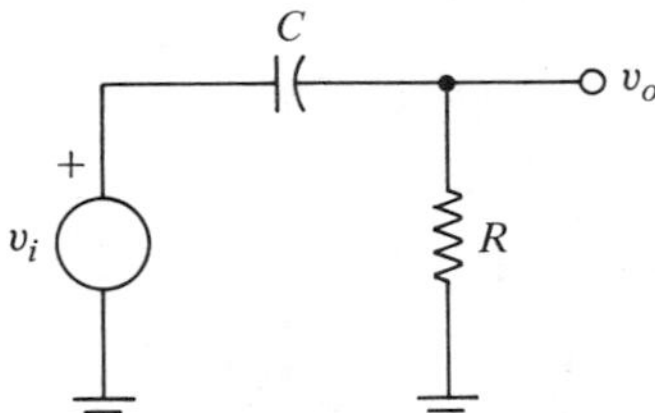

Fig. 9-60

9-25. In the steady state what is $v(t)$ in Fig. 9-61?

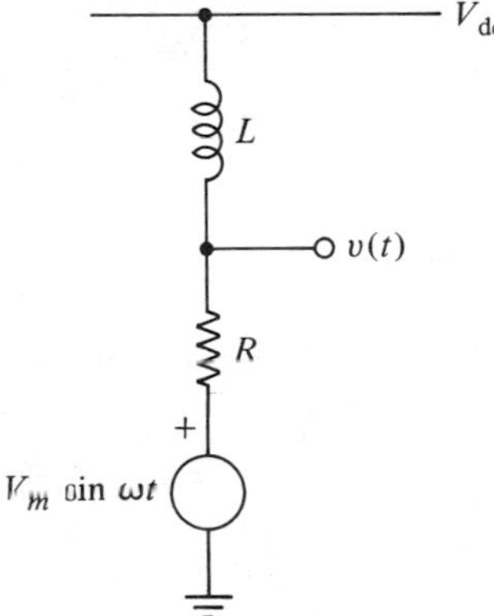

Fig. 9-61

9-26. In Fig. 9-62 the frequency of the sine wave is high enough to make the ac voltage across the capacitor and the ac current through the inductor negligible. Determine the steady-state expressions for $i_o(t)$ and $v_o(t)$.

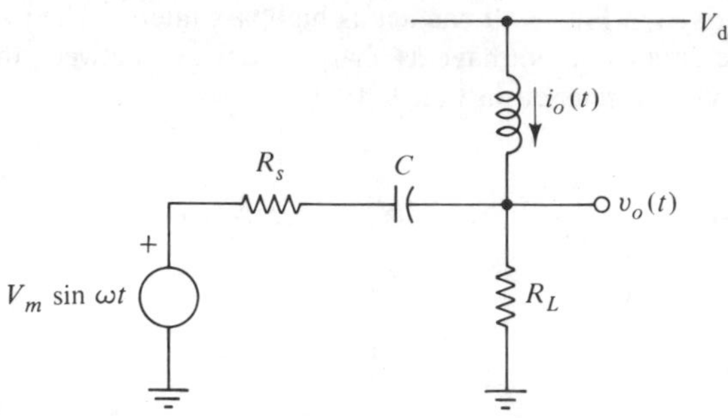

Fig. 9-62

9-27. In Fig. 9-63 steady state prevails. The frequency ω is high enough to make the ac voltage across the capacitor and the ac current through the inductor negligible. Obtain $v_1(t)$ and $v_2(t)$.

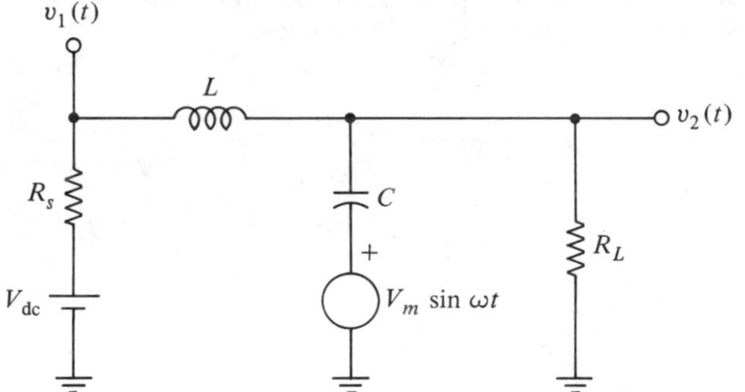

Fig. 9-63

9-28. In Fig. 9-64 $R \gg 1/\omega C$ and $\omega L \gg R$. Steady state prevails. Obtain the approximate expressions for $v_1(t)$ and $v_2(t)$.

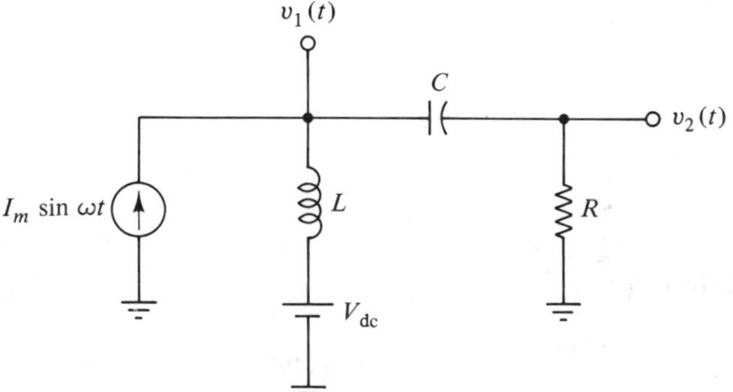

Fig. 9-64

9-29. Given the bandpass function

$$T(s) = \frac{s\omega_b}{s^2 + s\omega_b + \omega_p^2}$$

(**a**) Show that ω_p represents the frequency at which the magnitude curve peaks and ω_b represents the bandwidth, which is defined as the difference of the two frequencies at which the magnitude curve is $1/\sqrt{2}$ times the peak magnitude.

(**b**) Show that at the two frequencies obtained in (a) the phase is $\pm\pi/4$. The positive sign is associated with the lower frequency and the negative sign with the upper.

9-30. Design a bandpass filter with the following specifications.

$$R_s = R_L = 500\ \Omega$$

$$f_p = \frac{1}{2\pi} \times 10^5 \text{ Hz}$$

$$f_b = \frac{1}{2\pi} \times 2 \times 10^4 \text{ Hz}$$

9-31. A bandpass filter is shown in Fig. 9-65. What happens to the magnitude curve if R is doubled in value?

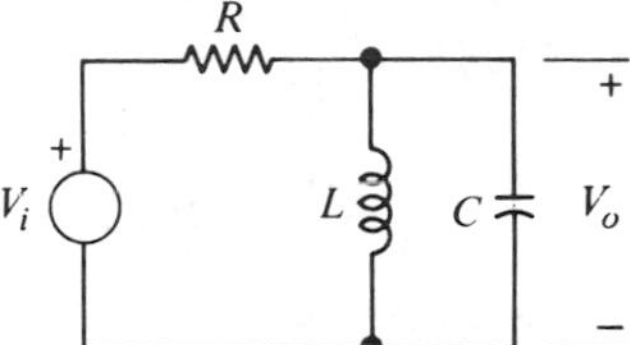

Fig. 9-65

9-32. Calculate the center frequency, bandwidth, and the peak magnitude for the bandpass circuits shown in Fig. 9-66.

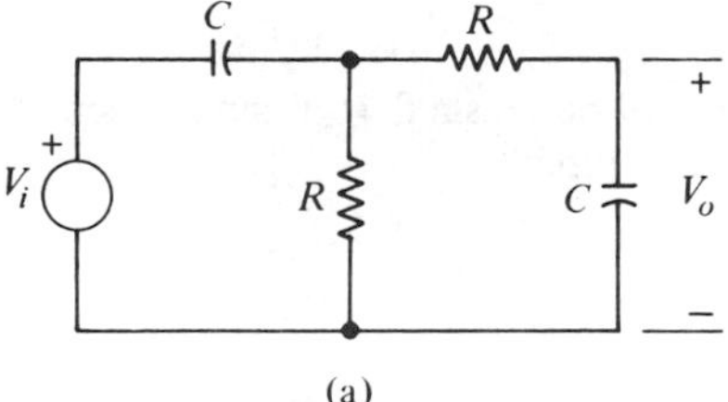

(a)

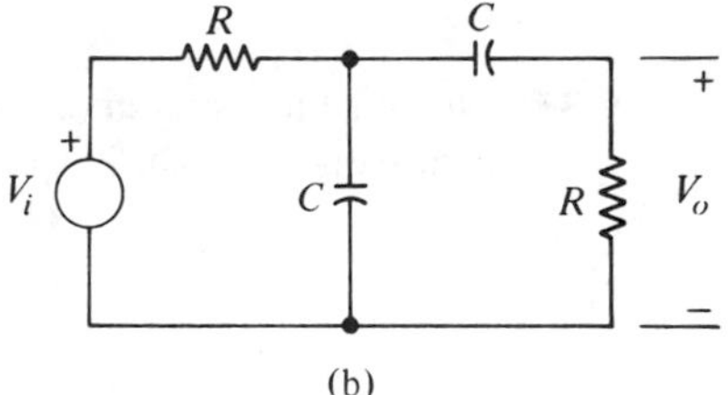

(b)

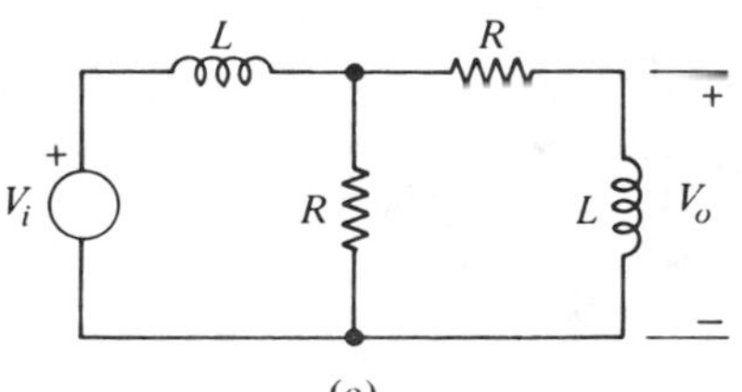

(c)

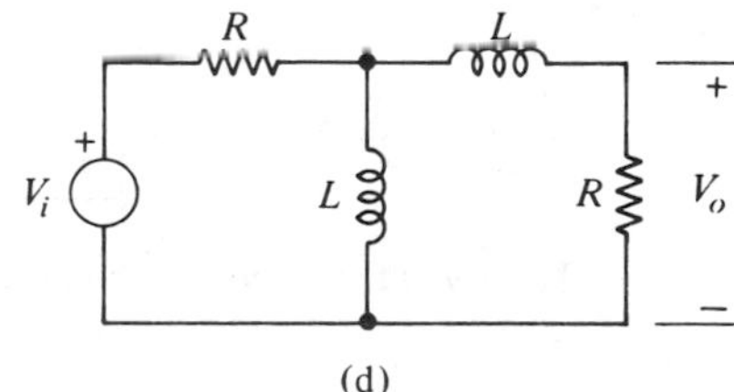

(d)

Fig. 9-66

9-33. Given $T = T_1 T_2$. If one of the functions is lowpass and the other highpass, can T be bandpass? Explain.

9-34. What kind of filtering is done by the networks shown in Fig. 9-67?

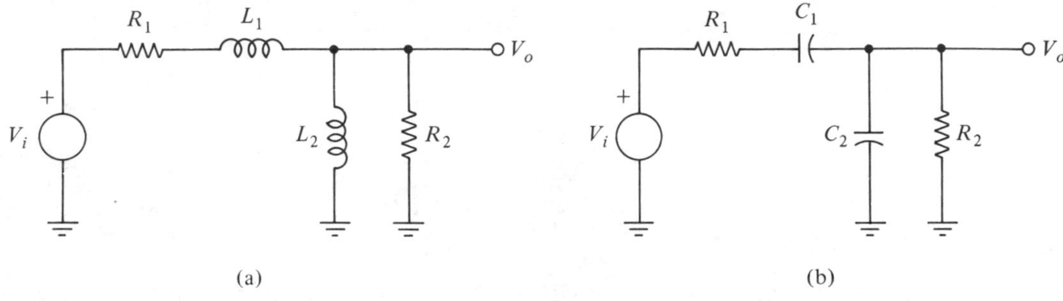

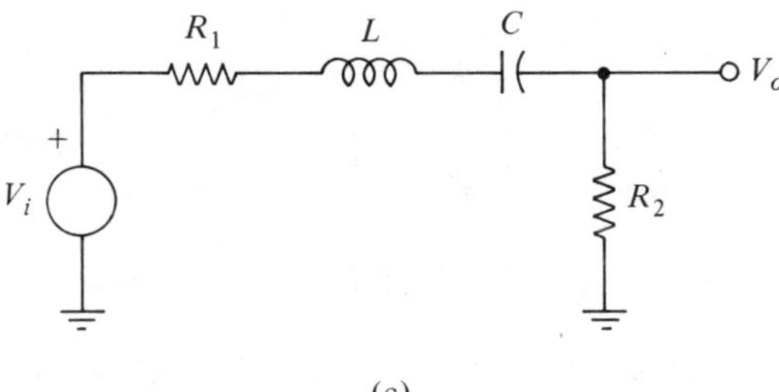

Fig. 9-67

9-35. The input to the system shown in Fig. 9-68 is $\sin 0.1t + \sin t + \sin 10t$. For all practical purposes what is the steady-state output?

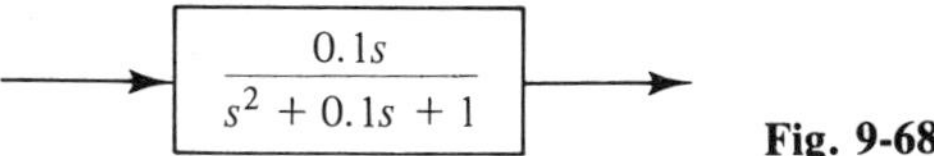

Fig. 9-68

9-36. Sketch the input and the steady-state output waveforms of the system shown in Fig. 9-69.

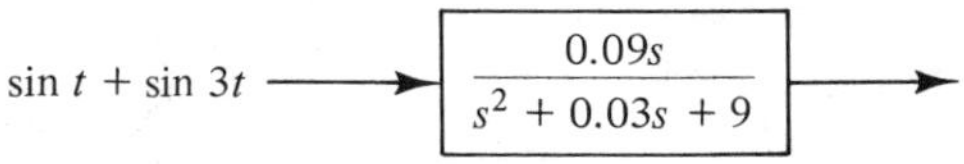

$\sin t + \sin 3t$ → $\boxed{\dfrac{0.09s}{s^2 + 0.03s + 9}}$ →

Fig. 9-69

9-37. Given the bandstop function

$$T(s) = \frac{s^2 + \omega_r^2}{s^2 + s\omega_b + \omega_r^2}$$

(**a**) Show that ω_b represents the difference of the two frequencies at which the magnitude is $1/\sqrt{2}$ times the magnitude at $\omega = 0$ and $\omega = \infty$.
(**b**) Show that at the two frequencies found in (a) the phase is $\pm\pi/4$. The positive sign is associated with the higher frequency and the negative sign with the lower.

9-38. (**a**) Obtain another network that meets the specifications of Example 9-7.
(**b**) What is the output if $v_i = 10 + 5 \sin 120\ \pi t$?

9-39. In Fig. 9-70, the bandwidth of the stopband is to be reduced without affecting the frequency of rejection. How can this result be achieved?

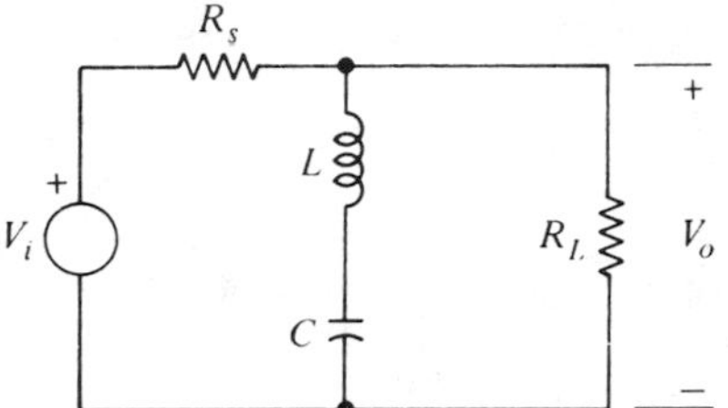

Fig. 9-70

9-40. In Fig. 9-71 for what setting of k is V_o/V_i a bandstop function?

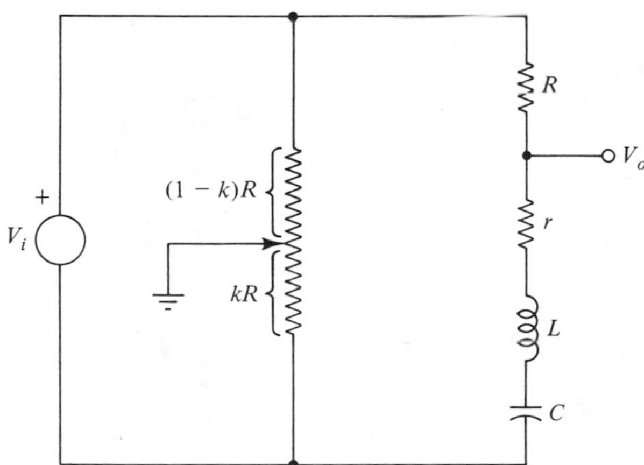

Fig. 9-71

9-41. For the circuit shown in Fig. 9-72 sketch the magnitude of the transfer function vs. ω for $k = 0, \frac{1}{2}$, and 1. Give values of various levels.

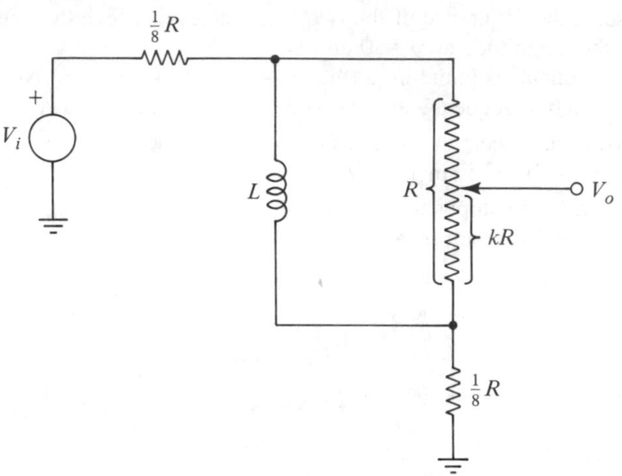

Fig. 9-72

9-42. Refer to the circuit shown in Fig. 9-73. Show that depending on the setting of k the low frequencies can be boosted or attenuated.

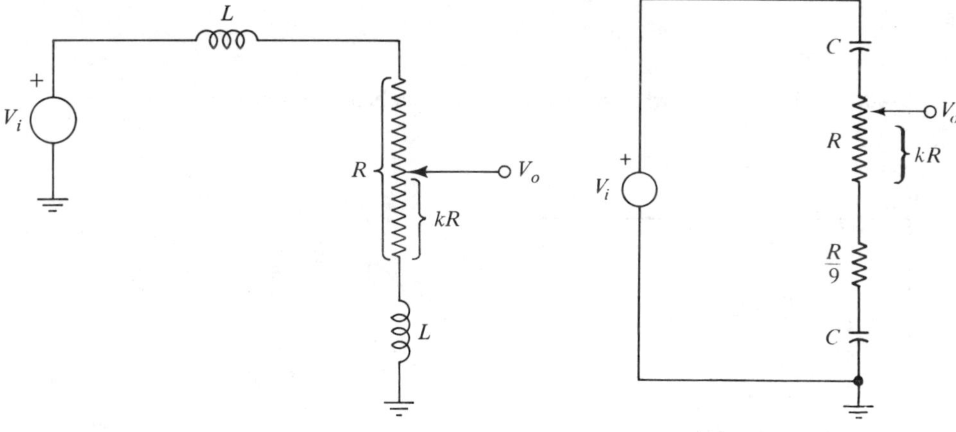

Fig. 9-73

Fig. 9-74

9-43. In Fig. 9-74, depending on the potentiometer setting k, high frequencies are either boosted or attenuated. Show this. (If the output is loaded, k also affects low frequencies.)

9-44. In Fig. 9-75, the frequency of the input is fixed at ω_0. The resistance R is varied from 0 to ∞.

(**a**) Sketch the amplitude and phase of the output voltage v_o as a function of R.

(**b**) The resistor R is adjusted to $1/\omega_0 C$. Voltages v_a and v_o are connected, respectively, to the horizontal and vertical amplifiers of an oscilloscope. What is the resulting display?

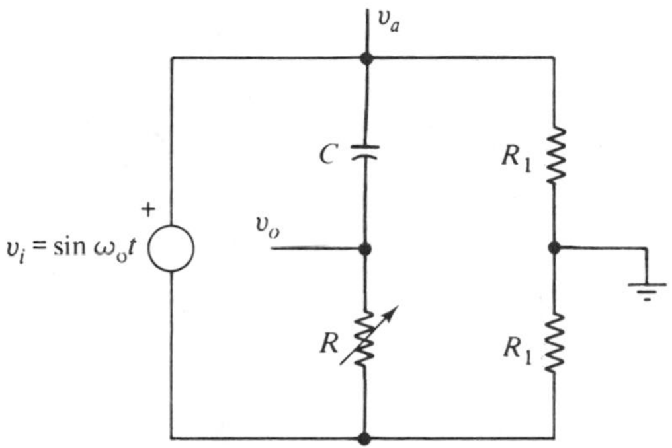

Fig. 9-75

9-45. Show that V_o/V_i is second-order all-pass for both circuits shown in Fig. 9-76.

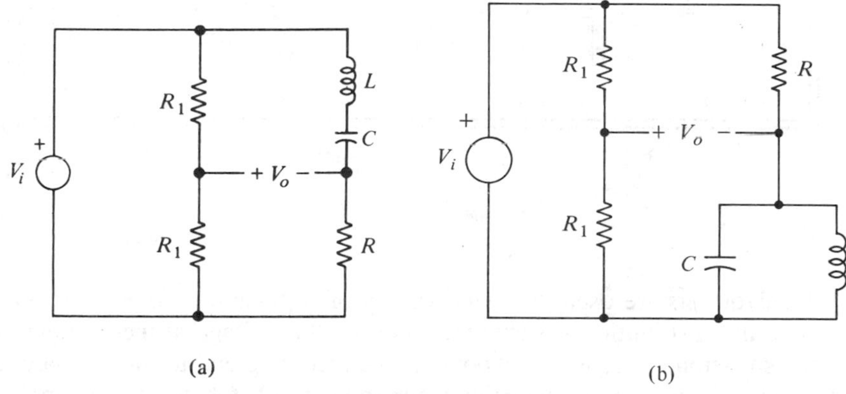

Fig. 9-76

9-46. Obtain a realization for $\dfrac{V_o}{V_i} = \dfrac{1}{2}\left(1 - \dfrac{2\alpha}{s + \alpha}\right)$.

CHAPTER 10

TRANSFORMERS

Transformers are used in a wide variety of applications. In electric power transmission and distribution systems they step up the voltage at the sending end to reduce transmission losses and step down at the receiving end to make it safer and easier to utilize. Transformers change voltages and currents to any desired amplitude, large or small. They transform impedances and match load impedances to source impedances for maximum output voltage or power transfer. They provide dc isolation between circuits and make it possible for the input and output sides to operate at different reference levels. They can invert or split signals by producing equal amplitude but opposite polarity sine waves with respect to a common reference. In conjunction with *RLC* elements they perform various filtering operations. In this chapter we learn about transformer models and how they are used in circuits.

10-1 MUTUALLY COUPLED CIRCUITS

We used the relationship $v = L(di/dt)$ to define inductance L in Chapter 1. Here we digress a little and start a development in terms of magnetic flux in order to broaden the concept of inductance.

An inductor is obtained by winding a wire to form a coil. Two such inductors with turns N_1 and N_2 are shown in Fig. 10-1. The magnetic fluxes threading through

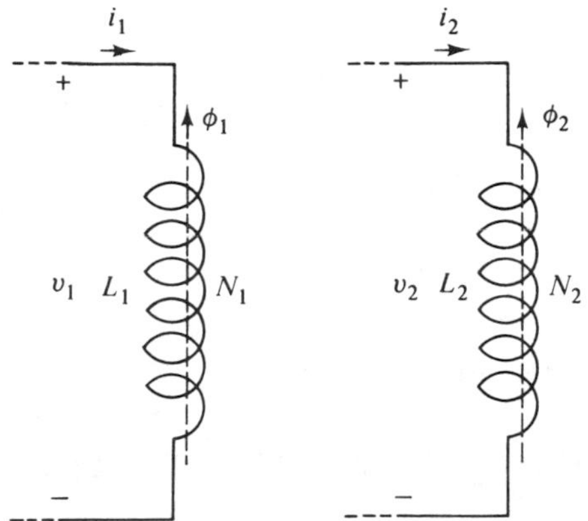

Fig. 10-1

the coils are designated by ϕ_1 and ϕ_2. Experimental observations indicate that the voltages across the coils are related to the number of turns and flux by the relationship

$$v_1 = N_1\frac{d\phi_1}{dt}, \qquad v_2 = N_2\frac{d\phi_2}{dt} \tag{10-1}$$

In linear, homogeneous, and isotropic media the flux produced by the current in the coil is proportional to the number of turns and the current. Thus

$$\phi_1 = k_1N_1i_1, \qquad \phi_2 = k_2N_2i_2 \tag{10-2}$$

where the proportionality constant k is related to the geometry of construction and the permeability of the material used for the coils.

Because of the linear relationship between flux and current, the voltages across the inductors can be expressed in terms of the currents rather than the fluxes through them.

$$v_1 = N_1\frac{d\phi_1}{dt} = k_1N_1^2\frac{di_1}{dt}, \qquad v_2 = N_2\frac{d\phi_2}{dt} = k_2N_2^2\frac{di_2}{dt} \tag{10-3}$$

If we now let

$$L_1 = k_1N_1^2, \qquad L_2 = k_2N_2^2 \tag{10-4}$$

we can write Eq. (10-3) as

$$v_1 = L_1\frac{di_1}{dt}, \qquad v_2 = L_2\frac{di_2}{dt} \tag{10-5}$$

Up to this point we implicitly assumed that the flux through a coil is due solely to the current in that coil. It is easy to construct a situation where such is not the case. All we need do is bring one coil physically into the vicinity of the other in Fig. 10-1 so that their magnetic fields interact (see Fig. 10-2). Of course, such an interaction can be avoided by magnetically shielding the coils from each other. However,

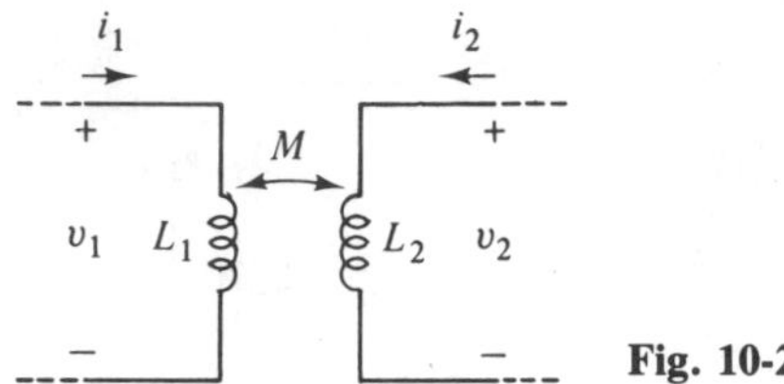

Fig. 10-2

in the absence of such shielding the voltages across the coils are no longer given by Eq. (10-5). We must modify the terminal relationship to include the effects of the mutual interaction.

Again the voltages across the coils are related to the flux through the coils by

$$v_1 = N_1 \frac{d\phi_1}{dt}, \qquad v_2 = N_2 \frac{d\phi_2}{dt} \tag{10-6}$$

However, ϕ_1 and ϕ_2 now have two components, one due to each current.

$$\phi_1 = \phi_{1s} \pm \phi_{1m}, \qquad \phi_2 = \phi_{2s} \pm \phi_{2m} \tag{10-7}$$

where the subscripts s and m stand for the self and mutual values. Thus ϕ_{1s} is the flux caused in coil 1 by the current in coil 1 (the self term), whereas ϕ_{1m} is the flux caused in coil 1 by the current in coil 2 (the mutual term). Similarly, the flux through coil 2 is due to the current in coil 2 (ϕ_{2s}) and the current in coil 1 (ϕ_{2m}). Depending on the relative direction of the two components, the flux through each coil is either additive or subtractive—hence the + or − signs in Eq. (10-7). A little thought should indicate that if the two components of the flux are additive in one coil, they are also additive in the other coil; that is, in the two equations the + or − signs go together.

The flux ϕ_{1s} is produced by i_1 circulating in N_1 turns; flux ϕ_{1m} is produced by i_2 circulating in N_2 turns. So as in Eq. (10-2), we can write

$$\phi_{1s} = k_{1s} N_1 i_1, \qquad \phi_{1m} = k_{12} N_2 i_2 \tag{10-8}$$

Similarly,

$$\phi_{2s} = k_{2s} N_2 i_2, \qquad \phi_{2m} = k_{21} N_1 i_1 \tag{10-9}$$

The proportionality constants (k's) depend on the geometry and the medium. It should therefore be evident that $k_{12} = k_{21} = k_m$. These relationships allow us to restate Eq. (10-6) in terms of currents rather than fluxes.

$$\begin{aligned} v_1 &= N_1 \frac{d\phi_1}{dt} = N_1 \frac{d}{dt}(\phi_{1s} \pm \phi_{1m}) = k_{1s} N_1^2 \frac{di_1}{dt} \pm k_m N_1 N_2 \frac{di_2}{dt} \\ v_2 &= N_2 \frac{d\phi_2}{dt} = N_2 \frac{d}{dt}(\phi_{2s} \pm \phi_{2m}) = k_{2s} N_2^2 \frac{di_2}{dt} \pm k_m N_1 N_2 \frac{di_1}{dt} \end{aligned} \tag{10-10}$$

The various inductances can be defined as follows.

$$L_1 = k_{1s}N_1^2 = \text{self-inductance of coil 1}$$
$$L_2 = k_{2s}N_2^2 = \text{self-inductance of coil 2} \tag{10-11}$$
$$M = k_m N_1 N_2 = \text{mutual inductance of coils 1 and 2}$$

Although we are familiar with the designation of self-inductance, or simply inductance, the concept of mutual inductance is new to us. Nonetheless, if we think in terms of the sources that produce the two components of the flux linking each coil and realize that it is the time rate of change of the *total flux* that produces the terminal voltage, we see mutual inductance as an extension of the concept of self-inductance.

To express mutual inductance in terms of self-inductance, the relations given in Eq. (10-11) are used.

$$M = k_m N_1 N_2 = k_m \sqrt{\frac{L_1}{k_{1s}}}\sqrt{\frac{L_2}{k_{2s}}} = \frac{k_m}{\sqrt{k_{1s}k_{2s}}}\sqrt{L_1 L_2}$$
$$M = k\sqrt{L_1 L_2} \tag{10-12}$$

where

$$k = \frac{k_m}{\sqrt{k_{1s}k_{2s}}}$$

The constant k is known as *the coefficient of coupling*. When $k = 0$, the two coils are decoupled from each other, and terminal voltages are due to the self-inductances only. When $k = 1$, the maximum possible coupling exists between the two coils. The coefficient of coupling k is a positive number between zero and one. The mutual inductance is positive.

When expressed in terms of inductances, Eq. (10-10) becomes

$$v_1 = L_1\frac{di_1}{dt} \pm M\frac{di_2}{dt}, \qquad v_2 = L_2\frac{di_2}{dt} \pm M\frac{di_1}{dt} \tag{10-13}$$

Depending on the direction of the coil winding and the relative position of the coils, the voltage due to the mutual inductance either *aids or opposes the voltage due to the self-inductance*. To determine its sign, we can conduct the simple experiment shown in Fig. 10-3. We drive one of the coils, say, coil 1, with a voltage source. The other coil is left open-circuited. Since $i_2 = 0$, Eq. (10-13) simplifies to

$$\left.\begin{aligned} v_1(t) &= L_1\frac{di_1}{dt} \\ v_2(t) &= \pm M\frac{di_1}{dt}\end{aligned}\right\} v_2(t) = \pm\frac{M}{L_1}v_1(t) \tag{10-14}$$

So except for the scale factor M/L_1, $v_2(t)$ is either an inverted or a noninverted version of the input $v_1(t)$. Suppose that we use a sine wave for $v_1(t)$. To facilitate mea-

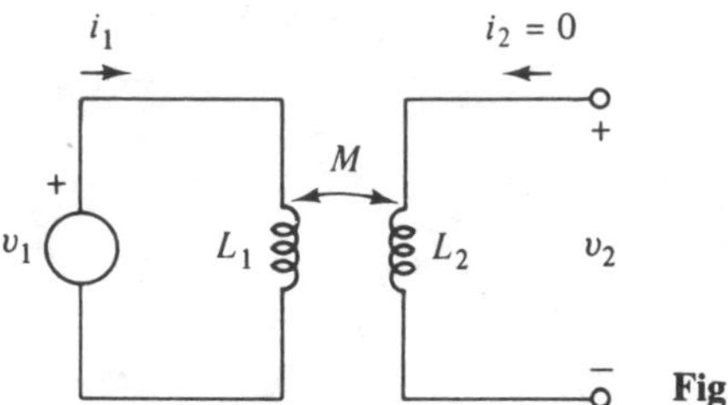

Fig. 10-3

surements, we connect the coils to a common ground and display the $v_1(t)$ and $v_2(t)$ waveforms simultaneously on an oscilloscope. The two sine waves are either *in phase* as in Fig. 10-4(a) or *out of phase* as in Fig. 10-4(b). Alternatively, we can connect one signal to the vertical and the other to the horizontal amplifier of the oscilloscope. If the slope of the resulting straight line is positive, the signals are in phase; if the slope is negative, the signals are out of phase.

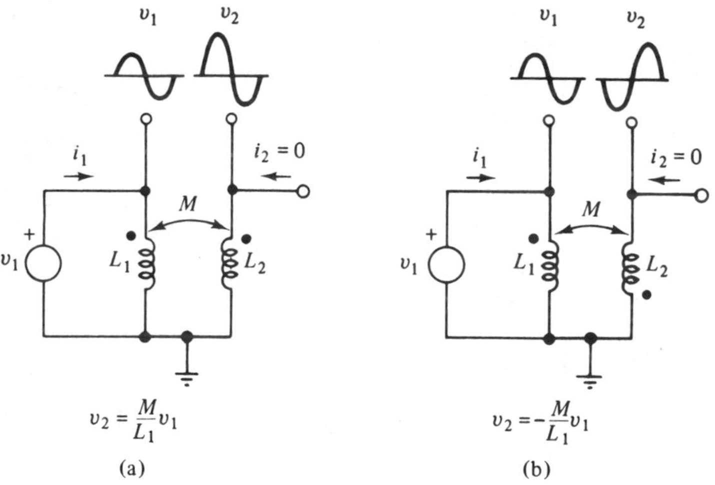

Fig. 10-4

We now mark with a dot the two terminals that produce in-phase voltages—that is, voltages that go up and down together. These terminals are called *corresponding terminals*. In Fig. 10-4(a) the corresponding terminals are the two top (or bottom) terminals. In Fig. 10-4(b), because the voltages are out of phase, the corresponding terminals are one on top and the other at the bottom.

Having thus designated the corresponding terminals, we are ready to state the rule for determining the sign of the voltage due to mutual induction *relative* to the sign of the voltage due to self-induction.

If both currents are directed into or away from corresponding terminals, the voltage due to mutual induction is of the same sign as the voltage due to self-induc-

tion. If one current enters a dotted terminal and the other a nondotted terminal, then voltages due to mutual and self-induction have opposite signs.

In Fig. 10-5(a), i_1 and i_2 enter the corresponding terminals. So mutual and self-induction voltages have the *same* sign.

$$v_1 = L_1\frac{di_1}{dt} + M\frac{di_2}{dt}, \qquad v_2 = L_2\frac{di_2}{dt} + M\frac{di_1}{dt}$$

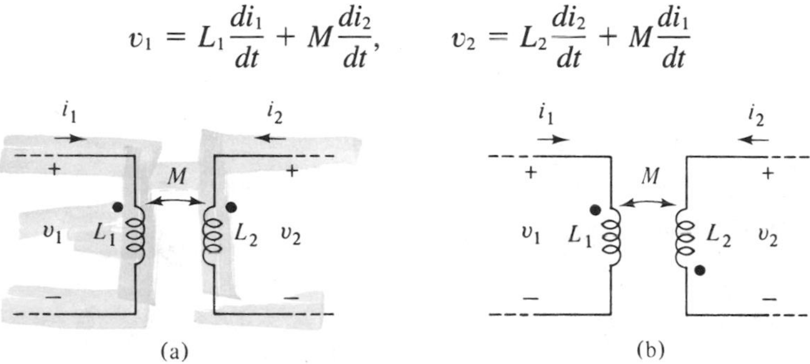

Fig. 10-5

In Fig. 10-5(b), i_1 enters a dotted and i_2 enters a nondotted terminal. Consequently, the sign of the mutual induction voltage is the *opposite* of the sign of the self-induction voltage.

$$v_1 = L_1\frac{di_1}{dt} - M\frac{di_2}{dt}, \qquad v_2 = L_2\frac{di_2}{dt} - M\frac{di_1}{dt}$$

In Fig. 10-6(a), the currents enter corresponding terminals. As a result, the mutual and self-inductance terms have the *same* sign.

$$v_1 = L_1\frac{di_1}{dt} + M\frac{di_2}{dt}, \qquad v_2 = -L_2\frac{di_2}{dt} - M\frac{di_1}{dt}$$

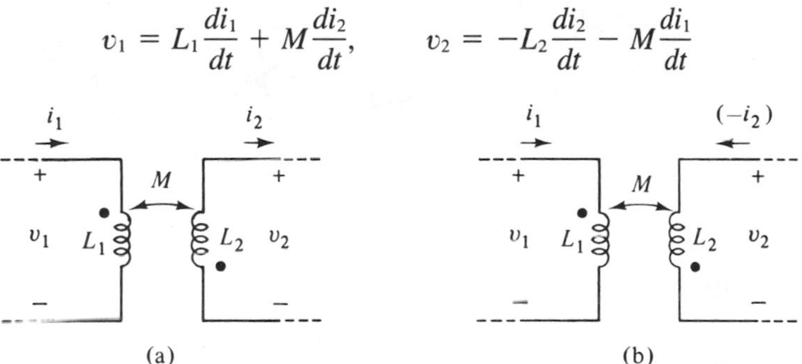

Fig. 10-6

Note that in the expression for v_2 *both terms are negative. The sign is dictated by the self-inductance term.* It is negative because i_2 as given will make v_2 negative. Alternatively, we can restate this problem as in Fig. 10-6(b), where both the direction and the sign of i_2 are reversed. Since this double reversal is equivalent to no reversal, the two circuits of Fig. 10-6 are identical. However, by reference to Fig. 10-6(b), we note that i_1 enters a dotted and $(-i_2)$ enters a nondotted terminal. Thus mutual and self-inductance terms have *opposite* signs.

$$v_1 = L_1\frac{di_1}{dt} - M\frac{d(-i_2)}{dt}, \qquad v_2 = L_2\frac{d(-i_2)}{dt} - M\frac{di_1}{dt}$$

Of course, this set of equations is identical with the preceding set.

The characteristics of mutually coupled coils are described by two equations because we are dealing with *four terminals*. These equations can be stated either in the time domain or the frequency domain.

$$v_1(t) = L_1\frac{di_1(t)}{dt} \pm M\frac{di_2(t)}{dt}, \qquad v_2(t) = L_2\frac{di_2(t)}{dt} \pm M\frac{di_1(t)}{dt} \tag{10-15}$$

$$V_1(s) = sL_1I_1(s) \pm sMI_2(s), \qquad V_2(s) = sL_2I_2(s) \pm sMI_1(s) \tag{10-16}$$

In writing the frequency-domain equations, it is assumed that initial conditions are zero—that is, $i_1(0) = i_2(0) = 0$.

10-2 SERIES AND PARALLEL CONNECTION OF MUTUALLY COUPLED COILS

The coils of a mutually coupled circuit can be connected in the *series-aiding* or *series-opposing* mode as shown in Fig. 10-7. In either case, we obtain a two-terminal circuit. The equivalent inductance of the combinations can be found as follows.

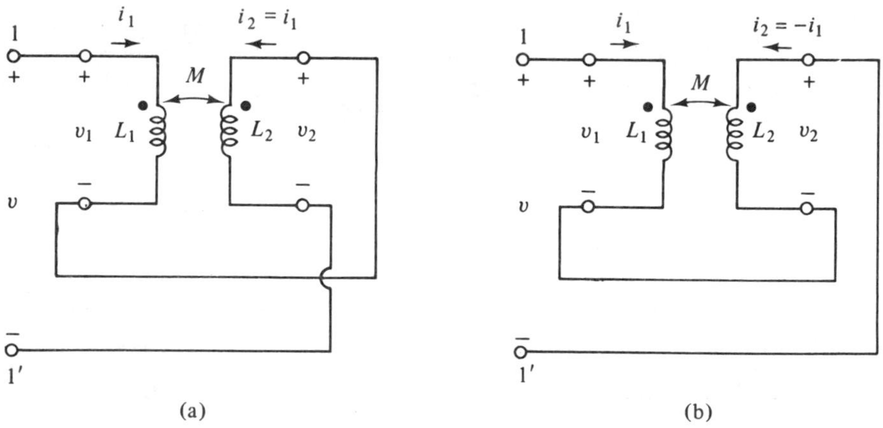

Fig. 10-7

In Fig. 10-7(a), the coils are connected in the series-aiding mode because the current i_1, which goes through both coils, enters corresponding terminals. The coupled equations are

$$v_1 = L_1\frac{di_1}{dt} + M\frac{di_2}{dt}, \qquad v_2 = L_2\frac{di_2}{dt} + M\frac{di_1}{dt}$$

Since $i_2 = i_1$ and $v = v_1 + v_2$, the result is

$$v = \underbrace{\left(L_1\frac{di_1}{dt} + M\frac{di_1}{dt}\right)}_{v_1} + \underbrace{\left(L_2\frac{di_1}{dt} + M\frac{di_1}{dt}\right)}_{v_2} = (L_1 + L_2 + 2M)\frac{di_1}{dt} \tag{10-17}$$

$$v = L_{eq1}\frac{di_1}{dt} \tag{10-18}$$

where

$$L_{eq1} = L_1 + L_2 + 2M = L_1 + L_2 + 2k\sqrt{L_1L_2} \tag{10-19}$$

Note that the equivalent inductance is greater than the sum of the individual self-inductances. For the case of $L_1 = L_2 = L$ and $k = 1$, we obtain $L_{eq1} = 4L$. (This result is to be expected, since the inductance is proportional to the square of the number of turns and the series-aiding connection has twice as many turns as the individual coils.)

Similarly, the series-opposing ($i_2 = -i_1$) connection of Fig. 10-7(b) gives

$$v = \underbrace{\left(L_1\frac{di_1}{dt} - M\frac{di_1}{dt}\right)}_{v_1} - \underbrace{\left(-L_2\frac{di_1}{dt} + M\frac{di_1}{dt}\right)}_{v_2} = (L_1 + L_2 - 2M)\frac{di_1}{dt} \tag{10-20}$$

$$v = L_{eq2}\frac{di_1}{dt} \tag{10-21}$$

where

$$L_{eq2} = L_1 + L_2 - 2M = L_1 + L_2 - 2k\sqrt{L_1L_2} \tag{10-22}$$

Here the equivalent inductance is less than the sum of the self-inductances. For the case of $L_1 = L_2 = L$ and $k = 1$, L_{eq2} is zero.

If we subtract L_{eq2} from L_{eq1}, we find

$$L_{eq1} - L_{eq2} = (L_1 + L_2 + 2M) - (L_1 + L_2 - 2M) = 4M$$

$$M = \tfrac{1}{4}(L_{eq1} - L_{eq2}) \tag{10-23}$$

Thus the mutual inductance can be determined by making two inductance measurements that are taken with the coils connected in series, first one way and then the other. One-fourth the difference of the smaller measurement from the larger measurement is the mutual inductance. To complete the modeling of the two coupled coils, we also need to measure the self-inductances. These inductance measurements are done on each coil separately while the other coil is open-circuited.

At first glance Eq. (10-22) may suggest that, for certain combinations of L_1 and L_2, L_{eq2} may become negative. However, it should be realized that a negative inductance results in *negative energy stored* ($\frac{1}{2}L_{eq2}i^2$), which implies that the equivalent inductance can become a *source of energy*. Clearly, we cannot expect to extract energy out of a passive system composed of two mutually coupled coils connected in series opposition! Indeed, we can use this energy argument to justify that $L_{eq2} \geq 0$ and hence $k \leq 1$ (see Problem 10-3). Also from Eq. (10-22) we see that

$$L_{eq2} \geq L_{eq2}\big|_{k=1} = (L_1 - L_2)^2$$

The right-hand side, being a squared function, is always positive. Hence, L_{eq2} can never become negative.

The coils of a mutually coupled circuit can also be connected in parallel, as in Fig. 10-8, with corresponding ends either tied together or tied in opposition. The equivalent inductance seen from terminals $1-1'$ is given by

$$L_{eq3} = \frac{L_1L_2 - M^2}{L_1 + L_2 - 2M} = \frac{L_1L_2(1 - k^2)}{L_1 + L_2 - 2k\sqrt{L_1L_2}} \tag{10-24a}$$

$$L_{eq4} = \frac{L_1L_2 - M^2}{L_1 + L_2 + 2M} = \frac{L_1L_2(1 - k^2)}{L_1 + L_2 + 2k\sqrt{L_1L_2}} \tag{10-24b}$$

where L_{eq3} is for Fig. 10-8(a) and L_{eq4} for Fig. 10-8(b). For $L_1 = L_2 = L$, these expressions simplify to

$$L_{eq3} = \frac{L}{2}(1 + k), \qquad L_{eq4} = \frac{L}{2}(1 - k)$$

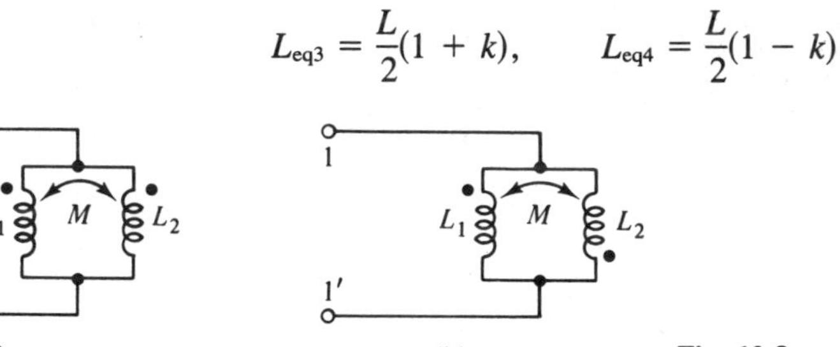

Fig. 10-8

10-3 EQUIVALENT CIRCUITS

The mutually coupled circuit of Fig. 10-9(a) is described by the set of equations

$$v_1 = L_1\frac{di_1}{dt} + M\frac{di_2}{dt}, \qquad v_2 = L_2\frac{di_2}{dt} + M\frac{di_1}{dt} \tag{10-25}$$

This set of equations also describes the terminal properties of the circuit shown in Fig. 10-9(b), as can be seen by expressing v_1 and v_2 as the sum of element voltages. The two circuits are *equivalent* with respect to their *terminal behavior*. As long as we are concerned with the relationships between terminal variables v_1, i_1, v_2, and i_2, the two circuits are indistinguishable from each other *even though their internal structure is different*. Note that there are no corresponding ends in Fig. 10-9(b).

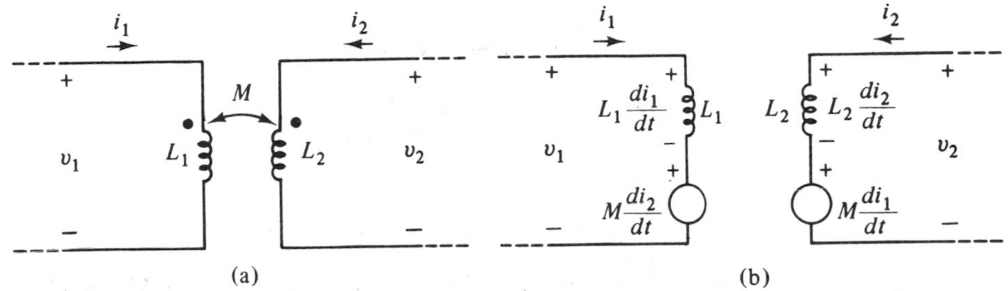

Fig. 10-9

Nor is their any mutual coupling between the coils. The voltages across the inductors are due to self-induction only. However, this circuit contains two *sources,* one on each side, to account for the interaction between the two coils. The source in loop 1, $M(di_2/dt)$, depends on di_2/dt and therefore conveys to loop 1 changes taking place in loop 2. On the other hand, the source in loop 2, $M(di_1/dt)$, depends on di_1/dt and thus conveys to loop 2 changes taking place in loop 1. Without these sources the two loops are isolated from each other: one cannot influence the other. The sources couple loop 1 to loop 2 and vice versa. Unlike all the sources seen and used so far, these sources *are not independent;* that is, their terminal voltages are not specified, irrespective of external influences. Rather, the voltages *depend* on events taking place in other parts of the circuit. Consequently, such sources are called *dependent sources.* (See Chapter 11 for discussion of dependent sources.) Thus the source $M(di_2/dt)$ depends on the time rate of change of the current in loop 2, whereas source $M(di_1/dt)$ depends on the time rate of change of the current in loop 1. Essentially, the equivalent circuit of Fig. 10-9(b) tells us that if we admit dependent sources, we can eliminate mutually coupled coils and analyze circuits by using the more familiar circuit elements (inductance and voltage source.)

The dependent sources in the equivalent circuit of Fig. 10-9(b) clearly show that *there is no coupling between the coils if the currents do not vary with time.* Mutual coupling depends on the *time rate of change* of currents. *Direct current cannot be transmitted in either direction.*

Other equivalent circuits that describe the terminal properties of mutually coupled coils can be constructed. For instance, we can rewrite Eq. (10-25) in the following form.

$$v_1 = L_1\frac{di_1}{dt} + M\frac{di_2}{dt} = (L_1 - M)\frac{di_1}{dt} + M\frac{d}{dt}(i_2 + i_1)$$

$$v_2 = L_2\frac{di_2}{dt} + M\frac{di_1}{dt} = (L_2 - M)\frac{di_2}{dt} + M\frac{d}{dt}(i_1 + i_2)$$

By interpreting these equations as representations of the mesh equations of two adjacent loops, we can easily draw the circuit of Fig. 10-10. In this equivalent representation M serves as the actual *coupling element* between the two loops and so makes

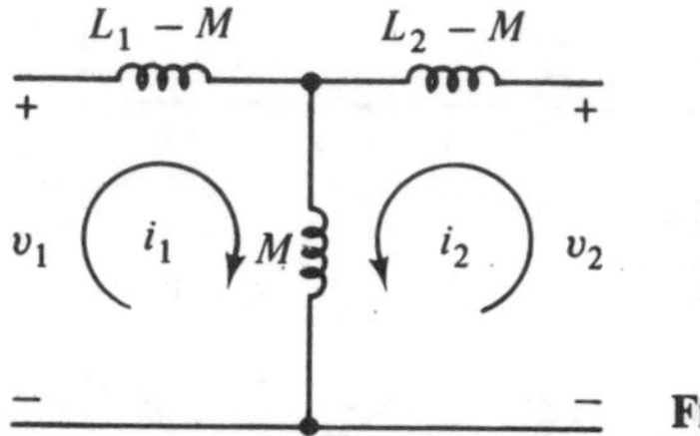

Fig. 10-10

sense from a physical standpoint. On the other hand, $(L_1 - M)$ or $(L_2 - M)$ may have a negative value and thereby represent a negative inductance that does not make sense physically. Regardless of what may occur internally, the terminal characteristics of this circuit are *identical* with those of mutually coupled coils.

The equivalent circuits given by Figs. 10-9(b) and 10-10 are by no means the only representations that can be used to describe the terminal behavior of mutually coupled coils. In the following sections we will develop additional equivalent circuits that are useful in analyzing circuits and interpreting results.

Example 10-1

In Fig. 10-11, obtain the input current i_i and the short-circuit current i_{sc}. The input voltage is applied at $t = 0$. Initial conditions are zero.

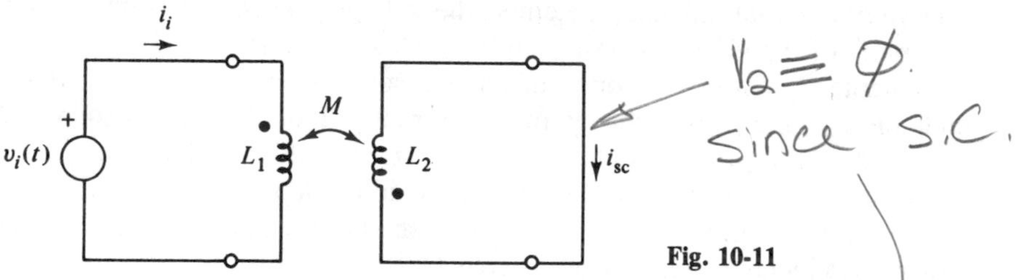

Fig. 10-11

Solution. To facilitate the writing of equations, we represent the circuit by using dependent sources as shown in Fig. 10-12. The dependent sources have their polarities reversed because i_1 enters a dotted and i_2 a nondotted terminal. As a result of the short circuit, we have on the output side

$$L_2 \frac{di_2}{dt} - M\frac{di_1}{dt} = 0$$

which gives

$$\frac{di_2}{dt} = \frac{M}{L_2}\frac{di_1}{dt}$$

Having thus expressed di_2/dt in terms of di_1/dt, we now refer to the input.

$$v_i = L_1 \frac{di_1}{dt} - M\frac{di_2}{dt} = L_1\frac{di_1}{dt} - M\left(\frac{M}{L_2}\frac{di_1}{dt}\right)$$

$$= \left(\frac{L_1 L_2 - M^2}{L_2}\right)\frac{di_1}{dt}$$

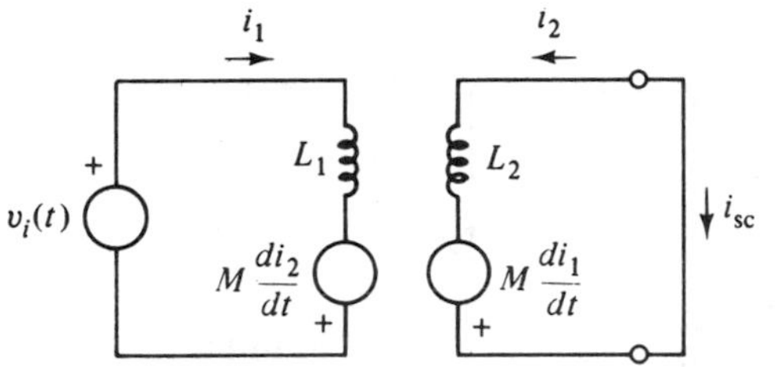

Fig. 10-12

It follows that

$$\frac{di_1}{dt} = \frac{L_2}{L_1L_2 - M^2} v_i$$

$$i_1(t) = \frac{L_2}{L_1L_2 - M^2} \int_0^t v_i(t')\,dt'$$

$$\frac{di_2}{dt} = \frac{M}{L_2}\frac{di_1}{dt} = \frac{M}{L_1L_2 - M^2} v_i$$

$$i_2(t) = \frac{M}{L_1L_2 - M^2} \int_0^t v_i(t')\,dt'$$

Note that $i_1(0) = 0$ and $i_2(0) = 0$, and so initial conditions are satisfied.

$$\left.\begin{aligned} i_i(t) &= i_1(t) = \frac{L_2}{L_1L_2 - M^2} \int_0^t v_i(t')\,dt' \\ i_{sc}(t) &= -i_2(t) = -\frac{M}{L_1L_2 - M^2} \int_0^t v_i(t')\,dt' \end{aligned}\right\} \text{Ans.}$$

Example 10-2

In Fig. 10-13, obtain $i_1(t)$ and $v_2(t)$. The two independent sources are applied at $t = 0$. The initial conditions are zero.

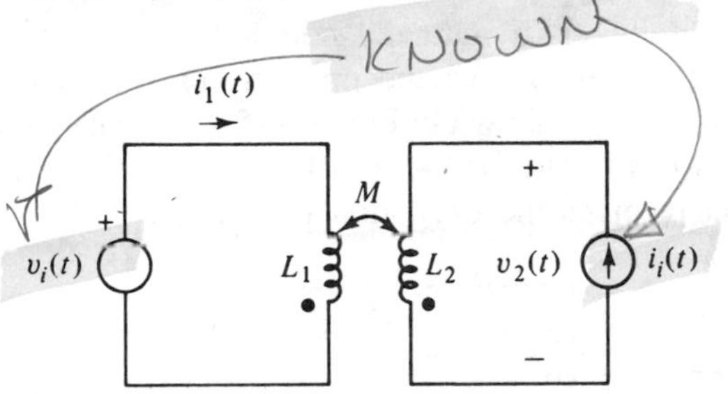

Fig. 10-13

Solution. Again, we redraw the circuit by using dependent sources as shown in Fig. 10-14. In the original circuit *both* i_1 and i_2 leave corresponding terminals. Hence the dependent-source polarities are with the positive sign on top (just like the voltages across L_1 and L_2, which are caused by i_1 and i_2 and therefore have the positive sign on the top side of the inductors).

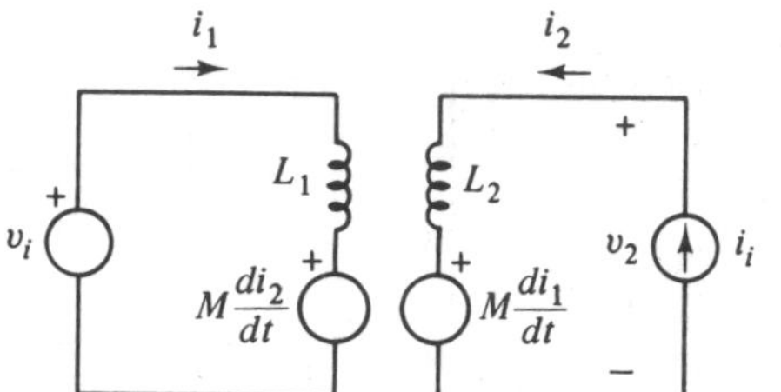

Fig. 10-14

Recognizing that $i_2 = i_i$, we sum voltages around the first loop to obtain

$$v_i = L_1\frac{di_1}{dt} + M\frac{di_2}{dt} = L_1\frac{di_1}{dt} + M\frac{di_i}{dt}$$

Then

$$\frac{di_1}{dt} = \frac{1}{L_1}\left(v_i - M\frac{di_i}{dt}\right)$$

$$i_1(t) = \frac{1}{L_1}\int_0^t v_i(t')\,dt' - \frac{M}{L_1}i_i(t) \quad \text{Ans.}$$

By summing voltages around the second loop and using the expression for di_1/dt just developed, we have

$$v_2 = L_2\frac{di_i}{dt} + M\frac{di_1}{dt} = L_2\frac{di_i}{dt} + \frac{M}{L_1}\left(v_i - M\frac{di_i}{dt}\right)$$

$$v_2(t) = \frac{M}{L_1}v_i(t) + \left(\frac{L_1L_2 - M^2}{L_1}\right)\frac{di_i(t)}{dt} \quad \text{Ans.}$$

10-4 TRANSFORMERS WITH TIGHT COUPLING

A transformer with tight coupling is a mutually coupled circuit with $k \cong 1$. To achieve the tight coupling, the coils are wound on iron cores. Schematically, the iron core is designated by two bars as shown in Fig. 10-15. These bars take the place of the symbol M with its two arrowheads. A transformer may have two or more windings. The winding that receives the excitation is generally called the *primary*

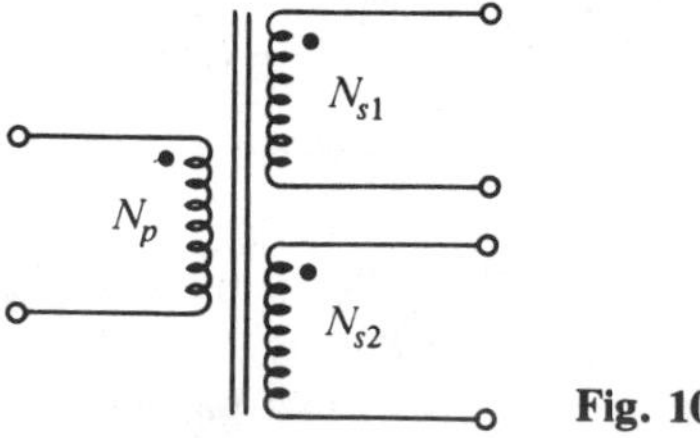

Fig. 10-15

winding. The other windings are called *secondary* windings. The primary winding is drawn on one side of the core, and all secondary windings are drawn on the other side. Either the number of turns on each winding is given or, as is often the case, the turns ratio between primary and secondary windings is given.

In addition to inductance, windings also have resistance. The winding resistance is shown as a separate resistance in series with the coils as in Fig. 10-16(a). Henceforth these resistances are considered to be part of the source and load resistances. The designation 1: n implies that for every turn on the left there are n turns on the right. Note that the direction of i_2 is taken here opposite to the direction used in preceding circuits. The implication is that signal or power flow is from left to right. The equivalent circuit is shown in Fig. 10-16(b). The dependent source voltages are in *opposition* to the self-inductance voltages v_{L1} and v_{L2} because i_1 and i_2 do not enter corresponding terminals.

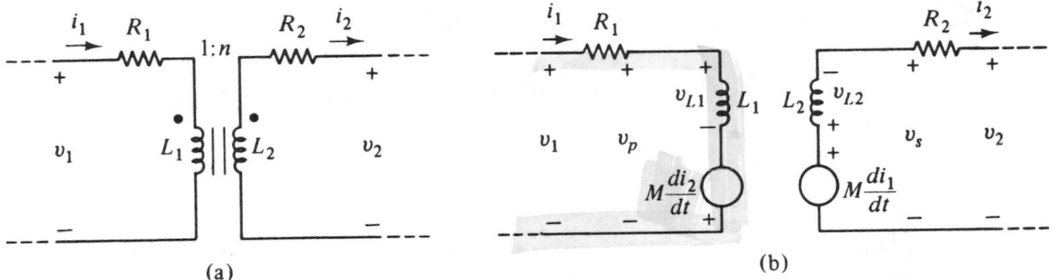

Fig. 10-16

Let us convert the equivalent circuit of Fig. 10-16(b) into a more suitable form that describes the terminal properties of a transformer. From the primary (left) side we have

$$v_p(t) = L_1\frac{di_1(t)}{dt} - M\frac{di_2(t)}{dt}$$

$$\frac{di_1(t)}{dt} = \frac{v_p(t)}{L_1} + \frac{M}{L_1}\frac{di_2(t)}{dt}$$

Integrating this expression between 0 and t gives

$$i_1(t) - i_1(0) = \frac{1}{L_1}\int_0^t v_p(t')\,dt' + \frac{M}{L_1}[i_2(t) - i_2(0)]$$

Since $M = k\sqrt{L_1L_2}$, we can express $i_1(t)$ as

$$i_1(t) = \frac{1}{L_1}\int_0^t v_p(t')\,dt' + k\sqrt{\frac{L_2}{L_1}}i_2(t) + i_1(0) - k\sqrt{\frac{L_2}{L_1}}i_2(0) \qquad (10\text{-}26)$$

Similarly, from the secondary side we obtain

$$v_s(t) = -L_2\frac{di_2(t)}{dt} + M\frac{di_1(t)}{dt} = -L_2\frac{di_2}{dt} + M\left[\frac{v_p(t)}{L_1} + \frac{M}{L_1}\frac{di_2(t)}{dt}\right]$$

$$= k\sqrt{\frac{L_2}{L_1}}v_p(t) - (1 - k^2)L_2\frac{di_2(t)}{dt} \tag{10-27}$$

Next, we let the number of turns of the primary and secondary windings be represented by N_1 and N_2, respectively. We also let the turns ratio be represented by $n = N_2/N_1$. Since self-inductance is proportional to the square of the number of turns and both coils are wound on the same core, we have

$$\frac{L_2}{L_1} = \frac{N_2^2}{N_1^2} = n^2 \tag{10-28}$$

Equations (10-26) and (10-27) can then be written

$$i_1(t) = \frac{1}{L_1}\int_0^t v_p(t')\,dt' + kni_2(t) + i_1(0) - kni_2(0) \tag{10-29a}$$

$$v_s(t) = knv_p(t) - (1 - k^2)L_2\frac{di_2(t)}{dt} \tag{10-29b}$$

Using these two equations, we can construct an equivalent circuit to represent the terminal characteristics of the transformer. By interpreting Eq. (10-29a) as a statement of Kirchhoff's Current Law applied to the top terminal on the primary side and Eq. (10-29b) as a statement of Kirchhoff's Voltage Law applied to the secondary loop, we draw the equivalent circuit shown in Fig. 10-17. The mutual interaction between the primary and secondary circuits is accounted for by the *current-dependent* current source $[kni_2(t)]$ on the primary side and by the *voltage-dependent* voltage source $[knv_p(t)]$ on the secondary side. If the secondary current $i_2(t)$ does not vary with time, then it must stay at its initial value—that is, $i_2(t) = i_2(0)$—in which case the two secondary-dependent current sources that are present on the primary side add to zero. Thus constant currents in the secondary circuit cannot influence the primary circuit in any way. Similarly, if $i_1(t)$ is constant, $v_p(t) = 0$ (because of L_1), and so the secondary circuit is unaffected by the primary circuit. *The transformer simply does not pass dc in either direction.*

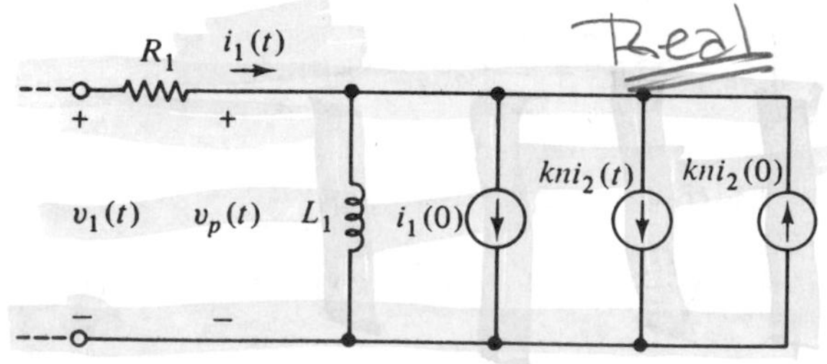

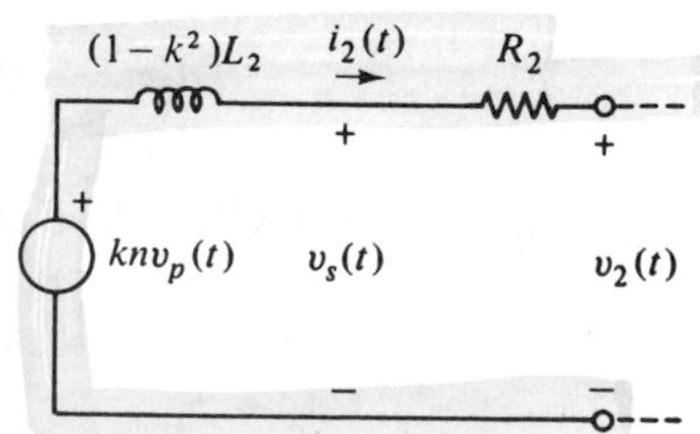

Fig. 10-17

We may wonder why the two sides of the transformer are represented by two different equivalent circuits. After all, the two sides differ physically only in the number of turns on the windings. Furthermore, the excitation can be applied to either side or, for that matter, to both sides at the same time. Why the difference? The answer is that in the development of the equivalent circuit we rearranged the equations with left-to-right transmission in mind. By rearranging the equations differently, we can obtain other equivalent circuits. In other words, the equivalent circuits are not unique. Of course, the equivalent circuit of Fig. 10-17 can just as well be used if the excitation is applied on the right and the output taken on the left even though the development favors signal transmission in the other direction.

We now make a number of *assumptions* to simplify the equivalent circuit given in Fig. 10-17.

1. Initial conditions are zero—that is, $i_1(0) = 0$, $i_2(0) = 0$.
2. Losses are zero—that is, $R_1 = 0$, $R_2 = 0$.
3. The current taken by L_1 is zero—that is, $L_1 = \infty$.
4. The coefficient of coupling is unity—that is, $k = 1$.

How well these assumptions are met in practice depends on the particular application. For instance, if the primary is driven by a source that has an internal resistance R_s much higher than R_1, then R_1 can be neglected relative to R_s. Similarly, if the load resistance R_L is much higher than R_2, R_2 can be neglected. Also, the more turns put on the primary, the larger L_1 becomes, and hence the more negligible the current taken by L_1 becomes. Correspondingly, L_2 must have a larger number of turns in order to maintain the turns ratio at the desired value ($n = L_2/L_1$). Under these assumptions the equivalent circuit of Fig. 10-17 simplifies considerably. It reduces to the equivalent circuit shown in Fig. 10-18, where, for reference, the original circuit is also drawn. This model describes *the ideal transformer*—one that transforms voltages and current according to

$$v_2 = nv_1, \qquad i_2 = \frac{1}{n} i_1 \tag{10-30}$$

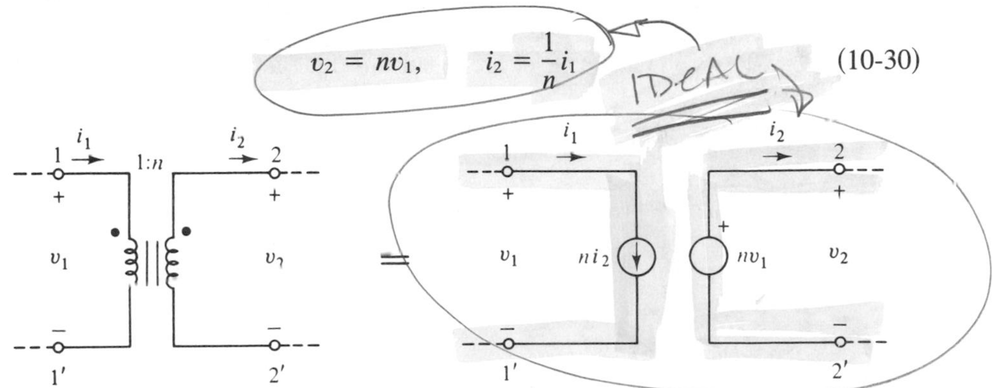

Fig. 10-18

These equations are valid only for time-varying signals. Under dc excitation both the primary and the secondary voltages eventually drop to zero, in which case primary and secondary windings can be replaced with short circuits.

In using the ideal model for the transformer, it is best to take terminal variables in the same sense as shown in Fig. 10-18. If any terminal variable is designated in an opposite sense, it can always be reversed to conform with Fig. 10-18, provided that we put a negative sign in front of the variable.

The equivalent circuit does not change if both input and output terminals are reversed—that is, if the dots are placed at the bottom instead of on top. On the other hand, if one dot is on top and the other at the bottom, then, in the equivalent circuit, the direction of the current source and the polarity of the voltage source must both be reversed.

If the turns ratio is specified from left to right as $n : 1$ instead of $1 : n$ as shown, n is replaced by $1/n$ in the equivalent circuit.

Referring to Fig. 10-18 or Eq. (10-30), the following important observations can be made concerning the ideal transformer.

1. If $n = 1$ (secondary and primary windings have the same number of turns),

$$v_2 = v_1, \qquad i_2 = i_1$$

   Although a pair of wires connecting input to output also produces the same result, the transformer
   (a) does not pass dc and thus allows different dc currents to flow in each winding without one dc current affecting the other.
   (b) allows the designation of voltages with respect to separate references on the input and output sides or allows the grounding of one side while the other is "floated."
2. If $n > 1$ (secondary winding has more turns than the primary),

$$v_2 > v_1, \qquad i_2 < i_1$$

   So, from primary to secondary, voltage is stepped up while current is stepped down. Transformers are used in this capacity to obtain high alternating voltages.
3. If $n < 1$ (secondary winding has fewer turns than the primary),

$$v_2 < v_1, \qquad i_2 > i_1$$

   Hence, from primary to secondary, voltage is stepped down while current is stepped up. Transformers are used in this capacity to obtain large alternating currents.

Example 10-3

The transformer in Fig. 10-19 is ideal. Obtain the input current $i_i(t)$ and the output voltage $v_o(t)$.

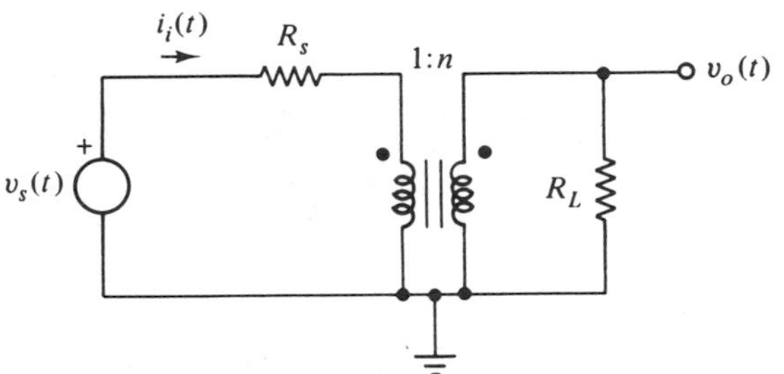

Fig. 10-19

Solution. Replace the transformer with its equivalent circuit as shown in Fig. 10-20. Although there are three sources acting on this network, only one is independent—namely, $v_s(t)$. The current source ni_2 depends on the current through the load R_L, whereas the voltage source nv_p depends on the voltage v_p across the input of the transformer. We now write one equation from each side to relate v_p and i_2 to the source v_s.

$$v_p = v_s - (ni_2)R_s \qquad \text{(primary)}$$

$$nv_p = i_2 R_L \qquad \text{(secondary)}$$

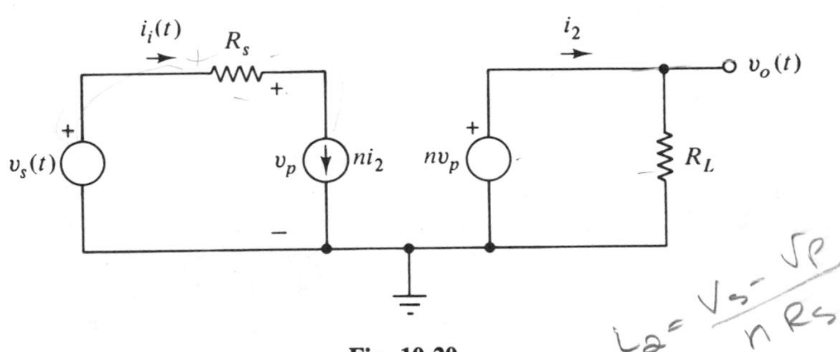

Fig. 10-20

In rearranged form these equations become

$$(1)v_p + (nR_s)i_2 = v_s$$

$$(n)v_p - (R_L)i_2 = 0$$

The two unknowns, v_p and i_2, are obtained by solving these equations simultaneously. Substituting i_2 from the first equation into the second, we have

$$nv_p - R_L\frac{(v_s - v_p)}{nR_s} = 0$$

which gives

$$v_p = v_s\frac{R_L}{n^2R_s + R_L}$$

The solution for i_2 is

$$i_2 = \frac{nv_p}{R_L} = v_s\frac{n}{n^2R_s + R_L}$$

Since $i_i = ni_2$ and $v_o = nv_p$, we have

$$\left.\begin{aligned} i_i &= v_s \frac{n^2}{n^2R_s + R_L} \\ v_o &= v_s \frac{nR_L}{n^2R_s + R_L} \end{aligned}\right\} \text{Ans.}$$

Example 10-4

The transformer in Fig. 10-21 is ideal. Obtain the steady-state primary and secondary currents and the output voltage.

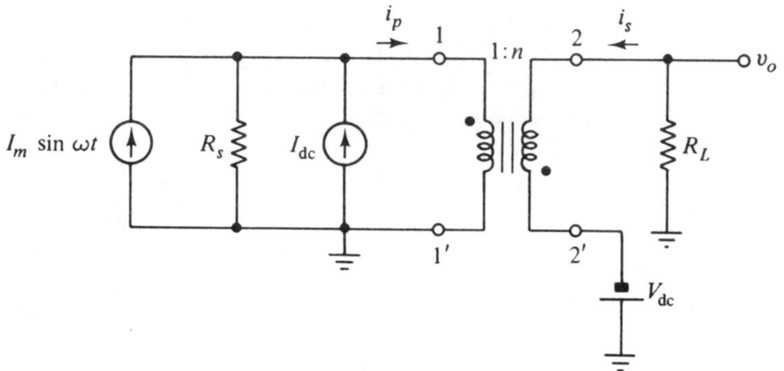

Fig. 10-21

Solution. Three independent sources are exciting the transformer: two dc and one ac. We determine first the steady-state currents and voltages produced by the dc sources by replacing the transformer with short circuits on both sides as shown in Fig. 10-22(a). (When currents do not vary with time, primary and secondary voltages are zero.) Inspection of the circuit shows that

$$i_{pdc} = I_{dc}, \qquad i_{sdc} = \frac{V_{dc}}{R_L}, \qquad v_{odc} = -V_{dc}$$

We determine next the steady-state currents and voltages produced by the ac source from Fig. 10-22(b), where the excitation is represented as a voltage source in series with R_s. The direction and the sign of i_s are reversed to bring the model of the transformer in conformity with Fig. 10-18. Since one dot is on top and the other on the bottom, the direction of the current-dependent current source and the polarity of the voltage-dependent voltage source are both reversed (from that given in Fig. 10-18). Using the results of Example 10-3 (with n replaced by $-n$), we find

$$i_{pac} = I_m R_s \left(\frac{n^2}{n^2R_s + R_L} \right) \sin \omega t$$

$$v_{oac} = -I_m R_s \left(\frac{nR_L}{n^2R_s + R_L} \right) \sin \omega t$$

$$i_{sac} = -\frac{v_{oac}}{R_L} = I_m R_s \left(\frac{n}{n^2R_s + R_L} \right) \sin \omega t$$

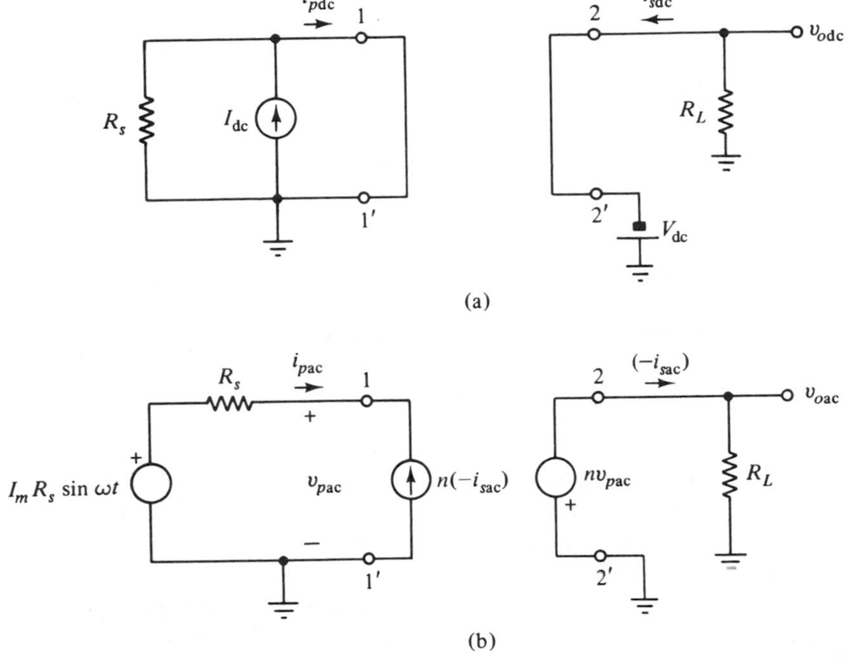

Fig. 10-22

By superposition, the primary and secondary currents and the output voltage are obtained.

$$\left.\begin{aligned} i_p &= i_{pdc} + i_{pac} = I_{dc} + \frac{I_m R_s n^2}{n^2 R_s + R_L} \sin \omega t \\ i_s &= i_{sdc} + i_{sac} = \frac{V_{dc}}{R_L} + \frac{I_m R_s n}{n^2 R_s + R_L} \sin \omega t \\ v_o &= v_{odc} + v_{oac} = -V_{dc} - \frac{I_m R_s R_L n}{n^2 R_s + R_L} \sin \omega t \end{aligned}\right\} \text{Ans.}$$

10-5 IMPEDANCE TRANSFORMATION WITH $k = 1$

A transformer transforms voltages and currents. As a result, it also *transforms resistances* from one value to another. To illustrate, refer to Fig. 10-23(a), where an ideal transformer is terminated in a resistive load. We wish to determine the resistance seen looking in from terminals 1–1'. In doing so, we replace the transformer by its ideal model as shown in Fig. 10-23(b) and proceed to calculate the v_1/i_1 ratio that represents R_1.

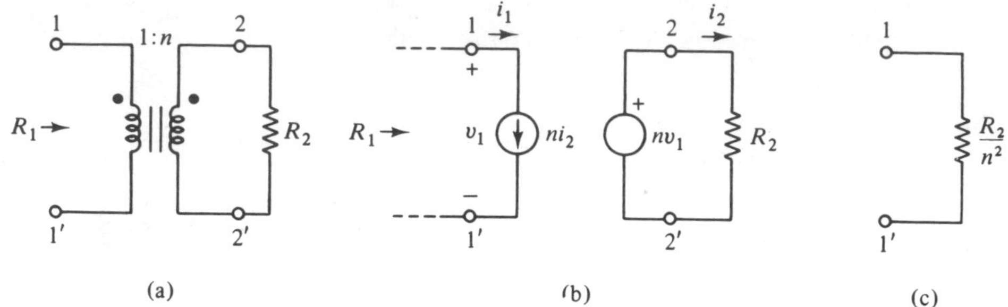

Fig. 10-23

$$i_1 = ni_2 = n\left(\frac{nv_1}{R_2}\right)$$

$$R_1 = \frac{v_1}{i_1} = \frac{R_2}{n^2} \qquad \text{(turns ratio } 1 : n) \tag{10-31}$$

This is an important and interesting result. It says that the resistance, looking in from one pair of terminals (1–1′), is the resistance connected across the other pair of terminals (2–2′) divided by the square of the turns ratio. If the turns ratio is greater than 1—that is, winding No. 2 has more turns than winding No. 1—the resistance is stepped down. Otherwise it is stepped up. As shown in Fig. 10-23(c), we can take out the entire transformer with its resistive termination and replace it with a single resistance. At terminals 1–1′ the actual circuit of Fig. 10-23(a) is indistinguishable from the equivalent circuit of Fig. 10-23(c).

If the turns ratio from 1–1′ to 2–2′ is $n : 1$ instead of $1 : n$, we replace n by $1/n$ in Eq. (10-31) and obtain

$$R_1 = n^2 R_2 \qquad \text{(turns ratio } n : 1) \tag{10-32}$$

Looking in from the terminals of the winding with the *lower number of turns,* we always see the *lower resistance*. On the other hand, looking in from the terminals of the winding with the *higher number of turns,* we always see the *higher resistance*. These resistance transformations are valid only for time-varying signals and do not apply for dc.

It is now easy to determine the Thévenin equivalent of an ideal transformer driven with a nonideal voltage source. [See Fig. 10-24(a).] Looking in from terminals 2–2′, we see an equivalent (Thévenin) circuit composed of a resistance in series with a voltage source. To find the resistance, we replace the independent voltage source $v_s(t)$ with a short circuit and look back as in Fig. 10-24(b). Since the turns ratio is $n : 1$, we see $n^2 R_s$. To find the open-circuit (and hence the Thévenin equivalent) voltage, we replace the transformer with its model as in Fig. 10-24(c). Since the secondary current is zero (open circuit), there is, also, no current in the primary, and all the source voltage appears across the primary. This voltage is then transformed and appears as nv_s across the open-circuited secondary terminals. Finally, we combine these results and obtain the complete equivalent circuit shown in Fig. 10-24(d).

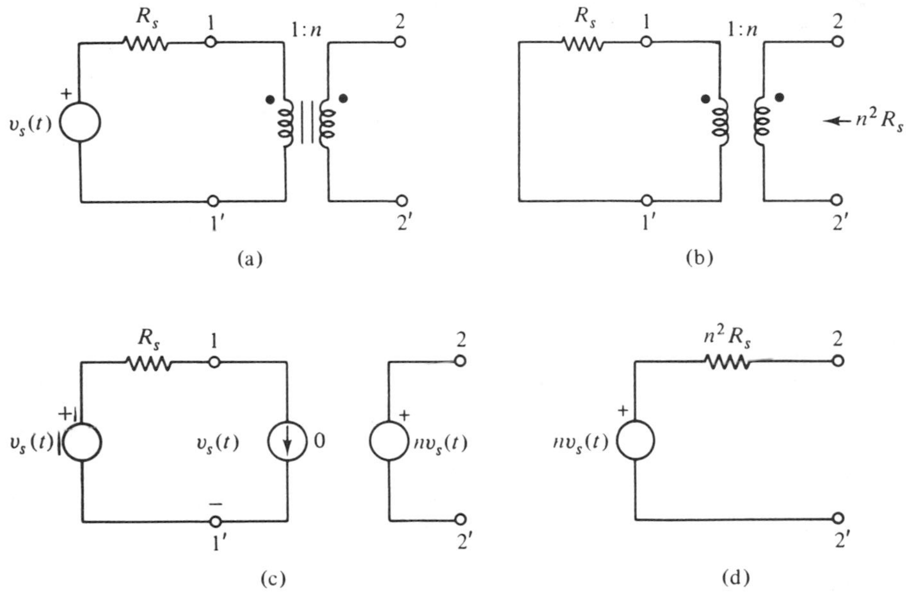

Fig. 10-24

Replacing a transformer with its Thévenin equivalent allows an easy calculation of voltages and currents in circuits without the need to evaluate the dependent sources associated with the transformer model.

The results derived here are equally valid for the more general case where R_s is replaced with Z_s. Using transformed variables, we obtain the equivalent circuit shown in Fig. 10-25.

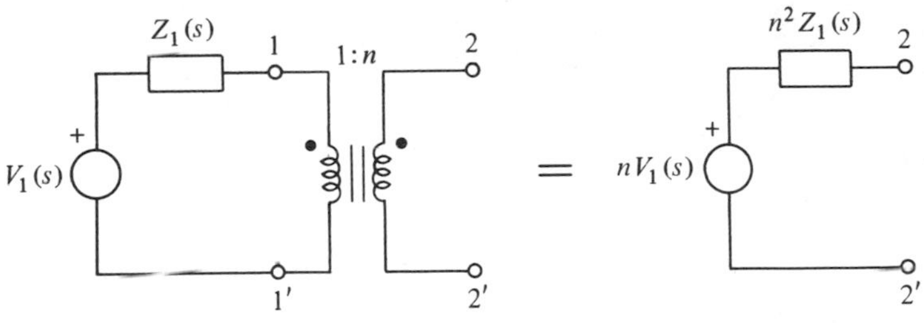

Fig. 10-25

Example 10-5

In the transformer circuit of Fig. 10-26, obtain the two source currents $I_1(s)$ and $I_2(s)$.

Solution. To find $I_1(s)$, we replace the circuit to the right of 1–1′ with its equivalent. This situation is shown in Fig. 10-27(a), where use is made of the results represented in Fig. 10-25 (with n replaced by $1/n$). By inspection of the circuit, we see that

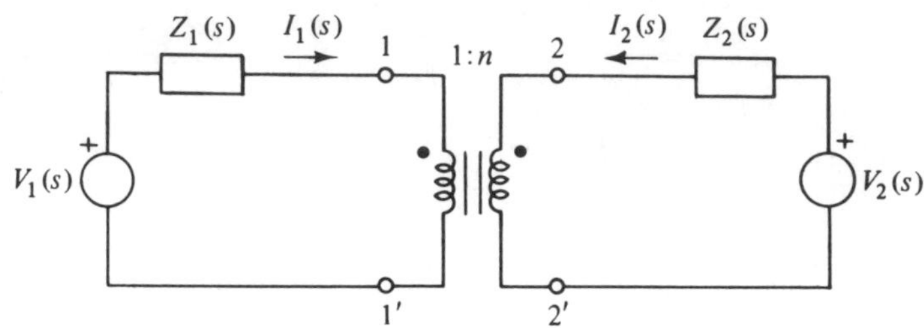

Fig. 10-26

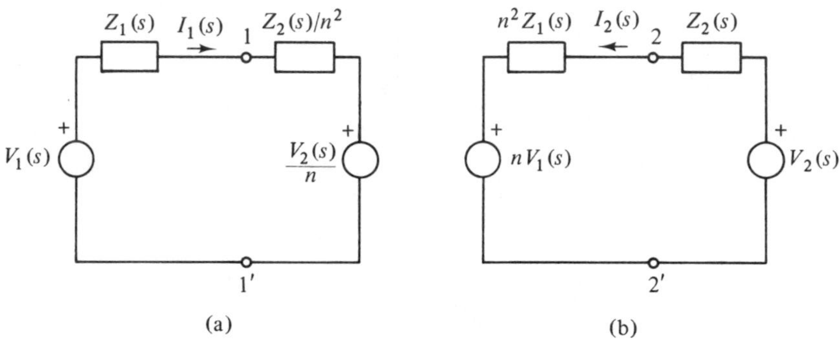

Fig. 10-27

$$I_1(s) = \frac{V_1(s) - (1/n)V_2(s)}{Z_1(s) + Z_2(s)/n^2} \quad \text{Ans.}$$

To find $I_2(s)$, we replace the circuit to the left of 2–2′ with its equivalent. This situation is shown in Fig. 10-27(b). By inspection, we obtain

$$I_2(s) = \frac{V_2(s) - nV_1(s)}{Z_2(s) + n^2Z_1(s)} \quad \text{Ans.}$$

Example 10-6

Refer to Fig. 10-28.

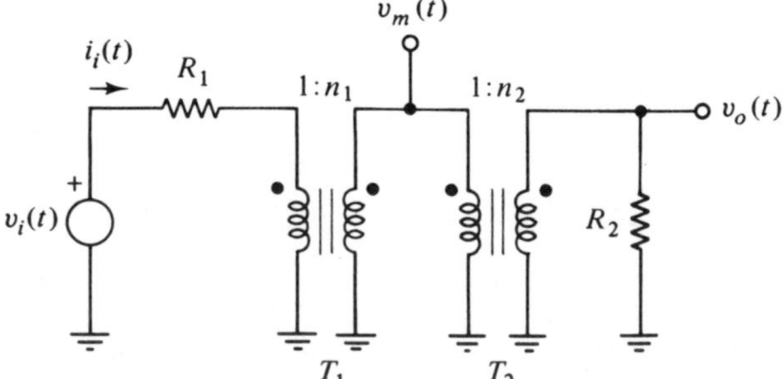

Fig. 10-28

(a) Obtain the input current $i_i(t)$ and the output voltage $v_o(t)$.
(b) What is the Thévenin equivalent facing R_2?
(c) Calculate the voltage $v_m(t)$ at the middle.

Solution.

(a) The resistance R_2 is transformed by transformer T_2, and it appears as a load of R_2/n_2^2 on transformer T_1. This resistance is further transformed by T_1, and it appears as a load of $R_2/n_1^2n_2^2$ on the source. So

$$i_i(t) = \frac{v_i(t)}{R_1 + R_2/(n_1^2n_2^2)} = \left(\frac{n_1^2n_2^2}{n_1^2n_2^2R_1 + R_2}\right)v_i(t) \quad \text{Ans.}$$

The current of $i_i(t)$ is transformed by T_1, and it appears as a current of $i_i(t)/n_1$ exciting the primary of transformer T_2. This current is further transformed by T_2, and it appears as an output current of $i_i(t)/n_1n_2$. Thus

$$v_o(t) = \frac{i_i(t)}{n_1n_2}R_2 = \left[\left(\frac{n_1^2n_2^2}{n_1^2n_2^2R_1 + R_2}\right)v_i(t)\right]\frac{R_2}{n_1n_2}$$

$$v_o(t) = n_1n_2\left(\frac{R_2}{n_1^2n_2^2R_1 + R_2}\right)v_i(t) \quad \text{Ans.}$$

(b) The resistance R_1 and the voltage source $v_i(t)$ are transformed by T_1 and T_2 in succession. The resulting equivalent (Thévenin) circuit is shown in Fig. 10-29. Note that we could have used this circuit to calculate the output voltage.

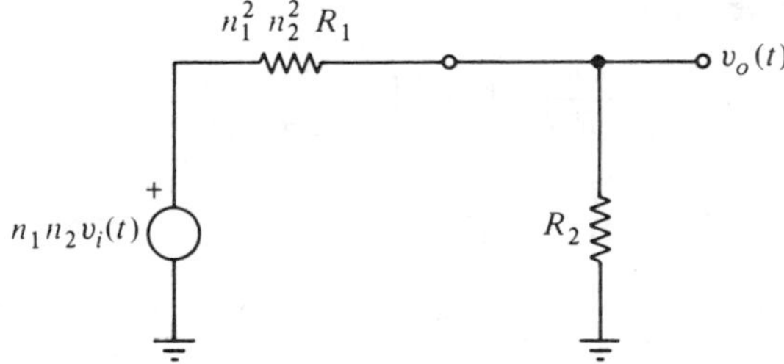

Fig. 10-29

(c) From the midpoint we look to the left and to the right and obtain the respective equivalent circuits. The midpoint voltage is calculated from the resulting equivalent circuit shown in Fig. 10-30.

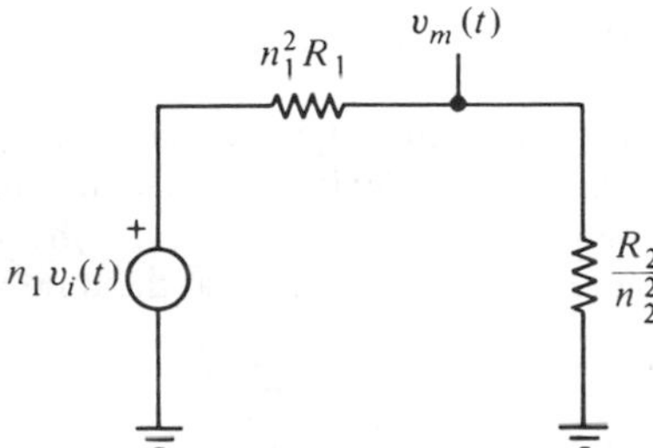

Fig. 10-30

$$v_m(t) = n_1 v_i(t) \frac{R_2/n_2^2}{n_1^2 R_1 + R_2/n_2^2} = n_1 \left(\frac{R_2}{n_1^2 n_2^2 R_1 + R_2} \right) v_i(t) \quad \text{Ans.}$$

Also note that the output voltage could have been calculated from this voltage—that is, $v_o(t) = n_2 v_m(t)$.

Example 10-7

Frequently, source and load resistances are fixed, and we face the problem of getting as large a signal as possible to the load. We do so by placing a transformer with the appropriate turns ratio between source and load. Show that such transformer coupling is advantageous.

Solution. The situation is illustrated in Fig. 10-31. The problem is to demonstrate that the voltage across the load can be maximized if n is chosen properly and that this voltage is larger than the voltage obtained by direct coupling of the source to the load.

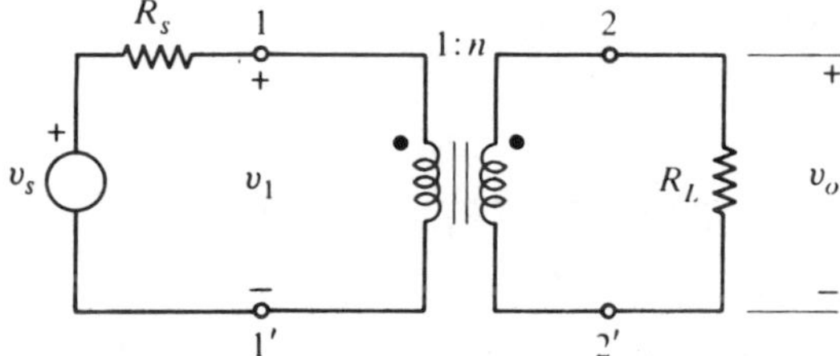

Fig. 10-31

First, we find the output. Since the circuit to the right of 1–1′ can be represented by a resistance of R_L/n^2, we have

$$v_1 = v_s \left(\frac{R_L/n^2}{R_s + R_L/n^2} \right) = v_s \left(\frac{R_L}{n^2 R_s + R_L} \right)$$

$$v_o = n v_1 = v_s \left(\frac{n R_L}{n^2 R_s + R_L} \right)$$

Next, we determine the n that maximizes v_o. Since v_o is zero for $n = 0$ and $n = \infty$, it must peak for some value of n. At this value of n, $dv_o/dn = 0$.

$$\frac{dv_o}{dn} = v_s R_L \left[\frac{(n^2 R_s + R_L) - n(2nR_s)}{(n^2 R_s + R_L)^2} \right] = 0$$

The slope of the v_o vs. n curve is zero for

$$R_L = n^2 R_s \qquad \text{or} \qquad R_s = \frac{R_L}{n^2} \tag{10-33}$$

We note that the condition for maximum output requires that *the load be matched to the equivalent resistance that it faces* ($R_L = n^2 R_s$) or, what amounts to the same thing, that *the source be matched to the equivalent resistance that it faces* ($R_s = R_L/n^2$). Since R_s and R_L are fixed, appropriate matching requires that the turns ratio be selected according to

$$n = \sqrt{\frac{R_L}{R_s}} \tag{10-34}$$

Under matched conditions the output is given by

$$v_o = v_s\left(\frac{nR_L}{n^2R_s + R_L}\right)\Bigg|_{n^2R_s=R_L} = \frac{n}{2}v_s = \frac{1}{2}\sqrt{\frac{R_L}{R_s}}v_s \tag{10-35}$$

If the source were connected to the load directly (without the benefit of the matching transformer), the output would have been

$$v_o' = v_s\left(\frac{R_L}{R_s + R_L}\right) \tag{10-36}$$

To compare the outputs with and without matching, eliminate v_s between Eqs. (10-35) and (10-36).

$$v_o = \frac{1}{2}\sqrt{\frac{R_L}{R_s}}\left(\frac{R_s + R_L}{R_L}\right)v_o'$$

$$v_o = \frac{1}{2}\left(\sqrt{\frac{R_s}{R_L}} + \sqrt{\frac{R_L}{R_s}}\right)v_o' \tag{10-37}$$

Since $(\sqrt{R_s/R_L} + \sqrt{R_L/R_s})$ has a minimum value of 2, which occurs when $R_s = R_L$, we see that

$$v_o \geq v_o'$$

Thus the output under matched conditions is equal to or greater than the output obtained by direct coupling. The amount of improvement depends on the R_s/R_L ratio. For example, if $R_s = 100\ \text{k}\Omega$ and $R_L = 1\ \text{k}\Omega$, then Eq. (10-37) shows that use of a matching transformer can increase the output voltage more than five times over direct coupling $[\frac{1}{2}(10 + 0.1) = 5.05]$. The same improvement is achieved if $R_s = 1\ \text{k}\Omega$ and $R_L = 100\ \text{k}\Omega$.

It is interesting to note that, for $R_L > 4R_s$, the matched circuit produces gain—that is, $v_o > v_s$ [see Eq. (10-35)], whereas the direct connection always attenuates the input signal.

It can be shown that, for sinusoidal signals and for source and load impedances specified by $Z_s(j\omega)$ and $Z_L(j\omega)$, maximum output voltage is achieved when $n = \sqrt{|Z_L|/|Z_s|}$ (see Problem 10-16).

10-6 POWER RELATIONSHIPS IN A TRANSFORMER

Consider the ideal transformer shown in Fig. 10-32. The input and output powers are

$$p_i(t) = v_1(t)i_1(t), \qquad p_o(t) = v_2(t)i_2(t)$$

In an ideal transformer

$$v_2(t) = nv_1(t), \qquad i_2(t) = \frac{i_1(t)}{n}$$

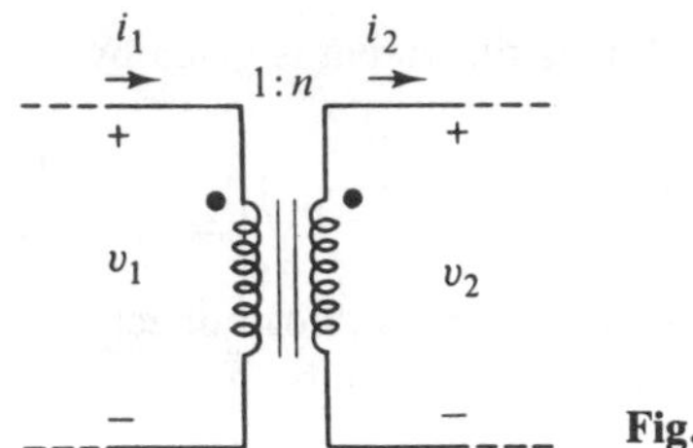

Fig. 10-32

Thus the output power can be expressed as

$$p_o(t) = v_2(t)i_2(t) = nv_1(t)\frac{i_1(t)}{n} = v_1(t)i_1(t) = p_i(t)$$

It should not be surprising that the output power equals the input power. An ideal transformer is lossless (no resistances to dissipate power), and so it transmits all the power that it receives.

Suppose that a source with *fixed source resistance* is to deliver power to a *resistive load that is also fixed*. If the source is connected directly to the load as shown in Fig. 10-33(a), the power delivered to the load is

$$p_L'(t) = i_L^2(t)R_L = \frac{R_L}{(R_s + R_L)^2}v_s^2(t) \tag{10-38}$$

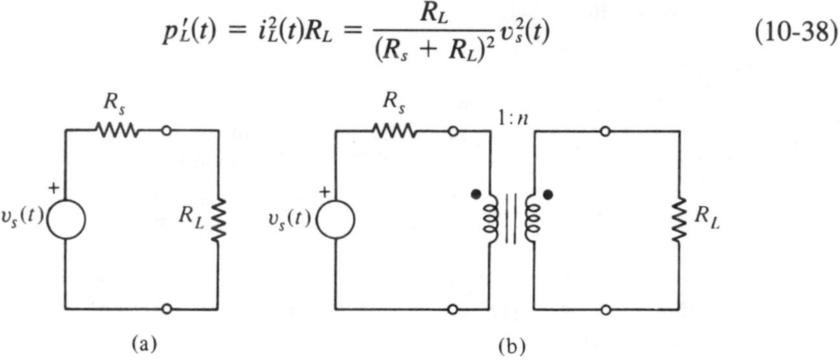

Fig. 10-33

On the other hand, if a transformer is connected between source and load as shown in Fig. 10-33(b) and n is chosen so that n^2R_s equals R_L, then the power delivered to the load becomes

$$p_L(t) = i_L^2(t)R_L\Big|_{n^2R_s=R_L} = \left[\frac{nv_s(t)}{n^2R_s + R_L}\right]^2 R_L\Big|_{n^2R_s=R_L} = \frac{1}{4}\frac{1}{R_s}v_s^2(t) \tag{10-39}$$

This equation gives the maximum amount of power that can be delivered from the source to the load. The condition on the turns ratio ($n = \sqrt{R_L/R_s}$) is the same as that required for maximum output voltage because, when the voltage is maximum across a resistor, the resistor dissipates the most power [as $p_L(t) = v_L^2(t)/R_L$ indicates].

In comparing Eqs. (10-38) and (10-39), we see that

$$p_L(t) = \frac{1}{4}\frac{1}{R_s}\frac{(R_s + R_L)^2}{R_L}p_L'(t) = \frac{1}{4}\left(\sqrt{\frac{R_s}{R_L}} + \sqrt{\frac{R_L}{R_s}}\right)^2 p_L'(t) \qquad (10\text{-}40)$$

Since $(\sqrt{R_s/R_L} + \sqrt{R_L/R_s}) \geq 2$, it follows that

$$p_L(t) \geq p_L'(t)$$

When the transformer matches R_L/n^2 to R_s or n^2R_s to R_L, more power is delivered to the load than when the load is connected directly to the source unless $R_L = R_s$. In this case, it is not necessary to use a transformer.

Example 10-8

All the power available from an amplifier with 128 Ω internal resistance is to be delivered to an 8 Ω speaker.

(a) What should be the turns ratio of the transformer?

(b) If 10 W of average power is to be delivered to the speaker, what should be the peak value of the input sine wave?

(c) Repeat (b) if the load were connected directly to the source.

Solution.

(a) From the circuit diagram shown in Fig. 10-34(a) we see that

$$n^2 8 = 128, \qquad n = 4$$

Thus a 4 : 1 step-down transformer is needed to deliver all the available power to the loudspeaker.

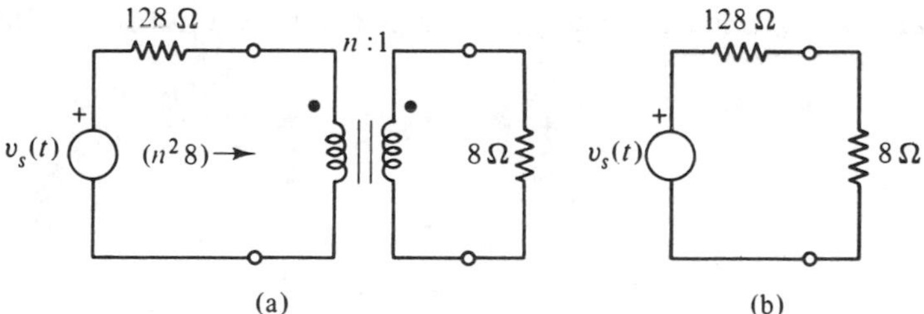

Fig. 10-34

(b) Under matched conditions the power delivered by the sinusoidal source is

$$p_L(t) = \frac{1}{4}\frac{1}{R_s}v_s^2(t) = \frac{1}{4}\frac{1}{R_s}V_m^2 \sin^2 \omega t = \frac{V_m^2}{8R_s}(1 - \cos 2\omega t)$$

Since the average value of a cosine wave over a period is zero, we have

$$(p_L)_{\text{av}} = \frac{V_m^2}{8R_s} = \frac{V_m^2}{1024} = 10$$

$$V_m = 101.2 \text{ V} \quad \text{Ans.}$$

(c) If the load were connected directly to the source, we see from Fig. 10-34(b) that

$$p_L'(t) = \left[\frac{v_s(t)}{136}\right]^2 8 = \frac{1}{2312} v_s^2(t)$$

$$= \frac{1}{2312} V_m^2 \sin^2 \omega t = \frac{V_m^2}{4624}(1 - \cos 2\omega t)$$

$$(p_L')_{av} = \frac{V_m^2}{4624} = 10$$

$$V_m = 215.0 \text{ V} \quad \text{Ans.}$$

10-7 THE AUTOTRANSFORMER

The autotransformer is a transformer that uses a single winding with one or more taps to transform voltages and currents. An iron core autotransformer with one tap is schematically shown in Fig. 10-35(a). The entire winding has $(N_1 + N_2)$ turns. The tap divides the winding into the N_1 and N_2 parts. The self-inductance L_1 (with N_1 turns) is the inductance seen between terminals 1 and 2 with terminal 3 open-circuited. The self-inductance L_2 (with N_2 turns) is the inductance seen between terminals 2 and 3 with terminal 1 open-circuited. Since the entire winding is on a common core, a time-varying current in one part produces a voltage in the other part. Consequently, there is mutual induction between L_1 and L_2. It is not necessary to show corresponding ends because the coil is wound in the same sense throughout. An autotransformer can also be thought of as a regular transformer that has the primary and secondary windings connected as shown in Fig. 10-35(b).

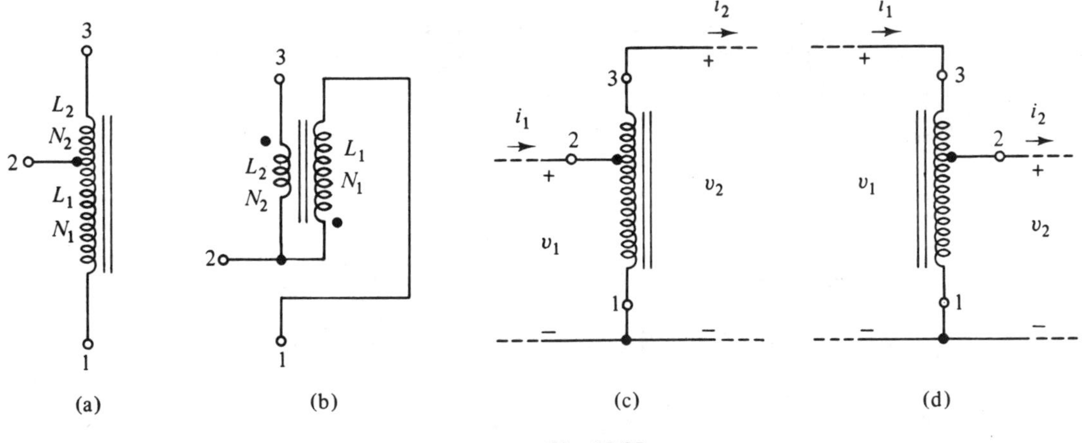

Fig. 10-35

The autotransformer steps up the voltage and steps down the current if the input is applied between 1 and 2 and the output is taken between 1 and 3. [See Fig.

10-35(c).] On the other hand, it steps down the voltage and steps up the current if the input is applied between 1 and 3 and the output is taken between 1 and 2. [See Fig. 10-35(d).] In either case, part of the winding (between 1 and 2) is common to both input and output.

To understand how the autotransformer works, Fig. 10-35(c) is redrawn in Fig. 10-36 with mutual and self-inductance designations. Because the coils are wound on the same iron core, we assume that the coefficient of coupling $k \cong 1$. Hence $M \cong \sqrt{L_1 L_2}$.

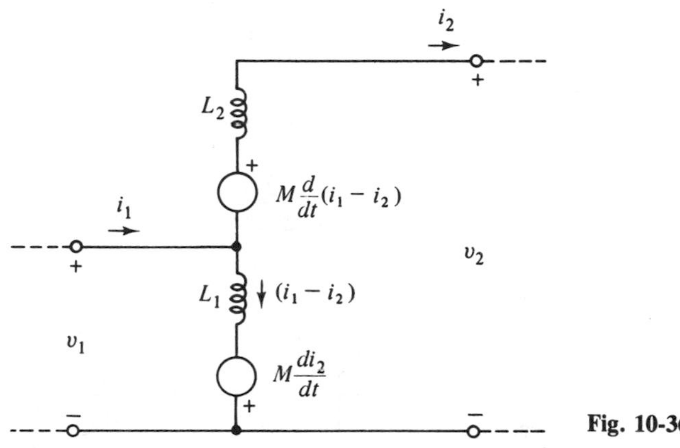

Fig. 10-36

For the bottom portion of the winding we can write

$$v_1 = L_1 \frac{d(i_1 - i_2)}{dt} - M\frac{di_2}{dt}$$

This equation can be solved for i_1 as follows.

$$\frac{di_1}{dt} = \frac{v_1}{L_1} + \left(1 + \frac{M}{L_1}\right)\frac{di_2}{dt} = \frac{v_1}{L_1} + \left(1 + \sqrt{\frac{L_2}{L_1}}\right)\frac{di_2}{dt} \tag{10-41}$$

$$i_1 = \frac{1}{L_1}\int v_1\, dt + \left(1 + \sqrt{\frac{L_2}{L_1}}\right)i_2$$

We now let n represent the turns ratio between N_2 and N_1—that is,

$$n = \frac{N_2}{N_1} = \sqrt{\frac{L_2}{L_1}} \tag{10-42}$$

Then i_1 becomes

$$i_1 = \frac{1}{L_1}\int v_1\, dt + ni_2 + i_2 \tag{10-43}$$

This equation can be interpreted to represent the terminal characteristics of the circuit shown in Fig. 10-37(a).

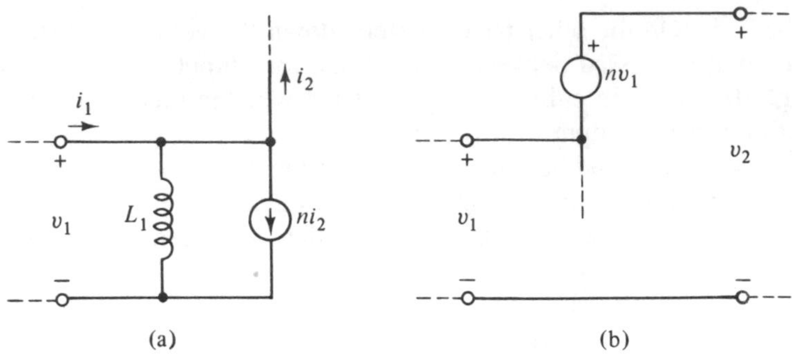

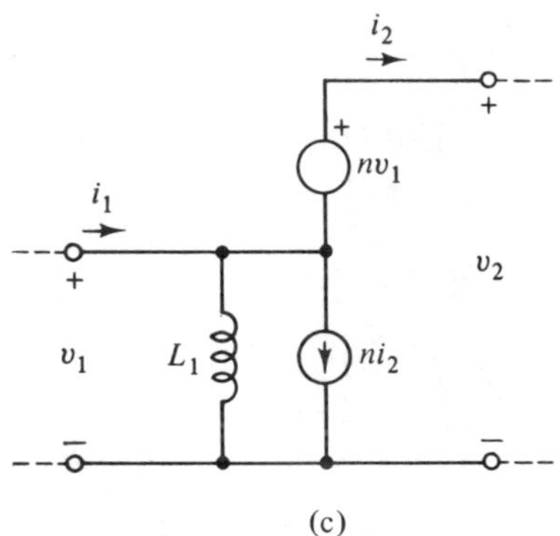

Fig. 10-37

For the top portion of the winding shown in Fig. 10-36 we can write

$$v_2 - v_1 = M\frac{d}{dt}(i_1 - i_2) - L_2\frac{di_2}{dt}, \qquad v_2 = v_1 + M\frac{di_1}{dt} - (M + L_2)\frac{di_2}{dt}$$

We can simplify the equation for v_2 by using the expression for di_1/dt given by Eq. (10-41).

$$v_2 = v_1 + \frac{M}{L_1}v_1 + M\left(1 + \sqrt{\frac{L_2}{L_1}}\right)\frac{di_2}{dt} - (M + L_2)\frac{di_2}{dt}$$

$$= v_1 + \sqrt{\frac{L_2}{L_1}}v_1 + (M + L_2)\frac{di_2}{dt} - (M + L_2)\frac{di_2}{dt}$$

$$v_2 = v_1 + nv_1 \tag{10-44}$$

This equation can be interpreted as representing the terminal characteristics of the circuit shown in Fig. 10-37(b).

The next step is to combine the two equivalent circuits given in Fig. 10-37(a) and (b) into one equivalent circuit—Fig. 10-37(c). Finally, we can take L_1 altogether out of the circuit by assuming that it draws negligible current (because L_1 is made large). The result is the equivalent circuit of the ideal autotransformer. (See Fig. 10-38.) The n and 1 designations on the autotransformer tell us that for every 1 turn on the lower portion of the winding there are n turns on the upper portion. By inspection of the equivalent circuit, we find the equations describing the terminal characteristics of the *ideal* autotransformer.

$$v_2 = v_1(1 + n), \qquad i_2 = \frac{i_1}{(1 + n)} \tag{10-45a}$$

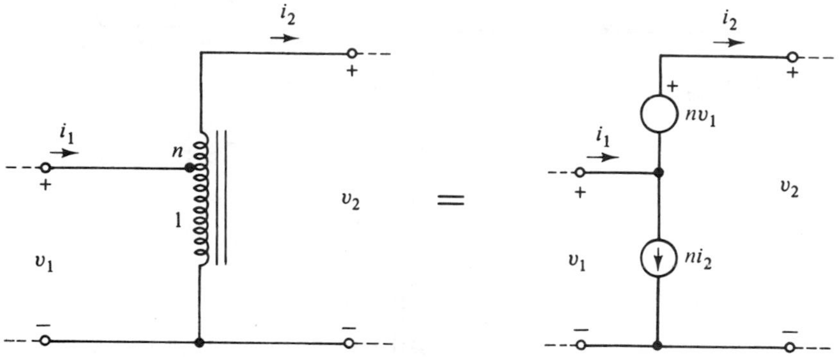

Fig. 10-38

While the voltage is stepped up, the current is stepped down so that $v_2 i_2 = v_1 i_1$, thereby indicating power transfer without loss. Note also that the output voltage is $v_1 + nv_1$; that is, it is composed of the input *plus* a voltage dependent on the input—hence the designation of *auto*transformer. If the output is taken across only the n turns and not across the entire $(1 + n)$ turns as indicated, the unity terms will not be present in Eq. (10-45a) and the autotransformer becomes a regular transformer (with a common input and output terminal).

When connected as shown in Fig. 10-39, the autotransformer can be represented by the accompanying equivalent circuit. In this case, voltages are stepped down and currents stepped up according to

$$v_2 = \frac{v_1}{1 + n}, \qquad i_2 = i_1(1 + n) \tag{10-45b}$$

A *variac* is an autotransformer with one fixed and one variable tap as shown in Fig. 10-40. Depending on the position of the wiper, $v_2 > v_1$ (2 below 3), $v_2 = v_1$ (2 at 3), or $v_2 < v_1$ (2 above 3). Thus a continuously adjustable output, which can go below or above the input, is obtained.

The relationships presented by Eqs. (10-45a) and (10-45b) are only valid for time-varying signals. They do not hold for dc voltages and currents.

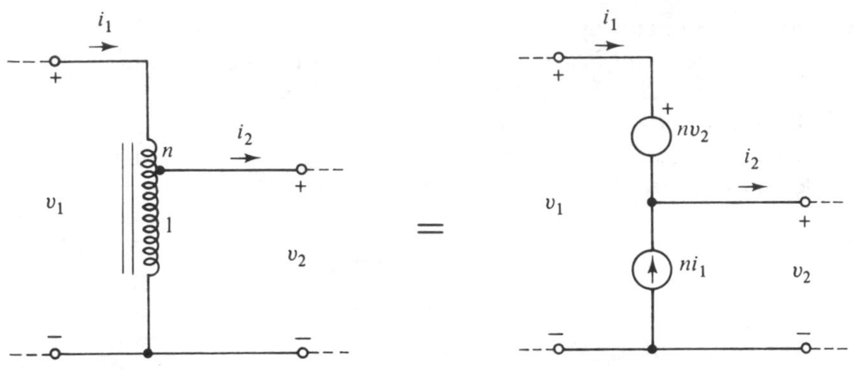

Fig. 10-39

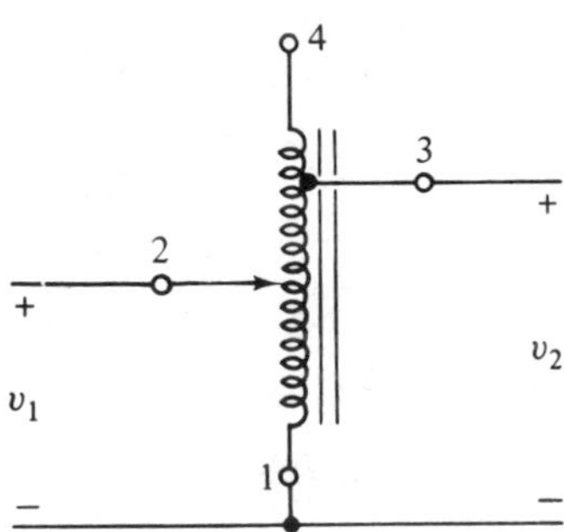

Fig. 10-40

10-8 STEP RESPONSE OF TRANSFORMERS

We know that a transformer does not pass dc voltages. This does not means, however, that the response is zero when *a step voltage* is applied. Since the input *changes* suddenly from zero to some dc level when the excitation is imposed on the transformer, initially there is a response due to this change even though the output must eventually drop to zero. A step-excited transformer is shown in Fig. 10-41(a), where primary and secondary resistances are considered negligible relative to R_s and R_L, respectively.

Calculating the step response if the transformer is considered ideal is simple enough. Such a response, however, will be wrong because the ideal model allows the transmission of dc voltages and currents through the transformer. In order to obtain the actual response, the transformer must be modeled by the more complicated but realistic equivalent circuit of Fig. 10-17. Using this model with zero initial conditions, we obtain the circuit of Fig. 10-41(b).

We go to the frequency domain to obtain the transform of the response. On the primary side we convert the voltage-source-R_s combination to an equivalent current-source-R_s circuit and then calculate $V_p(s)$ as follows.

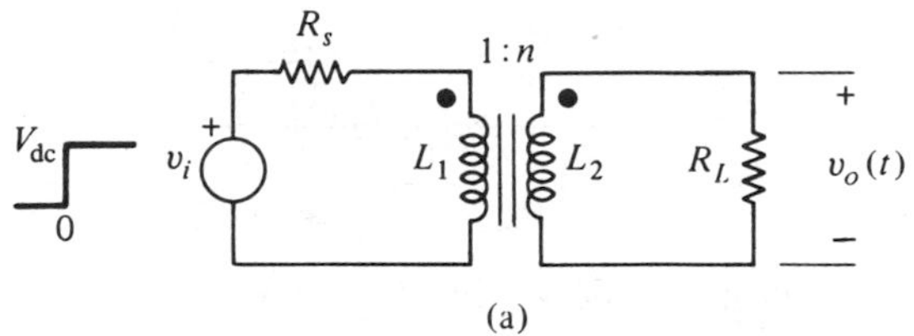

(a)

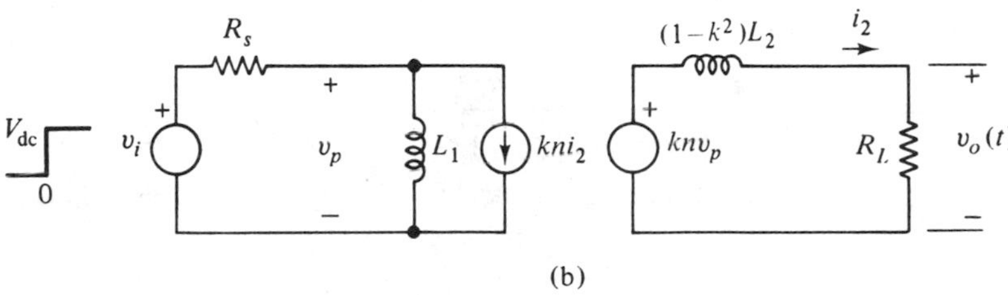

(b)

Fig. 10-41

$$V_p(s) = \left[\frac{V_i(s)}{R_s} - knI_2(s)\right]\left(\frac{sL_1R_s}{sL_1 + R_s}\right) \tag{10-46a}$$

On the secondary side we calculate $I_2(s)$.

$$I_2(s) = \frac{knV_p(s)}{s(1 - k^2)L_2 + R_L} \tag{10-46b}$$

Substituting the expression of $V_p(s)$ into the expression of $I_2(s)$ gives

$$I_2(s) = \frac{kn}{s(1 - k^2)L_2 + R_L}\left[\frac{V_i(s)}{R_s} - knI_2(s)\right]\left(\frac{sL_1R_s}{sL_1 + R_s}\right)$$

$$I_2(s)[s(1 - k^2)L_2 + R_L](sL_1 + R_s) + k^2n^2sL_1R_sI_2(s) = knsL_1V_i(s)$$

$$V_o(s) = I_2(s)R_L$$

$$= \frac{knsL_1R_LV_i(s)}{s^2(1 - k^2)L_1L_2 + s[(1 - k^2)L_2R_s + L_1R_L + k^2n^2L_1R_s] + R_LR_s}$$

The transfer function of the transformer is

$$T(s) = \frac{V_o(s)}{V_i(s)} = \frac{\dfrac{knR_L}{(1 - k^2)L_2}s}{s^2 + s\left[\dfrac{R_s}{L_1} + \dfrac{R_L + k^2n^2R_s}{(1 - k^2)L_2}\right] + \dfrac{R_LR_s}{(1 - k^2)L_1L_2}}$$

Since $n^2 = L_2/L_1$, $T(s)$ can be written

$$T(s) = \frac{\dfrac{knR_L}{(1 - k^2)L_2}s}{s^2 + s\dfrac{(R_sL_2 + R_LL_1)}{(1 - k^2)L_1L_2} + \dfrac{R_LR_s}{(1 - k^2)L_1L_2}} \tag{10-47}$$

We now write the denominator polynomial as

$$D(s) = s^2 + bs + c$$

where

$$b = \frac{R_sL_2 + R_LL_1}{(1 - k^2)L_1L_2}, \qquad c = \frac{R_LR_s}{(1 - k^2)L_1L_2}$$

The poles of $T(s)$ are obtained from

$$s = \frac{-b \pm \sqrt{b^2 - 4c}}{2} = \frac{-b}{2}\left(1 \mp \sqrt{1 - \frac{4c}{b^2}}\right) \tag{10-48}$$

where $$\frac{4c}{b^2} = \frac{4R_LR_s(1 - k^2)L_1L_2}{(R_sL_2 + R_LL_1)^2} = \frac{4(1 - k^2)}{(\sqrt{R_sL_2/R_LL_1} + \sqrt{R_LL_1/R_sL_2})^2}$$

Since

$$\left(\sqrt{\frac{R_sL_2}{R_LL_1}} + \sqrt{\frac{R_LL_1}{R_sL_2}}\right) \geq 2$$

it follows that

$$\frac{4c}{b^2} \leq (1 - k^2)$$

For tightly coupled circuits, $k \cong 1$. So $4c/b^2 \ll 1$. Consequently, we can use $\sqrt{1 + x} \cong 1 + (x/2)$ for $|x| \ll 1$ to approximate $\sqrt{1 - (4c/b^2)}$ with $[1 - \frac{1}{2}(4c/b^2)]$ and thereby simplify Eq. (10-48) to

$$s \cong -\frac{b}{2}\left[1 \mp \left(1 - \frac{2c}{b^2}\right)\right] = \begin{cases} -\dfrac{c}{b} \\ -b\left(1 - \dfrac{c}{b^2}\right) \cong -b \end{cases}$$

Then $D(s)$ can be approximated by

$$D(s) \cong \left(s + \frac{c}{b}\right)(s + b)$$

and $T(s)$ written

$$T(s) \cong \frac{\dfrac{nR_L}{(1 - k^2)L_2}s}{\left(s + \dfrac{1}{L_1/R_s + L_2/R_L}\right)\left[s + \left(\dfrac{1}{1 - k^2}\right)\left(\dfrac{R_s}{L_1} + \dfrac{R_L}{L_2}\right)\right]} \tag{10-49}$$

This transfer function describes *tightly coupled* coils. Both poles are on the negative real axis. Furthermore, because of division by $(1 - k^2)$, one pole is far removed from the origin. The tighter the coupling, the farther out this pole moves on the negative real axis and *the more widely separated the two poles become*.

We now calculate the step response.

$$V_o(s) = V_i(s)T(s) = \frac{V_{dc}}{s}\left[\frac{\dfrac{nR_L s}{(1 - k^2)L_2}}{(s - p_1)(s - p_2)}\right] = \frac{\dfrac{V_{dc}nR_L}{(1 - k^2)L_2}}{(s - p_1)(s - p_2)} \tag{10-50a}$$

where

$$p_1 = -\frac{1}{L_1/R_s + L_2/R_L} \tag{10-50b}$$

$$p_2 = -\frac{1}{1 - k^2}\left(\frac{R_s}{L_1} + \frac{R_L}{L_s}\right) \tag{10-50c}$$

Expansion into partial fractions yields

$$V_o(s) = V_{dc}\frac{nR_L}{(1 - k^2)L_2}\left[\frac{1/(p_1 - p_2)}{s - p_1} + \frac{1/(p_2 - p_1)}{s - p_2}\right] \tag{10-51}$$

$$v_o(t) = V_{dc}\frac{nR_L}{(1 - k^2)L_2}\frac{1}{p_1 - p_2}(e^{p_1 t} - e^{p_2 t}) \tag{10-52}$$

Since $|p_2| \gg |p_1|$, Eq. (10-51) simplifies to

$$\begin{aligned} v_o(t) &\cong V_{dc}\frac{nR_L}{(1 - k^2)L_2}\left(\frac{1}{-p_2}\right)(e^{p_1 t} - e^{p_2 t}) \\ &= V_{dc}\frac{nR_L}{R_L + n^2 R_s}(e^{p_1 t} - e^{p_2 t}) \end{aligned} \tag{10-53}$$

The exponentials $e^{p_1 t}$ and $e^{p_2 t}$ decay to zero with time constants of $1/|p_1|$ and $1/|p_2|$, respectively. Because $|p_1| \ll |p_2|$, it will take $e^{p_1 t}$ much longer to decay than $e^{p_2 t}$. Indeed, initially, while $e^{p_2 t}$ is decaying, $e^{p_1 t}$ can be taken as unity for all practical purposes. On the other hand, once $e^{p_2 t}$ has completely decayed, the response is governed by $e^{p_1 t}$. These arguments lead us to approximate Eq. (10-52) with two equations, depending on the time interval under consideration.

$$v_o(t) \cong \begin{cases} v_{o1}(t) = V_{dc}\dfrac{nR_L}{R_L + n^2 R_s}(1 - e^{p_2 t}) & t \ll \dfrac{1}{|p_1|} \\ v_{o2}(t) = V_{dc}\dfrac{nR_L}{R_L + n^2 R_s}e^{p_1 t} & t \gg \dfrac{1}{|p_2|} \end{cases} \tag{10-54}$$

The response $v_o(t)$ is sketched in Fig. 10-42. Also shown are $v_{o1}(t)$ (dashed curve) and $v_{o2}(t)$ (dotted curve). The output voltage is matched by $v_{o1}(t)$ at the lead-

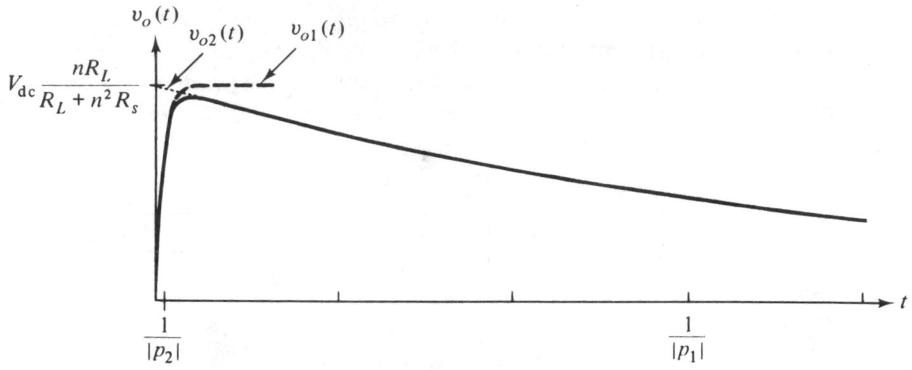

Fig. 10-42

ing edge and by $v_{o2}(t)$ at the trailing edge. The peak response is approximately equal to

$$V_{dc}\frac{nR_L}{R_L + n^2R_s} \tag{10-55}$$

Had we assumed the transformer to be ideal, at $t = 0$ the output would have jumped to the value given by Eq. (10-55) and stayed at that value! This problem shows that we cannot oversimplify models or make unrealistic assumptions without sacrificing accuracy of results or, what is worse, getting the wrong answer.

10-9 SINUSOIDAL STEADY-STATE RESPONSE OF TRANSFORMERS

A transformer circuit with sinusoidal excitation is shown in Fig. 10-43. In the sinusoidal steady state the output is given by

$$v_o(t) = V_m|T(j\omega)| \sin [\omega t + \theta_T(\omega)] \tag{10-56}$$

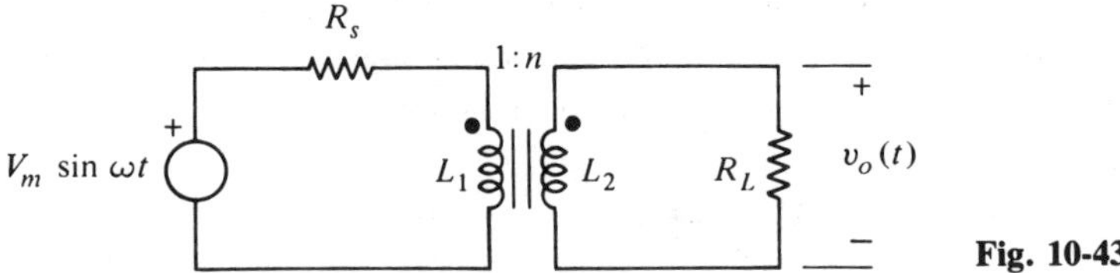

Fig. 10-43

where $T(j\omega) = |T(j\omega)|e^{j\theta_T(\omega)}$ represents the transfer function of the transformer evaluated at $s = j\omega$. The exact expression for $T(s)$ is given in Eq. (10-47). The approximate expression for $k \cong 1$ is given by Eq. (10-49) and is reproduced here for convenience.

$$T(s) = \frac{\dfrac{nR_L s}{(1-k^2)L_2}}{(s-p_1)(s-p_2)} \tag{10-57}$$

where

$$p_1 = -\frac{R_s R_L}{R_L L_1 + R_s L_2}, \qquad p_2 = -\frac{1}{1-k^2}\left(\frac{R_s}{L_1} + \frac{R_L}{L_2}\right)$$

The associated magnitude and phase functions are

$$|T(j\omega)| = \frac{\dfrac{nR_L\omega}{(1-k^2)L_2}}{\sqrt{\omega^2+p_1^2}\sqrt{\omega^2+p_2^2}} \tag{10-58}$$

$$\theta_T(\omega) = \frac{\pi}{2} - \tan^{-1}\left(\frac{\omega}{-p_1}\right) - \tan^{-1}\left(\frac{\omega}{-p_2}\right) \tag{10-59}$$

These functions are plotted in Fig. 10-44. A logarithmic scale is used for the frequency axis in order to display the characteristics in detail over a wide range of frequencies. As the magnitude curve shows, the transformer is bandpass in characteristics with three distinct ranges of operation. The more the two poles are separated, the more distinct these ranges become.

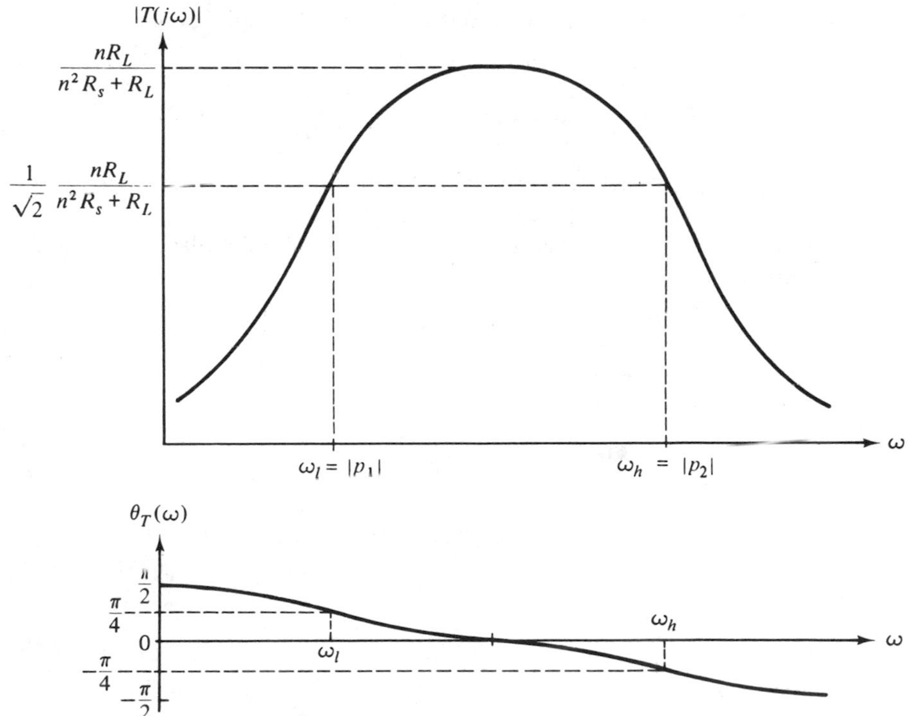

Fig. 10-44

In the *low-frequency region* $\sqrt{\omega^2 + p_2^2}$ can be replaced by $|p_2|$ and Eq. (10-58) simplified to

$$|T(j\omega)| \cong \frac{\dfrac{nR_L\omega}{(1-k^2)L_2}}{\sqrt{\omega^2 + p_1^2}\,|p_2|}$$

$$\cong \begin{cases} \omega \ll |p_1| & \dfrac{nR_L\omega}{(1-k^2)L_2|p_1||p_2|} = \dfrac{nR_L}{n^2R_s + R_L}\dfrac{\omega}{|p_1|} \\[2ex] \omega = |p_1| & \dfrac{nR_L|p_1|}{(1-k^2)L_2|p_1|\sqrt{2}\,|p_2|} = \dfrac{nR_L}{n^2R_s + R_L}\dfrac{1}{\sqrt{2}} \\[2ex] \omega \gg |p_1| & \dfrac{nR_L}{(1-k^2)L_2|p_2|} = \dfrac{nR_L}{n^2R_s + R_L} \end{cases} \tag{10-60}$$

At the low end of this region signals are attenuated. At the high end they are passed. At $\omega = |p_1|$ the magnitude is $1/\sqrt{2}$ times the value in the passband. This frequency is called *the lower cutoff frequency* and is designated by ω_l.

In the *midfrequency region* $\sqrt{\omega^2 + p_1^2}$ can be replaced by ω and $\sqrt{\omega^2 + p_2^2}$ by $|p_2|$. With these approximations Eq. (10-58) simplifies to

$$|T(j\omega)| \cong \frac{\dfrac{nR_L\omega}{(1-k^2)L_2}}{\omega|p_2|} = \frac{nR_L}{n^2R_s + R_L} \qquad (|p_1| \ll \omega \ll |p_2|) \tag{10-61}$$

This region is characterized by the flat portion shown in Fig. 10-44. The frequencies in this band are passed by the transformer.

In the *high-frequency region* $\sqrt{\omega^2 + p_1^2}$ can be replaced by ω and Eq. (10-58) simplifies to

$$|T(j\omega)| \cong \frac{\dfrac{nR_L}{(1-k^2)L_2}}{\sqrt{\omega^2 + p_2^2}}$$

$$\cong \begin{cases} \omega \ll |p_2| & \dfrac{nR_L}{(1-k^2)L_2|p_2|} = \dfrac{nR_L}{n^2R_s + R_L} \\[2ex] \omega = |p_2| & \dfrac{nR_L}{(1-k^2)L_2|p_2|\sqrt{2}} = \dfrac{nR_L}{n^2R_s + R_L}\dfrac{1}{\sqrt{2}} \\[2ex] \omega \gg |p_2| & \dfrac{nR_L}{(1-k^2)L_2\omega} = \dfrac{nR_L}{n^2R_s + R_L}\dfrac{|p_2|}{\omega} \end{cases} \tag{10-62}$$

At the low end of this region the signals are passed. At the high end they are attenuated. At $\omega = |p_2|$ the magnitude is $1/\sqrt{2}$ times the value in the passband. This frequency is called *the higher cutoff frequency* and is designated by ω_h.

The passband of the transformer is between the frequencies ω_l and ω_h. The *bandwidth* of the transformer is $(\omega_h - \omega_l)$ rad/s.

The phase starts out with $\pi/2$ radians in the low-frequency region and ends with $-\pi/2$ radians in the high-frequency region. In the passband it goes from $\pi/4$ to $-\pi/4$ radians.

10-10 TRANSFORMERS WITH LOOSE COUPLING

When the coils in a transformer are tightly coupled ($k \cong 1$), the transfer characteristics depend primarily on the turns ratio. When the coils are loosely coupled ($k \ll 1$), the transfer characteristics depened on coil inductances and on k. Thus k can be used as an additional parameter to control the frequency response.

A capacitor-tuned loosely coupled circuit that acts as a bandpass filter is shown in Fig. 10-45(a). To facilitate analysis, identical circuits are used on the primary and secondary sides.

The equivalent circuit representation of this network is given in Fig. 10-45(b). Since the self-inductances are equal, $M = k\sqrt{L_1L_2} = kL$. Further simplification results by going into the frequency domain and replacing the source and RC combina-

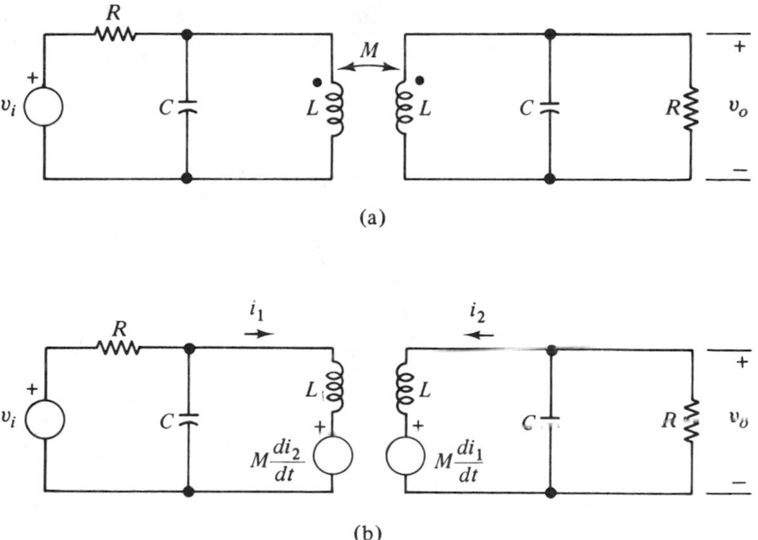

Fig. 10-45

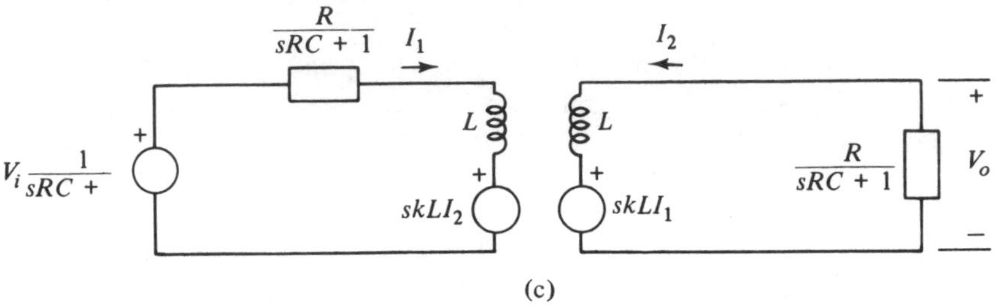

Fig. 10-45 (*cont.*)

tion with its Thévenin equivalent as shown in Fig. 10-45(c). Inspection of this network shows that

$$I_1 = \frac{[V_i/(sRC + 1)] - skLI_2}{R/(sRC + 1) + sL}, \qquad I_2 = -\frac{skLI_1}{R/(sRC + 1) + sL}$$

Elimination of I_1 results in

$$I_2 = -\left[\frac{skL}{R/(sRC + 1) + sL}\right]\left[\frac{V_i/(sRC + 1) - skLI_2}{R/(sRC + 1) + sL}\right] \tag{10-63}$$

After some algebra and using $V_o = -I_2R/(sRC + 1)$, we obtain the transfer function.

$$\frac{V_o}{V_i} = \frac{\left[\dfrac{k}{(1 - k^2)}\right]\delta\omega_o^2 s}{s^4 + 2\delta s^3 + \left[\delta^2 + \dfrac{2\omega_o^2}{(1 - k^2)}\right]s^2 + \left[\dfrac{2\delta\omega_o^2}{(1 - k^2)}\right]s + \dfrac{\omega_o^4}{(1 - k^2)}} \tag{10-64}$$

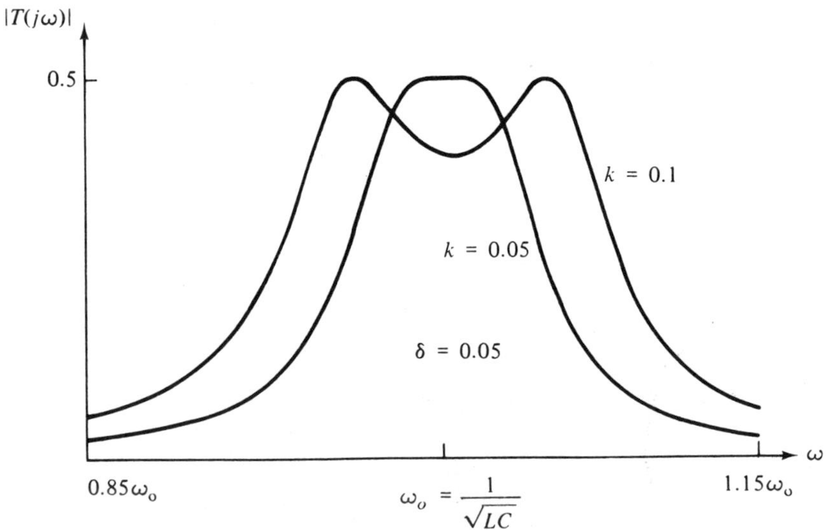

Fig. 10-46

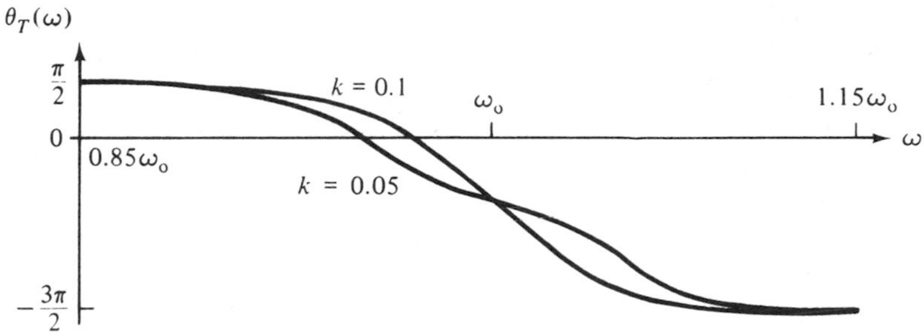

Figure. 10-46 *(cont.)*

where $\delta = \dfrac{1}{RC}$, $\qquad \omega_o = \dfrac{1}{\sqrt{LC}}$

The magnitude and phase functions associated with this fourth-order transfer function are plotted in Fig. 10-46 for $\delta = 0.05$ ($RC = 20$), using k as a parameter. As k is increased from 0.05 to 0.1, the bandwidth of the bandpass characteristics is almost doubled. Thus k can be used to control the width of the passband centered around the frequency $1/\sqrt{LC}$. By adjusting ω_o, δ, and k, we can position the passband at any specified center frequency and control its width. Such tuned circuits are widely used in radio and television circuits to separate stations and channels from each other.

10-11 SUMMARY

Voltages across coils are produced not only by the currents flowing in them $[L(di/dt)]$ but also by the currents flowing in adjacent coils $[\pm M(di'/dt)]$. The former is the voltage due to self-induction; the latter is the voltage due to mutual induction. Corresponding ends of mutually coupled coils are the ends that go up and down together in voltage. When currents enter corresponding ends, the voltage due to mutual induction has the same sign as the voltage due to self-induction. Otherwise it has the opposite sign. The sign of the self-induction voltage is determined by the v and i designations. The mutual inductance, just like the self-inductance, is positive. It can be determined from two self-inductance measurements obtained by connecting the two coils in series, first one way and then the other. The mutual inductance is one-fourth the difference of the larger reading from the smaller.

There are many equivalent circuit representations that describe the terminal characteristics of a pair of mutually coupled coils. The ideal transformer can be modeled simply by a current source on the input side and a voltage source on the output side. The input current source depends on the output current ($i_1 = ni_2$), and the output voltage source depends on the input voltage ($v_2 = nv_1$). A $1 : n$ step-up transformer takes the input voltage and steps it up to nv_1 volts. It also takes the output current, steps it up to ni_2 amperes, and presents it to the input. Thus the voltage is stepped up in one direction and the current in the other direction, so that $v_1 i_1 = v_2 i_2$. The ideal model does not hold for dc. Constant currents or voltages cannot be transmitted by the mutual coupling of coils.

A transformer transforms voltages and currents. Consequently, it also transforms impedances. On a $1 : n$ transformer an impedance connected at the output looks like Z/n^2 at the input. If $n > 1$, the impedance is stepped down. For $n < 1$ it is stepped up. Because of this property, transformers are used to match source impedances to load impedances and thus maximize the output voltage or the power transfer.

An autotransformer is a transformer with only one winding that is tapped. It has three terminals, one of which is the tap. The input is applied across one pair of terminals, and the output is taken across another. As a result, part of the winding is common to both input and output circuits. Autotransformers can be used to step up or step down voltages.

To obtain a more accurate representation of the terminal characteristics of the transformer, the ideal model is modified on the primary and secondary sides by the addition of inductances. When such a circuit is driven by a voltage source with internal resistance and is terminated in a resistive load, it produces a transfer function that is characterized by two poles. The tighter the coupling is made between the coils, the more widely separated the poles become. The step response of such a circuit exhibits a rather rapid initial rise in voltage followed by a slow decay to zero. The sinusoidal steady-state response is bandpass in characteristics with a wide bandwidth if the poles are widely separated. On the other hand, narrow bandwidths can be obtained by loosely coupled coils that are capacitively tuned on the input and output sides. The bandwidth of these circuits can be controlled by varying the coefficient of coupling.

PROBLEMS

10-1. Write the set of equations that describes the terminal properties of the mutually coupled coils shown in Fig. 10-47.

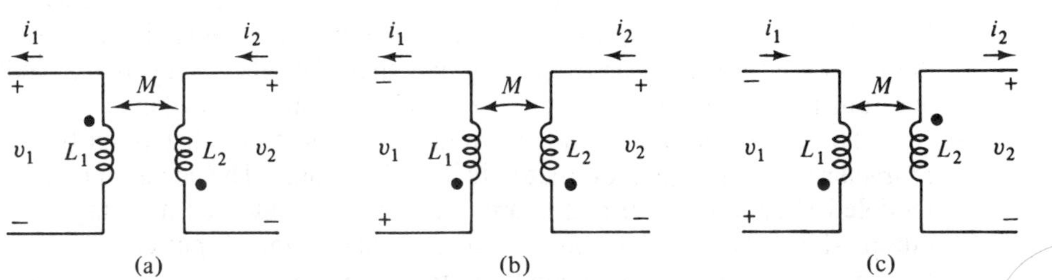

Fig. 10-47

10-2. Two mutually coupled coils are connected in series, first one way and then the other way, and the relative size of the two equivalent inductances are noted by measurement. Using this information, determine the corresponding ends.

10-3. When two mutually coupled coils are connected in series opposition, the resulting equivalent inductance is given by

$$L_{eq2} = L_1 + L_2 - 2k\sqrt{L_1 L_2}$$

From energy considerations we know that $L_{eq2} \geq 0$. In order to satisfy this condition, $k \leq 1$ for any value of L_1 and L_2. Show this.

10-4. Derive Eq. (10-24).

10-5. In Fig. 10-48, obtain the expressions for the voltages and currents indicated by a question mark. All sources are applied at $t = 0$, and initial conditions are zero.

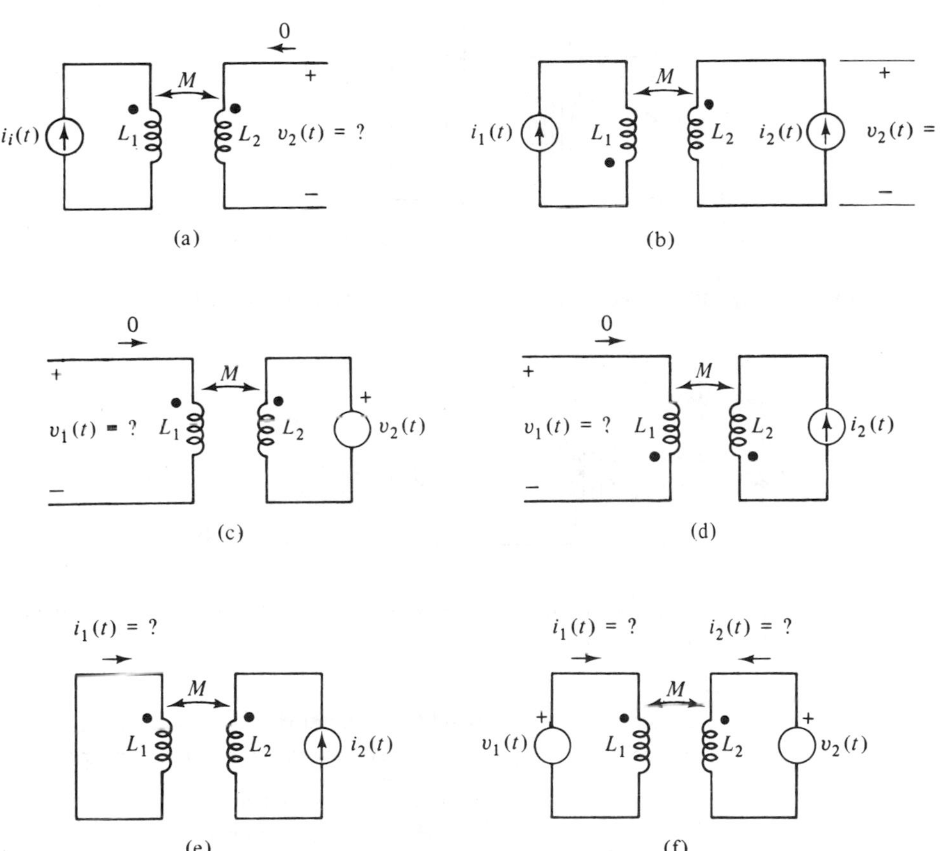

Fig. 10-48

10-6. In the circuits shown in Fig. 10-49, the transformers are ideal. Draw the corresponding equivalent circuits.

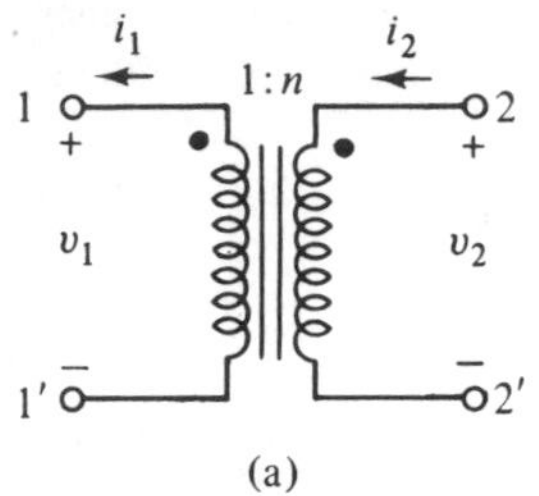

(a)

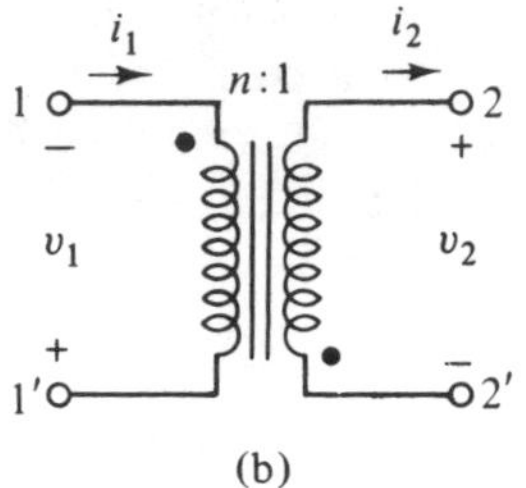

(b)

Fig. 10-49

10-7. In Fig. 10-50, the transformer is ideal. Obtain $v_1(t)$ and $v_2(t)$.

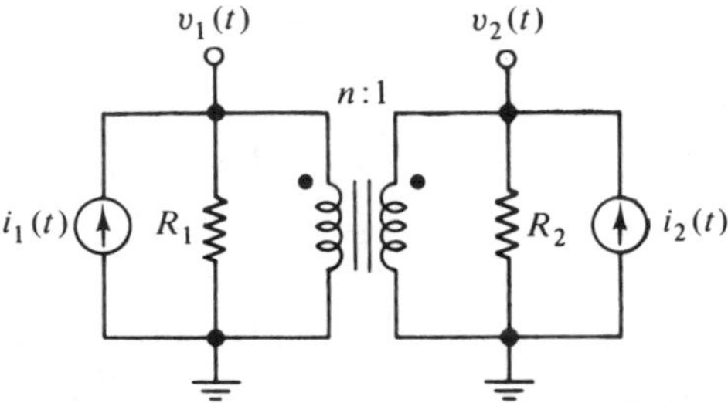

Fig. 10-50

10-8. In Fig. 10-51, the transformer is ideal. Obtain $i_1(t)$ and $i_2(t)$.

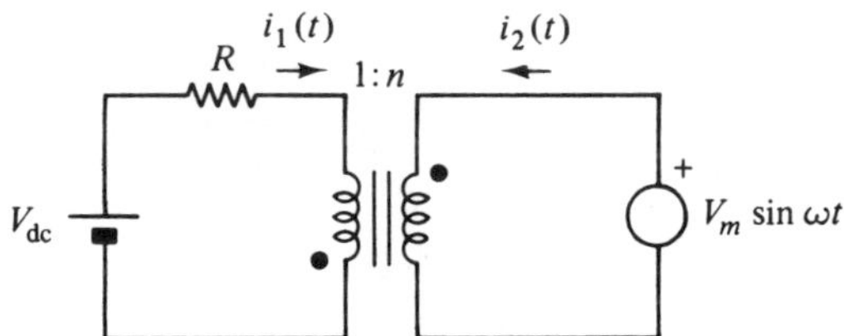

Fig. 10-51

10-9. To determine the coefficient of coupling between the primary and secondary of a transformer, the following measurements are taken.

Inductance of primary winding = 0.500 H
Inductance of secondary winding = 0.500 H
Inductance of the primary connected in series with the secondary

$$= \begin{cases} 1.992 \text{ H} & \text{(series aiding)} \\ 8 \text{ mH} & \text{(series opposing)} \end{cases}$$

What is k?

10-10. A transformer circuit and its equivalent representation are given in Fig. 10-52. What should be the value of L_1 so that i_{L1} is at least one-tenth of ni_2 in amplitude and thus negligible? Assume that currents are sinusoidal.

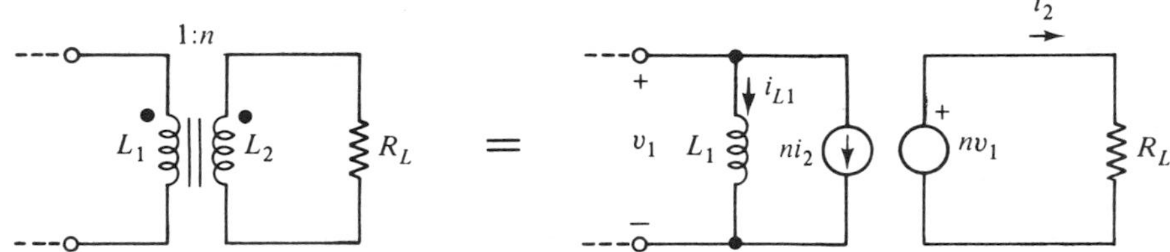

Fig. 10-52

10-11. Refer to Fig. 10-53.

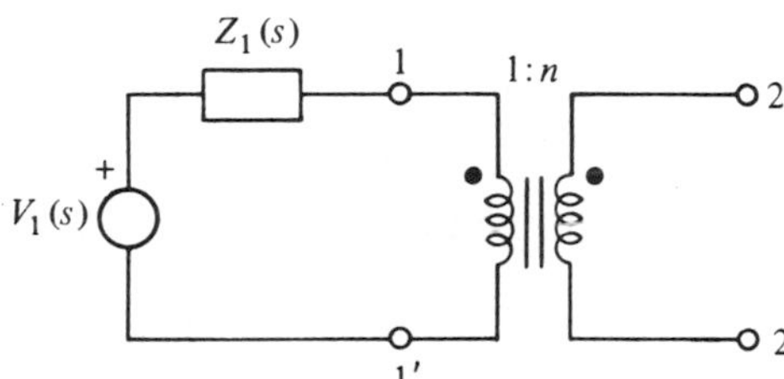

Fig. 10-53

(**a**) What is the open-circuit voltage at the output terminals?
(**b**) $V_1(s) = 0$. What is the impedance seen from the output terminals?
(**c**) Obtain the Thévenin equivalent representation.

10-12. In the circuit shown in Fig. 10-54, obtain $v_1(t)$ and $v_2(t)$. The transformer is ideal.

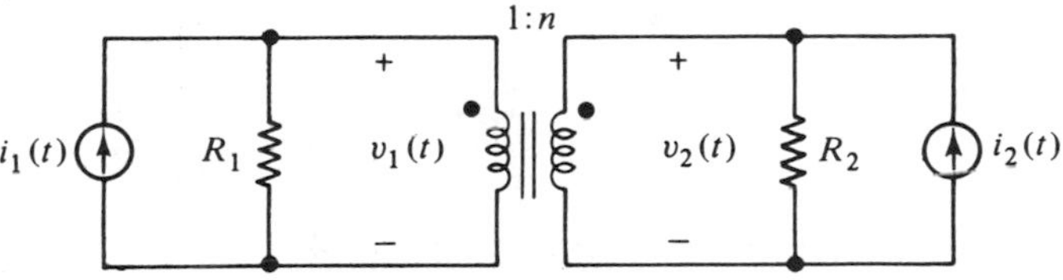

Fig. 10-54

10-13. Obtain the input impedance of the circuits shown in Fig. 10-55.

10-14. In Fig. 10-56, calculate $v_1(t)$, $v_2(t)$, and $v_3(t)$.

10-15. In Fig. 10-57, R_1, R_2, and R_3 are fixed. For what turns ratio is the output voltage maximum?

10-16. In Fig. 10-58, $v_i(t) = V_m \sin \omega t$. The steady-state output can be written as $v_o(t) = V_{mo} \sin(\omega t + \theta)$.
(**a**) Show that

$$V_{mo} = V_m \frac{n|Z_L|}{\sqrt{|Z_L|^2 + 2n^2(R_sR_L + X_sX_L) + n^4|Z_s|^2}}$$

where $Z_s = R_s + jX_s, \qquad Z_L = R_L + jX_L$
(**b**) Show that with Z_s and Z_L fixed, V_{mo} is maximum when

$$n = \sqrt{\frac{|Z_L|}{|Z_s|}}$$

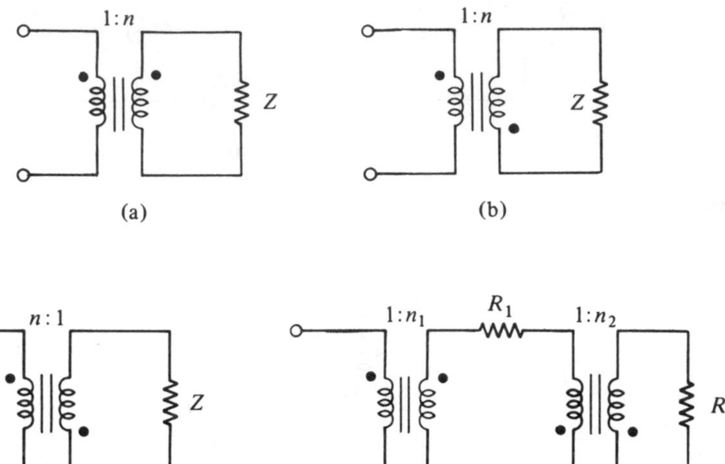

Fig. 10-55

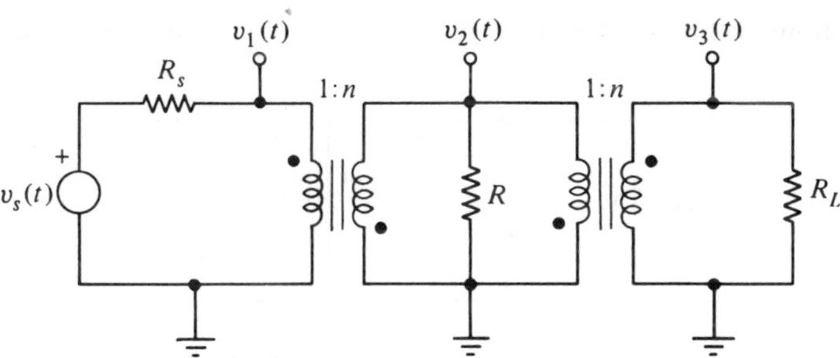

Fig. 10-56

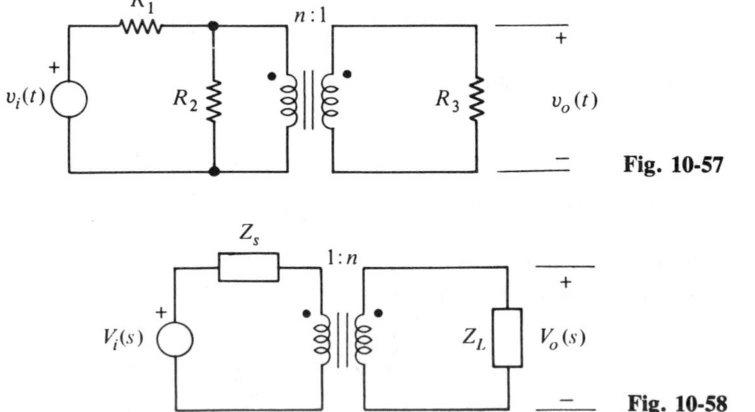

Fig. 10-57

Fig. 10-58

10-17. A power amplifier has an internal resistance of 144 Ω and an open-circuit voltage of 60 sin ωt.

(a) What is the maximum available average power?

(b) How would you deliver this power to a 16 Ω speaker?

(c) What is the voltage across the speaker terminals?

10-18. The autotransformer shown in Fig. 10-59 is ideal. Calculate the currents in the upper and lower portion of the winding.

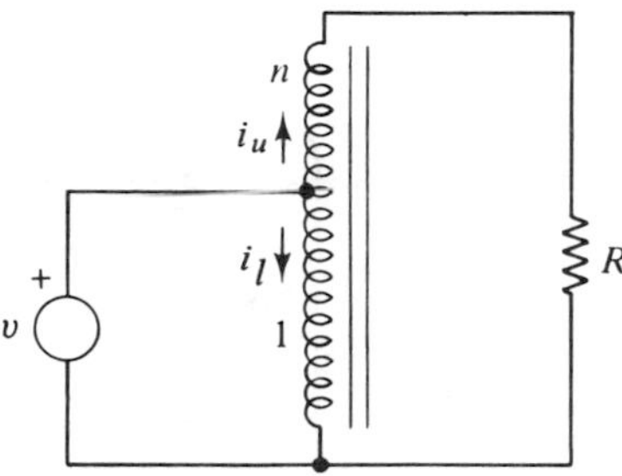

Fig. 10-59

10-19. Derive the equivalent circuit given in Fig. 10-39 and show that Eq. (10-45b) applies.

10-20. For each circuit shown in Fig. 10-60, calculate the input resistance. The autotransformer is ideal.

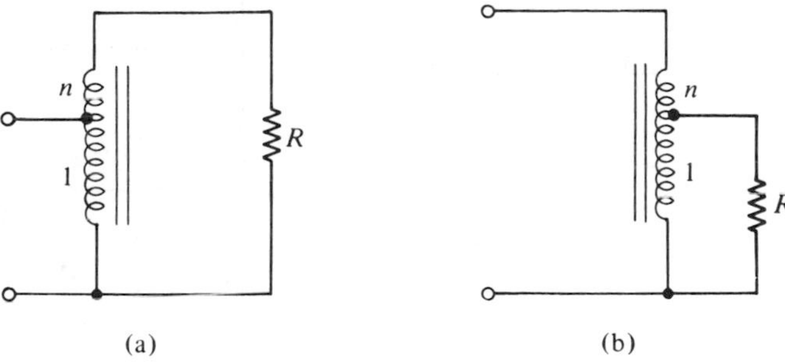

Fig. 10-60

10-21. For the circuit shown in Fig. 10-61, obtain the Thévenin equivalent circuit. The autotransformer is ideal.

10-22. Refer to Fig. 10-62. Assume that $k \cong 1$. Three equivalent circuits will be used to model the transformer.

(a) Show that model (a) predicts the leading edge of the response given by $v_{o1}(t)$ of Eq. (10-54).

(b) Show that model (b) predicts the peak response given by Eq. (10-55).

(c) Show that model (c) predicts the trailing edge of the response given by $v_{o2}(t)$ of Eq. (10-54).

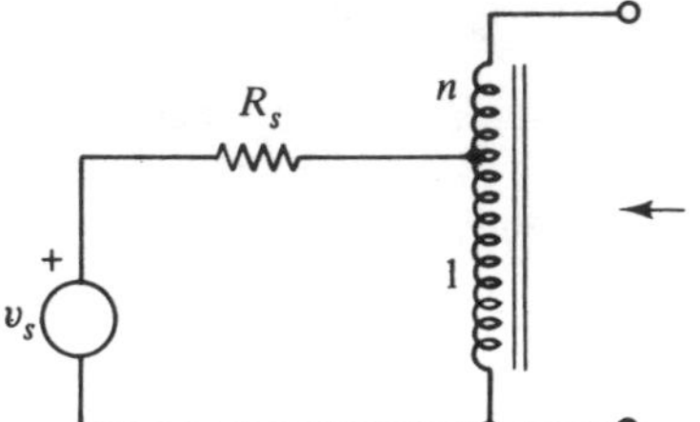

Fig. 10-61

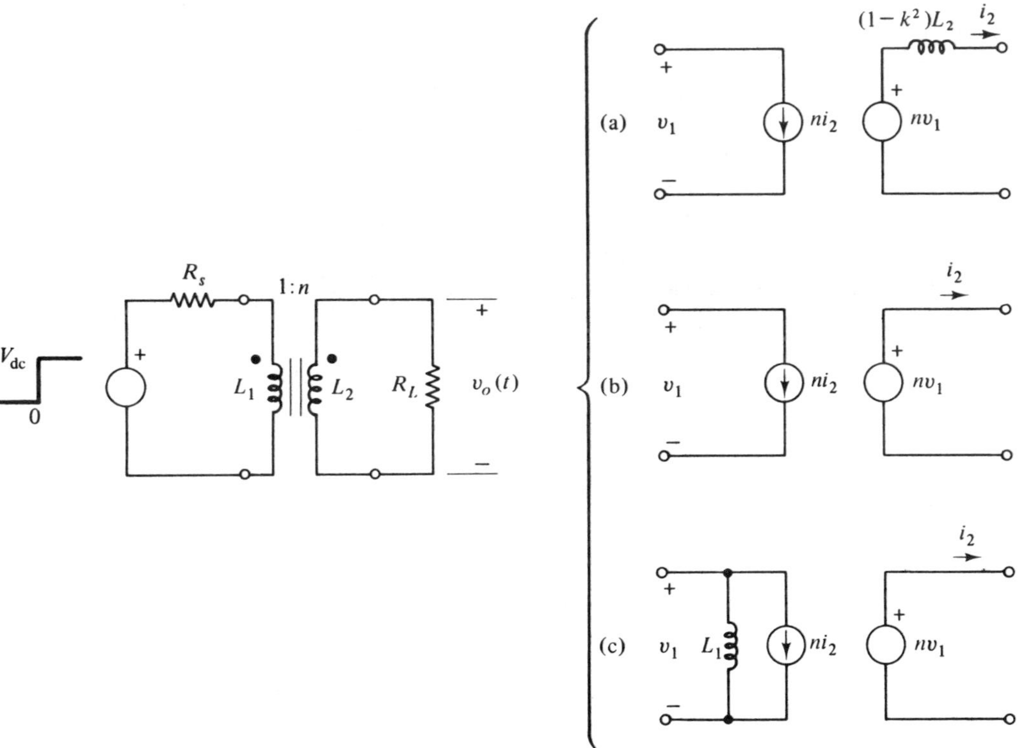

Fig. 10-62

10-23. In Fig. 10-63, the transformer is modeled by the equivalent circuit given in Fig. 10-41(b).

(**a**) Obtain the primary current $I_1(s)$.

(**b**) The input is a step V_{dc} volts high. Assume that the poles are widely separated and calculate $i_1(t)$.

10-24. Using Eq. (10-57), obtain the transfer function for the circuit shown in Fig. 10-64. Check the answer by direct calculation.

10-25. Derive Eq. (10-64).

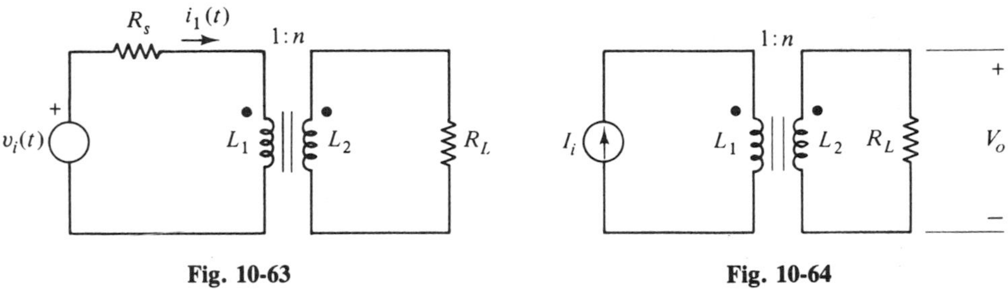

Fig. 10-63 Fig. 10-64

10-26. In Fig. 10-65, the secondary is center-tapped. For every turn on the primary there are n turns on the secondary. The transformer is ideal.

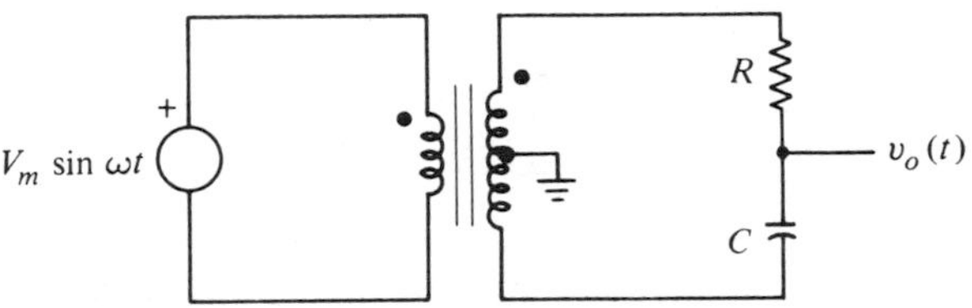

Fig. 10-65

(a) Obtain the steady-state expression for the output voltage.

(b) Let $n = 2$. Compare the output with the input as R is varied from 0 to ∞.

10-27. In Fig. 10-66, the current through the coil is at the steady-state value when the switch is opened. Approximately how long will it take before the output voltage reaches 15,000 V? What is the voltage across the switch at that instant?

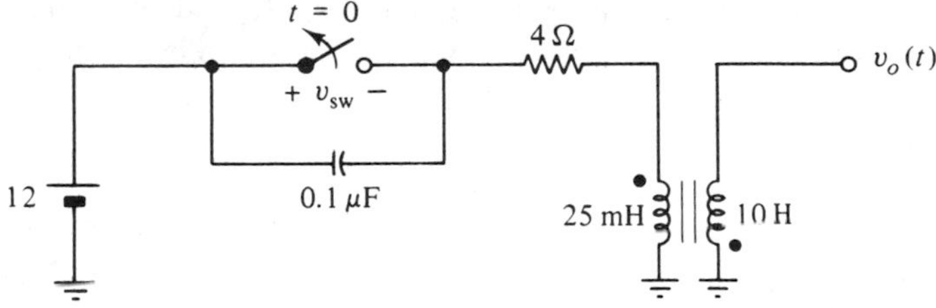

Fig. 10-66

CHAPTER 11

DEPENDENT SOURCES: MODELING, BIASING, AND GAIN CALCULATION

In the first nine chapters use was made of resistors, capacitors, inductors, and independent voltage and current sources to construct circuits. In Chapter 10 the concept of inductance was extended to include transformers as circuit elements. Here we introduce and discuss a new circuit element: the dependent source. Vacuum tubes and transistors are devices that are modeled with dependent sources when proper operating conditions are set up by independent sources. Dependent sources permit realizations that are impossible with *RLC* networks alone. For instance, we can amplify signals or build circuits that generate sine waves. We can use dependent sources in conjunction with *RC* elements to replace inductors. We can create negative elements, such as negative resistors, or raise and lower the magnitude of an impedance function. All these operations and more become possible if dependent sources are used in conjunction with *RLC* elements.

11-1 DEPENDENT SOURCES

An independent source fixes either the terminal voltage or the terminal current, irrespective of external influences. Thus a 10 V voltage source maintains at its terminals 10 V regardless of the circuit in which it is embedded. Similarly, a 2 A current source maintains a terminal current of 2 A, independent of conditions elsewhere. *At least one independent source is necessary to excite a network*. Without independent sources all responses in a network are zero.

A *dependent source,* on the other hand, is entirely controlled by voltages or currents that are elsewhere in the circuit. As a result, it is also called a *controlled source*. Its terminal voltage or current *depends on voltages or currents* established by independent sources *in other elements of the circuit*. A dependent source by itself cannot produce a response. It becomes activated—and hence has an effect on the response—only when independent sources excite the network.

There are two types of independent sources: voltage sources and current sources. There are four types of dependent sources: voltage-dependent voltage sources, voltage-dependent current sources, current-dependent voltage sources, and current-dependent current sources. These sources are shown in Fig. 11-1. The independent sources are on the left and the dependent sources on the right. Two of the dependent sources, K_1V and K_2V, depend on some voltage V in the network (shown at the top), whereas the other two, K_3I and K_4I, depend on some current I in the network (shown at the bottom). V and I are responses (not sources) in N. K_1 and K_4 are dimensionless; K_2 has the same dimension as admittance (mhos) and K_3 has the same dimension as impedance (ohms).

The dependent sources shown in Fig. 11-1 are linear-dependent sources. (Dependent sources given by KV^2, KI^3, and KVI are nonlinear and are not considered here.)

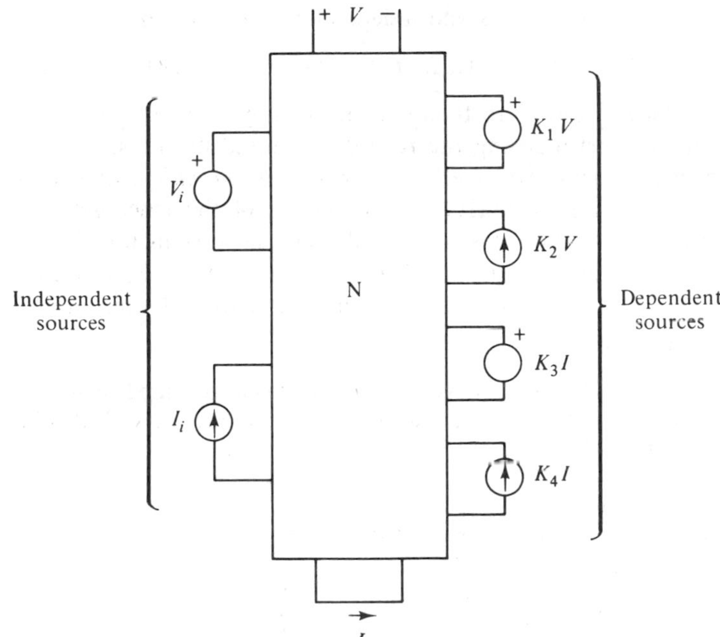

Fig. 11-1

When calculating responses in the network, *it is best to solve first for the dependent variables V and I*. In Fig. 11-1 six sources, two independent and four dependent, act on the network to produce V and I. To obtain V and I, we consider one source at a time while making all other sources zero (short-circuiting voltage sources and open-circuiting current sources) and calculate its contribution to the response through the appropriate transfer or input function. *In using the principle of superposition, we treat dependent sources as if they are independent;* that is, we assume that they can produce nonzero responses when acting by themselves. We can do so as long as we know that there are one or more *independent* sources of excitation, such as V_i and I_i, to activate the *dependent* sources. Thus from Fig. 11-1 we obtain

$$V = V_iT_1 + I_iT_2 + (K_1V)T_3 + (K_2V)T_4 + (K_3I)T_5 + (K_4I)T_6 \qquad (11\text{-}1)$$

$$I = V_iT_7 + I_iT_8 + (K_1V)T_9 + (K_2V)T_{10} + (K_3I)T_{11} + (K_4I)T_{12} \qquad (11\text{-}2)$$

Note that V appears on both sides of Eq. (11-1) and that I appears on both sides of Eq. (11-2). Such is always the case when superposition is used to calculate the dependent variables. Regrouping the V and I terms and putting the terms with the independent sources on the right, we obtain

$$V(1 - K_1T_3 - K_2T_4) - I(K_3T_5 + K_4T_6) = V_iT_1 + I_iT_2$$

$$-V(K_1T_9 + K_2T_{10}) + I(1 - K_3T_{11} - K_4T_{12}) = V_iT_7 + I_iT_8$$

These equations can be solved simultaneously for the unknown V and I in terms of the various T's and independent sources—that is,

$$V = f_1(V_i, I_i, T\text{'s}, K\text{'s}), \qquad I = f_2(V_i, I_i, T\text{'s}, K\text{'s})$$

Once V and I are thus calculated, any other response in the network can be found by superimposing the responses caused by the six known sources. *The final answer is always expressed as a function of the independent sources only* (since dependent sources themselves are functions of the independent sources). In solving problems, it is not necessary to calculate the various transfer or input functions explicitly. We merely use ordinary circuit-analysis techniques to calculate the responses. The following examples show how the solutions are obtained.

Example 11-1

In Fig. 11-2 the voltage from m to ground is sensed, converted to a voltage source K_1V_m, and fed back into the network as a voltage-dependent voltage source. Obtain the output voltage.

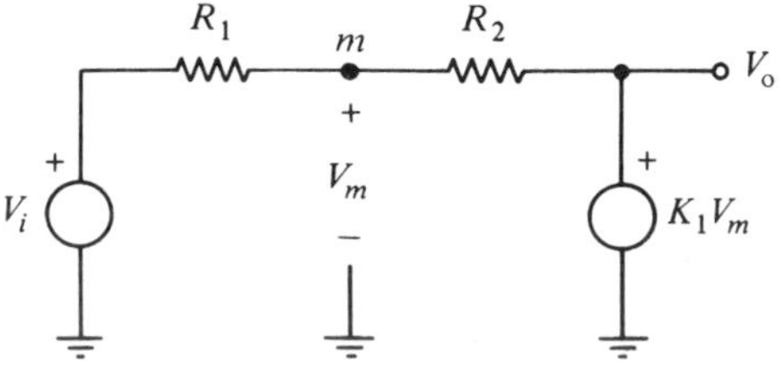

Fig. 11-2

Solution. We solve first for the dependent variable V_m. The independent source V_i and the dependent source K_1V_m act on the resistive network to produce V_m. Therefore we can use superposition to obtain

$$V_m = \frac{V_iR_2 + (K_1V_m)R_1}{R_1 + R_2}$$

We then solve for V_m explicitly.

$$V_m = V_i\left[\frac{R_2}{R_1(1 - K_1) + R_2}\right]$$

Thus V_m is obtained as a function of the independent source V_i. The output voltage is given by

$$V_o = K_1V_m = \left[\frac{K_1R_2}{R_1(1 - K_1) + R_2}\right]V_i \quad \text{Ans.}$$

Example 11-2

In Fig. 11-3 the voltage across the inductor is sensed, converted to a current source K_2V_L, and fed back into the network as a voltage-dependent current source. Obtain the current through the inductor.

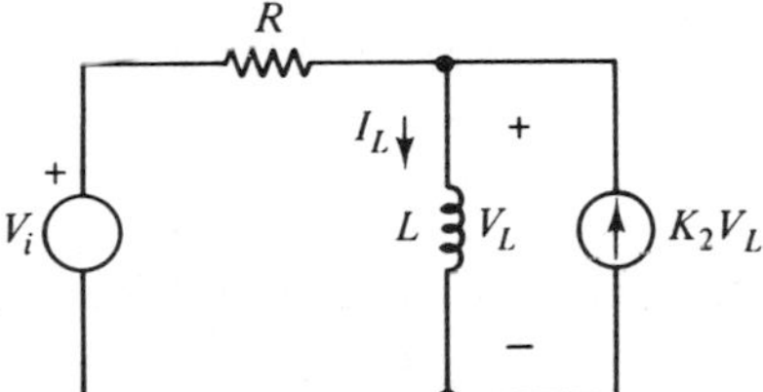

Fig. 11-3

Solution. We solve first for the dependent variable V_L. The independent source V_i and the dependent source K_2V_L act on the network together to produce V_L. Using superposition, we find

$$V_L = V_i\left(\frac{sL}{R + sL}\right) + (K_2V_L)\left(\frac{RsL}{R + sL}\right)$$

We then solve explicitly for V_L and obtain it as a function of the independent source V_i.

$$V_L = \frac{V_i[sL/(R + sL)]}{1 - K_2[RsL/(R + sL)]} = \left[\frac{sL}{sL(1 - K_2R) + R}\right]V_i$$

The current through the inductor is given by

$$I_L = \frac{V_L}{sL} = \left[\frac{1}{sL(1 - K_2R) + R}\right]V_i \quad \text{Ans.}$$

Example 11-3

In Fig. 11-4 the current through the voltage source is sensed, converted to a voltage source K_3I, and fed back into the network as a current-dependent voltage source. Obtain the current through the voltage source V_i.

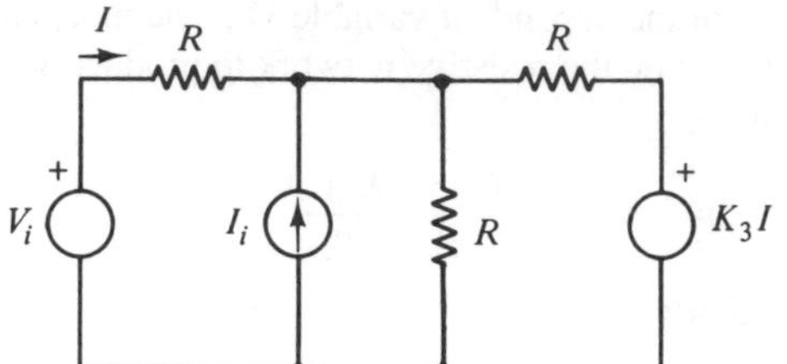

Fig. 11-4

Solution. Three sources, two independent and one dependent, excite the network and produce I.

$$I = V_i\left(\frac{1}{R + R/2}\right) + I_i\left(-\frac{R/2}{R + R/2}\right) + (K_3I)\left(-\frac{1/2}{R + R/2}\right)$$

Solving for I, we obtain

$$I\left(1 + \frac{K_3}{3R}\right) = V_i\left(\frac{2}{3R}\right) - I_i\left(\frac{1}{3}\right)$$

$$I = \frac{2V_i - I_iR}{3R + K_3} \quad \text{Ans.}$$

Note that the answer is in terms of the two independent sources.

Example 11-4

In Fig. 11-5 the current in the middle is sensed, converted to a current source K_4I_m, and fed back into the network as a current-dependent current source. Obtain V_o.

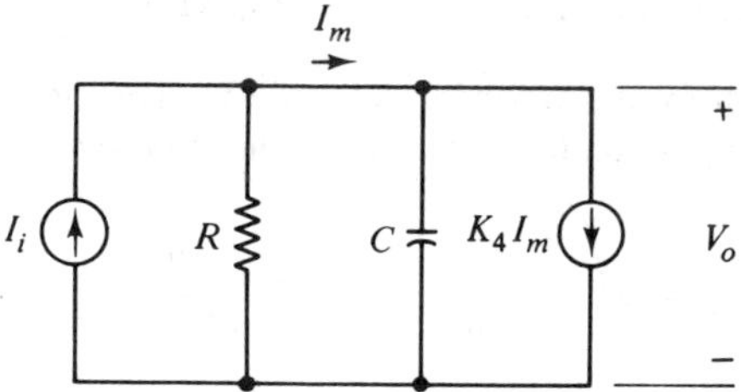

Fig. 11-5

Solution. By superposition, we obtain I_m.

$$I_m = I_i\left(\frac{R}{R + 1/sC}\right) + (K_4I_m)\left(\frac{1/sC}{R + 1/sC}\right)$$

$$I_m = \left(\frac{sRC}{sRC + 1 - K_4}\right)I_i$$

The voltage V_o is given by

$$V_o = I_m(1 - K_4)\frac{1}{sC} = \left[\frac{(1 - K_4)R}{sRC + 1 - K_4}\right]I_i \quad \text{Ans.}$$

Example 11-5

In Fig. 11-6 one independent and two dependent sources excite the network. Obtain I_o.

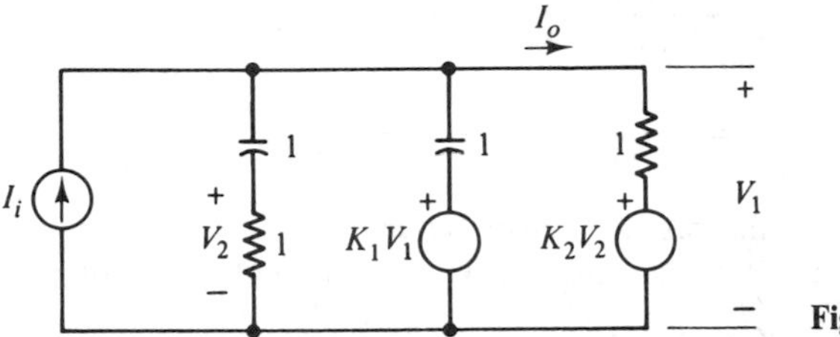

Fig. 11-6

Solution. Besides the independent source I_i, two voltage-dependent voltage sources, K_1V_1 and K_2V_2, excite the network. Nonetheless, all responses in the network, including V_1 and V_2, are ultimately dependent on I_i only. The problem cannot be solved without first determining V_1 and V_2 in terms of I_i. Making use of the principle of superposition, we write two equations, one for V_1 and the other for V_2.

$$V_1 = I_iT_1 + K_1V_1T_2 + K_2V_2T_3 \tag{11-3}$$

$$V_2 = I_iT_4 + K_1V_1T_5 + K_2V_2T_6 \tag{11-4}$$

where $T_1 = \dfrac{s+1}{s^2+3s+1}$

$$T_2 = \frac{s(s+1)}{s^2+3s+1} = sT_1$$

$$T_3 = \frac{s+1}{s^2+3s+1} = T_1$$

$$T_4 = \left(\frac{s}{s+1}\right)T_1$$

$$T_5 = \left(\frac{s}{s+1}\right)T_2 = \left(\frac{s^2}{s+1}\right)T_1$$

$$T_6 = \left(\frac{s}{s+1}\right)T_3 = \left(\frac{s}{s+1}\right)T_1$$

We can rewrite Eqs. (11-3) and (11-4) in terms of T_1.

$$V_1 = T_1(I_i + K_1V_1s + K_2V_2)$$

$$V_2 = \frac{s}{s+1}[T_1(I_i + K_1V_1s + K_2V_2)] = \frac{s}{s+1}V_1$$

When rearranged, these equations become

$$V_1(1 - sK_1T_1) - V_2(K_2T_1) = I_iT_1, \qquad -V_1(s) + V_2(s+1) = 0$$

We solve these equations simultaneously for the two unknown voltages V_1 and V_2.

$$V_1 = \frac{I_i(s+1)T_1}{(1 - sK_1T_1)(s+1) - s\,K_2T_1} = \left[\frac{(s+1)}{(1/T_1 - sK_1)(s+1) - sK_2}\right]I_i$$

$$= \left[\frac{(s+1)}{s^2(1-K_1) + s(3 - K_1 - K_2) + 1}\right]I_i$$

$$V_2 = \left(\frac{s}{s+1}\right)V_1 = \left[\frac{s}{s^2(1-K_1) + s(3-K_1-K_2) + 1}\right]I_i$$

Having thus expressed the two dependent variables in terms of the independent excitation I_i, we are now ready to calculate I_o. By inspection of Fig. 11-6, we have

$$I_o = \frac{V_1 - K_2V_2}{1}$$

$$I_o = I_i\left[\frac{s(1-K_2) + 1}{s^2(1-K_1) + s(3-K_1-K_2) + 1}\right] \quad \text{Ans.}$$

11-2 THÉVENIN AND NORTON EQUIVALENT CIRCUITS

Suppose that we look into a circuit from a pair of terminals. If the circuit is composed of independent sources (including initial condition sources), dependent sources, resistors, capacitors, and inductors, then the terminal properties of the circuit are described completely by the Thévenin or Norton equivalent circuit. See Fig. 11-7.

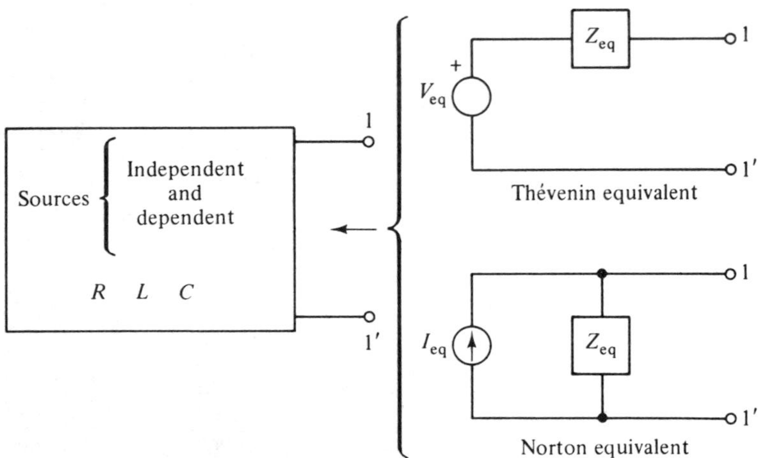

Fig. 11-7

The only difference between this representation and others used in preceding chapters is that we have generalized the equivalent representation by admitting dependent sources.

The Thévenin or Norton equivalent circuit can be found by a two-step procedure. First, V_{eq} or I_{eq} is calculated. Then a separate calculation is made for Z_{eq}.

To determine V_{eq}, we open-circuit terminals 1–1′ (this step is not necessary if the terminals are not connected to another circuit) and calculate the open-circuit voltage V_{oc} (across 1–1′). We then have $V_{eq} = V_{oc}$. To determine I_{eq}, we short-circuit terminals 1–1′ and calculate the short-circuit current I_{sc} (from 1 to 1′). We then have $I_{eq} = I_{sc}$.

To obtain Z_{eq}, *we first set to zero all independent sources* within the network. If there are any initial conditions, they, too, are set to zero. However, *we do not turn off the dependent sources*. The network is thus rendered dead in spite of the presence of any dependent sources (which by themselves produce no response). Then we apply either a voltage source V or a current source I to the terminals in order to excite the network and calculate the resulting current I or voltage V. The equivalent impedance is obtained by forming the V/I ratio. This procedure is illustrated in Fig. 11-8. In simple circuits without any dependent sources, we can also determine Z_{eq} by using the series and parallel combination rules.

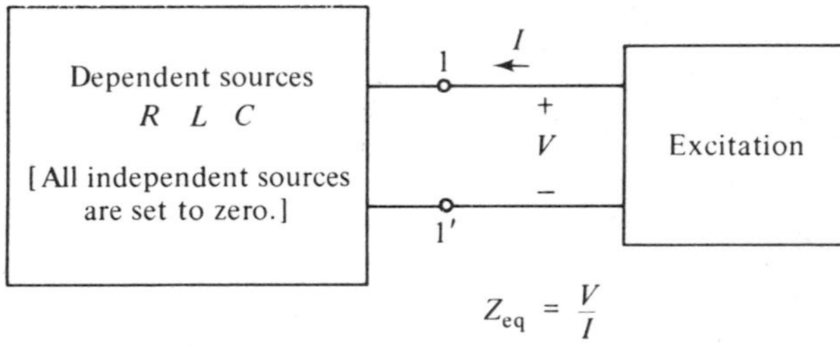

Fig. 11-8

There is also an indirect, one-step method for obtaining the Thévenin or Norton equivalent circuit if the network is independently excited. Although a little more work is involved, both V_{eq} and Z_{eq} (or I_{eq} and Z_{eq}) are obtained by a single calculation. To see how, refer to Fig. 11-9. The original network, *with all its sources, independent as well as dependent, intact,* is loaded by some impedance Z_L. It does not matter what Z_L is as long as it is labeled in such a way that it cannot be confused with any other impedance within the network. We will use Z_L only as a means of separating and identifying terms. From the Thévenin equivalent representation given in Fig. 11-9 we see that

$$I_L = \frac{V_{eq}}{Z_{eq} + Z_L} \tag{11-5}$$

$$V_L = V_{eq}\frac{Z_L}{Z_{eq} + Z_L} \tag{11-6}$$

Therefore by using any method, if we calculate either I_L or V_L from the original network and rearrange the resulting expression (through appropriate factoring) so that Z_L *is by itself in the denominator,* then Z_{eq} and V_{eq} can easily be identified by com-

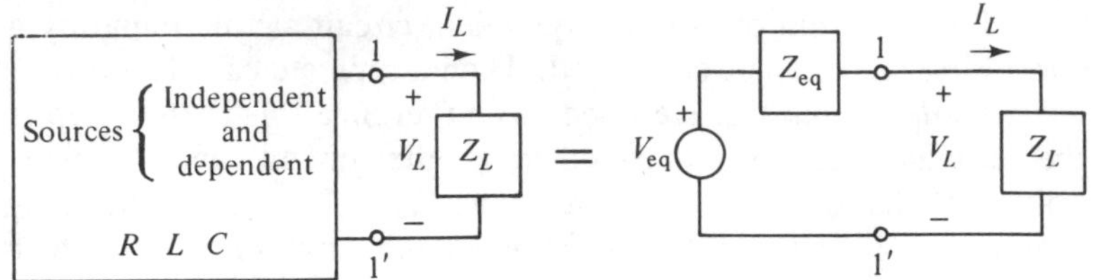

Fig. 11-9

parison to Eq. (11-5) or Eq. (11-6). For instance, suppose that the expression for the load current is obtained in the form

$$I_L = \frac{a}{b + cZ_L} \tag{11-7}$$

where a, b, and c do not depend on Z_L. We can isolate Z_L by factoring c out. Then we compare the resulting expression term by term with Eq. (11-5).

$$I_L = \frac{a/c}{b/c + Z_L} = \frac{V_{eq}}{Z_{eq} + Z_L} \tag{11-8a}$$

$$V_{eq} = \frac{a}{c}, \qquad Z_{eq} = \frac{b}{c} \tag{11-8b}$$

So from the calculation of I_L alone we obtain *both* V_{eq} and Z_{eq} and hence the complete Thévenin equivalent circuit. The Norton equivalent circuit can be obtained similarly. Note also that $I_{eq} = V_{eq}/Z_{eq}$.

This one-step procedure requires calculation of I_L or V_L while the network is loaded by Z_L, which complicates the calculations somewhat. Since it is easier to calculate I_L when $Z_L = 0$ and V_L when $Z_L = \infty$, the method can be modified as follows. First, we short-circuit terminals 1–1′ and calculate I_{sc}. Then we open-circuit terminals 1–1′ and calculate V_{oc}. From Eqs. (11-5) and (11-6) we have

$$I_{sc} = I_L\big|_{Z_L=0} = \frac{V_{eq}}{Z_{eq}} \tag{11-9}$$

$$V_{oc} = V_L\big|_{Z_L=\infty} = V_{eq} \tag{11-10}$$

$$\frac{V_{oc}}{I_{sc}} = \frac{V_{eq}}{V_{eq}/Z_{eq}} = Z_{eq} \tag{11-11}$$

Thus V_{eq} is obtained from the open-circuit voltage, and Z_{eq} *is obtained from the ratio of open-circuit voltage to short-circuit current*. Even though two calculations are made to determine the equivalent circuit, one with terminals open-circuited and the other with terminals short-circuited, each calculation is easier to perform than that necessary for the general termination Z_L.

The indirect method requires the presence of independent sources within the network to produce the terminal voltage and current. If the network is dead, as is the case when only dependent sources are present, both I_L and V_L are zero, and so Z_{eq} cannot be determined. However, we can introduce an independent source ourselves into the network so as to excite it. For instance, we can *cut any wire within the network and insert an independent voltage source,* or we can *connect an independent current source between any two nodes in the network.* We can even connect more than one independent source for excitation, provided that voltage sources are introduced in series and current sources in parallel with existing elements. In any event, regardless of the type, number, and placement of excitations, the impedance, looking into the network, is given by V_{oc}/I_{sc}. Alternatively, with the extraneous independent sources connected for excitation, the expressions for I_L or V_L (for an arbitrary load Z_L) are determined and Z_{eq} obtained (after proper factorization) by comparison to Eqs. (11-5) or (11-6). The resulting V_{eq} is ignored because the network is dead.

These techniques of obtaining equivalent circuits are not new. They have been utilized in previous chapters. However, here they have been generalized to include dependent sources.

We turn next to a number of examples to see how these various methods are used. Although only one method is used to solve each example problem, it should be clear that the others are equally applicable.

Example 11-6

Show that negative impedances can be generated by the arrangement given in Fig. 11-10.

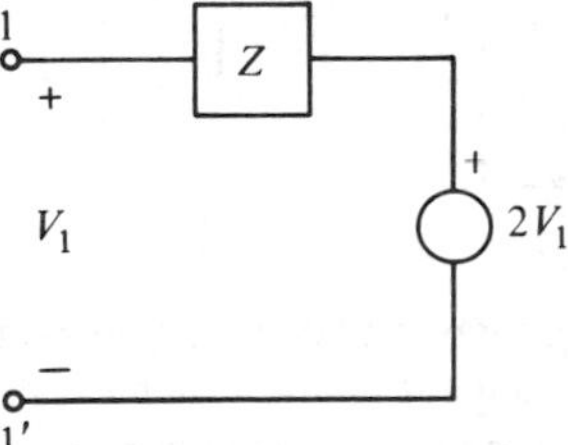

Fig. 11-10

Solution. Looking in at the terminals, we see the impedance Z in series with the voltage source $2V_1$. At first it may seem as if this circuit cannot be further simplified, since it appears to be in the Thévenin equivalent form. However, closer examination shows that *the source is not independent.* It depends on the input voltage V_1. Therefore *the network is dead and representable solely by an impedance* Z_{eq}. Stated differently, in the Thévenin equivalent representation, $V_{eq} = 0$. To obtain Z_{eq}, we connect a voltage source at the input terminals, determine the resulting input current, and form the voltage to current ratio. Referring to Fig. 11-11(a), we see that

$$I_1 = \frac{V_1 - 2V_1}{Z} = -\frac{V_1}{Z}$$

$$Z_{eq} = \frac{V_1}{I_1} = -Z \quad \text{Ans.}$$

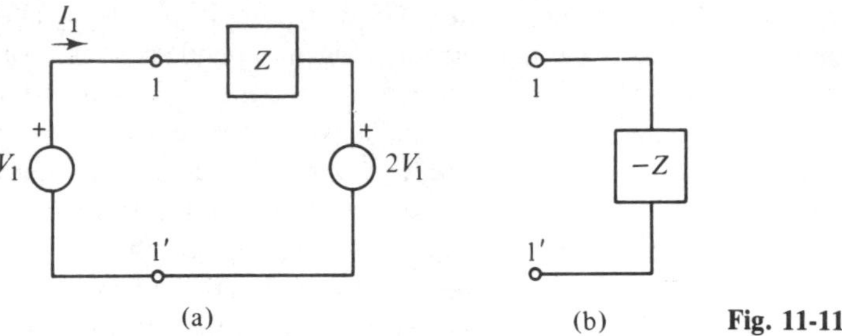

(a) (b) **Fig. 11-11**

Thus the terminal properties of the original network are indistinguishable from the network shown in Fig. 11-11(b). If Z represents the impedance of a resistor R, then at terminals 1–1′ we see $-R$. If Z represents the impedance of a capacitor C, at the input we see $-C$ and so on.

As this example indicates, *we can generate negative elements with dependent sources.*

Example 11-7

Show that impedances can be inverted by the arrangement shown in Fig. 11-12.

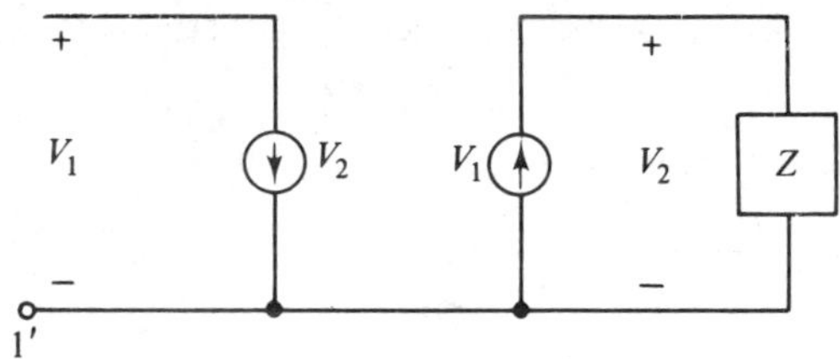

Fig. 11-12

Solution. The circuit contains two voltage-dependent current sources. One of them depends on the input voltage and the other on the voltage across the impedance Z. *Since there are no independent sources within the network, the terminal characteristics can be represented by a single equivalent impedance.* To obtain this impedance, we drive the network with a current source as shown in Fig. 11-13(a).

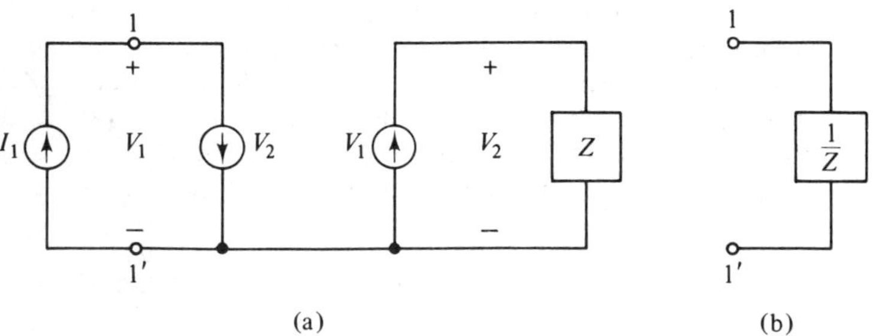

(a) (b)

Fig. 11-13

By inspection of the network, we see that

$$I_1 = V_2, \qquad V_2 = V_1 Z$$

So

$$I_1 = V_1 Z$$

$$Z_{eq} = \frac{V_1}{I_1} = \frac{1}{Z} \quad \text{Ans.}$$

Thus an impedance Z connected at the output side of the original network looks like $1/Z$ at the input. We can call this circuit an impedance inverter. For instance, if a capacitance C is connected at the output $(Z = 1/sC)$, we see at the input $Z_{eq} = 1/Z = sC$, which represents the impedance of a C-henry inductor.

We can invert impedances by the use of dependent sources.

Example 11-8

In Fig. 11-14, what is the output impedance?

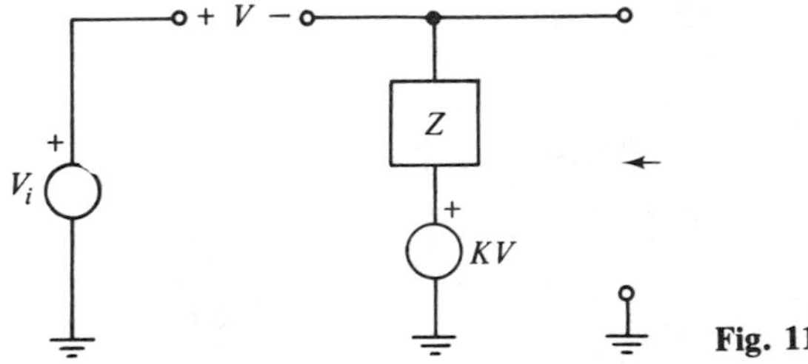

Fig. 11-14

Solution. Looking in from the output terminals, we see a circuit composed of an impedance and two sources. One of these sources, KV, is dependent; so we leave it in. The other source, V_i, is independent. We make it zero. The resulting network is drawn in Fig. 11-15. To obtain the output impedance, we calculate the V_2/I_2 ratio. Note that we need not designate (as we did in the two preceding examples) the type of source—voltage or current—that produces V_2 and I_2. We need not even know where they come from or how they are established. *It may be helpful to show a voltage or current source at the terminals, but doing so is not necessary.* We simply assume a V_2 or an I_2 and

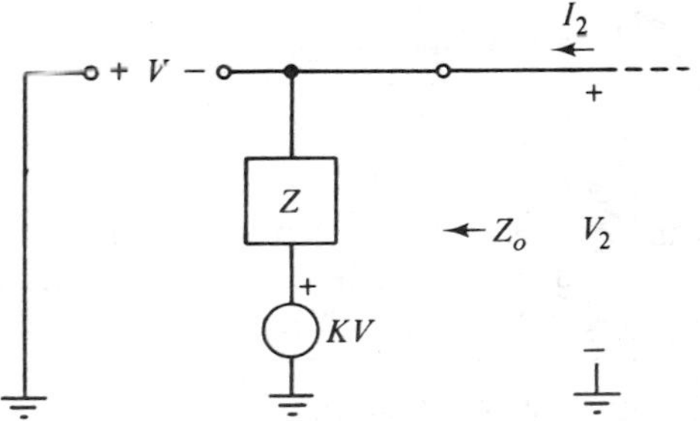

Fig. 11-15

proceed to obtain the relationship between them as imposed by the network to their left. Inspection of Fig. 11-15 shows that

$$V = -V_2 \qquad \text{and} \qquad I_2 = \frac{V_2 - KV}{Z}$$

Combining these equations, we have

$$I_2 = \frac{V_2 + KV_2}{Z} = \frac{V_2(1 + K)}{Z}$$

It follows that

$$Z_o = \frac{V_2}{I_2} = \frac{Z}{1 + K} \quad \text{Ans.}$$

Example 11-9

Refer to Fig. 11-16.

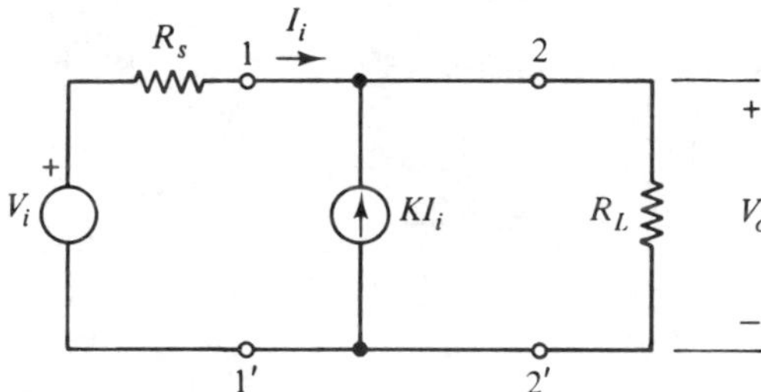

Fig. 11-16

(a) What does the source see (what is the equivalent resistance to the right of 1–1′)?
(b) What does the load see (what is the equivalent resistance to the left of 2–2′)?

Solution.

(a) Using superposition, we obtain the dependent variable I_i.

$$I_i = \underbrace{\frac{V_i}{R_s + R_L}}_{\text{Due to } V_i} + \underbrace{(-KI_i)\frac{R_L}{R_s + R_L}}_{\text{Due to } KI_i}$$

$$I_i = \frac{V_i}{R_s + R_L(1 + K)} = \frac{V_i}{R_s + R_{\text{eq1}}}$$

where $R_{\text{eq1}} = R_L(1 + K)$

So the source sees an equivalent resistance that is $(1 + K)$ times the load resistance. It does not see any equivalent source because the circuit to the right of 1–1′ does not contain any *independent* source. Consequently, in Fig. 11-16 we can remove the circuit to the right of 1–1′ and replace it with a single resistance: $R_L(1 + K)$. This situation is shown schematically in Fig. 11-17(a).
With dependent sources we can make impedances larger.

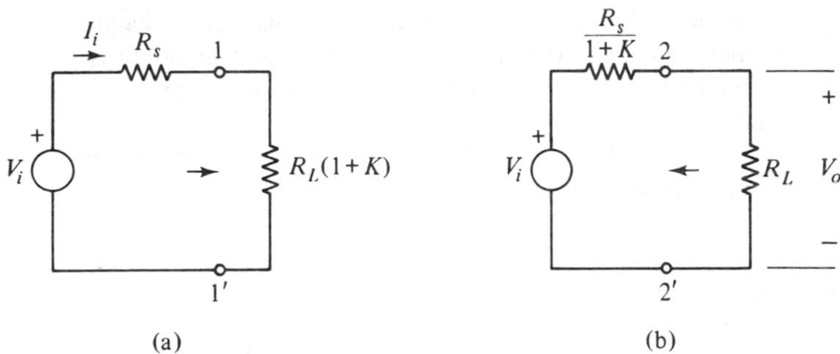

Fig. 11-17

(b) From Fig. 11-16 we see that

$$V_o = (1 + K)I_iR_L$$

Using the expression for I_i found in (a), we get

$$V_o = (1 + K)\left[\frac{V_i}{R_s + R_L(1 + K)}\right]R_L \tag{11-12}$$

To obtain the equivalent circuit facing R_L, we must put Eq. (11-12) in the form represented in Eq. (11-6). We do so by factoring out $(1 + K)$ and thus putting R_L by itself in the denominator.

$$V_o = V_i\left[\frac{R_L}{R_s/(1 + K) + R_L}\right] = V_{\text{eq}2}\frac{R_L}{R_{\text{eq}} + R_L} \tag{11-13}$$

where

$$V_{\text{eq}2} = V_i, \qquad R_{\text{eq}2} = \frac{R_s}{1 + K}$$

We see from Eq. (11-13) that the load R_L faces an equivalent circuit composed of a source $V_{\text{eq}2}$ connected in series with a resistance $R_{\text{eq}2}$. This Thévenin equivalent representation is shown schematically in Fig. 11-17(b).

If we make $V_i = 0$, looking in from 2–2′, we see an equivalent resistance of $R_s/(1 + K)$, which is the source resistance divided by $1 + K$. Thus *with dependent sources we can make impedances smaller.*

Example 11-10

Obtain the Norton equivalent of the circuit shown in Fig. 11-18.

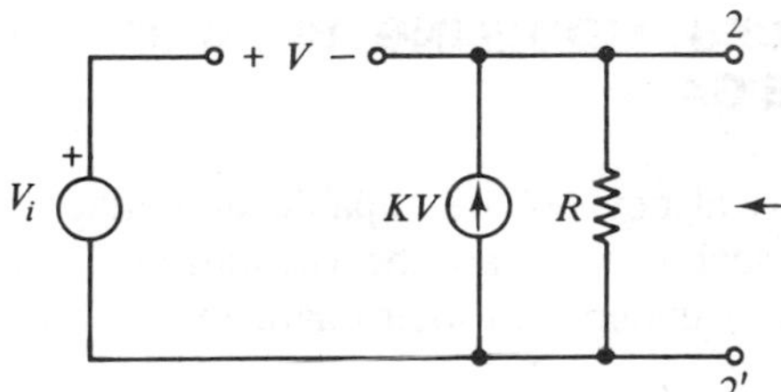

Fig. 11-18

Solution. The circuit consists of an independent voltage source V_i and a voltage-dependent current source KV. The Norton equivalent circuit is composed of an impedance in parallel with a current source. Let us determine this impedance by the V_{oc}/I_{sc} method.

We obtain V_{oc} directly from Fig. 11-18 after expressing the dependent variable V in terms of the independent variable V_i.

$$V = V_i - (KV)R$$

Then

$$V = \frac{V_i}{1 + KR}$$

$$V_{oc} = V_i - V = V_i\left(1 - \frac{1}{1 + KR}\right) = V_i\frac{KR}{1 + KR}$$

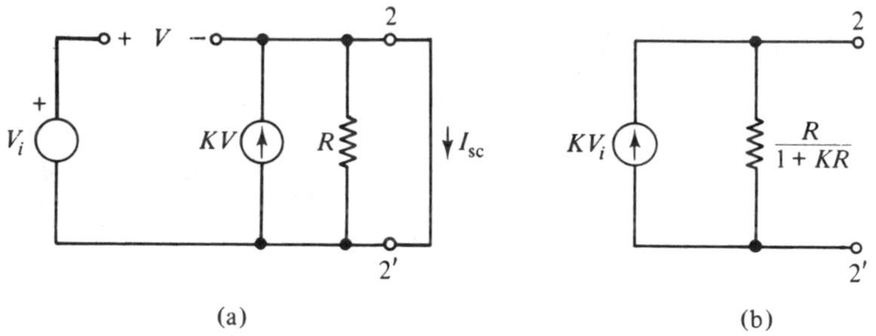

Fig. 11-19

We obtain I_{sc} from Fig. 11-19(a). Again we calculate the dependent variable V first and then I_{sc}.

$$V = V_i, \qquad I_{sc} = KV = KV_i$$

Thus

$$Z_{eq} = \frac{V_{oc}}{I_{sc}} = V_i\frac{KR}{1 + KR}\frac{1}{KV_i} = \frac{R}{1 + KR}$$

No separate calculation is necessary to determine the equivalent current source, since it is equal to I_{sc}. The resulting Norton equivalent circuit is shown in Fig. 11-19(b).

11-3 THREE-TERMINAL DEVICES: MODELING, BIASING, AND DETERMINING THE GAIN

Certain three-terminal electrical devices are capable of voltage, current, or power amplification. Examples of such devices are the vacuum tube and the transistor. In order to utilize them, we must understand their characteristics and set up proper dc and ac operating conditions.

A systematic, three-step procedure is used in the *design* of linear circuits involving such devices.

1. *Obtain the model* (equivalent circuit) that describes the characteristics at the three terminals.
2. *Establish the operating point,* using resistors and dc sources. This step is called *biasing*.
3. *Introduce the ac signal* without disturbing the dc voltages and currents established above.

Similarly, a three-step procedure is used for *analysis*.

1. *Use* the appropriate circuit model.
2. *Determine* the operating point to see that the device is properly biased and hence that the model used describes the characteristics of the device about the operating point.
3. *Calculate* the gain (transfer function) for the signal that is used as input.

Device modeling is not an easy task for several reasons. In general, device characteristics

1. Cannot be described by simple mathematical relations.
2. Vary from one unit to the next.
3. Vary with environmental factors, such as change in temperature.
4. Are either too complicated for developing a physical feel of how the device operates or too simple to give accurate results.

To illustrate, consider the three-terminal device given in Fig. 11-20(a). Three currents and three voltages are associated with the three terminals. However, only two currents (i_1, i_2) and two voltages (v_1, v_2) are designated on the diagram because the remaining variables can easily be determined. The current coming out of 3 is by Kirchhoff's Current Law ($i_1 + i_2$), and the voltage between 1–2 is by Kirchhoff's Voltage Law ($v_1 - v_2$). Suppose that we look into the device via leads 1 and 3. A single i_1 vs. v_1 curve would have described the terminal characteristics if lead 2 were not present. Because of lead 2, however, we would expect i_2 or v_2 to have an influence on the i_1 vs. v_1 curve. To describe this influence, we draw a family of curves, using i_2 or v_2 as a parameter. This kind of representation is shown in Fig. 11-20(b), where each curve is for a fixed but different value of i_2 or v_2. Similarly, if we look into the device via leads 2 and 3, we would expect the i_2 vs. v_2 characteristics to be dependent on i_1 or v_1. This dependence is shown in Fig. 11-20(c), where each curve is for a fixed but different value of i_1 or v_1. Thus *two sets of curves, i_1 vs. v_1 and i_2 vs. v_2, each controlled by a variable from the other set, are necessary to describe the characteristics of the three-terminal device.*

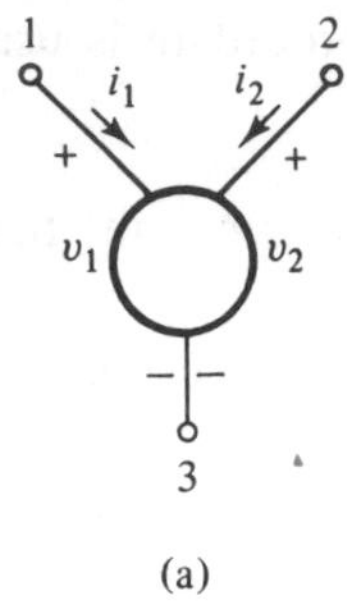

(a)

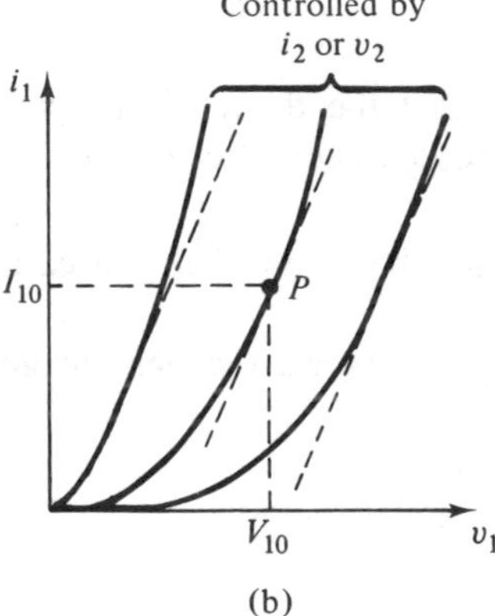

(b)

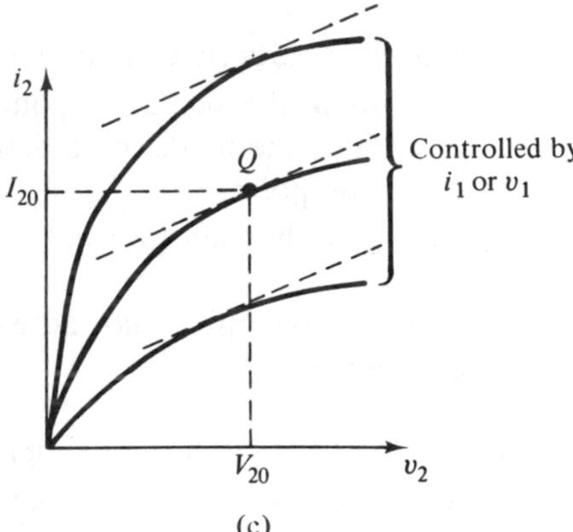

(c)

Fig. 11-20

Several remarks about these characteristic curves should be made.

1. Other parameters, such as temperature, may have an effect on these curves.
2. There may be considerable variation in characteristics among several units of the same type.
3. The curves represent the low-frequency behavior of the device, since they are taken by using dc or slowly varying voltages and currents. The curves are meaningless for high-frequency signals. More sophisticated measurements are necessary to describe the high-frequency characteristics.
4. The curves are not describable by simple mathematical relationships. However, we can approximate them over a limited region by linear, parallel, equidistant lines (shown dashed), thereby making them more tractable mathematically.

To model the device, an approximate expression for i_1 as a function of v_1 is obtained about some operating point P [see Fig. 11-20(b)] with either i_2 or v_2 acting as a parameter. Then an equivalent circuit that is governed by the *same* terminal relationship is constructed. In the equivalent circuit *the parameter comes in as a dependent source*. Similarly, an approximate expression for i_2 as a function of v_2 is obtained about some operating point Q [see Fig. 11-20(c)] with either i_1 or v_1 acting as a parameter. From this expression an equivalent circuit is constructed in which the effect of the parameter is represented by a dependent source. So two equivalent circuits, one representing the characteristics between 1–3 and the other representing the characteristics between 2–3, are used to model the device. These equivalent circuits have a common terminal (3).

Several examples of how to determine the circuit model of the device from its characteristic curves will be presented shortly.

The characteristics represented by the circuit model match the characteristics given by the actual curves (obtained by measurement) only over a limited region. For instance, if the device curves are linearized about points P and Q in Fig. 11-20(b) and (c), then the accuracy of the model diminishes if the operation is moved away from P and Q. Consequently, proper external circuitry must be used to ensure that operation is at or near P and Q. In other words, the device must be *biased* properly. Typical biasing circuits are shown in Fig. 11-21. In Fig. 11-21(a), V_{1b} and R_1 are chosen so that $i_1 = I_{10}$ and $v_1 = V_{10}$ when no external signal is present. Thus operating point $P(I_{10}, V_{10})$ is established. Similarly, V_{2b} and R_2 are chosen so that $i_2 = I_{20}$ and $v_2 = V_{20}$ when no external signal is present. Thus operating point $Q(I_{20}, V_{20})$ is established. Without the dc sources V_{1b} and V_{2b}, the device cannot be properly biased. In cases where V_{1b} is of the same sign as V_{2b}, a single dc source can be used to establish both operating points. This situation is shown in Fig. 11-21(b). The operating points are also known as *quiescent points,* since the device voltages and currents stay at these points indefinitely until signals are applied to cause variations of voltages and currents about them.

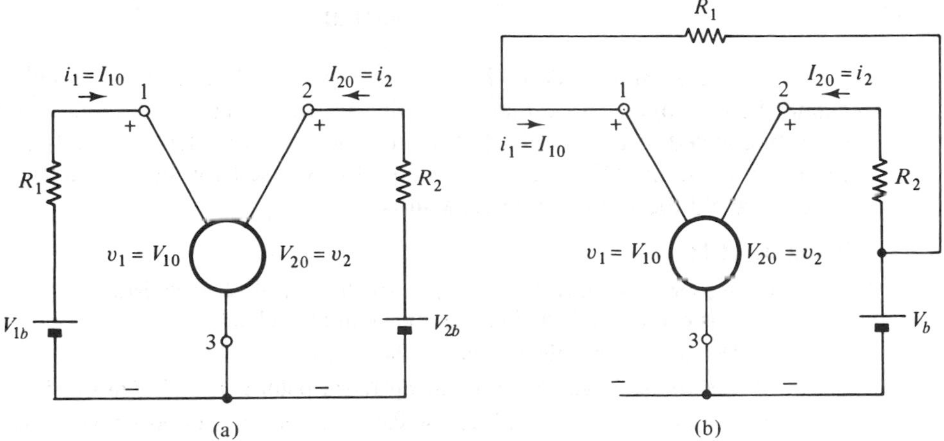

Fig. 11-21

A typical method of coupling an ac signal into and out of the device without upsetting the bias currents and voltages appears in Fig. 11-22. Capacitors C_1 and C_2 serve two functions. On the one hand, in the steady state, they become open circuits for dc, thereby disengaging the source and load from the bias circuitry. On the other hand, over a desired band of frequencies, they become short circuits (for all practical purposes) for the ac signals, thereby coupling the source and load to the device. The device currents and voltages are, by superposition, the sum of the dc (bias) and ac (signal) currents and voltages. *The gain of the circuit is* $V_o(s)/V_i(s)$ with $V_{1b} = V_{2b} = 0$. It is important to realize that sources V_{1b} and V_{2b} are used only to establish the device operating points, which, in turn, determine the values of the circuit elements in the equivalent representation. Once the appropriate circuit model is obtained, we can set the bias sources to zero and calculate the gain. Of course, in practice, we cannot turn off the dc sources without adversely affecting the operation of the device. However, the ac signal can be readily measured in the presence of the bias currents and voltages and hence the gain determined experimentally. Here gain and transfer functions are synonymous. Both describe the input-output relationship in the network.

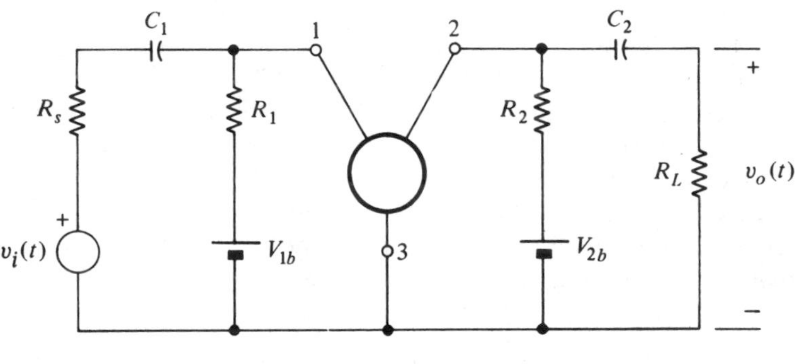

Fig. 11-22

When the input is dc or has a dc component that is to be passed, capacitors cannot be employed, since they block the dc. In this case, the input and output are directly coupled to the circuit. The source and load impedances then become part of the biasing circuit. Direct coupling may also be used for slowly varying signals in order to avoid the use of large capacitors.

Example 11-11

A three-terminal device, which has the linearized characteristics shown in Fig. 11-23(a), is connected in a circuit as shown in Fig. 11-23(b).

(a) Obtain the equivalent circuit of the device.

(b) Determine R_1 and R_2 to set the operating point at $i_2 = 100$ mA and $v_2 = 10$ V.

(c) The input signal, $v_i(t)$, is sinusoidal. The frequency of operation is such that the ac voltage across the capacitor is negligible. Calculate the ac gain.

(d) The input is $v_i = 0.05 \sin \omega t$. What is v_o?

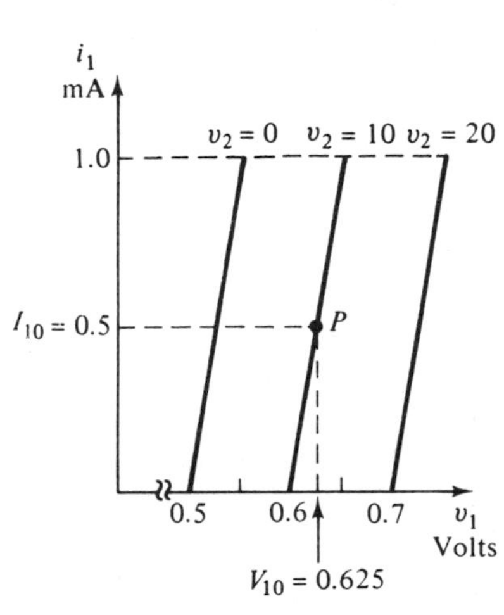

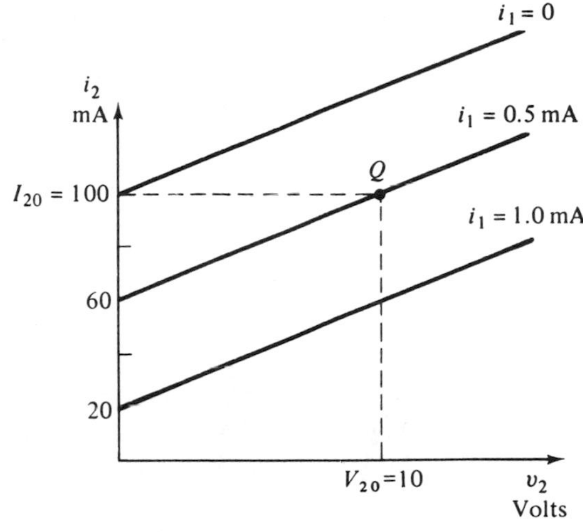

(a)

(b)

Fig. 11-23

Solution.

(a) From the input characteristics we see that i_1 is a function of v_1 and v_2. The constant-v_2 lines have a slope of 1 mA/0.05 V, and the horizontal separation between them is 0.1 V/10 V of v_2.

The equation for the $v_2 = 0$ line is

$$i_1 = \frac{1}{0.05}(v_1 - 0.5)$$

where i_1 is in milliamperes and v_1 is in volts. As Fig. 11-23(a) shows, the parameter v_2 changes the v_1-axis intercept by moving it to the right 0.1 V for every 10 V of v_2. For v_2 volts, the intercept is displaced to the right $(0.1/10)v_2$ volts. Hence the expression for i_1 in milliamperes becomes

$$i_1 = \frac{1}{0.05}\left[\left(v_1 - \frac{0.1}{10}v_2\right) - 0.5\right] = 20v_1 - 0.2v_2 - 10 \qquad (11\text{-}14)$$

We can solve this equation for v_1 in order to obtain the expression for v_1 as a function of i_1 and v_2:

$$v_1 = 0.05i_1 + 0.01v_2 + 0.5 \qquad (11\text{-}15)$$

Either Eq. (11-14) or Eq. (11-15) can be used to construct the input equivalent circuit. One gives the Norton, the other the Thévenin equivalent circuit. In Fig. 11-24(a), the Thévenin equivalent representation, which is a restatement of Eq. (11-15) in terms of circuit elements, is given. As the equivalent circuit and Eq. (11-15) show, the input voltage is the sum of three terms (voltages). The first term, $0.05i_1$, is due to the input current and thus can be represented as the voltage across a

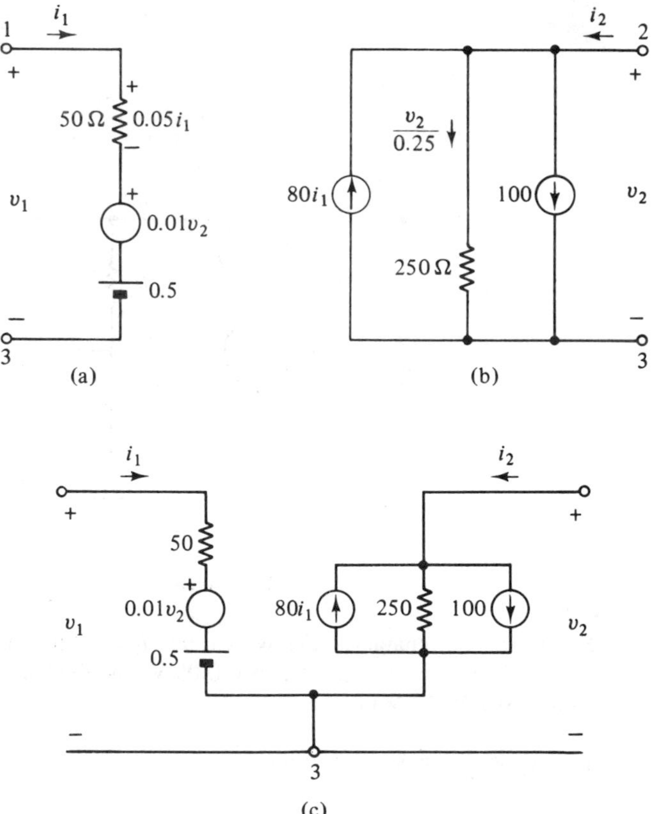

Fig. 11-24

0.05 kΩ resistor. The second term, $0.01v_2$, is due to the voltage at the output terminals and so can be represented as a voltage-dependent voltage source. The third term, 0.5, is constant; it can be represented as a dc voltage source.

From the output characteristics we see that i_2 is a function of v_2 and i_1. The constant-i_1 lines have a slope of 40 mA/10 V, and the vertical separation between them is 40 mA/0.5 mA of i_1.

The equation for the $i_1 = 0$ line is

$$i_2 = 100 + \frac{40}{10}v_2$$

where i_1 is in milliamperes and v_2 is in volts. As Fig. 11-23(b) shows, the parameter i_1 changes the i_2-axis intercept by moving it down 40 mA for every 0.5 mA of i_1. For i_1 milliamperes, the intercept is displaced downward $(40/0.5)i_1$ milliamperes. So the expression for i_2 in milliamperes becomes

$$i_2 = 100 + \frac{40}{10}v_2 - \frac{40}{0.5}i_1 = 100 + \frac{v_2}{0.25} - 80i_1 \qquad (11\text{-}16)$$

This equation for v_2 can be solved to obtain the expression for v_2 as a function of i_2 and i_1.

$$v_2 = 0.25i_2 + 20i_1 - 25 \qquad (11\text{-}17)$$

Equation (11-16) results in the Norton equivalent representation; Eq. (11-17) gives the Thévenin equivalent. In Fig. 11-24(b), the Norton equivalent circuit is given. As the equivalent circuit and Eq. (11-16) show, the output current is the sum of the three terms (currents). The first term, 100, is constant and so can be represented as a dc current source. The second term, $v_2/0.25$, is due to the output voltage and hence can be represented as the current through a 0.25 kΩ resistor. The third term, $-80i_1$, is due to the current at the input and thus can be represented as a current-dependent current source.

By putting the input and output equivalent circuits together, the complete equivalent circuit of the device is obtained. See Fig. 11-24(c). This equivalent representation is not unique. For instance, we could just as easily have used the Thévenin instead of the Norton equivalent representation for the output. Usually the nature of the characteristic curves may lead us to choose one over the other. In general, if the lines are more nearly vertical, the Thévenin equivalent representation using voltage sources is preferable. On the other hand, if the lines are more nearly horizontal, the Norton equivalent representation using current sources gives a truer picture of the nature of the device.

(b) To determine the resistor values for setting the operating point, we redraw Fig. 11-23(b) as in Fig. 11-25 (by replacing the capacitor with an open circuit) and mark on the diagram the operating point voltages and currents, which are obtained from Fig. 11-23(a): $I_{10} = 0.5$, $V_{10} = 0.625$, $I_{20} = 100$, and $V_{20} = 10$. Note that it is not necessary to specify both P and Q points. When one is specified, the other can be determined from the characteristic curves. In this case, I_{20} and V_{20} are specified, which fix point Q in Fig. 11-23(a). At point Q on the output curves we see that $i_1 = I_{10} = 0.5$. With I_{10} and V_{20} thus known, point P and hence V_{10} can be determined from the input curves (or the input equivalent circuit).

By inspection of the bias circuit given in Fig. 11-25, we obtain

$$I_{10} = \frac{30 - V_{10}}{R_1}, \qquad I_{20} = \frac{30 - V_{20}}{R_2}$$

$$0.5 = \frac{30 - 0.625}{R_1}, \quad 100 = \frac{30 - 10}{R_2}$$

$$R_1 = 58.75 \text{ k}\Omega, \qquad R_2 = 0.2 \text{ k}\Omega \quad \text{Ans.}$$

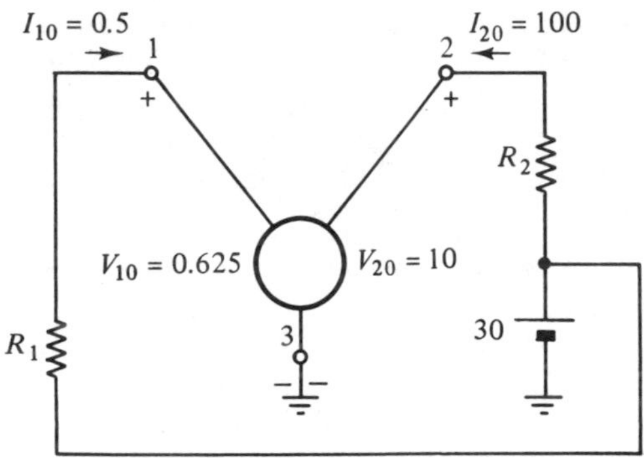

Fig. 11-25

(c) To determine the ac gain, we replace the dc source with a short circuit (since its effect has already been taken into consideration in the bias calculations) and the capacitor with a short circuit (since the ac voltage across it is assumed to be negligible). Consequently, Fig. 11-23(b) can be redrawn as in Fig. 11-26(a). Since $R_1 \gg 50\ \Omega$, it can be neglected. In other words, the Thévenin equivalent to the left of 1–3 is, for all practical purposes, v_i in series with 50 Ω. We then replace the device with its equivalent circuit given in Fig. 11-24(c), keeping in mind that we no longer are interested in dc values and so need not consider the 0.5 V dc voltage source on the input side and the 100 mA dc current source on the output side. These sources affect the operating point but not the ac gain. As a result, Fig. 11-26(a) can be redrawn as in Fig. 11-26(b). By inspection of this circuit, we write two equations, one from the input and the other from the output side, and solve for the two dependent variables i_{1ac} and v_{2ac}.

$$i_{1ac} = \frac{v_i - 0.01v_{2ac}}{0.050 + 0.050}, \qquad v_{2ac} = 80i_{1ac}\frac{0.25 \times 0.20}{0.25 + 0.20}$$

$$i_{1ac} + 0.1v_{2ac} = 10v_i, \qquad 80i_{1ac} - 9v_{2ac} = 0$$

$$i_{1ac} + 0.1 \times \frac{80}{9}i_{1ac} = 10v_i$$

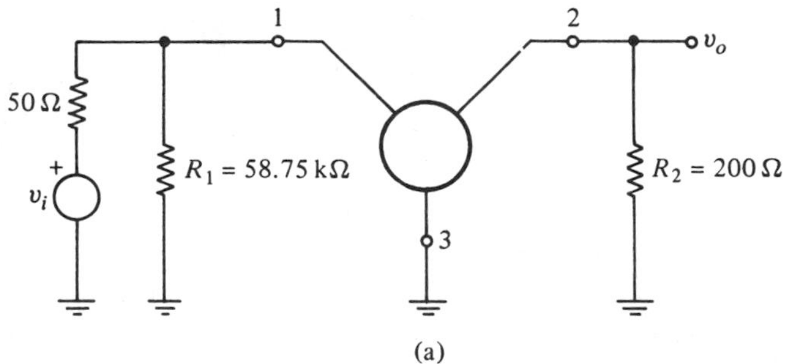

(a)

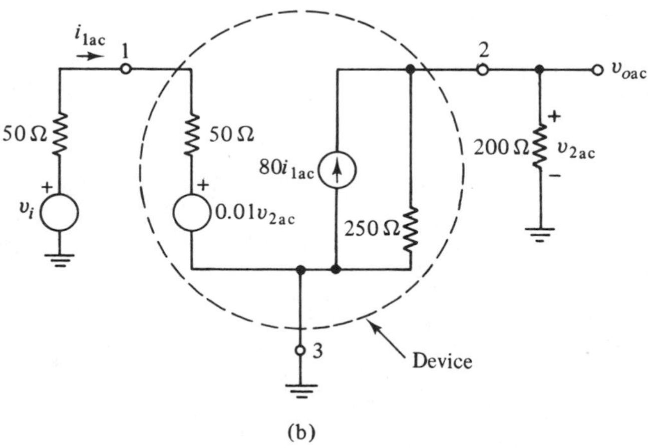

(b)

Fig. 11-26

$$i_{1ac} = \frac{90}{17}v_i = 5.29v_i$$

$$v_{2ac} = \frac{800}{17}v_i = 47.06v_i$$

Since $v_{oac} = v_{2ac}$, we have

$$\text{Gain} = \frac{v_{oac}}{v_i} = 47.06 \quad \text{Ans.}$$

(d) The dc portion of the output is $V_{20} = 10$. The ac portion of the output is $v_{2ac} = 47.06v_i$. Hence, by superposition, the output is

$$v_o = V_{20} + v_{2ac} = 10 + 47.06v_i$$

Since $v_i = 0.05 \sin \omega t$, we have

$$v_o = 10 + 2.353 \sin \omega t \quad \text{Ans.}$$

This device, in conjunction with the external circuit, can amplify signals by a factor of 47.06.

Example 11-12

The characteristics of a voltage-controlled device are shown in Fig. 11-27(a). This device is connected in the circuit of Fig. 11-27(b) to amplify the sinusoidal signal v_i. Obtain the operating point and the gain. Assume that the ac voltages across the capacitors are negligible.

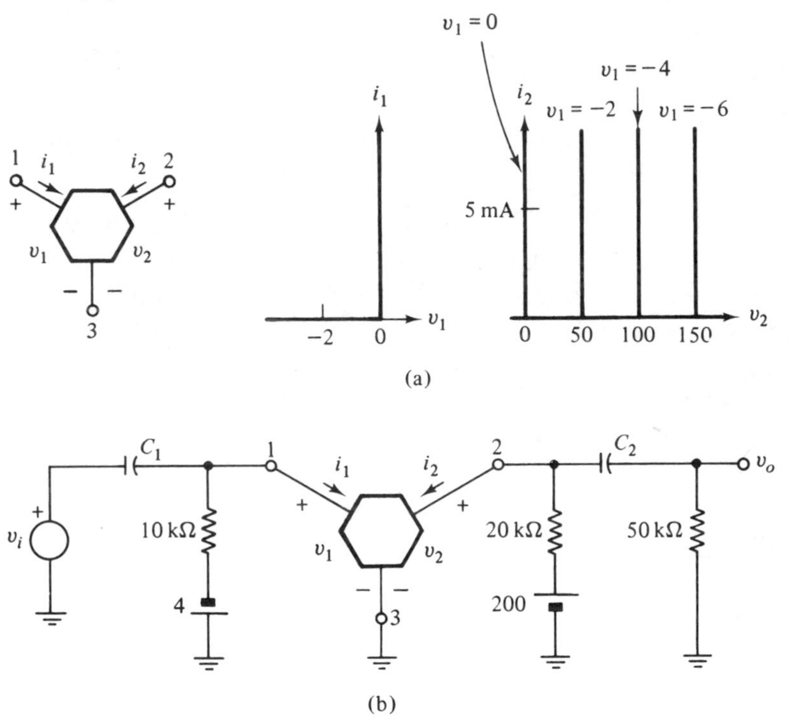

Fig. 11-27

Solution. It is not possible to characterize the i_1 vs. v_1 curve by a single equation. We need two equations, one for each straight line, to describe the input characteristic mathematically. Thus if the device is operating along the vertical line, we have

$$i_1 \geq 0, \qquad v_1 = 0$$

to describe its characteristic. The circuit model of the device is a short circuit ($v_i = 0$) between leads 1 and 3, provided that the $i_1 \geq 0$ constraint is met. On the other hand, if the device is operating along the horizontal line, we have

$$i_1 = 0, \qquad v_1 \leq 0$$

to describe its input behavior. The circuit model for the device is then an open circuit ($i_1 = 0$) between leads 1 and 3, provided that the $v_1 \leq 0$ constraint is met. Whether the device is operated entirely along the vertical line (short-circuit model) or the horizontal line (open-circuit model) depends on the input bias circuit and the signal amplitude. Although it is also possible to operate part of the time along the $v_1 = 0$ line and part of the time along the $i_1 = 0$ line as the ac signal varies with time, we will assume here that operation is confined to one region only. To determine the region of operation, we refer to the circuit diagram given in Fig. 11-27b. Suppose that we assume operation is along the vertical line. Then $v_1 = 0$; and by inspection of the input circuit, we see that the input bias current is $i_{1dc} = -4/10 = -0.4$mA. This result leads to contradiction because $(i_{1dc}, v_{1dc}) = (-0.4, 0)$ is not a point on the input characteristic curve and so is not a valid solution. Hence, as biased, the device must be operating along the horizontal line. Then $i_{1dc} = 0$; and by inspection of the input circuit, we see that the input voltage is $v_{1\,dc} = -4$. Since $(i_{1\,dc}, v_{1\,dc}) = (0, -4)$ is a point on the input characteristic curve, we see that the device is set up to operate about the -4 V level. Consequently the equivalent circuit between 1 and 3 is an open circuit [provided that $v_1 = (v_{1dc} + v_{1ac}) \leq 0$].

The output characteristics of the device are vertical lines, indicating that on the output side the device acts like a voltage source. Furthermore, we see that the value of the voltage source depends on the input voltage v_1. As Fig.11-27(a) shows, for every -2V of v_1, the output voltage shifts to the right 50 V. So the output characteristics are mathematically described by

$$v_2 = \left(\frac{50}{-2}\right)v_1 = -25v_1$$

The corresponding circuit model on the output side (between leads 2 and 3) is a voltage-dependent voltage source. The complete circuit model is shown in Fig.11-28(a).

With the device replaced by its equivalent circuit and the capacitors replaced by open circuits, the original circuit of Fig.11-27(b) can be redrawn as Fig.11-28(b) in order to show all the bias currents and voltages. With $v_{1dc} = -4$, the circuit model (or the output characteristic curves) gives

$$v_{2dc} = -25v_{1dc} = (-25)(-4) = 100$$

From Fig.11-28(b) we see that

$$i_{2dc} = \frac{200 - v_{2dc}}{20} = 5$$

Then the operating points on the input and output sides are

$$(i_1, v_1) = (0, -4), \qquad (i_2, v_2) = (5, 100) \qquad \text{Ans.}$$

To calculate the gain for the input v_i, we turn off the dc sources, replace the capacitors with short circuits, and use the circuit model for the device. Form the resulting circuit, shown in Fig.11-28(c), we obtain

$$v_{oac} = -25v_{1ac} = -25v_i$$

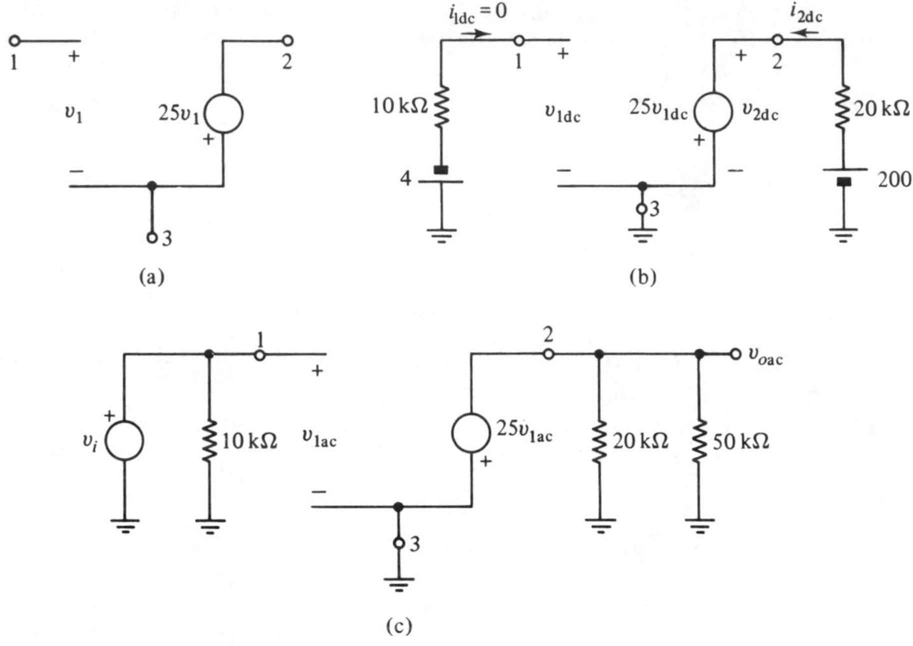

Fig. 11-28

Therefore the gain is

$$\frac{v_{oac}}{v_i} = -25 \quad \text{Ans.}$$

Example 11-13

Refer to the circuit and device characteristics given in Fig. 11-29.

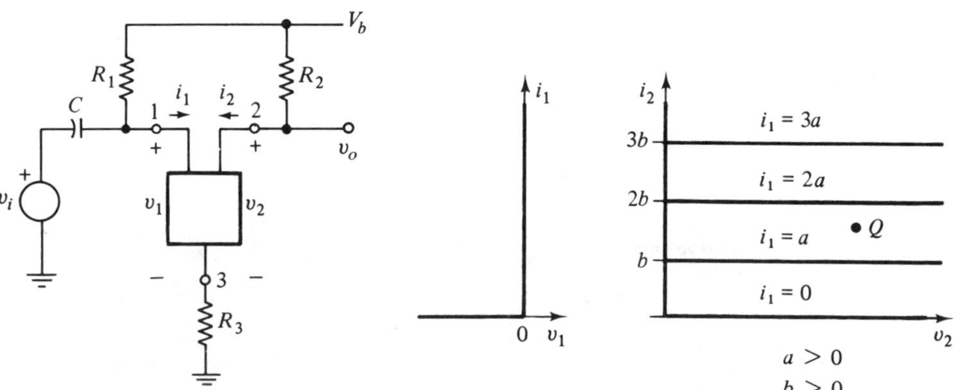

Fig. 11-29

(a) Obtain the model for the device, assuming that it will be operated about the Q point shown.
(b) Determine the operating point.
(c) Calculate the gain. Assume that the ac voltage across the capacitor is negligible.
(d) What resistance does the source see?
(e) What resistance is seen when looking in from the output terminals?
(f) What is the Thévenin equivalent circuit when looking in from the output terminals? Consider only the input signal—that is, make $V_b = 0$.

Solution.

(a) The output characteristics of the device are horizontal lines, indicating that the device acts like a current source. Furthermore, we see that the value of the current source depends on the input current i_1. For each "a" units of i_1, the output current shifts up "b" units. Hence the output characteristics are described by

$$i_2 = \frac{b}{a} i_1$$

The corresponding circuit model is a current-dependent current source.

The output curves indicate that $i_1 \geq 0$. When this constraint is applied to the input curve, we see that $v_1 = 0$, which means that a short circuit can be used in the equivalent representation. The complete model of the device is shown in Fig. 11-30(a).

(b) The operating point can be determined from the circuit of Fig. 11-30(b), which is obtained from Fig. 11-29 by replacing the capacitor with an open circuit and the device with its equivalent representation. By inspection of the circuit, we see that

$$V_b = i_{1dc}R_1 + i_{1dc}\left(1 + \frac{b}{a}\right)R_3$$

Thus

$$i_{1dc} = \frac{V_b}{R_1 + (1 + b/a)R_3}$$

$$v_{2dc} = V_b - \frac{b}{a}i_{1dc}R_2 - i_{1dc}\left(1 + \frac{b}{a}\right)R_3$$

$$v_{2dc} = V_b - \left[\frac{b}{a}R_2 + \left(1 + \frac{b}{a}\right)R_3\right]\left[\frac{V_b}{R_1 + (1 + b/a)R_3}\right]$$

The input and output operating points are

$$(i_1, v_1) = (i_{1dc}, 0), \qquad (i_2, v_2) = \left(\frac{b}{a}i_{1dc}, v_{2dc}\right) \quad \text{Ans.}$$

It should be clear that $i_{1dc} \geq 0$ and $v_{2dc} \geq 0$; otherwise we cannot justify the use of the device-equivalent circuit represented in Fig. 11-30(a). The model is valid as long as i_{1dc} and v_{2dc} are nonnegative.

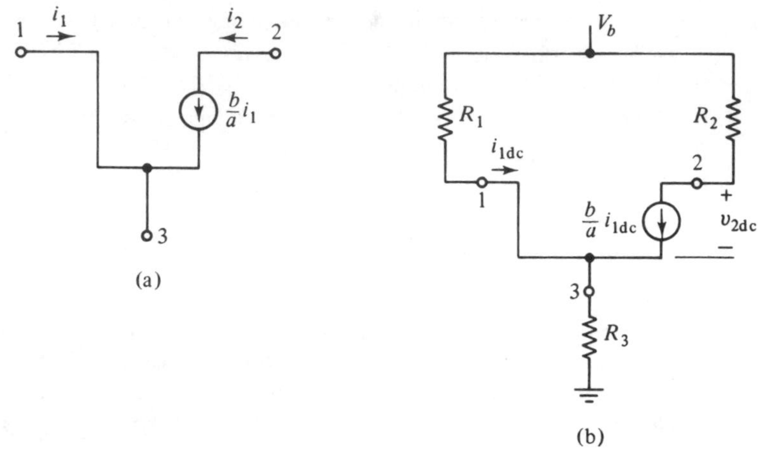

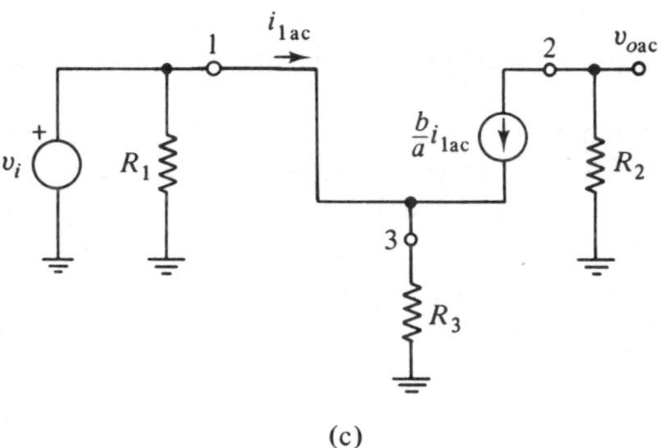

(c)

Fig. 11-30

(c) The gain can be calculated from the circuit of Fig. 11-30(c), which is obtained from Fig. 11-29 by replacing the capacitor with a short circuit, by turning off V_b (grounding the top line), and by replacing the device with its equivalent representation. Inspection of the circuit shows that

$$v_i = i_{1\,\mathrm{ac}}\left(1 + \frac{b}{a}\right)R_3$$

It follows that

$$i_{1\mathrm{ac}} = \frac{v_i}{(1 + b/a)R_3} \qquad (11\text{-}18)$$

$$v_{o\mathrm{ac}} = -\frac{b}{a} i_{1\mathrm{ac}} R_2 = -\frac{b}{a}\frac{v_i R_2}{(1 + b/a)R_3} = -\frac{R_2}{(1 + a/b)R_3} v_i$$

$$\text{Gain} = \frac{v_{o\mathrm{ac}}}{v_i} = -\frac{R_2}{(1 + a/b)R_3} \quad \text{Ans.}$$

(d) To obtain the resistance seen by the source, we turn off V_b (which is an independent source) and replace the capacitor with a short circuit. The result is Fig. 11-30(c). The source sees R_1 in parallel with the resistance of the circuit to the right of R_1. From Eq. (11-18) we know that this latter resistance is $v_i/i_{1\,ac} = (1 + b/a)R_3$. So

$$R_i = \frac{R_1(1 + b/a)R_3}{R_1 + (1 + b/a)R_3} \quad \text{Ans.}$$

(e) To obtain the output resistance, we redraw Fig. 11-30(c) with $v_i = 0$. The result is Fig. 11-31(a), from which we determine $R_o = v/i$ as follows.

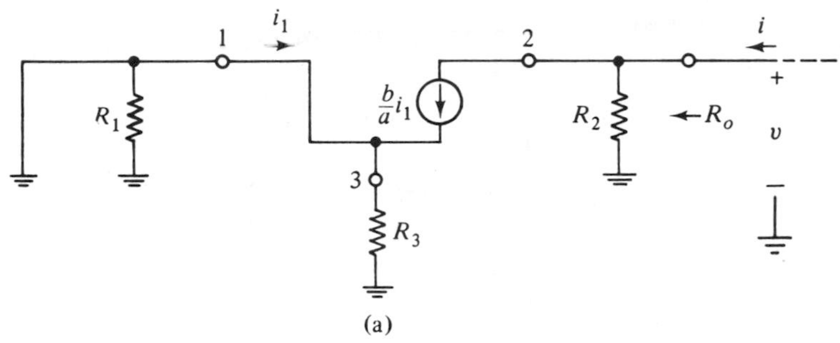

(a)

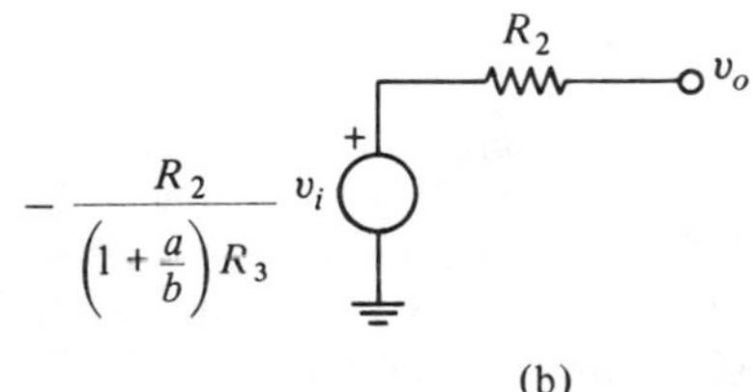

(b)

Fig. 11-31

Because of the short circuit from 1 to ground, the voltage from 3 to ground is zero.

$$0 = i_1\left(1 + \frac{b}{a}\right)R_3$$

Thus

$$i_1 = 0, \qquad i = \frac{v}{R_2}$$

$$R_o = \frac{v}{i} = R_2 \quad \text{Ans.}$$

(f) From (c) we obtain the open-circuit voltage caused by the signal:

$$v_{oc} = -\frac{R_2}{(1 + a/b)R_3}v_i$$

From (e) we have the output resistance:

$$R_o = R_2$$

The Thévenin equivalent can therefore be drawn as in Fig. 11-31(b).

Example 11-14

In Fig. 11-32 a dc voltage is applied to the circuit at $t = 0$. The model of the device labeled K is as given. Show that a sine wave is generated at the output if K is properly adjusted.

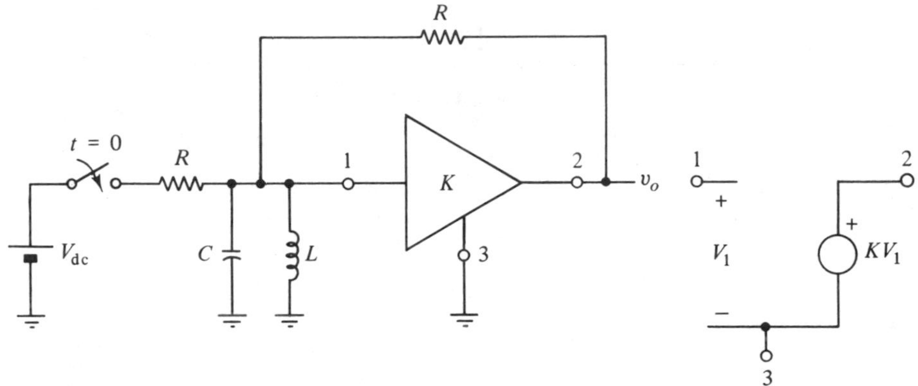

Fig. 11-32

Solution. The circuit is redrawn in Fig. 11-33(a) after replacing the device with its model. The circuit can be simplified by replacing the two resistor-source combinations with their Norton equivalent representations as shown in Fig. 11-33(b). The two resistors and the two current sources can then be combined into a single Norton representation that drives the LC circuit as shown in Fig. 11-33(c). (Note that here V_{dc} is divided by s in order to transform the input voltage into the frequency domain.)

We obtain $V_1(s)$ by multiplying the input current with the impedance of the circuit.

$$V_1 = \left(\frac{V_{dc}}{s}\frac{1}{R} + K\frac{V_1}{R}\right)\left[\frac{1}{2/R + sC + 1/sL}\right]$$

$$= \left(\frac{V_{dc}}{s} + KV_1\right)\left[\frac{(1/RC)s}{s^2 + s(2/RC) + 1/LC}\right]$$

$$V_1\left[s^2 + s(2 - K)\frac{1}{RC} + \frac{1}{LC}\right] = \frac{V_{dc}}{RC}$$

$$V_1 = \frac{V_{dc}/RC}{s^2 + s(2 - K)/RC + 1/LC}$$

$$V_o = KV_1 = \frac{K(V_{dc}/RC)}{s^2 + s(2 - K)/RC + 1/LC}$$

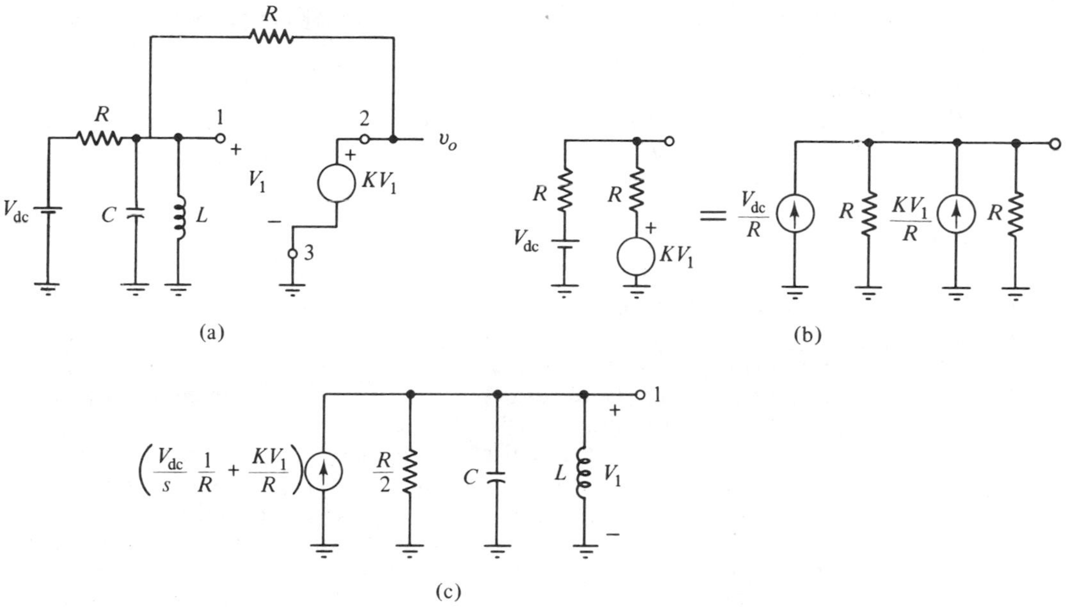

Fig. 11-33

If the output is to be a sine wave, the coefficient of the s term in the denominator polynomial must be zero. Therefore adjust K to 2. The output voltage then becomes

$$V_o = \frac{(2/RC)V_{dc}}{s^2 + (1/LC)} = 2V_{dc}\frac{1}{R}\sqrt{\frac{L}{C}}\left(\frac{1/\sqrt{LC}}{s^2 + 1/LC}\right)$$

$$v_o(t) = 2V_{dc}\frac{1}{R}\sqrt{\frac{L}{C}}\sin\frac{1}{\sqrt{LC}}t \quad \text{Ans.}$$

Example 11-15

(a) A two-terminal device and its terminal characteristics are shown in Fig. 11-34(a). Obtain the mathematical and the circuit models of the device.

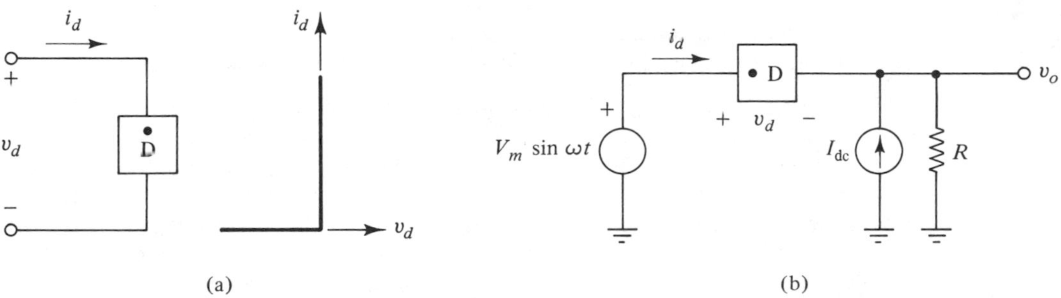

Fig. 11-34

(b) The device is used in the circuit of Fig. 11-34(b). Sketch the output voltage. Assume $V_m > I_{dc}R$.

Solution.

(a) The device is piecewisely linear, that is, there are two straight line segments. Hence two equations, one for each straight line segment, are needed to describe the device.

$$v_d = 0 \qquad \text{provided } i_d > 0 \tag{11-19a}$$

$$i_d = 0 \qquad \text{provided } v_d < 0 \tag{11-19b}$$

The device is on (conducting) when $i_d > 0$; the voltage across it then is zero. Therefore the device can be modelled with a short circuit as shown in Fig. 11-35(a). It is important to realize that the constraint $i_d > 0$ is part of the *on model,* and hence it must be placed next to the short circuit. Failure to do so would imply i_d could also be negative, a result that is precluded by the device characteristic shown in Fig. 11-34(a). The vertical straight line does not cover the entire i_d axis but just the upper half. The device is off (not conducting) when $v_d < 0$, and therefore the current through it is zero. Hence the device can be modelled with an open circuit as shown in Fig. 11-35(b). It is important to realize that the constraint $v_d < 0$ is part of the *off model,* and hence it must be placed across the open circuit. Failure to do so would imply v_d could also be positive, a result that is precluded by the device characteristic shown in Fig. 11-34(a). The horizontal straight line does not cover the entire v_d axis but just the left half.

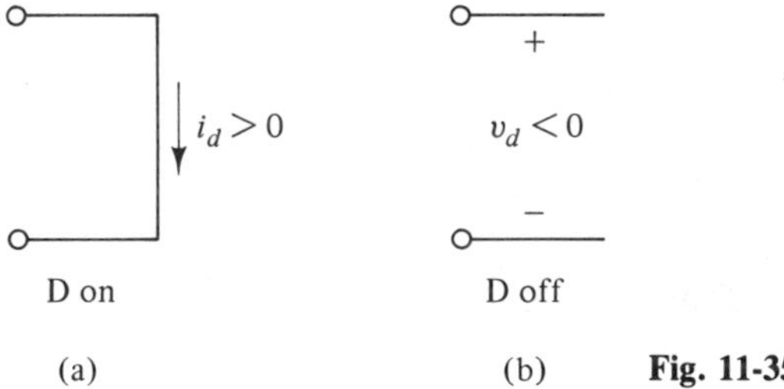

(a) (b) **Fig. 11-35**

The device is completely characterized by the mathematical model given by Eqs. (11-19a) and (11-19b). Alternatively the device is completely characterized by the circuit model given by Figs. 11-35(a) and (b). Note that the device cannot be characterized by a single equation or circuit. Depending on the conditions imposed by the external circuit, the device is either ON [Eq. (11-19a), Fig. 11-35(a)] or OFF [Eq. (11-19b), Fig. 11-35(b)]. When $i_d = 0$ and $v_d = 0$, either model can be used.

(b) When the device is used in the circuit of Fig. 11-34(b), it is not immediately obvious whether the ON or the OFF model should be used to characterize it. At this point we have two choices. We can assume the device is on ($v_d = 0$) and then, using the ON model, we find the resulting i_d. If i_d turns out to be positive, our assumption is correct and the ON model can be used to find all the remaining currents and voltages in the circuit. If i_d turns out to be negative, our assumption is incorrect, and the OFF model should be used. Or, to begin with we can assume the device is off ($i_d = 0$), and then, using the OFF model, we find the resulting v_d. If v_d turns out to be negative, our assumption is correct, and the OFF model can be used to find all remaining currents and voltages in the circuit. If v_d turns out to be positive, our assumption is incorrect, and the ON model should be used.

Let us assume the device is on. The circuit of Fig. 11-34(b) can then be drawn as in Fig. 11-36(a). We now calculate i_d and check to see what condition must be satisfied to assure that it is positive.

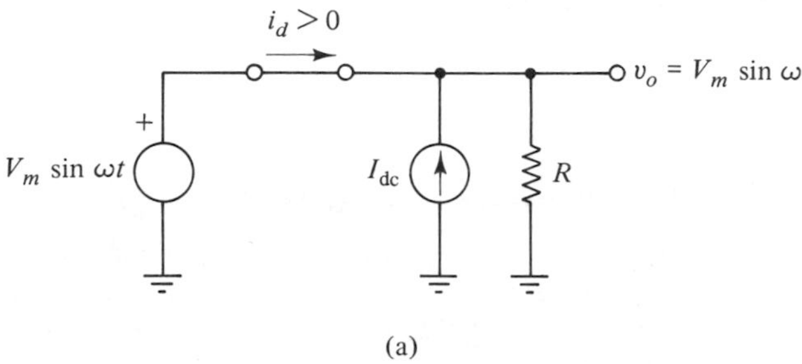

(a)

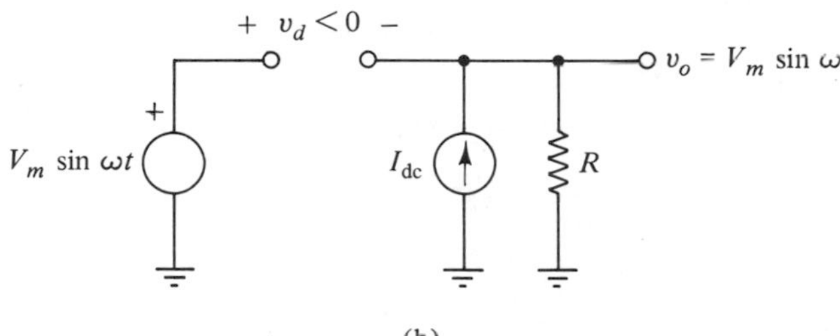

(b)

Fig. 11-36

$$i_d = \frac{V_m \sin \omega t}{R} - I_{dc} > 0 \tag{11-20}$$

$$V_m \sin \omega t > I_{dc}R \tag{11-21}$$

So, for all times that $V_m \sin \omega t$ exceeds $I_{dc}R$, the device is on, and we can use Fig. 11-36(a) to obtain the output as

$$v_o = V_m \sin \omega t \qquad (V_m \sin \omega t > I_{dc}R) \tag{11-22}$$

Obviously for all other times when Eq. (11-21) is not satisfied, the device is off, and the circuit of Fig. 11-34(b) can be drawn as in Fig. 11-36(b). In this case,

$$v_o = I_{dc}R \qquad (V_m \sin \omega t < I_{dc}R) \tag{11-23}$$

As an independent check on the validity of times during which the output is $I_{dc}R$, v_d is calculated in Fig. 11-36(b), and the constraint condition $v_d < 0$ is applied.

$$v_d = V_m \sin \omega t - I_{dc}R < 0$$

$$V_m \sin \omega t < I_{dc}R$$

This result is in agreement with that given by Eq. (11-23).

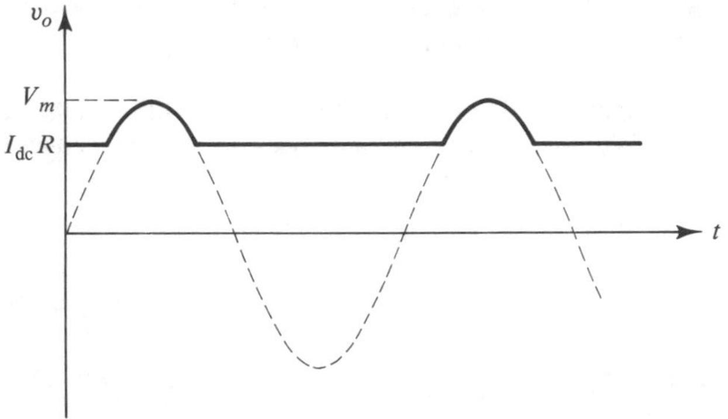

Fig. 11-37

The output waveform is shown in Fig. 11-37. The dashed curve represents the input voltage. When it exceeds $I_{dc}R$, the device turns on and connects the input to the output. When the input falls below $I_{dc}R$, the device is off, and the current source establishes an output voltage level of $I_{dc}R$.

Example 11-16

(a) Sketch the v_o vs. v_i transfer characteristic of the circuit shown in Fig. 11-38. The device characteristics are given in Fig. 11-34(a).

(b) What is the output waveform if $v_i = V_m \sin \omega t$, where $V_m > V_{dc}(R_1/R_2)$?

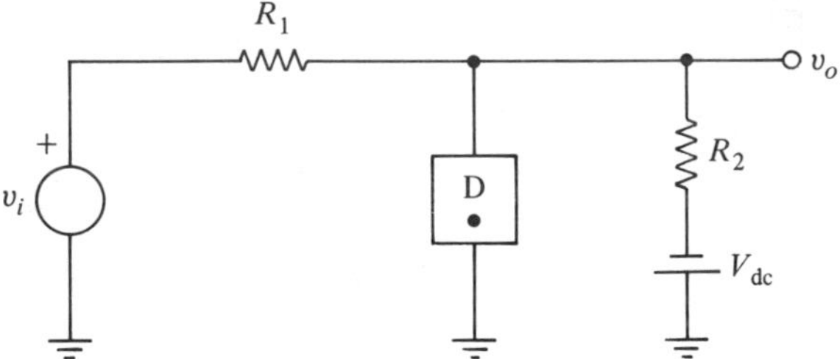

Fig. 11-38

Solution.

(a) The device is either on or off. At this point we don't know what the situation is. Obviously there will be values of v_i that will assure that the device is off. Assume this to be the case. (We could just as well start out with the opposite assumption that for some values of v_i the device will be on and then proceed accordingly.) When the OFF model is used for the device, the given circuit can be drawn as in Fig. 11-39(a).

To find out what range of v_i values will keep the device off, we calculate v_d, set it less than zero, and then solve for the condition on v_i.

$$v_d = -\frac{v_i R_2 - V_{dc} R_1}{R_1 + R_2} < 0$$

$$v_i > V_{dc}\frac{R_1}{R_2} \tag{11-24}$$

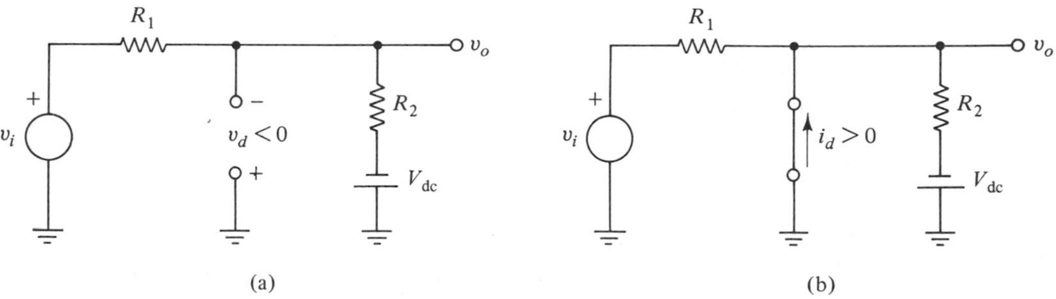

Fig. 11-39

The resulting output is obtained from Fig. 11-39(a).

$$v_o = \frac{v_i R_2 - V_{dc} R_1}{R_1 + R_2} = \frac{R_2}{R_1 + R_2}\left(v_i - V_{dc}\frac{R_1}{R_2}\right), \qquad v_i > V_{dc}\frac{R_1}{R_2} \qquad (11\text{-}25)$$

On the other hand, when $v_i < V_{dc}(R_1/R_2)$, the device is on, and therefore the ON model should be used in the given circuit. The result is the circuit of Fig. 11-39(b). The output then becomes

$$v_o = 0, \qquad v_i < V_{dc}\frac{R_1}{R_2} \qquad (11\text{-}26)$$

Using Eqs. (11-25) and (11-26), the transfer characteristics can be sketched as shown in Fig. 11-40(a). The output is either zero or positive.

(b) When a sine wave of amplitude $V_m > V_{dc}(R_1/R_2)$ is applied to the circuit, only the positive tips of the sine wave are passed (with attenuation) as shown in Fig. 11-40(b). By adjusting V_{dc} or the R_1/R_2 ratio, the portion of the sine wave that appears at the output can be controlled.

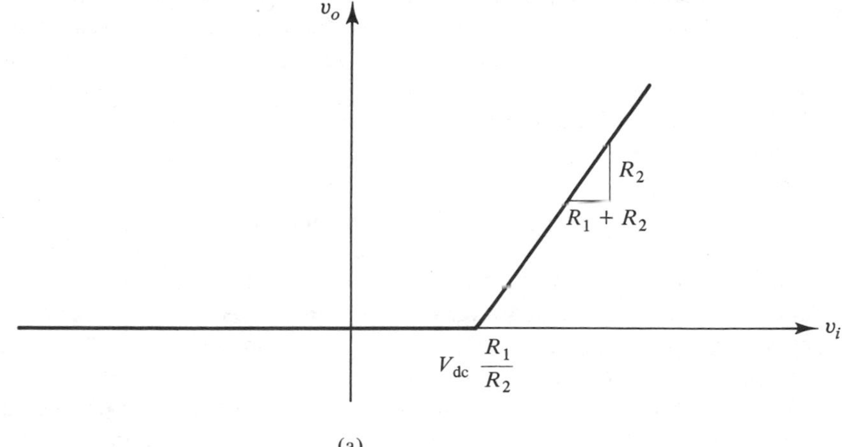

Fig. 11-40

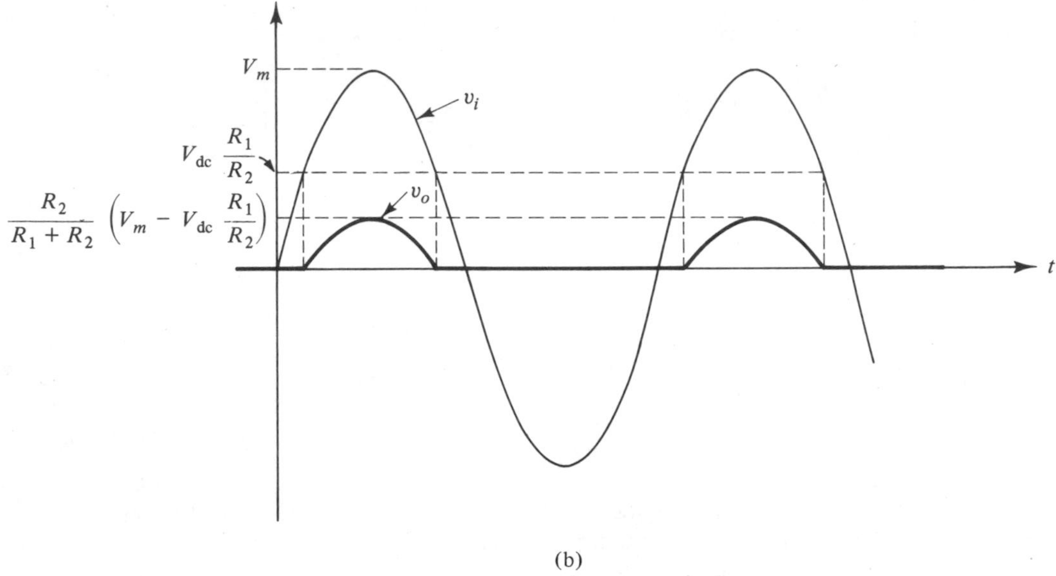

(b)

Fig. 11-40 (cont.)

11-4 SUMMARY

An independent source imposes in a network a voltage or current constraint that is solely determined by the source itself. On the other hand, a dependent source is completely controlled by some voltage or current in the network. By itself, it cannot produce any response. Together with independent sources, it produces responses that are unattainable from *RLC* networks alone.

In calculating responses, the dependent sources can be treated like independent sources. Superposition, Thévenin and Norton equivalent representations can be used on dependent as well as independent sources. Even though stating a response in terms of a dependent source or variable is not incorrect, it should be realized that such an answer does not reflect the true nature of the response, since the dependent source or variable itself is expressible in terms of the independent sources in the network.

Looking into a pair of terminals of a network composed of *R*' s, *L*'s, *C*'s, and dependent sources, we see an equivalent impedance. This impedance can be obtained by forming the V/I ratio at the terminals. If the network contains, in addition, one or more independent sources, its terminal behavior is completely characterized by adding either an equivalent voltage source in series with the impedance or an equivalent current source in parallel with the impedance. The equivalent voltage source is the voltage across the open-circuited terminals, whereas the equivalent current source is the current through the short-circuited terminals. The equivalent impedance can also be found from the ratio V_{oc}/I_{sc}.

Three-terminal devices are characterized by two sets of i vs. v curves or expressions. Each set is for one pair of terminals with a voltage or current from the other pair of terminals acting as a coupling between the two pairs of terminals. In circuit representation, this coupling is accomplished by dependent sources. Generally the characteristics of a device change from one region to another. As a result, a circuit model represents the behavior of the device at its terminals only in the region where the model equations are obtained. In the center of the region is the operating point, which is where we want the device to function. To establish the operating points on the input and output sides, we use resistors in conjunction with dc sources. Having thus biased the device, we introduce the signal to be amplified or processed. If the dc component of the signal is of no concern, then we use coupling capacitors that allow the passage of the ac signal but block the dc, thereby separating the dc (biasing) and ac (signal gain) functions of the circuit.

PROBLEMS

11-1. In Fig. 11-41, the voltage across 1–1′ is sensed, converted to a voltage source K_1V, and fed back into the network as shown. Obtain the output voltage.

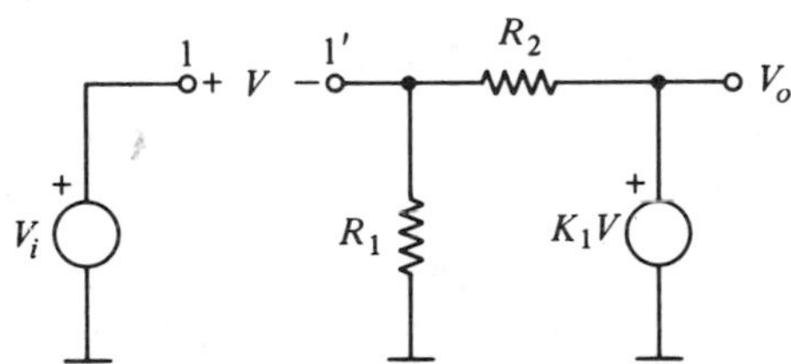

Fig. 11-41

11-2. In Fig. 11-42, the voltage across the capacitor is sensed, converted to a current source K_2V_c, and fed back into the network as shown. Obtain the current through the capacitor.

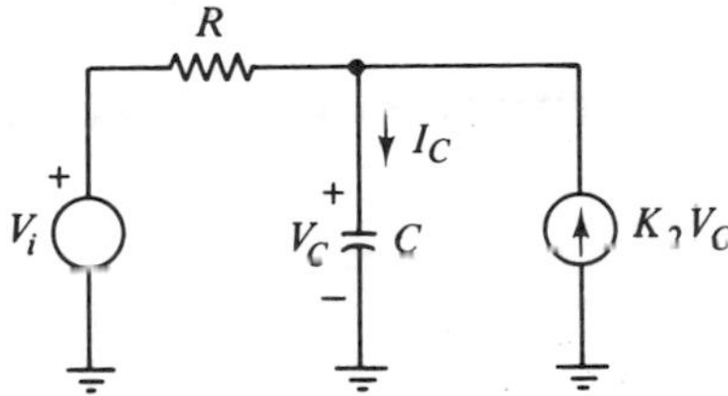

Fig. 11-42

11-3. In Fig. 11-43, the current through the independent voltage source is sensed, converted to a voltage source K_3I_1, and fed back into the network as shown. Obtain the voltage across the inductor.

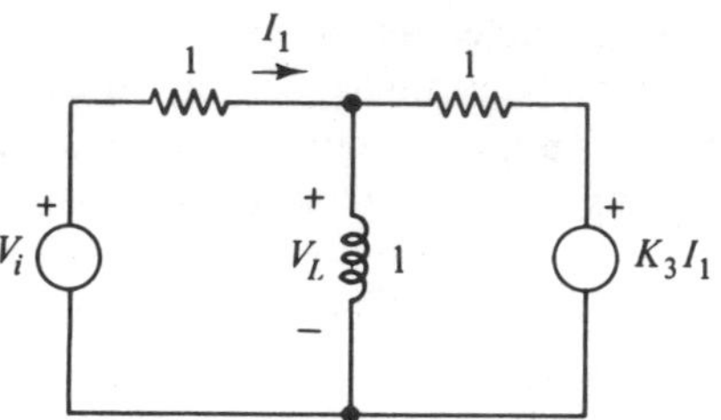

Fig. 11-43

11-4. In Fig. 11-44, the current through the resistor is sensed, converted to a current source $K_4 I_R$, and fed back into the network as shown. Obtain the current through the resistor.

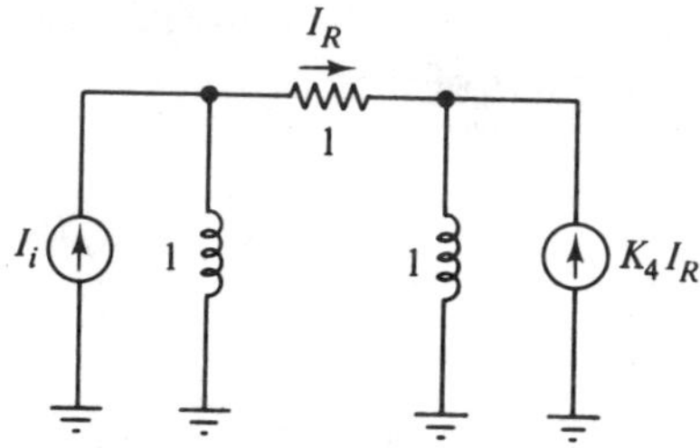

Fig. 11-44

11-5. In Fig. 11-45, one independent and two dependent sources excite the network. Obtain V_o.

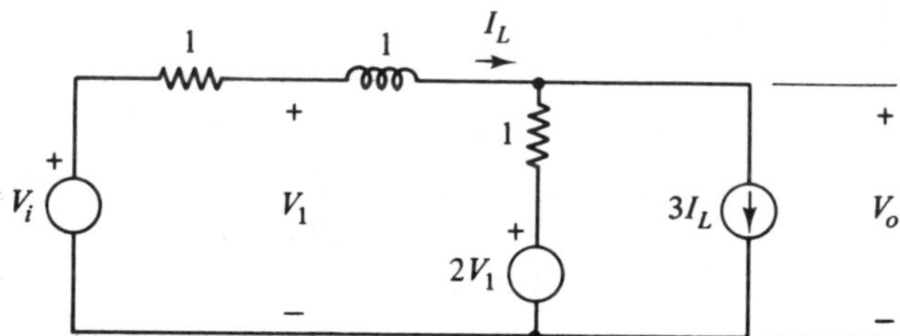

Fig. 11-45

11-6. In Fig. 11-46, obtain the input impedance by driving the network with a current source.

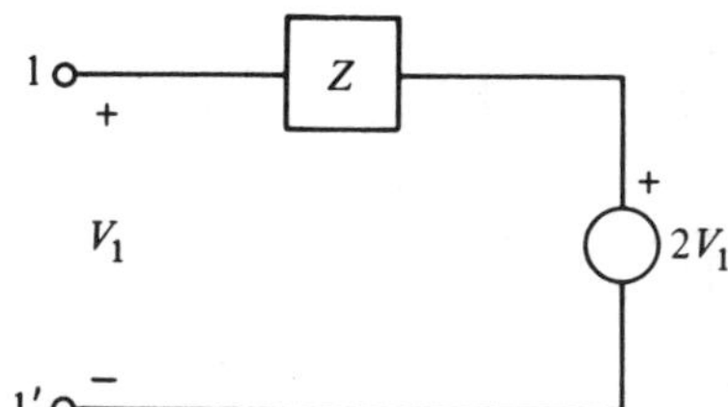

Fig. 11-46

11-7. Show that negative impedances can be generated by the arrangement given in Fig. 11-47.

11-8. What is the input impedance of the circuit shown in Fig. 11-48?

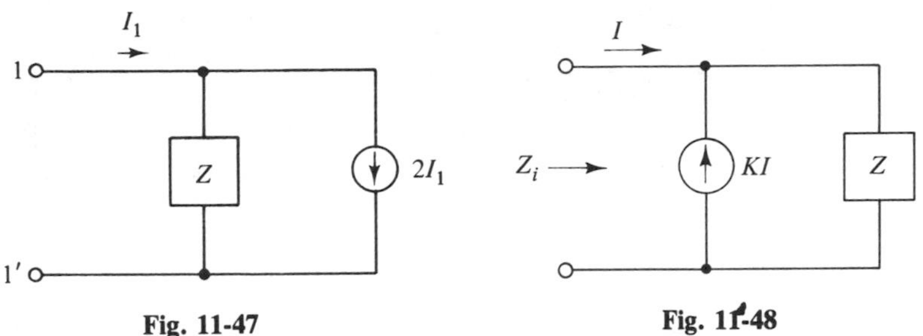

Fig. 11-47

Fig. 11-48

11-9. (**a**) Drive the network of Fig. 11-49 with a voltage source and obtain its input impedance.

(**b**) If Z represents the impedance of 1 μF capacitor and $K_1 = K_2 = 10^{-3}$, what does Z_i represent?

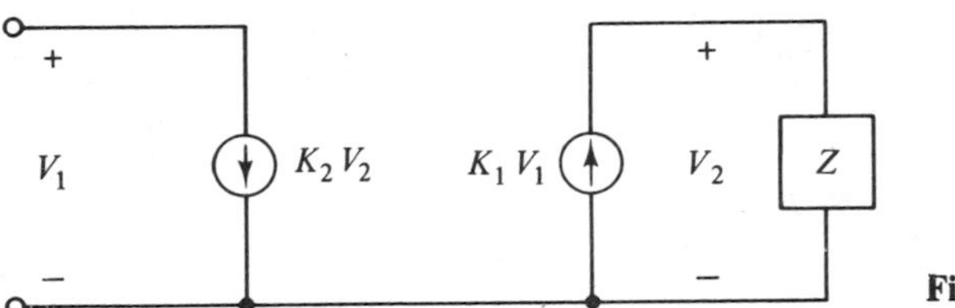

Fig. 11-49

11-10. Calculate the input impedance of the network shown in Fig. 11-50.

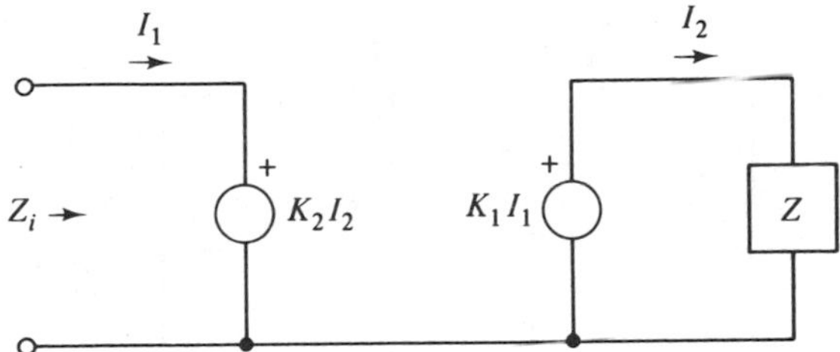

Fig. 11-50

11-11. What other electrical element has the same teminal properties as the circuit shown in Fig. 11-51?

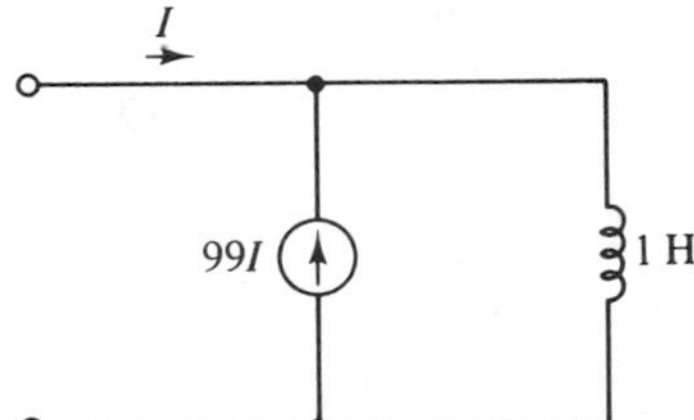

Fig. 11-51

11-12. The circuits shown in Fig. 11-52 can be simplified by eliminating the depending sources. Draw the resulting networks.

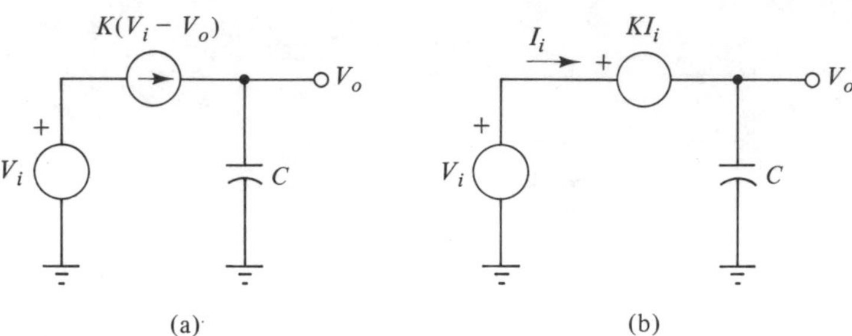

Fig. 11-52

11-13. Obtain another circuit which has the same input characteristics as that of the circuit shown in Fig. 11-53.

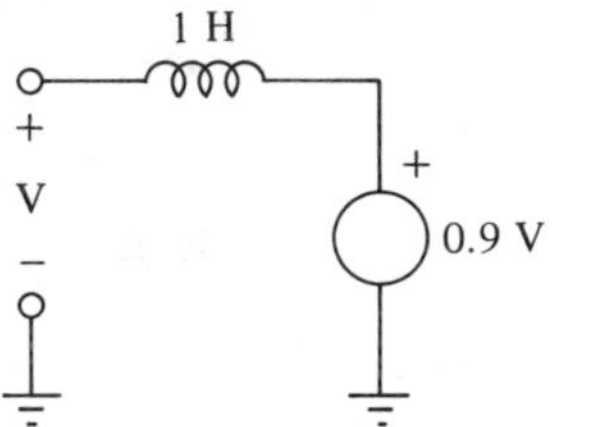

Fig. 11-53

11-14. Obtain the input impedance of the networks shown in Fig. 11-54.

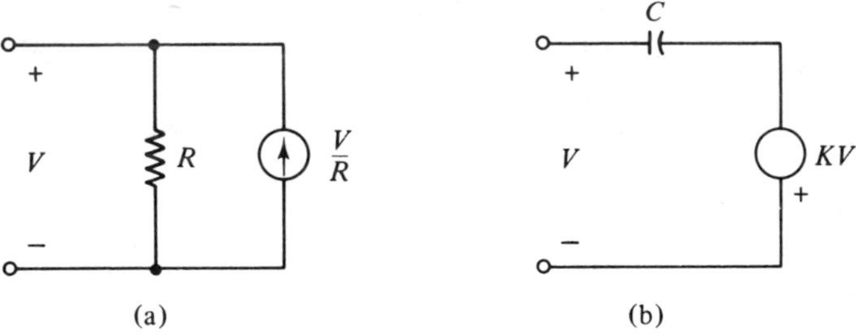

Fig. 11-54

11-15. Obtain the input impedance of the network shown in Fig. 11-55 by each of the following methods.

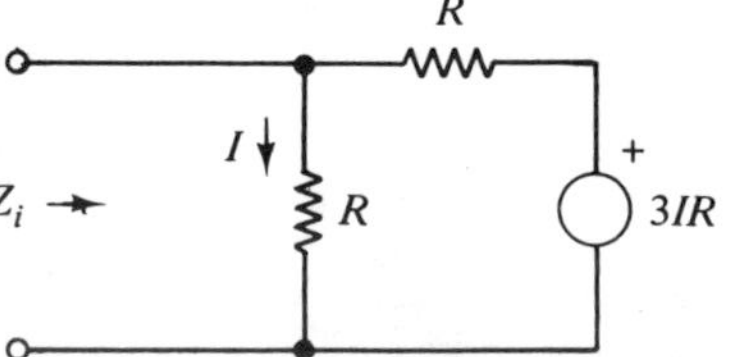

Fig. 11-55

(**a**) Connect a voltage source V_1 across the input terminals and calculate the resulting current I_1. Then form the V_1/I_1 ratio.
(**b**) Connect a current source I_1 across the input terminals and calculate the resulting voltage V_1. Then form the V_1/I_1 ratio.
(**c**) Connect a voltage source in series with the dependent source. At the input terminals calculate the open-circuit voltage V_{oc} and the short-circuit current I_{sc}. Then form the V_{oc}/I_{sc} ratio.
(**d**) Connect a current source in parallel with the R on the left. At the input terminals calculate the open-circuit voltage V_{oc} and the short-circuit current I_{sc}. Then form the V_{oc}/I_{sc} ratio.
(**e**) Connect a voltage source in series with the dependent source. Then connect a load R_L across the input terminals. Calculate the current through R_L. Rearrange the result and obtain the input impedance.
(**f**) Try a scheme of your own.

11-16. Refer to Fig. 11-56.

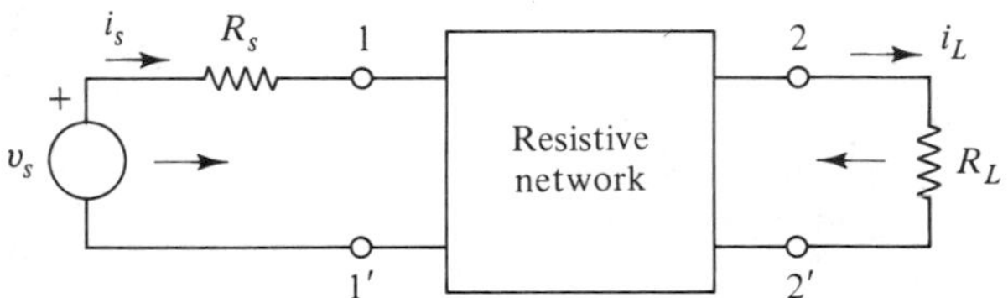

Fig. 11-56

(**a**) Given $i_s = Av_s/(BR_s + C)$ where A, B, and C are independent of R_s. What does the source v_s see?
(**b**) Given

$$i_L = \frac{a}{R_L}\left(\frac{v_s}{\dfrac{c}{R_L} - b}\right)$$

where a, b, and c are independent of R_L. What does the load R_L see?

11-17. Refer to Fig. 11-57.

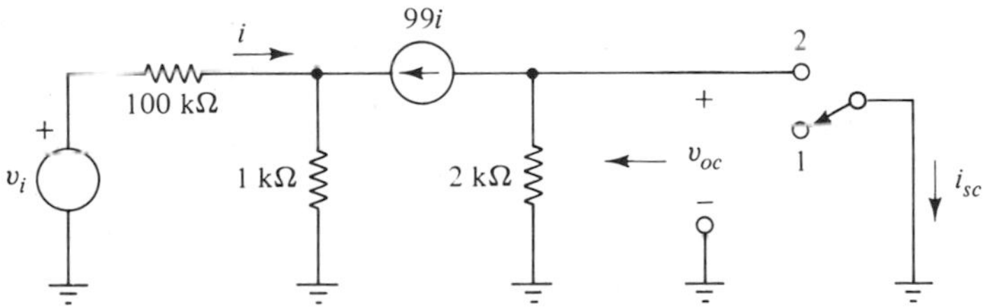

Fig. 11-57

(**a**) The switch is at 1. What is v_{oc}?
(**b**) The switch is at 2. What is i_{sc}?
(**c**) What is the Norton equivalent circuit to the left of the arrow shown?
(**d**) What does the source v_i see?

11-18. Refer to Fig. 11-58.

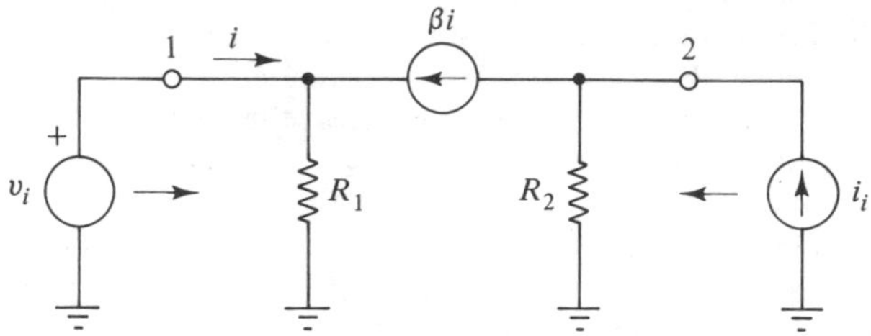

Fig. 11-58

(a) What is the Thévenin equivalent circuit seen by the source v_i?
(b) What is the Norton equivalent circuit seen by the source i_i?

11-19. In Fig. 11-59 $v = a/[(b/R) - c]$, where a, b, and c are independent of R. What is in the box?

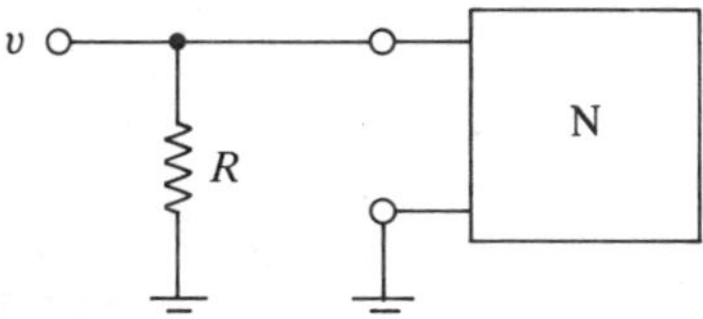

Fig. 11-59

11-20. In Fig. 11-60 $v_i = i_i a + b$. What is the Norton equivalent circuit seen by the current source i_i?

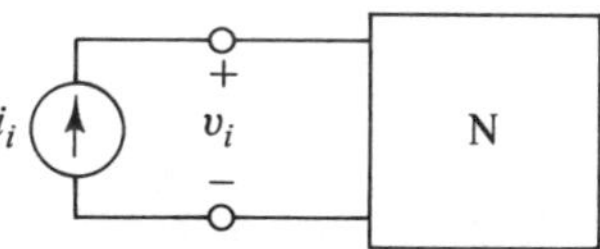

Fig. 11-60

11-21. Refer to Fig. 11-61.

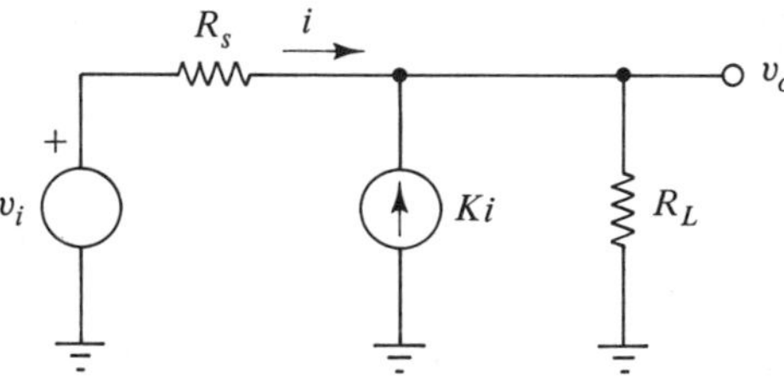

Fig. 11-61

(a) What does the source v_i see?
(b) What does the load R_L see?
(c) What is the gain v_o/v_i?

11-22. Refer to Fig. 11-62.
(a) The switch is at 2. What is v_{oc}?
(b) The switch is at 1. What is i_{sc}?
(c) What is the equivalent circuit to the left of the arrow shown?

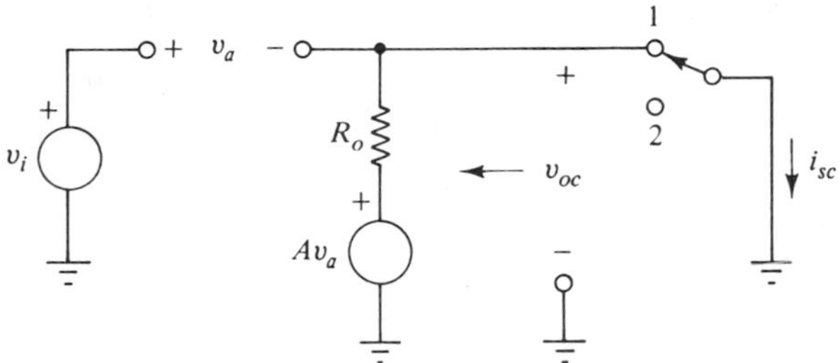

Fig. 11-62

11-23. Refer to Fig. 11-63.

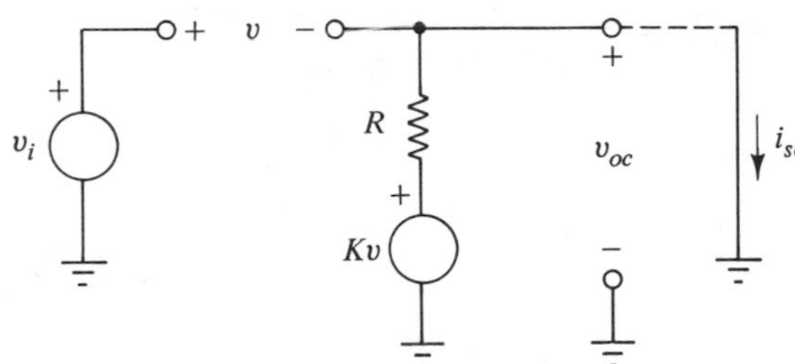

Fig. 11-63

(a) The output terminals are open circuited. What is v_{oc}?
(b) The output terminals are short circuited. What is i_{sc}?

11-24. In Fig. 11-64 what is the input equivalent circuit?

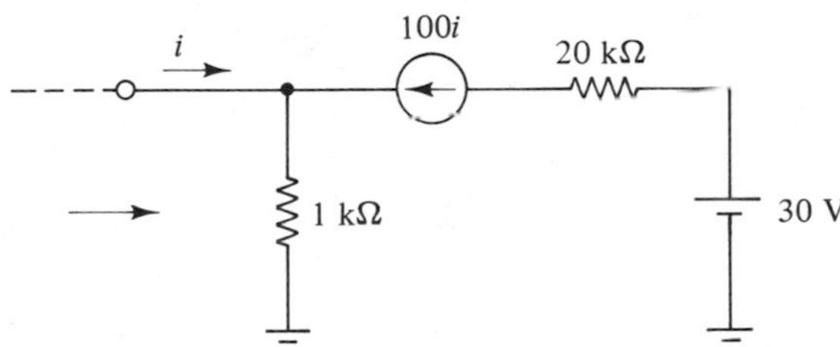

Fig. 11-64

11-25. Refer to Fig. 11-65.

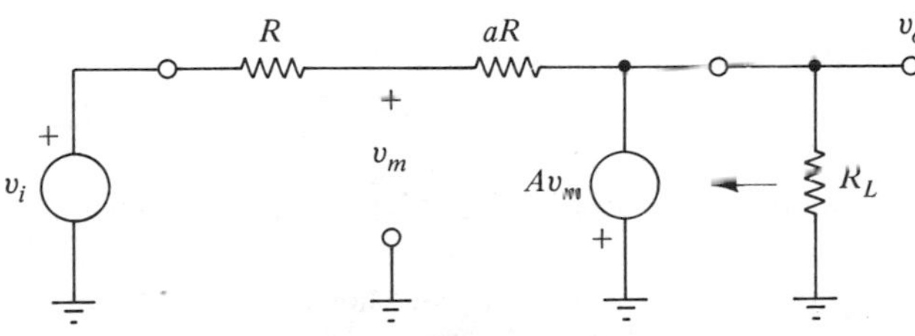

Fig. 11-65

(a) Obtain v_o as a function of v_i.
(b) From (a) above obtain the Thévenin equivalent circuit facing the load R_L.
(c) What does the source v_i see?

11-26. In Fig. 11-66 obtain v and v_o as A is made infinitely large.

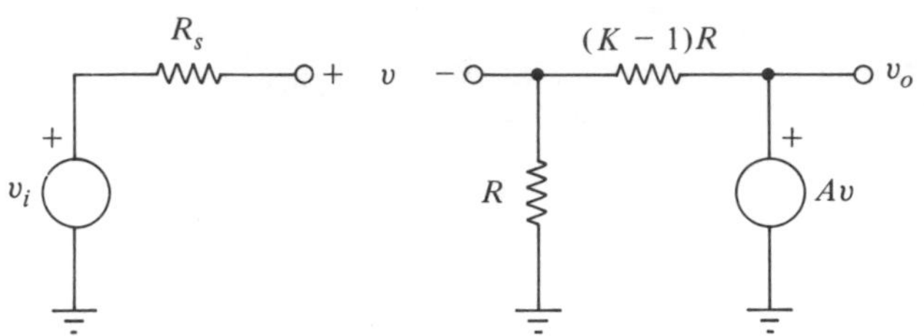

Fig. 11-66

11-27. The input and output characteristics of several three-terminal devices are shown in Fig. 11-67. Obtain the input and output equivalent circuits. In all cases, operation is about the point marked Q.

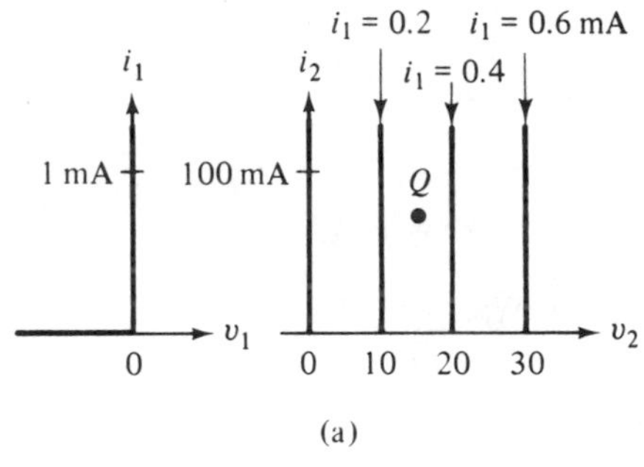

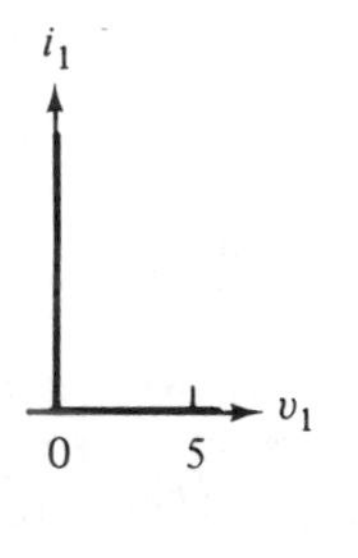

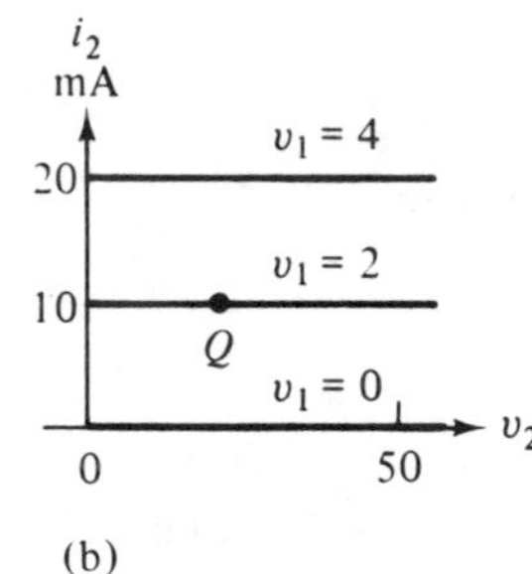

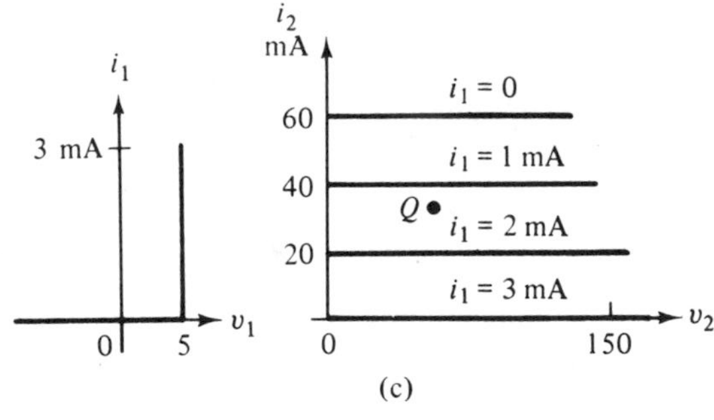

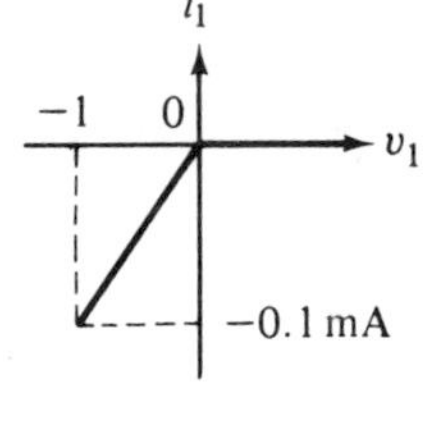

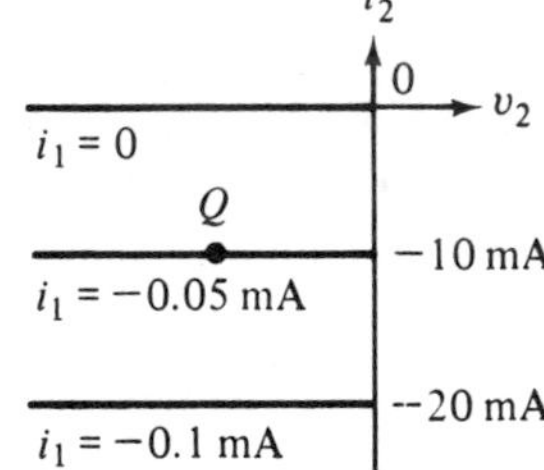

Fig. 11-67

11-28. The input characteristics of a device are shown in Fig. 11-68. What is the input equivalent circuit of the device?

11-29. The input and output characteristics of a new device are shown in Fig. 11-69.

(a) Obtain the equivalent circuit of the device.

(b) Show how you would establish the operating point $(i_1, v_1) = (-b, 0)$.

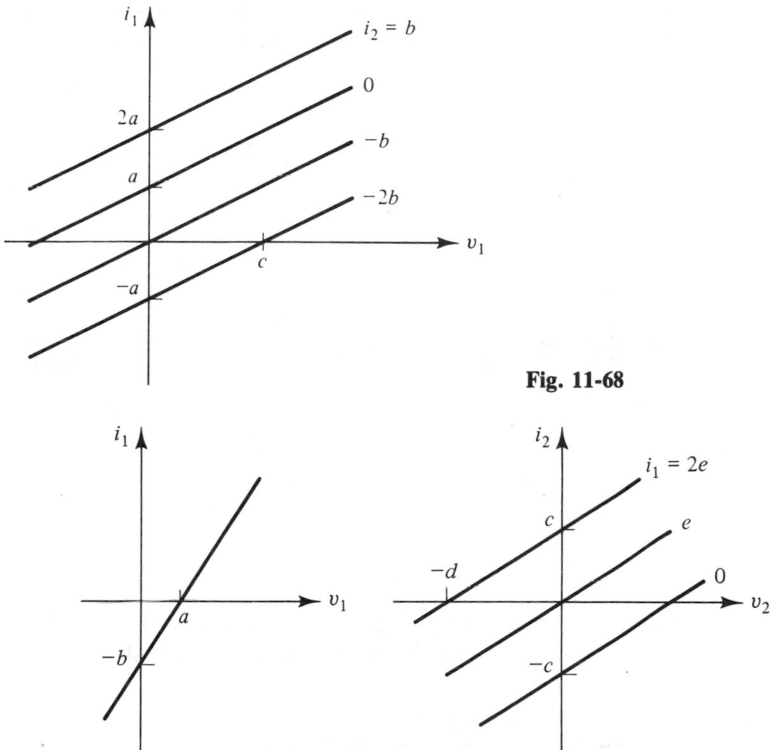

Fig. 11-68

Fig. 11-69

11-30. The output characteristics of a device are shown in Fig. 11-70. If the device is to operate about the point Q, what is its output equivalent circuit?

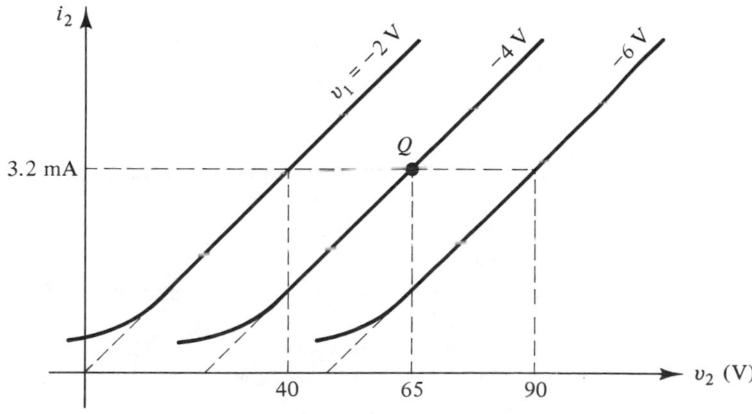

Fig. 11-70

11-31. The device that is characterized by the curves of Fig. 11-67(a) is connected in the circuit of Fig. 11-71. Calculate the operating points and the gain. The ac voltage across the capacitor is negligible.

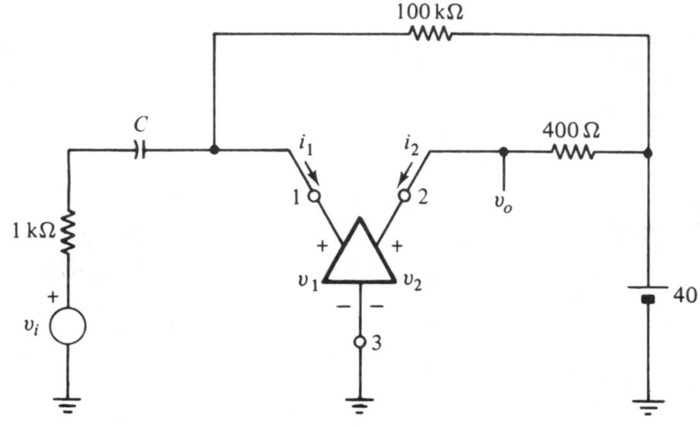

Fig. 11-71

11-32. The device that is characterized by the curves of Fig. 11-67(c) is connected in the circuit of Fig. 11-72. Calculate the output voltage. Assume that v_i is such that $i_1 > 0$.

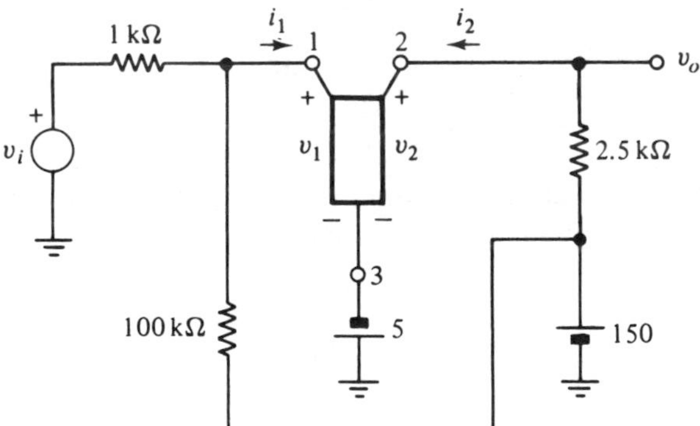

Fig. 11-72

11-33. The device used in Fig. 11-73 has the input and output characteristic curves shown.
(a) What are the input and output operating points?
(b) If $v_i = \sin \omega t$, what is i_L? Assume the capacitors are large enough to have negligible ac voltages.

11-34. The device used in Fig. 11-74 has the input and output characteristic curves as shown.
(a) What are the bias values?
(b) What is the gain? Assume the capacitors are large.
(c) If $v_i = 10^{-3} \sin \omega t$, what is v_2? v_o?

11-35. The characteristic curves of a device are shown in Fig. 11-75. If operation is to be confined to $i_a < 0$, obtain the equivalent circuit of the device.

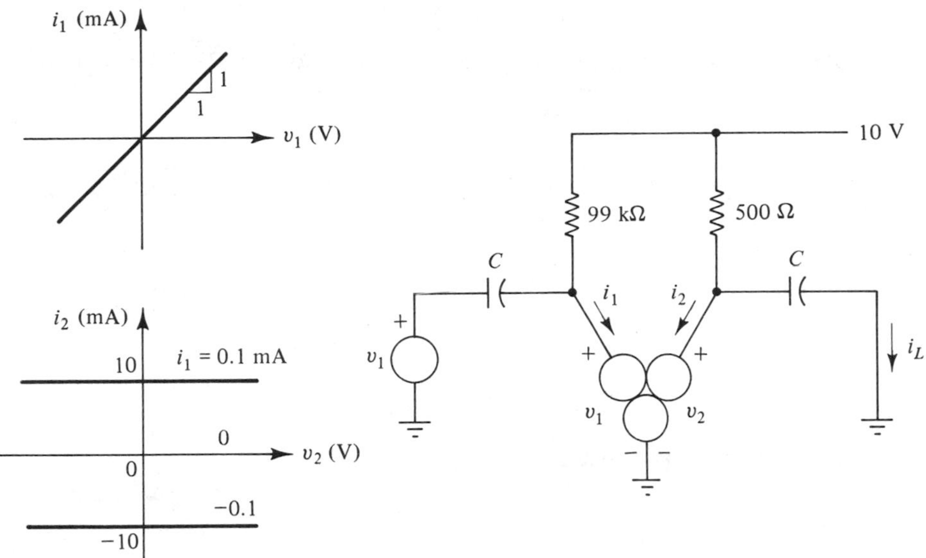

Fig. 11-73

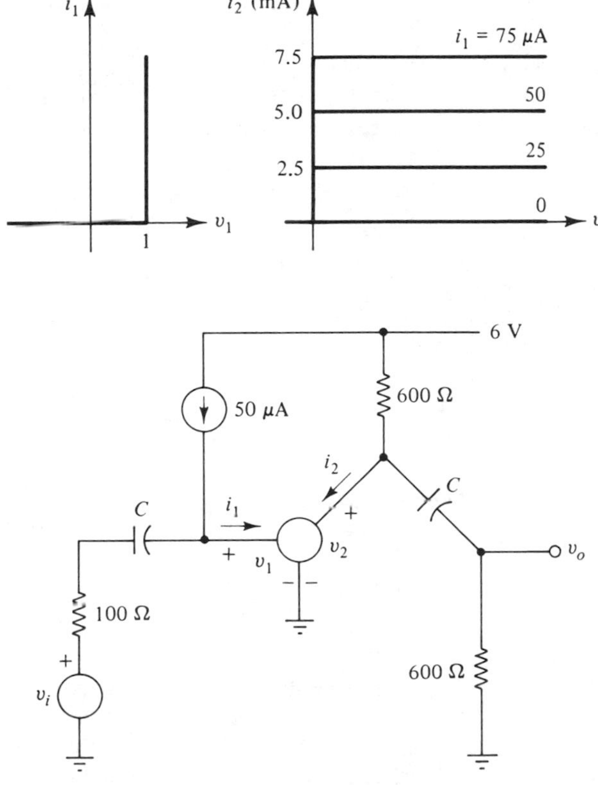

Fig. 11-74

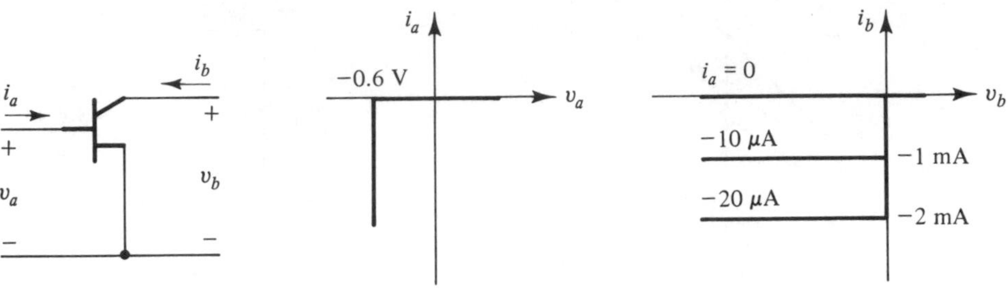

Fig. 11-75

11-36. Refer to Fig. 11-76.

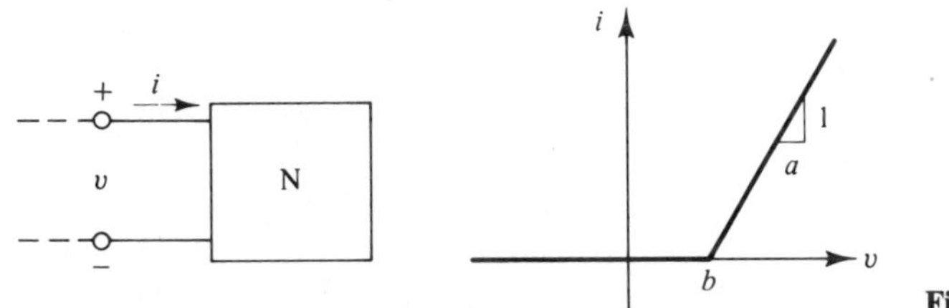

Fig. 11-76

(**a**) How would you model N?
(**b**) If the circuit external to N is a short circuit, what is i?

11-37. Refer to Fig. 11-77. For proper operation $i_b > 0$ and $v_{ca} > 0$.

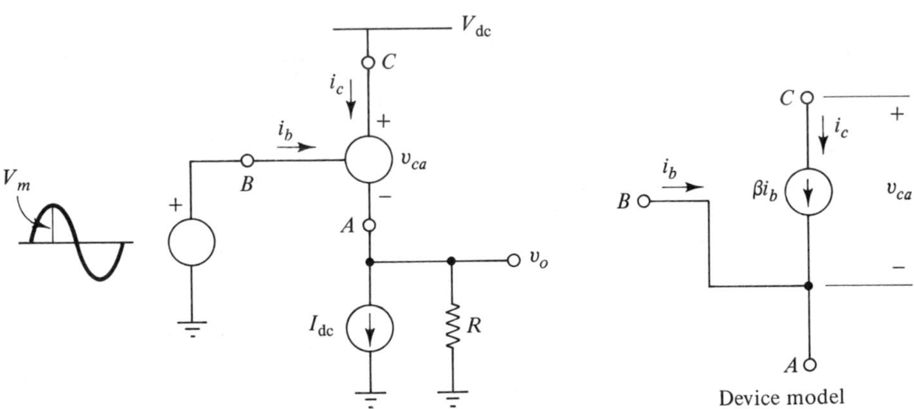

Fig. 11-77

(**a**) Find quiescent values.
(**b**) What is the voltage gain A_v?
(**c**) Signalwise what does the source v_i see?
(**d**) Signalwise what is the Thévenin equivalent circuit facing R?
(**e**) For proper operation what constraint must be placed on v_i?

11-38. The model of a three terminal device is shown in Fig. 11-78. Draw the input and output characteristic curves of this device. Give values.

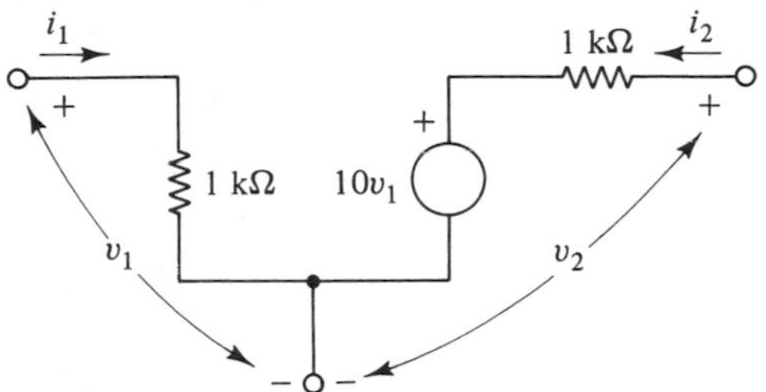

Fig. 11-78

11-39. Refer to Fig. 11-79. The device characteristics are as shown.

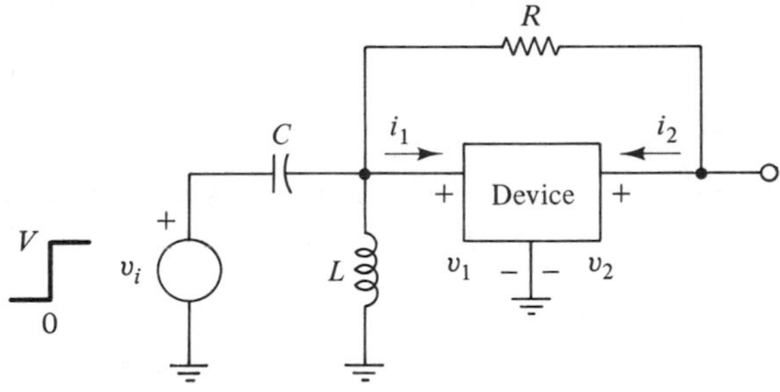

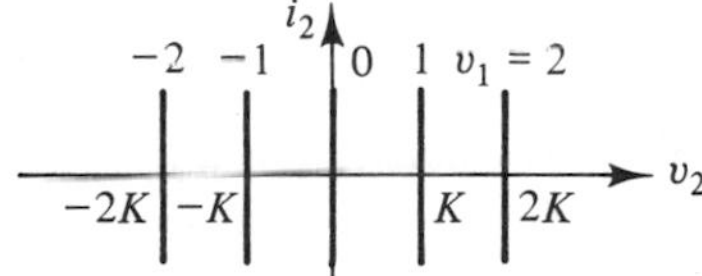

Fig. 11-79

(**a**) For what value of K are the poles of V_2/V_i on the imaginary axis?
(**b**) What is the resulting output if the input is a step function as shown?

11-40. Assume in Fig. 11-80 C is very large. Steady state prevails. Find v_c and v_o.

11-41. Obtain an equivalent representation of the circuit shown in Fig. 11-81(a) in the form shown in Fig. 11-81(b). The boxes represent impedances and the circles dependent voltage sources.

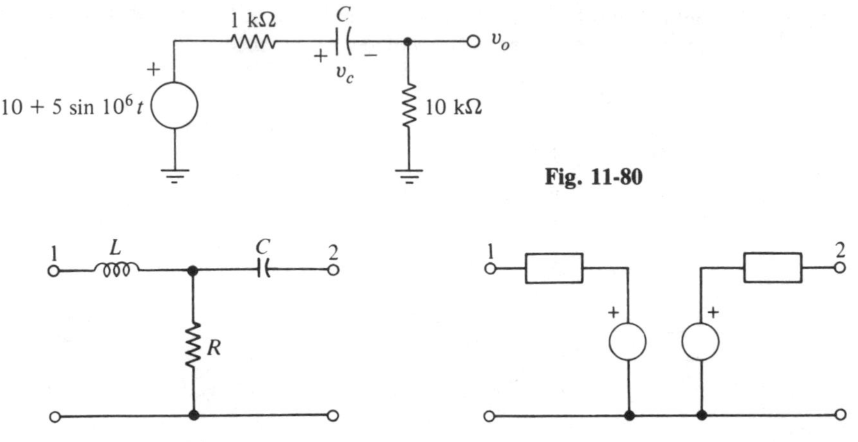

Fig. 11-80

Fig. 11-81

11-42. The two terminal characteristic of a device under test is a V-shaped curve as shown in Fig. 11-82. What is the model of the device?

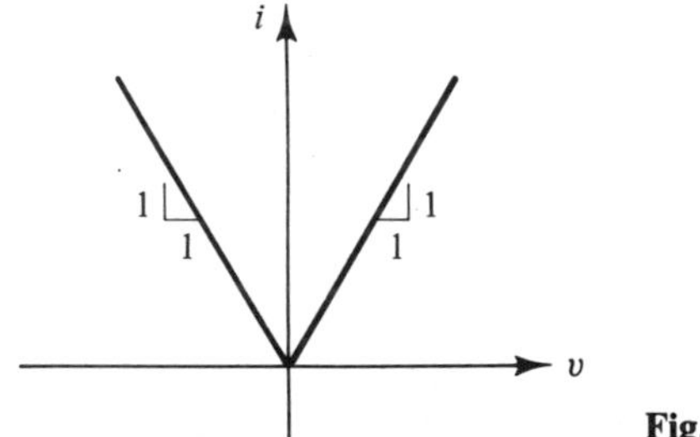

Fig. 11-82

11-43. The piecewise linear characteristics of the device in the circuit of Fig. 11-83 are as shown.

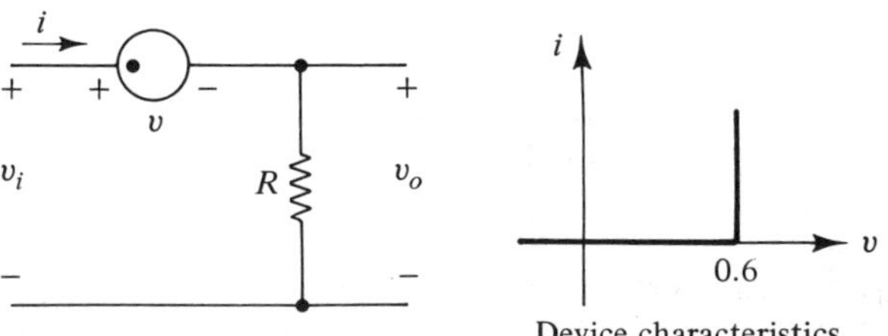

Fig. 11-83

(**a**) Obtain the v_o vs. v_i curve.
(**b**) The input is a sine wave of amplitude 1 V. Sketch the output voltage.

11-44. In all the circuits shown in Fig. 11-84, the devices are characterized by the model developed in Example 11-15. In each case obtain the circuit transfer characteristic and the output if the input is $V_m \sin \omega t$.

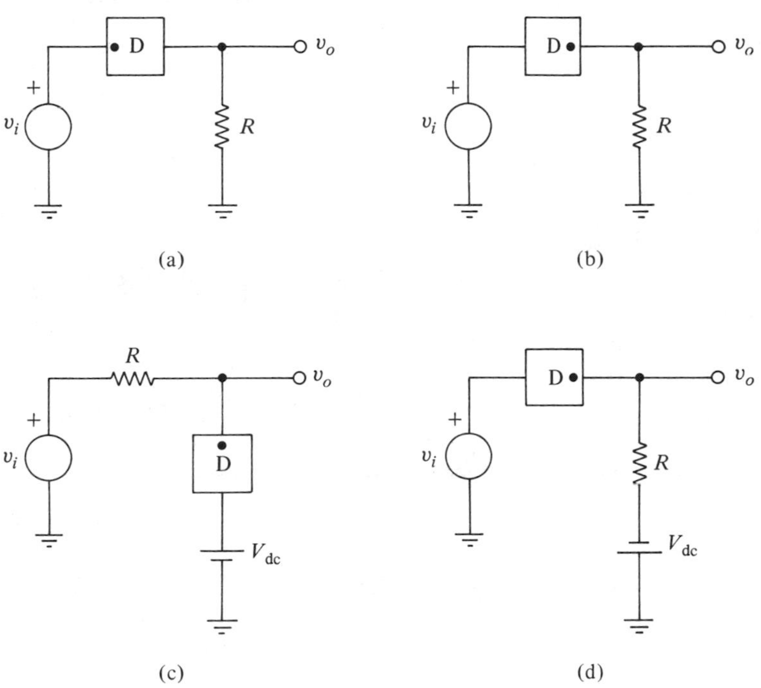

Fig. 11-84

CHAPTER 12

FOURIER SERIES AND APPLICATIONS

In Chapter 1, resistors, inductors, and capacitors are presented as linear elements and are used as such in the chapters that follow. In Chapter 11, linear voltage or current dependent sources are introduced as additional electrical elements and are used in conjunction with resistors, inductors, and capacitors to generate more versatile circuits. Linear elements result in linear networks which produce responses that are directly proportional to the independent sources of excitation, provided the sources are considered one at a time. There are also electrical elements that exhibit nonlinear characteristics. The introduction of a single nonlinear element in an otherwise linear network may result in responses that are not directly related to an independent source of excitation. In general, such networks are quite difficult to analyze. However, if the input is periodic and steady-state responses are of interest only, then Fourier series representations of the signals may be used to obtain solutions. The Fourier series representation can also be used in linear networks to obtain steady-state responses to periodic excitations. In this chapter, we learn how to expand a periodic function into the Fourier series and how to apply the results in the solution of practical circuit problems.

12-1 PERIODIC FUNCTIONS

A function $f(t)$ is periodic if for all t a positive constant T can be found such that

$$f(t + T) = f(t) \tag{12-1}$$

The smallest value of T that satisfies Eq. (12-1) is called the *period* of $f(t)$. A periodic function is shown in Fig. 12-1. As the dots indicate, the value of the function at some arbitrary time t_1 is the same as the value at time $t_1 + T$. The waveform repeats itself every T seconds. Hence it has a repetition frequency f_r or $1/T$ Hz.

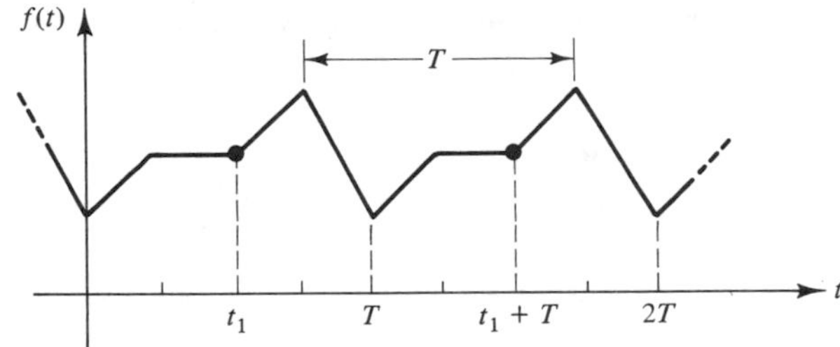

Fig. 12-1

12-2 FOURIER SERIES

Suppose that a function $f(t)$ satisfies the following conditions, known as Dirichlet conditions:

1. $f(t)$ is periodic with period T.
2. $f(t)$ is single valued and defined for all t except possibly at a finite number of points within a period.
3. $f(t)$ and $f'(t)$ are sectionally continuous within a period.

Then, the Fourier series expansion of $f(t)$ is given by

$$f(t) = \frac{a_0}{2} + \sum_{n=1}^{\infty} \left(a_n \cos \frac{2\pi n}{T} t + b_n \sin \frac{2\pi n}{T} t \right) \tag{12-2}$$

where

$$\frac{a_0}{2} = \frac{1}{T} \int_0^T f(t)\, dt \tag{12-3a}$$

$$a_n = \frac{2}{T} \int_0^T f(t) \cos \frac{2\pi n}{T} t\, dt \tag{12-3b}$$

$$b_n = \frac{2}{T}\int_0^T f(t)\sin\frac{2\pi n}{T}t\,dt \tag{12-3c}$$

$$n = \text{integer}$$

Note that Eq. (12-3a) can be obtained from Eq. (12-3b) by letting $n = 0$ and then solving for $a_0/2$.

The Dirichlet conditions are sufficient conditions for the Fourier series expansion of $f(t)$. Necessary and sufficient conditions are not known. Dirichlet conditions are easily met by waveforms encountered in engineering practice.

In Eqs. (12-3), the lower and upper limits of integration can be changed to t_0 and $t_0 + T$ respectively without affecting the results. See Problem 12-1. The initial time t_0 can have any value. For example, if t_0 is chosen $-T/2$, the limits of integration become $-T/2$ and $T/2$.

If we look at Fig. 12-1, we don't see sinusoidal waves. Yet, remarkably enough, the given $f(t)$ can be reconstructed using sine and cosine waves and a constant. As long as we know how to express $f(t)$ mathematically *over the time interval of a period T,* we can use Eqs. (12-3) to determine the a_n and b_n coefficients and then use Eqs. (12-2) to express $f(t)$ *for all time t* in the form of a trigonometric series.

As Eq. (12-3a) shows, the $a_0/2$ term in the Fourier series expansion represents the average value of $f(t)$ taken over a period. The next two terms, corresponding to $n = 1$, give $a_1 \cos(2\pi/T)t + b_1 \sin(2\pi/T)t$. Thus taken together they form *the fundamental or first harmonic component* of $f(t)$. The fundamental frequency f is $1/T$. This frequency is also called the repetition frequency or the first harmonic frequency. It is frequently expressed in radians per second, $\omega = 2\pi f = 2\pi/T$, and the fundamental component is written in terms of ω as $a_1 \cos \omega t + b_1 \sin \omega t$. The following two terms in the Fourier series expansion, corresponding to $n = 2$, are $a_2 \cos 2\omega t + b_2 \sin 2\omega t$. They form *the second harmonic component* of $f(t)$. The second harmonic frequency is 2ω rad/s. The *third harmonic component* of $f(t)$ is $a_3 \cos 3\omega t + b_3 \sin 3\omega t$. The mth harmonic component is $a_m \cos m\omega t + b_m \sin m\omega t$. Here m is an integer. Thus any arbitrary periodic waveform satisfying the Dirichlet conditions can be rebuilt first by generating a dc term ($a_0/2$) and an infinite number of harmonically related sine and cosine waves of appropriate amplitudes (a_n and b_n coefficients) and then by adding them all together. The resulting infinite series converges to $f(t)$ if $f(t)$ is continuous. If $f(t)$ is discontinuous at $t = t_a$, that is, if it jumps, then the series converges to the midpoint of the jump, which is $[f(t_a^-) + f(t_a^+)]/2$.

A necessary condition for convergence is that a_n and b_n coefficients approach zero as n approaches infinity. This means that the higher harmonic terms, important as they are in the *exact reproduction* of the given waveform, may be left out without significantly affecting the waveform. Thus, a truncated Fourier series may be used to obtain a reasonable approximation of $f(t)$. The smoother $f(t)$, the easier it is to approximate it with a few terms of the Fourier series. For example, if $f(t)$ and $f'(t)$ are continuous, then $f(t)$ is quite a smooth function in which case the dc term and the fundamental component alone may replicate $f(t)$ with a sufficient degree of accuracy or even exactly for some special waveforms. These will be seen in the examples that soon follow.

The a_n and b_n coefficients are evaluated by using Eqs. (12-3). We now show how these equations are obtained. We assume that the infinite trigonometric series

$$f(t) = \frac{a_0}{2} + \sum_{n=1}^{\infty} (a_n \cos n\omega t + b_n \sin n\omega t) \tag{12-4}$$

coverages uniformly to a given arbitrary periodic waveform such as shown in Fig. 12-1 except at points where $f(t)$ is not defined or is discontinuous.

To determine a_n, we multiply both sides of Eq. (12-4) with $\cos m\omega t$, where m is an integer, and integrate from 0 to $T = 2\pi/\omega$.

$$\int_0^{2\pi/\omega} f(t) \cos m\omega t \, dt = \int_0^{2\pi/\omega} \left[\frac{a_0}{2} + \sum_{n=1}^{\infty} (a_n \cos n\omega t + b_n \sin n\omega t)\right] \cos m\omega t \, dt \tag{12-5}$$

Because uniform convergence is assumed, integration and summation can be interchanged and Eq. (12-5) written as

$$\begin{aligned}\int_0^{2\pi/\omega} f(t) \cos m\omega t \, dt &= \frac{a_0}{2}\int_0^{2\pi/\omega} \cos m\omega t \, dt + \sum_{n=1}^{\infty}\left[a_n \int_0^{2\pi/\omega} \cos n\omega t \cos m\omega t \, dt\right] \\ &\quad + \sum_{n=1}^{\infty}\left[b_n \int_0^{2\pi/\omega} \sin n\omega t \cos m\omega t \, dt\right]\end{aligned} \tag{12-6}$$

For $m = 0$, this equation simplifies to

$$\begin{aligned}\int_0^{2\pi/\omega} f(t) \, dt &= \frac{a_0}{2}\int_0^{2\pi/\omega} dt + \sum_{n=1}^{\infty}\left[a_n \int_0^{2\pi/\omega} \cos n\omega t \, dt\right] \\ &\quad + \sum_{n=1}^{\infty}\left[b_n \int_0^{2\pi/\omega} \sin n\omega t \, dt\right]\end{aligned} \tag{12-7}$$

Each integral within the infinite summation signs represents the area under a sinusoidal waveform taken over n periods and is therefore zero as shown below.

$$\begin{aligned}\int_0^{2\pi/\omega} f(t) \, dt &= \frac{a_0}{2} t \Big|_0^{2\pi/\omega} + \sum_{n=1}^{\infty} a_n \left(\frac{\sin n\omega t}{n\omega}\right)\Bigg|_0^{2\pi/\omega} + \sum_{n=1}^{\infty} b_n \left(\frac{-\cos n\omega t}{n\omega}\right)\Bigg|_0^{2\pi/\omega} \\ &= a_0 \frac{\pi}{\omega} + \sum_{n=1}^{\infty} a_n \frac{\sin n2\pi}{n\omega} + \sum_{n=1}^{\infty} -b_n\left(\frac{\cos n2\pi - 1}{n\omega}\right) = a_0 \frac{\pi}{\omega}\end{aligned}$$

Solving for $a_0/2$, we obtain

$$\frac{a_0}{2} = \frac{\omega}{2\pi}\int_0^{2\pi/\omega} f(t) \, dt = \frac{1}{T}\int_0^{T} f(t) \, dt \tag{12-8}$$

Equation (12-8) is the same as Eq. (12-3a) given earlier and shows that $a_0/2$ represents the average value of the given function taken over a period. Hence, the constant term in the trigonometric series expansion of $f(t)$ represents the average value of the waveform.

Also for $m \neq 0$ Eq. (12-6) can be simplified. It is left as an exercise in Problem 12-2 to show that

$$\int_0^{2\pi/\omega} \cos m\omega t \, dt = 0 \qquad m \neq 0 \tag{12-9a}$$

$$\int_0^{2\pi/\omega} \cos n\omega t \cos m\omega t \, dt = \begin{cases} 0 & m \neq n \\ \pi/\omega & m = n \end{cases} \tag{12-9b}$$

$$\int_0^{2\pi/\omega} \sin n\omega t \cos m\omega t \, dt = 0 \tag{12-9c}$$

When Eqs. (12-9) are used in Eq. (12-6), all terms on the right-hand side become zero except for one term, which corresponds to $m = n$ in Eq. (12-9b). The result is

$$\int_0^{2\pi/\omega} f(t) \cos n\omega t \, dt = a_n \frac{\pi}{\omega}$$

which when solved for a_n yields

$$a_n = \frac{\omega}{\pi} \int_0^{2\pi/\omega} f(t) \cos n\omega t \, dt = \frac{2}{T} \int_0^T f(t) \cos \frac{2\pi n}{T} t \, dt \tag{12-10}$$

This equation is the same as Eq. (12-3b) given earlier.

To determine b_n, we go through a similar procedure. First, we multiply both sides of Eq. (12-4) with $\sin m\omega t$ and then integrate from 0 to $2\pi/\omega$.

$$\int_0^{2\pi/\omega} f(t) \sin m\omega t \, dt = \int_0^{2\pi/\omega} \left[\frac{a_0}{2} + \sum_{n=1}^{\infty} (a_n \cos n\omega t + b_n \sin n\omega t) \right] \sin m\omega t \, dt \tag{12-11}$$

Interchanging the orders of integration and summation, we write

$$\int_0^{2\pi/\omega} f(t) \sin m\omega t \, dt = \frac{a_0}{2} \int_0^{2\pi/\omega} \sin m\omega t \, dt + \sum_{n=1}^{\infty} \left[a_n \int_0^{2\pi/\omega} \cos n\omega t \sin m\omega t \, dt \right]$$
$$+ \sum_{n=1}^{\infty} \left[b_n \int_0^{2\pi/\omega} \sin n\omega t \sin m\omega t \, dt \right] \tag{12-12}$$

Again, it is left as an exercise to show that

$$\int_0^{2\pi/\omega} \sin m\omega t \, dt = 0 \tag{12-13a}$$

$$\int_0^{2\pi/\omega} \cos n\omega t \sin m\omega t \, dt = 0 \tag{12-13b}$$

$$\int_0^{2\pi/\omega} \sin n\omega t \sin m\omega t \, dt = \begin{cases} 0 & m \neq n \\ \dfrac{\pi}{\omega} & m = n \end{cases} \tag{12-13c}$$

When Eqs. (12-13) are used in Eq. (12-12), all terms on the right-hand side become zero except for one term, which corresponds to $m = n$ in Eq. (12-13c). The result is

$$\int_0^{2\pi/\omega} f(t) \sin n\omega t \, dt = b_n \frac{\pi}{\omega}$$

which when solved for b_n yields

$$b_n = \frac{\omega}{\pi} \int_0^{2\pi/\omega} f(t) \sin n\omega t \, dt = \frac{2}{T} \int_0^T f(t) \sin \frac{2\pi n}{T} t \, dt \tag{12-14}$$

This equation is the same as Eq. (12-3c) given earlier.

12-3 ODD AND EVEN FUNCTIONS AND HALF-WAVE SYMMETRY

A function $f(t)$ is *odd* when

$$f(-t) = -f(t) \tag{12-15}$$

This means that as we travel an equal amount in time forward or backward from the origin, we find the function to be the same except for a reversal in sign.

Examples of odd functions are shown in Fig. 12-2(a). As can be seen from the waveforms, for any arbitrarily chosen time t_1, $f(-t_1) = -f(t_1)$.

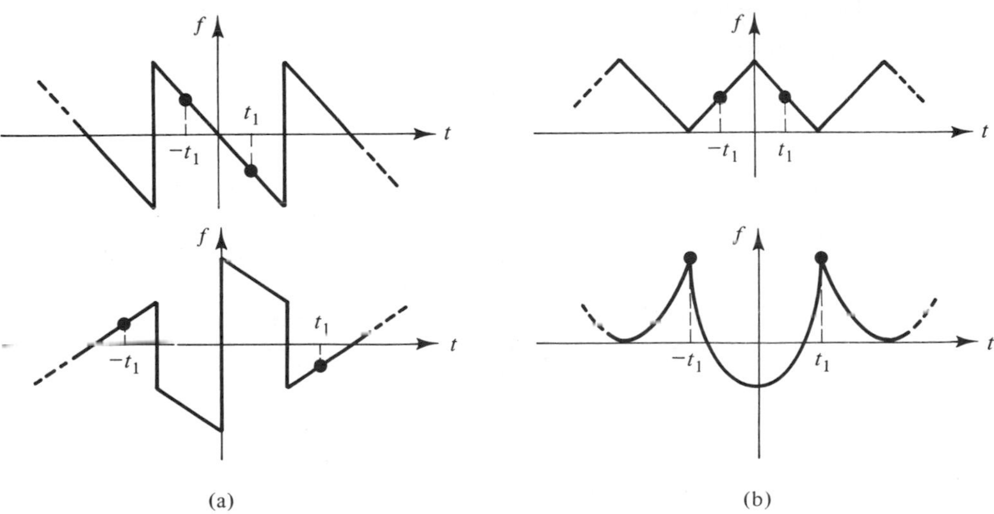

Fig. 12-2

The sine wave is an odd function because

$$\sin(-\omega t) = -\sin \omega t$$

If $f_1(t)$ and $f_2(t)$ are odd functions, then their sum, $f_1(t) + f_2(t)$, is also odd. Therefore the part of the Fourier series given by

$$\sum_{n=1}^{\infty} b_n \sin \frac{2\pi n}{T} t$$

forms a function that is odd.

A function is *even* when

$$f(-t) = f(t) \tag{12-16}$$

This means that as we travel equal amounts in time to the left and right of the origin, we find the function to have the same value. The function is symmetric with respect to the vertical axis.

Examples of even functions are shown in Fig. 12-2(b). As can be seen from the waveforms, for any arbitrarily chosen time t_1, $f(-t_1) = f(t_1)$. A constant is an even function also.

The cosine wave is an even function because

$$\cos(-\omega t) = \cos \omega t$$

If $f_1(t)$ and $f_2(t)$ are even functions, then their sum, $f_1(t) + f_2(t)$, is also even. Therefore the part of the Fourier series given by

$$\frac{a_0}{2} + \sum_{n=1}^{\infty} a_n \cos \frac{2\pi n}{T} t$$

forms a function that is even.

From the properties of odd and even functions we see that *if $f(t)$ is an odd function*, then its Fourier series expansion contains only sine waves, that is,

$$f(t) = \sum_{n=1}^{\infty} b_n \sin \frac{2\pi n}{T} t \tag{12-17a}$$

where

$$b_n = \frac{2}{T} \int_0^T f(t) \sin \frac{2\pi n}{T} \pm dt = \frac{2}{T} \int_{-T/2}^{T/2} f(t) \sin \frac{2\pi n}{T} t\, dt$$

The integrand for b_n, being the product of two odd functions, $[f(t)$ and $\sin (2\pi n/T)t]$, is an even function. Hence, the integral from $-T/2$ to $T/2$ can be replaced by twice the integral from 0 to $T/2$. As a result, the expression for b_n can be written as

$$b_n = \frac{4}{T} \int_0^{T/2} f(t) \sin \frac{2\pi n}{T} t\, dt \tag{12-17b}$$

On the other hand, *if $f(t)$ is an even function,* then its Fourier series expansion contains only a constant and cosine waves, that is,

$$f(t) = \frac{a_0}{2} + \sum_{n=1}^{\infty} a_n \cos \frac{2\pi n}{T} t \tag{12-18a}$$

where

$$a_0 = \frac{1}{T} \int_0^T f(t)\, dt = \frac{1}{T} \int_{-T/2}^{T/2} f(t)\, dt$$

$$a_n = \frac{2}{T} \int_0^T f(t) \cos \frac{2\pi n}{T} t\, dt = \frac{2}{T} \int_{-T/2}^{T/2} f(t) \cos \frac{2\pi n}{T} t\, dt$$

The integrand for a_n, being the product of two even functions, $[f(t)$ and $\cos (2\pi n/T)t]$, is an even function. Hence for a_0 and a_n both, the integrals from $-T/2$ to $T/2$ can be replaced by twice the integrals from 0 to $T/2$. As a result, the expressions for a_0 and a_n become

$$a_0 = \frac{2}{T} \int_0^{T/2} f(t)\, dt \tag{12-18b}$$

$$a_n = \frac{4}{T} \int_0^{T/2} f(t) \cos \frac{2\pi n}{T} t\, dt \tag{12-18c}$$

The function $f(t)$ possesses *half-wave symmetry* when

$$f\left(t \pm \frac{T}{2}\right) = -f(t) \tag{12-19}$$

This means that the function remains the same if it is shifted to the left or right by half a period and then flipped over with respect to the horizontal axis.

Examples of functions with half-wave symmetry are shown in Fig. 12-3. The solid lines represent the given waveforms and the dashed lines their half-period shifted forms which when flipped over (multiplied by -1) coincide with the original waveform. Additionally, we see that the triangular wave shown on the left is an odd function, whereas the square wave on the right is even.

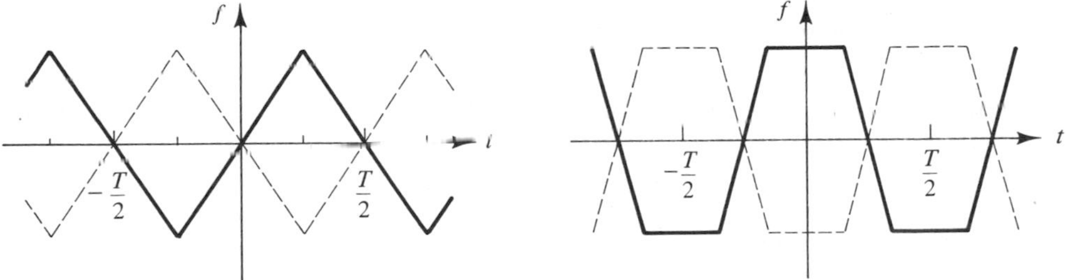

Fig. 12-3

Cosine and sine waves possess half-wave symmetry because

$$\cos\frac{2\pi}{T}\left(t \pm \frac{T}{2}\right) = \cos\left(\frac{2\pi}{T}t \pm \pi\right) = -\cos\frac{2\pi}{T}t \tag{12-20a}$$

$$\sin\frac{2\pi}{T}\left(t \pm \frac{T}{2}\right) = \sin\left(\frac{2\pi}{T}t \pm \pi\right) = -\sin\frac{2\pi}{T}t \tag{12-20b}$$

If we look at the nth harmonic term in the Fourier series, we see that

$$\cos\frac{2\pi n}{T}\left(t \pm \frac{T}{2}\right) = \cos\left(\frac{2\pi n}{T}t \pm n\pi\right) = \begin{cases} -\cos\dfrac{2\pi n}{T}t & n \text{ odd} \\ +\cos\dfrac{2\pi n}{T}t & n \text{ even} \end{cases} \tag{12-21a}$$

$$\sin\frac{2\pi n}{T}\left(t \pm \frac{T}{2}\right) = \sin\left(\frac{2\pi n}{T}t \pm n\pi\right) = \begin{cases} -\sin\dfrac{2\pi n}{T}t & n \text{ odd} \\ +\sin\dfrac{2\pi n}{T}t & n \text{ even} \end{cases} \tag{12-21b}$$

Note that these functions possess *half-wave symmetry only for odd values of n*.

We now make use of these results to show that waveforms with *half-wave symmetry contain only odd harmonics*.

Since functions with half-wave symmetry have zero average value, their Fourier series expansions are given by

$$f(t) = \sum_{n=1}^{\infty}\left(a_n \cos\frac{2\pi n}{T}t + b_n \sin\frac{2\pi n}{T}t\right) \tag{12-22}$$

When evaluating the a_n and b_n coefficients, we start with Eqs. (12-3) and split the integrals into two: one extends from 0 to $T/2$ and the other from $T/2$ to T. The expression for a_n can be written as

$$a_n = \frac{2}{T}\int_0^T f(t)\cos\frac{2\pi n}{T}t\,dt = \frac{2}{T}\int_0^{T/2} f(t)\cos\frac{2\pi n}{T}t\,dt + \frac{2}{T}\int_{T/2}^{T} f(t)\cos\frac{2\pi n}{T}t\,dt \tag{12-23}$$

Because of the half-wave symmetry, we can replace $f(t)$ with $-f[t - (T/2)]$ in the second integral.

$$a_n = \frac{2}{T}\int_0^{T/2} f(t)\cos\frac{2\pi n}{T}t\,dt + \frac{2}{T}\int_{T/2}^{T}\left[-f\left(t - \frac{T}{2}\right)\right]\cos\frac{2\pi n}{T}t\,dt \tag{12-24}$$

We now make use of the results of Eq. (12-21a) and write Eq. (12-24) as

$$a_n = \frac{2}{T}\int_0^{T/2} f(t)\cos\frac{2\pi n}{T}t\,dt + \begin{cases} \dfrac{2}{T}\displaystyle\int_{T/2}^{T}\left[-f\left(t-\frac{T}{2}\right)\right]\left[-\cos\frac{2\pi n}{T}\left(t-\frac{T}{2}\right)\right]dt & n \text{ odd} \\ \dfrac{2}{T}\displaystyle\int_{T/2}^{T}\left[-f\left(t-\frac{T}{2}\right)\right]\left[+\cos\frac{2\pi n}{T}\left(t-\frac{T}{2}\right)\right]dt & n \text{ even} \end{cases} \tag{12-25}$$

Finally, we let $t' = t - (T/2)$ in the second integral and obtain

$$a_n = \frac{2}{T}\int_0^{T/2} f(t)\cos\frac{2\pi n}{T}t\,dt + \begin{cases} \dfrac{2}{T}\displaystyle\int_{0}^{T/2}[-f(t')]\left[-\cos\frac{2\pi n}{T}t'\right]dt' & n \text{ odd} \\ \dfrac{2}{T}\displaystyle\int_{0}^{T/2}[-f(t')]\left[+\cos\frac{2\pi n}{T}t'\right]dt' & n \text{ even} \end{cases} \tag{12-26}$$

For n odd the second integral is the same as the first. For n even it is the negative of the first. Hence the expression for a_n becomes

$$a_n = \begin{cases} \dfrac{4}{T}\displaystyle\int_0^{T/2} f(t)\cos\frac{2\pi n}{T}t\,dt & n \text{ odd} \\ 0 & n \text{ even} \end{cases} \tag{12-27a}$$

Similarly, we can show that

$$b_n = \begin{cases} \dfrac{4}{T}\displaystyle\int_0^{T/2} f(t)\sin\frac{2\pi n}{T}t\,dt & n \text{ odd} \\ 0 & n \text{ even} \end{cases} \tag{12-27b}$$

In summary, we can make the following statements. If $f(t)$ possesses *half-wave symmetry,* then its Fourier series representation contains only odd harmonics and is given by

$$f(t) = \sum_{\substack{n=1 \\ \text{odd}}}^{\infty}\left(a_n\cos\frac{2\pi n}{T}t + b_n\sin\frac{2\pi n}{T}t\right) \tag{12-28a}$$

where

$$a_n = \frac{4}{T}\int_0^{T/2} f(t)\cos\frac{2\pi n}{T}t\,dt \qquad n \text{ odd}$$

$$b_n = \frac{4}{T}\int_0^{T/2} f(t)\sin\frac{2\pi n}{T}t\,dt \qquad n \text{ odd}$$

If $f(t)$ possesses *half-wave* symmetry and is in addition an *even* function, then $b_n = 0$, and only *odd-harmonic* cosine terms are present as shown below.

$$f(t) = \sum_{\substack{n=1 \\ \text{odd}}}^{\infty} a_n\cos\frac{2\pi n}{T}t \tag{12-28b}$$

where

$$a_n = \frac{8}{T}\int_0^{T/4} f(t)\cos\frac{2\pi n}{T}t\,dt \qquad n \text{ odd only}$$

If $f(t)$ possesses *half-wave* symmetry and is in addition an *odd* function, then $a_n = 0$, and only *odd-harmonic* sine terms are present as shown below.

$$f(t) = \sum_{\substack{n=1\\ \text{odd}}}^{\infty} b_n \sin\frac{2\pi n}{T}t\,dt \tag{12-28c}$$

where

$$b_n = \frac{8}{T}\int_0^{T/4} f(t)\sin\frac{2\pi n}{T}t\,dt \qquad n \text{ odd only}$$

It is left as an exercise (Problem 12-5) to show that the a_n and b_n coefficients simplify to the expressions given above.

12-4 FOURIER SERIES REPRESENTATION OF VARIOUS WAVEFORMS

In this section we develop the Fourier series representation of a number of waveforms and discuss the results.

Example 12-1

(a) Obtain the Fourier series representation of the square wave shown in Fig. 12-4.

(b) What is the effect of the fundamental and the various harmonics in the shaping of the waveform?

(c) Repeat (a) if the waveform is shifted up by B units.

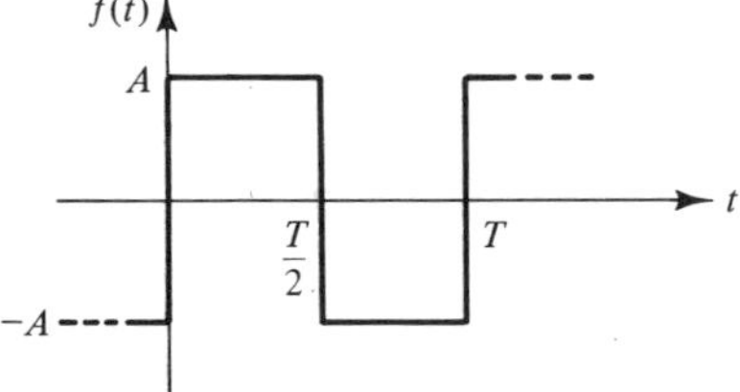

Fig. 12-4

Solution

(a) The function in Fig. 12-4 is an odd function because for any time t_1, $f(-t_1) = -f(t_1)$. Therefore its Fourier series representation will contain only sine waves. The function also possesses half-wave symmetry because $f[t_1 \pm (T/2)] = -f(t_1)$. Therefore, it will contain only odd harmonics. Hence, use can be made of Eq. (12-28c) to write $f(t)$ as

$$f(t) = \sum_{\substack{n=1 \\ \text{odd}}}^{\infty} b_n \sin \frac{2\pi n}{T} t \tag{12-29a}$$

where

$$b_n = \frac{8}{T} \int_0^{T/4} f(t) \sin \frac{2\pi n}{T} t \, dt \qquad n \text{ odd} \tag{12-29b}$$

We now evaluate b_n using the expression for $f(t)$ for $0 < t < T/4$, which is $f(t) = A$.

$$b_n = \frac{8}{T} \int_0^{T/4} A \sin \frac{2\pi n}{T} t \, dt = \frac{8A}{T} \left(\frac{-\cos \dfrac{2\pi n}{T} t}{\dfrac{2\pi n}{T}} \right) \Bigg|_0^{T/4}$$

$$= \frac{4A}{\pi n} \left(1 - \cos \frac{\pi n}{2} \right) \Bigg|_{n \text{ odd}} = \frac{4A}{\pi n} \tag{12-30}$$

Substituting this value of b_n in Eq. (12-29a), we get

$$f(t) = \frac{4A}{\pi} \sum_{\substack{n=1 \\ \text{odd}}}^{\infty} \frac{1}{n} \sin \frac{2\pi n}{T} t \qquad \text{Ans.} \tag{12-31}$$

This series converges to the square wave shown in Fig. 12-4 except at the discontinuities (jumps), where it converges to the midpoint values of the discontinuities. For example, at $t = T/2$, the series converges to

$$\frac{1}{2}\left[f\left(\frac{T^-}{2}\right) + f\left(\frac{T^+}{2}\right) \right] = \frac{1}{2}[A + (-A)] = 0$$

(b) To see the amplitudes of the various harmonics, Eq. (12-31) is written as

$$f(t) = \frac{4A}{\pi} \left(\sin \frac{2\pi}{T} t + \frac{1}{3} \sin \frac{6\pi}{T} t + \frac{1}{5} \sin \frac{10\pi}{T} t + \cdots \right) \tag{12-32}$$

Note that the amplitudes decrease as $1/n$, that is, the third harmonic component is $1/3$ as large as the fundamental, the fifth harmonic is $1/5$ as large, and so on. In general, waveforms that have discontinuities (jumps) like the square wave have, for n large, harmonic amplitudes that decrease as $1/n$ but not any faster.

A crude but reasonable approximation of the square wave can be made by using just the fundamental component

$$f_1(t) = \frac{4A}{\pi} \sin \frac{2\pi}{T} t$$

This is shown in Fig. 12-5(a). During the first half of the cycle, the fundamental wave with its amplitude of $4A/\pi = 1.27A$ tries to approximate the amplitude A of the square wave. However, by itself, the fundamental is not steep enough at the

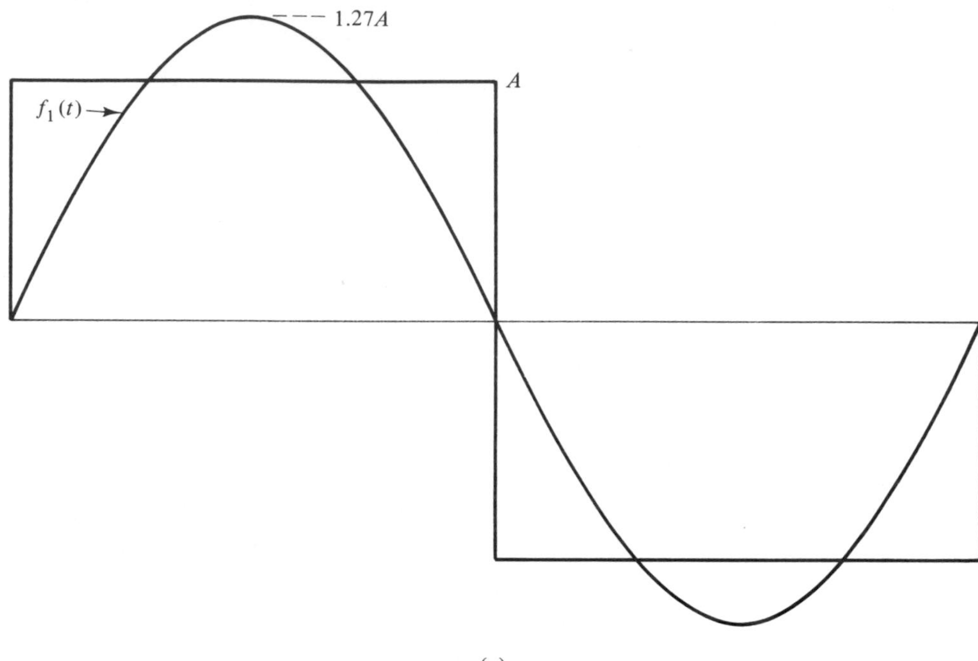

(a)

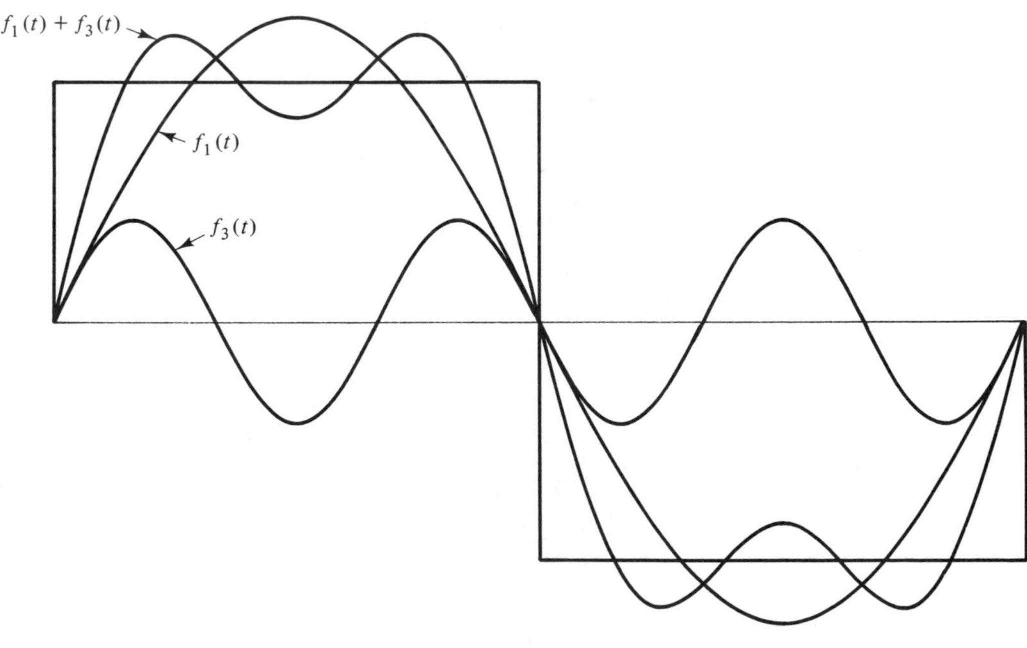

(b)

Fig. 12-5

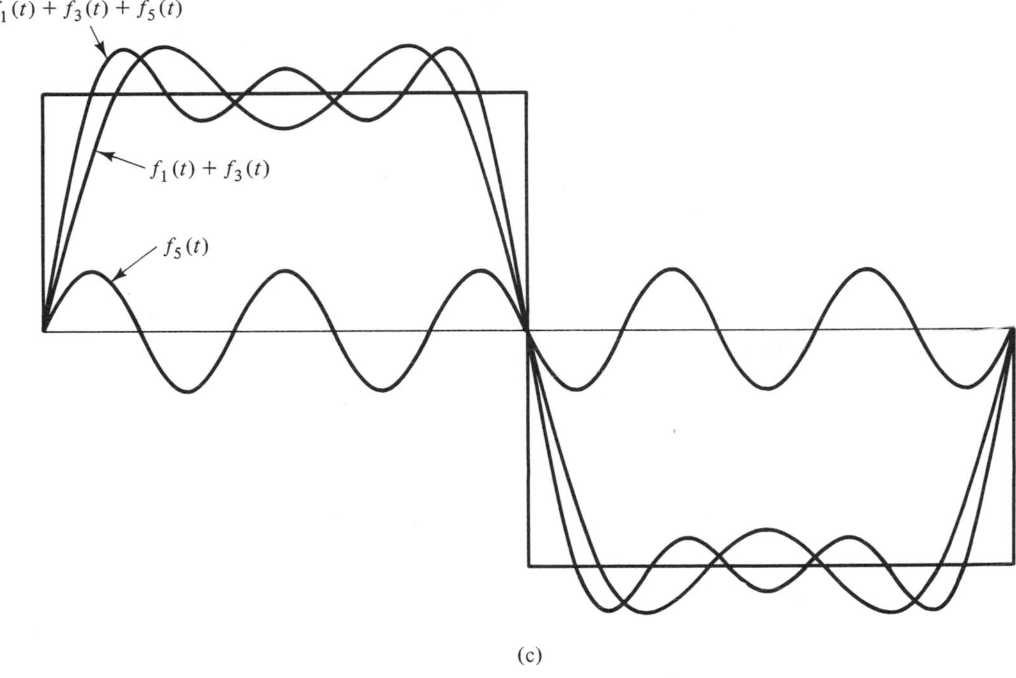

(c)

Fig. 12-5 cont.

edges. Nor is it flat enough on top. Figure 12-5(b) shows what happens when the third harmonic component,

$$f_3(t) = \frac{4A}{3\pi} \sin \frac{6\pi}{T} t$$

is added. The nature of the $f_3(t)$ waveform is such that it augments the $f_1(t)$ waveform at the edges, thereby making the sides steeper. It also helps flatten the top, since it is in opposition to $f_1(t)$ in that region. As a result, the sum waveform, $f_1(t) + f_3(t)$, forms a better approximation to the square wave. A still better fit is obtained when the fifth harmonic,

$$f_5(t) = \frac{4A}{5\pi} \sin \frac{10\pi}{T} t$$

is added as shown in Fig. 12-5(c). The relationship of $f_5(t)$ to the previous sum function, $f_1(t) + f_3(t)$, is such that it further enhances the steepness of the sides while it adds or subtracts from the midsection at the appropriate places to produce a new sum waveform, $f_1(t) + f_3(t) + f_5(t)$, which is more ripply on top but is overall closer to being a constant. As higher harmonics are added, the waveform improves further, but not as dramatically as it did with the first few harmonics, because the higher harmonics have lower amplitudes. Nonetheless, however insignificant their amplitudes may be, all harmonics (infinite number of them) are needed if the square wave is to be constructed exactly.

(c) If the waveform is shifted up by B units, then the Fourier series representation is obtained by adding the constant B to the expression derived in (a).

$$f(t) = B + \frac{4A}{\pi} \sum_{\substack{n=1 \\ \text{odd}}}^{\infty} \frac{1}{n} \sin \frac{2\pi n}{T} t \quad \text{Ans.} \tag{12-33}$$

Example 12-2

(a) Obtain the Fourier series representation of the triangular wave shown in Fig. 12-6.

(b) What is the effect of the various harmonics in the shaping of the waveform?

(c) Show that the Fourier series of the triangular wave shown in Fig. 12-6 can be obtained from the Fourier series of the square wave shown in Fig 12-4 through appropriate operations.

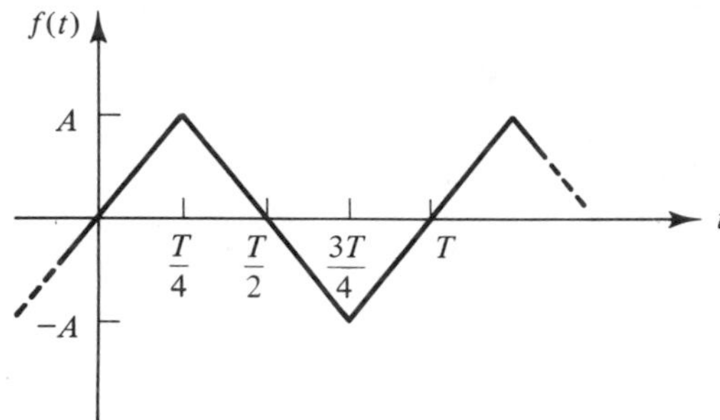

Fig. 12-6

Solution

(a) The triangular waveform shown is an odd function. Furthermore it possesses half-wave symmetry. Therefore its Fourier series representation will contain only odd harmonic sine waves. Hence, use can be made of Eq. (12-28c) to write $f(t)$ as

$$f(t) = \sum_{\substack{n=1 \\ \text{odd}}}^{\infty} b_n \sin \frac{2\pi n}{T} t \tag{12-34a}$$

where

$$b_n = \frac{8}{T} \int_0^{T/4} f(t) \sin \frac{2\pi n}{T} t \, dt \qquad n \text{ odd} \tag{12-34b}$$

Over the range of integration, $f(t)$ is described by $(4A/T)t$. Hence, the expression for b_n can be written as

$$b_n = \frac{8}{T} \int_0^{T/4} \frac{4A}{T} t \sin \frac{2\pi n}{T} t \, dt \tag{12-35}$$

Integrating by parts, we obtain

$$b_n = \frac{32A}{T^2} \left[t \left(\frac{-\cos \frac{2\pi n}{T} t}{\frac{2\pi n}{T}} \right) \Bigg|_0^{T/4} - \int_0^{T/4} \left(\frac{-\cos \frac{2\pi n}{T} t}{\frac{2\pi n}{T}} \right) dt \right] \tag{12-36}$$

$$= \frac{32A}{T^2}\left\{\frac{T^2}{8\pi n}\left(-\cos\frac{n\pi}{2}\right) + \left[\left(\frac{T}{2\pi n}\right)^2 \sin\frac{2\pi n}{T}t\right]_0^{T/4}\right\} \qquad (12\text{-}37)$$

$$= \frac{8A}{n\pi}\left(-\frac{1}{2}\cos\frac{n\pi}{2} + \frac{1}{n\pi}\sin\frac{n\pi}{2}\right) \qquad (12\text{-}38)$$

Since n is odd, $\cos(n\pi/2) = 0$. Therefore b_n can be expressed as

$$b_n = \frac{8A}{n^2\pi^2}\sin\frac{n\pi}{2} = (-1)^{(n+3)/2}\frac{8A}{n^2\pi^2} \qquad n \text{ odd} \qquad (12\text{-}39)$$

Substituting Eq. (12-39) in Eq. (12-34a), we obtain the Fourier series representation of the triangular wave as

$$f(t) = \frac{8A}{\pi^2}\sum_{\substack{n=1\\ \text{odd}}}^{\infty}\left(\frac{\sin\frac{n\pi}{2}}{n^2}\right)\sin\frac{2\pi n}{T}t \quad \text{Ans.} \qquad (12\text{-}40)$$

(b) To see the amplitudes of the various harmonics, Eq. (12-40) is written as

$$f(t) = \frac{8A}{\pi^2}\left(\sin\frac{2\pi}{T}t - \frac{1}{9}\sin\frac{6\pi}{T}t + \frac{1}{25}\sin\frac{10\pi}{T}t - \cdots\right) \qquad (12\text{-}41)$$

Note that the amplitudes decrease as $1/n^2$, that is, the third harmonic is $1/9$ as large as the fundamental, the fifth harmonic is $1/25$ as large, and so on. In general, waveforms that are continuous but have discontinuous first derivatives like the triangular waveform have, for n large, harmonic amplitudes that decrease $1/n^2$ but not any faster. (The first derivative of the triangular wave is a square wave with jumps at $t = \frac{1}{4}T, \frac{3}{4}T, \frac{5}{4}T$, etc.) Because of this $1/n^2$ dependence of harmonic amplitudes, the triangular wave can be reasonably approximated with fewer sine waves than the square wave. As shown in Fig. 12-7(a), the fundamental component,

$$f_1(t) = \frac{8A}{\pi^2}\sin\frac{2\pi}{T}t$$

alone forms a good basis for the triangular wave. Its amplitude, $8A/\pi^2 = 0.81A$, is close to the peak value of A of the triangular wave. Its slope at $t = 0$, $16A/\pi T = 5.1A/T$, is slightly higher than the slope of the triangular wave, which is $4A/T$. When the third harmonic

$$f_3(t) = -\frac{8A}{9\pi^2}\sin\frac{6\pi}{T}t$$

is added to the fundamental, the waveform improves considerably [see Fig. 12-7b]. Even though the third harmonic amplitude is only one-ninth of the fundamental, it is in step with the fundamental near the peak of the triangular waveform and out of step at the edges, thereby providing the necessary corrections for a straight line. The fifth and higher harmonics contribute to a better approximation though in a much less noticeable way since their amplitudes are so much smaller.

(c) Consider the square wave $f(t)$ shown in Fig. 12-8(a). If t is replaced with $t + (T/4)$, the square wave is shifted to the left by $T/4$ seconds as shown in Fig.

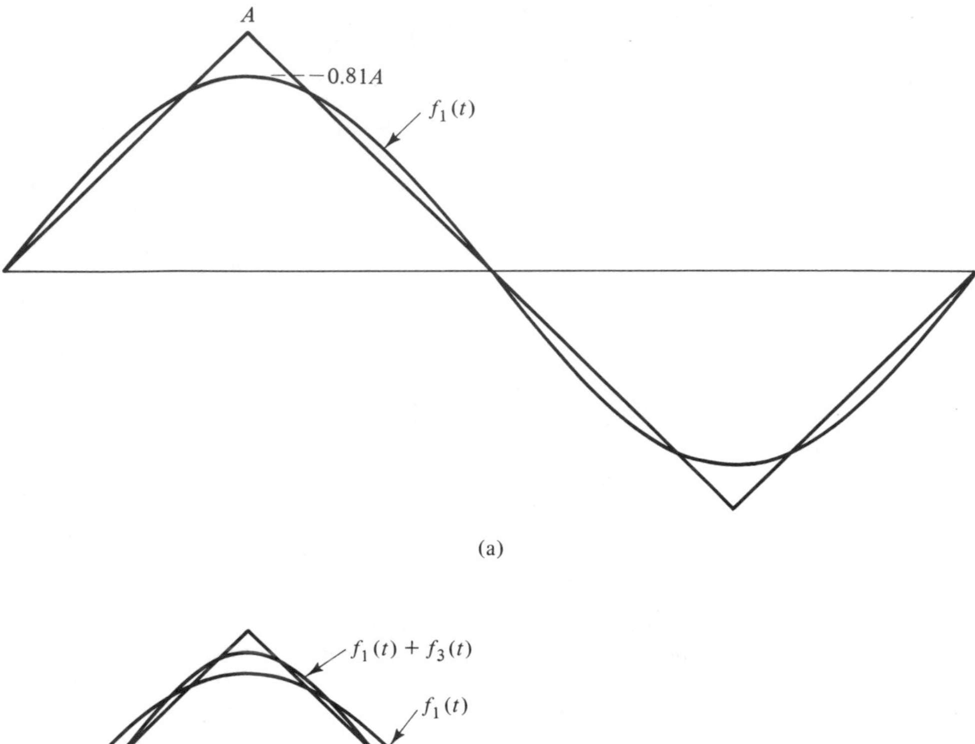

(a)

(b)

Fig. 12-7

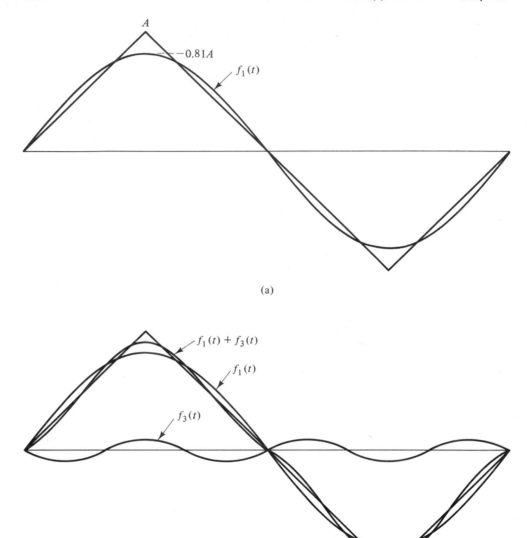

12-8(b). If this shifted square wave is integrated, starting with $t = 0$, the triangular wave shown in Fig. 12-8(c) results. Since integration represents *the accumulated area under the square wave* as a function of time, the area increases linearly with time until it reaches $A \times (T/4)$ at $t = T/4$. Between $t = T/4$ and $3T/4$, negative area is accrued. Therefore, starting with $t = T/4$, the area decreases linearly until $t = 3T/4$, at which time the total area accumulated becomes

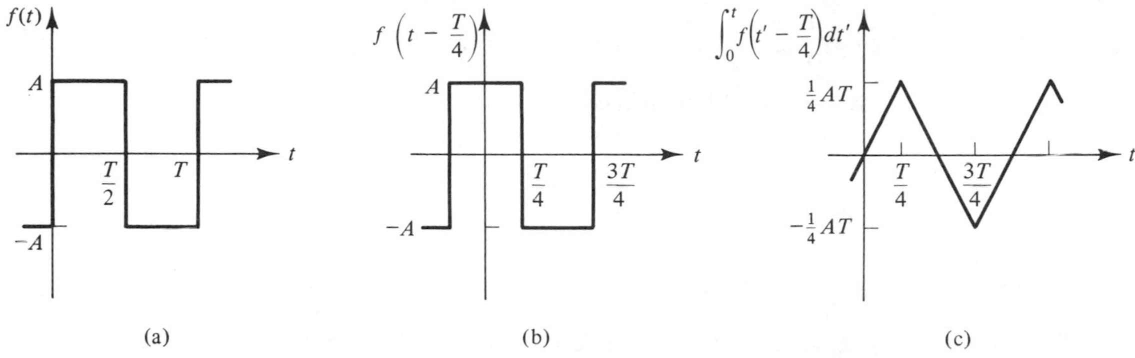

Fig. 12-8

$$A \times \frac{T}{4} + (-A) \times \frac{T}{2} = -A \times \frac{T}{4}$$

Because the square wave switches between $-A$ and A every $T/2$ seconds, alternately positive and negative areas are accumulated, resulting in the generation of the triangular waveform shown. This means that the Fourier series of the triangular wave can be obtained by replacing t with $[t + (T/4)]$ in the Fourier series expression of the square wave given by Eq. (12-31) and then integrating the resulting function.

$$f_{\text{sq}}(t) = \frac{4A}{\pi} \sum_{n \text{ odd}} \frac{1}{n} \sin \frac{2\pi n}{T} t \tag{12-42}$$

$$f_{\text{sq}}\left(t + \frac{T}{4}\right) = \frac{4A}{\pi} \sum_{n \text{ odd}} \frac{1}{n} \sin \frac{2\pi n}{T}\left(t + \frac{T}{4}\right) \tag{12-43}$$

$$= \frac{4A}{\pi} \sum_{n \text{ odd}} \frac{1}{n} \sin \left(\frac{2\pi n}{T} t + \frac{n\pi}{2}\right)$$

$$f_{\text{tr}}(t) = \int_0^t f_{\text{sq}}\left(t' + \frac{T}{4}\right) dt'$$

$$= \int_0^t \left[\frac{4A}{\pi} \sum_{n \text{ odd}} \frac{1}{n} \sin \left(\frac{2\pi n}{T} t' + \frac{n\pi}{2}\right)\right] dt'$$

$$= \frac{4A}{\pi} \sum_{n \text{ odd}} \left| \frac{-\cos\left(\frac{2\pi n}{T} t' + \frac{n\pi}{2}\right)}{n\left(\frac{2\pi n}{T}\right)} \right|_0^t$$

$$= \frac{2AT}{\pi^2} \sum_{n \text{ odd}} \frac{1}{n^2} \left[\cos \frac{n\pi}{2} - \cos \left(\frac{2\pi n}{T} t + \frac{n\pi}{2}\right)\right] \tag{12-44}$$

For n odd, $\cos n\pi/2 = 0$. Using $\cos(a + b) = \cos a \cos b - \sin a \sin b$, the second cosine term can be simplified as follows.

$$\cos\left(\frac{2\pi n}{T}t + \frac{n\pi}{2}\right) = \cos\frac{2\pi n}{T}t\cos\frac{n\pi}{2} - \sin\frac{2\pi n}{T}t\sin\frac{n\pi}{2} = -\sin\frac{n\pi}{2}\sin\frac{2\pi n}{T}t$$

Hence, Eq. (12-44) reduces to

$$f_{tr} = \frac{2AT}{\pi^2}\sum_{\substack{n=1\\ \text{odd}}}^{\infty}\left(\frac{\sin\frac{n\pi}{2}}{n^2}\right)\sin\frac{2\pi n}{T}t \tag{12-45}$$

This equation represents the Fourier series of the triangular waveform of Fig. 12-8(c). Its amplitude is $AT/4$, whereas the triangular waveform shown in Fig. 12-6 has an amplitude of A. Therefore, we change the amplitudes of the sine waves in Eq. (12-45) by multiplying them with $4/T$ and obtain

$$f(t) = \frac{8A}{\pi^2}\sum_{\substack{n=1\\ \text{odd}}}^{\infty}\left(\frac{\sin\frac{n\pi}{2}}{n^2}\right)\sin\frac{2\pi n}{T}t \quad \text{Ans.} \tag{12-46}$$

This result agrees with the Fourier series representation obtained in (a) above.

Example 12-3

The periodic function shown in Fig. 12-9 looks like a cosine wave, but it is not. It is piecewisely parabolic. It is an even function. It possesses half-wave symmetry and is given over half of its period by

$$f(t) = -\frac{16}{T^2}\left(t^2 - \frac{T^2}{16}\right), \qquad -\frac{T}{4} \le t \le \frac{T}{4}$$

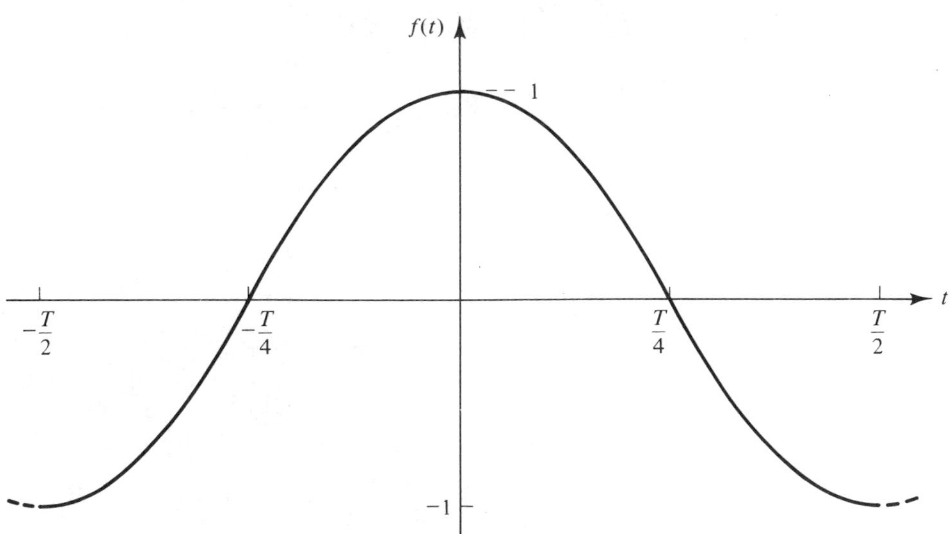

Fig. 12-9

(a) Sketch the first and second derivatives of $f(t)$.
(b) Obtain the Fourier series expansion of $f(t)$ and discuss the result.
(c) Show that this Fourier series representation can also be obtained from the triangular waveform expansion given in Example 12-2.

Solution.

(a) The first derivative of

$$f(t) = -\frac{16}{T^2}\left(t^2 - \frac{T^2}{16}\right) \qquad |t| \leq \frac{T}{4} \tag{12-47}$$

has also half-wave symmetry and is given by

$$f'(t) = -\frac{32}{T^2}t \qquad |t| \leq \frac{T}{4} \tag{12-48}$$

It is sketched in Fig. 12-10(a). Note that it is a piecewisely linear and continuous function.

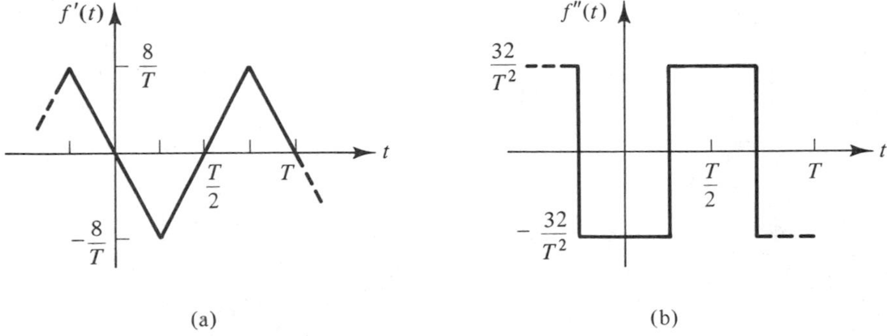

Fig. 12-10

The second derivative of $f(t)$ has also half-wave symmetry and is given by

$$f''(t) = -\frac{32}{T^2} \qquad |t| < \frac{T}{4} \tag{12-49}$$

It is sketched in Fig. 12-10(b). Note that it is discontinuous at $T/4$, $3T/4$, etc..

(b) The given $f(t)$ has half-wave symmetry. It is also an even function. Therefore, its Fourier series representation will contain only odd harmonic cosine waves. Using Eq. (12-28b), we can write

$$f(t) = \sum_{\substack{n=1 \\ \text{odd}}}^{\infty} a_n \cos\frac{2\pi n}{T}t \tag{12-50a}$$

where

$$a_n = \frac{8}{T}\int_0^{T/4} f(t)\cos\frac{2\pi n}{T}t\,dt \qquad n \text{ odd only} \tag{12-50b}$$

Over the range of integration $f(t)$ is given by

$$-\frac{16}{T^2}\left(t^2 - \frac{T^2}{16}\right)$$

Hence, the expression for a_n becomes

$$a_n = \frac{8}{T}\int_0^{T/4}\left[-\frac{16}{T^2}\left(t^2 - \frac{T^2}{16}\right)\right]\cos\frac{2\pi n}{T}t\,dt \tag{12-51}$$

$$= \frac{8}{T}\int_0^{T/4}\cos\frac{2\pi n}{T}t\,dt - \frac{128}{T^3}\int_0^{T/4}t^2\cos\frac{2\pi n}{T}t\,dt$$

$$= \frac{8}{T}\left(\frac{\sin\frac{2\pi n}{T}t}{\frac{2\pi n}{T}}\right)\Bigg|_0^{T/4} - \frac{128}{T^3}\left[t^2\left(\frac{\sin\frac{2\pi n}{T}t}{\frac{2\pi n}{T}}\right)\Bigg|_0^{T/4} - \int_0^{T/4}\left(\frac{\sin\frac{2\pi n}{T}t}{\frac{2\pi n}{T}}\right)2t\,dt\right]$$

$$= \frac{4}{n\pi}\sin\frac{n\pi}{n} - \frac{64}{T^2}\frac{1}{n\pi}\left(\frac{T^2}{16}\sin\frac{n\pi}{2}\right) + \frac{128}{T^2}\frac{1}{n\pi}\int_0^{T/4}t\sin\frac{2\pi n}{T}t\,dt$$

$$= -\frac{128}{n\pi T^2}\left[t\left(\frac{-\cos\frac{2\pi n}{T}t}{\frac{2\pi n}{T}}\right)\Bigg|_0^{T/4} + \int_0^{T/4}\left(\frac{-\cos\frac{2\pi n}{T}t}{\frac{2\pi n}{T}}\right)dt\right]$$

$$= \frac{128}{n\pi T^2}\left\{\frac{T^2}{8n\pi}\cos\frac{n\pi}{2} + \left[\left(\frac{T}{2\pi n}\right)^2\sin\frac{2\pi n}{T}t\right]_0^{T/4}\right\}$$

$$= \frac{32}{n^3\pi^3}\sin\frac{n\pi}{2}$$

Substituting the value of a_n in Eq. (12-50a), we obtain

$$f(t) = \frac{32}{\pi^3}\sum_{\substack{n=1\\ \text{odd}}}^{\infty}\frac{\left(\sin\frac{n\pi}{2}\right)}{n^3}\cos\frac{2\pi n}{T}t \quad \text{Ans.} \tag{12-52a}$$

$$f(t) = \frac{32}{\pi^3}\left(\cos\frac{2\pi}{T}t - \frac{1}{27}\cos\frac{6\pi}{T}t + \frac{1}{125}\cos\frac{10\pi}{T}t - \cdots\right. \tag{12-52b}$$

Note that the amplitude of the harmonics decreases as $1/n^3$, that is, the third harmonic is 1/27 as large as the fundamental, the fifth harmonic is 1/125 as large, and so on. In general, continuous functions with continuous first derivatives have, for n large, harmonic amplitudes that decrease as $1/n^3$ but not any faster. The parabolic curve [Fig. 12-9] is continuous and has a continuous first derivative [Fig. 12-10(a)]. But its second derivative [Fig. 12-10(b)] is discontinuous. Because of this $1/n^3$ dependence of harmonic amplitudes, an excellent approximation of the parabolic wave can be made by using just the fundamental component,

$$f_1(t) = \frac{32}{\pi^3}\cos\frac{2\pi}{T}t$$

With its amplitude of $32/\pi^3 = 1.03$, the fundamental is only slightly higher in amplitude than the peak value of the parabola. At $t = -T/4$, the slope of the fundamental, $64/\pi^2 T = 6.49/T$, is slightly less than the slope of $8/T$ of the parabola. See Fig. 12-11. If the third harmonic,

$$f_3(t) = \frac{32}{\pi^3}\frac{1}{27}\cos\frac{6\pi}{T}t$$

with its very small amplitude, were added on, it would provide minor improvement. This is why it is not shown in Fig. 12-11.

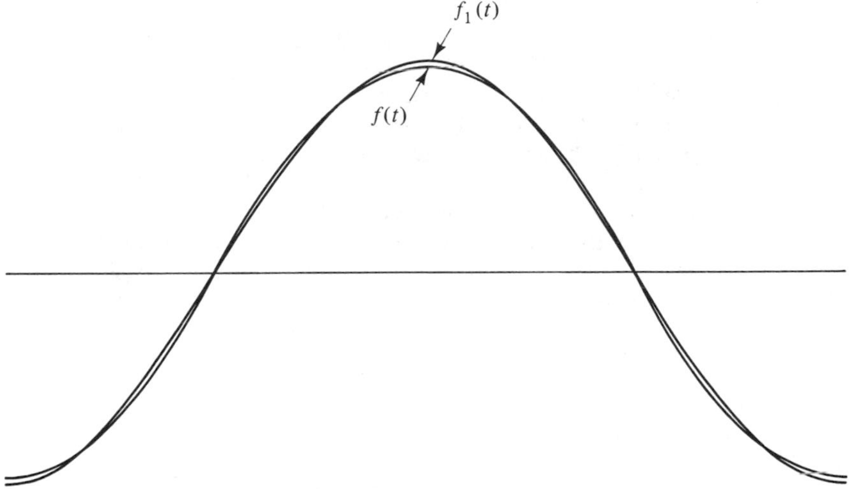

Fig. 12-11

(c) Since the derivative of the given parabolic waveform is the triangular waveform shown in Fig. 12-10(a), the integral of the Fourier series of the triangular waveform obtained in Example 12-2 should result in the Fourier series of the parabolic curve, provided the dc term is removed, the scale is properly adjusted, and the polarity is reversed.

We start with the expression of the triangular wave given by Eq. (12-40).

$$f_{tr}(t) = \frac{8A}{\pi^2}\sum_{\substack{n=1\\ \text{odd}}}^{\infty}\frac{\left(\sin\dfrac{n\pi}{2}\right)}{n^2}\sin\frac{2\pi n}{T}t \tag{12-53}$$

This function and its integral are sketched in Fig. 12-12.

Starting with $t = 0$, the integral results in an area that increases with t until $t = T/2$, at which time it attains its highest value. This value represents the area under the first triangle and is given by

$$\frac{1}{2}\times\frac{T}{2}\times A = \frac{AT}{4}$$

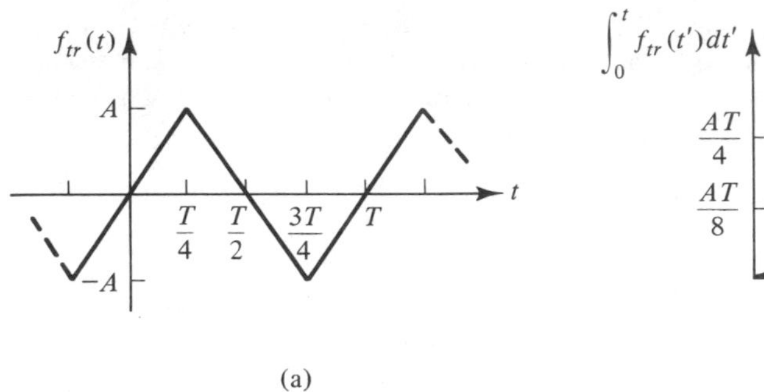

(a)

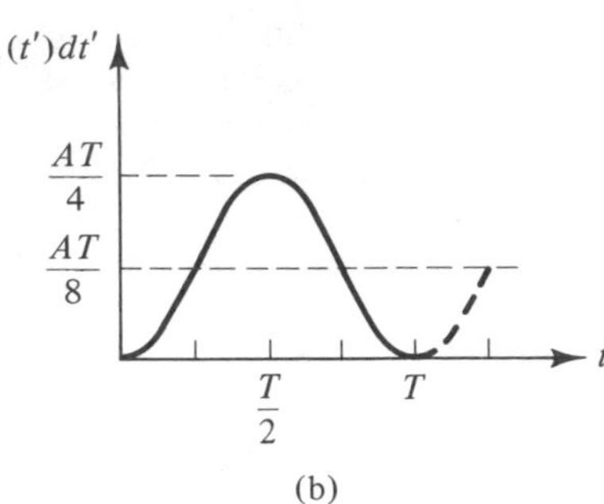

(b)

Fig. 12-12

From $t = T/2$ to T, an equal amount of negative area is accumulated, and correspondingly the integral decreases down to zero as shown in Fig. 12-12(b). By inspection of the integral we see that it has an average value of $AT/8$. If this average value is removed, the curve drops down by $AT/8$, resulting in a parabolic curve of amplitude $AT/8$. If it is then multiplied by $-8/AT$, the parabolic curve of Fig. 12-9 is obtained. When these operations of integration, average value removal, scale change, and sign reversal are performed on the triangular waveform of Eq. (12-53), we obtain the desired parabolic waveform of amplitude 1.

$$
\begin{aligned}
f(t) &= -\frac{8}{AT}\left[\int_0^t \frac{8A}{\pi^2}\sum_{\substack{n=1\\ \text{odd}}}^{\infty}\left(\frac{\sin\frac{n\pi}{2}}{n^2}\right)\sin\frac{2\pi n}{T}t'\,dt' - \frac{AT}{8}\right] \\
&= 1 - \frac{64}{\pi^2 T}\sum_{\substack{n=1\\ \text{odd}}}^{\infty}\left(\frac{\sin\frac{n\pi}{2}}{n^2}\right)\int_0^t \sin\frac{2\pi n}{T}t'\,dt' \\
&= 1 - \frac{64}{\pi^2 T}\sum_{\substack{n=1\\ \text{odd}}}^{\infty}\frac{\left(\frac{\sin n\pi}{2}\right)}{n^2}\,\frac{\left(-\cos\frac{2\pi n}{T}t'\right)}{\frac{2\pi n}{T}}\Bigg|_0^t \\
&= 1 - \frac{32}{\pi^3}\sum_{\substack{n=1\\ \text{odd}}}^{\infty}\frac{\left(\sin\frac{n\pi}{2}\right)}{n^3}\left(1 - \cos\frac{2\pi n}{T}t\right) \\
&= 1 - \frac{32}{\pi^3}\sum_{\substack{n=1\\ \text{odd}}}^{\infty}\frac{\left(\sin\frac{n\pi}{2}\right)}{n^3} + \frac{32}{\pi^3}\sum_{\substack{n=1\\ \text{odd}}}^{\infty}\left(\frac{\sin\frac{n\pi}{2}}{n^3}\right)\cos\frac{2\pi n}{T}t
\end{aligned}
\tag{12-54}
$$

The sum

$$
\sum_{\substack{n=1\\ \text{odd}}}^{\infty}\left(\frac{\sin\frac{n\pi}{2}}{n^3}\right) = 1 - \frac{1}{27} + \frac{1}{125} - \frac{1}{343} + \cdots
$$

is a well known series which converges to $\pi^3/32$. Hence Eq. (12-54) can be written as

$$f(t) = \frac{32}{\pi^3} \sum_{\substack{n=1 \\ \text{odd}}}^{\infty} \left(\frac{\sin \dfrac{n\pi}{2}}{n^3} \right) \cos \frac{2\pi n}{T} t \quad \text{Ans.} \tag{12-55}$$

This result agrees with Eq. (12-52a).

Example 12-4

(a) Obtain the Fourier series of the periodic waveform shown in Fig. 12-13(a).

(b) Making use of the results of (a) above, obtain the Fourier series of the waveforms shown in Fig. 12-13(b), (c), and (d).

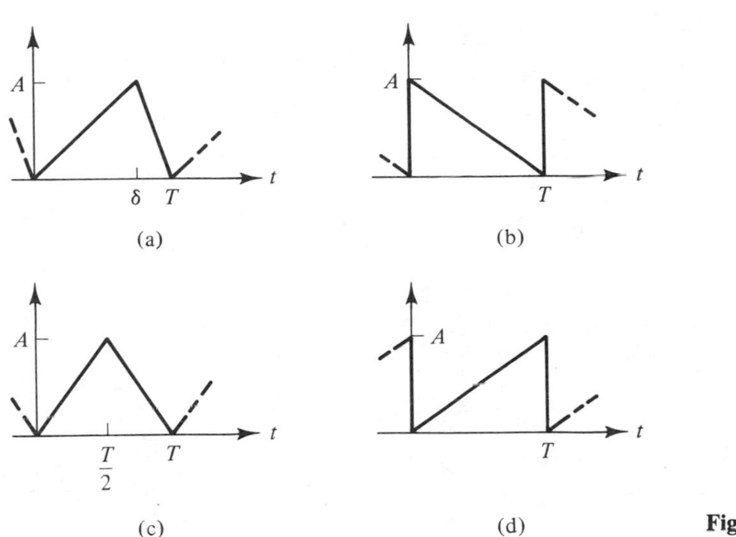

Fig. 12-13

Solution.

(a) The function shown in Fig. 12-13(a) is neither even nor odd. It does not have zero average value and does not possess half-wave symmetry. Therefore, its Fourier series expansion will contain all the a_n and b_n terms. Since the function is continuous with discontinuous first derivatives at $t = \delta$ and T, we expect the amplitudes of the harmonics to vanish no faster than $1/n^2$ as n becomes large.

The function is piecewisely linear. Therefore it will take two equations to describe it over its period.

$$f(t) = \frac{A}{\delta} t \qquad 0 \le t \le \delta \tag{12-56a}$$

$$f(t) = A - \left(\frac{A}{T - \delta} \right)(t - \delta) = A\left(\frac{T - t}{T - \delta} \right) \qquad \delta \le t \le T \tag{12-56b}$$

The various coefficients are calculated as follows.

$$\frac{a_0}{2} = \frac{1}{T}\int_0^T f(t)\,dt = \frac{1}{T}\left[\int_0^\delta \frac{A}{\delta}t\,dt + \int_\delta^T A\left(\frac{T-t}{T-\delta}\right)dt\right] = \frac{A}{2} \tag{12-57a}$$

$$\begin{aligned} a_n &= \frac{2}{T}\int_0^T f(t)\cos\frac{2\pi n}{T}t\,dt \\ &= \frac{2}{T}\left[\int_0^\delta \frac{A}{\delta}t\cos\frac{2\pi n}{T}t\,dt + \int_\delta^T A\left(\frac{T-t}{T-\delta}\right)\cos\frac{2\pi n}{T}t\,dt\right] \\ &= \frac{A}{2\pi^2 n^2}\left(\frac{T}{\delta}\right)\left(\frac{T}{T-\delta}\right)\left(\cos\frac{2\pi n}{T}\delta - 1\right) \end{aligned} \tag{12-57b}$$

$$\begin{aligned} b_n &= \frac{2}{T}\int_0^T f(t)\sin\frac{2\pi n}{T}t\,dt \\ &= \frac{2}{T}\left[\int_0^\delta \frac{A}{\delta}t\sin\frac{2\pi n}{T}t\,dt + \int_\delta^T A\left(\frac{T-t}{T-\delta}\right)\sin\frac{2\pi n}{T}t\,dt\right] \\ &= \frac{A}{2\pi^2 n^2}\left(\frac{T}{\delta}\right)\left(\frac{T}{T-\delta}\right)\sin\frac{2\pi n}{T}\delta \end{aligned} \tag{12-57c}$$

The details of obtaining the above expressions are left as an exercise. See Problem 12-11. The resulting Fourier series is given by

$$f(t) = \frac{a_0}{2} + \sum_{n=1}^{\infty}\left(a_n\cos\frac{2\pi n}{T}t + b_n\sin\frac{2\pi n}{T}t\right)$$

$$\begin{aligned} f(t) &= \frac{A}{2} + \sum_{n=1}^{\infty}\left\{\left[\frac{A}{2\pi^2 n^2}\left(\frac{T}{\delta}\right)\left(\frac{T}{T-\delta}\right)\left(\cos\frac{2\pi n}{T}\delta - 1\right)\right]\cos\frac{2\pi n}{T}t\right. \\ &\qquad \left. + \left[\frac{A}{2\pi^2 n^2}\left(\frac{T}{\delta}\right)\left(\frac{T}{T-\delta}\right)\left(\sin\frac{2\pi n}{T}\delta\right)\right]\sin\frac{2\pi n}{T}t\right\} \\ &= \frac{A}{2} + \frac{A}{2\pi^2}\left(\frac{T}{\delta}\right)\left(\frac{T}{T-\delta}\right)\sum_{n=1}^{\infty}\frac{1}{n^2}\left[\left(\cos\frac{2\pi n}{T}\delta - 1\right)\cos\frac{2\pi n}{T}t\right. \\ &\qquad \left. + \left(\sin\frac{2\pi n}{T}\delta\right)\sin\frac{2\pi n}{T}t\right] \quad \text{Ans.} \end{aligned} \tag{12-58}$$

(b). The sawtooth waveform for Fig. 12-13(b) can be obtained from the waveform of Fig. 12-13(a) by letting $\delta = 0$. Since a_n and b_n take the indeterminate form of 0/0 for $\delta = 0$, L'Hospital's rule is used in Eqs. (12-57) to evaluate them.

$$a_n = \lim_{\delta\to 0}\left[\frac{A}{2\pi^2}\left(\frac{T}{\delta}\right)\left(\frac{T}{T-\delta}\right)\frac{\left(\cos\frac{2\pi n}{T}\delta - 1\right)}{n^2}\right]$$

$$= \frac{AT}{2\pi^2 n^2} \lim_{\delta\to 0} \left[\frac{\cos \dfrac{2\pi n}{T}\delta - 1}{\delta} \right]$$

$$= \frac{AT}{2\pi^2 n^2} \lim_{\delta\to 0} \left[\frac{\dfrac{d}{d\delta}\left(\cos \dfrac{2\pi n}{T}\delta - 1\right)}{\dfrac{d}{d\delta}(\delta)} \right]$$

$$= \frac{AT}{2\pi^2 n^2} \lim_{\delta\to 0} \left(-\frac{2\pi n}{T} \sin \frac{2\pi n}{T}\delta \right) = 0 \tag{12-59a}$$

$$b_n = \lim_{\delta\to 0} \left[\frac{A}{2\pi^2}\left(\frac{T}{\delta}\right)\left(\frac{T}{T-\delta}\right) \frac{\left(\sin \dfrac{2\pi n}{T}\delta\right)}{n^2} \right]$$

$$= \frac{AT}{2\pi^2 n^2} \lim_{\delta\to 0} \left[\frac{\sin \dfrac{2\pi n}{T}\delta}{\delta} \right] = \frac{AT}{2\pi^2 n^2} \lim_{\delta\to 0} \left[\frac{\dfrac{d}{d\delta}\left(\sin \dfrac{2\pi n}{T}\delta\right)}{\dfrac{d}{d\delta}(\delta)} \right]$$

$$= \frac{AT}{2\pi^2 n^2} \lim_{\delta\to 0} \left(\frac{2\pi n}{T} \cos \frac{2\pi n}{T}\delta \right) = \frac{A}{n\pi} \tag{12-59b}$$

Hence, $f(t)$ can be written as

$$f(t) = \frac{A}{2} + \sum_{n=1}^{\infty} \frac{A}{n\pi} \sin \frac{2\pi n}{T} t \quad \text{Ans.} \tag{12-60}$$

Alternatively, this result can be arrived at with less work by evaluating directly the b_n coefficients for the sawtooth waveform shown in Fig. 12-13b. Note that $[f(t) - (A/2)]$ contains only sine waves and is therefore an odd function. That this is the case can be seen directly from Fig. 12-13(b) if the waveform is dropped by $A/2$ (dc term removed), in which case an odd function results. Since this odd function does not possess half-wave symmetry, the Fourier series contains all harmonic terms.

The triangular waveform of Fig. 12-13(c) can be obtained from Fig. 12-13(a) by letting $\delta = T/2$. Using Eqs. (12-57), we can evaluate the a_n and b_n coefficients.

$$a_n = \frac{2A}{n\pi}\left[\sin n\pi + \frac{1}{n\pi}(\cos n\pi - 1) \right] = \begin{cases} -\dfrac{4A}{n^2\pi^2} & n \text{ odd} \\ 0 & n \text{ even} \end{cases} \tag{12-61a}$$

$$b_n = \frac{A}{\pi^2} \frac{2}{T} \frac{\sin n\pi}{n^2} = 0 \tag{12-61b}$$

Hence, $f(t)$ can be written as

$$f(t) = \frac{A}{2} - \sum_{\substack{n=1 \\ \text{odd}}}^{\infty} \frac{4A}{n^2\pi^2} \cos \frac{2\pi n}{T} t \quad \text{Ans.} \tag{12-62}$$

Note that $f(t)$ given by Eq. (12-62) is an even function. This can be seen also from Fig. 12-13(c). Furthermore, with the average value removed, the waveform possesses half-wave symmetry, and hence only n odd terms are present.

The sawtooth waveform of Fig. 12-13(d) can be obtained from Fig. 12-13(a) by letting $\delta = T$. The a_n and b_n coefficients are obtained using Eq. (12-57). Again L'Hospital's rule is used to evaluate the $0/0$ indeterminate forms. The results are

$$a_n = 0 \tag{12-63a}$$

$$b_n = -\frac{A}{n\pi} \tag{12-63b}$$

Hence, $f(t)$ can be written as

$$f(t) = \frac{A}{2} - \sum_{n=1}^{\infty} \frac{A}{n\pi} \sin \frac{2\pi n}{T} t \quad \text{Ans.} \tag{12-64}$$

It should not be surprising that Eqs. (12-64) and (12-60) are alike except for a negative sign. After all, if the average values are taken out, the left- and right-going sawtooth waveforms of Fig. 12-13(b) and 12-13(d) have equal but opposite ordinates for any given t.

12-5 TRIGONOMETRIC, POLAR, AND EXPONENTIAL FORMS OF THE FOURIER SERIES

So far we have dealt with the *trigonometric* form of the Fourier expansion of a periodic function. For convenience, it is repeated here.

$$f(t) = \frac{a_0}{2} + \sum_{n=1}^{\infty} \left(a_n \cos \frac{2\pi n}{T} t + b_n \sin \frac{2\pi n}{T} t \right) \tag{12-65a}$$

where

$$\frac{a_0}{2} = \frac{1}{T} \int_0^T f(t)\, dt \tag{12-65b}$$

$$a_n = \frac{2}{T} \int_0^T f(t) \cos \frac{2\pi n}{T} t\, dt \tag{12-65c}$$

$$b_n = \frac{2}{T} \int_0^T f(t) \sin \frac{2\pi n}{T} t\, dt \tag{12-65d}$$

Making use of the trigonometric identity

$$a \cos \theta + b \sin \theta = \begin{cases} \sqrt{a^2 + b^2} \sin \left(\theta + \tan^{-1} \dfrac{a}{b} \right) \\ \sqrt{a^2 + b^2} \cos \left(\theta - \tan^{-1} \dfrac{b}{a} \right) \end{cases}$$

the trigonometric form of the Fourier series can be converted to *polar* form.

$$f(t) = \begin{cases} \dfrac{a_0}{2} + \sum_{n=1}^{\infty} \sqrt{a_n^2 + b_n^2} \sin \left(\dfrac{2\pi n}{T} t + \tan^{-1} \dfrac{a_n}{b_n} \right) & \text{(12-66a)} \\ \dfrac{a_0}{2} + \sum_{n=1}^{\infty} \sqrt{a_n^2 + b_n^2} \cos \left(\dfrac{2\pi n}{T} t - \tan^{-1} \dfrac{b_n}{a_n} \right) & \text{(12-66b)} \end{cases}$$

Whether the sine or the cosine form is used, $\sqrt{a_n^2 + b_n^2}$ represents the *amplitude* of each harmonic. The *phase* of each harmonic is represented by $\tan^{-1} (a_n/b_n)$ when the sine form is used or by $-\tan^{-1} (b_n/a_n)$ when the cosine form is used. Making use of Euler's identities

$$\cos \theta = \frac{e^{j\theta} + e^{-j\theta}}{2}, \qquad \sin \theta = \frac{e^{j\theta} - e^{-j\theta}}{2j}$$

the trigonometric form of the Fourier series can also be converted to the *exponential* form.

$$\begin{aligned} f(t) &= \frac{a_0}{2} + \sum_{n=1}^{\infty} \left[a_n \left(\frac{e^{j(2\pi n/T)t} + e^{-j(2\pi n/T)t}}{2} \right) - b_n \left(\frac{e^{j(2\pi n/T)t} - e^{-j(2\pi n/T)t}}{2j} \right) \right] \\ &= \frac{a_0}{2} + \sum_{n=1}^{\infty} \left[\left(\frac{a_n - jb_n}{2} \right) e^{j(2\pi n/T)t} + \left(\frac{a_n + jb_n}{2} \right) e^{-j(2\pi n/T)t} \right] \qquad \text{(12-67)} \\ &= c_0 + \sum_{n=1}^{\infty} (c_n e^{j(2\pi n/T)t} + c_{-n} e^{-j(2\pi n/T)t}) = \sum_{n=-\infty}^{\infty} c_n e^{j(2\pi n/T)t} \end{aligned}$$

where

$$c_0 = \frac{a_0}{2} = \frac{1}{T} \int_0^T f(t)\, dt = \text{Average value of } f(t) \qquad \text{(12-68a)}$$

$$\begin{aligned} c_n &= \frac{a_n - jb_n}{2} = \frac{1}{2} \left[\frac{2}{T} \int_0^T f(t) \cos \frac{2\pi n}{T} t\, dt - j \frac{2}{T} \int_0^T f(t) \sin \frac{2\pi n}{T} t\, dt \right] \\ &= \frac{1}{T} \int_0^T f(t) \left(\cos \frac{2\pi n}{T} t - j \sin \frac{2\pi n}{T} t \right) dt \\ &= \frac{1}{T} \int_0^T f(t) e^{-j(2\pi n/T)t}\, dt \qquad \text{(12-68b)} \end{aligned}$$

$$c_{-n} = \frac{a_n + jb_n}{2} = \frac{1}{T} \int_0^T f(t) e^{j(2\pi n/T)t}\, dt = c_n^* \qquad \text{(12-68c)}$$

Hence, without resorting to the calculation of the a_n and b_n coefficients, the *exponential* form of the Fourier series can be obtained directly from

$$f(t) = \sum_{n=-\infty}^{\infty} c_n e^{j(2\pi n/T)t} \tag{12-69a}$$

where

$$c_n = \frac{1}{T}\int_0^T f(t)e^{-j(2\pi n/T)t}\,dt \tag{12-69b}$$

Note that the summation ranges from $n = -\infty$ to $n = \infty$, and only one formula is needed to calulate c_n. However, because the resulting general expression for c_n becomes indeterminate for $n = 0$, it is best to evaluate c_0 separately by letting $n = 0$ in Eq. (12-69b) before integration.

Whereas the a_n and b_n coefficients are real numbers, the c_n coefficients, in general, are complex. Twice the magitude of c_n represents the amplitude of the nth harmonic, since

$$2|c_n| = \begin{cases} |a_n - jb_n| = \sqrt{a_n^2 + b_n^2} & n > 0 \\ |a_n + jb_n| = \sqrt{a_n^2 + b_n^2} & n < 0 \end{cases} \tag{12-70}$$

The angle of c_n is given by

$$\theta_{cn} = \begin{cases} -\tan^{-1}\dfrac{b_n}{a_n} & n > 0 \\ +\tan^{-1}\dfrac{b_n}{a_n} & n < 0 \end{cases} \tag{12-71}$$

In comparison to Eqs. (12-66b) we see that θ_{cn} represents the phase of the nth harmonic *if $n > 0$ and cosinusoidal represenation is used.*

Note further that magnitude of c_n is an even function of n [Eq. (12-70)] whereas the angle of c_n is an odd function of n [Eq. (12-71)].

Starting with Eq. (12-67), still another form of the Fourier series expansion can be developed.

$$f(t) = \frac{a_0}{2} + \sum_{n=1}^{\infty}\left[\left(\frac{a_n - jb_n}{2}\right)e^{j(2\pi n/T)t} + \left(\frac{a_n + jb_n}{2}\right)e^{-j(2\pi n/T)t}\right] \tag{12-72}$$

Since the second term within the summation is the complex conjugate of the first term, we can write Eq. (12-72) as

$$f(t) = \frac{a_0}{2} + 2\sum_{n=1}^{\infty}\text{Re}\left[\left(\frac{a_n - jb_n}{2}\right)e^{j(2\pi n/T)t}\right] = \frac{a_0}{2} + \sum_{n=1}^{\infty}\text{Re}\,[(a_n - jb_n)e^{j(2\pi n/T)t}] \tag{12-73}$$

Recognizing that $a_0/2 = c_0$ and $a_n - jb_n = 2c_n$, we can simplify Eq. (12-73) and obtain a Fourier series representation that involves only positive values of n.

$$f(t) = c_0 + \sum_{n=1}^{\infty} \text{Re}\,[2c_n e^{j(2\pi n/T)t}] \tag{12-74}$$

If c_n is put in exponential form, $|c_n|e^{j\theta_{c_n}}$, Eq. (12-74) can be simplified and put in polar form as shown below.

$$f(t) = c_0 + \sum_{n=1}^{\infty} \text{Re}\,[2|c_n|e^{j[(2\pi n/T)t+\theta_{cn}]}]$$

$$= c_0 + \sum_{n=1}^{\infty} 2|c_n| \cos\left(\frac{2\pi n}{T}t + \theta_{c_n}\right) \tag{12-75}$$

Replacing c_0 with $a_0/2$, $2|c_n|$ with $\sqrt{a_n^2 + b_n^2}$, and θ_{c_n} with $-\tan^{-1}(b_n/a_n)$ results in Eq. (17-66b).

12-6 AMPLITUDE AND PHASE SPECTRA

The exponential representation of the Fourier series of a periodic function is given by

$$f(t) = \sum_{n=-\infty}^{\infty} c_n e^{j(2\pi n/T)t} \tag{12-76a}$$

where

$$c_n = \frac{1}{T}\int_0^T f(t)e^{-j(2\pi n/T)t}\,dt = |c_n|e^{j\theta_{c_n}} \tag{12-76b}$$

As Eq. (12-76b) shows, both $|c_n|$ and θ_{c_n} are functions of $n/T = nf$, which represents the harmonic frequency under consideration. A plot of the value of $|c_n|$ at each discrete frequency nf gives the *amplitude spectrum* of $f(t)$. Since $2|c_n|$ represents the amplitude of each cosinusoid in the Fourier series expansion, the amplitude spectrum gives, at a glance, the relative size of the harmonics of the waveform. A plot of the value of θ_{c_n} at each discrete frequency nf gives the *phase spectrum* of $f(t)$. The phase spectrum gives the phase of each *cosinusoid* in the Fourier series expansion. Amplitude and phase spectra, taken together, supply all the information necessary to construct the Fourier series.

As an illustration consider the rectangular waveform shown in Fig. 12-14. This function is neither odd nor even. Neither does it possess half-wave symmetry. To obtain its spectra, we evaluate c_n using Eq. (12-76b) and then determine its magnitude and angle.

$$c_n = \frac{1}{T}\int_0^T f(t)e^{-j(2\pi n/T)t}\,dt$$

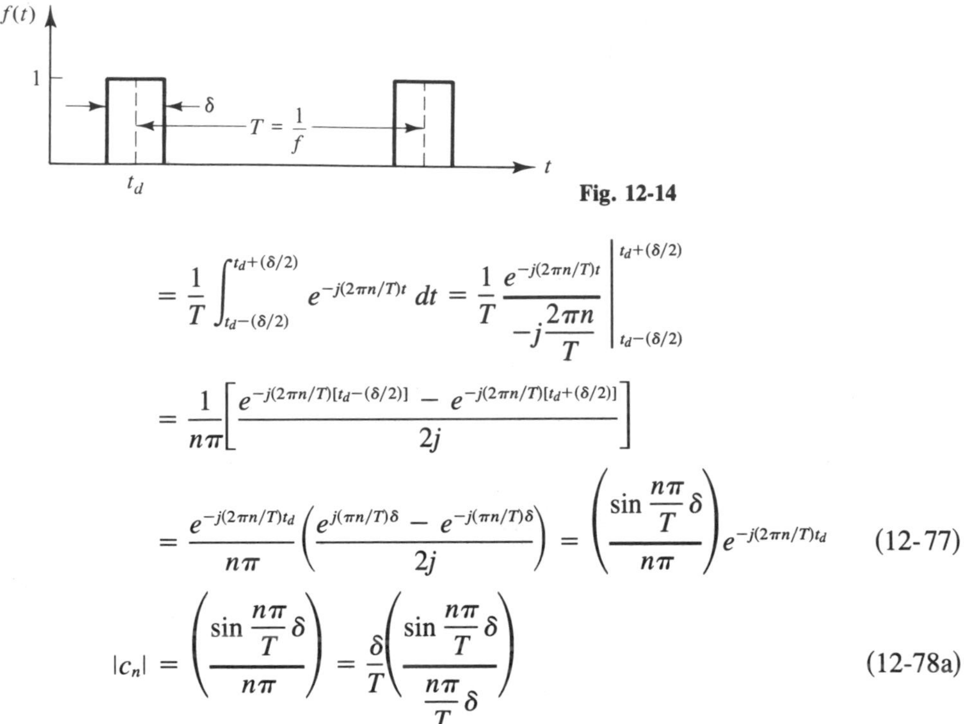

Fig. 12-14

$$= \frac{1}{T}\int_{t_d-(\delta/2)}^{t_d+(\delta/2)} e^{-j(2\pi n/T)t}\,dt = \frac{1}{T}\frac{e^{-j(2\pi n/T)t}}{-j\dfrac{2\pi n}{T}}\Bigg|_{t_d-(\delta/2)}^{t_d+(\delta/2)}$$

$$= \frac{1}{n\pi}\left[\frac{e^{-j(2\pi n/T)[t_d-(\delta/2)]} - e^{-j(2\pi n/T)[t_d+(\delta/2)]}}{2j}\right]$$

$$= \frac{e^{-j(2\pi n/T)t_d}}{n\pi}\left(\frac{e^{j(\pi n/T)\delta} - e^{-j(\pi n/T)\delta}}{2j}\right) = \left(\frac{\sin\dfrac{n\pi}{T}\delta}{n\pi}\right)e^{-j(2\pi n/T)t_d} \tag{12-77}$$

$$|c_n| = \left(\frac{\sin\dfrac{n\pi}{T}\delta}{n\pi}\right) = \frac{\delta}{T}\left(\frac{\sin\dfrac{n\pi}{T}\delta}{\dfrac{n\pi}{T}\delta}\right) \tag{12-78a}$$

$$\theta_{c_n} = -\frac{2\pi n}{T}t_d \tag{12-78b}$$

The magnitude function, $|c_n|$, is plotted vs. $n/T = nf$ in Fig. 12-15(a). To facilitate the drawing, n/T is assumed to be a continuous variable, and the dashed envelope curve shown is obtained. To evaluate c_0, use is made in Eq. (12-78a) of the fact that

$$\lim_{x\to 0}\frac{\sin x}{x} = 1$$

The result is $c_0 = \delta/T$. Whenever $(n\pi/T)\delta$ is a multiple of π, $\sin(n\pi/T)\delta = 0$. The first zero value is obtained when $n/T = 1/\delta$; the next when $n/T = 2/\delta$, etc. Since n/T is not a continuous but a discrete variable, the value of $|c_n|$ is taken only at 0, $1/T$, $2/T$, $3/T$, etc. and is shown by the length of the vertical bar extending to the dashed curve. This length represents one-half the value of the amplitude of each harmonic. The bar at $n = 0$ represents the dc value of the waveform. Figure 12-15(a) represents the amplitude spectrum of the rectangular wave.

The phase function, θ_{c_n}, is plotted vs. n/T in Fig. 12-15(b). Again, n/T is assumed to be a continuous variable, and the dashed curve is plotted. Then ordinates are erected at discrete frequencies of n/T to obtain the phase. The length of each bar represents the phase of each cosinusoid. Figure 12-15(b) represents the phase spectrum of the rectangular wave.

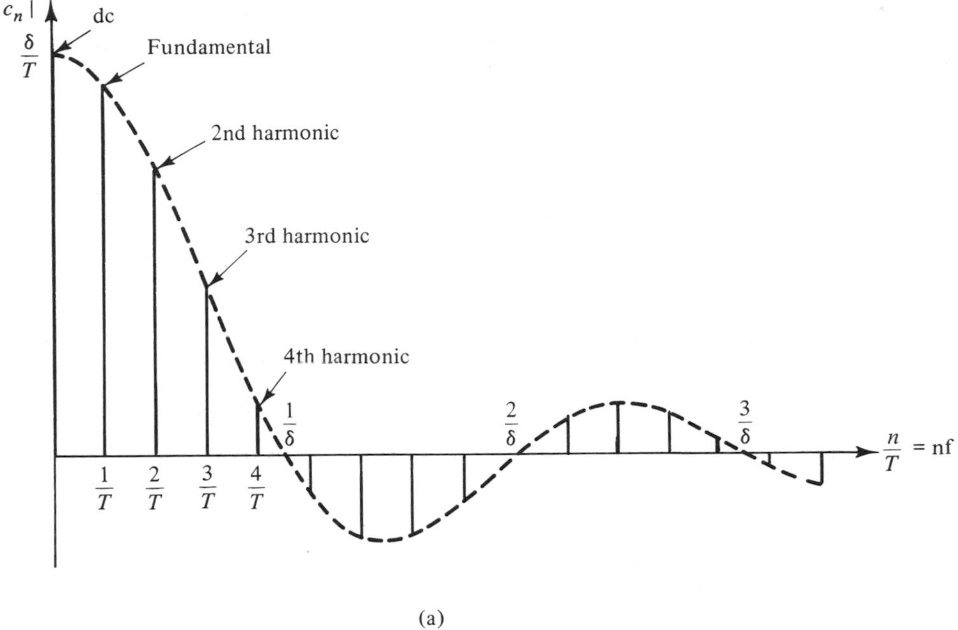

$|c_n|$
dc
$\frac{\delta}{T}$
Fundamental
2nd harmonic
3rd harmonic
4th harmonic
$\frac{1}{\delta}$
$\frac{2}{\delta}$
$\frac{3}{\delta}$
$\frac{n}{T}$ = nf
$\frac{1}{T}$
$\frac{2}{T}$
$\frac{3}{T}$
$\frac{4}{T}$

(a)

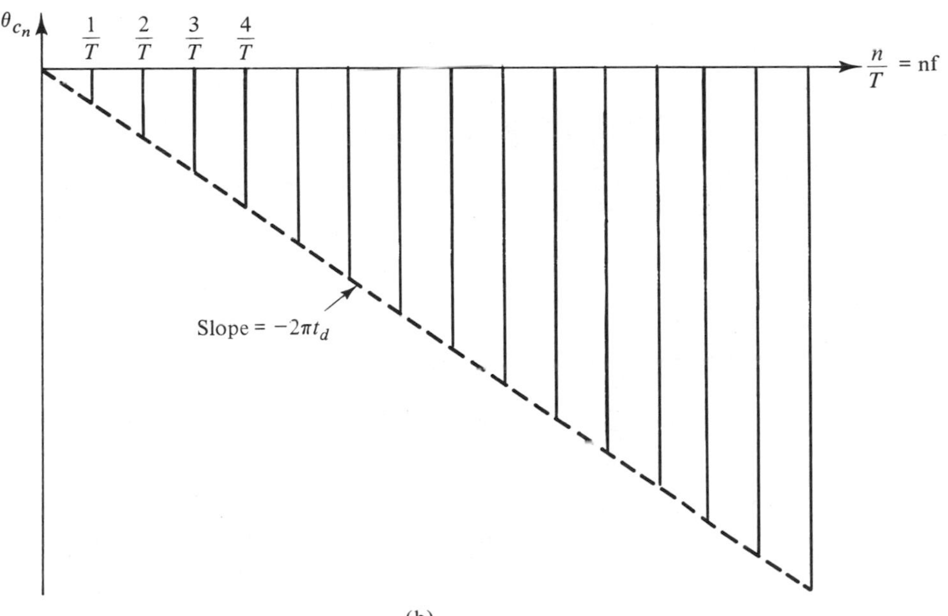

θc_n
$\frac{1}{T}$
$\frac{2}{T}$
$\frac{3}{T}$
$\frac{4}{T}$
$\frac{n}{T}$ = nf
Slope = $-2\pi t_d$

(b)

Fig. 12-15

[Strictly speaking a magnitude function, such as $|c_n|$, by definition should not be negative at all, that is, the negative bars of Fig. 12-15(a) should be reversed and drawn up, and the change in sign taken care of by adding an angle of π to the phase function. Then, if desired, $\cos(\phi + \pi)$ can be written as $-\cos\phi$, which brings us back where we started. Realizing this, $|c_n|$ is allowed to become negative, thereby making it easier to express the phase function.]

Using the results of Eqs. (12-78) in Eq. (12-76a) and in Eq. (12-75), the Fourier series of the rectangular waveform can be written as

$$f(t) = \sum_{n=-\infty}^{\infty} c_n e^{j(2\pi n/T)t} = \sum_{n=-\infty}^{\infty} \left(\frac{\sin \frac{n\pi}{T}\delta}{n\pi} \right) e^{j(2\pi n/T)(t-t_d)} \tag{12-79}$$

$$f(t) = c_0 + \sum_{n=1}^{\infty} 2|c_n| \cos\left(\frac{2\pi n}{T}t + \theta_{c_n}\right) = \frac{\delta}{T} + \frac{2}{\pi}\sum_{n=1}^{\infty} \left(\frac{\sin \frac{n\pi}{T}\delta}{n} \right) \cos\left[\frac{2\pi n}{T}(t - t_d)\right] \tag{12-80}$$

From these equations we see that the linear phase characteristic shown in Fig. 12-15(b) results in a time delay of t_d seconds. This is to be expected from the discussion of filters presented in Chapter 9, Section 1. Note also that t_d has no effect on the amplitude spectrum. This is always true when a waveform is merely shifted along the time axis forward or backward. In this case the unshifted version corresponds to a rectangular pulse centered about $t = 0$. See Fig. 12-14 for $t_d = 0$. The corresponding Fourier series representation is

$$f(t) = \frac{\delta}{T} + \frac{2}{\pi}\sum_{n=1}^{\infty} \left(\frac{\sin \frac{n\pi}{T}\delta}{n} \right) \cos \frac{2\pi n}{T}t \qquad (t_d = 0) \tag{12-81}$$

Suppose that we hold the period of this rectangular waveform constant, thus fixing its fundamental frequency. If we now vary δ, we will control how long the pulse will be "on," that is, how long it will stay at the 1 level. Such a variation in δ will affect the amplitude spectrum. The phase spectrum, being independent of δ, is unaffected. The amplitude spectrum is given by

$$|c_n| = \frac{\sin \frac{n\pi}{T}\delta}{n\pi} \tag{12-82}$$

and is sketched in Fig. 12-16 for three values of the δ/T ratio.

When $\delta/T = \frac{1}{2}$, the waveform becomes a square wave as shown in Fig. 12-16(a). The zero crossings of the $(\sin x)/x$ curve occur at n/T for n even. Therefore all even harmonics amplitudes are zero. The resulting $f(t)$ is given by

$$f(t) = 0.5 + \frac{2}{\pi}\sum_{\substack{n=1 \\ \text{odd}}}^{\infty} \frac{\sin(0.5n\pi)}{n} \cos \frac{2\pi n}{T}t \tag{12-83}$$

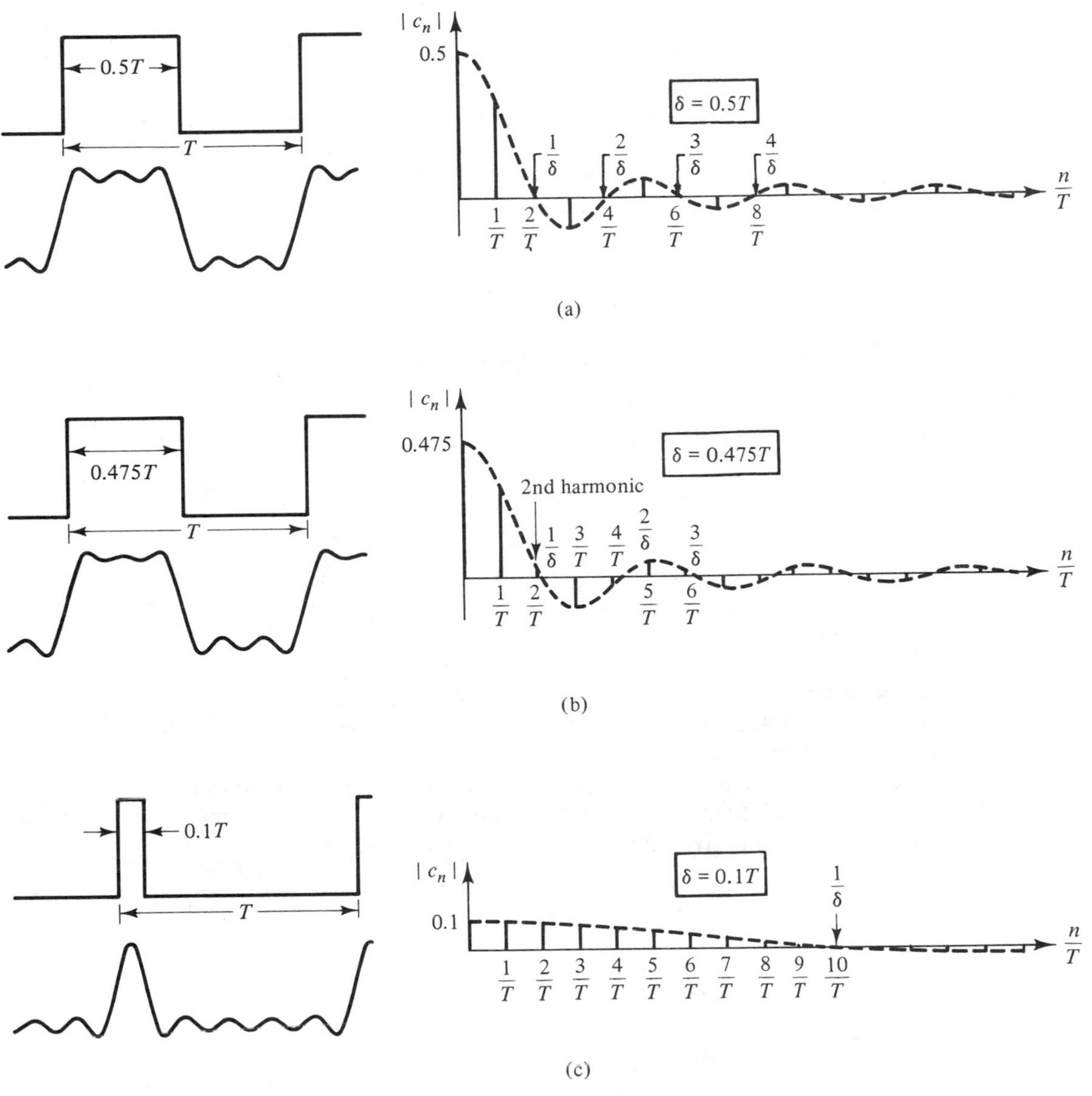

Fig. 12-16

Because the amplitudes decrease as $2/\pi \times 1/n$, the square wave can be approximated quite well by considering only terms through the fifth harmonic.

$$f(t) \cong 0.5 + 0.637 \cos \frac{2\pi}{T}t - 0.212 \cos \frac{6\pi}{T}t + 0.127 \cos \frac{10\pi}{T}t \quad (12\text{-}84)$$

The resulting waveform is shown in Fig. 12-16(a).

When $\delta/T = 0.475$, the waveform becomes slightly unsymmetrical as shown in Fig. 12-16(b). As a result, the even harmonics no longer fall at the zero crossings of the $(\sin x)/x$ curve and therefore come through. See Fig. 12-16(b). In particular, the second harmonic, however small, makes its appearance. Use is made of this fact in the design of function generators to produce square waves with two equal halves. One merely observes the second harmonic content of the waveform and reduces it to a minimum by varying the symmetry-adjust control. The $f(t)$ for $\delta/T = 0.475$ is given by

$$f(t) = 0.475 + \frac{2}{\pi}\sum_{n=1}^{\infty} \frac{\sin(0.475n\pi)}{n} \cos\frac{2\pi n}{T}t \tag{12-85}$$

An approximation to this $f(t)$ is obtained by using the first five harmonics.

$$f(t) \cong 0.475 + 0.635 \cos\frac{2\pi}{T}t + 0.05 \cos\frac{4\pi}{T}t - 0.206 \cos\frac{6\pi}{T}t - 0.049 \cos\frac{8\pi}{T}t + 0.118 \cos\frac{10\pi}{T}t \tag{12-86}$$

Note that the second harmonic amplitude, 0.05, is quite small in comparison to the fundamental amplitude of 0.635. The waveform generated by Eq. (12-86) is shown in Fig. 12-16(b).

When $\delta/T = 0.1$, the waveform becomes quite narrow, being "on" only 10% of the time as shown in Fig. 12-16(c). As the amplitude spectrum shows, the amplitude at each harmonic is much smaller than in the previous cases. More importantly, because the zero crossings of the $(\sin x)/x$ curve are much farther out, the harmonic amplitudes decrease slowly, making the effect of the higher harmonics more significant than before. The corresponding $f(t)$ and its approximation through the fifth harmonic are given by

$$f(t) = 0.1 + \frac{2}{\pi}\sum_{n=1}^{\infty} \frac{\sin(0.1n\pi)}{n} \cos\frac{2\pi n}{T}t \tag{12-87}$$

$$f(t) \cong 0.1 + 0.197 \cos\frac{2\pi}{T}t + 0.187 \cos\frac{4\pi}{T}t + 0.172 \cos\frac{6\pi}{T}t + 0.151 \cos\frac{8\pi}{T}t + 0.127 \cos\frac{10\pi}{T}t \tag{12-88}$$

In Fig. 12-16(c), a plot of Eq. (12-88) is shown. Unlike the previous cases, it obviously takes more than the dc term and the first five harmonics to produce a reasonable approximation to the given waveform. Because the pulse width is much smaller than the period, the series converges very slowly. This can be seen when the amplitudes of the fundamental and the succeeding harmonics are compared: 0.197, 0.187, 0.172, 0.151, and 0.127. From another viewpoint, we see that it would require a large number of harmonically related sine waves, each with half-wave symmetry, to produce the highly unsymmetrical pulse waveform. A much narrower pulse, say $\delta/T = 0.01$, would result in a series that converges very slowly. Only when a large number of terms are used can one expect the waves to come constructively together to produce the narrow pulses and to fall destructively out of step to produce the long zeros in between.

12-7 MEAN-SQUARE ERROR IN TRUNCATED SERIES

The Fourier series is an infinite series. It takes an infinite number of harmonics to reconstruct a given periodic waveform $f(t)$ with sinusoidal waves. If we truncate the series, we get an approximation to the waveform. If terms through the kth harmonic only are used, the exponential form of the truncated Fourier series becomes

$$f_A(t) = \sum_{n=-k}^{k} c_n e^{j(2\pi n/T)t} \tag{12-89a}$$

where, as before, c_n is given by

$$c_n = \frac{1}{T}\int_0^T f(t)e^{-j(2\pi n/T)t}\,dt \tag{12-89b}$$

In these equations $f_A(t)$ represents the function that approximates (hence the subscript A) the given periodic waveform $f(t)$. If k is taken as infinity, then $f_A(t) = f(t)$ except at the discontinuities of $f(t)$ (where the infinite series converges to the average value).

Certainly $f_A(t)$ is not the only function that can be used to approximate $f(t)$. Indeed, one can set up a different exponential series, say $f_D(t)$, that uses the same number of terms as $f_A(t)$ but has coefficients that are different from c_n.

$$f_D(t) = \sum_{n=-k}^{k} d_n e^{j(2\pi n/T)t} \tag{12-90}$$

The subscript D is to remind us that this is a different approximation. How do we now determine the d_n coefficients for a good fit to the given waveform $f(t)$? Obviously we want to minimize the difference between $f(t)$ and $f_D(t)$ as much as possible. This, however, cannot be done for all t. While the difference can be made zero at discrete points of time, it will assume positive or negative values at other times in between. Rather than concentrating on the point-by-point difference, we can obtain a single overall measure of the quality of the approximation by determining the average value of *the square of the error* (difference) taken over the entire period T.

The squaring operation serves two purposes. First, being always positive, it prevents positive and negative values of errors from cancelling each other out over the period. Second, it gives more weight to large errors than small. Thus, by summing (integrating) the square of the error and then dividing by T to find the average value, we get a single number to represent the quality of the approximation. The smaller this number, the better the overall approximation. Denoting the error function $\epsilon(t)$ as

$$\epsilon(t) = f(t) - f_D(t)$$

we now obtain the mean-square error, MSE, as follows.

$$\text{MSE} = \frac{1}{T}\int_0^T \epsilon^2(t)\,dt = \frac{1}{T}\int_0^T [f(t) - f_D(t)]^2\,dt \tag{12-91}$$

$$= \frac{1}{T}\int_0^T [f^2(t) - 2f(t)f_D(t) + f_D^2(t)]\,dt$$

$$= \frac{1}{T}\int_0^T f^2(t)\,dt - \frac{2}{T}\int_0^T f(t)f_D(t)\,dt + \frac{1}{T}\int_0^T f_D^2(t)\,dt \tag{12-92}$$

$$= \text{MS}_1 + \text{MS}_2 + \text{MS}_3 \tag{12-93}$$

The first integral, MS_1, represents the mean-square value of the given $f(t)$ and is given by

$$\text{MS}_1 = \frac{1}{T}\int_0^T f^2(t)\,dt \tag{12-94}$$

The second integral, MS_2, can be evaluated using the expression for $f_D(t)$ given by Eq. (12-90).

$$\text{MS}_2 = -\frac{2}{T}\int_0^T f(t)\,f_D(t)\,dt = -\frac{2}{T}\int_0^T \left[f(t)\sum_{n=-k}^{k}(d_n e^{j(2\pi n/T)t})\right]dt$$

$$= -\frac{2}{T}\sum_{n=-k}^{k}\left[d_n \int_0^T f(t)e^{j(2\pi n/T)t}\,dt\right] = -2\sum_{n=-k}^{k} d_n\left[\frac{1}{T}\int_0^T f(t)e^{j(2\pi n/T)t}\,dt\right] \tag{12-95}$$

When the expression within the brackets above is compared to Eq. (12-89b) we recognize that it represents c_{-n}. Hence Eq. (12-95) can be written as

$$\text{MS}_2 = -2\sum_{n=-k}^{k} c_{-n}d_n = -\sum_{n=-k}^{k}(c_{-n}d_n + c_n d_{-n}) \tag{12-96}$$

The third integral, MS_3, represents the mean-square value of $f_D(t)$.

$$\text{MS}_3 = \frac{1}{T}\int_0^T f_D^2(t)\,dt = \frac{1}{T}\int_0^T \left(\sum_{n=-k}^{k} d_n e^{j(2\pi n/T)t}\right)^2 dt \tag{12-97}$$

Some of the terms in the integrand are constant. They are the result of multiplying symmetrically placed terms ($d_{-m}e^{-j(2\pi m/T)t} \times d_m e^{j(2\pi m/T)t} = d_{-m}d_m$). Taken all together, they form

$$\sum_{n=-k}^{k} d_{-n}d_n$$

The remaining terms all have $e^{\pm j(2\pi m/T)t}$ as the time-dependent factor. Since for any integer m

$$\int_0^T e^{\pm j(2\pi m/T)t}\,dt = \left.\frac{e^{\pm j(2\pi m/T)t}}{\pm j\dfrac{2\pi m}{T}}\right|_0^T = \frac{e^{\pm j2\pi m}-1}{\pm j\dfrac{2\pi m}{T}} = 0 \tag{12-98}$$

these terms do not contribute to MS_3. Hence MS_3, can be simplified to

$$MS_3 = \frac{1}{T}\int_0^T \left(\sum_{n=-k}^{k} d_{-n}d_n\right) dt = \left(\sum_{n=-k}^{k} d_{-n}d_n\right)\left(\frac{1}{T}\int_0^T dt\right) = \sum_{n=-k}^{k} d_{-n}d_n \tag{12-99}$$

We now combine MS_2 with MS_3 and rearrange the result.

$$MS_2 + MS_3 = -\sum_{n=-k}^{k} (c_{-n}d_n + c_nd_{-n}) + \sum_{n=-k}^{k} (d_{-n}d_n) \tag{12-100}$$

$$= \sum_{n=-k}^{k} [d_{-n}d_n - (c_{-n}d_n + c_nd_{-n})] \tag{12-101}$$

The coefficients with negative subscripts are the conjugates of the coefficients with the positive subscripts. [If this were not the case, the trigonometric forms of $f_A(t)$ and $f_D(t)$ would not have harmonic amplitudes that are real.] Hence, Eq. (12-101) can be written as

$$MS_2 + MS_3 = \sum_{n=-k}^{k} [d_nd_n^* - (c_n^*d_n + c_nd_n^*) + (c_nc_n^* - c_nc_n^*)]$$

$$= \sum_{n=-k}^{k} (c_n - d_n)(c_n^* - d_n^*) - \sum_{n=-k}^{k} c_nc_n^*$$

$$= \sum_{n=-k}^{k} (c_n - d_n)(c_n - d_n)^* - \sum_{n=-k}^{k} c_nc_n^*$$

This expression can be simplified by recognizing that for any complex function z, $zz^* = |z|^2$.

$$MS_2 + MS_3 = \sum_{n=-k}^{k} |c_n - d_n|^2 - \sum_{n=-k}^{k} |c_n|^2 \tag{12-102}$$

Finally, Eqs. (12-94) and (12-102) are used in Eq. (12-93) to obtain the mean-square error.

$$MSE = \frac{1}{T}\int_0^T f^2(t)\,dt + \sum_{n=-k}^{k} |c_n - d_n|^2 - \sum_{n=-k}^{k} |c_n|^2 \tag{12-103}$$

Now that we have obtained the expression for MSE, how do we minimize it? The function $f(t)$ is given; it cannot be adjusted. The c_n coefficients are fixed, too, since they are obtained using the given $f(t)$ as shown in Eq. (12-98b). Only the d_n coefficients, associated with the new but different approximation given by Eq. (12-90), are free to be chosen. In Eq. (12-103), d_n appears only in the middle term, which is positive, being always squared. Hence, MSE attains its minimum value when this middle term is made zero by equating d_n to c_n.

$$d_n = c_n = \frac{1}{T}\int_0^T f(t)e^{-j(2\pi n/T)t}\, dt \tag{12-104}$$

This is a very interesting result. It says that if we are given the task of selecting the dc term d_0 and the k coefficients, $d_n = |d_n|e^{j\theta_{dn}}$, in the finite trigonometric series given by

$$f_D(t) = \sum_{n=-k}^{k} d_n e^{j(2\pi n/T)t} = d_0 + 2\sum_{n=1}^{k} |d_n| \cos\left(\frac{2\pi n}{T}t + \theta_{dn}\right) \tag{12-105}$$

such that the mean-square error between $f_D(t)$ and a given periodic function $f(t)$ is minimum, then the rule for obtaining the unknown d_n coefficients is the same as the rule for evaluating the c_n coefficients which form the basis for the Fourier series representation of $f(t)$. Stated differently, if a given periodic function $f(t)$ is approximated by a truncated Fourier series $f_A(t)$, then the mean-square error between $f(t)$ and $f_A(t)$ is minimum. At this point it should be clear that an error-minimization criterion different from the least mean-square would result in a different set of rules for the determination of the d_n coefficients. As a result the waveform it produces will look different, since it approximates the given $f(t)$ in a different sense.

Using $c_n = d_n$ in Eq. (12-103), we can now find the MSE in a truncated Fourier series.

$$\text{MSE} = \frac{1}{T}\int_0^T f^2(t)\, dt - \sum_{n=-k}^{k} |c_n|^2 \tag{12-106}$$

The larger the k, the smaller the MSE. As k approaches infinity, MSE approaches zero. Consider for example the square wave shown in Fig. 12-17. Its Fourier series expansion is given by Eq. (12-31), which is repeated here for convenience.

$$f(t) = \frac{4}{\pi}\sum_{\substack{n=1\\ \text{odd}}}^{\infty} \frac{1}{n}\sin\frac{2\pi n}{T}t \tag{12-107}$$

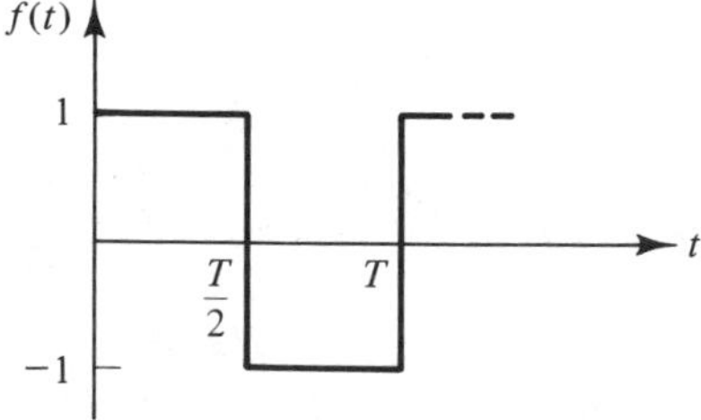

Fig. 12-17

As shown in Eq. (12-75), the amplitude of each harmonic is twice the magnitude of c_n. Hence, we have

$$|c_n| = \frac{2}{n\pi} \qquad n \text{ odd} \tag{12-108}$$

Because the dc term is zero, the expression for MSE can be written as

$$\text{MSE} = \frac{1}{T}\int_0^T f^2(t)\,dt - 2\sum_{\substack{n=1\\ \text{odd}}}^{k} |c_n|^2 \tag{12-109}$$

Since $f^2(t) = 1$, MSE becomes

$$\text{MSE} = \frac{1}{T}\int_0^T dt - 2\sum_{\substack{n=1\\ \text{odd}}}^{k} \frac{4}{n^2\pi^2} = 1 - \frac{8}{\pi^2}\sum_{\substack{n=1\\ \text{odd}}}^{k} \frac{1}{n^2} \tag{12-110}$$

Table 12-1 lists the values of MSE as a function of k.

TABLE 12-1

k	1	3	5	7	9
MSE	0.1894	0.0994	0.0669	0.0504	0.0404

As the number of harmonics used in the approximation is increased, the MSE becomes smaller. If the full Fourier series is used ($k = \infty$), MSE becomes zero, because

$$\sum_{\substack{n=1\\ \text{odd}}}^{\infty} \frac{1}{n^2} = \frac{\pi^2}{8} \tag{12-111}$$

As k approaches infinity, a curious phenomenon known as Gibb's phenomenon appears at points where $f(t)$ jumps. On either side of the discontinuity, the approximating function exhibits ringing. Figure 12-18 shows what happens at the positive jump of a square wave. The drawing covers a time span of only $0.1T$ centered about the jump. Hence, it gives quite an expanded view of the transition period. Curve (a) corresponds to the waveform obtained when terms through $k = 99$ (99th harmonic) are used for the approximation, whereas curve (b) is for $k = 999$. Note that the larger k results in a waveform that is not only faster rippling but also faster decaying. However, the peak amplitudes of the ripples are *not* correspondingly smaller. In fact, as $k\to\infty$, the ripples get compressed about the discontinuity and vanish almost instantaneously but result in a 9% overshoot as shown on either side of the jump. This Gibb's phenomenon is seen in all Fourier series representations that approximate functions with discontinuities. For example, the sawtooth waveforms of Figs. 12-13(b) and 12-13(d) behave about their jumps much like the square wave of Fig. 12-18.

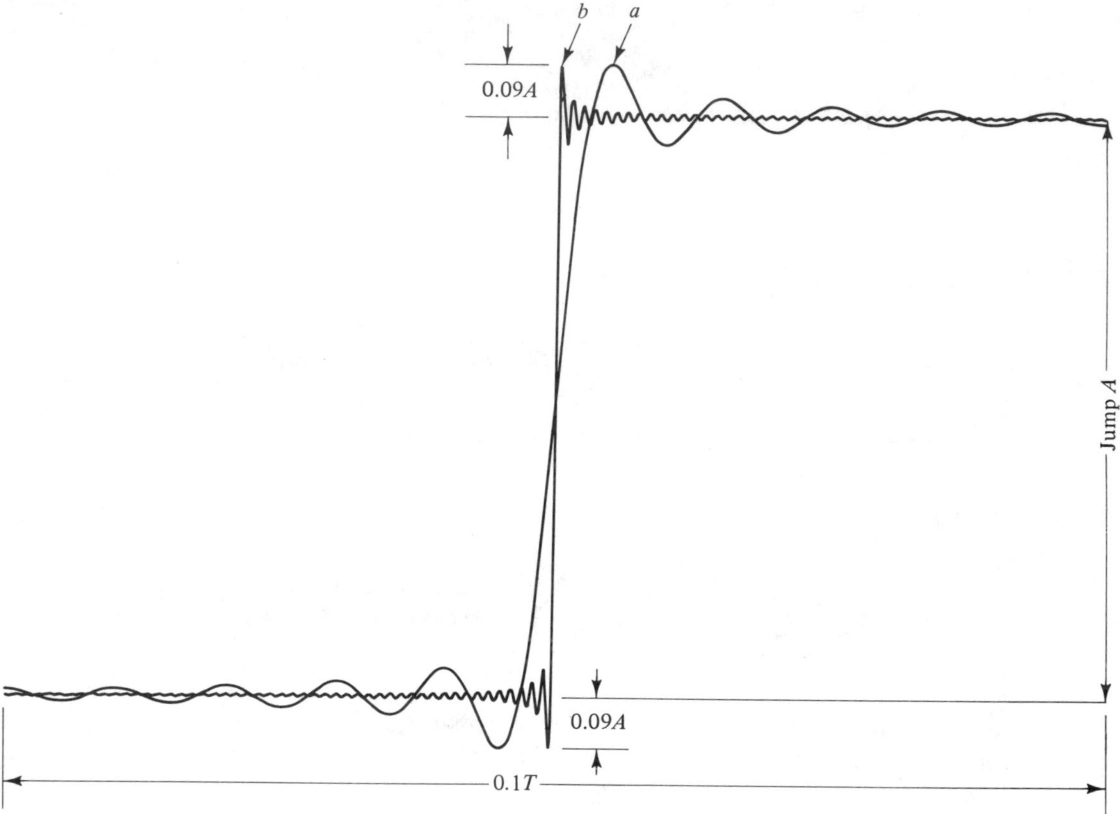

Fig. 12-18

12-8 POWER RELATIONSHIPS

As shown in the previous section, the mean-square error of a truncated Fourier series representing a periodic waveform $f(t)$ is

$$\text{MSE} = \frac{1}{T}\int_0^T f^2(t)\,dt - \sum_{n=-k}^{k} |c_n|^2 \tag{12-112}$$

where the Fourier coefficients c_n are given by

$$c_n = \frac{1}{T}\int_0^T f(t)e^{-j(2\pi n/T)t}\,dt \tag{12-113}$$

If the series is made infinite, $k = \infty$, the MSE becomes zero, and hence Eq. (12-112) simplifies to

$$\frac{1}{T}\int_0^T f^2(t)\,dt = \sum_{n=-\infty}^{\infty} |c_n|^2 = c_0^2 + 2\sum_{n=1}^{\infty} |c_n|^2 \tag{12-114}$$

From Eq. (12-70) we know that

$$|c_n| = \frac{1}{2}\sqrt{a_n^2 + b_n^2} \tag{12-115}$$

where a_n and b_n coefficients represent the coefficients in the trigonometric form of the Fourier series. See Eq. (12-3). So, Eq. (12-114) can be alternatively written as

$$\frac{1}{T}\int_0^T f^2(t)\,dt = \left(\frac{a_0}{2}\right)^2 + \frac{1}{2}\sum_{n=1}^{\infty} (a_n^2 + b_n^2) \tag{12-116}$$

The result given by Eq. (12-116) or Eq. (12-114) is known as the *Parseval's* relation. Since $a_0/2$ represents the dc (average) value of $f(t)$ and $\sqrt{a_n^2 + b_n^2}$ the amplitude of the nth harmonic, Parseval's relation can be stated as

mean-square value of $f(t)$ = (average value)^2

+ $\frac{1}{2}$ (sum of the squares of harmonic amplitudes)

The square root of the mean-square value represents the rms value (see Chapter 8, Sec. 11) of $f(t)$ and is here designated by F_{rms}. Furthermore, $\sqrt{a_n^2 + b_n^2}/\sqrt{2}$ represents the rms value of the nth harmonic. So, we can write

$$F_{\text{rms}} = \sqrt{\frac{1}{T}\int_0^T f^2(t)\,dt} = \sqrt{\left(\frac{a_0}{2}\right)^2 + \frac{1}{2}\sum_{n=1}^{\infty} (a_n^2 + b_n^2)} \tag{12-117a}$$

$$= \sqrt{(dc)^2 + \sum_{n=1}^{\infty} (\text{rms}_n)^2} \tag{12-117b}$$

Once the Fourier series representation of a function is known, its rms value can be obtained using Eq. (12-117). When the rms value of a waveform is known, the average power delivered to a resistor by that waveform can be calculated using V_{rms}^2/R or $I_{\text{rms}}^2 R$.

As is discussed in Chapter 3, Sec. 6, the power delivered to a two-terminal network is

$$p(t) = v(t)i(t) \tag{12-118}$$

If the waveforms are periodic, then the average power delivered to the network is obtained from

$$p_{\text{av}} = \frac{1}{T}\int_0^T v(t)i(t)\,dt \tag{12-119}$$

If the Fourier series representations are used for $v(t)$ and $i(t)$, then we have

$$p_{\text{av}} = \frac{1}{T}\int_0^T \left(\sum_{n=-\infty}^{\infty} c_{nv}e^{j(2\pi n/T)t}\right)\left(\sum_{m=-\infty}^{\infty} c_{mi}e^{j(2\pi m/T)t}\right) dt \qquad (12\text{-}120)$$

where c_{nv} and c_{mi} are the complex Fourier coefficients for $v(t)$ and $i(t)$.

The product of the two infinite sums in Eq. (12-120) is itself an infinite sum. Some of the terms are time dependent and some are constant. The time-dependent terms have $e^{\pm jk(2\pi/T)t}$ as a factor, where k is an integer. When these terms are integrated over a period, the result is zero. The remaining constant terms are the result of multiplying a $\pm n$th term with $m = \mp n$th term and give

$$(c_{-nv}e^{-j(2\pi n/T)t})(c_{ni}e^{j(2\pi n/T)t}) + (c_{nv}e^{j(2\pi n/T)t})(c_{-ni}e^{-j(2\pi n/T)t}) = c_{-nv}c_{ni} + c_{nv}c_{-ni}$$

Since c_{nv} and c_{ni} are complex, they can be written in exponential form as $|c_{nv}|e^{j\theta_{nv}}$ and $|c_{ni}|e^{j\theta_{ni}}$. Furthermore $c_{-nv} = c_{nv}^*$ and $c_{-ni} = c_{ni}^*$. Hence, we have

$$\begin{aligned}
c_{-nv}c_{ni} + c_{nv}c_{-ni} &= (c_{nv})^*(c_{ni}) + (c_{nv})(c_{ni})^* \\
&= |c_{nv}|e^{-j\theta_{nv}} \times |c_{ni}|e^{j\theta_{ni}} + |c_{nv}|e^{j\theta_{nv}} \times |c_{ni}|e^{-j\theta_{ni}} \\
&= |c_{nv}||c_{ni}|[e^{j(\theta_{ni}-\theta_{nv})} + e^{-j(\theta_{ni}-\theta_{nv})}] \\
&= 2|c_{nv}||c_{ni}|\cos(\theta_{ni} - \theta_{nv}) \\
&= 2|c_{nv}||c_{ni}|\cos(\theta_{nv} - \theta_{ni}) \qquad (12\text{-}121)
\end{aligned}$$

These terms taken all together form

$$c_{0v}c_{0i} + \sum_{n=1}^{\infty} 2|c_{nv}||c_{ni}|\cos(\theta_{nv} - \theta_{ni}) \qquad (12\text{-}122)$$

Hence the expression for the average power becomes

$$\begin{aligned}
p_{\text{av}} &= \frac{1}{T}\int_0^T \left[c_{0v}c_{0i} + 2\sum_{n=1}^{\infty}|c_{nv}||c_{ni}|\cos(\theta_{nv} - \theta_{ni})\right] dt \qquad (12\text{-}123) \\
&= \left[c_{0v}c_{0i} + 2\sum_{n=1}^{\infty}|c_{nv}||c_{ni}|\cos(\theta_{nv} - \theta_{ni})\right]\frac{1}{T}\int_0^T dt \\
&= c_{0v}c_{0i} + 2\sum_{n=1}^{\infty}|c_{nv}||c_{ni}|\cos(\theta_{nv} - \theta_{ni}) \qquad (12\text{-}124)
\end{aligned}$$

The $|c_{nv}|$ and $|c_{ni}|$ coefficients are related to the nth harmonic voltage and current amplitudes V_n and I_n by

$$c_{0v} = V_{dc}, \qquad |c_{nv}| = \frac{1}{2}V_n, \qquad c_{0i} = I_{dc}, \qquad |c_{ni}| = \frac{1}{2}I_n \qquad (12\text{-}125)$$

Hence p_{av} can be written as

$$p_{\text{av}} = V_{\text{dc}}I_{\text{dc}} + \sum_{n=1}^{\infty}\frac{1}{2}V_nI_n\cos\theta_n \qquad (12\text{-}126)$$

where θ_n represents the phase difference between the nth harmonic voltage and current sinusoids while $\cos\theta_n$ is the corresponding power factor (see Chapter 8, Sec. 8). Finally, we can express p_{av} in terms of rms values and power factors as

$$p_{av} = V_{dc}I_{dc} + \sum_{n=1}^{\infty} V_{n\,rms}I_{n\,rms}\cos\theta_n \tag{12-127}$$

Equation (12-127) allows us to calculate the average power delivered to a two terminal network in terms of the harmonic components of the input voltage and input current waveforms. The expression shows that the total average power is the sum of the average powers produced by the dc values and by each harmonic taken one at a time. The mth harmonic component of $v(t)$ does not react with the nth $(m \neq n)$ harmonic component of $i(t)$ to produce average power. Only like frequency terms contribute to power.

Example 12-5

The voltage across a resistor is $v(t) = V_{dc} + V_m \sin\omega t$. What is the average power delivered to the resistor?

Solution. The voltage across the resistor is periodic with $T = 2\pi/\omega$. The waveform is composed of two terms only: a dc term and a fundamental term having an rms value of $V_m/\sqrt{2}$. All other harmonics are zero. The rms value of this waveform is obtained using Eq. (12-117).

$$V_{rms} = \sqrt{(\text{dc})^2 + (\text{rms})^2} = \sqrt{(V_{dc})^2 + \left(\frac{V_m}{\sqrt{2}}\right)^2} = \sqrt{V_{dc}^2 + \frac{1}{2}V_m^2}$$

Hence the average power delivered to the resistor is

$$p_{av} = \frac{V_{rms}^2}{R} = \frac{V_{dc}^2 + \frac{1}{2}V_m^2}{R} \qquad \text{Ans.}$$

Example 12-6

What is the average power delivered by the sawtooth current waveform of Fig. 12-19?

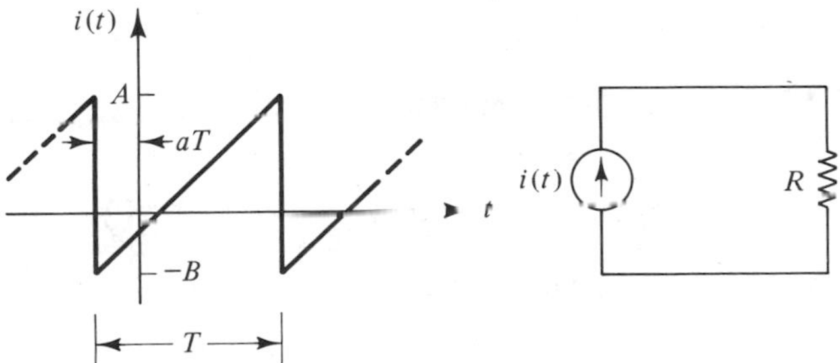

Fig. 12-19

Solution

Method 1 The expression for $i(t)$ is

$$i(t) = \frac{(A+B)}{T}(t + aT) - B \qquad -aT < t < T(1-a)$$

The average power delivered is

$$p_{av} = \frac{1}{T}\int_{-aT}^{T-aT} i^2(t)R\,dt = \frac{R}{T}\int_{-aT}^{T(1-a)} \left[\frac{(A+B)}{T}(t+aT) - B\right]^2 dt$$

$$= \frac{R(A+B)^2}{T^3}\int_{-aT}^{T(1-a)} \left[t + \left(aT - \frac{BT}{A+B}\right)\right]^2 dt$$

$$= \frac{R(A+B)^2}{T^3}\int_{-aT}^{T(1-a)} \left[t^2 + 2Tt\left(a - \frac{B}{A+B}\right) + T^2\left(a - \frac{B}{A+B}\right)^2\right] dt$$

$$= \frac{R(A+B)^2}{T^3}\left[\frac{t^3}{3} + Tt^2\left(a - \frac{B}{A+B}\right) + tT^2\left(a - \frac{B}{A+B}\right)^2\right]_{-aT}^{T(1-a)}$$

$$= R(A+B)^2\left[\frac{(1-a)^3}{3} + (1-a)^2\left(a - \frac{B}{A+B}\right) + (1-a)\left(a - \frac{B}{A+B}\right)^2 + \frac{a^3}{3} - a^2\left(a - \frac{B}{A+B}\right) + a\left(a - \frac{B}{A+B}\right)^2\right]$$

$$= \left[\frac{(A+B)^2}{3} - AB\right]R = \frac{(A^2 - AB + B^2)}{3}R \qquad \text{Ans.}$$

Note that p_{av} is independent of a, which controls the amount of the time shift.

Method 2 The sawtooth waveform of Fig. 12-19 is different from that of Fig. 12-13(d) in three ways. Its peak-to-peak amplitude is $(A + B)$ instead of A. Its average value is $\frac{1}{2}(A - B)$ instead of $\frac{1}{2}A$. It is shifted in time by aT seconds. When these three changes are incorporated in Eq. (12-64), which represents the Fourier series of the waveform of Fig. 12-13(d), we obtain the Fourier series of the waveform of Fig. 12-19.

$$i(t) = \frac{1}{2}(A-B) - \sum_{n=1}^{\infty}\frac{(A+B)}{n\pi}\sin\frac{2\pi n}{T}(t + aT) \tag{12-128}$$

The rms value of the nth harmonic is $(A + B)/n\pi\sqrt{2}$. Using the dc and rms values in Eq. (12-117), we obtain the rms value of $i(t)$.

$$I_{rms} = \sqrt{(\text{dc})^2 + \sum_{n=1}^{\infty}(\text{rms}_n)^2}$$

$$= \sqrt{\frac{1}{4}(A-B)^2 + \sum_{n=1}^{\infty}\left(\frac{A+B}{n\pi\sqrt{2}}\right)^2} = \sqrt{\frac{1}{4}(A-B)^2 + \frac{(A+B)^2}{2\pi^2}\sum_{n=1}^{\infty}\frac{1}{n^2}}$$

The infinite summation yields

$$\sum_{n=1}^{\infty}\frac{1}{n^2} = \frac{\pi^2}{6}$$

Hence, I_{rms} can be written as

$$I_{\text{rms}} = \sqrt{\frac{1}{4}(A - B)^2 + \frac{(A + B)^2}{2\pi^2}\frac{\pi^2}{6}} = \frac{1}{2}\sqrt{(A - B)^2 + \frac{(A + B)^2}{3}}$$

$$= \sqrt{\frac{A^2 - AB + B^2}{3}}$$

The average power can be calculated using this rms value.

$$p_{\text{av}} = I_{\text{rms}}^2 R = \left(\frac{A^2 - AB + B^2}{3}\right)R \quad \text{Ans.}$$

Example 12-7

What is the average power delivered by the triangular voltage source of Fig. 12-20?

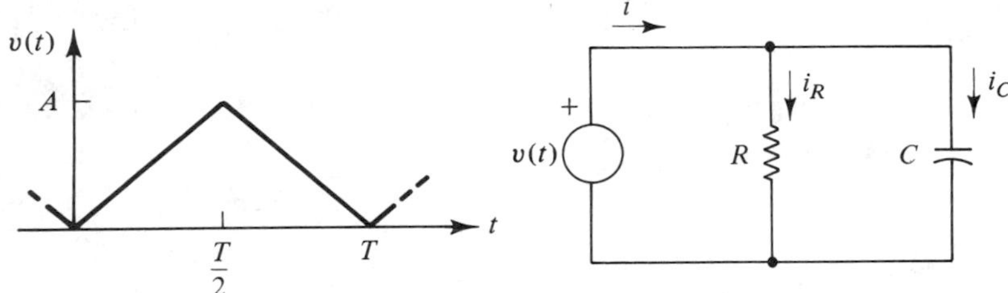

Fig. 12-20

Solution

Method 1 The current delivered by the voltage source is

$$i(t) = i_R(t) + i_C(t) = \frac{v(t)}{R} + C\frac{dv(t)}{dt}$$

From Eq. (12-62) we obtain the Fourier series for $v(t)$.

$$v(t) = \frac{A}{2} - \sum_{\substack{n=1\\ \text{odd}}}^{\infty} \frac{4A}{n^2\pi^2}\cos\frac{2\pi n}{T}t \tag{12-129}$$

Upon differentiation $v(t)$ becomes

$$\frac{dv(t)}{dt} = \sum_{\substack{n=1\\ \text{odd}}}^{\infty} \frac{8A}{n\pi T}\sin\frac{2\pi n}{T}t \tag{12-130}$$

Hence $i(t)$ can be written as

$$i(t) = \frac{1}{R}\left[\frac{A}{2} - \sum_{\substack{n=1\\ \text{odd}}}^{\infty} \frac{4A}{n^2\pi^2}\cos\frac{2\pi n}{T}t\right] + C\sum_{\substack{n=1\\ \text{odd}}}^{\infty} \frac{8A}{n\pi T}\sin\frac{2\pi n}{T}t \tag{12-131}$$

$$= \frac{A}{2R} + \frac{4A}{R\pi^2}\sum_{\substack{n=1\\ \text{odd}}}^{\infty} \frac{1}{n^2}\left(\frac{2\pi RCn}{T}\sin\frac{2\pi n}{T}t - \cos\frac{2\pi n}{T}t\right)$$

Using the trigonometry identity of

$$a \sin \theta - b \cos \theta = -\sqrt{a^2 + b^2} \cos \left(\theta + \tan^{-1} \frac{a}{b} \right)$$

we obtain

$$i(t) = \frac{A}{2R} - \frac{4A}{R\pi^2} \sum_{\substack{n=1 \\ \text{odd}}}^{\infty} \frac{1}{n^2} \sqrt{1 + \left(\frac{2\pi RCn}{T} \right)^2} \cos \left(\frac{2\pi n}{T} t + \tan^{-1} \frac{2\pi RCn}{R} \right) \tag{12-132}$$

The dc and the nth harmonic amplitudes of $v(t)$ and $i(t)$ are obtained from Eqs. (12-129) and (12-132). Division of peak values by $\sqrt{2}$ gives the rms values.

$$V_{\text{dc}} = \frac{A}{2}, \qquad V_{n\,\text{rms}} = \frac{4A}{n^2 \pi^2 \sqrt{2}}$$

$$I_{\text{dc}} = \frac{A}{2R}, \qquad I_{n\,\text{rms}} = \frac{4A}{n^2 R \pi^2 \sqrt{2}} \sqrt{1 + \left(\frac{2\pi RCn}{T} \right)^2}$$

Comparing the same two equations for the nth harmonic, we see that the phase difference between $v(t)$ and $i(t)$ is

$$\theta_n = \tan^{-1} \frac{2\pi RCn}{T}$$

The power factor, $\cos \theta_n$, is evaluated using the triangle of Fig. 12-21.

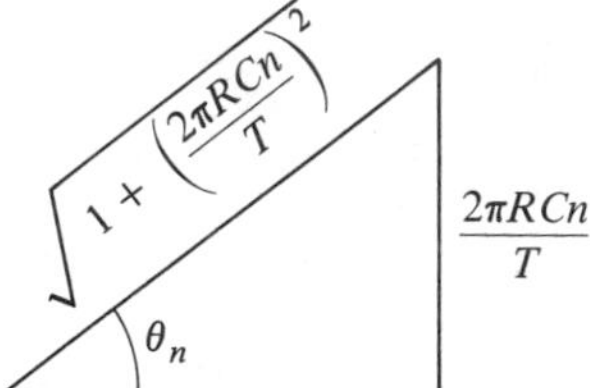

Fig. 12-21

$$\cos \theta_n = \frac{1}{\sqrt{1 + \left(\frac{2\pi RCn}{T} \right)^2}}$$

From Eq. (12-127) the average power delivered to the RC network is

$$p_{\text{av}} = V_{\text{dc}} I_{\text{dc}} + \sum_{\substack{n=1 \\ \text{odd}}}^{\infty} V_{n\,\text{rms}} I_{n\,\text{rms}} \cos \theta_n$$

$$= \frac{A^2}{4R} + \sum_{\substack{n=1 \\ \text{odd}}}^{\infty} \frac{4A}{n^2 \pi^2 \sqrt{2}} \frac{4A}{n^2 R \pi^2 \sqrt{2}} \sqrt{1 + \left(\frac{2\pi RCn}{T} \right)^2} \times \frac{1}{\sqrt{1 + \left(\frac{2\pi RCn}{T} \right)^2}}$$

$$= \frac{A^2}{4A} + \frac{8A^2}{\pi^4 R} \sum_{\substack{n=1 \\ \text{odd}}}^{\infty} \frac{1}{n^4}$$

When evaluated, the infinite summation yields

$$\sum_{\substack{n=1\\ \text{odd}}}^{\infty} \frac{1}{n^4} = \frac{\pi^4}{96}$$

Hence p_{av} becomes

$$p_{av} = \frac{A^2}{4R} + \frac{8A^2}{\pi^4 R}\frac{\pi^4}{96} = \frac{A^2}{3R} \quad \text{Ans.}$$

Method 2 For a capacitor $i_C(t) = C[dv_C(t)/dt]$. Therefore, if the voltage across it is a sine wave, the current through it will be a cosine wave. Thus, for each harmonic, $v_C(t)$ and $i_C(t)$ will be 90° out of phase, resulting in a power factor that is zero. Hence, the average power delivered to the capacitor is zero. The voltage source needs to supply power to the resistor only. Since the voltage across the resistor is

$$v(t) = \frac{A}{2} - \sum_{\substack{n=1\\ \text{odd}}}^{\infty} \frac{4A}{n^2\pi^2} \cos\frac{2\pi n}{T}t$$

the average power delivered to it is

$$p_{av} = \frac{V_{rms}^2}{R} \tag{12-133}$$

where V_{rms} is determined by Eq. (12-117b).

$$V_{rms} = \sqrt{(\text{dc})^2 + \sum_{n=1}^{\infty} (\text{rms}_n)^2}$$

$$= \sqrt{\frac{A^2}{4} + \sum_{\substack{n=1\\ \text{odd}}}^{\infty} \left(\frac{4A}{n^2\pi^2\sqrt{2}}\right)^2} = A\sqrt{\frac{1}{4} + \frac{8}{\pi^4}\sum_{\substack{n=1\\ \text{odd}}}^{\infty} \frac{1}{n^4}}$$

Substituting $\pi^4/96$ for the infinite summation and using Eq. (12-133), we obtain

$$p_{av} = \frac{A^2}{R}\left(\frac{1}{4} + \frac{8}{\pi^4}\frac{\pi^4}{96}\right) = \frac{A^2}{3R} \quad \text{Ans.}$$

Method 3 The average power can also be obtained from

$$p_{av} = \frac{1}{T}\int_0^T \frac{v^2(t)}{R}\,dt = \frac{A^2}{3R} \quad \text{Ans.} \tag{12-134}$$

The details of the integration are left as an exercise. See Problem 12-21.

12-9 FUNCTIONS WITH FINITE FOURIER SERIES

All the periodic functions considered so far have Fourier series expansions that contain an infinite number of terms. There are also functions that can be represented by *finite trigonometric series*. Such representations should not be confused with the truncated versions of infinite series where the aim is to get a reasonable approximation with as few terms as possible. Rather, the interest here is in *exact* representation with a finite number of terms. Consider, for example, the function

$$f(t) = (1 + 0.5 \cos 2\pi t) \cos 20\pi t \tag{12-135}$$

This function does not represent a cosine wave. Nonetheless, it can be thought of as a 10 Hz cosine wave, the amplitude of which is varied at the much slower rate of 1 Hz. Such waves are called *amplitude-modulated* waves. It is not immediately obvious that this function is periodic. However, the plot of $f(t)$ in Fig. 12-22 for $t \geq 0$ shows that it has a period T of 1 second. Hence, $f(t)$ can be represented by a Fourier series. Since $f(t)$ is an even function with zero average value, its expansion will take the form

$$f(t) = \sum_{n=1}^{\infty} a_n \cos 2\pi nt$$

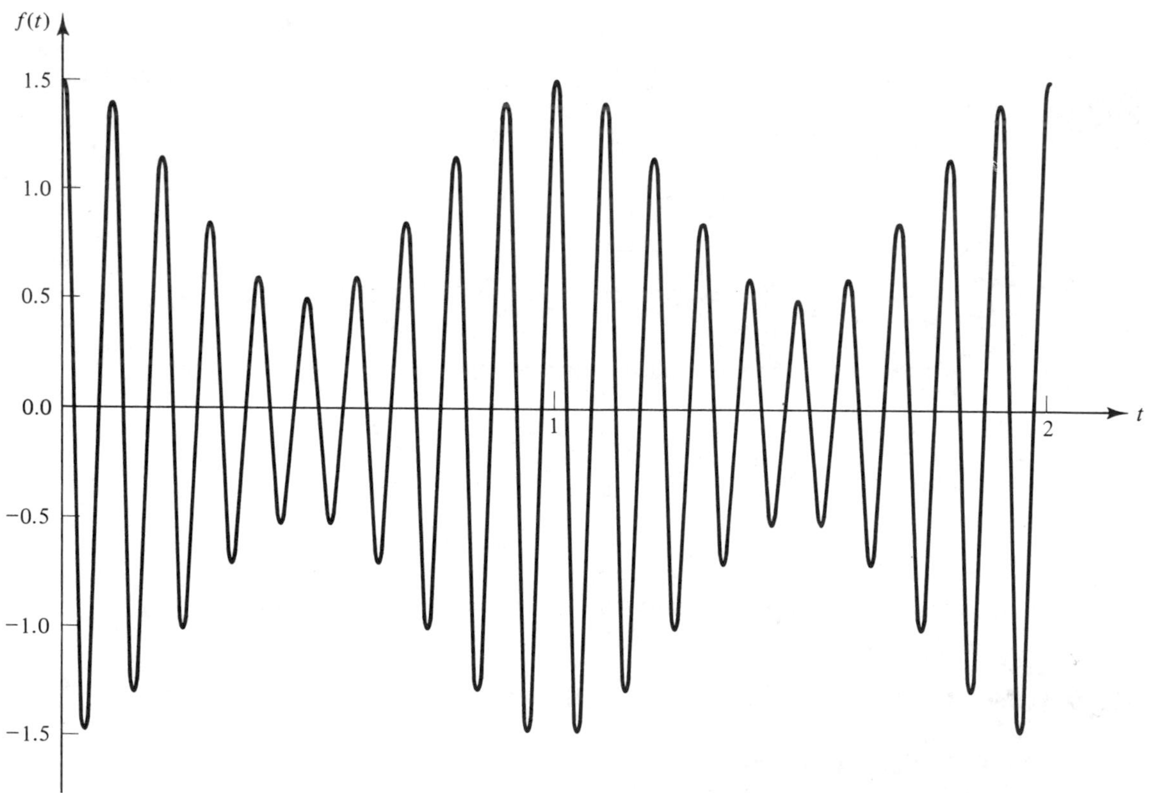

Fig. 12-22

where

$$a_n = 2\int_0^1 f(t)\cos 2\pi nt\,dt = 2\int_0^1 [(1 + 0.5\cos 2\pi t)\cos 20\pi t]\cos 2\pi nt\,dt \tag{12-136}$$

It will take some effort to perform the indicated integration to evaluate a_n. Fortunately there is an easier way to solve this problem. Using the trigonometric identity

$$2\cos A\cos B = \cos(A + B) + \cos(A - B)$$

in Eq. (12-135), we obtain

$$\begin{aligned} f(t) &= \cos 20\pi t + 0.5\cos 2\pi t\cos 20\pi t \\ &= \cos 20\pi t + 0.25\cos 22\pi t + 0.25\cos 18\pi t \\ &= 0.25\cos 2\pi\times 9t + \cos 2\pi\times 10t + 0.25\cos 2\pi\times 11t \end{aligned} \tag{12-137}$$

Equation (12-137) represents the Fourier series expansion of the waveform given by Eq. (12-135). It is a finite series but is exact. It contains only three terms with frequencies 9, 10, and 11 Hz, respectively. Since $T = 1$, the fundamental frequency is 1 Hz. Therefore the three terms present are the 9th, 10th, and 11th harmonic frequencies. All other frequencies, including the fundamental, are absent. The 10th harmonic has the largest amplitude (1); the 9th and 11th harmonic amplitudes are smaller (0.25). Thus, the situation here is quite different from all the previous examples, where the fundamental frequency was always present and had the largest amplitude.

That there exist waveforms with a missing fundamental or other harmonics and with harmonic amplitudes that are greater than the fundamental should not be surprising. Indeed, it is rather easy to *construct* such waveforms. All we have to do is to pick a bunch of sinusoidal waves, the frequencies of which are all harmonically related to some fundamental frequency which may or may not be present. Then we can assign any arbitrary amplitude and phase to each harmonic and add the resulting terms to form a periodic waveform. For example, consider

$$f(t) = A + B\sin(\omega t + \theta) + C\cos(1.25\omega t + \psi) \tag{12-138}$$

where A, B, C, ω, θ, and ψ are arbitrary constants. The frequencies of the sinusoidal and cosinusoidal waves are ω and 1.25ω, respectively. Since these two frequencies are not integer multiples of each other, we don't know what the fundamental frequency is—or for that matter we can't even tell whether the waveform is periodic. However, if it is periodic, then ω and 1.25ω should be integer multiples, n_1 and n_2, of some fundamental frequency, say ω_f.

$$\omega = n_1\omega_f$$

$$1.25\omega = n_2\omega_f$$

This set of equations gives an n_2/n_1 ratio of 1.25 to 1, which is not a ratio of integers. However, it can be converted to a ratio of integers as shown below.

$$\frac{n_2}{n_1} = 1.25 = 1.25 \times \frac{4}{4} = \frac{5}{4}$$

With $n_1 = 4$ and $n_2 = 5$, we see that $\omega = n_1\omega_f = 4\omega_f$ and $1.25\omega = n_2\omega_f = 5\omega_f$. Hence, the second and third terms in Eq. (12-138) represent the fourth and fifth harmonic terms of $f(t)$. All other harmonic terms, including the fundamental, are absent. The period of $f(t)$ is given by

$$T = \frac{2\pi}{\omega_f} = \frac{2\pi}{\omega/n_1} = \frac{8\pi}{\omega}$$

An infinite variety of periodic functions can be constructed by assigning different values to the A, B, C, ω, θ, and ψ constants of Eq. (12-138). If ω is kept the same, all the functions will have the same period but the waveforms will be different.

Just to show how important the effect of phase alone can be, the function given by

$$f(t) = \sin 2\pi t + \frac{1}{3}\sin(6\pi t + \theta)$$

is plotted in Fig. 12-23 for $\theta = 0$ and $\theta = \pi$. Although both functions have the same period and their harmonics have the same amplitude, the resulting waveforms are remarkably different.

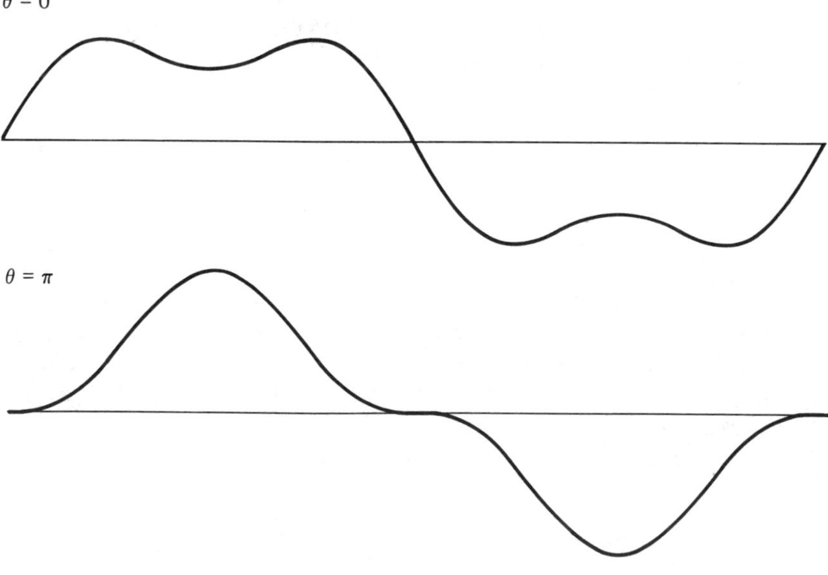

Fig. 12-23

12-10 GENERATION OF HARMONICS

In a *linear* circuit with left half-plane poles, all steady-state responses produced by a single sinusoidal source of frequency ω are sinusoidal and of the same frequency. Only their amplitudes and phases are different. On the other hand, if the circuit is *nonlinear,* the sine waves become distorted. As a result, harmonics are generated. For an example we will study the hyperbolic tangent type nonlinearity encountered in amplifiers.

The transfer characteristic (input-output relationship) of an ideal amplifier is given by

$$v_o = Kv_i$$

This is a linear relationship, where K is a constant that represents the gain of the amplifier. When such an amplifier is driven by $v_i = V_m \sin \omega t$, it produces an output of $v_o = KV_m \sin \omega t$, which is a scaled replica of the input. The dashed lines in Fig. 12-24 show the transfer characteristic and the output waveform for the ideal amplifier.

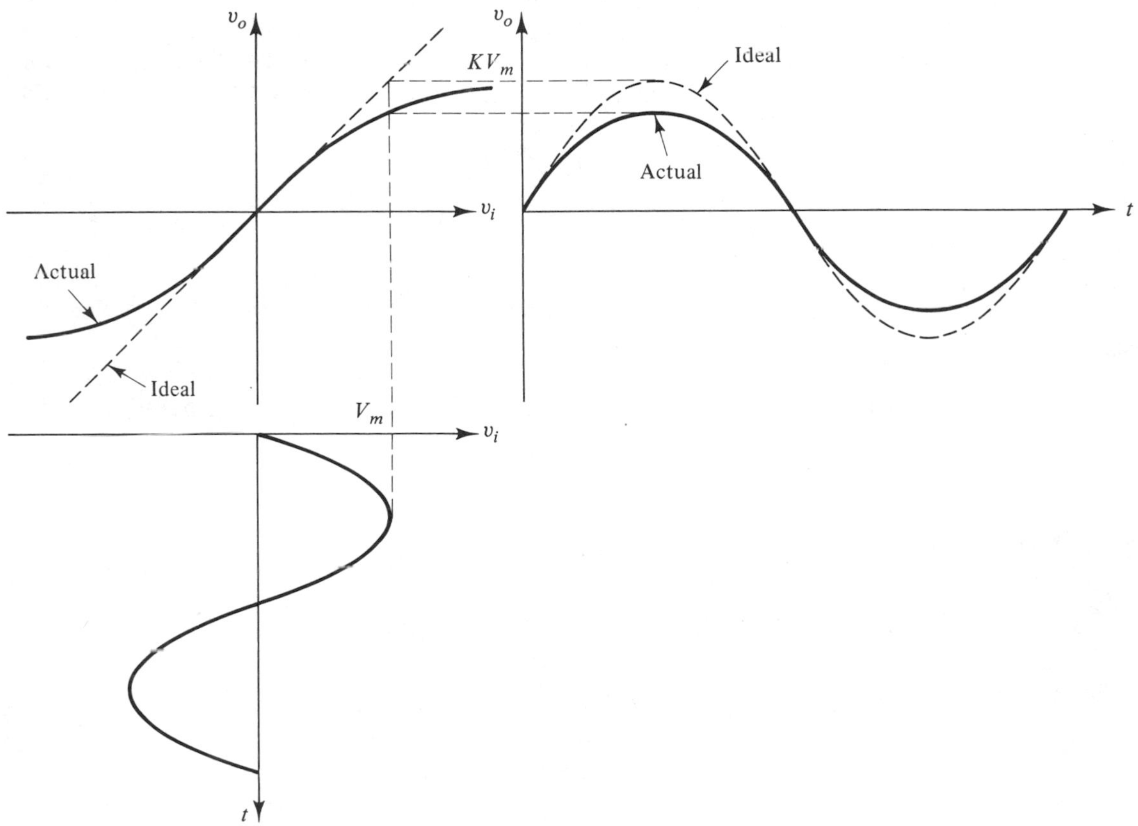

Fig. 12-24

The transfer characteristic of a *nonideal* amplifier is given by

$$v_o = KV_T \tanh \frac{v_i}{V_T} \tag{12-139}$$

where K and V_T are constants. This is not a linear relationship. For example, if we double the input v_i, the output v_o does not quite double. When a sinusoidal input voltage is applied to this amplifier, the output voltage will not be a scaled replica of the input. Instead a waveform that is somewhat flattened at the top and at the bottom will result as shown in the diagram. The larger the amplitude V_m of the input sine wave, the more distorted (flattened) will the output waveform become. The output is given by

$$v_o = KV_T \tanh \frac{v_i}{V_T} = KV_T \tanh\left(\frac{V_m}{V_T}\sin \omega t\right)$$

Though not sinusoidal, this waveform is periodic with $T = 2\pi/\omega$. It has no dc term. Since both sine and tanh functions are odd, the output is an even function. Furthermore, it has half-wave symmetry. See waveform of Fig. 12-24. Hence the Fourier series of $v_o(t)$ will contain only odd harmonic cosine waves. (In practice there will also be some small even harmonic terms present, because it is impossible to construct actual amplifiers with characteristics that are exactly odd.) Thus we can write

$$v_o = \sum_{\substack{n=1\\ \text{odd}}}^{\infty} a_n \cos n\omega t$$

where

$$a_n = \frac{4\omega}{\pi}\int_0^{\pi/2\omega} KV_T \tanh\left(\frac{V_m}{V_T}\sin \omega t\right)\cos n\omega t\, dt$$

This integration is rather involved. A better and much faster approach would be to make use of the series approximation for the hyperbolic tangent function

$$\tanh x \cong x - \frac{x^3}{3} \qquad |x| \ll 1$$

and obtain directly a finite but approximate trigonometric expansion for v_o.

$$v_o = KV_T \tanh\frac{v_i}{V_T} \cong KV_T\left[\frac{v_i}{V_T} - \frac{1}{3}\left(\frac{v_i}{V_T}\right)^3\right] = Kv_i - \frac{K}{3V_T^2}v_i^3$$

$$= KV_m \sin \omega t - \frac{KV_m^3}{3V_T^2}\sin^3 \omega t \qquad \left(\left|\frac{v_i}{V_T}\right| \ll 1\right)$$

Making use of the trigonometric identity

$$\sin^3 x = \frac{1}{4}(3 \sin x - \sin 3x)$$

we can simplify the expression for v_o to

$$v_o \cong KV_m \sin \omega t - \frac{KV_m^3}{12V_T^2}(3 \sin \omega t - \sin 3\omega t)$$

$$= KV_m\left[1 - \frac{1}{4}\left(\frac{V_m}{V_T}\right)^2\right] \sin \omega t + KV_m \frac{1}{12}\left(\frac{V_m}{V_T}\right)^2 \sin 3\omega t \qquad \frac{V_m}{V_T} \ll 1 \qquad (12\text{-}140)$$

If V_m is made quite small in comparison to the constant V_T, then Eq. (12-140) simplifies further to

$$v_o \cong KV_m \sin \omega t$$

This also would have been the result if the amplifier had been linear. From Eq. (12-140) we see that, for signals of small amplitude, the effect of hyperbolic tangent type nonlinearity is twofold. The gain for the fundamental frequency is slightly reduced, from K to $K[1 - \frac{1}{4}(V_m/V_T)^2]$. More importantly, a distortion-producing third-harmonic term of amplitude $(KV_m/12)(V_m/V_T)^2$ is generated. The larger the V_m/V_T ratio, the more noticeable becomes the distortion. The third harmonic term reaches its minimum value when the fundamental reaches its maximum value and vice versa. As a result, the two terms oppose each other, and the output waveform is symmetrically flattened. See Fig. 12-24. Such third harmonic distortion terms are quite common in amplifiers, particularly when they are driven with large signals.

As a measure of the amount of distortion produced by amplifiers, a figure of merit, called *total harmonic distortion* (*THD*), is used. It is defined by

$$\text{THD} = \frac{\text{rms value of waveform without the dc and the fundamental}}{\text{rms value of fundamental}}$$

The rms value of the waveform without the dc and fundamental terms can be obtained using Eq. (12-117b). Hence, THD can be written as

$$\text{THD} = \frac{\sqrt{\sum_{n=2}^{\infty} (\text{rms}_n)^2}}{\text{rms}_1} \qquad (12\text{-}141)$$

The lower the distortion, the more the output looks like a sine wave, and hence the smaller are the higher harmonic amplitudes and correspondingly the THD. Since the amount of distortion produced varies with the input signal amplitude, THD is calculated for a specified V_m. For the amplifier with the hyperbolic tangent nonlinearity, the THD is given by

$$\text{THD} = \frac{\sqrt{\sum_{\substack{n=3\\ \text{odd}}}^{\infty} \text{rms}_n^2}}{\text{rms}_1} \cong \frac{\text{rms}_3}{\text{rms}_1} = \frac{KV_m \frac{1}{12}\left(\frac{V_m}{V_T}\right)^2 \frac{1}{\sqrt{2}}}{KV_m\left[1 - \frac{1}{4}\left(\frac{V_m}{V_T}\right)^2\right]\frac{1}{\sqrt{2}}} = \frac{1}{12}\frac{\left(\frac{V_m}{V_T}\right)^2}{\left[1 - \frac{1}{4}\left(\frac{V_m}{V_T}\right)^2\right]}$$

which for $\frac{1}{4}(V_m/V_T)^2 \ll 1$ simplifies to

$$\text{THD} \cong \frac{1}{12}\left(\frac{V_m}{V_T}\right)^2$$

For $V_m/V_T = 0.1$, THD is $0.01/12 = 0.00083$ or 0.083%.

12-11 APPLICATION OF FOURIER SERIES TO NETWORK PROBLEMS

The Fourier series can be used to obtain the steady-state responses in a linear network that is excited by a nonsinusoidal, periodic input. The procedure involves three steps. First the input is decomposed into its sinusoidal components using the Fourier series expansion. Then the sinusoidal steady-state response produced by a general term of the series is calculated using the method outlined in Section 3 or 5 of Chapter 8. Finally the responses caused by the individual terms are superimposed to obtain the total response.

Although this procedure is easy to apply, the results appear as infinite sums and hence may sometimes be difficult to interpret, in which case other methods of solution may be more appropriate. We now look at a number of examples where Fourier series is used in the solution of network problems.

Example 12-8

In Fig. 12-25 the shape of the current pulses is not specified. However, it is known that the pulses are quite narrow, that is, $\delta \ll T$. The RC network is used as a first-order lowpass filter to convert the current pulses to a dc voltage and at the same time produce negligible ac. The resistor R_L is fixed. What size must the capacitor C be if the amplitude of the fundamental component of the steady-state output voltage is to be no more than 10% of the dc output?

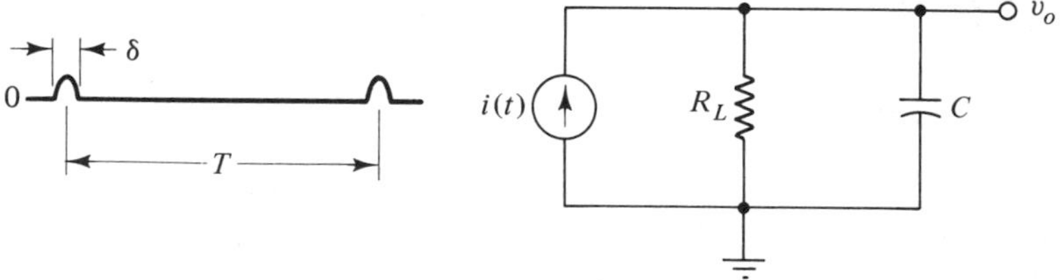

Fig. 12-25

Solution. Although the $i(t)$ waveform is not specified, the expression for its average (dc) value can nonetheless be set up.

$$i_{\text{av}} = \frac{1}{T}\int_{-T/2}^{T/2} i(t)dt = I_{\text{dc}} \tag{12-142}$$

The amplitudes of the harmonics are independent of the origin of time. For convenience of calculation, let us therefore place $t = 0$ at the center of the current pulse, thereby making $i(t)$ an even function. Its Fourier series representation is

$$i(t) = \sum_{n=1}^{\infty} a_n \cos \frac{2\pi n}{T} t \qquad (12\text{-}143)$$

where

$$a_n = \frac{2}{T} \int_{-T/2}^{T/2} i(t) \cos \frac{2\pi n}{T} t \, dt$$

For the fundamental component, we have

$$a_1 = \frac{2}{T} \int_{-T/2}^{T/2} i(t) \cos \frac{2\pi}{T} t \, dt \qquad (12\text{-}144)$$

In Fig. 12-26 $i(t)$ and $\cos (2\pi/T)t$ are sketched. Because the current is zero over most of the period, the product term [the integrand in Eq. (12-144)] too will be zero most of the time, except for the narrow segment of time lasting δ seconds. Over this interval of time, the value of the cosine term is essentially 1 as shown. Hence the product term is essentially $i(t)$. As a result a_1 can be approximated as

$$a_1 \cong \frac{2}{T} \int_{-T/2}^{T/2} i(t) \, dt \qquad (12\text{-}145)$$

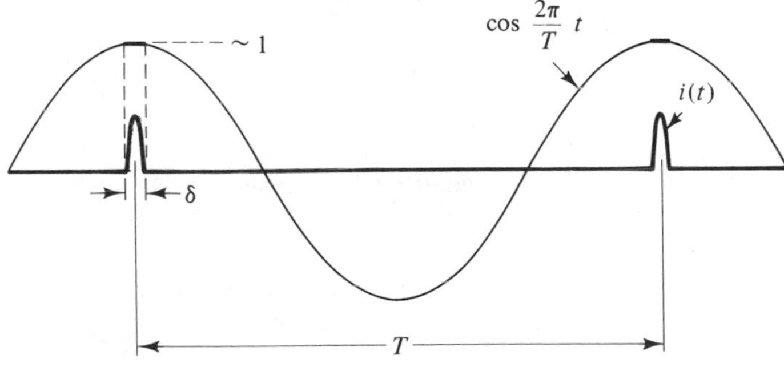

Fig. 12-26

When Eqs. (12-142) and (12-145) are compared, we see that

$$a_1 = 2I_{dc}$$

This is an interesting and important result which has far more general applicability than indicated for the present example. It states that *the amplitude of the fundamental is twice the average value* for all waveforms that are zero except for a short segment of time during the period. Indeed, the same evaluation procedure can be used to demonstrate that the second and even higher harmonics will have amplitudes that are twice the average value provided the waveform is narrow enough. [Refer to Fig. 12-16(c) to see the general shape of the amplitude spectrum of such narrow pulses.]

To find out how the network processes the input, we must calculate the transfer function. From Fig. 12-25, we have

$$T(s) = \frac{V_o(s)}{I_i(s)} = Z_i(s) = \frac{1}{Y_i(s)} = \frac{1}{sC + \dfrac{1}{R_L}} = \frac{R_L}{sR_LC + 1} \tag{12-146}$$

Since we are interested in the steady-state response due to the dc and fundamental input terms only, we evaluate $T(s)$ for $s = 0$ and $s = j(2\pi/T)$.

$$T(0) = R_L$$

$$T\left(j\frac{2\pi}{T}\right) = \frac{R_L}{1 + j\dfrac{2\pi}{T}R_LC} = \frac{R_L}{\sqrt{1 + \left(\dfrac{2\pi R_LC}{T}\right)^2}} \angle -\tan^{-1}\frac{2\pi R_LC}{T}$$

The steady-state output due to the dc component of the input is

$$v_{odc} = i_{av} \times T(0) = I_{dc}R_L$$

The steady-state output due to the fundamental component of the input (of a_1 in amplitude) is

$$v_{of} = a_1 \left|T\left(j\frac{2\pi}{T}\right)\right| \cos\left(\frac{2\pi}{T}t + \theta_T\right)$$

$$= 2I_{dc}\frac{R_L}{\sqrt{1 + \left(\dfrac{2\pi R_LC}{T}\right)^2}} \cos\left(\frac{2\pi}{T}t - \tan^{-1}\frac{2\pi R_LC}{T}\right)$$

If the amplitude of the fundamental component of the output voltage is to be no more than 10% of the dc value, we must satisfy the condition

$$2I_{dc}\frac{R_L}{\sqrt{1 + \left(\dfrac{2\pi R_LC}{T}\right)^2}} \le 0.1I_{dc}R_L$$

Solving for C, we obtain

$$C \ge \frac{T}{2\pi}\frac{\sqrt{399}}{R_L} \qquad \text{Ans.}$$

If $R_L = 1\ \text{K}\Omega$ and $T = 1/60$ seconds, then C must have a value of

$$C \ge \frac{1}{120\pi}\frac{\sqrt{399}}{10^3} = 53\ \mu\text{F}$$

The sum of the harmonics in the output constitutes a ripple on the dc voltage. For a given load R_L, the larger the C that is used the smaller becomes the ripple.

Example 12-9

Refer to Fig. 12-27.

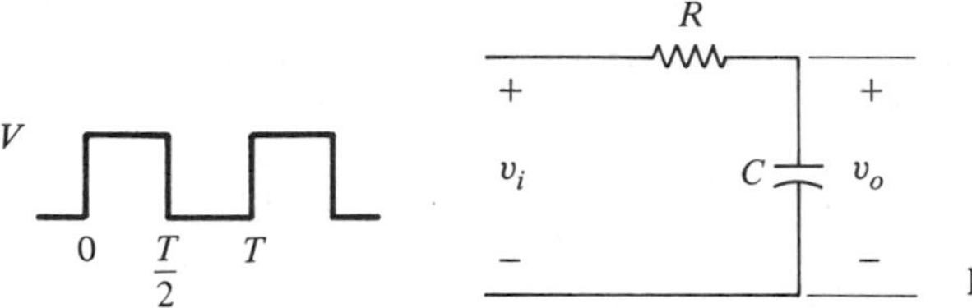

Fig. 12-27

(a) Obtain the steady-state response. Discuss the result.
(b) Sketch the response produced by the terms through the fifteenth harmonic if the bandwidth of the filter BW is related to the fundamental frequency by $BW = \omega_f$. Repeat for $BW = 15\omega_f$. Discuss the results.

Solution

(a) The average value of the input square wave is $V/2$. Using this value in conjunction with the result of Example 12-1, we obtain the Fourier series representation of the input waveform.

$$v_i(t) = \frac{V}{2} + \frac{2V}{\pi} \sum_{\substack{n=1 \\ \text{odd}}}^{\infty} \frac{1}{n} \sin n\omega_f t$$

where $\omega_f = 2\pi/T$ represents the fundamental frequency. The amplitudes of the various harmonics are given by

$$a_n = \frac{2V}{\pi n}$$

The transfer function of the network is

$$T(s) = \frac{V_o(s)}{V_i(s)} = \frac{\dfrac{1}{sC}}{R + \dfrac{1}{sC}} = \frac{1}{1 + sRC} \tag{12-147}$$

This $T(s)$ represents the transfer function of a first-order lowpass filter. See discussion in Sec. 2 of Chapter 9. Its magnitude and phase characteristics are continuous functions of ω and are obtained from

$$T(j\omega) = \frac{1}{1 + j\omega RC}$$

$$|T(j\omega)| = \frac{1}{\sqrt{1 + (\omega RC)^2}}$$

$$\theta_T(\omega) = -\tan^{-1} \omega RC$$

The dc component of the input produces a steady-state output of

$$v_{odc} = \frac{V}{2}T(0) = \frac{V}{2} \tag{12-148}$$

The nth harmonic of the input, corresponding to the discrete frequency of $n\omega_f$, produces a steady-state output of

$$v_{on}(t) = \frac{2V}{\pi n} \mid T(jn\omega_f) \mid \sin (n\omega_f t + \theta_T) \tag{12-149}$$

where

$$\mid T(jn\omega_f) \mid = \frac{1}{\sqrt{1 + (n\omega_f RC)^2}}$$

$$\theta_T = -\tan^{-1} n\omega_f RC$$

[In some of these equations the letter T designates both the transfer function $T(s)$ and the period T, but this should not cause any confusion].

The input can be thought of as an infinite number of voltage sources, each of which produces its own unique output. Therefore, the output can be obtained by superimposing (summing) all the individual outputs. Using the results of Eqs. (12-148) and (12-149), $v_o(t)$ can be expressed as

$$\begin{aligned} v_o(t) &= \frac{V}{2} + \frac{2V}{\pi} \sum_{\substack{n=1 \\ \text{odd}}}^{\infty} \frac{1}{n} \mid T(jn\omega_f) \mid \sin (n\omega_f t + \theta_T) \\ &= \frac{V}{2} + \frac{2V}{\pi} \sum_{\substack{n=1 \\ \text{odd}}}^{\infty} \frac{1}{n\sqrt{1 + (n\omega_f RC)^2}} \sin (n\omega_f t - \tan^{-1} n\omega_f RC) \quad \text{Ans.} \end{aligned} \tag{12-150}$$

In order to see how the circuit processes the input waveform, we look at Fig. 12-28, where the amplitude spectrum of the input and the magnitude characteristic of the lowpass filter are displayed.

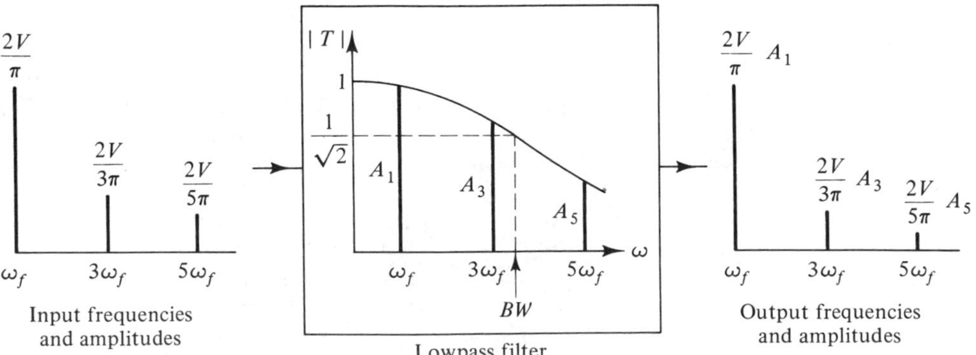

Fig. 12-28

At the fundamental frequency, the input amplitude of $2V/\pi$ is multiplied by the magnitude A_1 of the transfer function to produce the output amplitude of $2VA_1/\pi$. Similarly, the third harmonic amplitude $2V/3\pi$ is multiplied by A_3 to produce $2VA_3/3\pi$ and so on. Thus the input amplitude spectrum is reshaped by the lowpass filter to produce the output amplitude spectrum. A similar diagram can be constructed to show how the phase is altered.

(b) Although the expression for the output voltage is easily obtained, it is difficult to visualize what its waveform is by looking at the infinite summation. Even with the aid of Fig. 12-28, we see what is happening but not what the result is. From Eq. (9-8) we know that the bandwidth BW of this filter is $1/RC$. See also Fig. 12-28. Frequencies lower than $1/RC$ are passed more or less and frequencies higher than $1/RC$ are attenuated more or less. Since the outcome of the filter depends on the relationship between the bandwidth BW and the fundamental frequency ω_f, it is best to express Eq. (12-150) using BW in place of $1/RC$.

$$v_o(t) = \frac{V}{2} + \frac{2V}{\pi}\sum_{\substack{n=1\\ \text{odd}}}^{\infty} \frac{1}{n\sqrt{1 + \left(\dfrac{n\omega_f}{BW}\right)^2}} \sin\left(n\omega_f t - \tan^{-1}\frac{n\omega_f}{BW}\right) \tag{12-151}$$

This equation is approximated by truncating it to $n_{\max} = 15$ and is plotted in Fig. 12-29 for $BW = \omega_f$ and $BW = 15\omega_f$. When $BW = \omega_f$, the bandwidth is quite narrow; only the fundamental component is within the passband. As a result, the

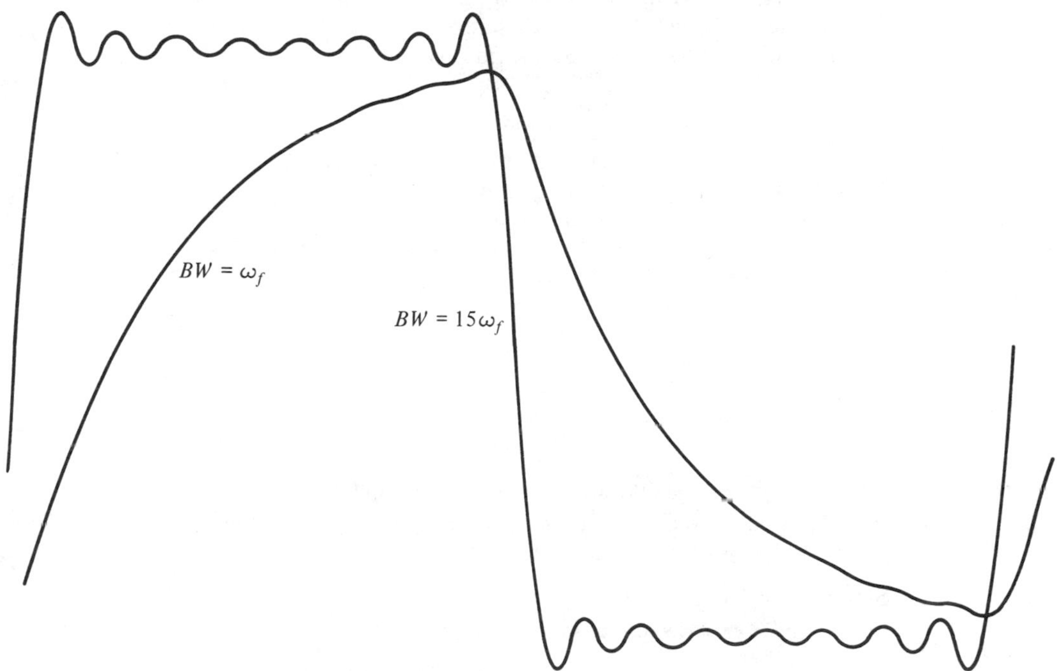

Fig. 12-29

waveform is rather "sluggish." It takes a long time to make the transition between the 0 and the V levels on its way up and on its way down. This is to be expected because the transition is primarily formed by the fundamental component, which is the slowest-varying waveform. The contribution of the other harmonics is such that the overall waveform looks surprisingly like an exponential. When $BW = 15\omega_f$, the bandwidth is quite wide; harmonics through the fifteenth are passed. Hence, more of the components that make up the square wave appear at the output. As a result, the transition between the two levels takes less time. Unlike the narrow-bandwidth case, here the transition waveforms do not look like exponentials, which is rather misleading. Of course, had we used the infinite series rather than the finite series for plotting, the exponential nature of the waveform would have emerged, even though there is no way of knowing that this would be the case by looking at Eq. (12-151).

The solution of this problem is given also in Example 16 of Chapter 6. The method of solution used there shows the exact exponential nature of the waveform. Rather than using the frequency-domain concept of bandwidth $BW = 1/RC$, there the time-domain concept of time constant $\tau = RC$ is used to relate the circuit constants to the period T of the input. The two concepts are related by $\tau = 1/BW$. Thus, a large bandwidth implies a short time constant and hence faster exponential transitions. Although Eq. (12-150) or (12-151) gives the exact expression for the output, practically speaking, these equations are useless because the results are difficult to interpret. The power and beauty of the Fourier series is lost here. By contrast, the methods of Chapter 6 are ideally suited to this problem. They are direct and easy to use, give exact results, and provide physical insight about the operation of the circuit.

Example 12-10

Refer to Fig. 12-30.

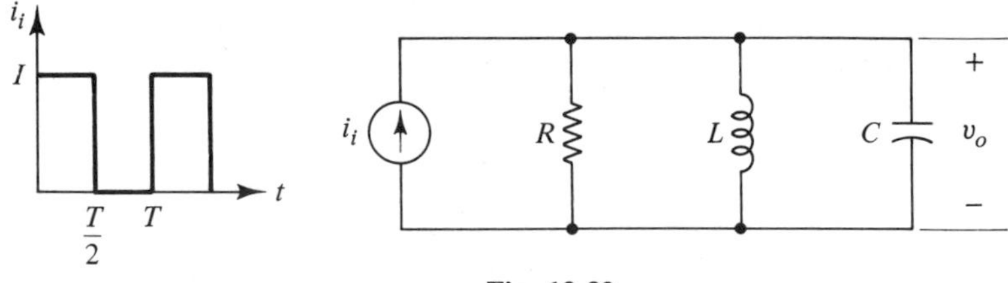

Fig. 12-30

(a) Obtain the expression for the steady-state output voltage.

(b) The circuit is tuned to the fundamental frequency of the input square wave. What is the steady-state output? Discuss its waveform.

Solution

(a) The Fourier series of the input waveform is

$$i_i(t) = \frac{T}{2} + \frac{2I}{\pi} \sum_{\substack{n=1 \\ \text{odd}}}^{\infty} \frac{1}{n} \sin n\omega_f t$$

where $\omega_f = 2\pi/T$. The input current can be regarded as a constant plus individual sine waves (with frequencies ω_f, $3\omega_f$, $5\omega_f$, . . .) all acting on the network one at a time. Any one of the sine waves can be represented by

$$\underbrace{\frac{2I}{n\pi}}_{\text{Amplitude}} \sin \underbrace{n\omega_f}_{\text{Frequency}} t \qquad (n = 1, 3, 5, \ldots) \tag{12-152}$$

The output of the network is related to its input by

$$T(s) = \frac{V_o(s)}{I_i(s)} = R\left(\frac{s\omega_b}{s^2 + s\omega_b + \omega_p^2}\right) \tag{12-153}$$

where

$$\omega_b = \frac{1}{RC}, \qquad \omega_p = \frac{1}{\sqrt{LC}}$$

From Eq. (12-153) we obtain the magnitude and phase of $T(s)$ for $s = j\omega$, where ω represents the input frequency.

$$|T(j\omega)| = R\frac{\omega\omega_b}{\sqrt{(\omega_p^2 - \omega^2)^2 + (\omega\omega_b)^2}} \tag{12-154a}$$

$$\theta_T = \frac{\pi}{2} - \tan^{-1}\left(\frac{\omega\omega_b}{\omega_p^2 - \omega^2}\right) \tag{12-154b}$$

The magnitude characteristic is that of a bandpass function with center frequency ω_p and bandwidth ω_b. See Sec. 4 of Chapter 9 for details.

The steady-state output due to the dc term in the input is

$$v_{odc} = \frac{I}{2} \times T(0) = 0$$

There is no dc term in the output because under constant excitation voltages across inductors approach zero after five time constants.

The steady-state output due to the single sinusoidal input given by Eq. (12-152) is

$$\frac{2I}{n\pi} \times |T(jn\omega_f)| \sin(n\omega_f t + \theta_T)$$

By superposition, the steady-state output is then obtained.

$$v_o = \frac{2I}{\pi}\sum_{\substack{n=1\\ \text{odd}}}^{\infty} \frac{|T(jn\omega_f)|}{n} \sin(n\omega_f t + \theta_T)$$

$$= \frac{2IR}{\pi}\sum_{\substack{n=1\\ \text{odd}}}^{\infty} \frac{1}{n}\left\{\frac{(n\omega_f)\omega_b}{\sqrt{[\omega_p^2 - (n\omega_f)^2]^2 + [(n\omega_f)\omega_b]^2}}\right\}$$

$$\sin\left[(n\omega_f)t + \frac{\pi}{2} - \tan^{-1}\frac{(n\omega_f)\omega_b}{\omega_p^2 - (n\omega_f)^2}\right]$$

$$= \frac{2IR}{\pi} \sum_{\substack{n=1 \\ \text{odd}}}^{\infty} \frac{\omega_f \omega_b}{\sqrt{[\omega_p^2 - (n\omega_f)^2]^2 + [(n\omega_f)\omega_b]^2}}$$

$$\times \cos\left[(n\omega_f)t - \tan^{-1}\frac{(n\omega_f)\omega_b}{\omega_p^2 - (n\omega_f)^2}\right] \quad \text{Ans.} \tag{12-155}$$

(b) The fundamental frequency of the input is ω_f. The circuit is tuned to this fundamental frequency by adjusting LC such that

$$\omega_p = \frac{1}{\sqrt{LC}} = \omega_f$$

Then, the expression of the output voltage simplifies to

$$v_o(t) = \frac{2IR}{\pi} \sum_{\substack{n=1 \\ \text{odd}}}^{\infty} \frac{\omega_b}{\sqrt{\omega_f^2(1 - n^2)^2 + n^2\omega_b^2}}$$

$$\times \cos\left[(n\omega_f)t - \tan^{-1}\frac{n\omega_b}{\omega_f(1 - n^2)}\right] \quad \text{Ans.} \tag{12-156}$$

This output waveform, though somewhat simpler than that given for the general case, is still difficult to visualize. To obtain a clear physical picture of what the network does, we refer to Fig. 12-31. The fundamental component of the input has frequency ω_f and amplitude $2I/\pi$. Since the filter is tuned to the fundamental frequency, it produces the greatest output at this frequency. See Fig. 12-31. Thus the fundamental component of the output has an amplitude of

$$\frac{2I}{\pi}|T(j\omega_f)| = \frac{2I}{\pi}A_1 = \frac{2IR}{\pi} \tag{12-157}$$

The third harmonic component of the input has a frequency of $3\omega_f$ and amplitude $2I/3\pi$. As shown in Fig. 12-31, at this frequency the magnitude of $T(j\omega)$ is much less than at the fundamental frequency. As a result, the third harmonic, which is smaller in amplitude than the fundamental to begin with, comes out of the filter with much smaller amplitude. The more selective the filter (the smaller the band-

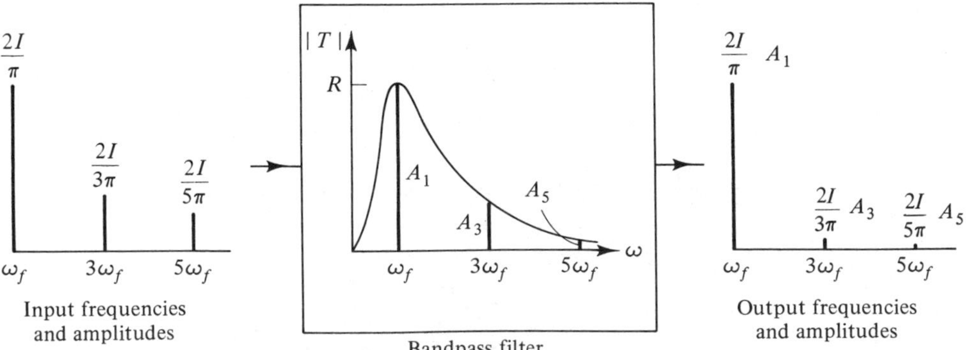

Fig. 12-31

width ω_b) is made, the more the third harmonic is attenuated. The third harmonic component of the output has an amplitude of

$$\frac{2I}{3\pi}|T(j3\omega_f)| = \frac{2I}{3\pi}A_3 = \frac{2IR}{\pi}\left[\frac{1}{\sqrt{9 + 64(\omega_f/\omega_b)^2}}\right] \tag{12-158}$$

This amplitude can be made very small compared to the fundamental amplitude by making ω_f/ω_b large. For example, if the bandwidth of the filter is 10% of the center frequency, $\omega_b = \omega_f/10$, then

$$\text{third harmonic amplitude} = \frac{\text{fundamental amplitude}}{\sqrt{6409}}$$

and therefore the third harmonic may be considered negligible.

The fifth harmonic component of the output is much smaller still because the fifth harmonic component of the input is small to begin with and the filter attenuates much more at the fifth harmonic frequency. The amplitude of this component is given by

$$\frac{2I}{5\pi}|T(j5\omega_f)| = \frac{2I}{5\pi}A_5 = \frac{2IR}{\pi}\left[\frac{1}{\sqrt{25 + 576(\omega_f/\omega_b)^2}}\right] \tag{12-159}$$

For $\omega_b = \omega_f/10$,

$$\text{fifth harmonic amplitude} = \frac{\text{fundamental amplitude}}{\sqrt{57{,}625}}$$

This discussion indicates that if the filter is highly selective ($\omega_b \ll \omega_f$), the output, for all practical purposes, is due to the fundamental component of the input. Thus we need consider only the $n = 1$ (fundamental) term in Eq. (12-156), and the output simplifies to a single sine wave.

$$v_o(t) \cong \frac{2IR}{\pi}\sin\omega_f t \tag{12-160}$$

This result is so interesting that it is illustrated graphically in Fig. 12-32. The filter simply selects the fundamental component of the input and rejects the higher harmonics. As a result, a sine wave is obtained with a square wave input. The sine wave and the square wave have the same frequency. Also note that the amplitude of the output sine wave $2IR/\pi$ is linearly related to the input square wave ampli-

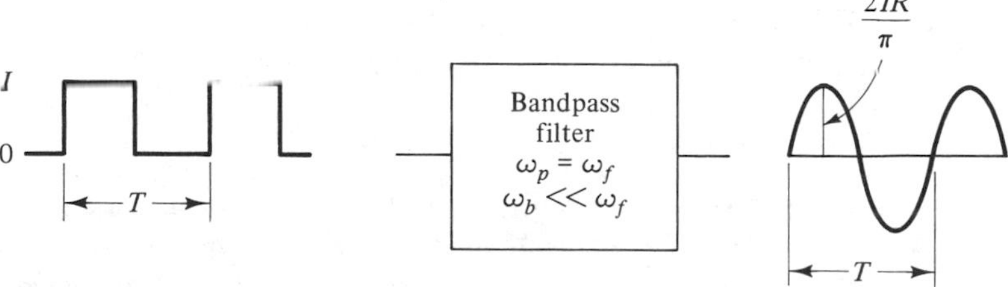

Fig. 12-32

tude I. It should be clear from this example that we can produce a third harmonic sine wave at the output if the filter is tuned to three times the fundamental frequency ($\omega_p = 3\omega_f$) and if the filter is sufficiently selective (see Problem 12-33). This result is even more remarkable because the output is not only a sine wave but also its frequency is three times the repetition frequency of the input square wave. The other higher harmonics can be selected similarly. However, their extraction in the presence of the lower harmonics, which have larger input amplitudes, is a more difficult task.

The result presented by Eq. (12-160) can be directly obtained from inspection of the circuit diagram given in Fig. 12-28. If the circuit is resonated (tuned) to the fundamental frequency of the input, then the impedance of the parallel LC network becomes infinite at that frequency. The fundamental component of the current i_i then flows through R to produce the fundamental component of the output voltage

$$v_{of} = i_{if}R = \frac{2I}{\pi}R \sin \omega_f t$$

If the circuit is selective (narrow bandwidth), the output is, for all practical purposes, $v_{of}(t)$. In this method of analysis, the usefulness of the Fourier series is clearly demonstrated. Contrast this simple approach to that used in Example 7-21(c), where the responses initiated by each input transition from low to high and high to low were summed to obtain the steady-state response—a cumbersome process indeed.

Example 12-11

In Fig. 12-33 the dc voltage V is applied to the network at $t = 0$ by closing the switch.

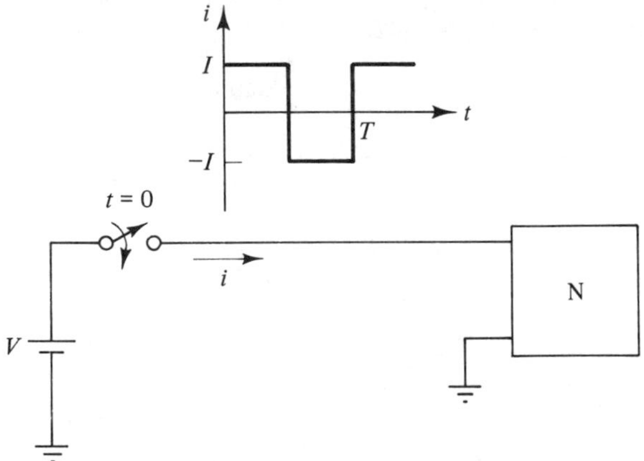

Fig. 12-33

(a) Design the network N such that the resulting input current is a square wave of peak-to-peak amplitude $2I$ and period T as shown. Explain the results.

(b) What is the waveshape of the current delivered by the voltage source if an additional inductor is placed across the input terminals of the network obtained in (a)?

Solution

(a) The input impedance $Z_i(s)$ or admittance $Y_i(s)$ of the network N determines the relationship between its input voltage $V_i(s)$ and input current $I_i(s)$. Here we have for $v_i(t)$ a step voltage and for $i_i(t)$ a square-wave current. The corresponding transforms are

$$V_i(s) = \frac{V}{s}$$

$$I_i(s) = \mathcal{L}\left\{\frac{4I}{\pi}\sum_{\substack{n=1\\ \text{odd}}}^{\infty}\frac{1}{n}\sin\frac{2\pi n}{T}t\right\} = \frac{4I}{\pi}\sum_{\substack{n=1\\ \text{odd}}}^{\infty}\frac{1}{n}\frac{\frac{2\pi n}{T}}{s^2+\left(\frac{2\pi n}{T}\right)^2}$$

Hence the network must have an input admittance of

$$Y_i(s) = \frac{I_i(s)}{V_i(s)} = \frac{\frac{8I}{T}\sum_{\substack{n=1\\ \text{odd}}}^{\infty}\frac{1}{s^2+\left(\frac{2\pi n}{T}\right)^2}}{\frac{V}{s}}$$

$$= \frac{8}{TZ_o}\sum_{\substack{n=1\\ \text{odd}}}^{\infty}\frac{s}{s^2+\left(\frac{2\pi n}{T}\right)^2} \tag{12-161}$$

where Z_o is a constant determined by $Z_o = V/I$. The first few terms of the infinite series are

$$Y_i(s) = \underbrace{\frac{8}{TZ_o}\left[\frac{s}{s^2+\left(\frac{2\pi}{T}\right)^2}\right]}_{Y_1} + \underbrace{\frac{8}{TZ_o}\left[\frac{s}{s^2+\left(\frac{6\pi}{T}\right)^2}\right]}_{Y_3} + \underbrace{\frac{8}{TZ_o}\left[\frac{s}{s^2+\left(\frac{10\pi}{T}\right)^2}\right]}_{Y_5} + \cdots \tag{12-162}$$

Being the sum of admittances, $Y_i(s)$ is composed of an infinite number of branches connected in parallel. The general expression for the admittance of the nth branch is

$$Y_n = \frac{8}{TZ_o}\left[\frac{s}{s^2+\left(\frac{2\pi n}{T}\right)^2}\right] \tag{12-163}$$

The corresponding impedance is

$$Z_n = \frac{1}{Y_n} = \frac{TZ_o}{8}\left[\frac{s^2 + \left(\frac{2\pi n}{T}\right)^2}{s}\right] = s\frac{TZ_o}{8} + \frac{1}{s\frac{2T}{n^2\pi^2 Z_o}} \tag{12-164}$$

Equation (12-164) can be written as

$$Z_n = sL_n + \frac{1}{sC_n}$$

where

$$L_n = \frac{TZ_o}{8}, \qquad C_n = \frac{2T}{n^2\pi^2 Z_o} \tag{12-165}$$

Thus each branch is composed of an inductor and a capacitor connected in series. The inductance of each branch is the same. However, the capacitance varies inversely with n^2. The resulting network is shown in Fig. 12-34. (This network representation can also be used to depict the input impedance of a lossless, open-circuited transmission line.)

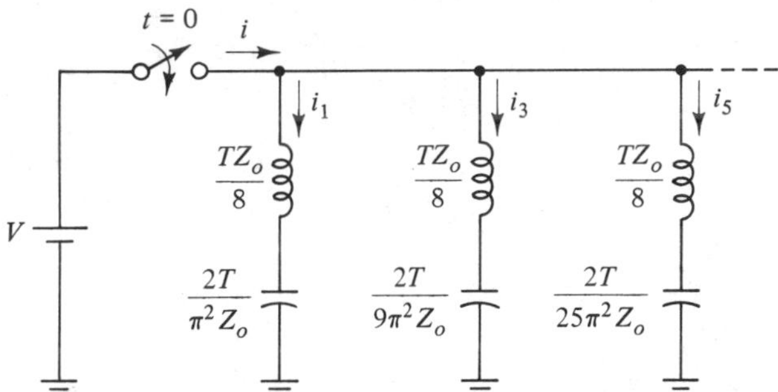

Fig. 12-34

A study of the network reveals how it generates the trigonometric form of the Fourier series of the square wave. Each branch is excited by the same step voltage V, but it produces its own current independent of the other branches. The current through the nth branch is obtained using Eq. (12-163).

$$I_n(s) = V_i(s)Y_n(s) = \frac{V}{s}\frac{8}{TZ_o}\left[\frac{s}{s^2 + \left(\frac{2\pi n}{T}\right)^2}\right] = \frac{4V}{n\pi Z_o}\left[\frac{\frac{2\pi n}{T}}{s^2 + \left(\frac{2\pi n}{T}\right)^2}\right]$$

$$i_n(t) = \frac{4V}{n\pi Z_o}\sin\frac{2\pi n}{T}t = \frac{4I}{n\pi}\sin\frac{2\pi n}{T}t \tag{12-166}$$

This current represents a typical term of the Fourier series. The required summation is carried out at the top node. Applying Kirchhoff's current law to this node we see how the square-wave current is evolved.

$$i = i_1 + i_3 + i_5 + \cdots = \frac{4I}{\pi} \sum_{\substack{n=1 \\ \text{odd}}}^{\infty} \frac{1}{n} \sin \frac{2\pi n}{T} t \qquad t \geq 0$$

Indeed this formulation can be generalized to obtain a network implementation for any step response that is an odd periodic function with positive Fourier coefficients. See Problem 12-40. (However, it should be realized that such results are unattainable in practice. Because actual inductors and capacitors are lossy, the current waveform eventually becomes zero.)

(b) Figure 12-35 shows the network with an added inductor across the input terminals. The current delivered by the voltage source $i_s(t)$ is the sum of $i_o(t)$ and $i(t)$, where $i(t)$ is the square-wave current obtained in (a) above. The current $i_o(t)$ is obtained from

$$i_o(t) = \frac{1}{L_o} \int_0^t V\, dt = \frac{V}{L_o} t$$

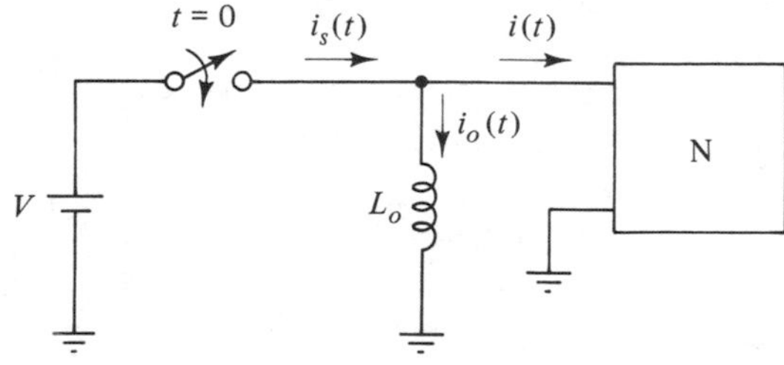

Fig. 12-35

Hence, we have

$$i_s(t) = \frac{V}{L_o} t + \frac{4I}{\pi} \sum_{\substack{n=1 \\ \text{odd}}}^{\infty} \frac{1}{n} \sin \frac{2\pi n}{T} t \qquad t \geq 0$$

The current is composed of a square-wave and a ramp function. The resulting waveform is shown in Fig. 12-36 for $V/L_o = 2I/T$.

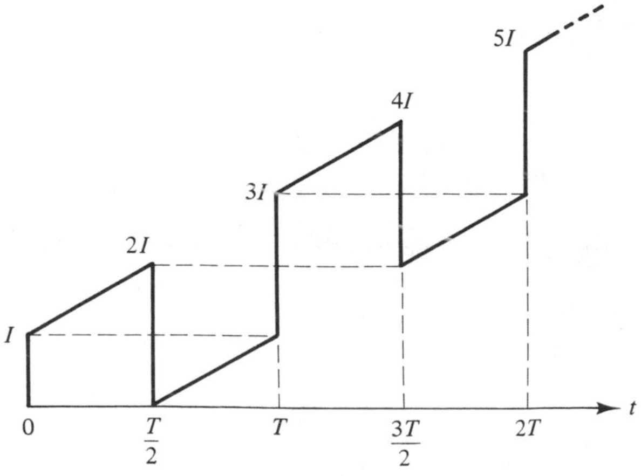

Fig. 12-36

12-12 SUMMARY

The trigonometric form of the Fourier series is

$$f(t) = \frac{a_0}{2} + \sum_{n=1}^{\infty} \left(a_n \cos \frac{2\pi n}{T} t + b_n \sin \frac{2\pi n}{T} t \right)$$

where

$$\frac{a_0}{2} = \frac{1}{T} \int_{t_o}^{t_o+T} f(t)\, dt$$

$$a_n = \frac{2}{T} \int_{t_o}^{t_o+T} f(t) \cos \frac{2\pi n}{T} t\, dt$$

$$b_n = \frac{2}{T} \int_{t_o}^{t_o+T} f(t) \sin \frac{2\pi n}{T} t\, dt$$

The constant t_o can have any value. It is usually taken as 0 or $-T/2$. If $f(t)$ is an even function, $f(-t) = f(t)$, then $b_n = 0$, and a_n can be obtained from

$$a_n = \frac{4}{T} \int_0^{T/2} f(t) \cos \frac{2\pi n}{T} t\, dt$$

If $f(t)$ is an odd function $f(-t) = -f(t)$, then $a_n = 0$, and b_n can be obtained from

$$b_n = \frac{4}{T} \int_0^{T/2} f(t) \sin \frac{2\pi n}{T} t\, dt$$

If $f(t)$ possesses half-wave symmetry, $f(t \pm T/2) = -f(t)$, then the Fourier series expansion contains odd harmonics only, and the a_n and b_n coefficients can be obtained from

$$a_n = \frac{4}{T} \int_0^{T/2} f(t) \cos \frac{2\pi n}{T} t\, dt \qquad n \text{ odd}$$

$$b_n = \frac{4}{T} \int_0^{T/2} f(t) \sin \frac{2\pi n}{T} t\, dt \qquad n \text{ odd}$$

If $f(t)$ possesses half-wave symmetry and is also an even function, then $f(t)$ is given by

$$f(t) = \sum_{\substack{n=1 \\ \text{odd}}}^{\infty} a_n \cos \frac{2\pi n}{T} t$$

where

$$a_n = \frac{8}{T}\int_0^{T/4} f(t)\cos\frac{2\pi n}{T}t\,dt$$

If $f(t)$ possesses half-wave symmetry and is also an odd function, then $f(t)$ is given by

$$f(t) = \sum_{\substack{n=1\\ \text{odd}}}^{\infty} b_n \sin\frac{2\pi n}{T}t$$

where

$$b_n = \frac{8}{T}\int_0^{T/4} f(t)\sin\frac{2\pi n}{T}t\,dt$$

The polar form of the Fourier series is

$$f(t) = \frac{a_0}{2} + \sum_{n=1}^{\infty}\sqrt{a_n^2 + b_n^2}\sin\left(\frac{2\pi n}{T}t + \tan^{-1}\frac{a_n}{b_n}\right)$$

$$f(t) = \frac{a_0}{2} + \sum_{n=1}^{\infty}\sqrt{a_n^2 + b_n^2}\cos\left(\frac{2\pi n}{T}t - \tan^{-1}\frac{b_n}{a_n}\right)$$

where the $a_0/2$, a_n, and b_n coefficients are the same as in the trigonometric form.

The exponential form of the Fourier series is

$$f(t) = \sum_{n=-\infty}^{\infty} c_n e^{j(2\pi n/T)t}$$

where

$$c_n = \frac{1}{T}\int_{t_o}^{t_o+T} f(t)e^{-j(2\pi n/T)t}\,dt$$

$$c_{-n} = c_n^*$$

The polar form can also be expressed in terms of the c_n coefficients.

$$f(t) = c_0 + 2\sum_{n=1}^{\infty}|c_n|\cos\left(\frac{2\pi n}{T}t + \theta_{c_n}\right)$$

where

$$|c_n| = \text{magnitude of } c_n$$

$$\theta_{c_n} = \text{angle of } c_n$$

Fourier series representations of commonly encountered waveforms are given as follows.

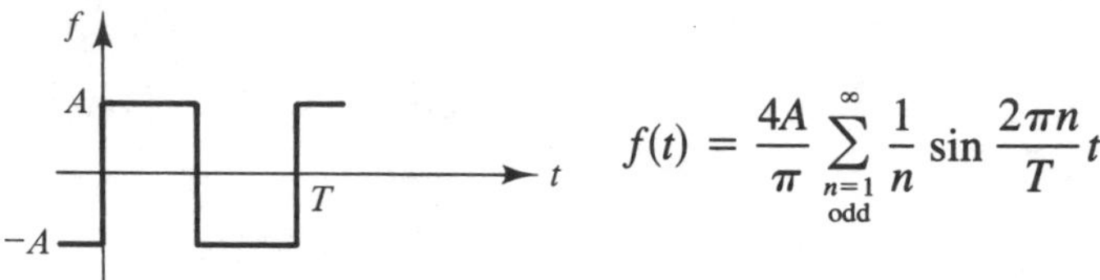

$$f(t) = \frac{4A}{\pi} \sum_{\substack{n=1 \\ \text{odd}}}^{\infty} \frac{1}{n} \sin \frac{2\pi n}{T} t$$

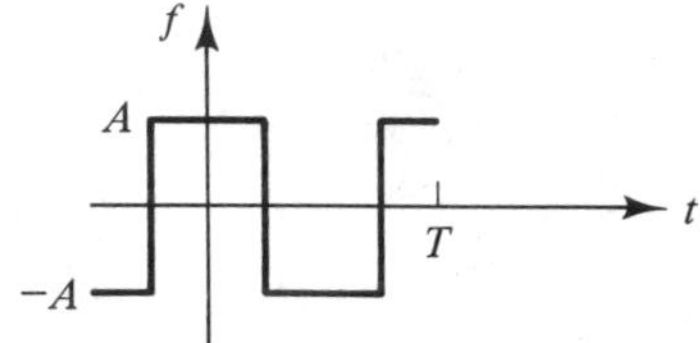

$$f(t) = \frac{4A}{\pi} \sum_{\substack{n=1 \\ \text{odd}}}^{\infty} \frac{1}{n} \sin \left(\frac{2\pi n}{T} t + n\frac{\pi}{2} \right) = \frac{4A}{\pi} \sum_{\substack{n=1 \\ \text{odd}}}^{\infty} \left(\frac{\sin \frac{n\pi}{2}}{n} \right) \cos \frac{2\pi n}{T} t$$

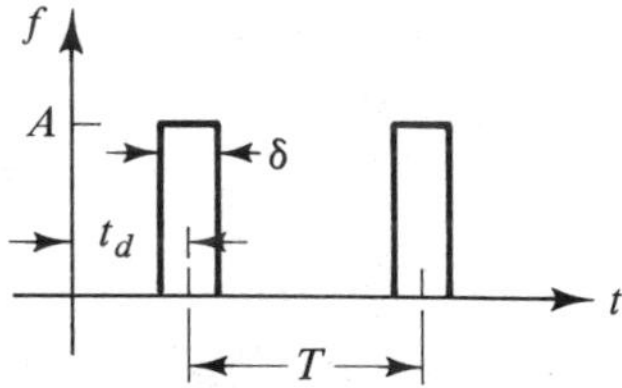

$$f(t) = \frac{A}{\pi} \sum_{n=-\infty}^{\infty} \left(\frac{\sin \frac{n\pi\delta}{T}}{n} \right) e^{j(2\pi n/T)(t-t_d)} = A\frac{\delta}{T} + \frac{2A}{\pi} \sum_{n=1}^{\infty} \left(\frac{\sin \frac{n\pi\delta}{T}}{n} \right) \cos \left[\frac{2\pi n}{T} (t - t_d) \right]$$

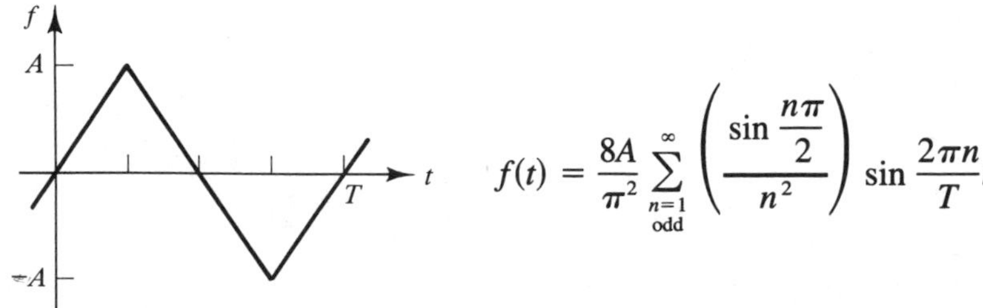

$$f(t) = \frac{8A}{\pi^2} \sum_{\substack{n=1 \\ \text{odd}}}^{\infty} \left(\frac{\sin \frac{n\pi}{2}}{n^2} \right) \sin \frac{2\pi n}{T} t$$

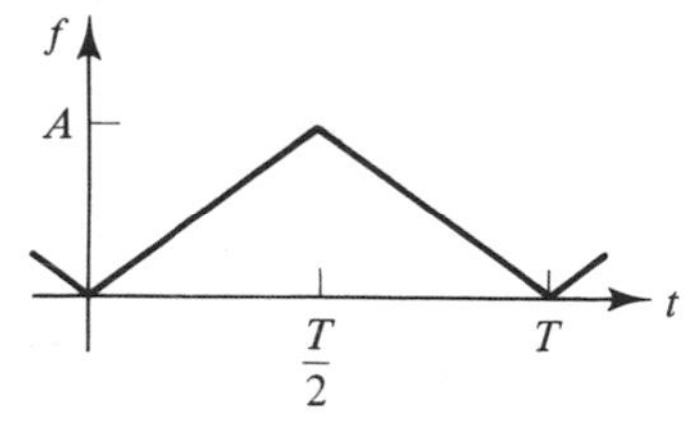

$$f(t) = \frac{A}{2} - \frac{4A}{\pi^2} \sum_{\substack{n=1 \\ \text{odd}}}^{\infty} \frac{1}{n^2} \cos \frac{2\pi n}{T} t$$

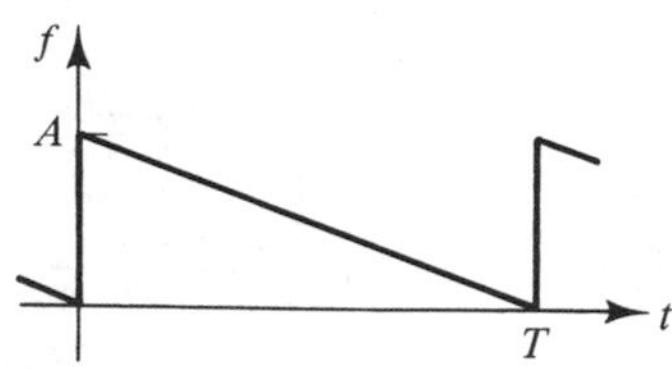

$$f(t) = \frac{A}{2} + \frac{A}{\pi} \sum_{n=1}^{\infty} \frac{1}{n} \sin \frac{2\pi n}{T} t$$

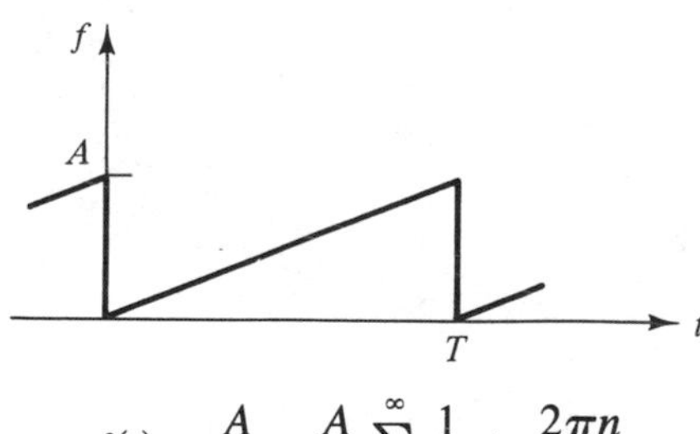

$$f(t) = \frac{A}{2} - \frac{A}{\pi} \sum_{n=1}^{\infty} \frac{1}{n} \sin \frac{2\pi n}{T} t$$

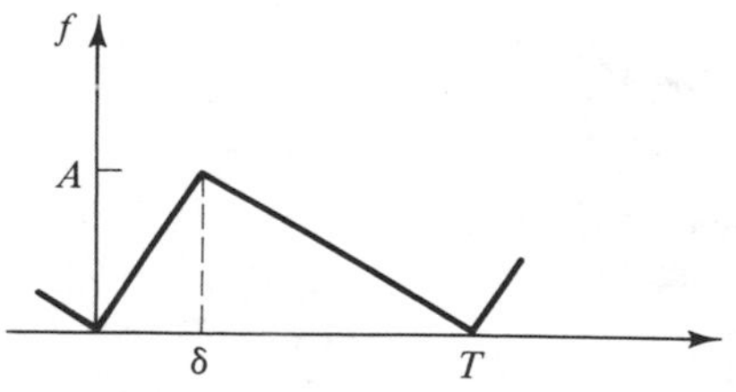

$$f(t) = \frac{A}{2} + \frac{A}{2\pi^2}\left(\frac{T}{\delta}\right)\left(\frac{T}{T-\delta}\right) \sum_{n=1}^{\infty} \frac{1}{n^2}\left[\left(\cos \frac{2\pi n\delta}{T} - 1\right) \cos \frac{2\pi n}{T} t + \left(\sin \frac{2\pi n\delta}{T}\right) \sin \frac{2\pi n}{T} t\right]$$

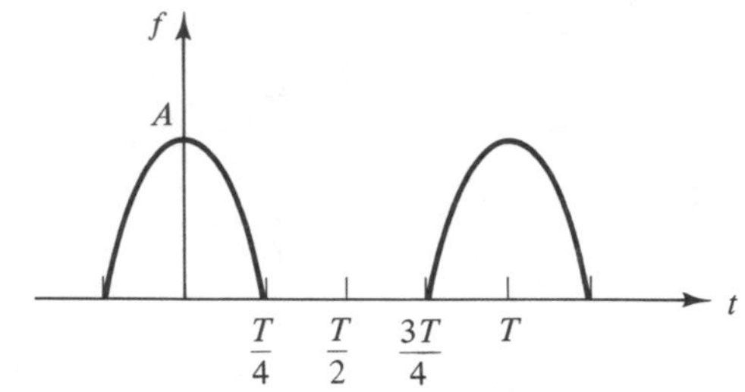

$$f(t) = \frac{A}{\pi} + \frac{A}{2}\cos\frac{2\pi}{T}t + \frac{2A}{\pi}\sum_{\substack{n=2\\ \text{even}}}^{\infty}\left[\frac{(-1)^{(n/2)+1}}{n^2-1}\right]\cos\frac{2\pi n}{T}t$$

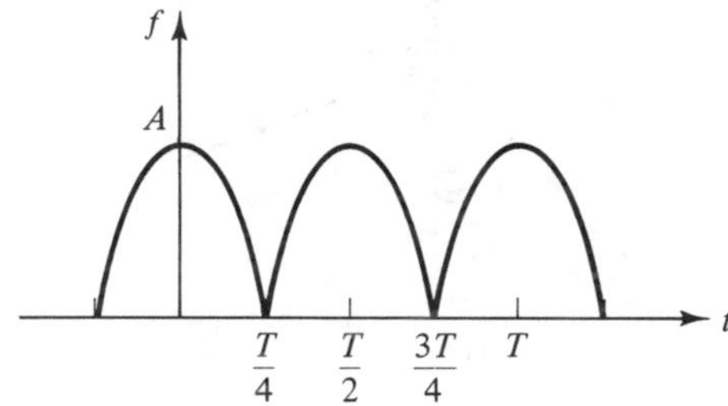

$$f(t) = \frac{2A}{\pi} + \frac{4A}{\pi}\sum_{\substack{n=2\\ \text{even}}}^{\infty}\left[\frac{(-1)^{(n/2)+1}}{n^2-1}\right]\cos\frac{2\pi n}{T}t$$

PROBLEMS

12-10. Show that

$$a_n = \frac{2}{T}\int_0^T f(t)\cos\frac{2\pi n}{T}t\,dt = \frac{2}{T}\int_{t_o}^{t_o+T} f(t)\cos\frac{2\pi n}{T}t\,dt$$

$$b_n = \frac{2}{T}\int_0^T f(t)\sin\frac{2\pi n}{T}t\,dt = \frac{2}{T}\int_{t_o}^{t_o+T} f(t)\sin\frac{2\pi n}{T}t\,dt$$

12-2. Prove Eqs. (12-9) and (12-13).

12-3. Prove Eq.(12-27b).

12-4. If a function has half-wave symmetry, then its average value is zero. Show this.

12-5. (**a**) The function $f(t)$ is even and has half-wave symmetry. Show that the expression for a_n can then be simplified from

$$a_n = \frac{4}{T}\int_0^{T/2} f(t)\cos\frac{2\pi n}{T}t\,dt$$

to

$$a_n = \frac{8}{T}\int_0^{T/4} f(t)\cos\frac{2\pi n}{T}t\,dt$$

(**b**) The function $f(t)$ is odd and has half-wave symmetry. Show that the expression for b_n can then be simplified from

$$b_n = \frac{4}{T}\int_0^{T/2} f(t)\sin\frac{2\pi n}{T}t\,dt$$

to

$$b_n = \frac{8}{T}\int_0^{T/4} f(t)\sin\frac{2\pi n}{T}t\,dt$$

12-6. Obtain the Fourier series representation of the functions shown in Fig. 12-37.

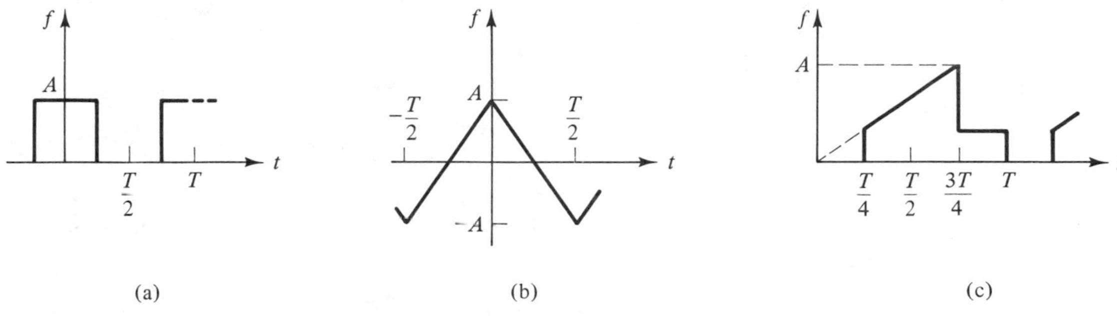

Fig. 12-37

12-7. Using the result of Example 12-2, derive the Fourier series of the square wave shown in Fig. 12-37(a).

12-8. Using the result of Example 12-3, derive the Fourier series of the triangular waveform shown in Fig. 12-37(b).

12-9. Given $f(t) = \frac{16}{3}t(1 - 4t^2)$ for $-\frac{1}{2} \le t \le \frac{1}{2}$. The period is 1s.
(**a**) Sketch $f(t)$, $f'(t)$, and $f''(t)$.
(**b**) Obtain the Fourier series expansion of $f(t)$ and discuss the result.

12-10. (**a**) Obtain the Fourier series for the two waveforms shown in Fig. 12-38.
(**b**) How would you obtain the Fourier series of the waveform of Fig. 12-38(b) directly from the Fourier series of the waveform of Fig. 12-38(a)?

12-11. Derive the results given in Eqs. (12-57) by evaluating the integrals.

12-12. Starting with Eqs. (12-57), let $\delta = T$, and derive the results given in Eqs. (12-63).

12-13. Refer to Fig. 12-39.
(**a**) Plot the amplitude spectrum.
(**b**) Obtain an approximation of $f(t)$ through the fifth harmonic.
(**c**) In what way would a plot of (b) above be different from the waveform shown in Fig. 12-16(c)?

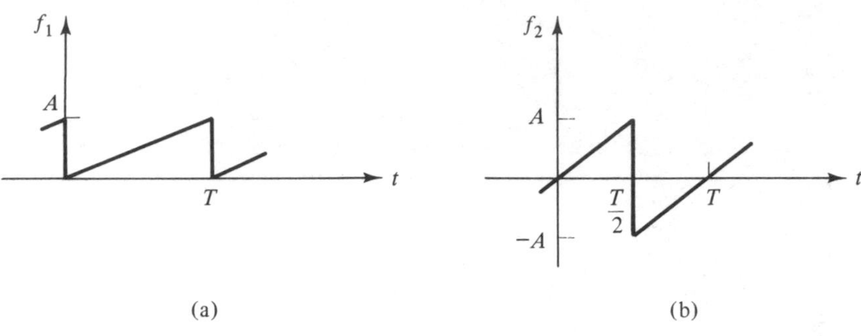

Fig. 12-38

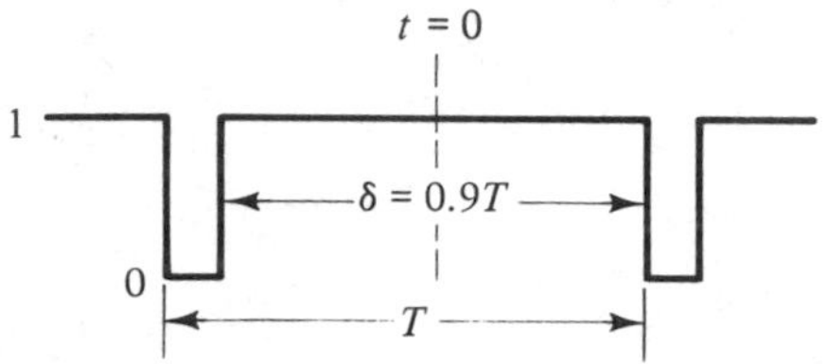

Fig. 12-39

12-14. Obtain the exponential form of the Fourier series for the waveform shown in Fig. 12-40.

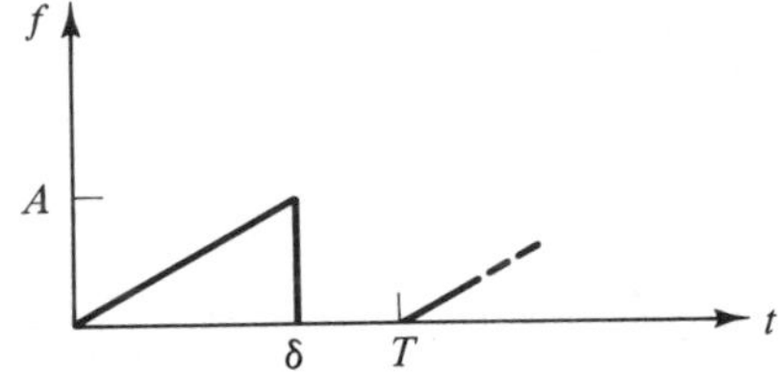

Fig. 12-40

12-15. An arbitrary periodic function $f(t)$ can be decomposed into the sum of its even and odd parts.

$$f(t) = f_e(t) + f_o(t)$$

(a) Show that $f_e(t)$ and $f_o(t)$ can be obtained by appropriate combination of $f(t)$ and $f(-t)$.

(b) Making use of the results of (a) obtain the waveforms of the even and odd parts of the function shown in Fig. 12-41.

(c) Obtain the Fourier series of $f(t)$ in trigonometric form.

12-16. **(a)** Obtain the Fourier series in exponential form for the two waveforms shown in Fig. 12-42.

(b) Take the sum of the two series obtained in (a). What waveform does the resulting series represent?

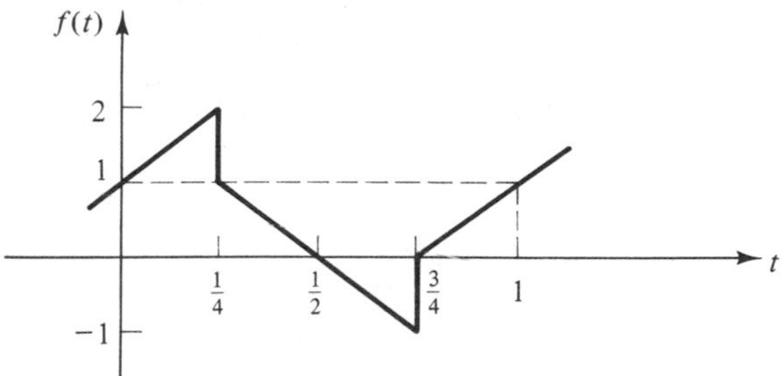

Fig. 12-41

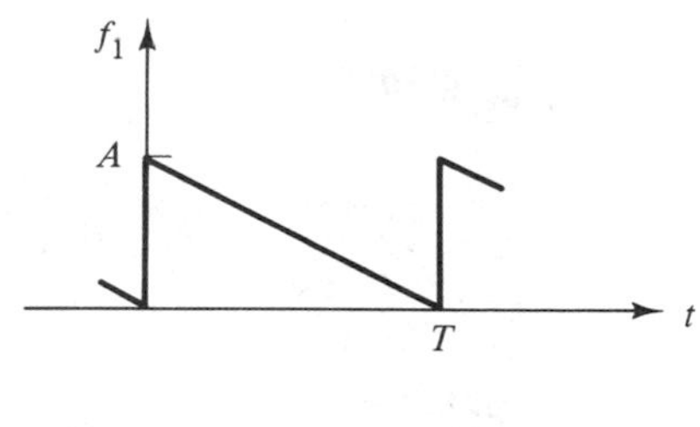

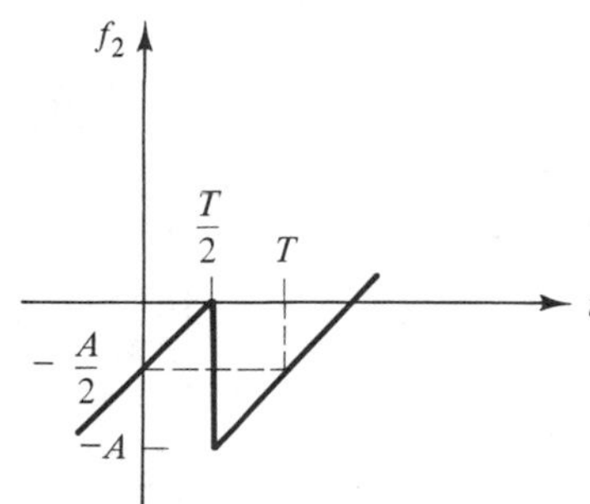

Fig. 12-42

12-17. Refer to Fig. 12-43.

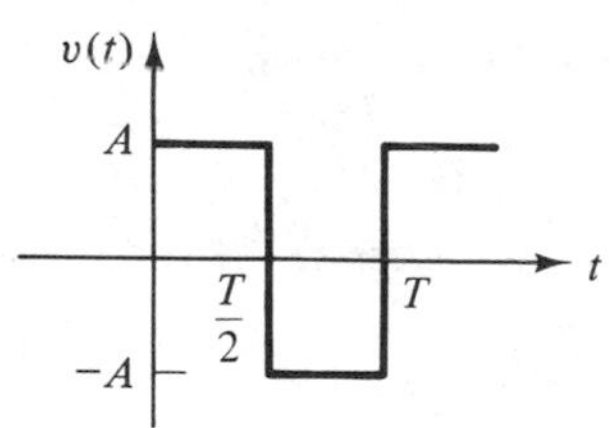

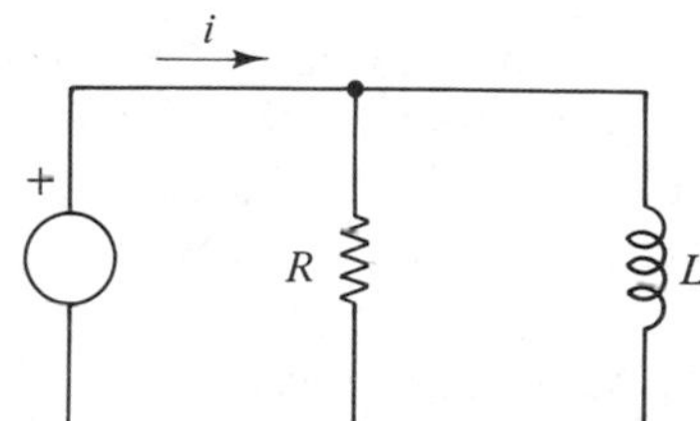

Fig. 12-43

(**a**) Determine by inspection the average power delivered by the voltage source.
(**b**) Obtain the exponential form of the Fourier series for the input current.
(**c**) Using the exponential forms of the input current and voltage, determine the average power delivered by the voltage source. Does it agree with (a)?
(**d**) Using the exponential form of voltage determine the average power delivered to the resistor. Does this result agree with (a)?

12-18. In Fig. 12-44, $f_1(t) = 1 - e^{-t/\tau}$ for $0 \leq t < T/2$ and $f_2(t) = e^{-[t-(T/2)]\tau}$ for $T/2 \leq t < T$. Assume $10\tau < T$.
(**a**) Obtain the coefficients of the exponential form of the Fourier series.
(**b**) Let $\tau = 0$. Show that the resulting function represents the Fourier series of a square wave.

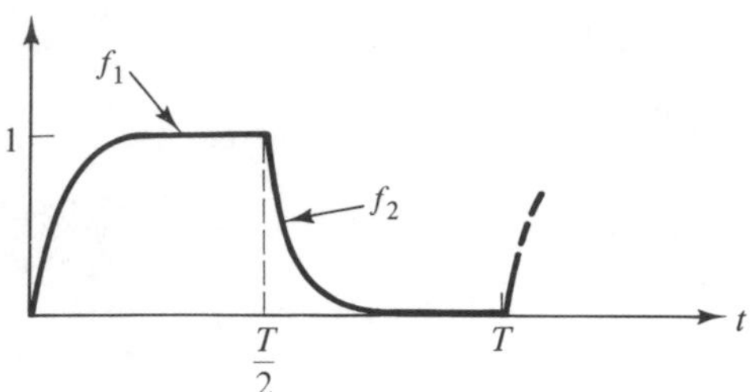

Fig. 12-44

12-19. (**a**) Find the Fourier series of the repeated single-cycle sine wave shown in Fig. 12-45. Assume $T \geq T_o$.
(**b**) Simplify the expression obtained in (a) for $T = T_o$.

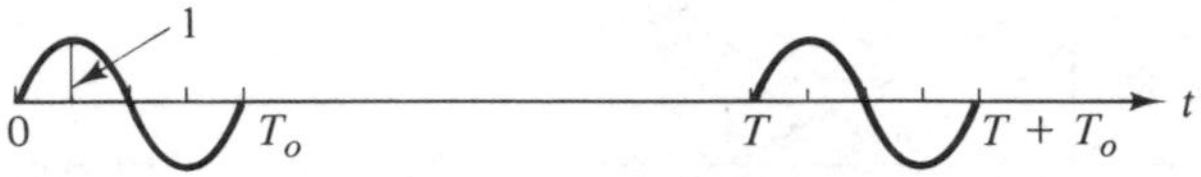

Fig. 12-45

12-20. For $-\frac{1}{2} > t > \frac{1}{2}$, the function $f(t)$ shown in Fig. 12-46(a) is defined by $f(t) = t$. Outside this time interval, the nature of the function is of no concern. Within the range of interest it is desired to express $f(t)$ as a trigonometric series. To achieve this, $f(t)$ must be made periodic. There are an infinite number of ways of doing this, four of which are shown in Figs. 12-46(b) through (e). Each has a different period T and a different waveshape. The one in Fig. 12-46(e) is an odd function with half-wave symmetry. It is defined by $f_e(t) = t$ for $0 \leq t \leq \frac{1}{2}$ and by $f_e(t) = \frac{1}{2} + \sin\ (t - \frac{1}{2})$ for $\frac{1}{2} \leq t \leq \frac{1}{2} + \pi/2$.
(**a**) Which harmonics are present in the waveforms f_b through f_e?
(**b**) Which waveforms will converge to $f(t)$ fastest?

12-21. Derive the result of Eq. (12-134).

12-22. Evaluate Eq. (12-136), and show that it reduces to the coefficients given in Eq. (12-137).

12.23. Determine whether the functions given below are periodic. If periodic, find the period.
(**a**) $f_1(t) = \sin t + \sin \pi t$
(**b**) $f_2(t) = \cos^{-1} (n \cos \omega t)$
(**c**) $f_3(t) = e^{\cos t}$
(**d**) $f_4(t) = \cos 1.5t + \sin 4t \cos 7.5t$
(**e**) $f_5(t) = 1$

12-24. The output current of a three-terminal device is controlled by the input voltage v_i in a square-law fashion, that is,

$$i_o = I_o\left(1 + \frac{v_i}{V_p}\right)^2, \qquad -V_p \leq v_i \leq 0$$

In this expression, I_o and V_p are constants.
(**a**) Sketch the i_o vs. v_i curve.

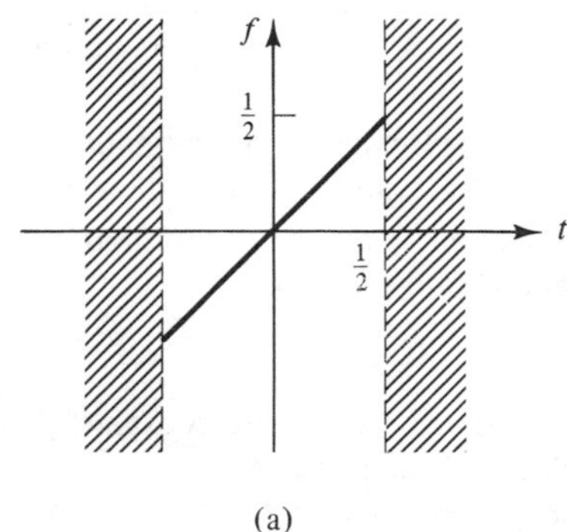

(a)

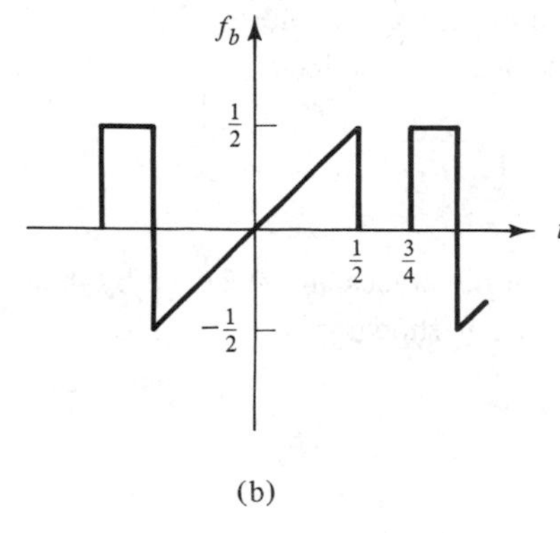

(b)

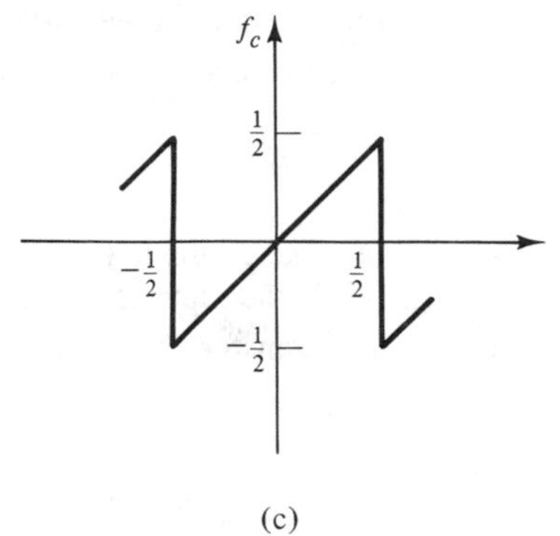

(c)

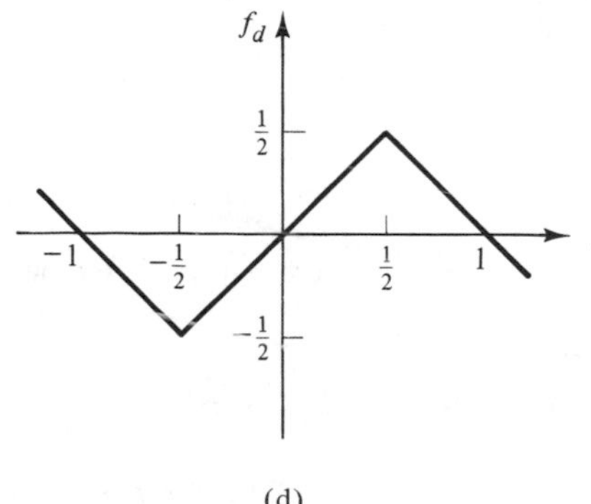

(d)

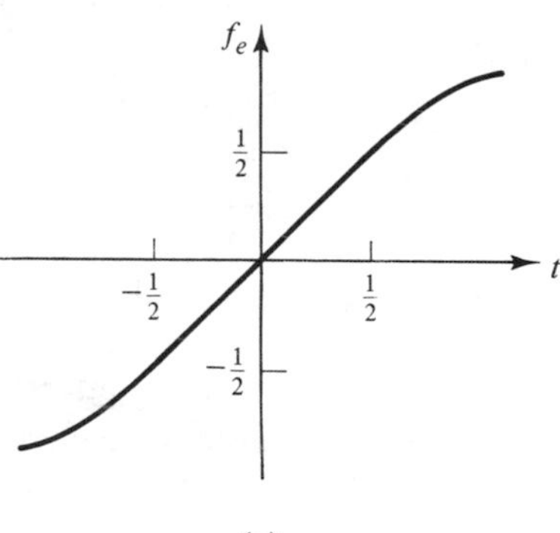

(e)

Fig. 12-46

(b) Sketch the output waveform if

$$v_i = -\frac{V_p}{2} + V_m \sin \omega t \qquad V_m \le \frac{V_p}{2}$$

(c) Give the amplitudes of the harmonics present in the output waveform of (b).
(d) What constraint must be placed on V_m if THD < 0.1?

12-25. The output current i_o of a three-terminal device is controlled by the input voltage v_i in an exponential fashion, that is,

$$i_o = I_s e^{v_i/V_T} \qquad v_i > 0$$

In this expression I_s and V_T are constants.
(a) Sketch the i_o vs. v_i curve.
(b) Sketch the output waveform if

$$v_i = V_{dc} + V_m \cos \omega t, \qquad V_m < V_{dc}$$

(c) What harmonics are present in the output waveform of (b)?

12-26. The transfer characteristics of a device are described by

$$v_o = \begin{cases} V & v_i > 0 \\ -V & v_i < 0 \end{cases}$$

(a) Sketch the transfer characteristic.
(b) If the input is a sine wave, what harmonics are generated by this device?

12-27. The transfer characteristic of a device is shown in Fig. 12-47.

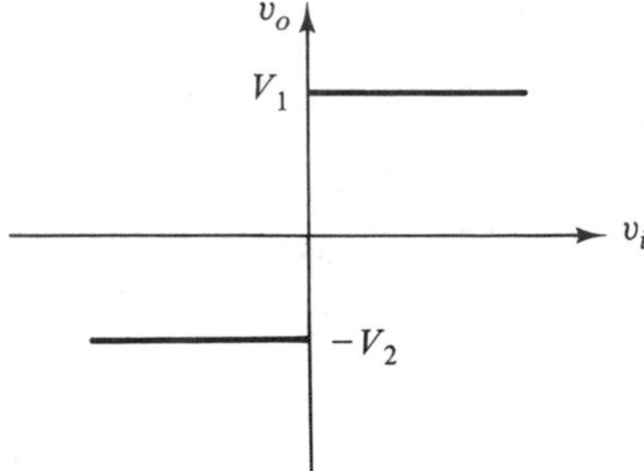

Fig. 12-47

(a) If the input is $v_i = V_m \sin \omega t$, what harmonics are present in the output? Assume $V_2 = V_1$.
(b) What is the effect of $V_2 \ne V_1$?

12-28. The transfer characteristic of a device is shown in Fig. 12-48.
(a) The input v_i is given by

$$v_i = V_m \sin \omega t$$

Under what condition is the output linearly related to the input?
(b) Assume $V_m > V$. What harmonics are present in the output?
(c) Set up the equations for evaluating the coefficients of the trigonometric form of the Fourier series.

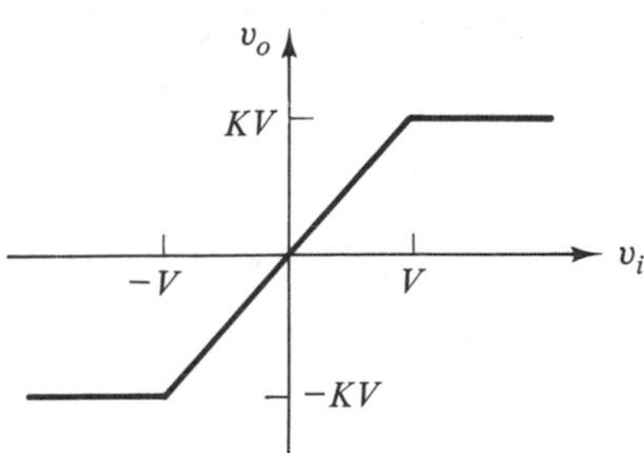

Fig. 12-48

12-29. The transfer characteristic of a device is shown in Fig. 12-49. Assume $v_i = V_m \cos \omega t$.

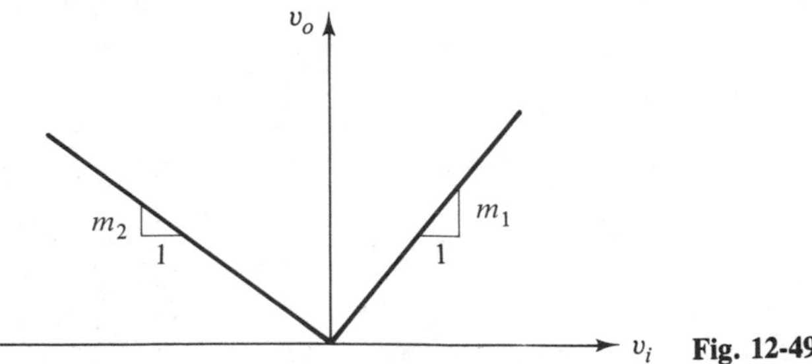

Fig. 12-49

(**a**) Let $m_2 = 0$. Draw the output waveform and obtain its Fourier series representation in trigonometic form.
(**b**) Let $m_2 = m_1$. Draw the output waveform and obtain its Fourier series representation in trigonometric form.
(**c**) Show that the answer to (b) can be obtained from the answer of (a) by using

$$v_{ob} = 2v_{oa} - m_1 v_i$$

(**d**) Explain what will happen to the result in (b) if m_2 is slightly different from m_1?

12-30. How is the fundamental component of the waveform shown in Fig. 12-50 related to its average value? The pulses are narrow compared to the period.

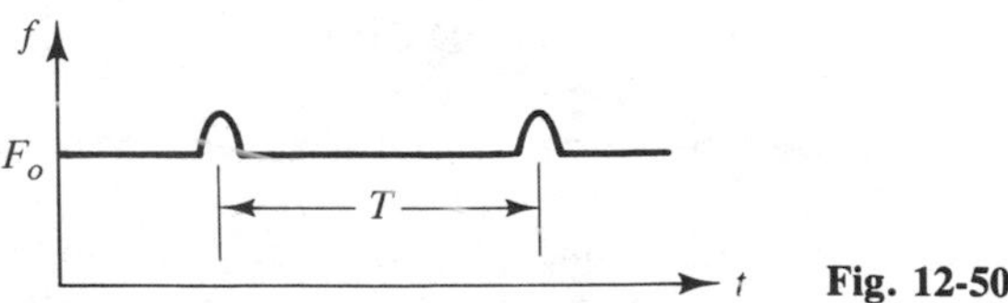

Fig. 12-50

12-31. In Fig. 12-51 R is fixed. The lowpass filter is used to produce a dc output with negligible ripple on it. If the fundamental component of the ripple is to be less than 10% of the dc output voltage, what must be the size of L? The input v_i is sinusoidal for $|t| \leq \frac{1}{2}T$.

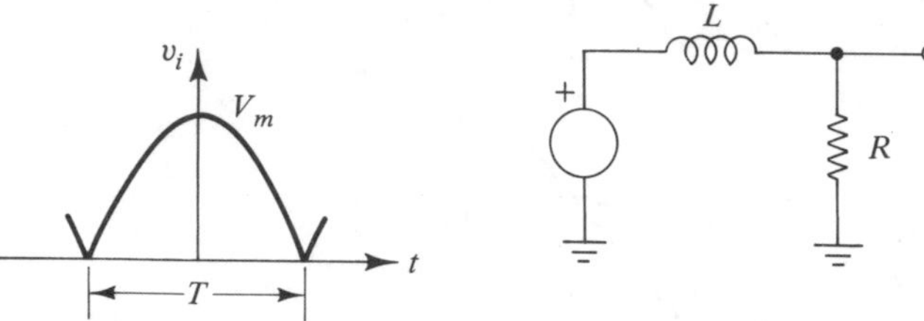

Fig. 12-51

12-32. The lowpass filter of Fig. 12-52 is used to get rid of the pulses riding on the output of a dc power supply. The load resistor R_L is fixed. The cutoff frequency ω_c is to be chosen such that the fundamental component of the output voltage is less than 0.1% of the dc component. Assuming that $\delta \ll T$, obtain the expresion for ω_c.

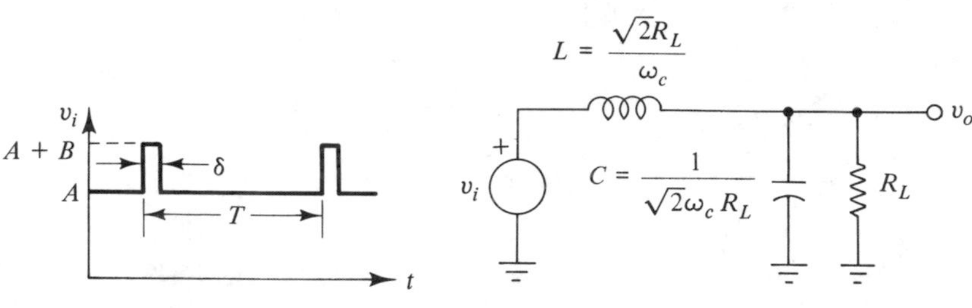

Fig. 12-52

12-33. In Fig. 12-53, the network is tuned to the third harmonic. Its bandwidth is 10% of the center frequency.

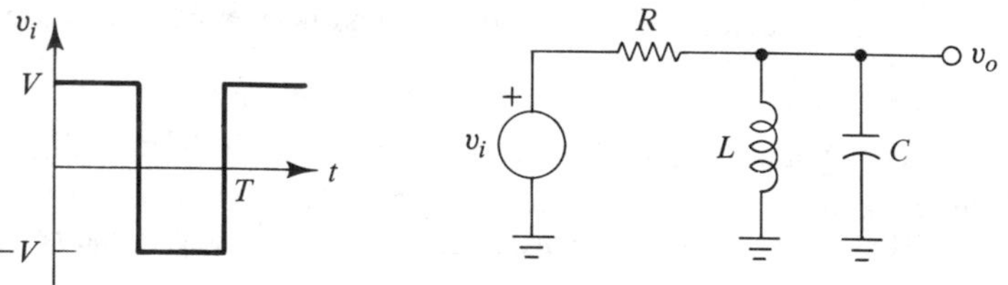

Fig. 12-53

(a) Obtain the fundamental, third, and fifth harmonic component of the output voltage.

(b) Compare the amplitude of the third harmonic output to the amplitude of the fundamental and fifth harmonic. Base your comparison on unity third-harmonic amplitude. Comment on the result.

12-34. The bandpass network of Fig. 12-54 is very selective. It is tuned to the fundamental frequency of the input waveform which is composed of very narrow pulses ($\delta \ll T$). Use the necessary approximations to obtain the expression for $v_o(t)$ with little effort.

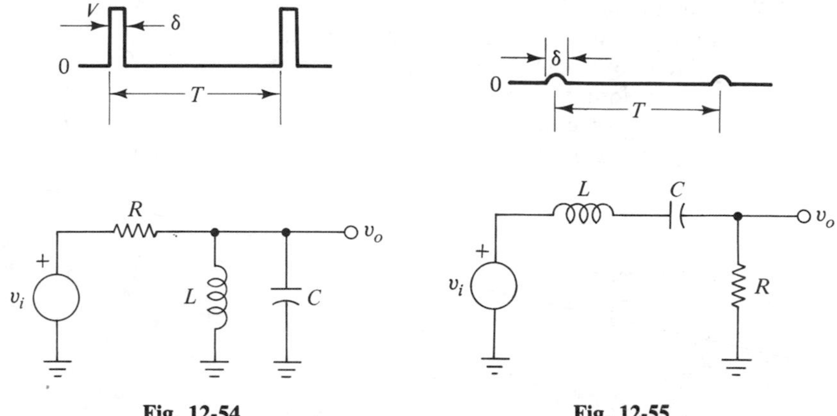

Fig. 12-54

Fig. 12-55

12-35. The bandpass network of Fig. 12-55 is highly selective. It is tuned to the fundamental frequency. The input is composed of sine-wave tips which drive the circuit intermittently ($\delta \ll T$) as shown. What does this circuit do? Explain.

12-36. The bandstop network of Fig. 12-56 is tuned to the fundamental frequency, that is, $T = 2\pi\sqrt{LC}$. It has a narrow bandwidth of rejection.

(a) Obtain the expression for the output voltage.

(b) Sketch $v_o(t)$. Give values.

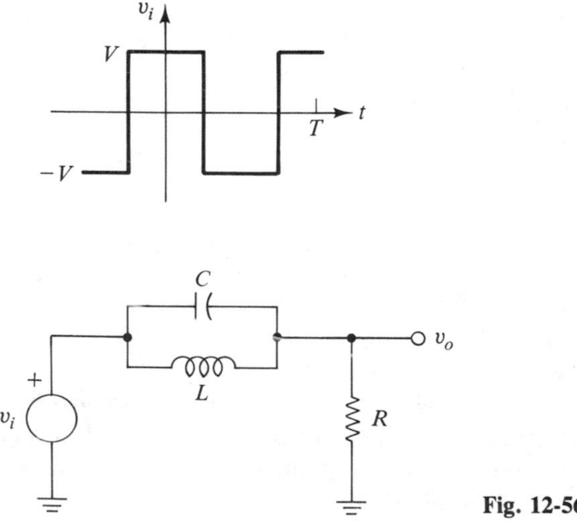

Fig. 12-56

12-37. Refer to Fig. 12-57.

(**a**) Design the network such that the resulting input voltage is a square-wave of peak-to-peak amplitude 2 V and period T as shown. Explain how the square current waveform is formed.

(**b**) What is the waveshape of the voltage across the current source if an additional capacitor is placed in series with the input to the network?

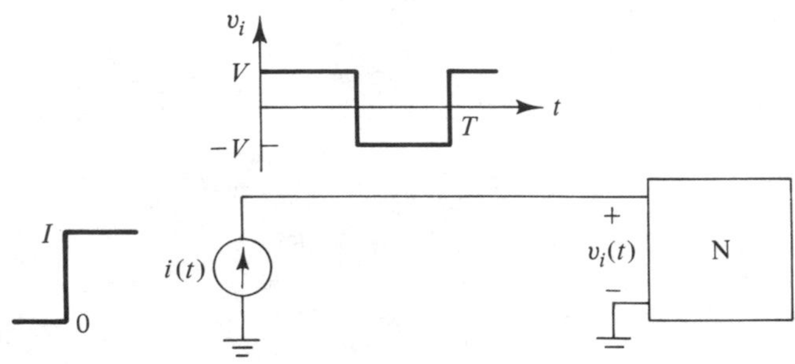

Fig. 12-57

12-38. Refer to Fig. 12-58.

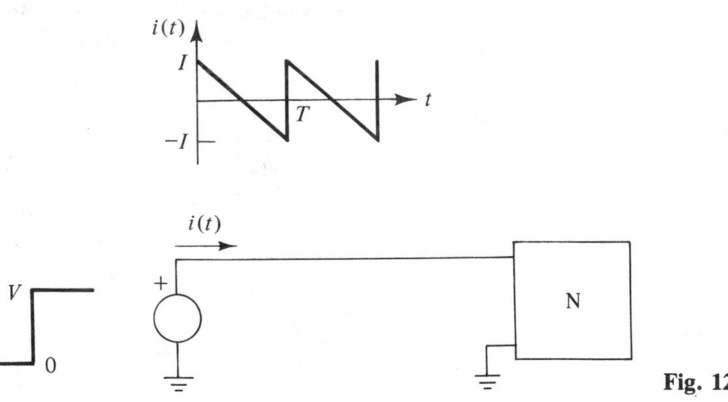

Fig. 12-58

(**a**) Design the network to produce the desired current.

(**b**) What happens to the input current waveform if an inductor of value $L_o = \frac{1}{2}T(V/I)$ is connected across the input terminals of N?

12-39. Refer to Fig. 12-59.

(**a**) Design the network to produce the desired input voltage waveform.

(**b**) How would you modify the network to produce a staircase voltage waveform?

12-40. In Fig. 12-60 $i(t)$ or $v(t)$ is a specified periodic function. If this function is odd and its Fourier series coefficients are all positive, then the network N is realizable with inductors and capacitors. Show this.

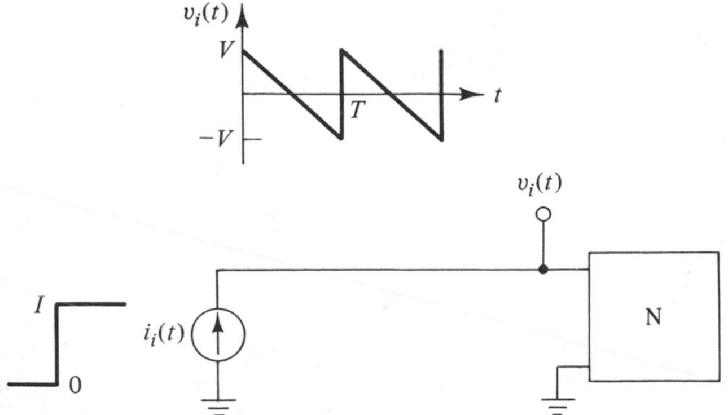

Fig. 12-59

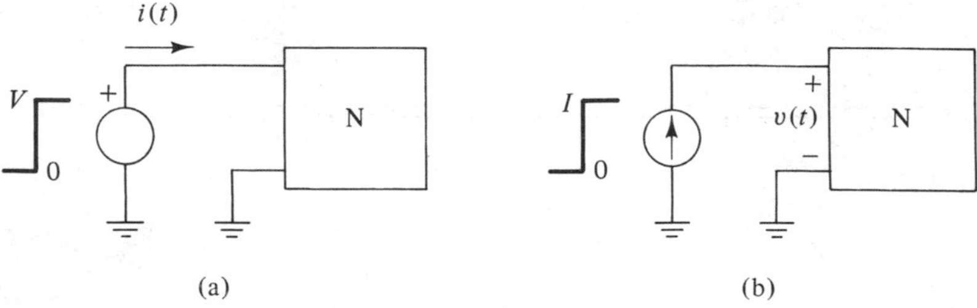

Fig. 12-60

APPENDIX 1

DETERMINANTS

Consider the set of n simultaneous, linear, and independent equations in n unknowns $x_1, x_2, \ldots, x_n$.

$$a_{11}x_1 + a_{12}x_2 + \cdots + a_{1n}x_n = b_1$$

$$a_{21}x_1 + a_{22}x_2 + \cdots + a_{2n}x_n = b_2$$

$$\vdots$$

$$a_{n1}x_1 + a_{n2}x_2 + \cdots + a_{nn}x_n = b_n$$

By Cramer's rule, the solution of this set is given by

$$x_1 = \frac{\Delta_1}{\Delta}$$

$$x_2 = \frac{\Delta_2}{\Delta}$$

$$\vdots$$

$$x_n = \frac{\Delta_n}{\Delta}$$

where

$$\Delta = \begin{vmatrix} a_{11} & a_{12} & \cdots & a_{1n} \\ a_{21} & a_{22} & \cdots & a_{2n} \\ \vdots & \vdots & & \vdots \\ a_{n1} & a_{n2} & \cdots & a_{nn} \end{vmatrix}$$

$$\Delta_1 = \begin{vmatrix} b_1 & a_{12} & \cdots & a_{1n} \\ b_2 & a_{22} & \cdots & a_{2n} \\ \vdots & \vdots & & \vdots \\ b_n & a_{n2} & \cdots & a_{nn} \end{vmatrix} \qquad \Delta_2 = \begin{vmatrix} a_{11} & b_1 & \cdots & a_{1n} \\ a_{21} & b_2 & \cdots & a_{2n} \\ \vdots & \vdots & & \vdots \\ a_{n1} & b_n & \cdots & a_{nn} \end{vmatrix}$$

$$\cdots \qquad \Delta_n = \begin{vmatrix} a_{11} & a_{12} & \cdots & b_1 \\ a_{21} & a_{22} & \cdots & b_2 \\ \vdots & \vdots & & \vdots \\ a_{n1} & a_{n2} & \cdots & b_n \end{vmatrix}$$

The Δ's are called determinants. An $n \times n$ determinant can be evaluated by expansion along any row or column. For instance, the value of Δ can be obtained by expansion along the first column.

$$\Delta = \begin{vmatrix} a_{11} & a_{12} & a_{13} & \cdots & a_{1n} \\ a_{21} & a_{22} & a_{23} & \cdots & a_{2n} \\ a_{31} & a_{32} & a_{33} & \cdots & a_{3n} \\ \vdots & \vdots & \vdots & & \vdots \\ a_{n1} & a_{n2} & a_{n3} & \cdots & a_{nn} \end{vmatrix}$$

$$= a_{11}M_{11} - a_{21}M_{21} + a_{31}M_{21} - \cdots + (-1)^{n+1}a_{n1}M_{n1}$$

where M_{ij} is a $(n - 1) \times (n - 1)$ determinant obtained from Δ by striking out the ith row and jth column. Alternatively, the value of Δ can be obtained by expansion along the first row:

$$\Delta = a_{11}M_{11} - a_{12}M_{12} + a_{13}M_{13} - \cdots + (-1)^{n+1}a_{1n}M_{1n}$$

The expansion of second- and third-order determinants is given below.

$$\Delta = \begin{vmatrix} a_{11} & a_{12} \\ a_{21} & a_{22} \end{vmatrix} = a_{11}a_{22} - a_{21}a_{12}$$

$$\Delta = \begin{vmatrix} a_{11} & a_{12} & a_{13} \\ a_{21} & a_{22} & a_{23} \\ a_{31} & a_{32} & a_{33} \end{vmatrix} = a_{11}\begin{vmatrix} a_{22} & a_{23} \\ a_{32} & a_{33} \end{vmatrix} - a_{21}\begin{vmatrix} a_{12} & a_{13} \\ a_{32} & a_{33} \end{vmatrix} + a_{31}\begin{vmatrix} a_{12} & a_{13} \\ a_{22} & a_{23} \end{vmatrix}$$

$$= a_{11}(a_{22}a_{33} - a_{32}a_{23}) - a_{21}(a_{12}a_{33} - a_{32}a_{13}) + a_{31}(a_{12}a_{23} - a_{22}a_{13})$$

$$= a_{11}a_{22}a_{33} + a_{21}a_{32}a_{13} + a_{31}a_{12}a_{23} - a_{11}a_{32}a_{23} - a_{21}a_{12}a_{33} - a_{31}a_{22}a_{13}$$

APPENDIX 2

ALGEBRA OF COMPLEX NUMBERS

1. COMPLEX NUMBERS

Let a and b represent real numbers like $-2.1, 0, 3.4$.

Let the letter j stand for $\sqrt{-1}$—that is, $j = \sqrt{-1}$.

An imaginary number is obtained by multiplying j with a real number. Thus ja and jb represent imaginary numbers. By this definition, $\sqrt{-3}$ is an imaginary number because it can be written $(\sqrt{-1})(\sqrt{3}) = j\sqrt{3}$. On the other hand, j^2 is a real number because $j^2 = -1$.

A complex number is obtained by summing a real number with an imaginary number. Thus $a + jb$ and $b + ja$ represent complex numbers.

A single letter in boldface type is used to designate a complex number:

$$\mathbf{z} = a + jb$$

The *real part* of $\mathbf{z}$ is a—that is,

$$\text{Re}\{\mathbf{z}\} = a$$

The *imaginary part* of $\mathbf{z}$ is b—that is,

$$\text{Im}\{\mathbf{z}\} = b$$

Thus the complex number $\mathbf{z}_1 = -2 + j3$ has a real part of -2 and an imaginary part of 3. The number $\mathbf{z}_2 = -j4 = 0 + j(-4)$ has a real part of 0 and an imaginary part of -4. It is important to note that the imaginary part of a complex number is real. *It does not contain the j*. What follows the j is the imaginary part.

Two complex numbers $\mathbf{z}_1$ and $\mathbf{z}_2$ are equal if

$$\text{Re}\,\{\mathbf{z}_1\} = \text{Re}\,\{\mathbf{z}_2\} \qquad \text{and} \qquad \text{Im}\,\{\mathbf{z}_1\} = \text{Im}\,\{\mathbf{z}_2\}$$

Thus if

$$\underbrace{c + jd}_{\mathbf{z}_1} = \underbrace{-2 + j}_{\mathbf{z}_2}$$

then $c = -2$ and $d = 1$.

The *complex conjugate* of $\mathbf{z} = a + jb$ is $\mathbf{z}^* = a - jb$. Thus a number is conjugated if j is replaced by $-j$. For instance, if $\mathbf{z} = -3 - j4$, then $\mathbf{z}^* = -3 + j4$.

2. THE COMPLEX PLANE

Real numbers are pictorially represented as points on a line. Complex numbers are pictorially represented as points in a plane formed by a horizontal and a vertical axis. See Fig. 1. The horizontal axis is called the *real axis*. If a number is real, it is represented as a point on the real axis. For instance, the number -3 is represented by the point P. The vertical axis is called the *imaginary axis*. If a number is imaginary, it is represented as a point on the vertical axis. To illustrate, the number $-j2$ is represented by the point Q. If a number is complex, such as $3 + j2$, it is represented as the point R. Note that the real part of this number is 3 and the imaginary part 2. The origin represents the number $\mathbf{z} = 0$. The entire plane is called the *complex plane*.

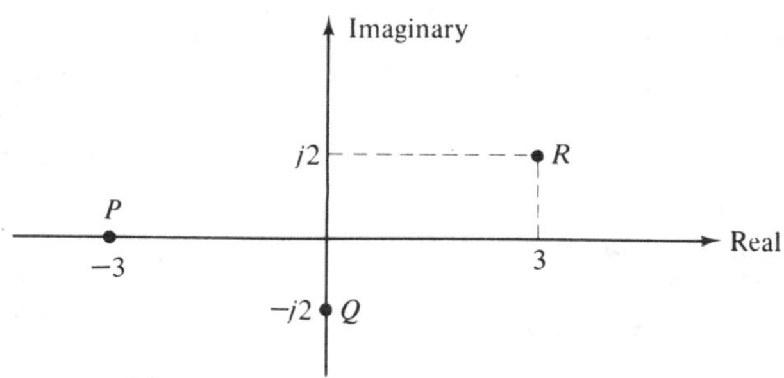

Fig. A2-1

In Fig. 1, a complex number is represented in terms of its real and imaginary parts, which together designate a point in the complex plane. Alternatively, the same point can be designated in terms of a directed line from the origin as shown in Fig. 2.

The length of the line, M, is called the *magnitude*, or absolute value, of the complex number $\mathbf{z}$. Symbolically, it is designated by $|\mathbf{z}| = M$. The magnitude is a *positive* number.

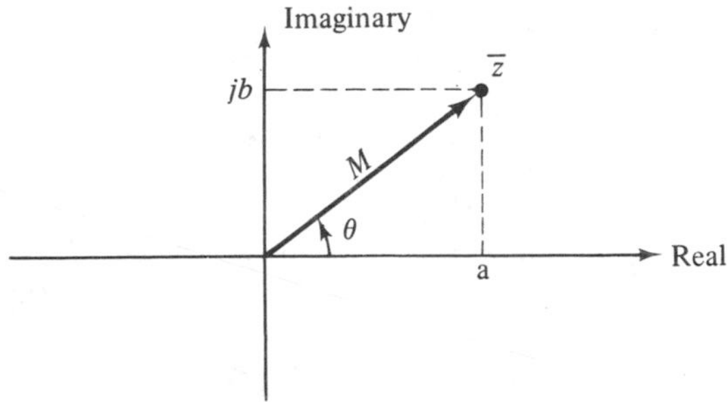

Fig. A2-2

The angle θ, taken counterclockwise from the positive real axis to the directed line, is called the *angle* or argument of $\mathbf{z}$. Depending on the sign of a and b, the line can be in any one of the four quadrants. For example, if a and b are both negative, the line is in the third quadrant corresponding to $\pi < \theta < 3\pi/2$. A negative angle implies clockwise rotation from the positive real axis.

Thus a pair of real numbers (a, b) or (M, θ) are used to designate a complex number. The real and imaginary parts (a, b) give the rectangular coordinates of the point; the magnitude and angle (M, θ) give the polar coordinates. The conversion formulas from one form to the other can easily be obtained. From Fig. 2 it is seen that

$$a = M \cos \theta, \qquad b = M \sin \theta \tag{1}$$

$$M = \sqrt{a^2 + b^2} = \sqrt{(\text{Re part})^2 + (\text{Im part})^2}, \qquad \theta = \tan^{-1} \frac{b}{a} = \tan^{-1} \left(\frac{\text{Im part}}{\text{Re part}} \right) \tag{2}$$

The first set of equations is used to convert from polar to rectangular coordinates. The second set is used to convert from rectangular to polar coordinates. For instance, if $(M, \theta) = 10, -3\pi/4)$, then

$$a = M \cos \theta = 10 \cos \left(-\frac{3\pi}{4} \right) = 10 \cos \frac{3\pi}{4} = -10 \cos \frac{\pi}{4} = -\frac{10}{\sqrt{2}} = -5\sqrt{2}$$

$$b = M \sin \theta = 10 \sin \left(-\frac{3\pi}{4} \right) = -10 \sin \frac{3\pi}{4} = -10 \sin \frac{\pi}{4} = -\frac{10}{\sqrt{2}} = -5\sqrt{2}$$

$$(a, b) = (-5\sqrt{2}, -5\sqrt{2})$$

In converting from rectangular to polar form, care should be taken in determining the correct angle θ. Depending on the sign of a and b, one of the following forms can be used.

$$a > 0, \quad b > 0, \quad \theta = \tan^{-1}\frac{b}{a} \quad \text{(I quadrant)} \tag{3a}$$

$$a < 0, \quad b > 0, \quad \theta = \pi - \tan^{-1}\frac{b}{|a|} \quad \text{(II quadrant)} \tag{3b}$$

$$a < 0, \quad b < 0, \quad \theta = \pi + \tan^{-1}\frac{|b|}{|a|} \quad \text{(III quadrant)} \tag{3c}$$

$$a > 0, \quad b < 0, \quad \theta = 2\pi - \tan^{-1}\frac{|b|}{a} \quad \text{(IV quadrant)} \tag{3d}$$

$$a = 0, \quad b > 0, \quad \theta = \frac{\pi}{2} \tag{3e}$$

$$a = 0, \quad b < 0, \quad \theta = \frac{3\pi}{2} \tag{3f}$$

$$a > 0, \quad b = 0, \quad \theta = 0 \tag{3g}$$

$$a < 0, \quad b = 0, \quad \theta = \pi \tag{3h}$$

In these expressions θ is in radians. The complex number is not altered if $k2\pi(k = 1, 2, 3, \ldots)$ is added or subtracted from θ. For instance, in Eq. (3c), instead of using $\theta = \pi + \tan^{-1} |b|/|a|$ to describe a point in the third quadrant, $\theta' = \theta - 2\pi = -\pi + \tan^{-1} |b|/|a|$ can be used. Even though $\theta' \neq \theta$, the complex number is representable by either (M, θ) or (M, θ'). In general, θ can be replaced with $\theta' = \theta \pm k2\pi(k = 0, 1, 2, \ldots)$.

As another example, consider the complex number represented in the rectangular form by $(a, b) = (\sqrt{3}/2, -1/2)$. The polar representation of the complex number (M, θ) is

$$M = \sqrt{a^2 + b^2} = \sqrt{\left(\frac{\sqrt{3}}{2}\right)^2 + \left(-\frac{1}{2}\right)^2} = \sqrt{\frac{3}{4} + \frac{1}{4}} = 1$$

$$\theta = \tan^{-1}\frac{b}{a} = 2\pi - \tan^{-1}\frac{|b|}{a} = 2\pi - \tan^{-1}\frac{1/2}{\sqrt{3}/2} = 2\pi - \tan^{-1}\frac{1}{\sqrt{3}}$$

$$= 2\pi - \frac{\pi}{6} = \frac{11}{6}\pi \text{ radians}$$

Alternatively, 2π can be subtracted from θ and $(M, \theta') = (1, -\pi/6)$ used to represent the complex number.

3. THE EXPONENTIAL REPRESENTATION

The set described by Eq. (1) can be converted to a single equation by combining the real and imaginary parts.

$$a + jb = M \cos\theta + jM \sin\theta$$

Then

$$a + jb = M(\cos\theta + j\sin\theta) \tag{4}$$

The function $f(\theta) = \cos\theta + j\sin\theta$ has interesting properties. It is a solution to the second-order, linear differential equation

$$f''(\theta) + f(\theta) = 0$$

and it satisfies the initial conditions

$$f(0) = 1, \qquad f'(0) = j$$

These results can easily be verified by substitution.

Again, by substitution, it can readily be demonstrated that the same differential equation and initial conditions are satisfied by the function $e^{j\theta}$. Therefore the following identity, known as *Euler's identity,* is established.

$$\cos\theta + j\sin\theta = e^{j\theta} \tag{5}$$

Consequently, Eq. (4) can be written

$$a + jb = Me^{j\theta} \tag{6}$$

Thus a complex number can be expressed in the *exponential* form as $Me^{j\theta}$.

The three forms of representing a complex number are summarized below.

Rectangular:	$a + jb$
Polar:	$M\underline{/\theta}$
Exponential:	$Me^{j\theta}$

Figure 2, Eq. (1), or Eq. (2) relates a and b to M and θ. For computational purposes, the polar form can easily be converted to the exponential form by replacing $\underline{/\theta}$ with $e^{j\theta}$.

4. ADDITION AND SUBTRACTION

Let $\mathbf{z}_1 = a + jb$ and $\mathbf{z}_2 = c + jd$ be two complex numbers. Their sum and difference are given by

$$\mathbf{z}_1 + \mathbf{z}_2 = (a + jb) + (c + jd) = (a + c) + j(b + d) \tag{7}$$

$$\mathbf{z}_1 - \mathbf{z}_2 = (a + jb) - (c + jd) = (a - c) + j(b - d) \tag{8}$$

Thus the real part of the sum, $(a + c)$, is sum of real parts, a and c. The imaginary part of the sum, $(b + d)$, is the sum of the imaginary parts. Similarly, the real and imaginary parts of the difference of two complex numbers are the differences of the real and imaginary parts of the two numbers. For example,

$$(3 + j4) + (1 - j) = (3 + 1) + j(4 - 1) = 4 + j3$$

$$(3 + j4) - (1 - j) = (3 - 1) + j[4 - (-1)] = 2 + j5$$

The addition and subtraction of complex numbers are easily performed if the numbers are expressed in rectangular form. If expressed in polar or exponential form, the numbers are first converted into rectangular form by using $e^{j\theta} = \cos\theta + j\sin\theta$ and then added or subtracted. For instance, if $\mathbf{z}_1 = 2\underline{/\pi/6}$ and $\mathbf{z}_2 = 6e^{-j\pi/3}$, then

$$\mathbf{z}_1 + \mathbf{z}_2 = \underbrace{2\underline{/\pi/6}}_{\text{Polar}} + \underbrace{6e^{-j\pi/3}}_{\text{Exp.}} = \underbrace{2e^{j\pi/6}}_{\text{Exp.}} + \underbrace{6e^{-j\pi/3}}_{\text{Exp.}}$$

$$= \underbrace{2\left(\left(\cos\frac{\pi}{6} + j\sin\frac{\pi}{6}\right)\right.}_{\text{Rectangular}} + \underbrace{6\left[\cos\left(-\frac{\pi}{3}\right) + j\sin\left(-\frac{\pi}{3}\right)\right]}_{\text{Rectangular}}$$

$$= 2\left(\frac{\sqrt{3}}{2} + j\frac{1}{2}\right) + 6\left(\frac{1}{2} - j\frac{\sqrt{3}}{2}\right) = (\sqrt{3} + 3) + j(1 - 3\sqrt{3})$$

When desired, the sum can be expressed in polar or exponential form, using Eq. (2).

$$\mathbf{z}_1 + \mathbf{z}_2 = \underbrace{(\sqrt{3} + 3)}_{a} + j\underbrace{(1 - 3\sqrt{3})}_{b} = M\underline{/\theta} = Me^{j\theta}$$

where $M = \sqrt{a^2 + b^2} = \sqrt{(\sqrt{3} + 3)^2 + (1 - 3\sqrt{3})^2} = 2\sqrt{10}$

$$\theta = \tan^{-1}\frac{b}{a} = \tan^{-1}\left(\frac{1 - 3\sqrt{3}}{\sqrt{3} + 3}\right) = 2\pi - \tan^{-1}\left(\frac{3\sqrt{3} - 1}{\sqrt{3} + 3}\right) \text{ radians}$$

5. MULTIPLICATION AND DIVISION

Let $\mathbf{z}_1 = M_1e^{j\theta_1}$ and $\mathbf{z}_2 = M_2e^{j\theta_2}$ be two complex numbers. Their product and quotient are given by

$$\mathbf{z}_1 \times \mathbf{z}_2 = (M_1e^{j\theta_1})(M_2e^{j\theta_2}) = M_1M_2e^{j(\theta_1+\theta_2)} \tag{9}$$

$$\frac{\mathbf{z}_1}{\mathbf{z}_2} = \frac{M_1e^{j\theta_1}}{M_2e^{j\theta_2}} = \frac{M_1}{M_2}e^{j(\theta_1-\theta_2)} \tag{10}$$

Thus the magnitude of the product, M_1M_2, is the product of the magnitudes M_1 and M_2. The angle of the product, $\theta_1 + \theta_2$, is the *sum* of the angles θ_1 and θ_2. Similarly, the magnitude of the quotient is the quotient of the magnitudes, and the angle of the quotient is the *difference* of the angles. For instance,

$$[3e^{j(\pi/12)}][2e^{-j(\pi/9)}] = 3 \times 2e^{j(\pi/12-\pi/9)} = 6e^{-j(\pi/36)}$$

$$\frac{3e^{j(\pi/12)}}{2e^{-j(\pi/9)}} = \frac{3}{2}e^{j[\pi/12-(-\pi/9)]} = 1.5e^{j(7/36)\pi}$$

The multiplication and division of complex numbers are readily performed if the numbers are expressed in exponential or polar form. If expressed in rectangular form, the numbers can first be converted into exponential form and then multiplied or divided. For example, if $\mathbf{z}_1 = -1 + j$ and $\mathbf{z}_2 = 1 - j$, then

$$\begin{aligned}\mathbf{z}_1 \times \mathbf{z}_2 &= \underbrace{(-1 + j)}_{\text{Rectangular}} \times \underbrace{(1 - j)}_{\text{Rectangular}} \\ &= \underbrace{[\sqrt{(-1)^2 + (1)^2}e^{j\tan^{-1}(1/-1)}]}_{\text{Exponential}}\underbrace{[\sqrt{(1)^2 + (-1)^2}e^{j\tan^{-1}(-1/1)}]}_{\text{Exponential}} \\ &= [\sqrt{2}e^{j(\pi-\pi/4)}][\sqrt{2}e^{j(2\pi-\pi/4)}] = [\sqrt{2}e^{j(3/4)\pi}][\sqrt{2}e^{j(7/4)\pi}] \\ &= 2e^{j(5/2)\pi}\end{aligned}$$

The product has a magnitude of 2 and angle $5\pi/2$. In the complex plane, an angle of $5\pi/2$ occupies the same position as an angle of $5\pi/2 - 2\pi = \pi/2$. So the product can be written

$$\mathbf{z}_1 \times \mathbf{z}_2 = 2e^{j(\pi/2)} = 2\underline{/\pi/2}$$

When desired, the product can be converted to rectangular form.

$$\mathbf{z}_1 \times \mathbf{z}_2 = 2\left(\cos\frac{\pi}{2} + j\sin\frac{\pi}{2}\right) = j2$$

Alternatively, the product can be obtained by multiplying the two numbers in their rectangular form. Using the rules of algebra for real numbers, $\mathbf{z}_1 \times \mathbf{z}_2$ becomes

$$\begin{aligned}\mathbf{z}_1 \times \mathbf{z}_2 &= (-1 + j) \times (1 - j) = (-1)(1 - j) + j(1 - j) \\ &= -1 + j + j + 1 = j2\end{aligned}$$

In general,

$$\mathbf{z}_1 \times \mathbf{z}_2 = (a + jb)(c + jd) = (ac - bd) + j(bc + ad)$$

Similarly, the quotient of $\mathbf{z}_1$ and $\mathbf{z}_2$ can be found as follows.

$$\frac{\mathbf{z}_1}{\mathbf{z}_2} = \frac{-1 + j}{1 - j} = \frac{\sqrt{2}e^{j(3/4)\pi}}{\sqrt{2}e^{j(7/4)\pi}} = e^{-j\pi} = \cos(-\pi) + j\sin(-\pi) = -1$$

Alternatively, the numerator and denominator of the quotient are multiplied by the complex conjugate of the denominator to convert the denominator into a real number, thereby simplifying the division.

$$\frac{\mathbf{z}_1}{\mathbf{z}_2} = \left(\frac{-1 + j}{1 - j}\right)\left(\frac{1 + j}{1 + j}\right) = \frac{-1(1 + j) + j(1 + j)}{1^2 - (j)^2} = \frac{-2}{2} = -1$$

In general,

$$\frac{\mathbf{z}_1}{\mathbf{z}_2} = \frac{a + jb}{c + jd} = \frac{a + jb}{c + jd} \times \frac{c - jd}{c - jd} = \frac{(ac + bd) + j(bc - ad)}{c^2 + d^2}$$

6. COMPLEX ALGEBRA

The rectangular form is used in the addition and subtraction of complex numbers. Either the rectangular or the exponential form is used in the multiplication and division. In mixed operations, like addition and multiplication, the rectangular form can be used throughout. Alternatively, the numbers can be converted from one form to another to perform an indicated operation and then reconverted back to the original form for the next operation.

Consider, for example, the evaluation of

$$\mathbf{z}_1 + \frac{\mathbf{z}_2 + \mathbf{z}_3}{\mathbf{z}_4}$$

where
$$\mathbf{z}_1 = j2$$
$$\mathbf{z}_2 = e^{j(\pi/3)}$$
$$\mathbf{z}_3 = -e^{-j(\pi/3)}$$
$$\mathbf{z}_4 = \frac{\sqrt{3} + j}{4}$$

The sequence of operations and the form of representation used for the complex numbers are as follows.

$$\mathbf{z}_2 + \mathbf{z}_3 \qquad \text{(rectangular)}$$

$$\frac{\mathbf{z}_2 + \mathbf{z}_3}{\mathbf{z}_4} \qquad \text{(rectangular or exponential)}$$

$$\mathbf{z}_1 + \frac{\mathbf{z}_2 + \mathbf{z}_3}{\mathbf{z}_4} \qquad \text{(rectangular)}$$

Although the division operation can be performed in either rectangular or exponential form, the rectangular form will be used here because the preceding and succeeding operations are in the rectangular form.

$$\mathbf{z}_2 + \mathbf{z}_3 = e^{j(\pi/3)} + [-e^{-j(\pi/3)}]$$

$$= \left[\cos\left(\frac{\pi}{3}\right) + j\sin\left(\frac{\pi}{3}\right)\right] + \left\{-\left[\cos\left(-\frac{\pi}{3}\right) + j\sin\left(-\frac{\pi}{3}\right)\right]\right\}$$

$$= \cos\frac{\pi}{3} + j\sin\frac{\pi}{3} - \cos\frac{\pi}{3} + j\sin\frac{\pi}{3} = j2\sin\frac{\pi}{3} = j\sqrt{3}$$

$$\frac{\mathbf{z}_2 + \mathbf{z}_3}{\mathbf{z}_4} = \frac{j\sqrt{3}}{(\sqrt{3} + j)/4} = j\frac{4\sqrt{3}}{\sqrt{3} + j} \times \frac{\sqrt{3} - j}{\sqrt{3} - j} = \frac{4\sqrt{3} + j12}{3 + 1} = \sqrt{3} + j3$$

$$\frac{\mathbf{z}_2 + \mathbf{z}_3}{\mathbf{z}_4} + \mathbf{z}_1 = (\sqrt{3} + j3) + (j2) = \sqrt{3} + j5 \quad \text{Ans.}$$

As another illustration, consider the evaluation of

$$\mathbf{z}_4 + \mathbf{z}_1\mathbf{z}_2\mathbf{z}_3$$

where the **z**'s are as given previously. Again, all the indicated operations can be performed by using the rectangular form for the complex numbers. However, here it is easier to use the exponential form to obtain the $\mathbf{z}_1\mathbf{z}_2\mathbf{z}_3$ product, which is then converted to the rectangular form and summed with $\mathbf{z}_4$.

$$\begin{aligned}\mathbf{z}_1\mathbf{z}_2\mathbf{z}_3 &= (j2)[e^{j(\pi/3)}][-e^{-j(\pi/3}] = [2e^{j\tan^{-1}(2/0)}][e^{j(\pi/3)}][-e^{-j(\pi/3)}]\\ &= [2e^{j(\pi/2)}][e^{j(\pi/3)}][-e^{-j(\pi/3)}] = -2e^{j(\pi/2)}\\ &= -2\left(\cos\frac{\pi}{2} + j\sin\frac{\pi}{2}\right) = -j2\end{aligned}$$

$$\mathbf{z}_1\mathbf{z}_2\mathbf{z}_3 + \mathbf{z}_4 = -j2 + \frac{\sqrt{3}+j}{4} = \frac{\sqrt{3}-j7}{4} \quad \text{Ans.}$$

When desired, this result can be converted to exponential form.

$$\begin{aligned}\frac{\sqrt{3}-j7}{4} &= \frac{\sqrt{(\sqrt{3})^2+(-7)^2}}{4}e^{j\tan^{-1}(-7/\sqrt{3})} = \frac{\sqrt{13}}{2}e^{j(2\pi - \tan^{-1}(7/\sqrt{3})}\\ &= \frac{\sqrt{13}}{2}e^{-j\tan^{-1}(7/\sqrt{3})}\end{aligned}$$

7. USEFUL RELATIONSHIPS

Let $\mathbf{z} = a + jb$. Then

$$\begin{aligned}\mathbf{z} + \mathbf{z}^* &= (a+jb) + (a-jb) = 2a = 2\,\mathrm{Re}\,\{\mathbf{z}\} = 2\,\mathrm{Re}\,\{\mathbf{z}^*\}\\ \mathbf{z} - \mathbf{z}^* &= (a+jb) - (a-jb) = j2b = j2\,\mathrm{Im}\,\{\mathbf{z}\} = -j2\,\mathrm{Im}\,\{\mathbf{z}^*\}\\ \mathbf{z} \times \mathbf{z}^* &= (a+jb)(a-jb) = a^2 + b^2 = |\mathbf{z}|^2 = |\mathbf{z}^*|^2\end{aligned}$$

Since

$$e^{j\theta} = \cos\theta + j\sin\theta$$

it follows that

$$\cos\theta = \mathrm{Re}\,\{e^{j\theta}\}, \qquad \sin\theta = \mathrm{Im}\,\{e^{j\theta}\}$$

$$|e^{j\theta}| = \sqrt{\cos^2\theta + \sin^2\theta} = 1, \qquad e^{-j\theta} = \cos\theta - j\sin\theta$$

$$\frac{e^{j\theta}+e^{-j\theta}}{2} = \cos\theta, \qquad \frac{e^{j\theta}-e^{-j\theta}}{2j} = \sin\theta$$

$$e^{j(\theta \pm k2\pi)} = e^{j\theta} \qquad (k = 0, 1, 2, \ldots)$$

$$e^{j(\pi/2)} = j, \qquad e^{-j(\pi/2)} = -j, \qquad e^{\pm j\pi} = -1, \qquad e^{\pm j2\pi} = 1$$

If α and ω are real numbers, then

$$\begin{aligned}\mathrm{Re}\,\{e^{(\alpha+j\omega)t}\} &= \mathrm{Re}\,\{e^{\alpha t}e^{j\omega t}\} = e^{\alpha t}\,\mathrm{Re}\,\{e^{j\omega t}\} = e^{\alpha t}\cos\omega t\\ \mathrm{Im}\,\{e^{(\alpha+j\omega)t}\} &= \mathrm{Im}\,\{e^{\alpha t}e^{j\omega t}\} = e^{\alpha t}\,\mathrm{Im}\,\{e^{j\omega t}\} = e^{\alpha t}\sin\omega t\end{aligned}$$

ANSWERS TO ODD-NUMBERED PROBLEMS

CHAPTER 1, page 37

1-1. (**a**) $i = -2$ A; (**b**) $i = -0.5$ A; (**c**) $i = -5$ A; (**d**) $i = 6$ A.
1-3. -5 A.
1-5. (**a**) -3 A; (**b**) -5 A.
1-7. (**a**) 15 V; (**b**) -10 V.
1-9. (**a**) $i = 4$ A; (**b**) $i = 25$ A; (**c**) $i = 5$ A.
1-11. (**a**) 6 V; (**b**) -5 V.
1-13. (**a**) 20 V; (**b**) 10 V; (**c**) 8 V; (**d**) 10 V.
1-15. A resistor of value 2 Ω.
1-17. 5 A.
1-19. -4 A.
1-21. $i = 0$, $v = -12$ V.
1-23. $i = 0.01 + 0.01 \cos t$.
1-25. (**a**)

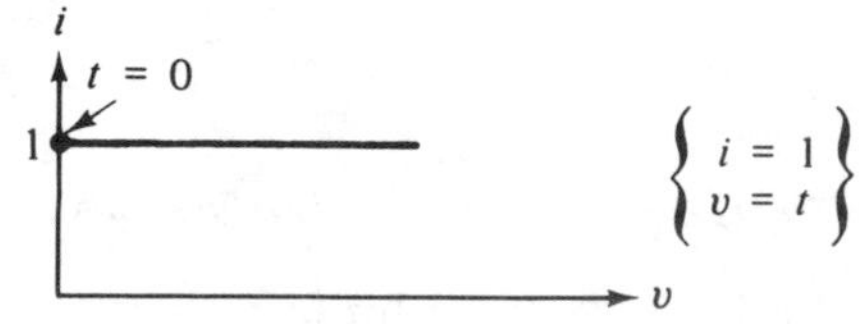

$$\begin{Bmatrix} i = 1 \\ v = t \end{Bmatrix}$$

(b)

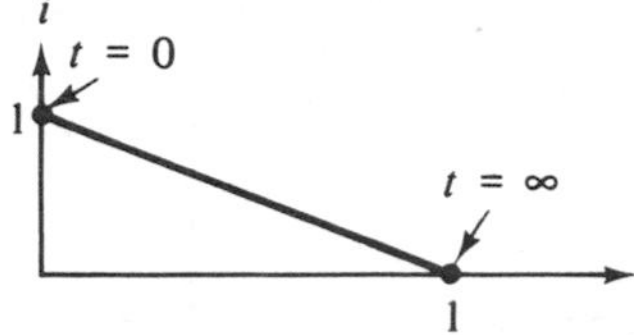

$$\left\{\begin{array}{l} i = e^{-t} \\ v = 1 - e^{-t} \end{array}\right\} \; i = 1 - v$$

1-27. $v(t) = \begin{cases} \frac{1}{4}t^2 & 0 \leq t \leq 2 \\ -\frac{1}{4}t^2 + 2t - 2 & 2 \leq t \leq 4 \\ 2 & 4 \leq t \end{cases}$

1-29.

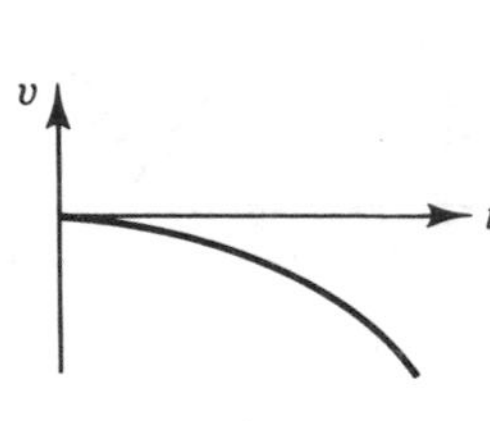

$v = -\frac{1}{2}t^2$

i

t = 0

v

$i = \sqrt{-2v}$

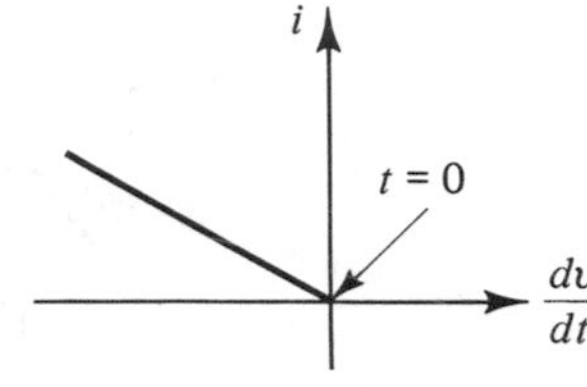

$i = -\dfrac{dv}{dt}$

1-31.

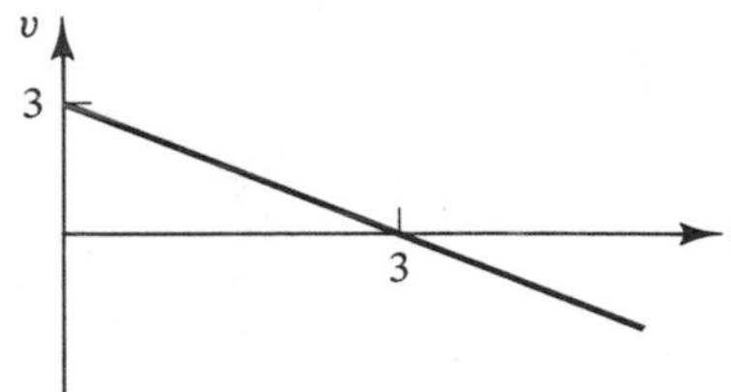

1-33 10 V.

1-35. **(a)**

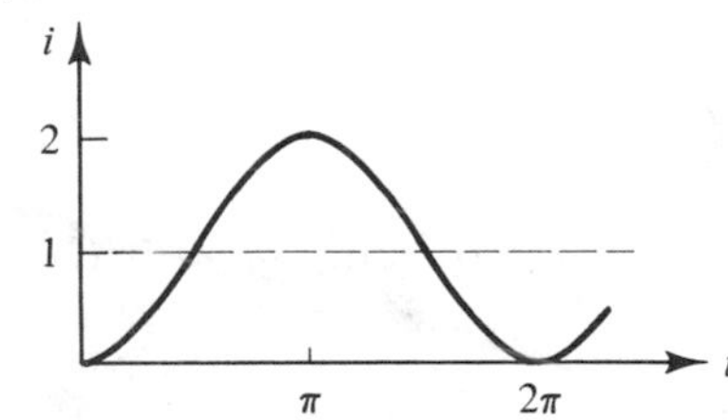

(b)

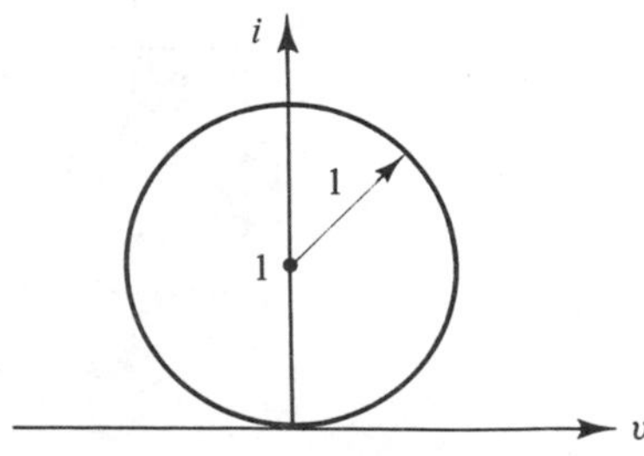

1-37.

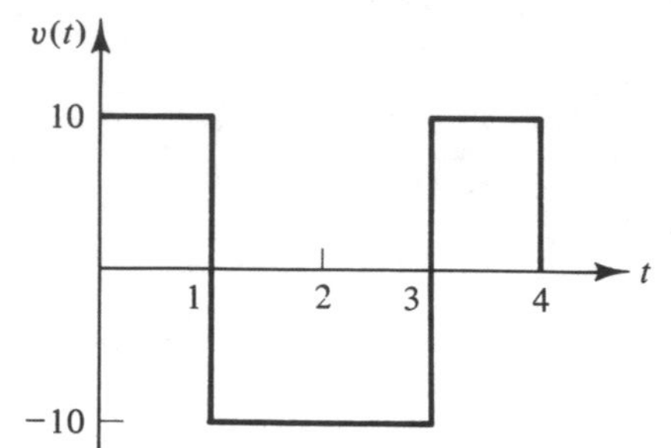

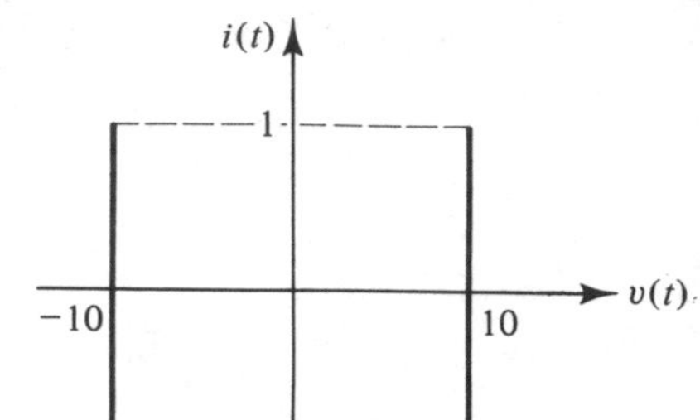

1-39.

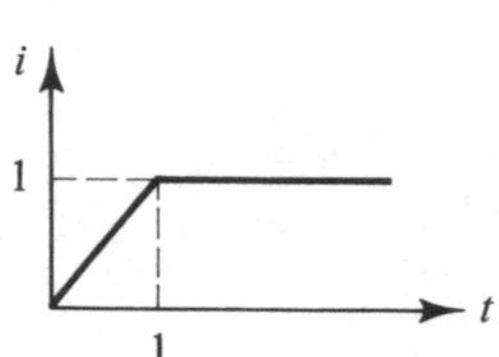

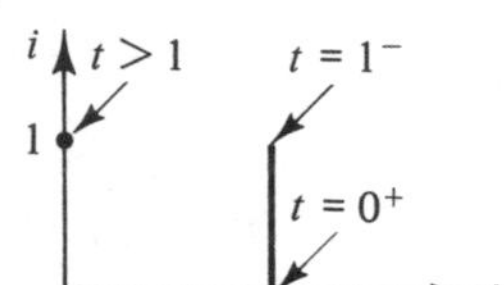

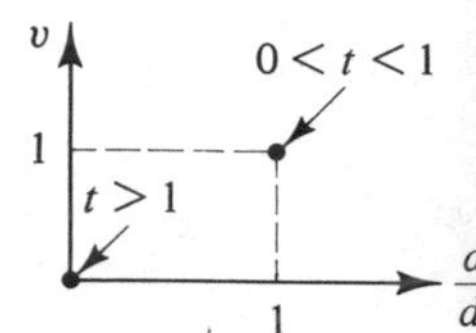

1-41.

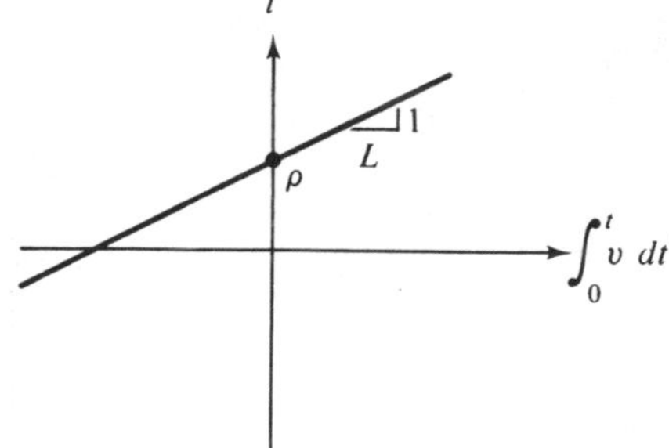

CHAPTER 2, page 93

2-1. **(a)** $R_1 + \dfrac{R_2R_3}{R_2 + R_3}$; **(b)** $\dfrac{R_1(R_2 + R_3)}{R_1 + R_2 + R_3}$; **(c)** $\dfrac{R}{2}$; **(d)** ∞; **(e)** 0; **(f)** 0; **(g)** R; **(h)** 1.

2-3. **(a)** $\frac{5}{11}\ \Omega$; **(b)** $\frac{5}{12}\ \Omega$.

2-5. **(a)** $\frac{11}{6}R$; **(b)** $\frac{1}{3}(R_1 + R_3)$.

2-7. **(a)**

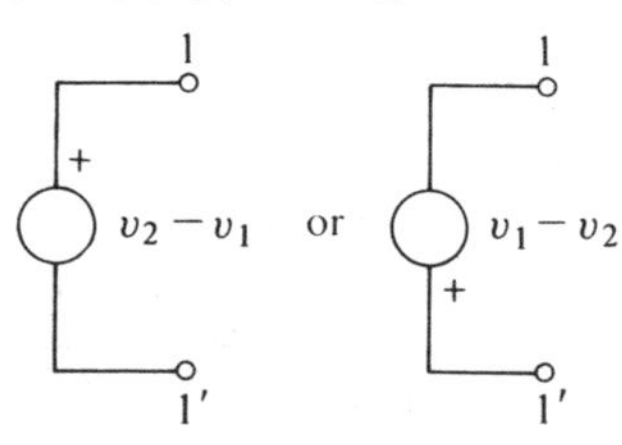

(b)

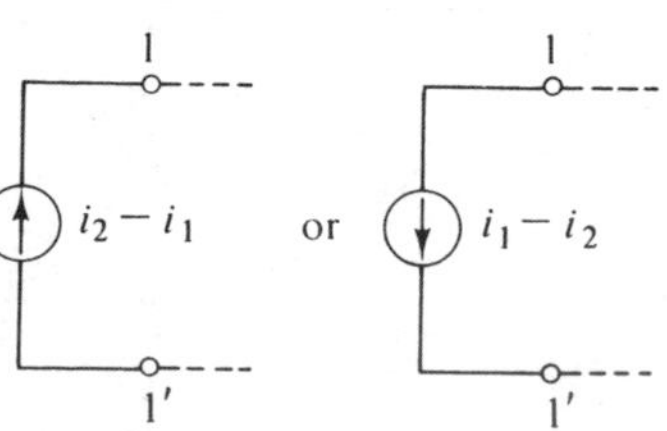

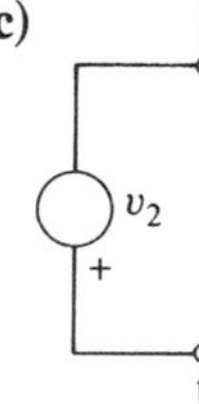

(d)

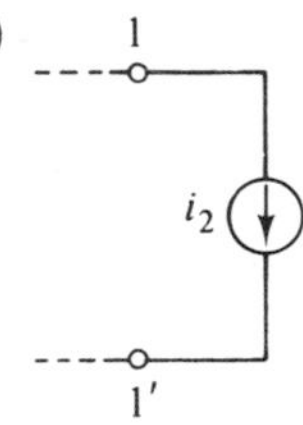

(e)

1 ○

Open circuit

1′ ○

2-9.

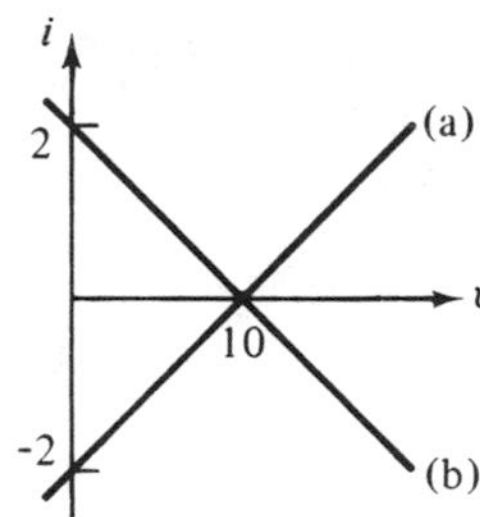

2-11.

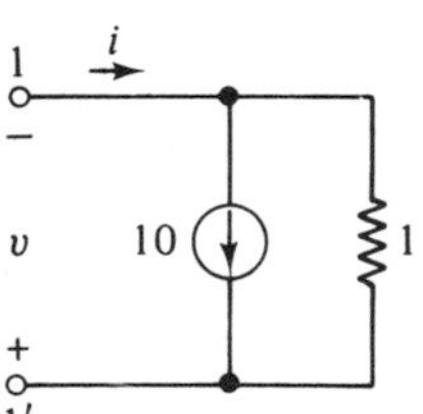

or

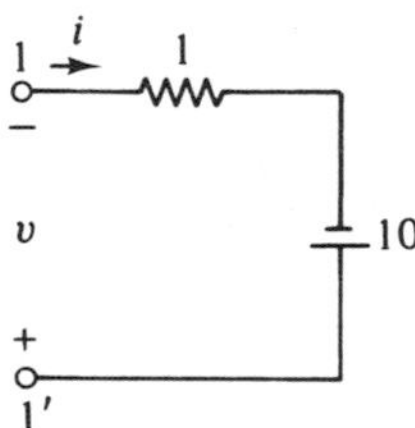

2-13.

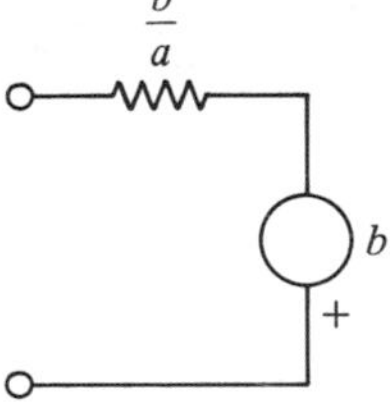

or

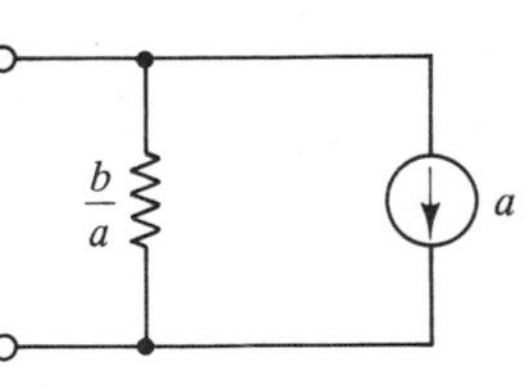

2-15.

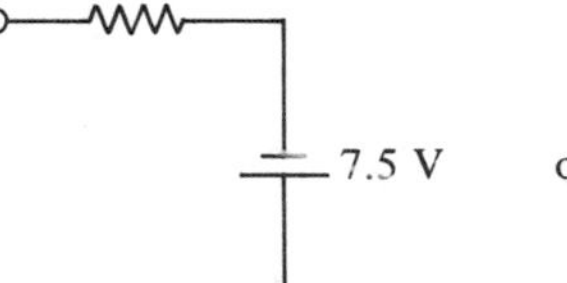

or

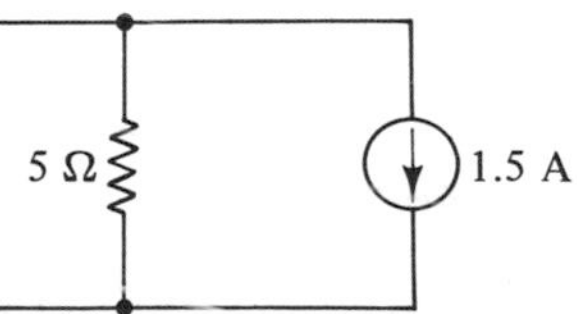

2-17. **(a)** $v = 0$; **(b)** $v = -4$ V; **(c)** $v = 30$ V; **(d)** $v = -10$ V; **(e)** $i = 0$; **(f)** $i = 8$ A; **(g)** $v = -25$ V; **(h)** $v = -5$ V; **(i)** $i = 30$ A; **(j)** $v = 0$; **(k)** $v = 0$; **(l)** $i = 0$.

2-19.

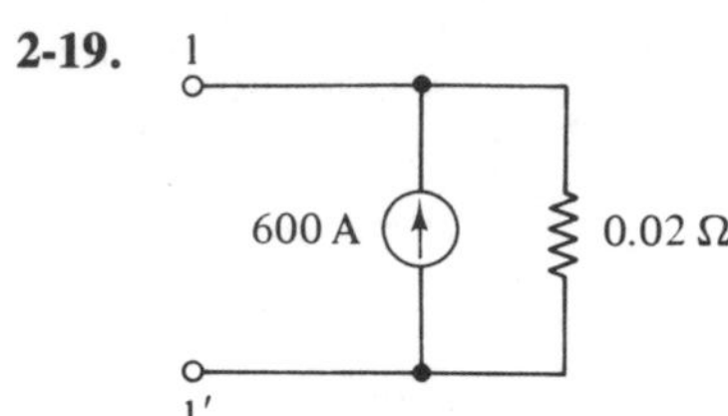

2-21.

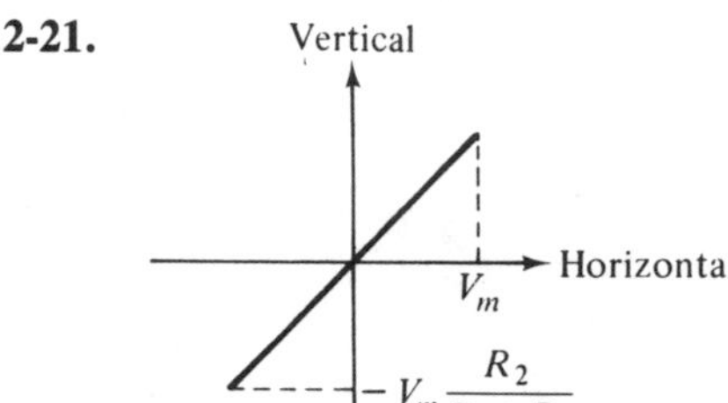

2-23. $v_1 = 442.5$ V, $v_2 = 356.5$ V, $v_3 = 270.5$ V.

2-25. $i = -15\ \mu$A.

2-27. (**a**) $R_L \leq \frac{10}{9}\ \Omega$; (**b**) $R_L \geq 90\ \Omega$.

2-29.

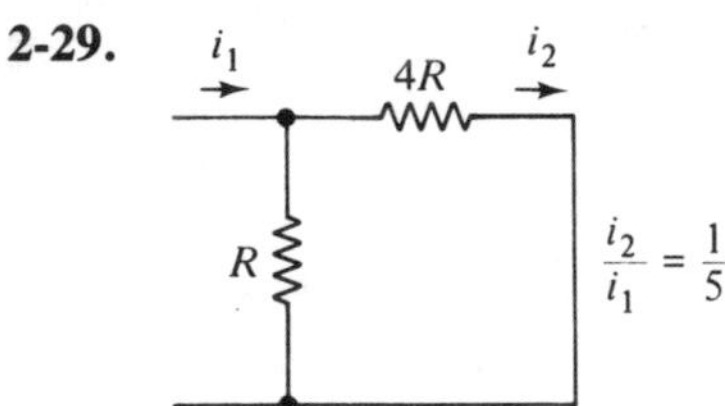

2-31. $R_1 = 2R$, $R_2 = R$.

2-33.

2-35. (**b**) $(R_1 + R_2) \gg R_s$.

2-37. $v_o = \alpha$.

2-39. (**a**) $v_o = V\frac{R_2}{R_2 + \alpha R_1}$; (**b**) $v_o = V\frac{R_2}{R_2 + (1-\alpha)R_1}$; (**c**) $v_o = V_1(1-\alpha) + V_2\alpha$;

(**d**) $v_o = V\dfrac{1-\alpha}{2-\alpha}$; (**e**) $v_o = \dfrac{V}{2\pi}\theta$ (θ in radians).

2-41.

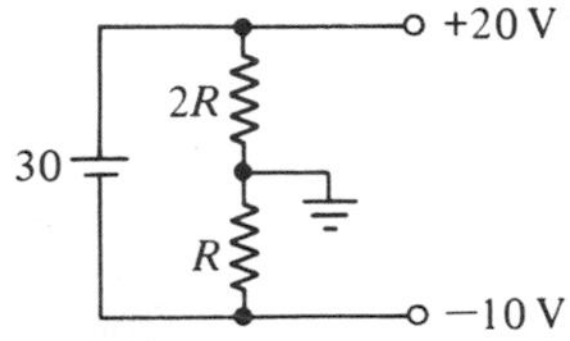

+20 V
2R
30
R
−10 V

2-43. $v_1 = -\dfrac{2}{3}V$,

$v_2 = -\dfrac{V}{3}$, $v_3 = \dfrac{V}{3}$.

2-45. (**a**) $v_o = i\dfrac{RR_L}{R+2R_L}$; (**b**) $v_o = i\dfrac{R}{2}$.

2-47. (**a**)

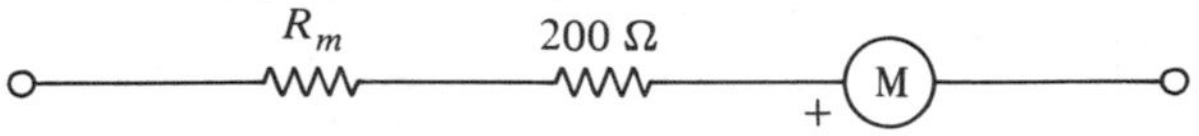

R_m 200 Ω + M

$$R_m = (2 \times 10^6 - 200)\ \Omega$$

(**b**) 40 V; when voltmeter is disconnected, the voltage is 50 V.

2-49. (**a**)

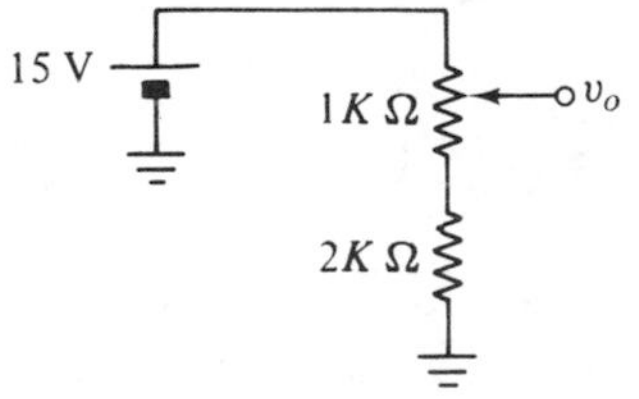

15 V
1K Ω
v_o
2K Ω

(**b**) 6 V; (**c**) 15 V.

2-51. (**a**) $\alpha = \frac{1}{2}$; (**b**) $\alpha = \frac{10}{21}$.

2-53. Use as is.

2-55. (**a**) 2 kΩ/V; (**b**) 20 kΩ.

2-57. 10 mA.

2-63. 0.1 Ω.

2-65. $V = IR$.

2-67. $v_o = V\dfrac{\Delta R}{R}$.

2-69. $v_o = -v\dfrac{\Delta R}{2R}$.

2-71. $9.90\ \text{k}\Omega \leq R_x \leq 10.10\ \text{k}\Omega$.

2-73. (**a**) $v_{o1} = 0$, $v_{o2} = 7.5$ V; (**b**) $\Delta v_{o1} = 74.63$ mV, $\Delta v_{o2} = 37.31$ mV.

2-75. $i = 2$ mA.

2-77. $i_o = v\left(\dfrac{\dfrac{R_3}{R_1 + R_3} - \dfrac{R_4}{R_2 + R_4}}{\dfrac{R_1R_3}{R_1 + R_3} + \dfrac{R_2R_4}{R_2 + R_4}}\right).$

2-79. 5°C below the oven temperature.

2-81.

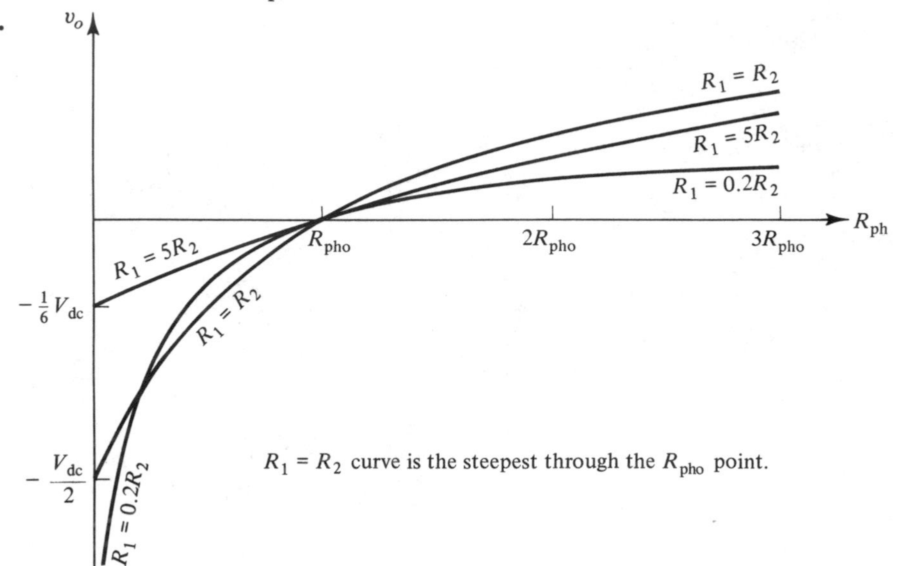

CHAPTER 3, page 146

3-1. **(a)** $v_o = i\left(\dfrac{R_1}{R_1 + R_2 + R_3}\right)R_3 + i\left(\dfrac{R_2}{R_1 + R_2 + R_3}\right)R_3;$

(b) $v_o = v\dfrac{R_2}{R_1 + R_2} - i\dfrac{R_1R_2}{R_1 + R_2};$ **(c)** $v_o = -iR;$

(d) $i_3 = \dfrac{v}{R_1 + R_2 + R_3} + i\dfrac{R_2}{R_1 + R_2 + R_3};$ **(e)** $v_o = v;$ **(f)** $v_o = -iR_1 - v;$

(g) $i = 10;$ **(h)** $i = 0;$ **(i)** $v_o = 0.$

3-3. The output will still be proportional to the sum of the input but the proportionality factor will be lower.

$$v_o = \left(\frac{v_1 + v_2 + \cdots + v_n}{n}\right)\left(\frac{R_L}{R_L + \dfrac{R}{n}}\right).$$

3-5.

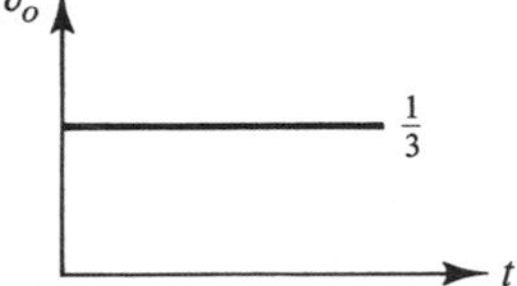

3-7.

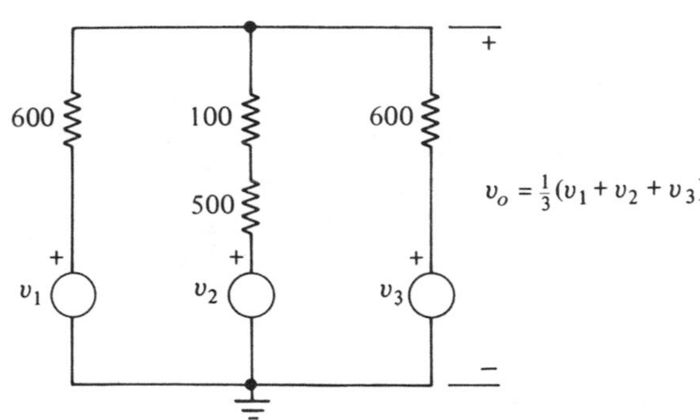

3-9.

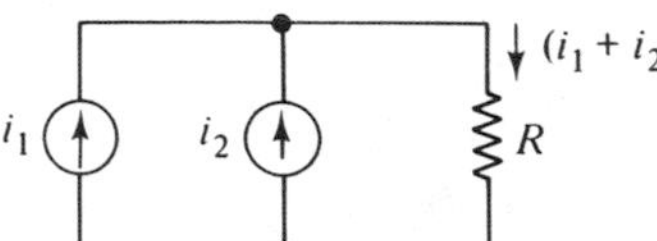

R can have any value including zero. ($R \neq \infty$)

3-11.

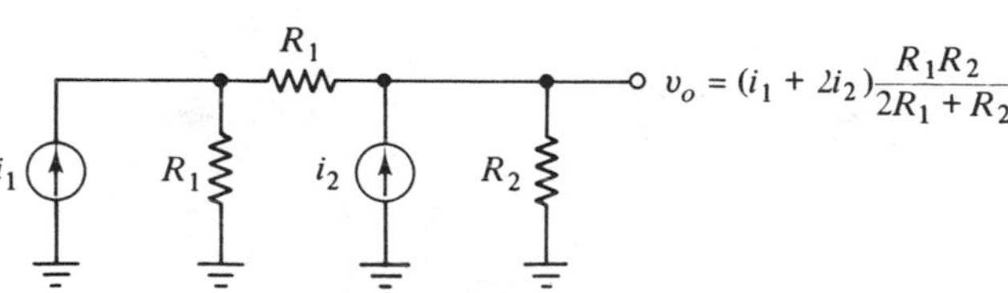

3-13.

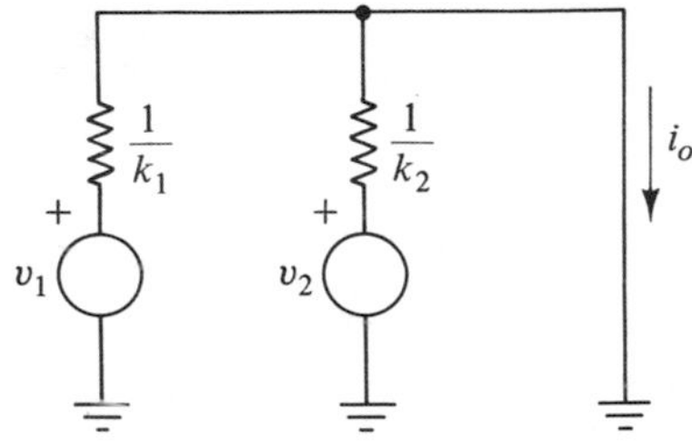

3-15. Both circuits are level shifters.
(**a**) $v_o = kV + v$; (**b**) $v_o = v - V_1(1 - k) + V_2 k$.

3-17.

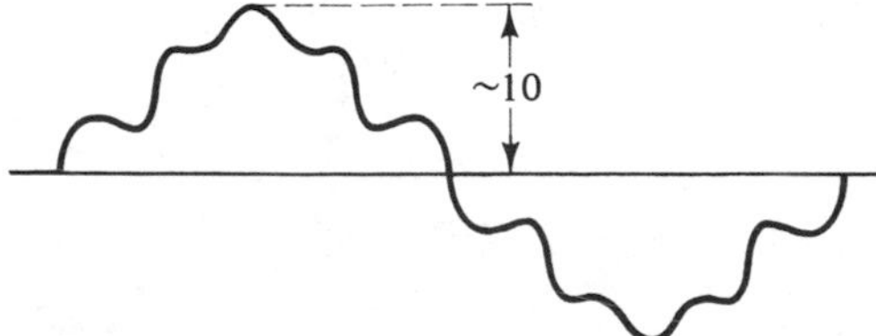

3-19. **(a)** $v_{\text{eq}} = i\dfrac{R_1R_2}{R_1 + R_2} + v\dfrac{R_1}{R_1 + R_2}$, $R_{\text{eq}} = \dfrac{R_1R_2}{R_1 + R_2}$;

(b) $v_{\text{eq}} = \dfrac{v_1R_2 + v_2R_1}{R_1 + R_2}$, $R_{\text{eq}} = \dfrac{R_1R_2}{R_1 + R_2}$; **(c)** $v_{\text{eq}} = -iR_1$, $R_{\text{eq}} = R_1$;

(d) $v_{\text{eq}} = 0$, $R_{\text{eq}} = \dfrac{R_1(R_2 + R_3)}{R_1 + R_2 + R_3}$; **(e)** $v_{\text{eq}} = -v_1 - iR$, $R_{\text{eq}} = R$;

(f) Does not exist.

3-21. **(a)**

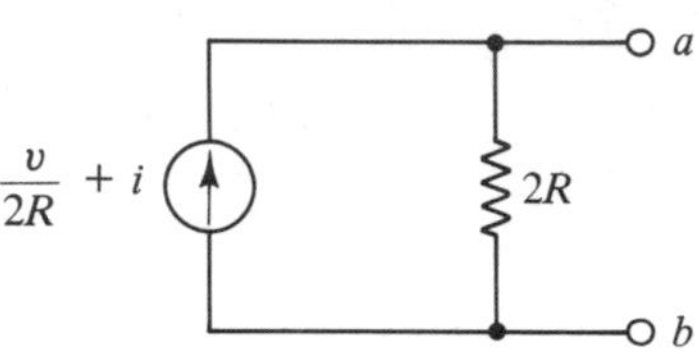

(b)

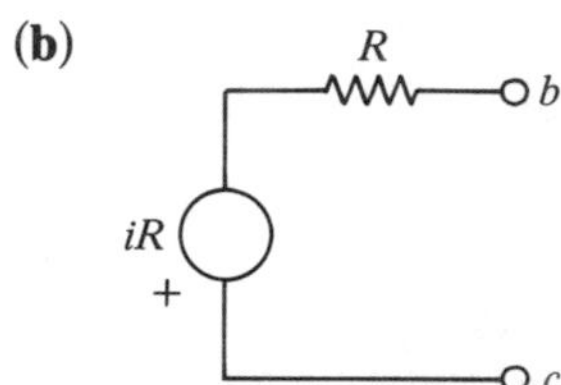

3-23. **(a)** $v_o = \frac{1}{15}(v_1 + 2v_2 + 4v_3 + 8v_4)$;
(b) $v_1 = v_2 = v_3 = 0$, $v_4 = 15$;
(c) $v_1 = v_3 = v_4 = 15$, $v_2 = 0$.

3-25. **(a)**

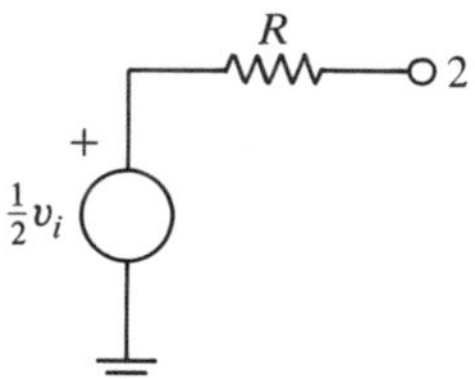

(b) It introduces 2 : 1 attenuation without altering the source resistance.

3-27. $R = 75\ \Omega$, $R' = 120\ \Omega$.

3-29. **(a)**

R_{eq} v_{eq} +

$$R_{\text{eq}} = \frac{(R_1 + R_3)(R_2 + R_4)}{R_1 + R_2 + R_3 + R_4}$$

$$v_{eq} = i\left(\frac{R_2R_3 - R_1R_4}{R_1 + R_2 + R_3 + R_4}\right)$$

(b) $i_o = \dfrac{v_{eq}}{R_{eq} + R_L}$ to the right.

3-31. **(a)** $v_o = \dfrac{1}{8}v_i$; **(b)** $v_o = i_i\dfrac{R}{13}$;

(c) $v_o = \left(\dfrac{v_1}{R_1} + \dfrac{v_2}{R_2} + \dfrac{v_3}{R_3} + \dfrac{v_4}{R_4}\right)\left(\dfrac{1}{\dfrac{1}{R_1} + \dfrac{1}{R_2} + \dfrac{1}{R_3} + \dfrac{1}{R_4}}\right)$;

(d) $i = 0$; **(e)** $i = 0$; **(f)** $v_m = 0$; **(g)** $i_m = 0$.

3-33. $i_o = 0$, $i_2 = \dfrac{v}{R_1 + \dfrac{R_2R_3}{R_2 + R_3}}$.

3-35.

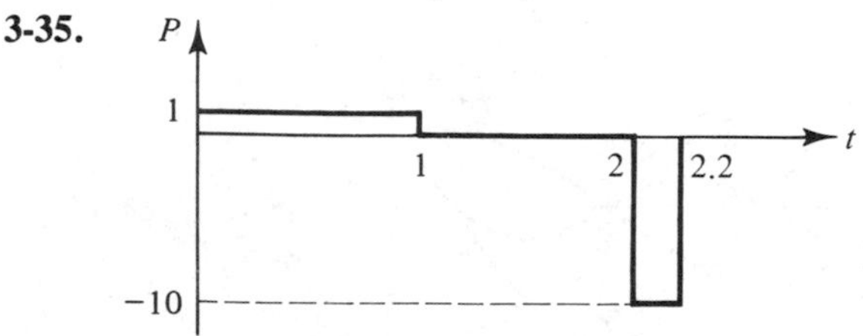

3-37. 0.5 A.

3-39. **(a)** 0.141 A; **(b)** 0.141 A.

3-41. The wattage rating of the resistors is halved.

3-43. 720 W.

3-45. $R_s = 0$.

3-47. $R = \dfrac{R_1R_2}{R_1 + R_2}$

3-49. **(a)** $R_1 = 0$, $p_L = \dfrac{v^2}{R_L}$;

(b) $R_2 = \infty$, $p_L = \left(\dfrac{v}{R_1 + R_L}\right)^2 R_L$;

(c) $R_L = \dfrac{R_1R_2}{R_1 + R_2}$, $p_L = \dfrac{v^2}{4R_1}\left(\dfrac{R_2}{R_1 + R_2}\right)$.

3-51. 200 μF.

3-53. 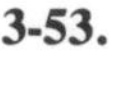

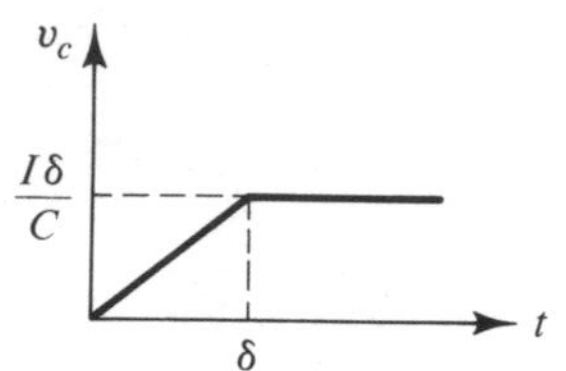

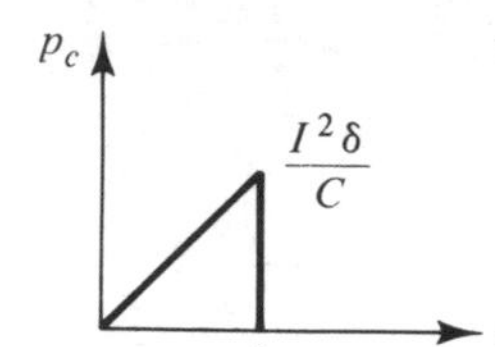

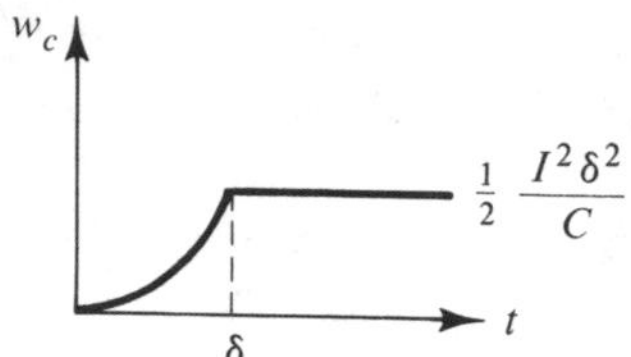

3-55.

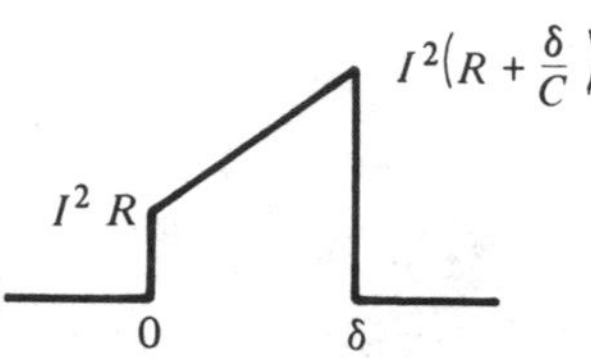

3-57. 1000 J.

3-59. $p = V^2\left(\frac{1}{R} + \frac{t}{L}\right)$, $w = V^2t\left(\frac{1}{R} + \frac{t}{2L}\right)$.

3-61. **(a)**

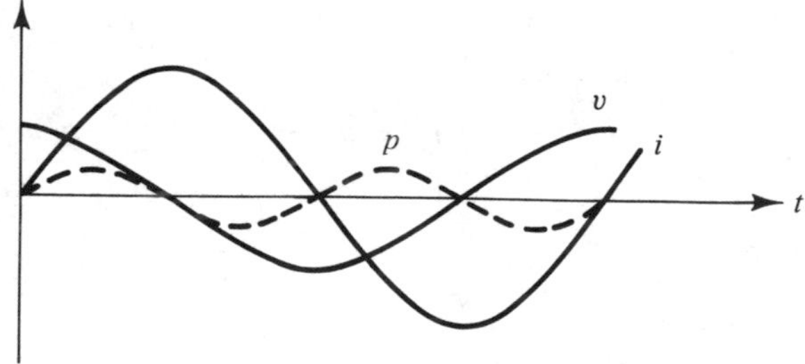

(b) $p_{av} = 0$; **(c)** $w_L = 0$.

CHAPTER 4, page 194

4-1. **(a)** $v_a + v_b + v_c = 0$

$v_d + v_e - v_c = 0$

(b) $v_a + v_b + v_d + v_e = 0$ (Kirchhoff's Voltage Law applied to outer loop)

4-3. **(a)**

$$L_1\frac{di_1}{dt} + \frac{1}{C}\int i_1\,dt - \frac{1}{C}\int i_2\,dt = v$$

$$-\frac{1}{C}\int i_1\,dt + L_2\frac{di_2}{dt} + \frac{1}{C}\int i_2\,dt = 0$$

(b)

$$L\frac{di_1}{dt} + i_1R - L\frac{di_2}{dt} = -v$$

$$-L\frac{di_1}{dt} + L\frac{di_2}{dt} + \frac{1}{C}\int i_2\,dt = v$$

(c) $i_1 R + \frac{1}{C}\int i_1\,dt - \frac{1}{C}\int i_2\,dt = v_1$

$$-\frac{1}{C}\int i_1\,dt + \frac{2}{C}\int i_2\,dt = V_2$$

4-5. (a) $\Delta = \begin{vmatrix} (R_1 + R_2 + R_3) & -R_3 \\ -R_3 & (R_3 + R_4 + R_5) \end{vmatrix}$ (b) $\Delta = \begin{vmatrix} 6 & -2 & -3 & 0 \\ -2 & 32 & 0 & -9 \\ -3 & 0 & 18 & -6 \\ 0 & -9 & -6 & 30 \end{vmatrix}$

4-7. (a) $\Delta = 45$; $v_o = \frac{2v_1 + 12v_2}{15}$; (b) $v_o = -\frac{5}{4}$; (c) $v_o = \frac{i_1 + 2i_2}{3}$;

(d) $v_o = -\frac{150}{7}$;

(e) $v_o = 0$; (f) $v_o = 0$.

4-9. $-v_1G_1 + C\frac{dv_2}{dt} + v_2(G_1 + G_2) + \frac{1}{L}\int v_2\,dt - \frac{1}{L}\int v_3\,dt - C\frac{dv_4}{dt} - v_4G_2 = i_1 - i_2$

4-11. (a) $v_1 = v$ (constraint)

$-\frac{1}{L}\int v_1\,dt + C\frac{dv_2}{dt} + G_2v_2 + \frac{1}{L}\int v_2\,dt - G_2v_3 = 0$ (node 2)

$-v_1G_1 - v_2G_2 + (G_1 + G_2)v_3 = i$ (node 3)

(b) $v_1 = v_a$ (constraint)

$-v_1G + Gv_2 + \frac{1}{L}\int v_2\,dt + \frac{1}{L}\int v_3\,dt = 0$ (supernode covering nodes 2 and 3)

$v_3 - v_2 = v_b$ (constraint)

4-13. (a) $i_o = \frac{35}{3}$; (b) $v_o = 7.5$; (c) $i_o = 0$; (d) $v_o = (v_1 + v_2 + v_3 + v_4)\frac{1}{4}$;

(e) $i_o = \frac{1}{2}$; (f) $i_o = -v$.

4-15. (a) $i_o = 0$; (b) $i_o = 0$.

4-17. $\Delta_3 = \begin{vmatrix} 1 & 0 & -10 \\ 0 & 1 & 0 \\ 0 & 0 & 10 \end{vmatrix}$

4-19. One possible solution is

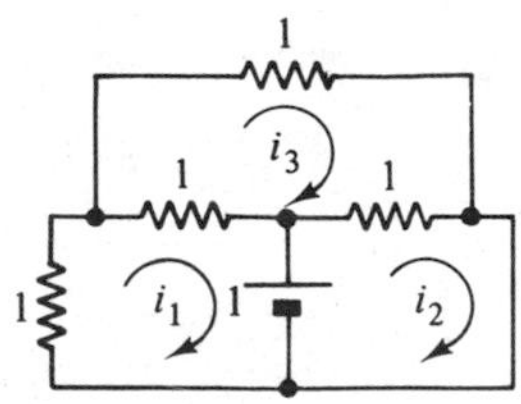

CHAPTER 5, page 259

5-1. **(a)** $\dfrac{s}{s^2+\omega^2}$; **(b)** $\dfrac{\omega}{(s+\alpha)^2+\omega^2}$; **(c)** $\dfrac{1}{s^2}$; **(d)** $\dfrac{\alpha}{s(s+\alpha)}$; **(e)** $\dfrac{\omega\cos\theta + s\sin\theta}{s^2+\omega^2}$;

(f) $\dfrac{\alpha_2-\alpha_1}{(s+\alpha_1)(s+\alpha_2)}$

5-3. **(a)** $Y(s) = \dfrac{s^2+2}{(s^2+1)^2}$; **(b)** $Y(s) = \dfrac{1}{s^3+s^2+s}$.

5-5. **(a)**

$$\Delta_l = \begin{vmatrix} \left(s+1+\dfrac{1}{s}\right) & -\left(s+\dfrac{1}{s}\right) & 0 \\ -\left(s+\dfrac{1}{s}\right) & \left(2s+1+\dfrac{1}{s}\right) & -s \\ 0 & -s & \left(s+\dfrac{1}{s}\right) \end{vmatrix}$$

$$\Delta_n = \begin{vmatrix} \left(s+1+\dfrac{1}{s}\right) & -\left(s+\dfrac{1}{s}\right) & 0 \\ -\left(s+\dfrac{1}{s}\right) & \left(s+1+\dfrac{2}{s}\right) & -\dfrac{1}{s} \\ 0 & -\dfrac{1}{s} & \left(s+\dfrac{1}{s}\right) \end{vmatrix}$$

(b)

$$\Delta_l = \begin{vmatrix} \left(R_s+R+\dfrac{1}{sC}\right) & -R & -\dfrac{1}{sC} \\ -R & \left(R+R_L+\dfrac{1}{sC}\right) & -\dfrac{1}{sC} \\ -\dfrac{1}{sC} & -\dfrac{1}{sC} & \left(sL+\dfrac{2}{sC}\right) \end{vmatrix}$$

$$\Delta_n = \begin{vmatrix} \left(sC+G_s+\dfrac{1}{sL}\right) & -sC & -\dfrac{1}{sL} \\ -sC & (2sC+G) & -sC \\ -\dfrac{1}{sL} & -sC & \left(sC+G_L+\dfrac{1}{sL}\right) \end{vmatrix}$$

5-7. **(a)** $\dfrac{s+1}{s+2}$; **(b)** $\dfrac{(1/C)s}{s^2+1/LC}$; **(c)** $s(L_1+L_2)$; **(d)** $\dfrac{1}{s(C_1+C_2)}$; **(e)** $\dfrac{s^2+1}{s^2+s+1}$;

(f) $\dfrac{s}{s^2+s+1}$; **(g)** $\dfrac{s^2+s+1}{s+1}$; **(h)** $\dfrac{s^2+s+1}{s(s+1)}$; **(i)** $\dfrac{s^5+4s^3+3s}{s^4+3s^2+1}$;

(j) 1; (k) $Z_1 + \dfrac{Z_2Z_3}{Z_2 + Z_3}$; (l) $\dfrac{Z_1(Z_2 + Z_3)}{Z_1 + Z_2 + Z_3}$;

(m) $$Z_i = \cfrac{1}{Y_1 + \cfrac{1}{Z_2 + \cfrac{1}{Y_3 + \cfrac{1}{Z_4 + \cfrac{1}{Y_5 + \cfrac{1}{Z_6 + \cfrac{1}{Y_7}}}}}}}$$

(n) $$Z_i = s + \cfrac{1}{s + \cfrac{1}{s + \cfrac{1}{s + \cfrac{1}{s + \cdots}}}} = s + \cfrac{1}{s + \cfrac{1}{Z_i}} = \frac{s \pm \sqrt{s^2 + 4}}{2}$$

5-9. (a) $Z_1Z_4 = Z_2Z_3$; (b) $Z_1Z_4 = Z_2Z_3$.

5-11. (a) $\dfrac{V_2}{I_1} = \dfrac{Z_1Z_2}{Z_1 + Z_2}$; (b) $\dfrac{V_2}{I_1} = \dfrac{Z_1Z_3}{Z_1 + Z_2 + Z_3}$; (c) $\dfrac{V_2}{V_1} = 1$; (d) $\dfrac{I_2}{V_1} = -\dfrac{1}{Z_2 + Z_3}$;

(e) $\dfrac{V_2}{V_1} = \dfrac{Z_4}{Z_3 + Z_4}$; (f) $\dfrac{V_2}{I_1} = Z_2$; (g) $\dfrac{I_2}{I_1} = -\dfrac{1}{2}$.

5-13. (a) $I_1 = 0.77\dfrac{V_1}{Z}$; (b) $I_1 = \dfrac{V_1}{Z}$.

5-15. (a) $V_{oc}(s) = \dfrac{s\gamma + \rho/C}{s^2 + \dfrac{1}{LC}}$; (b) $I_{sc}(s) = \dfrac{\rho + s\gamma C}{s}$; (c) $Z(s) = \dfrac{s\,1/C}{s^2 + \dfrac{1}{LC}}$;

(d)

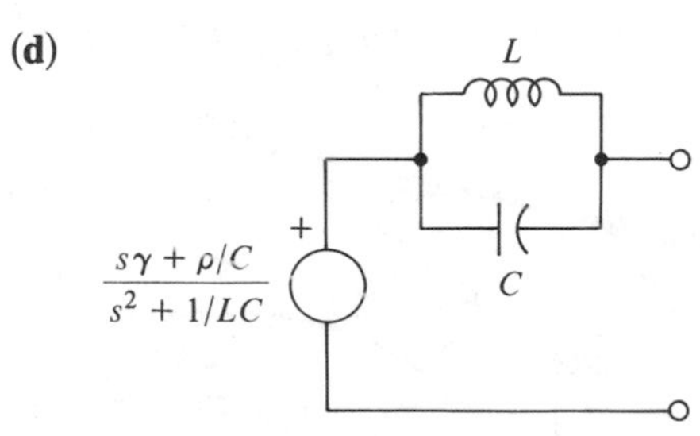

Thévenin

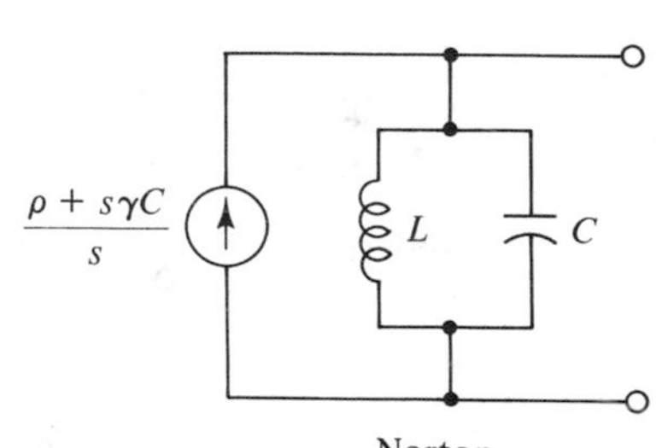

Norton

5-17. Unit-step function.

5-19. (a) $1\angle\pi$; (b) $\dfrac{1}{2\sqrt{65}}\angle\left(\dfrac{\pi}{2} - \tan^{-1}\left(\dfrac{7}{4}\right)\right)$

5-21. **(a)** $e^{-\alpha t}\sin\beta t$; **(b)** $a\cos\phi - b\sin\phi$; **(c)** $2a\cos\theta$ **(d)** $\tan^{-1}\left(\dfrac{-\sin\phi}{1+\cos\phi}\right)$;

(e) $2(1+\cos a)$; **(f)** -1;

(g) $-\sin t$; **(h)** $\cos a \cosh b$.

5-23. $s^2 + s2\alpha + \alpha^2 + \beta^2$.

5-25. $r(t) = A + Be^{-t} + C\sin(t+D) + Ee^{-t}\sin(t+F)$
A, B, C, D, E, F, are constants.

5-27. **(a)** $\sin t + \cos t = \sqrt{2}\cos\left(t - \dfrac{\pi}{4}\right) = \sqrt{2}\sin\left(t + \dfrac{\pi}{4}\right)$;

(b) $e^{-\alpha t}\left(a_1\cos\beta t + \dfrac{a_o - a_1\alpha}{\beta}\sin\beta t\right)$;

(c) $2(a\cos ct - b\sin ct) =$

$2\sqrt{a^2+b^2}\sin\left(ct + \tan^{-1}\dfrac{a}{-b}\right) = 2\sqrt{a^2+b^2}\cos\left(ct - \tan^{-1}\dfrac{-b}{a}\right)$;

(d) $\sqrt{2}\,e^{-t}\cos\left(t + \dfrac{\pi}{4}\right)$.

5-31. **(a)** $v_o(t) = e^{-t} - e^{-2t}$;
(b) $v_o(t) = 1 - \cos t$;
(c) $i_o(t) = e^{-t}$;
(d) $v_o(t) = 1$.

CHAPTER 6, page 314

6-1. **(a)** $v_{on} = e^{-t}$, $v_{of} = 0$; **(b)** $v_{on} = 1$, $v_{of} = 0$; **(c)** $v_{on} = \dfrac{2}{\sqrt{3}}e^{-t/2}\sin\dfrac{\sqrt{3}}{2}t$, $v_{of} = 0$;

(d) $v_o = t$ (because of multiple poles, forced and natural parts cannot be separated);

(e) $i_{on} = \dfrac{2}{\sqrt{3}}e^{-t/2}\sin\dfrac{\sqrt{3}}{2}t$, $i_{of} = 0$; **(f)** $i_n = \sin t$, $i_f = 0$;

(g) $i_n(t) = 0$, $i_f(t) = \sin t$.

6-3. $AT(0)$.

6-5. **(a)** $i(t) = \dfrac{V}{R}(1 - e^{-(R/L)t})$

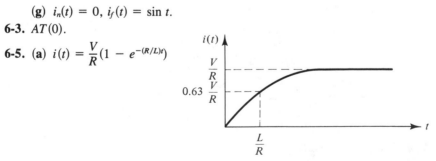

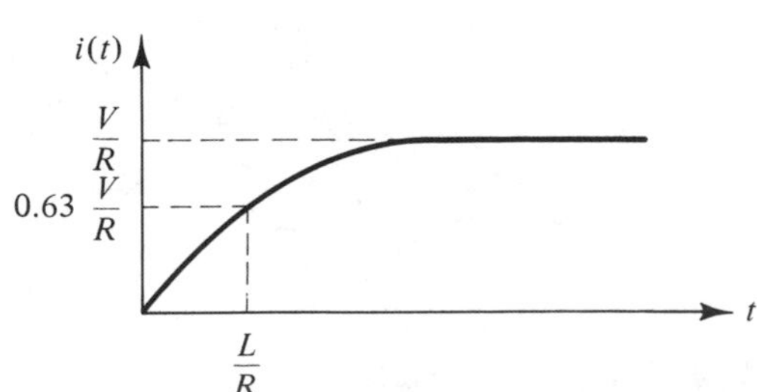

(b) $i(t) = I(1 - e^{-(R/L)t})$

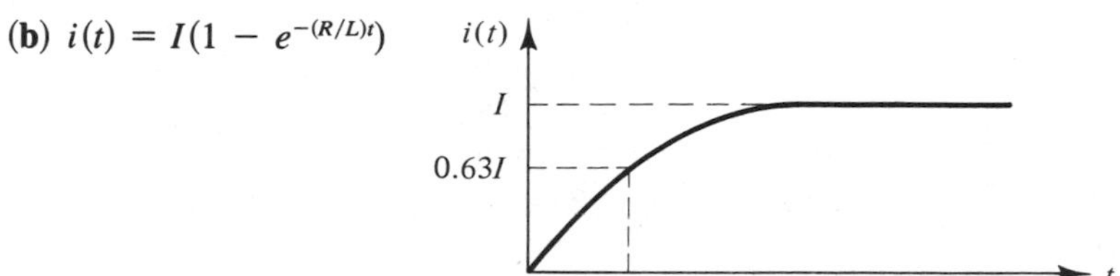

(c) $v_o(t) = IR(1 - e^{-t/RC})$

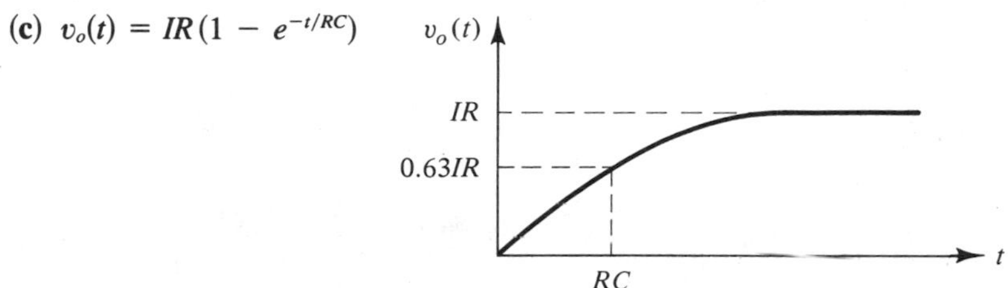

6-7. (a) $i(t) = e^{-t}$; (b) $v_o(t) = e^{-t}$; (c) $i_2(t) = I\dfrac{L_1}{L_1 + L_2}[1 - e^{-[R(L_1+L_2)/L_1L_2]t}]$;

(d) $v_o(t) = e^{-2t}$; (e) $i(t) = -0.5 + 0.75e^{-t_{ms}/4.8}$ mA; (f) $v_o(t) = \frac{5}{3}(1 - e^{-t_{ms}})$.

6-9. $v_o(t) = \dfrac{V_{dc}}{2}(1 + e^{-2t/RC})$.

6-11. (a) $v(t) = IR(1 - e^{-t/RC}),\ i(t) = Ie^{-t/RC}$;

(b) $v(t) = \dfrac{I}{C}t,\ i(t) = I$.

6-13. (a) $r(t) = 12 - 7e^{-t_{ms}/2}$;

(b) $r(t) = 10 - 16e^{-t_{\mu s}/25}$.

6-15. (a) $v_o(0^+) = (\rho_2 - \rho_1)R,\ v_o(\infty) = 0,\ \tau = \dfrac{L_1L_2}{L_1 + L_2}\Big/R$;

(b) $v_o(0^+) = \dfrac{\gamma_1R_2 + \gamma_2R_1}{R_1 + R_2},\ v_o(\infty) = \dfrac{\gamma_1C_1 + \gamma_2C_2}{C_1 + C_2},\ \tau = (R_1 + R_2)\dfrac{C_1C_2}{C_1 + C_2}$;

(c) $i(0^+) = -\dfrac{V_{dc}}{\dfrac{RR_2}{R + R_2}},\ i(\infty) = I_{dc} - \dfrac{V_{dc}}{R_2},\ \tau = RC$;

(d) $i(0^+) = I_{dc} + \dfrac{\gamma}{R_2},\ i(\infty) = \dfrac{V_{dc}}{R_1 + R_2} + I_{dc}\dfrac{R_2}{R_1 + R_2},\ \tau = \dfrac{R_1R_2}{R_1 + R_2}C$.

6-17. **(a)** $v_o(t) = \dfrac{\alpha}{\alpha - 1}(e^{-t} - e^{-\alpha t})$

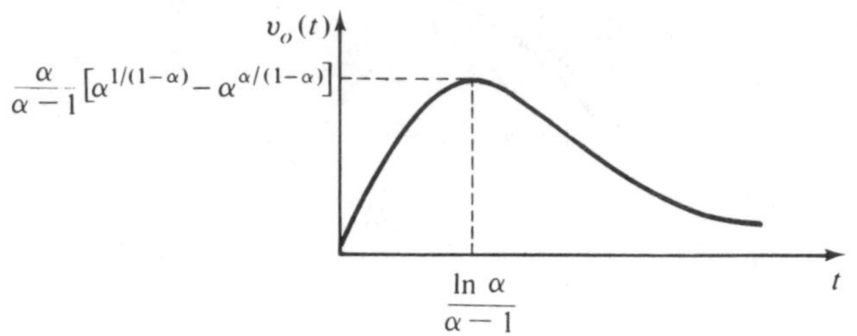

(b)

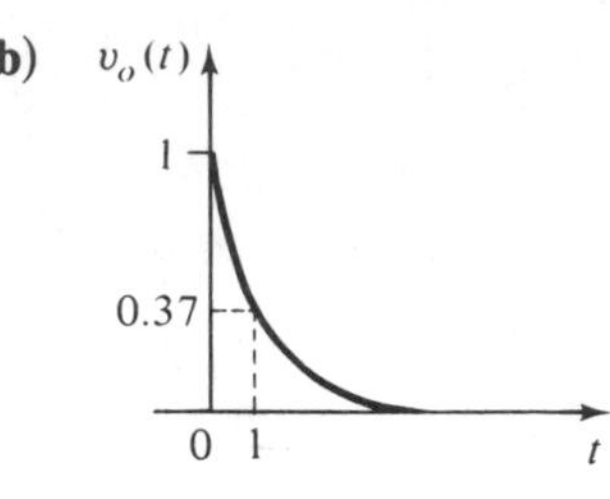

6-19. $v_o(t) = I_{dc}Re^{-2t/RC}$, $i_o(t) = I_{dc}(1 + e^{-2t/RC})$.

6-21. **(a)**

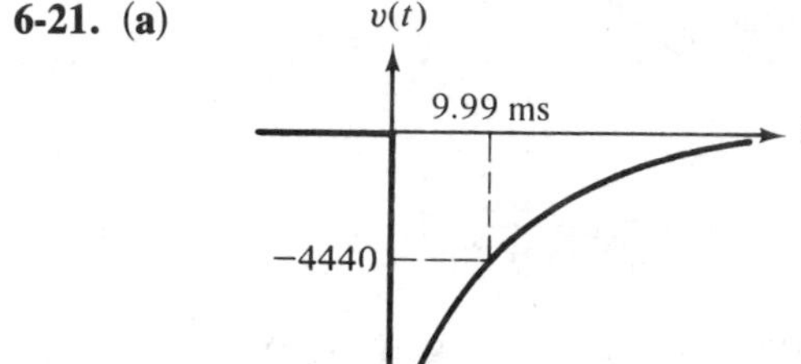

(b)

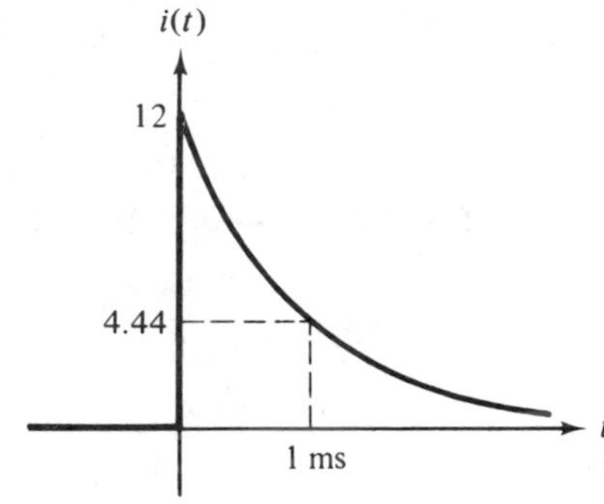

6-23 $i(0^+) = \dfrac{V_{dc} - \gamma}{R} - I_{dc}$, $v(0^+) = V_{dc}$, $i(\infty) = \dfrac{V_{dc}}{R} - I_{dc}$, $v(\infty) = V_{dc}$.

6-25. $v_o(t) = \dfrac{V_{dc}}{6}(2 + e^{-3t/2RC})$

6-27.

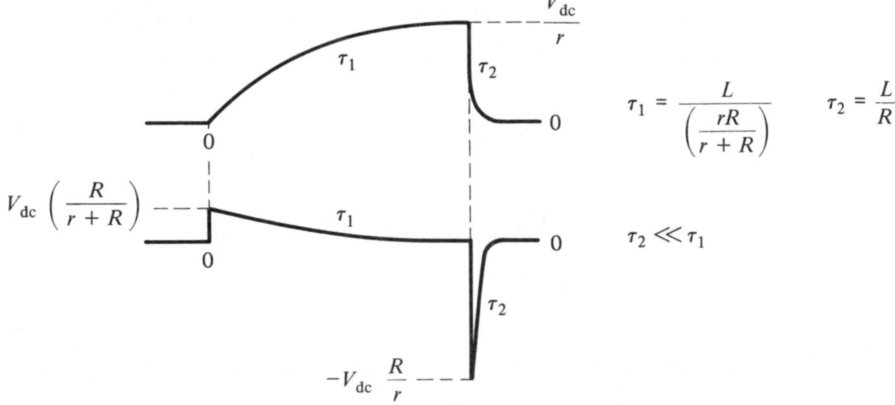

6-29.

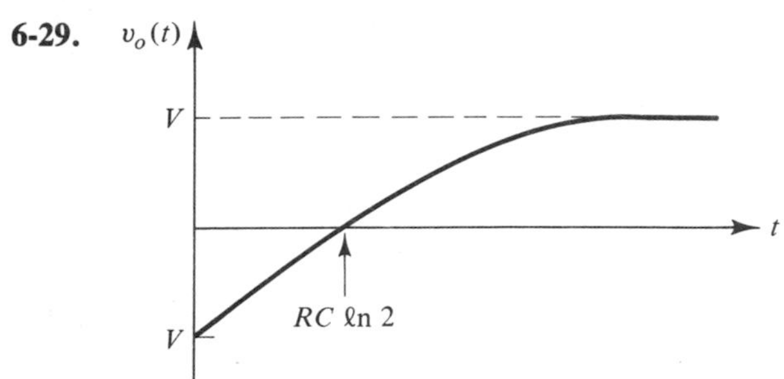

6-31. $v_{o1}(t) = -(V_1 + V_2)e^{-t/RC}$, $v_{o2}(t) = -V_2 + (V_1 + V_2)e^{-t/RC}$.

6-33. **(a)**

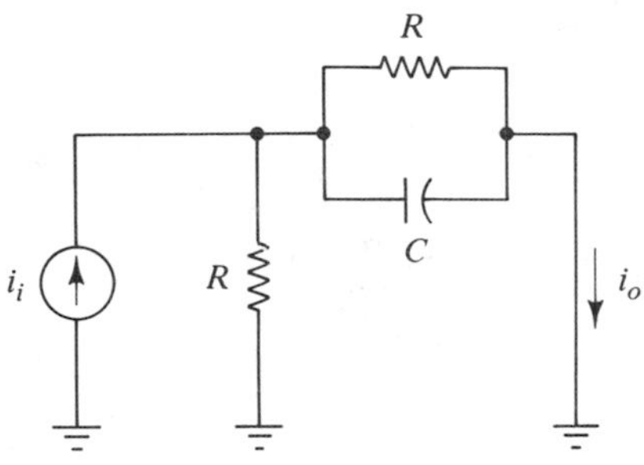

(b)

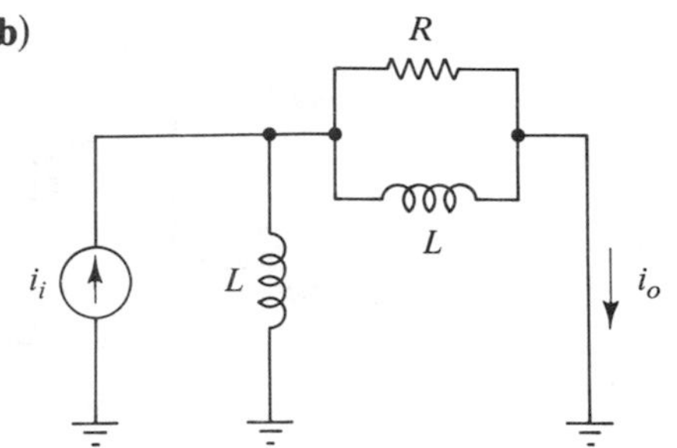

6-35. **(a)**

R_1 R_2 C

$\frac{R_1}{R_2} = 1.5$

or

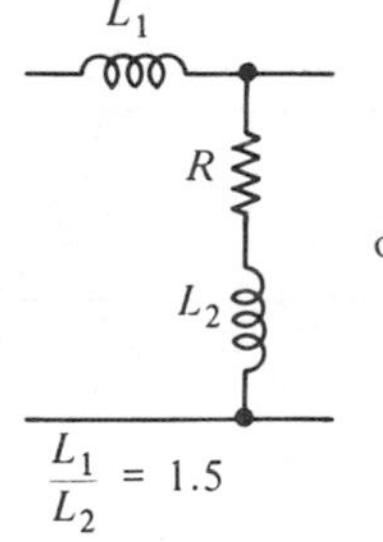

$\frac{L_1}{L_2} = 1.5$

or

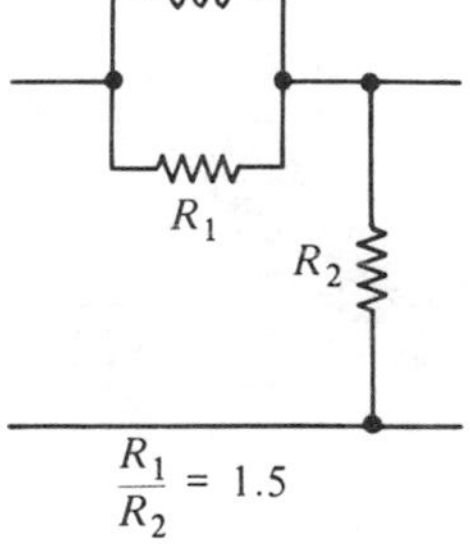

$\frac{R_1}{R_2} = 1.5$

(b)

C_1 R C_2

$\frac{C_2}{C_1} = 1.5$

or

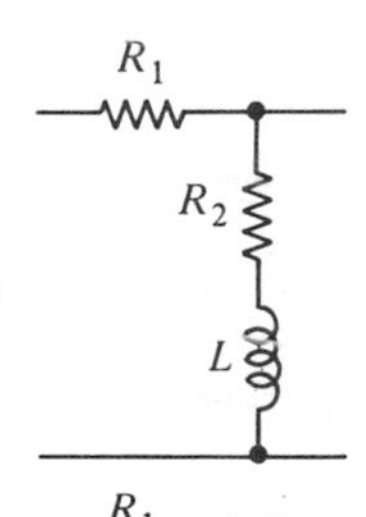

$\frac{R_1}{R_2} = 1.5$

or

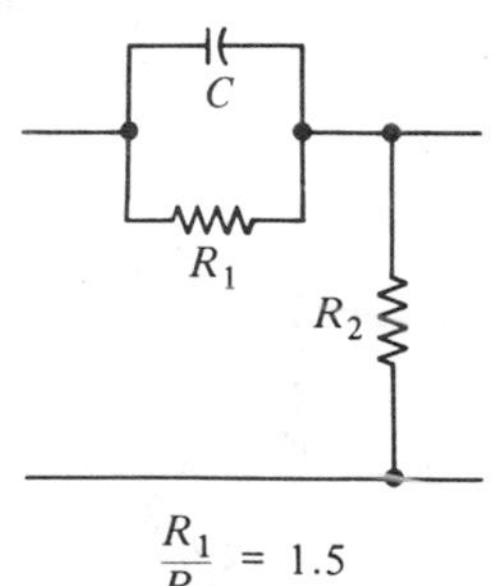

$\frac{R_1}{R_2} = 1.5$

6-37. (a)

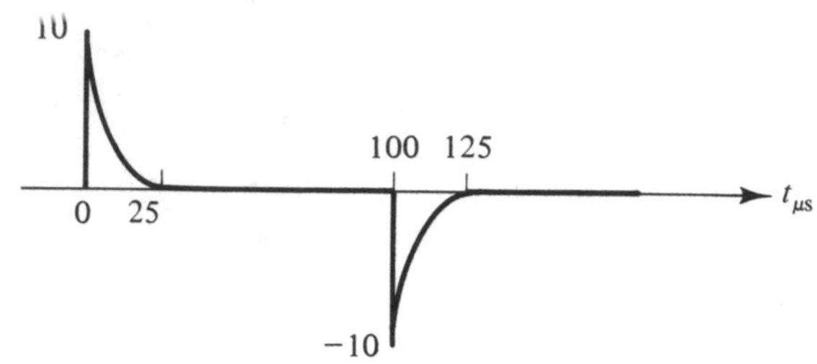

$$v_o(t) = \begin{cases} 10e^{-t_{\mu s}/5}, & 0 < t < 100\ \mu s \\ 10(e^{-t_{\mu s}/5} - e^{-(t_{\mu s}-100)/5}), & 100\ \mu s < t \end{cases}$$

(b)

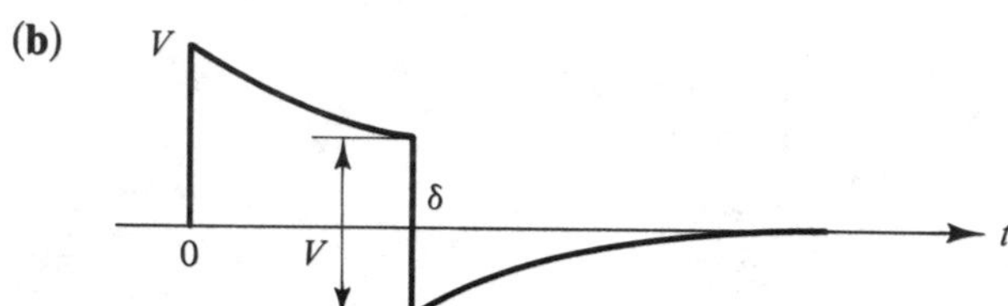

$$v_o(t) = \begin{cases} Ve^{-t/RC}, & 0 < t < \delta \\ V(e^{-t/RC} - e^{-(t-\delta)/RC}), & \delta < t \end{cases}$$

(c)

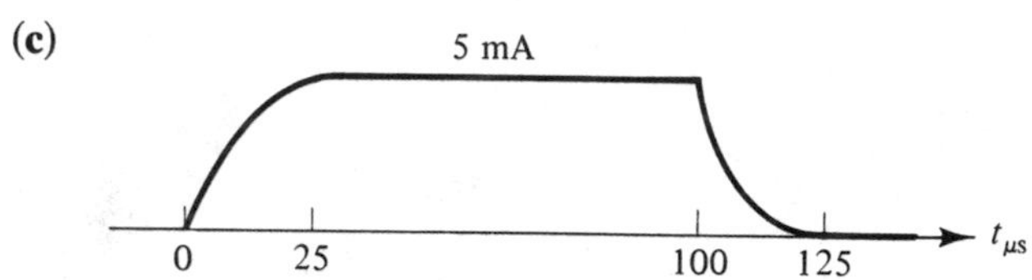

$$i(t) = \begin{cases} 5(1 - e^{-t_{\mu}/5}), & 0 \le t \le 100\ \mu s \\ 5(e^{-(t_{\mu s}-100)/5} - e^{-t_{\mu s}/5}), & 100\ \mu s \le t \end{cases}$$

(d)

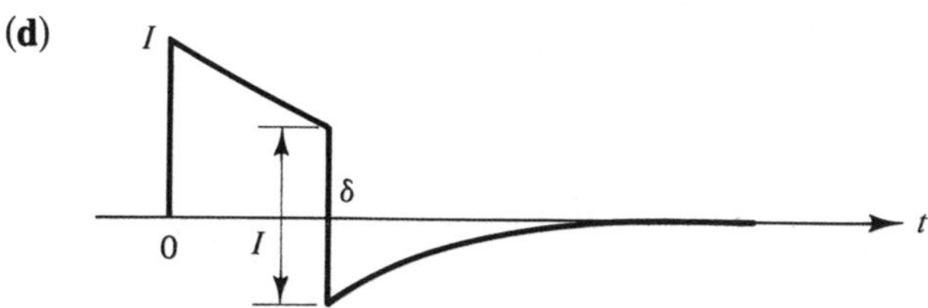

$$i(t) = \begin{cases} Ie^{-t/RC}, & 0 < t < \delta \\ I(e^{-t/RC} - e^{-(t-\delta)/RC}), & \delta > t \end{cases}$$

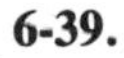

6-39.

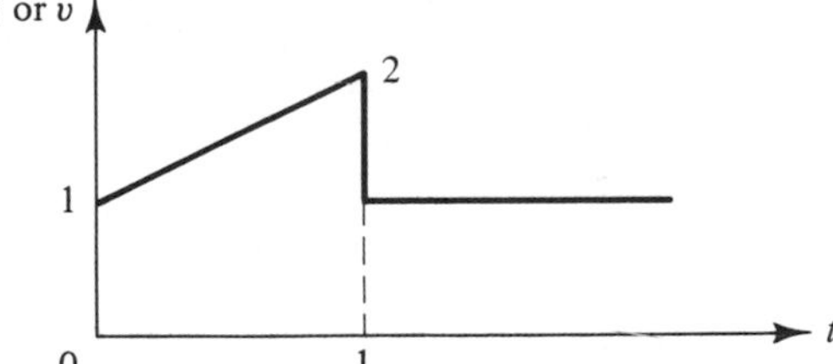

6-41.

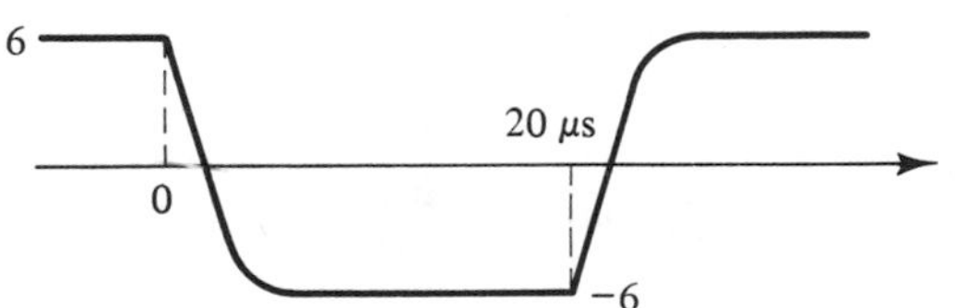

6-43.

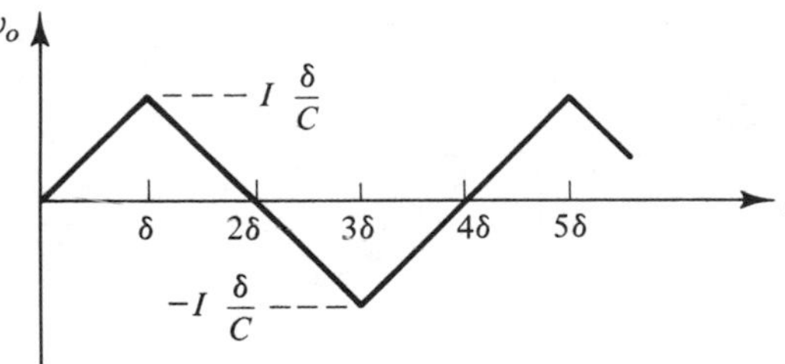

6-45. (a)

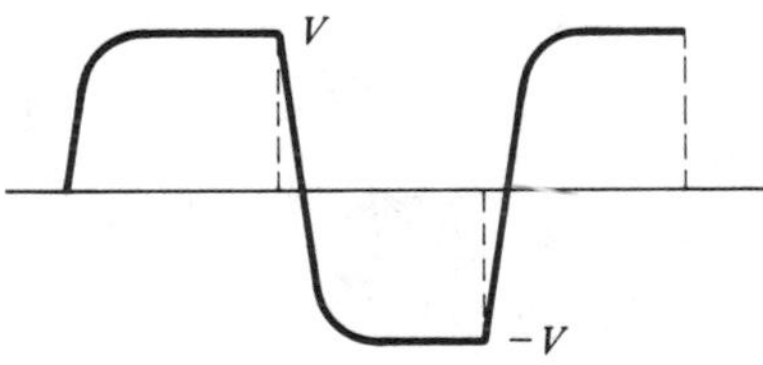

(b)

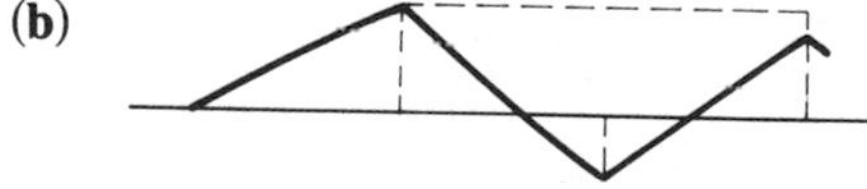

(c)

6-47.

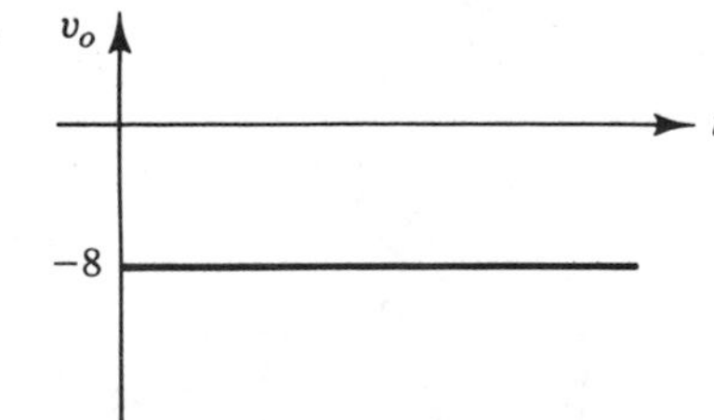

6-49. **(a)**

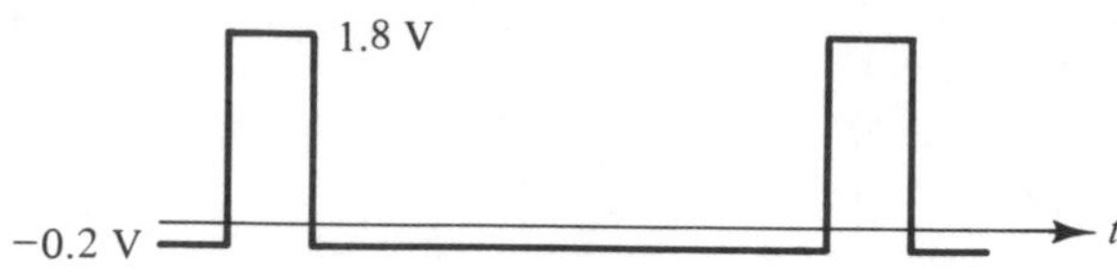

(b)

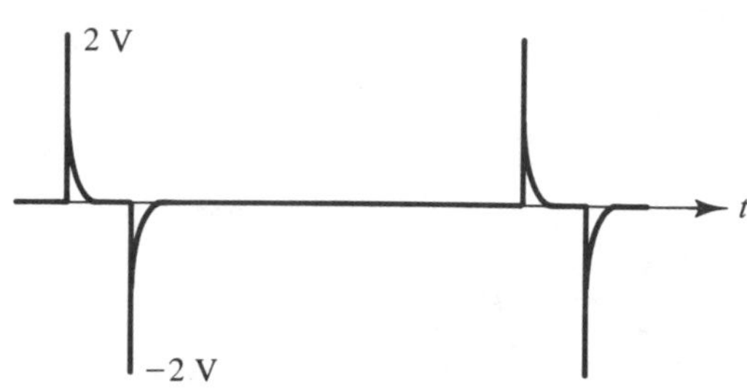

6-51. **(a)**

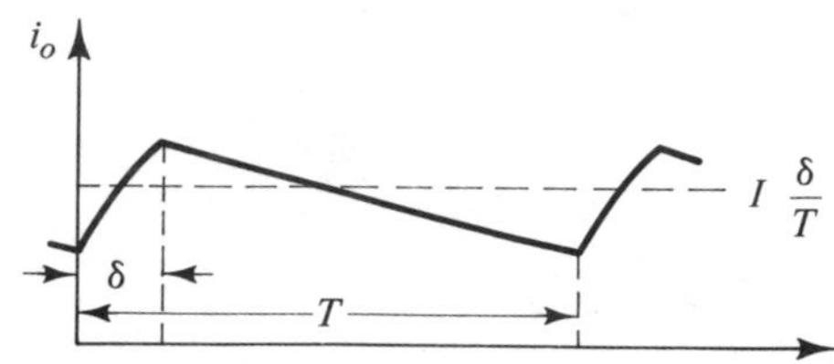

(b)

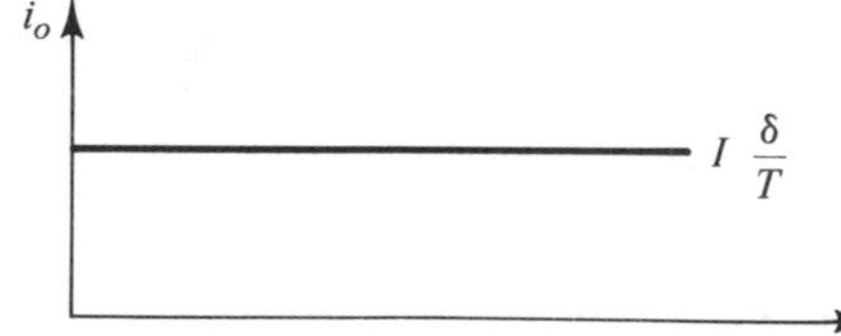

6-55. **(a)**

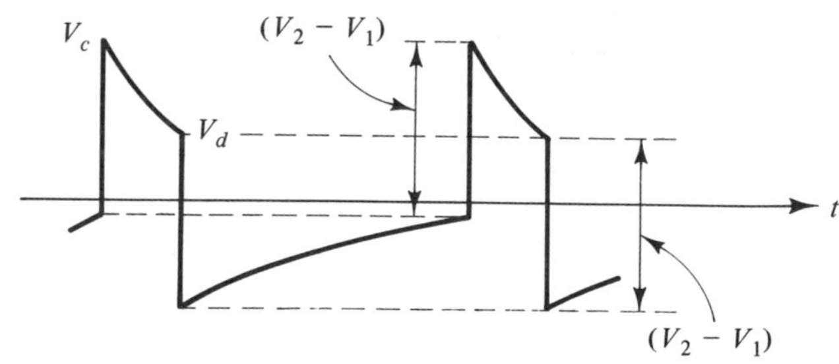

(b) $V_c = V_2 - V_a$, $V_d = V_2 - V_b$, where V_a and V_b are obtained from Eq. (6-44).
(c) $\overline{v_o} = 0$.

6-57. **(a)** Switch at dc: $v_o = v_i$

Switch at ac:

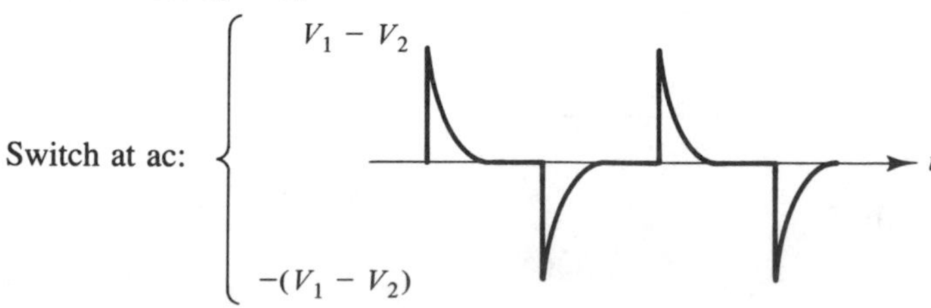

(**b**) Switch at dc: $v_o = v_i$

Switch at ac: $\begin{cases} \frac{1}{2}(V_1 - V_2) \\ -\frac{1}{2}(V_1 - V_2) \end{cases}$ → t

CHAPTER 7, page 403

7.1. $a_2 = 1$, $a_1 = 1$, $a_0 = 0$, $b_1 = 2$, $b_0 = 2$. The poles are at $-1 \pm j$. The zeros are at 0, -1.

7-3. *Hint:* Keeping in mind that α_1 is constant, rearrange the equation and use the α_2/α_1 ratio as a parameter.

7-5. $T_0 = \dfrac{R_1R_2/L_1L_2}{s^2 + s(R_1/L_1 + R_1/L_2 + R_2/L_2) + R_1R_2/L_1L_2}$.
The discriminant is positive and less than $(R_1/L_1 + R_1/L_2 + R_2/L_2)$.

7-7. $L = 1$, $C = \dfrac{1}{2}$, $R_1 = \dfrac{3}{5}$, $R_2 = \dfrac{1}{15}$.

7-9. $r(t) = -1 + 4e^{-t} - 2e^{-2t}$.

7-11. $r(t) = 2\alpha_1 te^{-\alpha_1 t}$.

7-15.

7-19. Choose L arbitrarily.

$$C = \frac{1}{L}\left(\frac{L_1L_2}{R_1R_2}\right)$$

$$R = \frac{L}{L_1/R_1 + L_2/R_2 + L_1/R_2}.$$

7-23. $\dfrac{3}{2}\dfrac{dy}{dt} + \dfrac{1}{2}y + \displaystyle\int_0^t y(t')\,dt'$.

7-25.

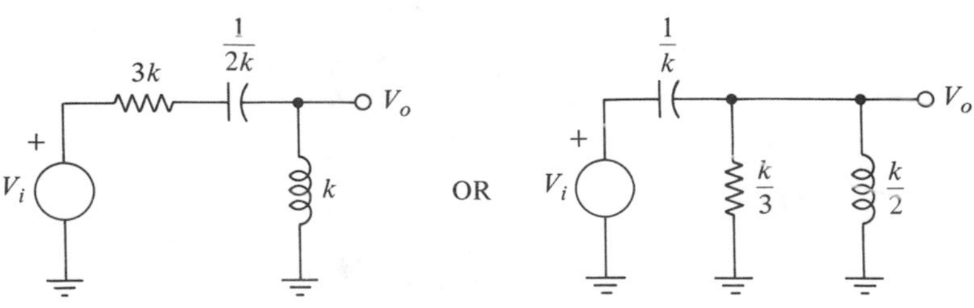

Any positive value can be used for k.

7-27. $a_2\dfrac{dr}{dt} + a_1 r + a_0 \displaystyle\int_0^t r\,dt'$.

7-29. **(a)** $r_1(t) = te^{-t}$; **(c)** $r(t) = 1 - 4te^{-t}$.

7-31. **(a)** Treat $R_1R_2 - C_1C_2$ circuit as a bridge.

(b) $v_o(t) = V\left(\dfrac{R_1 + R_2}{R_0 + R_1 + R_2}\right)\left(\dfrac{C_1}{C_1 + C_2}\right)(1 - e^{-t/\tau})$,

where $\tau = \left[\dfrac{R_0(R_1 + R_2)}{R_0 + (R_1 + R_2)}\right]\left(\dfrac{C_1C_2}{C_1 + C_2}\right)$;

(c) $v_o(t) = \dfrac{V}{10}(1 - e^{-t/0.1RC})$.

7-33. $v_o(t) = \dfrac{R_2}{R_1 + R_2} + \left(\dfrac{C_c}{C_c + C_s} - \dfrac{R_2}{R_1 + R_2}\right)e^{-t/\tau}$,

where $\tau = R_{\|}C_{\|} = \dfrac{R_1R_2}{R_1 + R_2}(C_c + C_s)$.

Condition for proper compensation: $R_1C_c = R_2C_s$.

7-35. $v_o(t) = \frac{1}{10}V$.

7-39. $\alpha_1 = \alpha - \lambda$, $\alpha_2 = \alpha + \lambda$.

7-41.

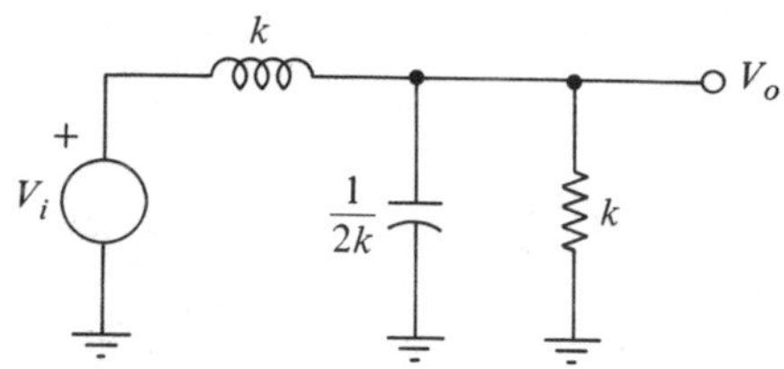

Any positive value can be used for k.

7-43. **(a)** $R > (1/2)\sqrt{L/C}$.

(b)

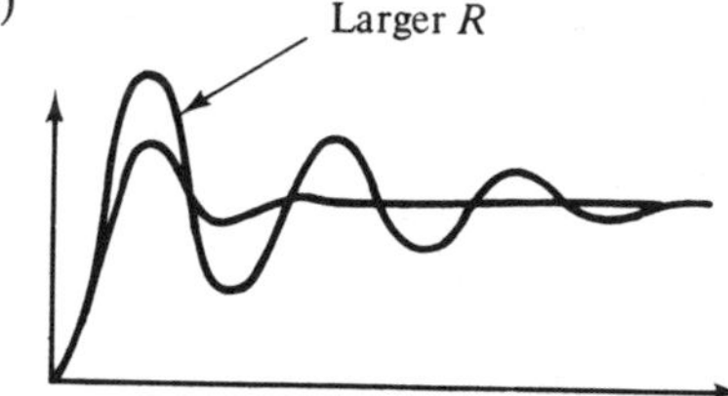

7-45.

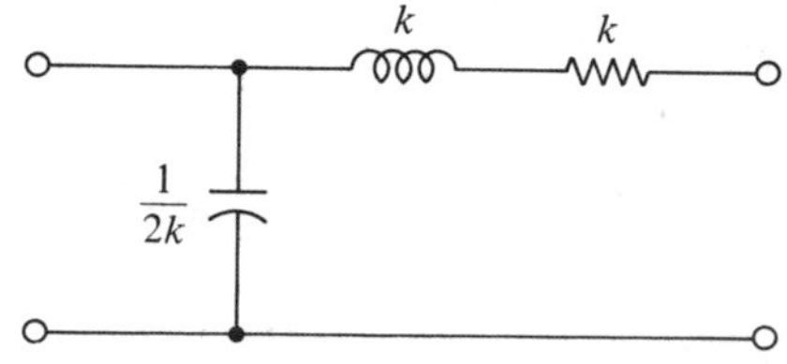

Any positive value can be used for k.

7-47. To obtain complex poles: $R > (1/2)\sqrt{L/C}$.
Vary L to obtain the response curves of Fig. 7-42(a).
Vary R to obtain the response curves of Fig. 7-42(b).

7-49. (**a**) $r(t) = \dfrac{1}{\sqrt{1-4a}}[e^{-[(1-\sqrt{1-4a})/2]t} - e^{-[(1+\sqrt{1-4a})/2]t}]$;

(**b**) $r(t) = \dfrac{2}{\sqrt{4a-1}} e^{-(1/2)t} \sin \dfrac{1}{2}\sqrt{4a-1}\,t$.

7-51. (**a**) $y(0^-) = -1,\ x(0^-) = 0$;
(**b**) $y(t) \cong 1 - 2e^{-(\delta/2)t} \cos t,\ x(t) \cong 2e^{-(\delta/2)t} \sin t$.
(**c**)

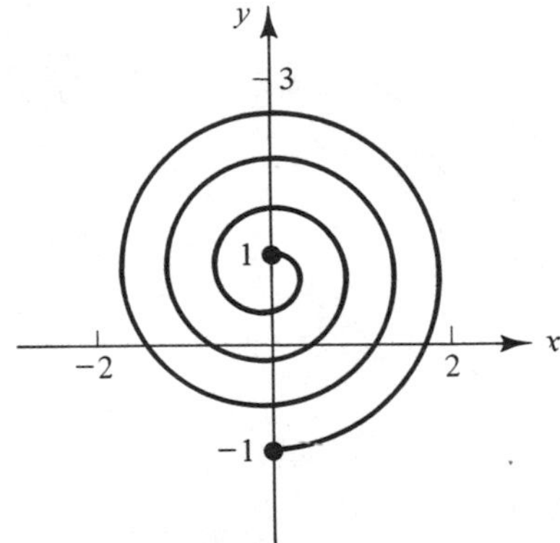

7-53.

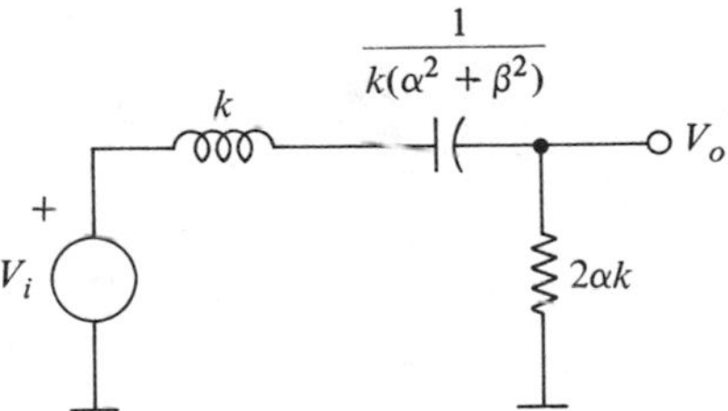

OR

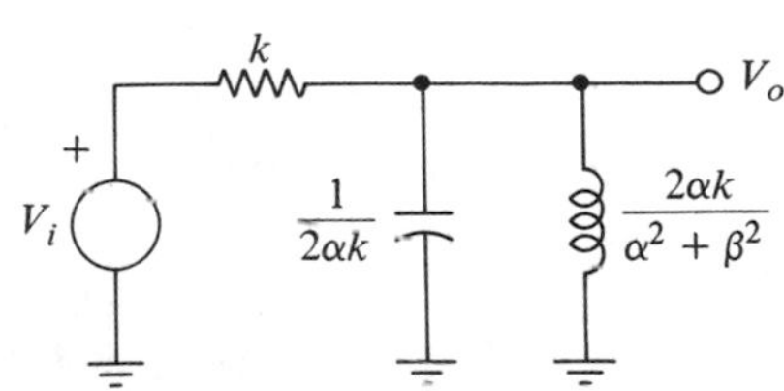

Any positive value can be used for k.

7-57. (**a**) $y(t) = 1 - e^{-t} \sin t,\ x(t) = 1 - e^{-t} \cos t$.
(**b**)

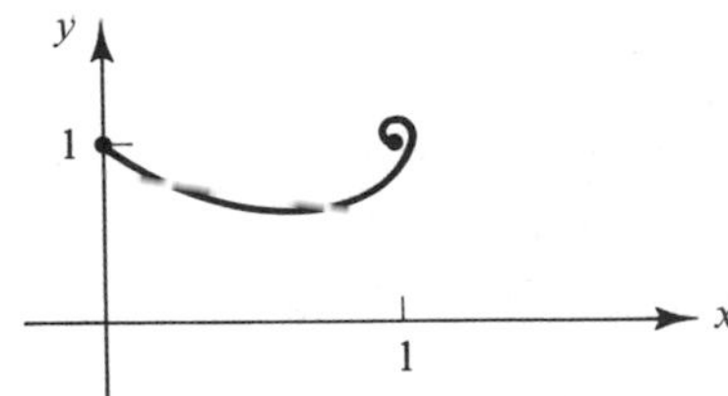

7-59. $r(t) = 1 + e^{-t}(\cos t - 3 \sin t)$.

7-61. $r(t) = e^{-t} \cos t$.

7-63.

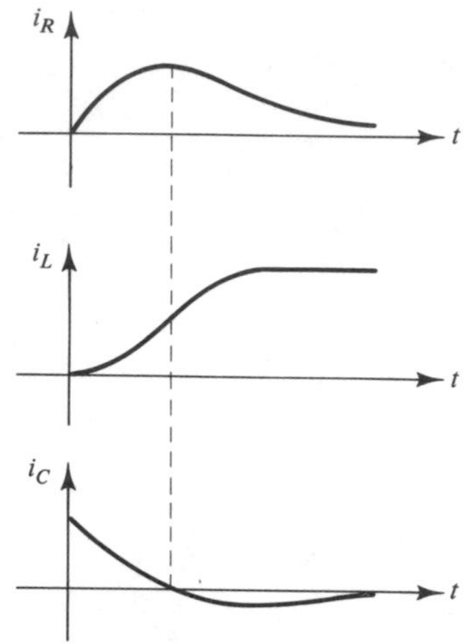

7-67. $i(t) \cong e^{-(R/2L)t}\left(\rho \cos \frac{t}{\sqrt{LC}} + \gamma\sqrt{\frac{C}{L}} \sin \frac{t}{\sqrt{LC}}\right)$

7-69. **(a)** $v_o(t) = -V_{dc} \cos \frac{t}{\sqrt{LC}}$; **(b)** $v_o(t) = -\frac{V_{dc}}{R}\sqrt{\frac{L}{C}} \sin \frac{t}{\sqrt{LC}}$.

7-71. **(a)** $R > \frac{1}{2}\sqrt{\frac{L}{C}}$

(b)

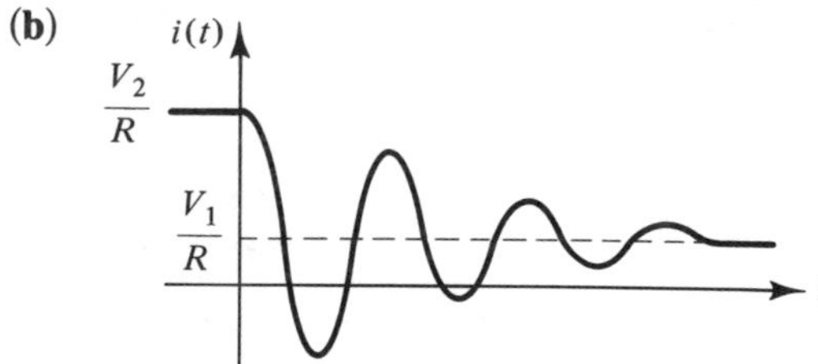

7-73. **(a)** $\rho = 1,\ \gamma = 2$

(b) $v(t) = e^{-t/4}\left(\cos \frac{\sqrt{15}}{4}t - \frac{67}{3\sqrt{15}} \sin \frac{\sqrt{15}}{4}t\right)$

7-75. $i(0^+) = \frac{V + \gamma}{R_1} - \rho,\ i(\infty) = \frac{V}{R_2}$

7-77. $i(0^+) = 0$.

7-79. **(a)** $L \geq 100\ R_L t_{OFF}$; **(b)** $C \geq \frac{12.5T}{L} t_{OFF}$.

7-81. (a) $$i(t) = \begin{cases} V\sqrt{\dfrac{C}{L}} \sin \dfrac{t}{\sqrt{LC}}, & 0 \le t \le \delta \\ V\sqrt{\dfrac{C}{L}}\left(\sin \dfrac{t}{\sqrt{LC}} - \sin \dfrac{t-\delta}{\sqrt{LC}}\right), & t \ge \delta \end{cases}$$

(b) $i(\delta) = V\sqrt{\dfrac{C}{L}} \sin \dfrac{\delta}{\sqrt{LC}}$, $v(\delta) = V\left(1 - \cos \dfrac{\delta}{\sqrt{LC}}\right)$.

7-83. (a) $v_o(t) = V\left(1 - \cos \dfrac{t}{\sqrt{LC}}\right)$; (b) $\delta = 2\pi\sqrt{LC}$.

7-85. $C = 0.1\ \mu\text{F}$.

7-87.

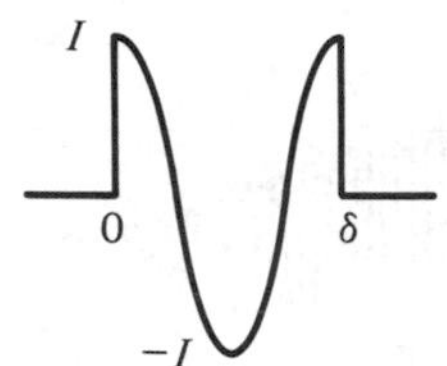

7-89. $T_a = \dfrac{a_0}{s^2 + sb_1 + b_0}$, $T_b = \dfrac{a_1 s}{s^2 + sb_1 + b_0}$, $T_c = \dfrac{a_2 s^2}{s^2 + sb_1 + b_0}$.

7-91.

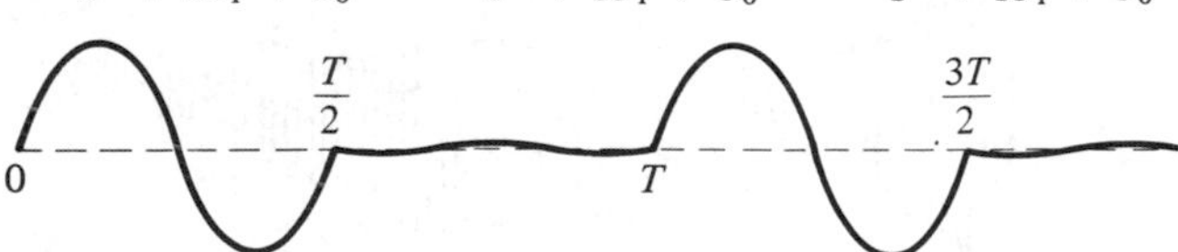

7-93.

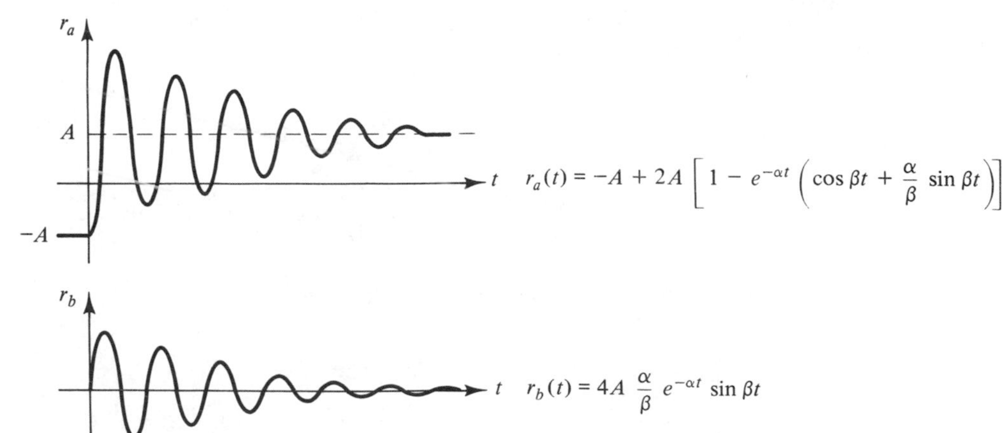

r_a
A
−A
t
$r_a(t) = -A + 2A\left[1 - e^{-\alpha t}\left(\cos \beta t + \dfrac{\alpha}{\beta} \sin \beta t\right)\right]$
r_b
t
$r_b(t) = 4A\,\dfrac{\alpha}{\beta}\,e^{-\alpha t} \sin \beta t$

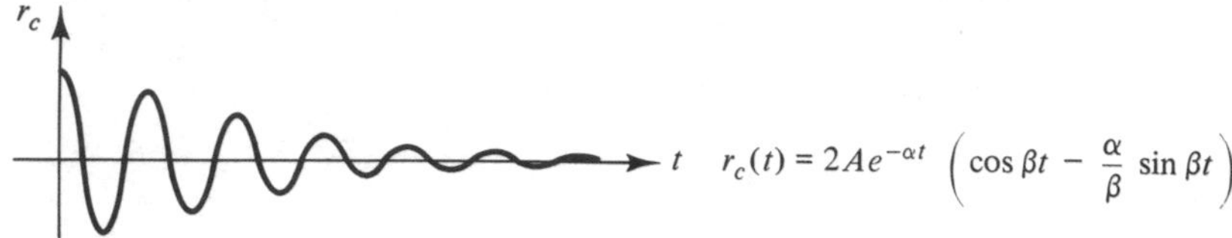

7-95.

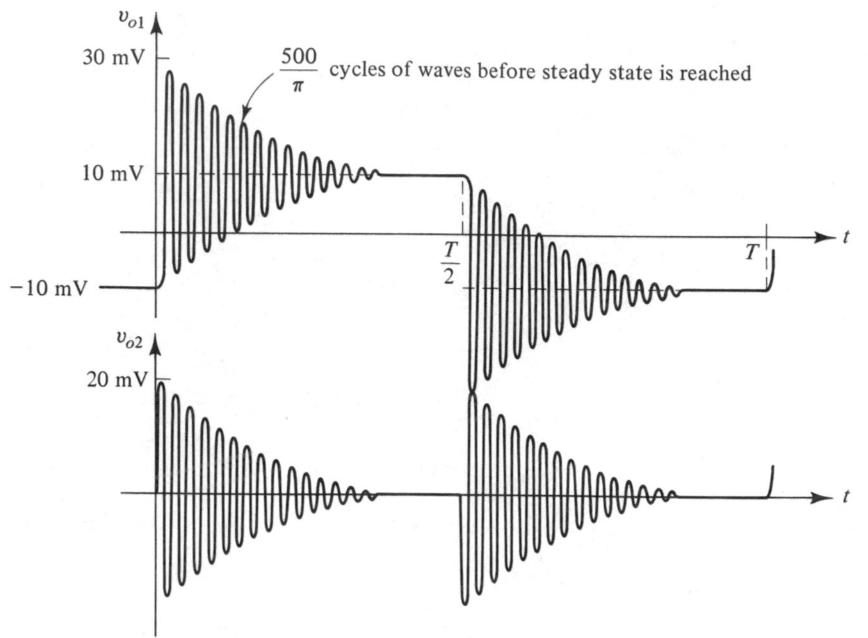

CHAPTER 8, page 486

8-1. $T = 4$ s, $\theta = -\dfrac{3\pi}{2}$.

8-3. **(a)** $v_o(t) = V_m\dfrac{\omega}{1+\omega^2}e^{-t} + \dfrac{V_m}{\sqrt{1+\omega^2}}\sin(\omega t - \tan^{-1}\omega)$;

(b) $v_o(t) = -\dfrac{V_m}{1+\omega^2}e^{-t} + \dfrac{V_m}{\sqrt{1+\omega^2}}\cos(\omega t - \tan^{-1}\omega)$;

(c) $\theta = \tan^{-1}\omega$, $v_o(t) = \dfrac{V_m}{\sqrt{1+\omega^2}}\sin\omega t$.

8-5. $v_o(t) = -\dfrac{5}{26}e^{-t} + \dfrac{5}{\sqrt{26}}\cos(5t - \tan^{-1}5)$.

8-7. $\omega = 6$.

8-9. $\theta = \frac{\pi}{4}$, $v_o(t) = \frac{1}{\sqrt{2}} \cos t$.

8-11. **(a)**

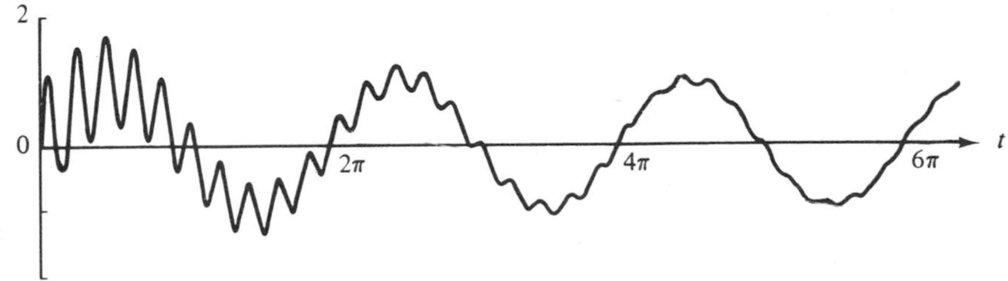

(b)

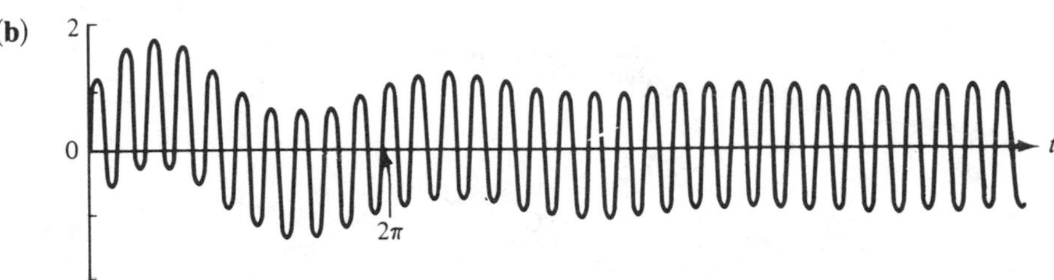

8-13. **(a)** $5(R_1 + R_2)C$; **(b)** $5\frac{L}{R_1 + R_2}$; **(c)** $10\frac{L}{R}$.

8-15. **(a)** $\omega = \frac{1}{\sqrt{LC}}$; **(b)** $\omega = \frac{1}{\sqrt{LC}}$.

8-17. **(a)** $v_{oss}(t) = \frac{1}{\sqrt{2}} \sin\left(t - \frac{\pi}{4}\right)$; **(b)** $i_{oss}(t) = \frac{1}{\sqrt{2}} \sin\left(t - \frac{\pi}{4}\right)$;

(c) $v_{oss}(t) = \sqrt{2} \cos\left(t + \frac{\pi}{4}\right)$; **(d)** $i_{oss}(t) = \frac{3}{\sqrt{2}} \sin\left(t - \frac{\pi}{4}\right)$;

(e) $v_{oss}(t) = V_1 \frac{R}{\sqrt{R^2 + \omega_1^2 L^2}} \sin\left(\omega_1 t - \tan^{-1} \frac{\omega_1 L}{R}\right)$

$+ V_2 \frac{R}{\sqrt{R^2 + \omega_2^2 L^2}} \sin\left(\omega_2 t - \tan^{-1} \frac{\omega_2 L}{R}\right)$;

(f) $v_{oss}(t) = \frac{I_1}{\sqrt{5}} \sin\left(t - \tan^{-1} \frac{1}{2}\right) + I_2 \frac{1}{2}\sqrt{\frac{5}{2}} \cos\left(2t + \tan^{-1} 2 - \frac{\pi}{4}\right)$;

(g) $i_{iss}(t) = V_m \frac{\sqrt{\omega^4 - \omega^2 + 1}}{1 + \omega^2} \sin\left(\omega t + \tan^{-1} \frac{\omega}{1 - \omega^2} - 2 \tan^{-1} \omega\right)$;

(h) $i_{oss}(t) = \frac{I_m}{3} \sin \omega t$; **(i)** $v_{oss}(t) = \frac{3}{\sqrt{0.82}} \sin\left(2t + 1 + \tan^{-1} \frac{1}{9}\right)$;

(j) $i_{iss}(t) = 0$.

8-19. $r_{ss}(t) = 3\sin\left(t - \dfrac{\pi}{2}\right) = -3\cos t.$

8-21. $A_3 = A_4 = \sqrt{A_1^2 + A_2^2 + 2A_1A_2\cos(\theta_1 - \theta_2)}.$

$$\theta = \tan^{-1}\left(\frac{A_1\sin\theta_1 + A_2\sin\theta_2}{A_1\cos\theta_1 + A_2\cos\theta_2}\right), \qquad \phi = \theta - \frac{\pi}{2}.$$

8-23. $A = \sqrt{5},\ \theta = \tan^{-1}\dfrac{1}{2}.$

8-25. **(a)** $\sqrt{2}\,\underline{/\tfrac{\pi}{4}}$; **(b)** $\sqrt{2}\sin\left(t + \dfrac{\pi}{4}\right) = \sqrt{2}\cos\left(t - \dfrac{\pi}{4}\right).$

8-27. **(a)** $\mathbf{V}_o = \dfrac{V_m}{\omega^4 - 3\omega^2 + 1}\underline{/0}$; **(b)** $\mathbf{I}_o = \dfrac{V_m}{2}\dfrac{\omega C}{1 - \omega^2 LC}\underline{/\pi/2}$;

(c) $\mathbf{V}_o = \dfrac{I_m\omega^3}{1 - 2\omega^2}\underline{/-\tfrac{\pi}{2}}$;

(d) $\mathbf{I}_o = \dfrac{I_m\omega RC}{\sqrt{(1 - \omega^2LC)^2 + \omega^2R^2C^2}}\underline{\Big/\dfrac{\pi}{2} - \tan^{-1}\dfrac{\omega RC}{1 - \omega^2LC}}$

(e) $\mathbf{V}_o = \dfrac{V_m + I_m}{\sqrt{1 + \omega^2}}\underline{/-\tan^{-1}\omega}$;

(f) $\mathbf{V}_o = V_m\dfrac{\omega(L - R^2C)}{\sqrt{R^2(1 - \omega^2LC)^2 + \omega^2(R^2C + L)^2}}\underline{\Big/\dfrac{\pi}{2} - \tan^{-1}\dfrac{\omega(R^2C + L)}{R(1 - \omega^2LC)}}.$

8-29. $10\sin\left(t + \tan^{-1}\dfrac{3}{4}\right)$

8-31. 10.

8-37.

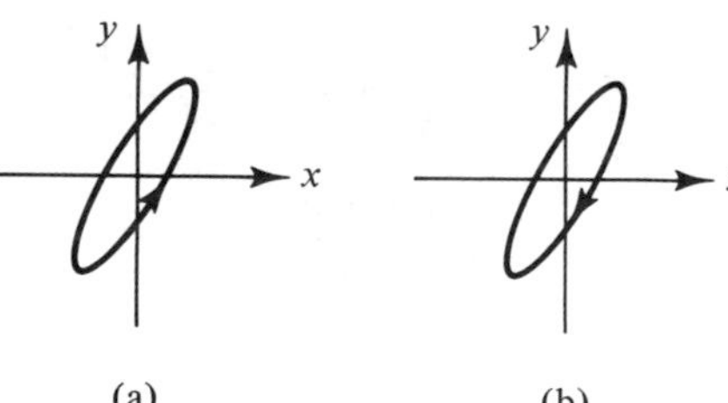

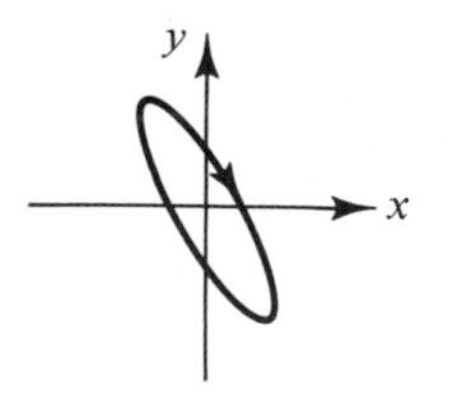

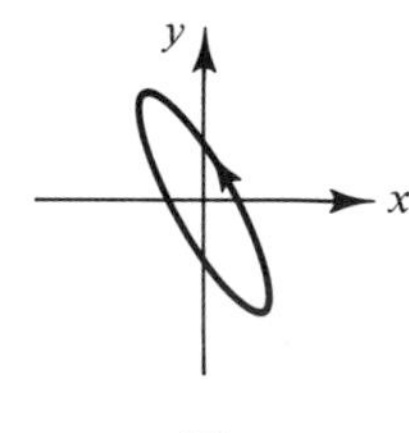

(a) (b) (c) (d)

8-39. **(a)** $s_1\begin{Bmatrix}\text{leads}\\ \text{lags}\end{Bmatrix}$ s_3 by $\begin{Bmatrix}-(\psi \pm \pi)\\ (\psi \pm \pi)\end{Bmatrix}$,

$s_2\begin{Bmatrix}\text{leads}\\ \text{lags}\end{Bmatrix}$ s_3 by $\begin{Bmatrix}-\theta - (\psi \pm \pi)\\ \theta + (\psi \pm \pi)\end{Bmatrix}$;

(b) $s_2\begin{Bmatrix}\text{leads}\\ \text{lags}\end{Bmatrix}$ s_1 by $\begin{Bmatrix}-\theta\\ \theta\end{Bmatrix}$.

8-43. $\omega = \dfrac{1}{\sqrt{LC}},\ \theta_1 - \theta_2 = \pi - 2\tan^{-1}R\sqrt{\dfrac{C}{L}}.$

8-47. $V_m = \dfrac{I_m}{\sqrt{\left(\dfrac{1}{R}\right)^2 + \left(\omega C - \dfrac{1}{\omega L}\right)^2}}, \qquad \theta = -\tan^{-1}\left(\dfrac{\omega C - \dfrac{1}{\omega L}}{\dfrac{1}{R}}\right);$

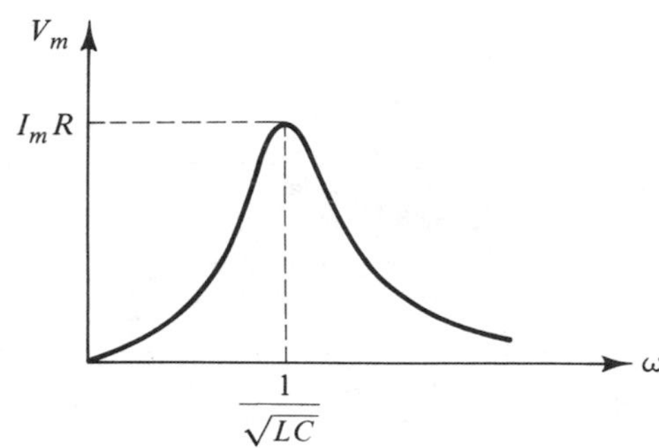

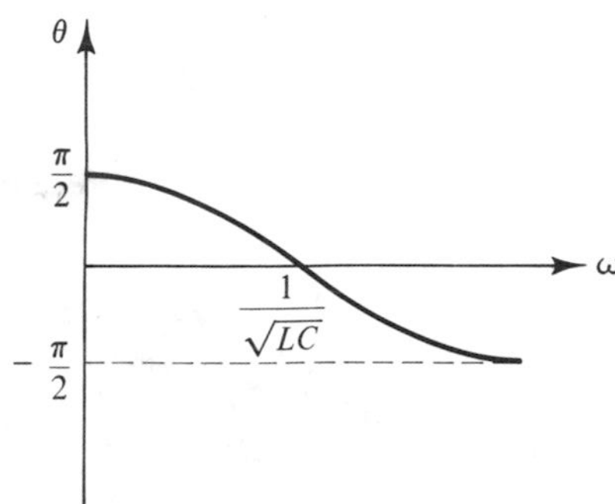

8-49 (**a**) $v_R(t) = \underbrace{I_m R}_{V_{mR}} \sin(\omega t + \theta), \qquad v_L(t) = \underbrace{\omega L I_m}_{V_{mL}} \sin\left(\omega t + \theta + \dfrac{\pi}{2}\right),$

$$v_C(t) = \underbrace{\frac{I_m}{\omega C}}_{V_{mC}} \sin\left(\omega t + \theta - \frac{\pi}{2}\right)$$

$$v(t) = \underbrace{I_m \sqrt{R^2 + \left(\omega L - \frac{1}{\omega C}\right)^2}}_{V_m} \sin\left[\omega t + \theta + \tan^{-1}\left(\frac{\omega L - 1/\omega C}{R}\right)\right];$$

(**b**)

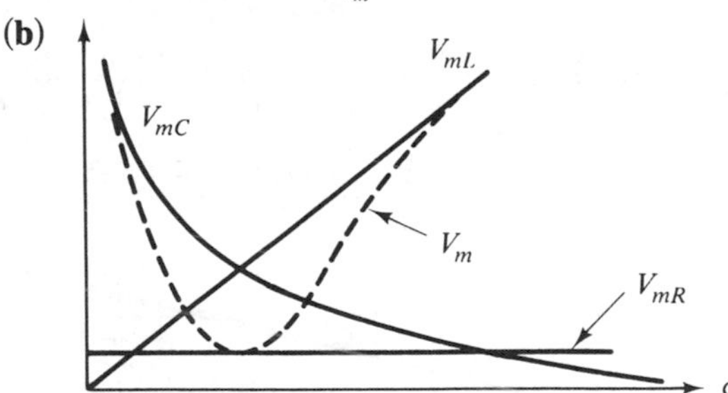

(**c**) $\dfrac{V_{mC}}{V_m} = \dfrac{1}{R}\sqrt{\dfrac{L}{C}}.$

8-51. $p_{av} = 0.$

8-53. (**a**) Power delivered by source = power delivered to R

$$= \frac{1}{2} V_m^2 \left[\frac{R}{R^2 + (\omega L - 1/\omega C)^2}\right].$$

Power delivered to L = power delivered to $C = 0$.

(**b**) Power delivered by source = power delivered to R

$$= \frac{1}{2}I_m^2\left[\frac{1/R}{(1/R)^2 + (\omega C - 1/\omega L)^2}\right]$$

Power delivered to L = power delivered to C = 0.

8-55. (**a**) $\text{PF} = \frac{R}{\sqrt{R^2 + \omega^2 L^2}}$; (**b**) PF = 0;

(**c**) $\text{PF} = \frac{R}{\sqrt{R^2 + \omega^2 L^2[\omega^2 LC - 1 + (R^2C/L)]^2}}$; (**d**) $C = \frac{L}{\omega^2 L^2 + R^2}$;

(**e**) $\omega = \sqrt{\frac{1}{LC} - \frac{R^2}{L^2}}$.

8-57. (**a**) $C = \frac{L}{R^2 + \omega^2 L^2}$; (**b**) $I_m = V_m \frac{R}{R^2 + \omega^2 L^2}$; $\theta = 0$.

8-59 (**a**) $p_{\text{av}} = \frac{1}{2}V_m I_m \cos\theta$; (**b**) $p_{\text{avN}} = p_{\text{av}}$; (**c**) $C = \frac{I_m \sin\theta}{\omega V_m}$;

(**d**) $i_L(t) = I_m \cos\theta \sin\omega t$;

(**e**) $\cos\left(\tan^{-1}\frac{V_m\omega C - I_m \sin\theta}{I_m\cos\theta}\right)\Big|_{C=I_m\sin\theta/V_m\omega C} = 1$.

8-61. (**a**) $\text{PF} = \frac{1}{\sqrt{1 + (\omega RC)^2}}$; (**b**) $L = \frac{1}{C\omega^2}$.

8-63. $Z(j\omega) = \frac{R_1(1 + j\omega R_2 C)}{1 + j\omega(R_1 + R_2)C}$, $|Z(j\omega)| = \frac{R_1\sqrt{1 + (\omega R_2 C)^2}}{\sqrt{1 + \omega^2 C^2 (R_1 + R_2)^2}}$

$\theta_Z = \tan^{-1}\omega R_2 C - \tan^{-1}\omega(R_1 + R_2)C$, $R(\omega) = \frac{R_1[1 + \omega^2 R_2 C^2(R_1 + R_2)]}{1 + \omega^2(R_1 + R_2)^2 C^2}$

$X(\omega) = \frac{-\omega R_1^2 C}{1 + \omega^2(R_1 + R_2)^2 C^2}$, $p_{\text{av}} = \frac{1}{2}I_m^2\left\{\frac{R_1[1 + \omega^2 R_2 C^2(R_1 + R_2)]}{1 + \omega^2(R_1 + R_2)^2 C^2}\right\}$

8-65. $Y(j\omega) = \frac{1}{Z(j\omega)}$, $|Y| = \frac{1}{|Z|}$, $\theta_Y = -\theta_Z$, $G = \frac{R}{R^2 + X^2}$,

$B = -\frac{X}{R^2 + X^2}$

8-67. (**a**) $V_{\text{dc}} = \frac{V}{2\sqrt{3}}$; (**b**) $V_{\text{rms}} = \frac{V}{2\sqrt{3}}$.

8-69. (**a**) $V_{\text{dc}} = V$; (**b**) $V_{\text{rms}} = V$.

8-71. 4.

8-73. $\sqrt{2}$.

CHAPTER 9, page 545

9-3. (a) $\alpha = \dfrac{R_L}{R_s + R_L}$, $\quad \omega_c = \sqrt{\left(1 + \dfrac{R_L}{R_s}\right)\dfrac{1}{LC}} = \dfrac{1}{\sqrt{2}}\left(\dfrac{1}{R_sC} + \dfrac{R_L}{L}\right)$;

(b) $\sqrt{\left(1 + \dfrac{R_L}{R_s}\right)\dfrac{1}{LC}} = \dfrac{1}{\sqrt{2}}\left(\dfrac{1}{R_sC} + \dfrac{R_L}{L}\right)$; (c) $L = \sqrt{2}\dfrac{R}{\omega_c}$, $\quad C = \dfrac{\sqrt{2}}{\omega_c R}$.

9-5. $\dfrac{I_o}{V_i} = \dfrac{1}{R}\left(\dfrac{\omega_c}{s + \omega_c}\right)$, where $\omega_c = \dfrac{R}{2L}$

9-7. (a) $\left|\dfrac{V_o}{V_i}\right| = \dfrac{1}{\sqrt{(1 - \omega^2R^2C^2)^2 + 9\omega^2R^2C^2}}$

- $\omega \ll \dfrac{1}{RC}$: $\cong 1$ — Low frequencies are passed.
- $\omega \gg \dfrac{1}{RC}$: $\cong \dfrac{1}{\omega^2R^2C^2}$ — High frequencies are attenuated.

(b) $\left|\dfrac{V_o}{V_i}\right| = \dfrac{1}{\sqrt{\left(1 - \dfrac{\omega^2L^2}{R^2}\right)^2 + \dfrac{9\omega^2L^2}{R^2}}}$

- $\omega \ll \dfrac{R}{L}$: $\cong 1$ — Low frequencies are passed.
- $\omega \gg \dfrac{R}{L}$: $\cong \dfrac{R^2}{\omega^2L^2}$ — High frequencies are attenuated.

9-9. $v_s \cong 25 + 0.00707 \sin\left(10^5t - \dfrac{\pi}{4}\right)$

$v_o \cong 25 + 7.07 \sin\left(10^5t + \dfrac{\pi}{4}\right)$

Very little of the ac signal contaminates the power supply output, whereas almost all of its reaches the other output.

9-13. (a)

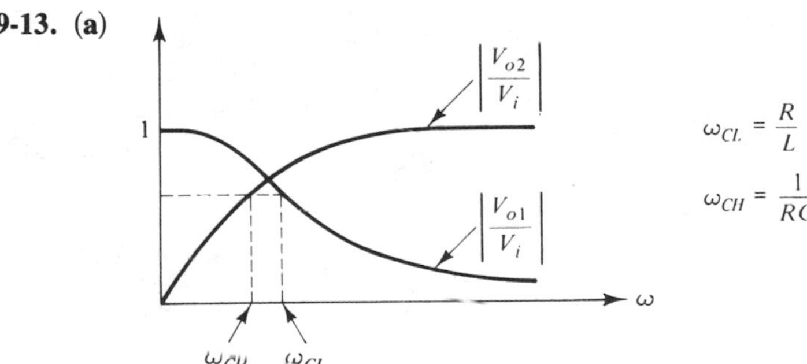

(b) $R^2 = \dfrac{L}{C}$.

9-15. (a) $R^2 = \dfrac{L}{C}$, $Z_i = R$;

(b) $\dfrac{V_{o1}}{V_i} = \dfrac{R}{R_s + R}\left(\dfrac{\omega_{cs}}{s + \omega_{cs}}\right), \dfrac{V_{o2}}{V_i} = \dfrac{R}{R_s + R}\left(\dfrac{s}{s + \omega_{cs}}\right)$, where $\omega_{cs} = \dfrac{R}{L} = \dfrac{1}{RC}$;

(c) $\theta_1 = -\dfrac{\pi}{4}, \theta_2 = \dfrac{\pi}{4}$.

9-19. **(a)** 2;

(b) $v_{o1}(t) = \dfrac{1}{2}\dfrac{1}{\sqrt{1+\omega^4}} \sin\left(\omega t - \tan^{-1}\dfrac{\omega\sqrt{2}}{1-\omega^2}\right)$

$$v_{o2}(t) = \frac{1}{2}\frac{\omega^2}{\sqrt{1+\omega^4}} \sin\left(\omega t + \pi - \tan^{-1}\frac{\omega\sqrt{2}}{1-\omega^2}\right).$$

9-21. **(a)** 1;

(b) $v_{o1}(t) = \dfrac{I_m}{\sqrt{1+\omega^4}} \sin\left(\omega t + \tan^{-1}\dfrac{\omega\sqrt{2}}{1-\omega^2}\right)$,

$$v_{o2}(t) = \frac{I_m\omega^2}{\sqrt{1+\omega^4}} \sin\left(\omega t + \pi - \tan^{-1}\frac{\omega\sqrt{2}}{1-\omega^2}\right).$$

9-23. **(a)** $\left|\dfrac{V_o}{V_i}\right| = \dfrac{(\omega RC)^2}{\sqrt{[(\omega RC)^2 - 1]^2 + 9(\omega RC)^2}}$ =

- $\omega \ll \dfrac{1}{RC}$: $\cong (\omega RC)^2$ — Low frequencies are attenuated.
- $\omega \gg \dfrac{1}{RC}$: $\cong 1$ — High frequencies are passed.

(b) $\left|\dfrac{V_o}{V_i}\right| = \dfrac{(\omega L/R)^2}{\sqrt{\left[\left(\dfrac{\omega L}{R}\right) - 1\right]^2 + 9\left(\dfrac{\omega L}{R}\right)^2}}$ =

- $\omega \ll \dfrac{R}{L}$: $\cong \left(\dfrac{\omega L}{R}\right)^2$ — Low frequencies are attenuated.
- $\omega \gg \dfrac{R}{L}$: $\cong 1$ — High frequencies are passed.

9-25. $v(t) = V_{dc} + V_m\dfrac{\omega L}{\sqrt{R^2 + \omega^2 L^2}} \sin\left(\omega t + \dfrac{\pi}{2} - \tan^{-1}\dfrac{\omega L}{R}\right)$.

9-27. $v_1(t) \cong V_{dc}\dfrac{R_L}{R_s + R_L}, v_2(t) \cong V_{dc}\dfrac{R_L}{R_s + R_L} + V_m \sin \omega t$.

9-35. $\sin t$.

9-41.

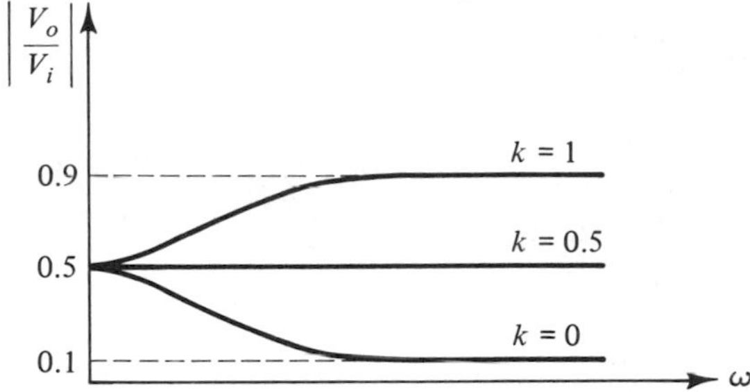

9-43.

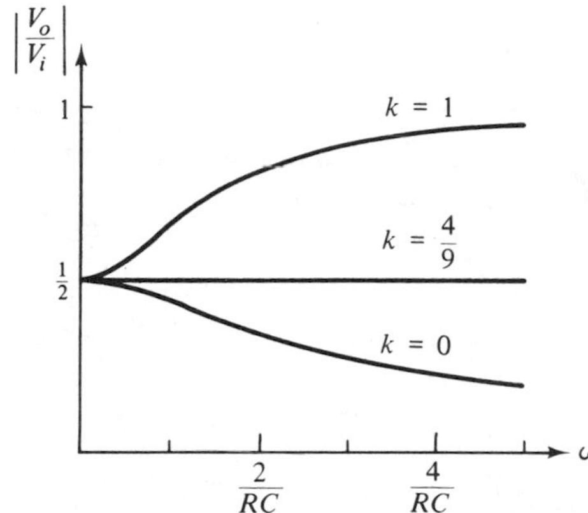

9-45. **(a)** $\dfrac{V_o}{V_i} = \dfrac{1}{2}\dfrac{s^2 - s(R/L) + (1/LC)}{s^2 + s(R/L) + (1/LC)}$; **(b)** $\dfrac{V_o}{V_i} = \dfrac{1}{2}\dfrac{s^2 - s(1/RC) + (1/LC)}{s^2 + s(1/RC) + (1/LC)}$.

CHAPTER 10, page 600

10-1. **(a)** $v_1 = -L_1\dfrac{di_1}{dt} - M\dfrac{di_2}{dt}$ **(b)** $v_1 = L_1\dfrac{di_1}{dt} - M\dfrac{di_2}{dt}$ **(c)** $v_1 = -L_1\dfrac{di_1}{dt} - M\dfrac{di_2}{dt}$

$v_2 = L_2\dfrac{di_2}{dt} + M\dfrac{di_1}{dt}$ $\qquad v_2 = L_2\dfrac{di_2}{dt} - M\dfrac{di_1}{dt}$ $\qquad v_2 = -L_2\dfrac{di_2}{dt} - M\dfrac{di_1}{dt}$

10-5. **(a)** $v_2(t) = M\dfrac{di_1}{dt}$; **(b)** $v_2(t) = L_2\dfrac{di_2(t)}{dt} - M\dfrac{di_1(t)}{dt}$; **(c)** $v_1(t) = \dfrac{M}{L_2}v_2(t)$;

(d) $v_1(t) = M\dfrac{di_2(t)}{dt}$; **(e)** $i_1(t) = -\dfrac{M}{L_1}i_2(t)$;

(f) $i_1(t) = \left(\dfrac{L_2}{L_1L_2 - M^2}\right)\displaystyle\int_0^t \left[v_1(t') - \dfrac{M}{L_2}v_2(t')\right] dt'$.

$i_2(t) = \left(\dfrac{L_1}{L_1L_2 - M^2}\right)\displaystyle\int_0^t \left[v_2(t') - \dfrac{M}{L_1}v_1(t')\right] dt'$.

10-7. $v_1(t) = \dfrac{R_1 n^2 R_2}{R_1 + n^2 R_2}\left(i_1 + \dfrac{i_2}{n}\right), \qquad v_2(t) = \dfrac{R_2 R_1/n^2}{R_2 + R_1/n^2}(i_2 + n i_1)$

10-9. $k = 0.992$

10-11. **(a)** $V_{oc}(s) = nV_1(s)$; **(b)** $Z_o(s) = n^2 Z_1(s)$;
(c)

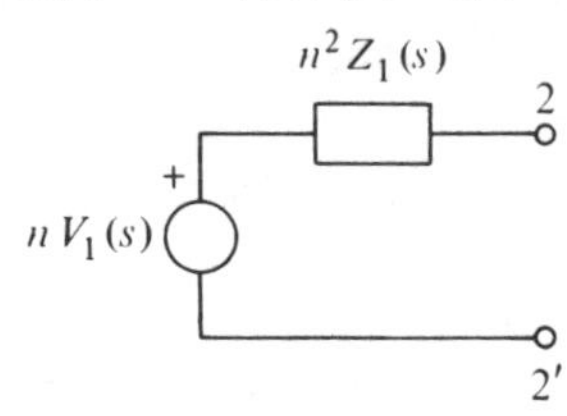

10-13. **(a)** $Z_i = \dfrac{Z}{n^2}$; **(b)** $Z_i = \dfrac{Z}{n^2}$; **(c)** $Z_i = n^2 Z$; **(d)** $Z_i = \dfrac{1}{n_1^2}\left(R_1 + \dfrac{R_2}{n_2^2}\right)$.

10-15. $n = \sqrt{\dfrac{R_1 R_2}{R_3(R_1 + R_2)}}$

10-17. **(a)** 3.125 W;
(b)

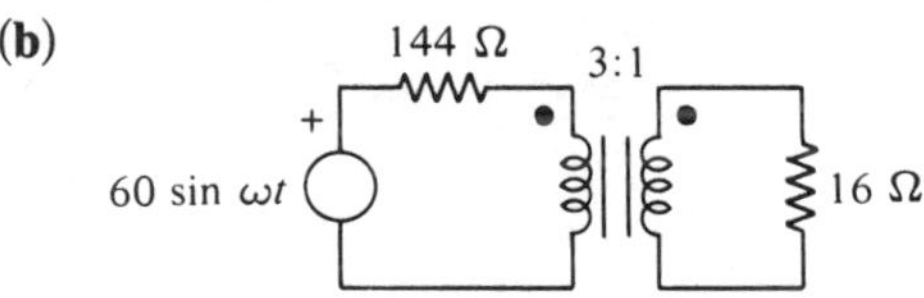

(c) $v_{sp} = 10 \sin \omega t$.

10-21.

$(1 + n)^2 R_s$

+

$v_s(1 + n)$

10-23. **(a)** $I_1(s) = \dfrac{1}{(1 - k^2)L_1}\left\{\left(s + \dfrac{R_L}{L_2}\right)\Big/\left[s^2 + s\dfrac{R_s L_2 + R_L L_1}{(1 - k^2)L_1 L_2} + \dfrac{R_L R_s}{(1 - k^2)L_1 L_2}\right]\right\}V_i(s)$

(b) $i_1(t) = \dfrac{V_{dc}}{R_s} + \dfrac{V_{dc}}{(p_1 - p_2)(1 - k^2)L_1}\left[\left(1 + \dfrac{R_L}{L_2 p_1}\right)e^{p_1 t} - \left(1 + \dfrac{R_L}{L_2 p_2}\right)e^{p_2 t}\right]$,

where p_1 and p_2 are as given in Eq. (10-50).

10-27. **(a)** 26.18 μs; **(b)** 750 V.

CHAPTER 11, page 645

11-1. $V_o = \left[\dfrac{K_1(R_1 + R_2)}{R_1(1 + K_1) + R_2}\right]V_i$

11-3. $V_L = \left[\dfrac{(1 + K_3)s}{s(2 + K_3) + 1}\right]V_i$

11-5. $V_o = \dfrac{2(s - 1)}{s - 3}V_i$

11-9. **(a)** $Z_i = \dfrac{1}{K_1K_2Z}$; **(b)** $Z_i = s$ (impedance of 1 H inductor).

11-11. A 100 H inductor.

11-13. A 10 H inductor.

11-15. $Z_i = -R$.

11-17. **(a)** $v_{oc} = -0.99\ v_i$; **(b)** $i_{sc} = -\dfrac{0.99}{2}v_i$

(c)

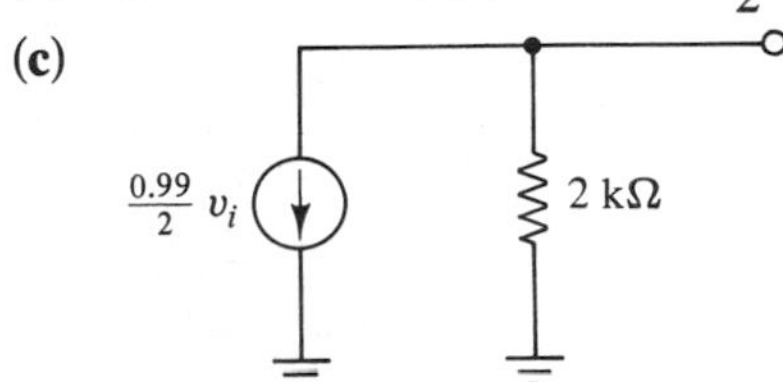

(d) 200 kΩ.

11-19.

$-b/c$

$\dfrac{a}{c}$

+

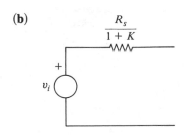

11-21. **(a)**

$R_s + (1 + K)R_L$

(b)

$\dfrac{R_s}{1 + K}$

+

v_i

(c) $\dfrac{R_L}{R_L + \dfrac{R_S}{1 + K}}$

11-23. **(a)** $v_{oc} = \dfrac{K}{1+K}v_i$; **(b)** $i_{sc} = \dfrac{Kv_i}{R}$.

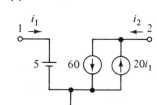

11-25. **(a)** $v_o = -\dfrac{Aa}{1+a+A}v_i$;

(b)

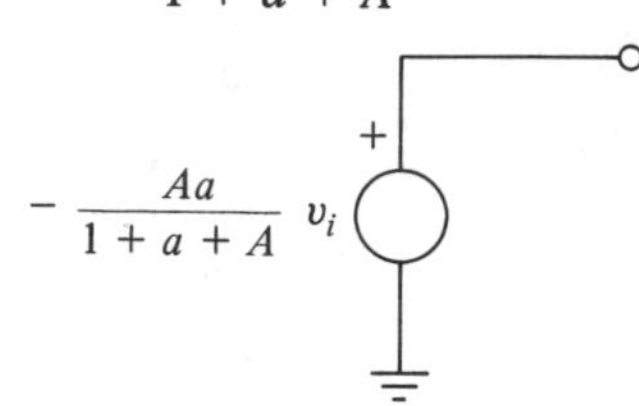

(c)

$R\,\dfrac{1+a+A}{1+A}$

11-27. (a)

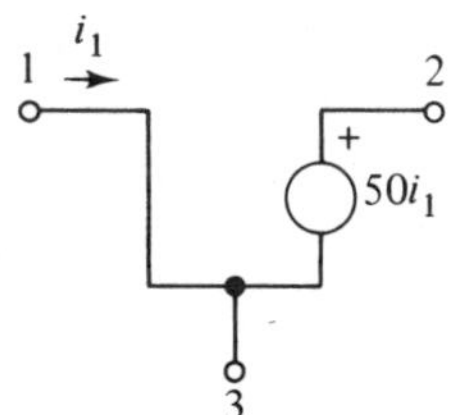

(b)

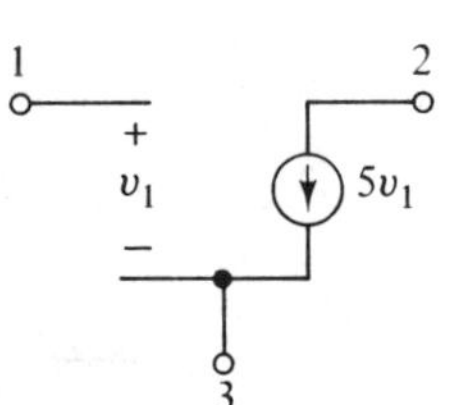

(c)

i_1 1 · i_2 2 · 5 · 60 · $20i_1$ · 3

(d)

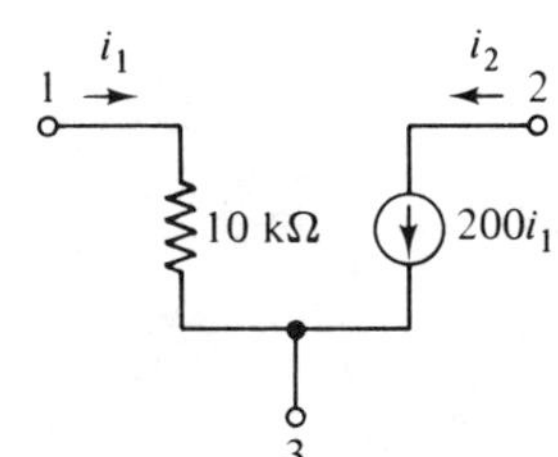

11-29. **(a)**

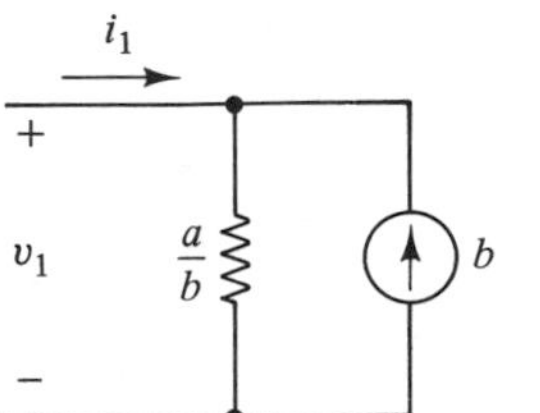

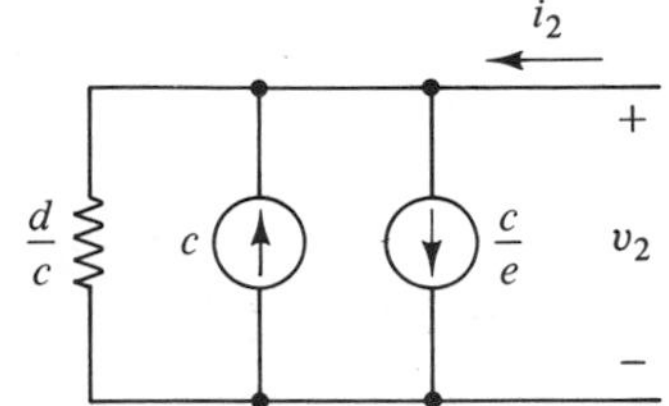

(b)

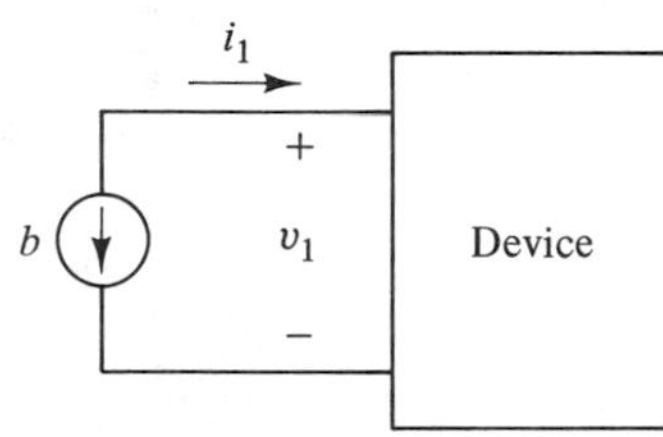

11-31. The operating points are $\begin{cases} (i_1,\ v_i) = (0.4 \text{ mA},\ 0) \\ i_2,\ v_2) = (50 \text{ mA},\ 20 \text{ V}) \end{cases}$

Gain = 50.

11-33. **(a)** $(i_{1\text{dc}},\ v_{1\text{dc}}) = (0.1 \text{ mA},\ 0.1)$, $(i_{2\text{dc}},\ v_{2\text{dc}}) = (10 \text{ mA},\ 5)$; **(b)** $i_L = -100 \sin \omega t$ mA.

11-35.

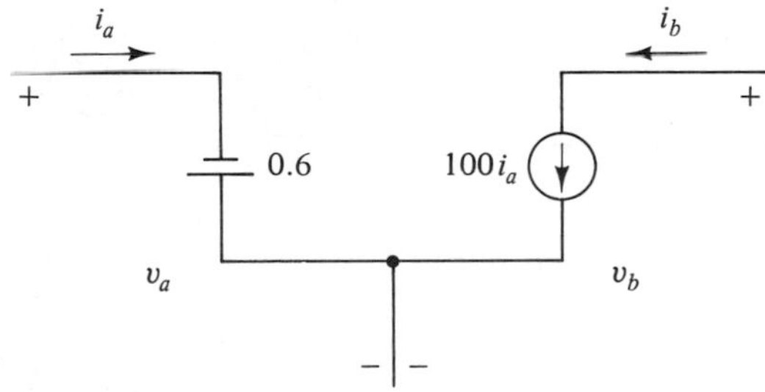

11-37. **(a)** $(i_b,\ v_{ba}) = \left(\dfrac{I_{dc}}{1+\beta},\ 0\right)$ **(b)** $A_v = 1$

$$(i_c,\ v_{ca}) = \left(\frac{\beta}{1+\beta} I_{dc},\ V_{dc}\right)$$

(c)

$(1 + \beta)R$

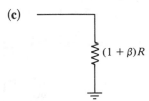

(d)

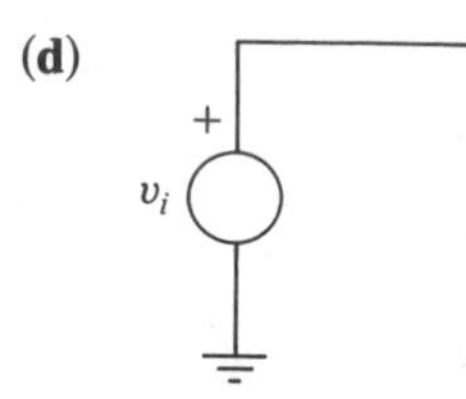

(e) $-I_{dc}R < v_i < V_{dc}$.

11-39. (a) $K = 1$; (b) $v_o = V \cos \dfrac{t}{\sqrt{LC}}$.

11-41.

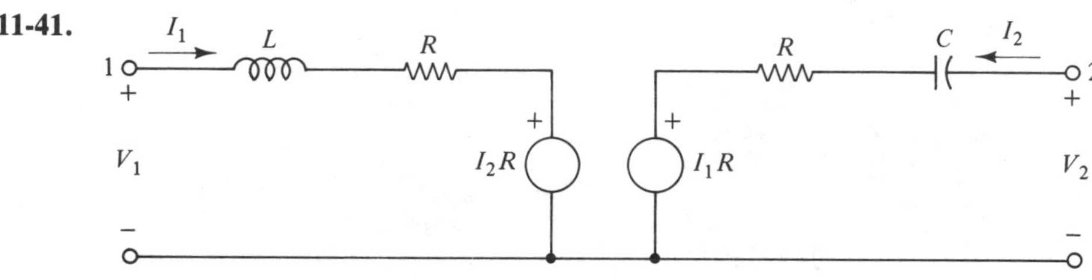

11-43. (a) (b)

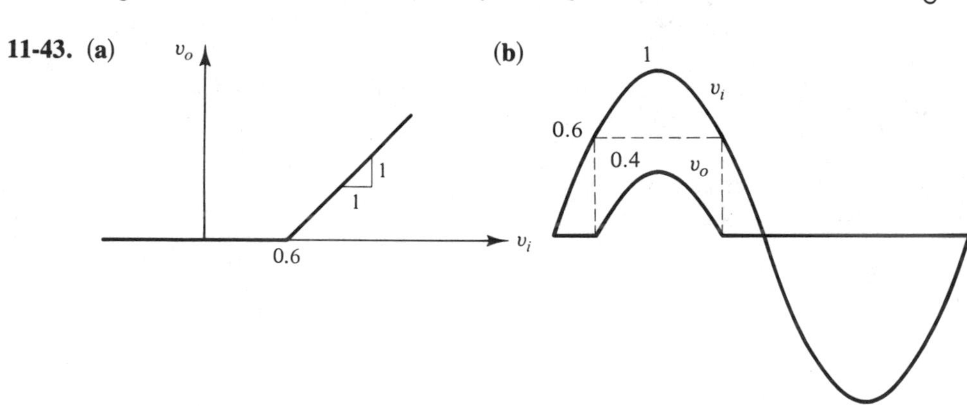

CHAPTER 12, page 732

12-9. (a)

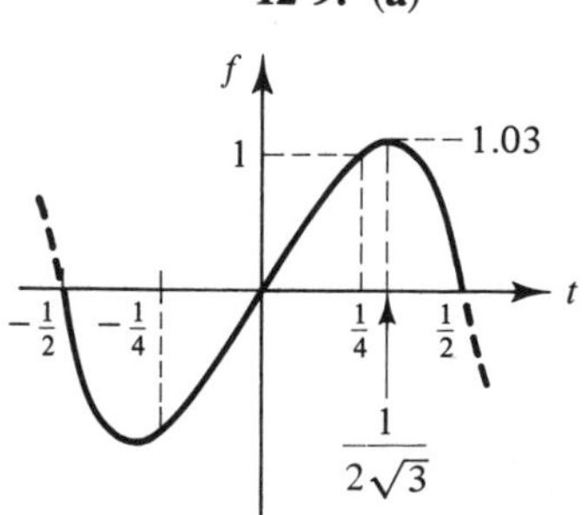

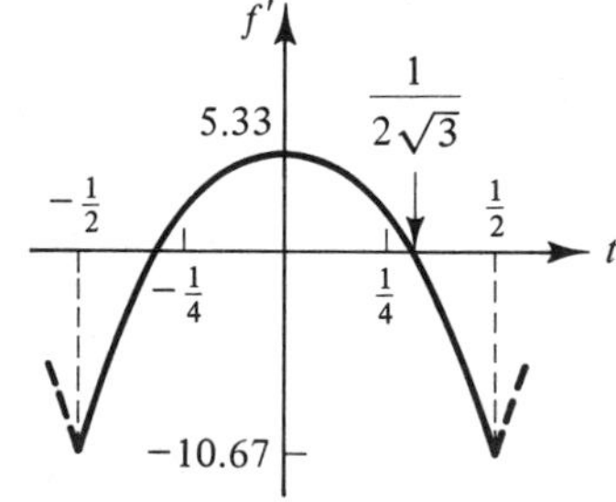

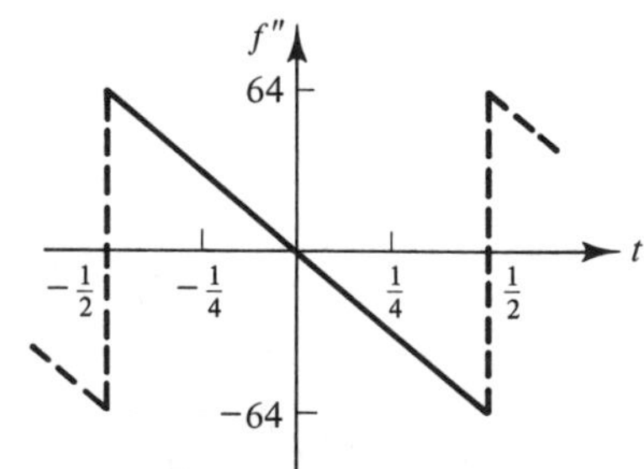

(b) $f(t) = \dfrac{32}{\pi^3} \sum_{n=1}^{\infty} \dfrac{(-1)^{n+1}}{n^3} \sin 2\pi n t$.

Since $f(t)$ and $f'(t)$ are continuous for all t but $f''(t)$ is discontinuous at $t = \pm\frac{1}{2}$, the harmonic amplitude decreases as $1/n^3$.

12-13. **(a)**

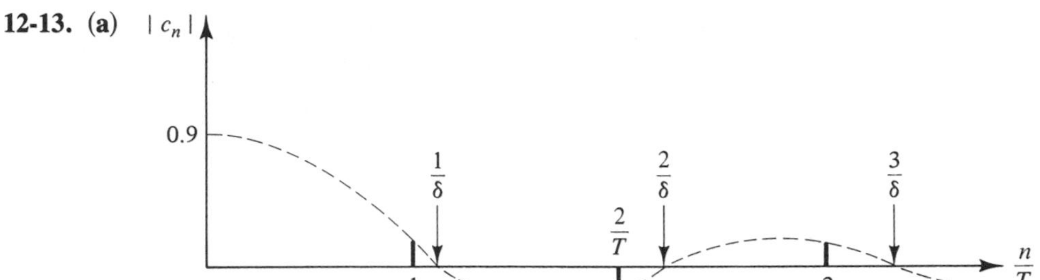

(b) $f(t) \cong 0.9 + 0.197 \cos \frac{2\pi}{T}t - 0.187 \cos \frac{4\pi}{T}t + 0.172 \cos \frac{6\pi}{T}t - 0.151 \cos \frac{8\pi}{T}t + 0.127 \cos \frac{10\pi}{T}t;$

(c) $f(t) = 1 - f_1\left(t + \frac{T}{2}\right)$, where $f_1(t)$ is the waveform of Fig. 12-16(c).

12-15. **(a)** $f_e(t) = \frac{1}{2}[f(t) + f(-t)], f_o(t) = \frac{1}{2}[f(t) - f(-t)]$;

(b)

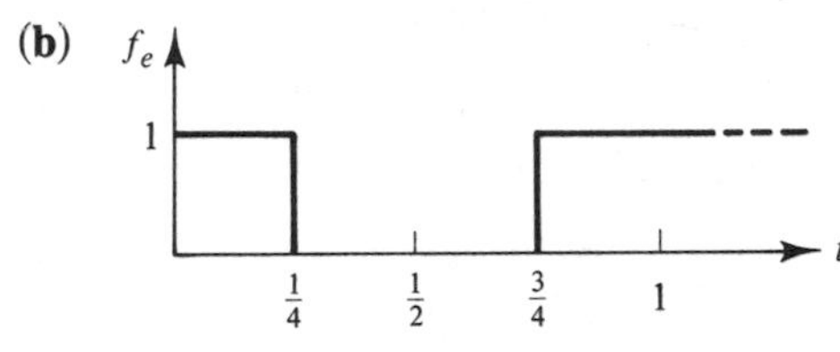

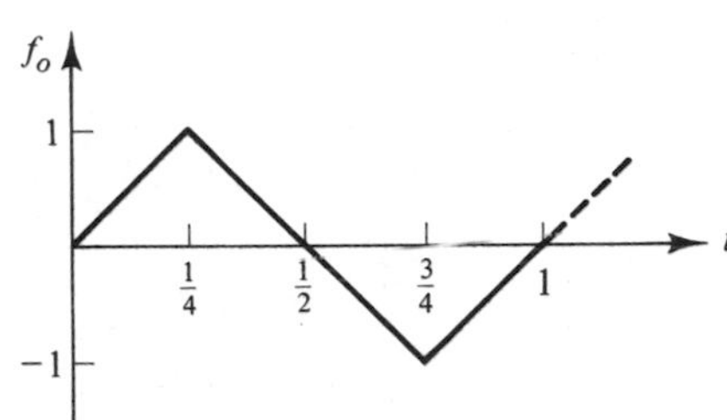

(c) $f(t) = \frac{1}{2} + \frac{2}{\pi}\sum_{\substack{n=1\\ \text{odd}}}^{\infty} \frac{\sin 0.5n\pi}{n}\left(\cos \frac{2\pi n}{T}t + \frac{4}{n\pi}\sin\frac{2\pi n}{T}t\right).$

12-17. **(a)** A^2/R; **(b)** $i(t) = \frac{AT}{4L} - \frac{2A}{\pi}\sum_{\substack{n=-\infty\\ \text{odd}}}^{\infty} \frac{1}{n}\left(\frac{T}{2n\pi L} + j\frac{1}{R}\right)e^{j(2\pi n/T)t};$

(c) Yes; **(d)** Yes.

12-19. **(a)** $f(t) = \frac{1}{2\pi}\left(\frac{T_o}{T}\right)\sum_{n=-\infty}^{\infty} \frac{1 - e^{-j(2\pi_n T_o/T)}}{1 - \left(\frac{nT_o}{T}\right)^2} e^{j(2\pi n/T)t};$

(b) $f(t) = \sin \frac{2\pi}{T}t.$

12-23. (**a**) Not periodic; (**b**) $T = \dfrac{2\pi}{\omega}$; (**c**) $T = 2\pi$; (**d**) $T = 4\pi$;

(**e**) T = any positive number.

12-25. (**a**)

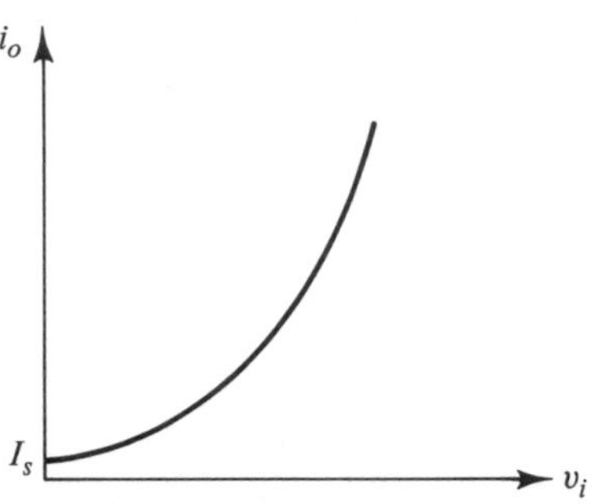

(**b**)

i_o

t

$\dfrac{\pi}{\omega}$ $\dfrac{2\pi}{\omega}$

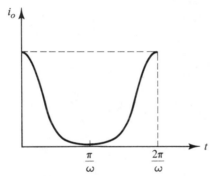

(**c**) $\omega, 2\omega, 3\omega, \ldots$.

12-27. (**a**) $\omega, 3\omega, 5\omega, \ldots$; (**b**) The average value of output waveform is not zero.

12-29. (**a**) $$v_o(t) = \frac{m_1 V_m}{\pi}\left(1 - 2\sum_{n=1}^{\infty} \frac{\cos\dfrac{n\pi}{2}}{n^2 - 1} \cos\frac{2\pi n}{T}t\right)$$

$$= \frac{m_1 V_m}{\pi}\left(1 + \frac{\pi}{2}\cos\frac{2\pi}{T}t + 2\sum_{\substack{n=2\\ \text{even}}}^{\infty} \frac{(-1)^{1+n/2}}{n^2 - 1}\cos\frac{2\pi n}{T}t\right)$$

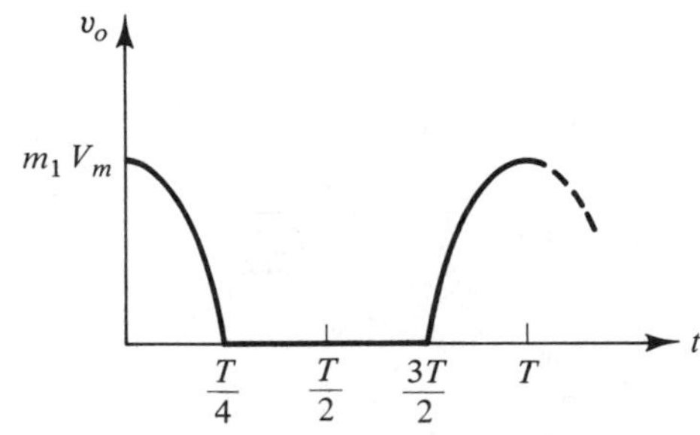

(b) $v_o(t) = \dfrac{2mV_m}{\pi}\left(1 + 2\sum_{\substack{n=2\\ \text{even}}}^{\infty} \dfrac{(-1)^{1+n/2}}{n^2-1}\cos\dfrac{2\pi n}{T}t\right)$

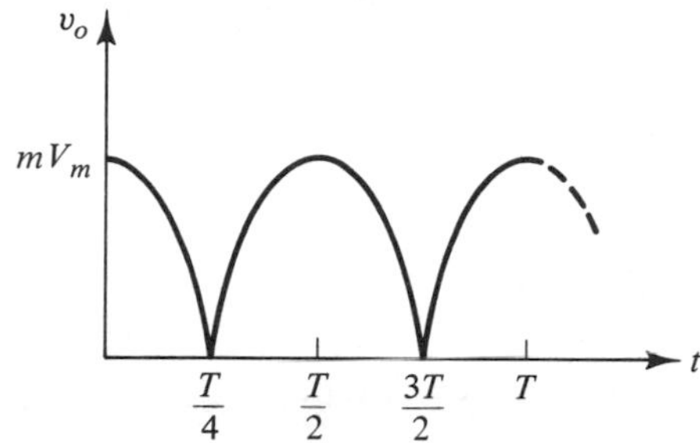

(d) Odd harmonic amplitudes will no longer be zero.

12-31. $L > \dfrac{RT}{6\pi}\sqrt{391}.$

12-33. (a) $v_o = \dfrac{12\text{ V}}{\pi\sqrt{6409}}\sin\left(\dfrac{2\pi}{T}t + \tan^{-1}\dfrac{80}{3}\right) + \dfrac{4\text{ V}}{3\pi}\sin\dfrac{6\pi}{T}t + \dfrac{12\text{ V}}{5\pi\sqrt{1033}}$
$\times \sin\left(\dfrac{10\pi}{T}t - \tan^{-1}\dfrac{32}{3}\right) + \cdots;$

(b) $\dfrac{V_{om3}}{V_{om1}} = \dfrac{\sqrt{6409}}{9} = 8.895,\ \dfrac{V_{om3}}{V_{om5}} = \dfrac{5\sqrt{1033}}{9} = 17.856,$

$v_o \cong \dfrac{4V}{3\pi}\sin\dfrac{6\pi}{T}t.$

12-35. $v_o \cong V_m \sin\dfrac{2\pi}{T}t$, where V_m is the amplitude of the fundamental component of the input voltage.

12-37. (a)

$\frac{TI}{8V}$ $\frac{TI}{8V}$ $\frac{TI}{8V}$

$\frac{2T}{\pi^2}\frac{V}{I}$ $\frac{2T}{9\pi^2}\frac{V}{I}$ $\frac{2T}{25\pi^2}\frac{V}{I}$

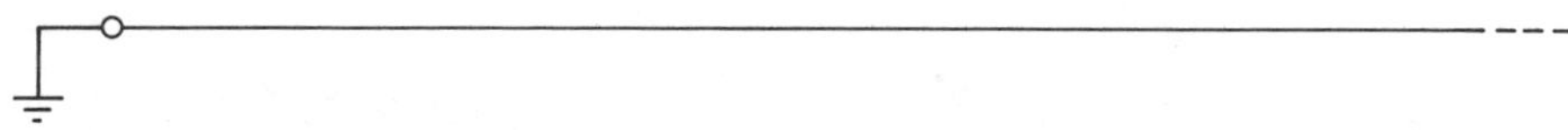

(**b**)

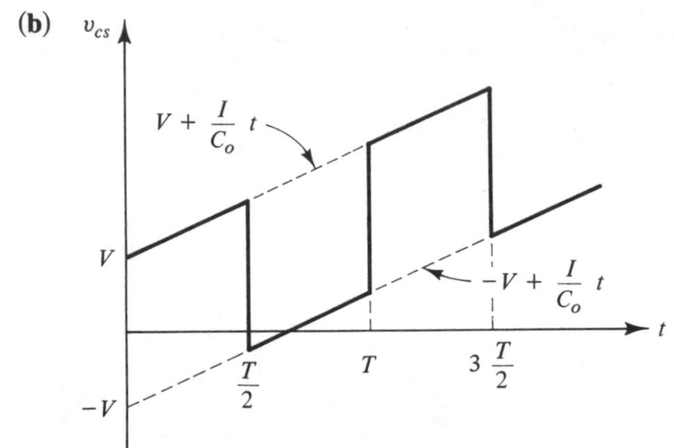

12-39. (**a**)

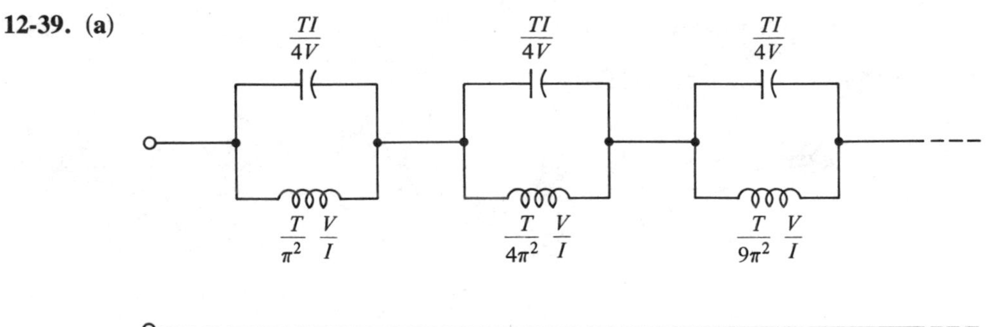

(**b**) Add *RC* network shown below in series with N, and take output across the current source.

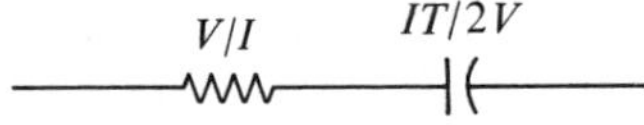

INDEX

E

F

G

H

I

K

L

T

U

V

Z